CUMULATIVE PROBABILITIES FOR THE STANDARD NORMAL I

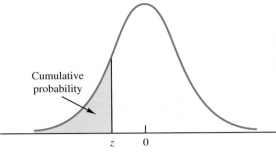

Cumulative probability

Entries in this table give the area under the curve to the left of the z value. For example, for z = −.85, the cumulative probability is .1977.

z	.00	.01	.02	.03	.04	.05	.06	.07	.08	.09
−3.0	.0013	.0013	.0013	.0012	.0012	.0011	.0011	.0011	.0010	.0010
−2.9	.0019	.0018	.0018	.0017	.0016	.0016	.0015	.0015	.0014	.0014
−2.8	.0026	.0025	.0024	.0023	.0023	.0022	.0021	.0021	.0020	.0019
−2.7	.0035	.0034	.0033	.0032	.0031	.0030	.0029	.0028	.0027	.0026
−2.6	.0047	.0045	.0044	.0043	.0041	.0040	.0039	.0038	.0037	.0036
−2.5	.0062	.0060	.0059	.0057	.0055	.0054	.0052	.0051	.0049	.0048
−2.4	.0082	.0080	.0078	.0075	.0073	.0071	.0069	.0068	.0066	.0064
−2.3	.0107	.0104	.0102	.0099	.0096	.0094	.0091	.0089	.0087	.0084
−2.2	.0139	.0136	.0132	.0129	.0125	.0122	.0119	.0116	.0113	.0110
−2.1	.0179	.0174	.0170	.0166	.0162	.0158	.0154	.0150	.0146	.0143
−2.0	.0228	.0222	.0217	.0212	.0207	.0202	.0197	.0192	.0188	.0183
−1.9	.0287	.0281	.0274	.0268	.0262	.0256	.0250	.0244	.0239	.0233
−1.8	.0359	.0351	.0344	.0336	.0329	.0322	.0314	.0307	.0301	.0294
−1.7	.0446	.0436	.0427	.0418	.0409	.0401	.0392	.0384	.0375	.0367
−1.6	.0548	.0537	.0526	.0516	.0505	.0495	.0485	.0475	.0465	.0455
−1.5	.0668	.0655	.0643	.0630	.0618	.0606	.0594	.0582	.0571	.0559
−1.4	.0808	.0793	.0778	.0764	.0749	.0735	.0721	.0708	.0694	.0681
−1.3	.0968	.0951	.0934	.0918	.0901	.0885	.0869	.0853	.0838	.0823
−1.2	.1151	.1131	.1112	.1093	.1075	.1056	.1038	.1020	.1003	.0985
−1.1	.1357	.1335	.1314	.1292	.1271	.1251	.1230	.1210	.1190	.1170
−1.0	.1587	.1562	.1539	.1515	.1492	.1469	.1446	.1423	.1401	.1379
−.9	.1841	.1814	.1788	.1762	.1736	.1711	.1685	.1660	.1635	.1611
−.8	.2119	.2090	.2061	.2033	.2005	.1977	.1949	.1922	.1894	.1867
−.7	.2420	.2389	.2358	.2327	.2296	.2266	.2236	.2206	.2177	.2148
−.6	.2743	.2709	.2676	.2643	.2611	.2578	.2546	.2514	.2483	.2451
−.5	.3085	.3050	.3015	.2981	.2946	.2912	.2877	.2843	.2810	.2776
−.4	.3446	.3409	.3372	.3336	.3300	.3264	.3228	.3192	.3156	.3121
−.3	.3821	.3783	.3745	.3707	.3669	.3632	.3594	.3557	.3520	.3483
−.2	.4207	.4168	.4129	.4090	.4052	.4013	.3974	.3936	.3897	.3859
−.1	.4602	.4562	.4522	.4483	.4443	.4404	.4364	.4325	.4286	.4247
−.0	.5000	.4960	.4920	.4880	.4840	.4801	.4761	.4721	.4681	.4641

CUMULATIVE PROBABILITIES FOR THE STANDARD NORMAL DISTRIBUTION

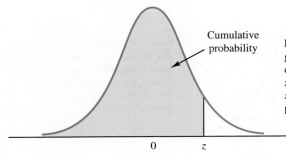

Cumulative probability

Entries in the table give the area under the curve to the left of the z value. For example, for $z = 1.25$, the cumulative probability is .8944.

z	.00	.01	.02	.03	.04	.05	.06	.07	.08	.09
.0	.5000	.5040	.5080	.5120	.5160	.5199	.5239	.5279	.5319	.5359
.1	.5398	.5438	.5478	.5517	.5557	.5596	.5636	.5675	.5714	.5753
.2	.5793	.5832	.5871	.5910	.5948	.5987	.6026	.6064	.6103	.6141
.3	.6179	.6217	.6255	.6293	.6331	.6368	.6406	.6443	.6480	.6517
.4	.6554	.6591	.6628	.6664	.6700	.6736	.6772	.6808	.6844	.6879
.5	.6915	.6950	.6985	.7019	.7054	.7088	.7123	.7157	.7190	.7224
.6	.7257	.7291	.7324	.7357	.7389	.7422	.7454	.7486	.7517	.7549
.7	.7580	.7611	.7642	.7673	.7704	.7734	.7764	.7794	.7823	.7852
.8	.7881	.7910	.7939	.7967	.7995	.8023	.8051	.8078	.8106	.8133
.9	.8159	.8186	.8212	.8238	.8264	.8289	.8315	.8340	.8365	.8389
1.0	.8413	.8438	.8461	.8485	.8508	.8531	.8554	.8577	.8599	.8621
1.1	.8643	.8665	.8686	.8708	.8729	.8749	.8770	.8790	.8810	.8830
1.2	.8849	.8869	.8888	.8907	.8925	.8944	.8962	.8980	.8997	.9015
1.3	.9032	.9049	.9066	.9082	.9099	.9115	.9131	.9147	.9162	.9177
1.4	.9192	.9207	.9222	.9236	.9251	.9265	.9279	.9292	.9306	.9319
1.5	.9332	.9345	.9357	.9370	.9382	.9394	.9406	.9418	.9429	.9441
1.6	.9452	.9463	.9474	.9484	.9495	.9505	.9515	.9525	.9535	.9545
1.7	.9554	.9564	.9573	.9582	.9591	.9599	.9608	.9616	.9625	.9633
1.8	.9641	.9649	.9656	.9664	.9671	.9678	.9686	.9693	.9699	.9706
1.9	.9713	.9719	.9726	.9732	.9738	.9744	.9750	.9756	.9761	.9767
2.0	.9772	.9778	.9783	.9788	.9793	.9798	.9803	.9808	.9812	.9817
2.1	.9821	.9826	.9830	.9834	.9838	.9842	.9846	.9850	.9854	.9857
2.2	.9861	.9864	.9868	.9871	.9875	.9878	.9881	.9884	.9887	.9890
2.3	.9893	.9896	.9898	.9901	.9904	.9906	.9909	.9911	.9913	.9916
2.4	.9918	.9920	.9922	.9925	.9927	.9929	.9931	.9932	.9934	.9936
2.5	.9938	.9940	.9941	.9943	.9945	.9946	.9948	.9949	.9951	.9952
2.6	.9953	.9955	.9956	.9957	.9959	.9960	.9961	.9962	.9963	.9964
2.7	.9965	.9966	.9967	.9968	.9969	.9970	.9971	.9972	.9973	.9974
2.8	.9974	.9975	.9976	.9977	.9977	.9978	.9979	.9979	.9980	.9981
2.9	.9981	.9982	.9982	.9983	.9984	.9984	.9985	.9985	.9986	.9986
3.0	.9987	.9987	.9987	.9988	.9988	.9989	.9989	.9989	.9990	.9990

Statistics for Business and Economics 14e Revised DATAfiles

Chapter 1

Nations	Table 1.1
Rogers	Table 1.5
CompactSUV	Exercise 25
Nations	Appendix 1.1
Chemitech	Appendix 1.1

Chapter 2

SoftDrink	Table 2.1
Websites	Exercise 4
Names2018	Exercise 5
Networks2012	Exercise 6
AirSurvey	Exercise 7
BaseballHall	Exercise 8
Majors	Exercise 9
HotelRatings	Exercise 10
Audit	Table 2.4
AptitudeTest	Table 2.8
Frequency	Exercise 11
NBAPlayerPts	Exercise 18
Airports	Exercise 19
CEOTime	Exercise 20
Endowments	Exercise 21
Franchise	Exercise 22
MarketIndexes	Exercise 23
EngineeringSalary	Exercise 24
BestPayingDegrees	Exercise 25
Marathon	Exercise 26
Restaurant	Table 2.9
Crosstab	Exercise 27
Crosstab2	Exercise 28
BrandValue	Table 2.12
FuelData2018	Table 2.12
Electronics	Table 2.12
Scatter	Exercise 36
MPG	Exercise 39
Snow	Exercise 40
Hypertension	Exercise 41
Smartphones	Exercise 42
ManagerTime	Exercise 43
NewSAT	Exercise 44
MedianHousehold	Exercise 45
Population2012	Exercise 46
StartUps	Exercise 47
BBB	Exercise 48
StocksBeta	Table 2.17
FortuneBest100	Exercise 52
Colleges	Exercise 54
ElectricVehicles	Exercise 57
Zoo	Exercise 58
PelicanStores	Table 2.19
Movies2016	Table 2.20
QueenCity	Case Problem 3
CutRate	Case Problem 4
Audit	Appendix 2.1
AptitudeTest	Appendix 2.1
SoftDrink	Appendix 2.1
Electronics	Appendix 2.1
SoftDrink	Appendix 2.2
Audit	Appendix 2.2
Restaurant	Appendix 2.2
Electronics	Appendix 2.2
Restaurant	Appendix 2.2
Restaurant	Appendix 2.2

Chapter 3

StartingSalaries	Table 3.1
MutualFund	Table 3.2
eICU	Exercise 7
AdvertisingSpend	Exercise 9
JacketRatings	Exercise 10
TelevisionViewing	Exercise 11
OnlineGame	Exercise 12
UnemploymentRates	Exercise 14
SFGasPrices	Exercise 26
Flights	Exercise 27
VarattaSales	Exercise 28
CellPhoneExpenses	Exercise 31
Advertising	Exercise 32
BestCities	Exercise 43
NCAA	Exercise 44
iPads	Exercise 45
MajorSalaries	Figure 3.8
Runners	Exercise 50
PharmacySales	Exercise 51
CellService	Exercise 52
AdmiredCompanies	Exercise 53
BorderCrossings	Exercise 54
Electronics	Table 3.6
StockComparison	Exercise 57
SmokeDetectors	Exercise 59
Russell	Exercise 60
BestPrivateColleges	Exercise 61
Coaches	Exercise 63
WaitTracking	Exercise 64
Sleep	Exercise 65
Smartphone	Exercise 66
Transportation	Exercise 67
FoodIndustry	Exercise 69
Travel	Exercise 70
NFLTeamValue	Exercise 71
SpringTraining	Exercise 72
PanamaRailroad	Exercise 75
PelicanStores	Table 3.9
Movies2016	Table 3.10
AsiaMBA	Case Problem 3
HeavenlyChocolates	Table 3.12
AfricanElephants	Table 3.13
StartingSalaries	Appendix 3.1
MajorSalaries	Appendix 3.1
Electronics	Appendix 3.1
StartingSalaries	Appendix 3.2
Electronics	Appendix 3.2
StartingSalaries	Appendix 3.2
MajorSalaries	Appendix 3.2

Chapter 4

CodeChurn	Exercise 10
Judge	Table 4.8
MarketBasket	Case Problem 2

Chapter 5

Coldstream12	Exercise 17

Chapter 7

EAI	Section 7.1
Morningstar	Exercise 14
ShadowStocks	Exercise 50
USCitiesPop	Appendix 7.2
MetAreas	Appendix 7.3

Chapter 8

Lloyds	Section 8.1
Houston	Exercise 5
TravelTax	Exercise 6
Setters	Exercise 7
TobaccoFires	Exercise 9
NewBalance	Table 8.3
Scheer	Table 8.3
CorporateBonds	Exercise 16
Miami	Exercise 17
JobSearch	Exercise 18
HongKongMeals	Exercise 19
AutoInsurance	Exercise 20
TeleHealth	Exercise 21
Guardians	Exercise 22
TeeTimes	Section 8.4
RightDirection	Exercise 37
CasualDining	Exercise 38
FedTaxErrors	Exercise 44
FedSickHours	Exercise 45
SleepHabits	Exercise 51
DrugCost	Exercise 52
Obesity	Exercise 53
35MPH	Exercise 65
UnderEmployed	Exercise 66
FloridaFraud	Exercise 67
Professional	Case Problem 1
GulfProp	Table 8.9
Auto	Case Problem 3
Lloyds	Appendix 8.1
NewBalance	Appendix 8.1
TeeTimes	Appendix 8.1
Lloyds	Appendix 8.2
NewBalance	Appendix 8.2
IntervalProp	Appendix 8.2

Essentials of Statistics
for Business and Economics 9e

David R. Anderson
University of Cincinnati

Dennis J. Sweeney
University of Cincinnati

Thomas A. Williams
Rochester Institute
of Technology

Jeffrey D. Camm
Wake Forest University

James J. Cochran
University of Alabama

Michael J. Fry
University of Cincinnati

Jeffrey W. Ohlmann
University of Iowa

Australia • Brazil • Mexico • Singapore • United Kingdom • United States

**Essentials of Statistics
for Business and Economics,
Ninth Edition**

David R. Anderson
Dennis J. Sweeney
Thomas A. Williams
Jeffrey D. Camm
James J. Cochran
Michael J. Fry
Jeffrey W. Ohlmann

Senior Vice President, Higher Ed Product,
Content, and Market Development:
Erin Joyner

Senior Product Team Manager:
Joe Sabatino

Senior Product Manager:
Aaron Arnsparger

Project Manager: John Rich

Content Manager: Conor Allen

Product Assistant: Renee Schnee

Marketing Manager: Chris Walz

Production Service: MPS Limited

Designer, Creative Studio:
Chris Doughman

Text Designer: Beckmeyer Design

Intellectual Property Analyst:
Reba Frederics

Intellectual Property Project Manager:
Nick Barrows

Cover Designer: Foo Toon Check
Cover Image:
© iStock.com/stockinasia

For product information and technology assistance, contact us at
Cengage Learning Asia Customer Service, 65-6410-1200

We reserve the right to refuse any product and/or technology assistance if this book is used outside Asia

For permission to use material from this text or product, submit all requests online at **www.cengage.com/permissions**
Further permissions questions can be e-mailed to
asia.permissionrequest@cengage.com

ISBN: 978-981-48-6631-6

Cengage Learning Asia Pte Ltd
151 Lorong Chuan
#02-08 New Tech Park
Singapore 556741

Cengage is a leading provider of customized learning solutions with office locations around the globe. In Asia, we have offices in 11 territories including Singapore, China, Japan, Korea, Malaysia and more. To locate your nearest local office or sales representative, kindly visit **www.cengageasia.com/office-address**

To learn more about Cengage digital solutions, e-learning options or titles, please visit **www.cengageasia.com**

Printed in Singapore
Print Number: 01   Print Year: 2019

Brief Contents

Contents

David R. Anderson. David R. Anderson is Professor Emeritus of Quantitative Analysis in the College of Business Administration at the University of Cincinnati. Born in Grand Forks, North Dakota, he earned his B.S., M.S., and Ph.D. degrees from Purdue University. Professor Anderson has served as Head of the Department of Quantitative Analysis and Operations Management and as Associate Dean of the College of Business Administration at the University of Cincinnati. In addition, he was the coordinator of the College's first Executive Program.

At the University of Cincinnati, Professor Anderson has taught introductory statistics for business students as well as graduate-level courses in regression analysis, multivariate analysis, and management science. He has also taught statistical courses at the Department of Labor in Washington, D.C. He has been honored with nominations and awards for excellence in teaching and excellence in service to student organizations.

Professor Anderson has coauthored 10 textbooks in the areas of statistics, management science, linear programming, and production and operations management. He is an active consultant in the field of sampling and statistical methods.

Dennis J. Sweeney. Dennis J. Sweeney is Professor Emeritus of Quantitative Analysis and Founder of the Center for Productivity Improvement at the University of Cincinnati. Born in Des Moines, Iowa, he earned a B.S.B.A. degree from Drake University and his M.B.A. and D.B.A. degrees from Indiana University, where he was an NDEA Fellow. Professor Sweeney has worked in the management science group at Procter & Gamble and spent a year as a visiting professor at Duke University. Professor Sweeney served as Head of the Department of Quantitative Analysis and as Associate Dean of the College of Business Administration at the University of Cincinnati.

Professor Sweeney has published more than 30 articles and monographs in the area of management science and statistics. The National Science Foundation, IBM, Procter & Gamble, Federated Department Stores, Kroger, and Cincinnati Gas & Electric have funded his research, which has been published in *Management Science, Operations Research, Mathematical Programming, Decision Sciences,* and other journals.

Professor Sweeney has coauthored 10 textbooks in the areas of statistics, management science, linear programming, and production and operations management.

Thomas A. Williams. Thomas A. Williams is Professor Emeritus of Management Science in the College of Business at Rochester Institute of Technology. Born in Elmira, New York, he earned his B.S. degree at Clarkson University. He did his graduate work at Rensselaer Polytechnic Institute, where he received his M.S. and Ph.D. degrees.

Before joining the College of Business at RIT, Professor Williams served for seven years as a faculty member in the College of Business Administration at the University of Cincinnati, where he developed the undergraduate program in Information Systems and then served as its coordinator. At RIT he was the first chairman of the Decision Sciences Department. He teaches courses in management science and statistics, as well as graduate courses in regression and decision analysis.

Professor Williams is the coauthor of 11 textbooks in the areas of management science, statistics, production and operations management, and mathematics. He has been a consultant for numerous *Fortune* 500 companies and has worked on projects ranging from the use of data analysis to the development of large-scale regression models.

Jeffrey D. Camm. Jeffrey D. Camm is the Inmar Presidential Chair and Associate Dean of Analytics in the School of Business at Wake Forest University. Born in Cincinnati, Ohio, he holds a B.S. from Xavier University (Ohio) and a Ph.D. from Clemson University. Prior to joining the faculty at Wake Forest, he was on the faculty of the University of Cincinnati. He has also been a visiting scholar at Stanford University and a visiting professor of business administration at the Tuck School of Business at Dartmouth College.

Dr. Camm has published over 40 papers in the general area of optimization applied to problems in operations management and marketing. He has published his research in *Science, Management Science, Operations Research, Interfaces,* and other professional journals. Dr. Camm was named the Dornoff Fellow of Teaching Excellence at the University of Cincinnati and he was the 2006 recipient of the INFORMS Prize for the Teaching of Operations Research Practice. A firm believer in practicing what he preaches, he has served as an operations research consultant to numerous companies and government agencies. From 2005 to 2010 he served as editor-in-chief of *Interfaces.* In 2017, he was named an INFORMS Fellow.

James J. Cochran.   James J. Cochran is Professor of Applied Statistics and the Rogers-Spivey Faculty Fellow at the University of Alabama. Born in Dayton, Ohio, he earned his B.S., M.S., and M.B.A. degrees from Wright State University and a Ph.D. from the University of Cincinnati. He has been at the University of Alabama since 2014 and has been a visiting scholar at Stanford University, Universidad de Talca, the University of South Africa, and Pole Universitaire Leonard de Vinci.

Professor Cochran has published over 40 papers in the development and application of operations research and statistical methods. He has published his research *in Management Science, The American Statistician, Communications in Statistics—Theory and Methods, Annals of operations Research, European Journal of Operational Research, Journal of Combinatorial Optimization. Interfaces, Statistics and Probability Letters,* and other professional journals. He was the 2008 recipient of the INFORMS Prize for the Teaching of Operations Research Practice and the 2010 recipient of the Mu Sigma Rho Statistical Education Award. Professor Cochran was elected to the International Statistics Institute in 2005 and named a Fellow of the American Statistical Association in 2011. He received the Founders Award in 2014 and the Karl E. Peace Award in 2015 from the American Statistical Association. In 2017 he received the American Statistical Association's Waller Distinguished Teaching Career Award and was named a Fellow of INFORMS, and in 2018 he received the INFORMS President's Award.

A strong advocate for effective statistics and operations research education as a means of improving the quality of applications to real problems, Professor Cochran has organized and chaired teaching effectiveness workshops in Montevideo, Uruguay; Cape Town, South Africa; Cartagena, Colombia; Jaipur, India; Buenos Aires, Argentina; Nairobi, Kenya; Buea, Cameroon; Kathmandu, Nepal; Osijek, Croatia; Havana, Cuba; Ulaanbaatar, Mongolia; and Chişinău, Moldova. He has served as an operations research consultant to numerous companies and not-for-profit organizations. He served as editor-in-chief of *INFORMS Transactions on Education* from 2006 to 2012 and is on the editorial board of *Interfaces, International Transactions in Operational Research, and Significance.*

Michael J. Fry.   Michael J. Fry is Professor of Operations, Business Analytics, and Information Systems and Academic Director of the Center for Business Analytics in the Carl H. Lindner College of Business at the University of Cincinnati. Born in Killeen, Texas, he earned a BS from Texas A&M University and M.S.E. and Ph.D. degrees from the University of Michigan. He has been at the University of Cincinnati since 2002, where he was previously Department Head and has been named a Lindner Research Fellow. He has also been a visiting professor at the Samuel Curtis Johnson Graduate School of Management at Cornell University and the Sauder School of Business at the University of British Columbia.

Professor Fry has published more than 25 research papers in journals such as *Operations Research, M&SOM, Transportation Science, Naval Research Logistics, IIE Transactions, Critical Care Medicine* and *Interfaces.* His research interests are in applying quantitative management methods to the areas of supply chain analytics, sports analytics, and public-policy operations. He has worked with many different organizations for his research, including Dell, Inc., Starbucks Coffee Company, Great American Insurance Group, the Cincinnati Fire Department, the State of Ohio Election Commission, the Cincinnati Bengals, and the Cincinnati Zoo & Botanical Garden. He was named a finalist for the Daniel H. Wagner Prize for Excellence in Operations Research Practice, and he has been recognized for both his research and teaching excellence at the University of Cincinnati.

Jeffrey W. Ohlmann.   Jeffrey W. Ohlmann is Associate Professor of Management Sciences and Huneke Research Fellow in the Tippie College of Business at the University of Iowa. Born in Valentine, Nebraska, he earned a B.S. from the University of Nebraska, and MS and Ph.D. degrees from the University of Michigan. He has been at the University of Iowa since 2003.

Professor Ohlmann's research on the modeling and solution of decision-making problems has produced more than 20 research papers in journals such as *Operations Research, Mathematics of Operations Research, INFORMS Journal on Computing, Transportation Science,* the *European Journal of Operational Research,* and *Interfaces.* He has collaborated with companies such as Transfreight, LeanCor, Cargill, the Hamilton County Board of Elections, and three National Football League franchises. Because of the relevance of his work to industry, he was bestowed the George B. Dantzig Dissertation Award and was recognized as a finalist for the Daniel H. Wagner Prize for Excellence in Operations Research Practice.

management methods to the areas of supply chain analytics, sports analytics, and public policy operations. He has worked with many different organizations for his research, including Dell Inc., Starbucks Coffee Company, Great American Insurance Group, the Cincinnati Fire Department, the State of Ohio Election Commission, the Cincinnati Bengals, and the Cincinnati Zoo & Botanical Garden. He was named a finalist for the Daniel H. Wagner Prize for Excellence in Operations Research Practice, and he has been recognized for both his research and teaching excellence at the University of Cincinnati.

Jeffrey W. Ohlmann. Jeffrey W. Ohlmann is Associate Professor of Management Sciences and Huneke Research Fellow in the Tippie College of Business at the University of Iowa. Born in Valentine, Nebraska, he earned a B.S. from the University of Nebraska, and MS and Ph.D. degrees from the University of Michigan. He has been at the University of Iowa since 2003.

Professor Ohlmann's research on the modeling and solution of decision-making problems has produced more than 20 research papers in journals such as Operation Research, Mathematics of Operations Research, INFORMS Journal on Computing, Transportation Science, the European Journal of Operational Research, and Interfaces. He has collaborated with companies such as Transfreight, LeanCor, Cargill, the Hamilton County Board of Elections, and three National Football League franchises. Because of the relevance of his work to industry, he was bestowed the George B. Dantzig Dissertation Award and was recognized as a finalist for the Daniel H. Wagner Prize for Excellence in Operations Research Practice.

This text is the 9th edition of *ESSENTIALS OF STATISTICS FOR BUSINESS AND ECONOMICS*. In this edition, we include procedures for statistical analysis using Excel 2016 and JMP Student Edition 14. In MindTap Reader, we also include instructions for using the exceptionally popular open-source language R to perform statistical analysis. We are excited to introduce two new coauthors, Michael J. Fry of the University of Cincinnati and Jeffrey W. Ohlmann of the University of Iowa. Both are accomplished teachers and researchers. More details on their backgrounds may be found in the About the Authors section.

The remainder of this preface describes the authors' objectives in writing *ESSENTIALS OF STATISTICS FOR BUSINESS AND ECONOMICS* and the major changes that were made in developing the 9th edition. The purpose of the text is to give students, primarily those in the fields of business administration and economics, a conceptual introduction to the field of statistics and its many applications. The text is applications-oriented and written with the needs of the nonmathematician in mind; the mathematical prerequisite is understanding of algebra.

Applications of data analysis and statistical methodology are an integral part of the organization and presentation of the text material. The discussion and development of each technique is presented in an application setting, with the statistical results providing insights to decisions and solutions to problems.

Although the book is applications oriented, we have taken care to provide sound methodological development and to use notation that is generally accepted for the topic being covered. Hence, students will find that this text provides good preparation for the study of more advanced statistical material. A bibliography to guide further study is included as an appendix.

The text introduces the student to the software packages of JMP Student Edition 14 and Microsoft® Office Excel 2016 and emphasizes the role of computer software in the application of statistical analysis. JMP is illustrated as it is one of the leading statistical software packages for both education and statistical practice. Excel is not a statistical software package, but the wide availability and use of Excel make it important for students to understand the statistical capabilities of this package. JMP and Excel procedures are provided in appendices so that instructors have the flexibility of using as much computer emphasis as desired for the course. MindTap Reader includes appendices for using R for statistical analysis. R is an open-source programming language that is widely used in practice to perform statistical analysis. The use of R typically requires more training than the use of software such as JMP or Excel, but the software is extremely powerful. To ease students' introduction to the R language, we also use RStudio which provides an integrated development environment for R.

Changes in the 9th Edition

We appreciate the acceptance and positive response to the previous editions of *Essentials of Statistics for Business and Economics*. Accordingly, in making modifications for this new edition, we have maintained the presentation style and readability of those editions. There have been many changes made throughout the text to enhance its educational effectiveness. The most substantial changes in the new edition are summarized here.

Content Revisions

- **Software.** In addition to step-by-step instructions in the software appendices for Excel 2016, we also provide instructions for JMP Student Edition 14 and R. This provides students exposure to and experience with the current versions of several of the most commonly used software for statistical analysis in business. Excel 2016 and

JMP appendices are contained within the textbook chapters, while R appendices are provided in MindTap Reader. In this latest edition, we no longer provide discussion of the use of Minitab.

- **Case Problems.** We have added 12 new case problems in this edition; the total number of cases is now 42. One new case on graphical display has been added to Chapter 2. Two new cases using discrete probability distributions have been added to Chapter 5, and one new case using continuous probability distributions has been added to Chapter 6. A new case on hypothesis testing has been added to Chapter 11, and two new cases on testing proportions have been added to Chapter 12. The 42 case problems in this book provide students the opportunity to work on more complex problems, analyze larger data sets, and prepare managerial reports based on the results of their analyses.

- **Examples and Exercises Based on Real Data.** In this edition, we have added headers to all Applications exercises to make the application of each problem more obvious. We continue to make a substantial effort to update our text examples and exercises with the most current real data and referenced sources of statistical information. We have added more than 160 new examples and exercises based on real data and referenced sources. Using data from sources also used by *The Wall Street Journal*, *USA Today*, *The Financial Times*, and others, we have drawn from actual studies and applications to develop explanations and create exercises that demonstrate the many uses of statistics in business and economics. We believe that the use of real data from interesting and relevant problems helps generate more student interest in the material and enables the student to learn about both statistical methodology and its application. The 9th edition contains more than 350 examples and exercises based on real data.

Features and Pedagogy

Authors Anderson, Sweeney, Williams, Camm, Cochran, Fry, and Ohlmann have continued many of the features that appeared in previous editions. Important ones for students are noted here.

Methods Exercises and Applications Exercises

The end-of-section exercises are split into two parts, Methods and Applications. The Methods exercises require students to use the formulas and make the necessary computations. The Applications exercises require students to use the chapter material in real-world situations. Thus, students first focus on the computational "nuts and bolts" and then move on to the subtleties of statistical application and interpretation.

Margin Annotations and Notes and Comments

Margin annotations that highlight key points and provide additional insights for the student are a key feature of this text. These annotations, which appear in the margins, are designed to provide emphasis and enhance understanding of the terms and concepts being presented in the text.

At the end of many sections, we provide Notes and Comments designed to give the student additional insights about the statistical methodology and its application. Notes and Comments include warnings about or limitations of the methodology, recommendations for application, brief descriptions of additional technical considerations, and other matters.

Data Files Accompany the Text

Over 200 data files accompany this text. Data files are provided in Excel format and step-by-step instructions on how to open Excel files in JMP are provided in Appendix 1.1. Files for use with R are provided in comma-separated-value (CSV) format for easy loading into the R environment. Step-by-step instructions for importing CSV files into R are provided in MindTap Reader Appendix R 1.2.

The data files can be accessed from WebAssign within the resources section, directly within the MindTap Reader by clicking on the DATAfile icon, or online directly at www.cengage.com/decisionsciences/anderson/sbe/14e.

Acknowledgments

We would like to acknowledge the work of our reviewers, who provided comments and suggestions of ways to continue to improve our text. Thanks to

AbouEl-Makarim Aboueissa,
University of Southern
Maine

Kathleen Arano
Fort Hays State University

Musa Ayar
Uw-baraboo/Sauk County

Kathleen Burke
SUNY Cortland

YC Chang
University of Notre
Dame

David Chen
Rosemont College and
Saint Joseph's University

Margaret E. Cochran
Northwestern State
University of Louisiana

Thomas A. Dahlstrom
Eastern University

Anne Drougas
Dominican University

Fesseha Gebremikael Strayer
University/Calhoun Community College

Malcolm C. Gold
University of Wisconsin—
Marshfield/Wood County

Joel Goldstein
Western Connecticut State
University

Jim Grant
Lewis & Clark College

Reidar Hagtvedt
University of Alberta
School of Business

Clifford B. Hawley
West Virginia University

Vance A. Hughey
Western Nevada College

Tony Hunnicutt
Ouachita Technical College

Stacey M. Jones
Albers School of Business
and Economics, Seattle
University

Dukpa Kim
University of Virginia

Rajaram Krishnan
Earlham College

Robert J. Lemke
Lake Forest College

Philip J. Mizzi
Arizona State University

Mehdi Mohaghegh Norwich
University

Mihail Motzev
Walla Walla University

Somnath Mukhopadhyay
The University of Texas
at El Paso

Kenneth E. Murphy
Chapman University

Ogbonnaya John Nwoha
Grambling State University

Claudiney Pereira
Tulane University

J. G. Pitt
University of Toronto

Scott A. Redenius
Brandeis University

Sandra Robertson
Thomas Nelson
Community College

Sunil Sapra
California State University,
Los Angeles

Kyle Vann Scott
Snead State Community
College

Rodney E. Stanley
Tennessee State University

Jennifer Strehler
Oakton Community College

Ronald Stunda
Valdosta State University

Cindy van Es
Cornell University

Jennifer VanGilder
Ursinus College

Jacqueline Wroughton
Northern Kentucky
University

Dmitry Yarushkin
Grand View University

David Zimmer
Western Kentucky University

We continue to owe debt to our many colleagues and friends for their helpful comments and suggestions in the development of this and earlier editions of our text. Among them are:

Mohammad Ahmadi
University of Tennessee
at Chattanooga

Lari Arjomand
Clayton College and State
University

Robert Balough
Clarion University

Philip Boudreaux
University of Louisiana

Mike Bourke
Houston Baptist University

James Brannon
University of Wisconsin—
Oshkosh

John Bryant
University of Pittsburgh

Peter Bryant
University of Colorado

Terri L. Byczkowski
University of Cincinnati

Robert Carver
Stonehill College

Richard Claycombe
McDaniel College

Robert Cochran
University of Wyoming

Robert Collins
Marquette University

David W. Cravens
Texas Christian University

Tom Dahlstrom
Eastern College

Gopal Dorai
William Patterson University

Nicholas Farnum
California State
University—Fullerton

Donald Gren
Salt Lake Community
College

Paul Guy
California State
University—Chico

Clifford Hawley
West Virginia University

Jim Hightower
California State
University, Fullerton

Alan Humphrey
University of Rhode Island

Ann Hussein
Philadelphia College of
Textiles and Science

C. Thomas Innis
University of Cincinnati

Ben Isselhardt
Rochester Institute of
Technology

Jeffery Jarrett
University of Rhode Island

Ronald Klimberg
St. Joseph's University

David A. Kravitz
George Mason University

David Krueger
St. Cloud State University

John Leschke
University of Virginia

Martin S. Levy
University of Cincinnati

John S. Loucks
St. Edward's University

David Lucking-Reiley
Vanderbilt University

Bala Maniam
Sam Houston State
University

Don Marx
University of Alaska,
Anchorage

Tom McCullough
University of California—
Berkeley

Ronald W. Michener
University of Virginia

Glenn Milligan
Ohio State University

Mitchell Muesham
Sam Houston State University

Roger Myerson
Northwestern University

Richard O'Connell
Miami University of Ohio

Alan Olinsky
Bryant College

Ceyhun Ozgur
Valparaiso University

Tom Pray
Rochester Institute
of Technology

Harold Rahmlow
St. Joseph's University

H. V. Ramakrishna
Penn State University at
Great Valley

Tom Ryan
Case Western Reserve
University

Bill Seaver
University of Tennessee

Alan Smith
Robert Morris College

Willbann Terpening
Gonzaga University

Ted Tsukahara
St. Mary's College of
California

Hroki Tsurumi
Rutgers University

David Tufte
University of New Orleans

Victor Ukpolo
Austin Peay State University

Ebenge Usip
Youngstown State
University

Cindy Van Es
Cornell University

Jack Vaughn
University of Texas-El Paso

Andrew Welki
John Carroll University

Ari Wijetunga
Morehead State University

J. E. Willis
Louisiana State University

Mustafa Yilmaz
Northeastern University

Gary Yoshimoto
St. Cloud State University

Yan Yu
University of Cincinnati

Charles Zimmerman
Robert Morris College

We thank our associates from business and industry who supplied the Statistics in Practice features. We recognize them individually by a credit line in each of the articles. We are also indebted to our senior product manager, Aaron Arnsparger; our learning designer, Brandon Foltz; our content manager, Conor Allen; our project manager at MPS Limited, Manoj Kumar; and others at Cengage for their editorial counsel and support during the prepartion of this text.

David R. Anderson
Dennis J. Sweeney
Thomas A. Williams
Jeffrey D. Camm
James J. Cochran
Michael J. Fry
Jeffrey W. Ohlmann

Chapter 1

Data and Statistics

CONTENTS

STATISTICS IN PRACTICE

Bloomberg Businessweek*

NEW YORK, NEW YORK

Bloomberg Businessweek is one of the most widely read business magazines in the world. Along with feature articles on current topics, the magazine contains articles on international business, economic analysis, information processing, and science and technology. Information in the feature articles and the regular sections helps readers stay abreast of current developments and assess the impact of those developments on business and economic conditions.

Most issues of *Bloomberg Businessweek* provide an in-depth report on a topic of current interest. Often, the in-depth reports contain statistical facts and summaries that help the reader understand the business and economic information. Examples of articles and reports include the impact of businesses moving important work to cloud computing, the crisis facing the U.S. Postal Service, and why the debt crisis is even worse than we think. In addition, *Bloomberg Businessweek* provides a variety of statistics about the state of the economy, including production indexes, stock prices, mutual funds, and interest rates.

Bloomberg Businessweek also uses statistics and statistical information in managing its own business. For example, an annual survey of subscribers helps the company learn about subscriber demographics, reading habits, likely purchases, lifestyles, and so on. *Bloomberg Businessweek* managers use statistical summaries from the survey to provide better services to subscribers and advertisers. One North American subscriber survey indicated that 64% of *Bloomberg Businessweek* subscribers are involved with computer purchases at work. Such statistics alert *Bloomberg*

Bloomberg Businessweek uses statistical facts and summaries in many of its articles. AP Images/Weng lei-Imaginechina

Businessweek managers to subscriber interest in articles about new developments in computers. The results of the subscriber survey are also made available to potential advertisers. The high percentage of subscribers involved with computer purchases at work would be an incentive for a computer manufacturer to consider advertising in *Bloomberg Businessweek*.

In this chapter, we discuss the types of data available for statistical analysis and describe how the data are obtained. We introduce descriptive statistics and statistical inference as ways of converting data into meaningful and easily interpreted statistical information.

*The authors are indebted to Charlene Trentham, Research Manager, for providing the context for this Statistics in Practice.

Frequently, we see the following types of statements in newspapers and magazines:

- Unemployment dropped to an 18-year low of 3.8% in May 2018 from 3.9% in April and after holding at 4.1% for the prior six months (*Wall Street Journal,* June 1, 2018).
- Tesla ended 2017 with around $5.4 billion of liquidity. Analysts forecast it will burn through $2.8 billion of cash this year (*Bloomberg Businessweek,* April 19, 2018).
- The biggest banks in America reported a good set of earnings for the first three months of 2018. Bank of America and Morgan Stanley made quarterly net profits of $6.9 billion and $2.7 billion, respectively (*The Economist,* April 21, 2018).
- According to a study from the Pew Research Center, 15% of U.S. adults say they have used online dating sites or mobile apps (*Wall Street Journal,* May 2, 2018).

- According to the U.S. Centers for Disease Control and Prevention, in the United States alone, at least 2 million illnesses and 23,000 deaths can be attributed each year to antibiotic-resistant bacteria (*Wall Street Journal,* February 13, 2018).

The numerical facts in the preceding statements—3.8%, 3.9%, 4.1%, $5.4 billion, $2.8 billion $6.9 billion, $2.7 billion, 15%, 2 million, 23,000—are called **statistics**. In this usage, the term *statistics* refers to numerical facts such as averages, medians, percentages, and maximums that help us understand a variety of business and economic situations. However, as you will see, the subject of statistics involves much more than numerical facts. In a broader sense, statistics is the art and science of collecting, analyzing, presenting, and interpreting data. Particularly in business and economics, the information provided by collecting, analyzing, presenting, and interpreting data gives managers and decision makers a better understanding of the business and economic environment and thus enables them to make more informed and better decisions. In this text, we emphasize the use of statistics for business and economic decision making.

Chapter 1 begins with some illustrations of the applications of statistics in business and economics. In Section 1.2 we define the term *data* and introduce the concept of a data set. This section also introduces key terms such as *variables* and *observations,* discusses the difference between quantitative and categorical data, and illustrates the uses of cross-sectional and time series data. Section 1.3 discusses how data can be obtained from existing sources or through survey and experimental studies designed to obtain new data. The uses of data in developing descriptive statistics and in making statistical inferences are described in Sections 1.4 and 1.5. The last four sections of Chapter 1 provide an introduction to business analytics and the role statistics plays in it, an introduction to big data and data mining, the role of the computer in statistical analysis, and a discussion of ethical guidelines for statistical practice.

1.1 Applications in Business and Economics

In today's global business and economic environment, anyone can access vast amounts of statistical information. The most successful managers and decision makers understand the information and know how to use it effectively. In this section, we provide examples that illustrate some of the uses of statistics in business and economics.

Accounting

Public accounting firms use statistical sampling procedures when conducting audits for their clients. For instance, suppose an accounting firm wants to determine whether the amount of accounts receivable shown on a client's balance sheet fairly represents the actual amount of accounts receivable. Usually the large number of individual accounts receivable makes reviewing and validating every account too time-consuming and expensive. As common practice in such situations, the audit staff selects a subset of the accounts called a sample. After reviewing the accuracy of the sampled accounts, the auditors draw a conclusion as to whether the accounts receivable amount shown on the client's balance sheet is acceptable.

Finance

Financial analysts use a variety of statistical information to guide their investment recommendations. In the case of stocks, analysts review financial data such as price/earnings ratios and dividend yields. By comparing the information for an individual stock with information about the stock market averages, an analyst can begin to draw a conclusion as to whether the stock is a good investment. For example, the average dividend yield for the S&P 500 companies for 2017 was 1.88%. Over the same period, the average dividend yield for Microsoft was 1.72% (Yahoo Finance). In this case, the statistical information on dividend yield indicates a lower dividend yield for Microsoft than the average dividend yield for the S&P 500 companies. This and other information about Microsoft would help the analyst make an informed buy, sell, or hold recommendation for Microsoft stock.

Marketing

Electronic scanners at retail checkout counters collect data for a variety of marketing research applications. For example, data suppliers such as The Nielsen Company and IRI purchase point-of-sale scanner data from grocery stores, process the data, and then sell statistical summaries of the data to manufacturers. Manufacturers spend hundreds of thousands of dollars per product category to obtain this type of scanner data. Manufacturers also purchase data and statistical summaries on promotional activities such as special pricing and the use of in-store displays. Brand managers can review the scanner statistics and the promotional activity statistics to gain a better understanding of the relationship between promotional activities and sales. Such analyses often prove helpful in establishing future marketing strategies for the various products.

Production

Today's emphasis on quality makes quality control an important application of statistics in production. A variety of statistical quality control charts are used to monitor the output of a production process. In particular, an x-bar chart can be used to monitor the average output. Suppose, for example, that a machine fills containers with 12 ounces of a soft drink. Periodically, a production worker selects a sample of containers and computes the average number of ounces in the sample. This average, or x-bar value, is plotted on an x-bar chart. A plotted value above the chart's upper control limit indicates overfilling, and a plotted value below the chart's lower control limit indicates underfilling. The process is termed "in control" and allowed to continue as long as the plotted x-bar values fall between the chart's upper and lower control limits. Properly interpreted, an x-bar chart can help determine when adjustments are necessary to correct a production process.

Economics

Economists frequently provide forecasts about the future of the economy or some aspect of it. They use a variety of statistical information in making such forecasts. For instance, in forecasting inflation rates, economists use statistical information on such indicators as the Producer Price Index, the unemployment rate, and manufacturing capacity utilization. Often these statistical indicators are entered into computerized forecasting models that predict inflation rates.

Information Systems

Information systems administrators are responsible for the day-to-day operation of an organization's computer networks. A variety of statistical information helps administrators assess the performance of computer networks, including local area networks (LANs), wide area networks (WANs), network segments, intranets, and other data communication systems. Statistics such as the mean number of users on the system, the proportion of time any component of the system is down, and the proportion of bandwidth utilized at various times of the day are examples of statistical information that help the system administrator better understand and manage the computer network.

Applications of statistics such as those described in this section are an integral part of this text. Such examples provide an overview of the breadth of statistical applications. To supplement these examples, practitioners in the fields of business and economics provided chapter-opening Statistics in Practice articles that introduce the material covered in each chapter. The Statistics in Practice applications show the importance of statistics in a wide variety of business and economic situations.

1.2 Data

Data are the facts and figures collected, analyzed, and summarized for presentation and interpretation. All the data collected in a particular study are referred to as the **data set** for the study. Table 1.1 shows a data set containing information for 60 nations that participate in the World Trade Organization. The World Trade Organization encourages the free flow of international trade and provides a forum for resolving trade disputes.

Elements, Variables, and Observations

Elements are the entities on which data are collected. Each nation listed in Table 1.1 is an element with the nation or element name shown in the first column. With 60 nations, the data set contains 60 elements.

A **variable** is a characteristic of interest for the elements. The data set in Table 1.1 includes the following five variables:

- WTO Status: The nation's membership status in the World Trade Organization; this can be either as a member or an observer.
- Per Capita Gross Domestic Product (GDP) ($): The total market value ($) of all goods and services produced by the nation divided by the number of people in the nation; this is commonly used to compare economic productivity of the nations.
- Fitch Rating: The nation's sovereign credit rating as appraised by the Fitch Group[1]; the credit ratings range from a high of AAA to a low of F and can be modified by + or −.
- Fitch Outlook: An indication of the direction the credit rating is likely to move over the upcoming two years; the outlook can be negative, stable, or positive.

Measurements collected on each variable for every element in a study provide the data. The set of measurements obtained for a particular element is called an **observation**. Referring to Table 1.1, we see that the first observation (Armenia) contains the following measurements: Member, 3615, BB-, and Stable. The second observation (Australia) contains the following measurements: Member, 49755, AAA, and Stable and so on. A data set with 60 elements contains 60 observations.

Scales of Measurement

Data collection requires one of the following scales of measurement: nominal, ordinal, interval, or ratio. The scale of measurement determines the amount of information contained in the data and indicates the most appropriate data summarization and statistical analyses.

When the data for a variable consist of labels or names used to identify an attribute of the element, the scale of measurement is considered a **nominal scale**. For example, referring to the data in Table 1.1, the scale of measurement for the WTO Status variable is nominal because the data "member" and "observer" are labels used to identify the status category for the nation. In cases where the scale of measurement is nominal, a numerical code as well as a nonnumerical label may be used. For example, to facilitate data collection and to prepare the data for entry into a computer database, we might use a numerical code for the WTO Status variable by letting 1 denote a member nation in the World Trade Organization and 2 denote an observer nation. The scale of measurement is nominal even though the data appear as numerical values.

The scale of measurement for a variable is considered an **ordinal scale** if the data exhibit the properties of nominal data and in addition, the order or rank of the data is meaningful. For example, referring to the data in Table 1.1, the scale of measurement for

---

[1]The Fitch Group is one of three nationally recognized statistical rating organizations designated by the U.S. Securities and Exchange Commission. The other two are Standard & Poor's and Moody's.

DATAfile

Nations

TABLE 1.1	Data Set for 60 Nations in the World Trade Organization			
Nation	**WTO Status**	**Per Capita GDP ($)**	**Fitch Rating**	**Fitch Outlook**
Armenia	Member	3,615	BB−	Stable
Australia	Member	49,755	AAA	Stable
Austria	Member	44,758	AAA	Stable
Azerbaijan	Observer	3,879	BBB−	Stable
Bahrain	Member	22,579	BBB	Stable
Belgium	Member	41,271	AA	Stable
Brazil	Member	8,650	BBB	Stable
Bulgaria	Member	7,469	BBB−	Stable
Canada	Member	42,349	AAA	Stable
Cape Verde	Member	2,998	B+	Stable
Chile	Member	13,793	A+	Stable
China	Member	8,123	A+	Stable
Colombia	Member	5,806	BBB−	Stable
Costa Rica	Member	11,825	BB+	Stable
Croatia	Member	12,149	BBB−	Negative
Cyprus	Member	23,541	B	Negative
Czech Republic	Member	18,484	A+	Stable
Denmark	Member	53,579	AAA	Stable
Ecuador	Member	6,019	B−	Positive
Egypt	Member	3,478	B	Negative
El Salvador	Member	4,224	BB	Negative
Estonia	Member	17,737	A+	Stable
France	Member	36,857	AAA	Negative
Georgia	Member	3,866	BB−	Stable
Germany	Member	42,161	AAA	Stable
Hungary	Member	12,820	BB+	Stable
Iceland	Member	60,530	BBB	Stable
Ireland	Member	64,175	BBB+	Stable
Israel	Member	37,181	A	Stable
Italy	Member	30,669	A−	Negative
Japan	Member	38,972	A+	Negative
Kazakhstan	Observer	7,715	BBB+	Stable
Kenya	Member	1,455	B+	Stable
Latvia	Member	14,071	BBB	Positive
Lebanon	Observer	8,257	B	Stable
Lithuania	Member	14,913	BBB	Stable
Malaysia	Member	9,508	A−	Stable
Mexico	Member	8,209	BBB	Stable
Peru	Member	6,049	BBB	Stable
Philippines	Member	2,951	BB+	Stable
Poland	Member	12,414	A−	Positive
Portugal	Member	19,872	BB+	Negative
South Korea	Member	27,539	AA−	Stable
Romania	Member	9,523	BBB−	Stable
Russia	Member	8,748	BBB	Stable
Rwanda	Member	703	B	Stable
Serbia	Observer	5,426	BB−	Negative
Singapore	Member	52,962	AAA	Stable
Slovakia	Member	16,530	A+	Stable

Slovenia	Member	21,650	A−	Negative
South Africa	Member	5,275	BBB	Stable
Spain	Member	26,617	A−	Stable
Sweden	Member	51,845	AAA	Stable
Switzerland	Member	79,888	AAA	Stable
Thailand	Member	5,911	BBB	Stable
Turkey	Member	10,863	BBB−	Stable
United Kingdom	Member	40,412	AAA	Negative
Uruguay	Member	15,221	BB+	Positive
United States	Member	57,638	AAA	Stable
Zambia	Member	1,270	B+	Negative

the Fitch Rating is ordinal because the rating labels, which range from AAA to F, can be rank ordered from best credit rating (AAA) to poorest credit rating (F). The rating letters provide the labels similar to nominal data, but in addition, the data can also be ranked or ordered based on the credit rating, which makes the measurement scale ordinal. Ordinal data can also be recorded by a numerical code, for example, your class rank in school.

The scale of measurement for a variable is an **interval scale** if the data have all the properties of ordinal data and the interval between values is expressed in terms of a fixed unit of measure. Interval data are always numerical. College admission SAT scores are an example of interval-scaled data. For example, three students with SAT math scores of 620, 550, and 470 can be ranked or ordered in terms of best performance to poorest performance in math. In addition, the differences between the scores are meaningful. For instance, student 1 scored $620 - 550 = 70$ points more than student 2, while student 2 scored $550 - 470 = 80$ points more than student 3.

The scale of measurement for a variable is a **ratio scale** if the data have all the properties of interval data and the ratio of two values is meaningful. Variables such as distance, height, weight, and time use the ratio scale of measurement. This scale requires that a zero value be included to indicate that nothing exists for the variable at the zero point. For example, consider the cost of an automobile. A zero value for the cost would indicate that the automobile has no cost and is free. In addition, if we compare the cost of $30,000 for one automobile to the cost of $15,000 for a second automobile, the ratio property shows that the first automobile is $30,000/$15,000 = 2 times, or twice, the cost of the second automobile.

Categorical and Quantitative Data

Data can be classified as either categorical or quantitative. Data that can be grouped by specific categories are referred to as **categorical data**. Categorical data use either the nominal or ordinal scale of measurement. Data that use numeric values to indicate how much or how many are referred to as **quantitative data**. Quantitative data are obtained using either the interval or ratio scale of measurement.

The statistical method appropriate for summarizing data depends upon whether the data are categorical or quantitative.

A **categorical variable** is a variable with categorical data, and a **quantitative variable** is a variable with quantitative data. The statistical analysis appropriate for a particular variable depends upon whether the variable is categorical or quantitative. If the variable is categorical, the statistical analysis is limited. We can summarize categorical data by counting the number of observations in each category or by computing the proportion of the observations in each category. However, even when the categorical data are identified by a numerical code, arithmetic operations such as addition, subtraction, multiplication, and division do not provide meaningful results. Section 2.1 discusses ways of summarizing categorical data.

Arithmetic operations provide meaningful results for quantitative variables. For example, quantitative data may be added and then divided by the number of observations to compute the average value. This average is usually meaningful and easily interpreted. In general, more alternatives for statistical analysis are possible when data are quantitative. Section 2.2 and Chapter 3 provide ways of summarizing quantitative data.

Cross-Sectional and Time Series Data

For purposes of statistical analysis, distinguishing between cross-sectional data and time series data is important. **Cross-sectional data** are data collected at the same or approximately the same point in time. The data in Table 1.1 are cross-sectional because they describe the five variables for the 60 World Trade Organization nations at the same point in time. **Time series data** are data collected over several time periods. For example, the time series in Figure 1.1 shows the U.S. average price per gallon of conventional regular gasoline between 2012 and 2018. From January 2012 until June 2014, prices fluctuated between $3.19 and $3.84 per gallon before a long stretch of decreasing prices from July 2014 to January 2015. The lowest average price per gallon occurred in January 2016 ($1.68). Since then, the average price appears to be on a gradual increasing trend.

Graphs of time series data are frequently found in business and economic publications. Such graphs help analysts understand what happened in the past, identify any trends over time, and project future values for the time series. The graphs of time series data can take on a variety of forms, as shown in Figure 1.2. With a little study, these graphs are usually easy to understand and interpret. For example, Panel (A) in Figure 1.2 is a graph that shows the Dow Jones Industrial Average Index from 2008 to 2018. Poor economic conditions caused a serious drop in the index during 2008 with the low point occurring in February 2009 (7062). After that, the index has been on a remarkable nine-year increase, reaching its peak (26,149) in January 2018.

The graph in Panel (B) shows the net income of McDonald's Inc. from 2008 to 2017. The declining economic conditions in 2008 and 2009 were actually beneficial to McDonald's as the company's net income rose to all-time highs. The growth in McDonald's net income showed that the company was thriving during the economic downturn as people were cutting back on the more expensive sit-down restaurants and seeking less-expensive alternatives offered by McDonald's. McDonald's net income continued to new all-time highs in 2010 and 2011, decreased slightly in 2012, and peaked in 2013. After three years of relatively lower net income, their net income increased to $5.19 billion in 2017.

Panel (C) shows the time series for the occupancy rate of hotels in South Florida over a one-year period. The highest occupancy rates, 95% and 98%, occur during the months

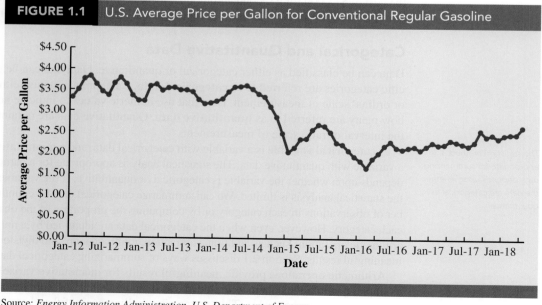

FIGURE 1.1   U.S. Average Price per Gallon for Conventional Regular Gasoline

Source: *Energy Information Administration, U.S. Department of Energy.*

FIGURE 1.2   A Variety of Graphs of Time Series Data

(A) Dow Jones Industrial Average Index

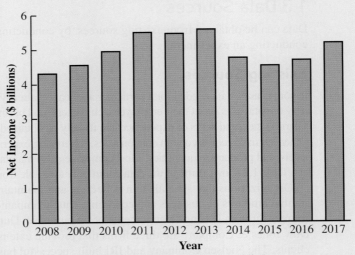

(B) Net Income for McDonald's Inc.

(C) Occupancy Rate of South Florida Hotels

of February and March when the climate of South Florida is attractive to tourists. In fact, January to April of each year is typically the high-occupancy season for South Florida hotels. On the other hand, note the low occupancy rates during the months of August to October, with the lowest occupancy rate of 50% occurring in September. High temperatures and the hurricane season are the primary reasons for the drop in hotel occupancy during this period.

N O T E S   +   C O M M E N T S

1. An observation is the set of measurements obtained for each element in a data set. Hence, the number of observations is always the same as the number of elements. The number of measurements obtained for each element equals the number of variables. Hence, the total number of data items can be determined by multiplying the number of observations by the number of variables.

2. Quantitative data may be discrete or continuous. Quantitative data that measure how many (e.g., number of calls received in 5 minutes) are discrete. Quantitative data that measure how much (e.g., weight or time) are continuous because no separation occurs between the possible data values.

1.3 Data Sources

Data can be obtained from existing sources, by conducting an observational study, or by conducting an experiment.

Existing Sources

In some cases, data needed for a particular application already exist. Companies maintain a variety of databases about their employees, customers, and business operations. Data on employee salaries, ages, and years of experience can usually be obtained from internal personnel records. Other internal records contain data on sales, advertising expenditures, distribution costs, inventory levels, and production quantities. Most companies also maintain detailed data about their customers. Table 1.2 shows some of the data commonly available from internal company records.

Organizations that specialize in collecting and maintaining data make available substantial amounts of business and economic data. Companies access these external data sources through leasing arrangements or by purchase. Dun & Bradstreet, Bloomberg, and Dow Jones & Company are three firms that provide extensive business database services to clients. The Nielsen Company and IRI built successful businesses collecting and processing data that they sell to advertisers and product manufacturers.

Data are also available from a variety of industry associations and special interest organizations. The U.S. Travel Association maintains travel-related information such as the number of

TABLE 1.2	Examples of Data Available from Internal Company Records
Source	**Some of the Data Typically Available**
Employee records	Name, address, social security number, salary, number of vacation days, number of sick days, and bonus
Production records	Part or product number, quantity produced, direct labor cost, and materials cost
Inventory records	Part or product number, number of units on hand, reorder level, economic order quantity, and discount schedule
Sales records	Product number, sales volume, sales volume by region, and sales volume by customer type
Credit records	Customer name, address, phone number, credit limit, and accounts receivable balance
Customer profile	Age, gender, income level, household size, address, and preferences

TABLE 1.3	Examples of Data Available from Selected Government Agencies
Government Agency	**Some of the Data Available**
Census Bureau	Population data, number of households, and household income
Federal Reserve Board	Data on the money supply, installment credit, exchange rates, and discount rates
Office of Management and Budget	Data on revenue, expenditures, and debt of the federal government
Department of Commerce	Data on business activity, value of shipments by industry, level of profits by industry, and growing and declining industries
Bureau of Labor Statistics	Consumer spending, hourly earnings, unemployment rate, safety records, and international statistics
DATA.GOV	More than 150,000 data sets including agriculture, consumer, education, health and manufacturing data

tourists and travel expenditures by states. Such data would be of interest to firms and individuals in the travel industry. The Graduate Management Admission Council maintains data on test scores, student characteristics, and graduate management education programs. Most of the data from these types of sources are available to qualified users at a modest cost.

The Internet is an important source of data and statistical information. Almost all companies maintain websites that provide general information about the company as well as data on sales, number of employees, number of products, product prices, and product specifications. In addition, a number of companies, including Google, Yahoo, and others, now specialize in making information available over the Internet. As a result, one can obtain access to stock quotes, meal prices at restaurants, salary data, and an almost infinite variety of information. Some social media companies such as Twitter provide application programming interfaces (APIs) that allow developers to access large amounts of data generated by users. These data can be extremely valuable to companies who want to know more about how existing and potential customers feel about their products.

Government agencies are another important source of existing data. For instance, the website DATA.GOV was launched by the U.S. government in 2009 to make it easier for the public to access data collected by the U.S. federal government. The DATA.GOV website includes more than 150,000 data sets from a variety of U.S. federal departments and agencies, but there are many other federal agencies who maintain their own websites and data repositories. Table 1.3 lists selected governmental agencies and some of the data they provide. Figure 1.3 shows the home page for the DATA.GOV website. Many state and local governments are also now providing data sets online. As examples, the states of California and Texas maintain open data portals at data.ca.gov and data.texas.gov, respectively. New York City's open data website is opendata.cityofnewyork.us, and the city of Cincinnati, Ohio, is at data.cincinnati-oh.gov.

Observational Study

In an *observational study* we simply observe what is happening in a particular situation, record data on one or more variables of interest, and conduct a statistical analysis of the resulting data. For example, researchers might observe a randomly selected group of customers that enter a Walmart supercenter to collect data on variables such as the length of time the customer spends shopping, the gender of the customer, the amount spent, and so on. Statistical analysis of the data may help management determine how factors such as the length of time shopping and the gender of the customer affect the amount spent.

As another example of an observational study, suppose that researchers were interested in investigating the relationship between the gender of the CEO for a *Fortune* 500 company and the performance of the company as measured by the return on equity (ROE). To obtain data, the researchers selected a sample of companies and recorded the gender of the CEO

FIGURE 1.3   DATA.GOV Homepage

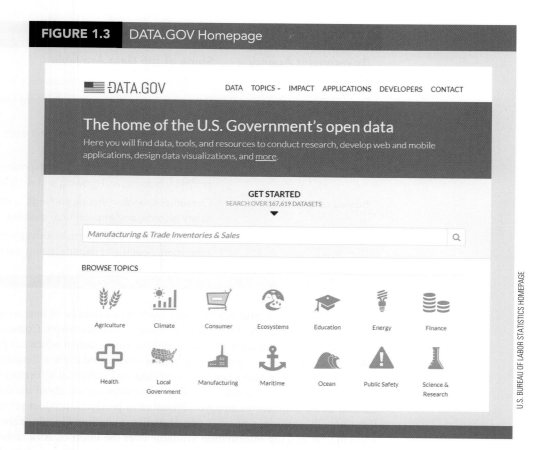

and the ROE for each company. Statistical analysis of the data can help determine the relationship between performance of the company and the gender of the CEO. This example is an observational study because the researchers had no control over the gender of the CEO or the ROE at each of the companies that were sampled.

Surveys and public opinion polls are two other examples of commonly used observational studies. The data provided by these types of studies simply enable us to observe opinions of the respondents. For example, the New York State legislature commissioned a telephone survey in which residents were asked if they would support or oppose an increase in the state gasoline tax in order to provide funding for bridge and highway repairs. Statistical analysis of the survey results will assist the state legislature in determining if it should introduce a bill to increase gasoline taxes.

Experiment

The largest experimental statistical study ever conducted is believed to be the 1954 Public Health Service experiment for the Salk polio vaccine. Nearly 2 million children in grades 1, 2, and 3 were selected from throughout the United States.

In Chapter 13, we discuss statistical methods appropriate for analyzing the data from an experiment.

The key difference between an observational study and an experiment is that an experiment is conducted under controlled conditions. As a result, the data obtained from a well-designed experiment can often provide more information as compared to the data obtained from existing sources or by conducting an observational study. For example, suppose a pharmaceutical company would like to learn about how a new drug it has developed affects blood pressure. To obtain data about how the new drug affects blood pressure, researchers selected a sample of individuals. Different groups of individuals are given different dosage levels of the new drug, and before and after data on blood pressure are collected for each group. Statistical analysis of the data can help determine how the new drug affects blood pressure.

The types of experiments we deal with in statistics often begin with the identification of a particular variable of interest. Then one or more other variables are identified and controlled so that data can be obtained about how the other variables influence the primary variable of interest.

Time and Cost Issues

Anyone wanting to use data and statistical analysis as aids to decision making must be aware of the time and cost required to obtain the data. The use of existing data sources is desirable when data must be obtained in a relatively short period of time. If important data are not readily available from an existing source, the additional time and cost involved in obtaining the data must be taken into account. In all cases, the decision maker should consider the contribution of the statistical analysis to the decision-making process. The cost of data acquisition and the subsequent statistical analysis should not exceed the savings generated by using the information to make a better decision.

Data Acquisition Errors

Managers should always be aware of the possibility of data errors in statistical studies. Using erroneous data can be worse than not using any data at all. An error in data acquisition occurs whenever the data value obtained is not equal to the true or actual value that would be obtained with a correct procedure. Such errors can occur in a number of ways. For example, an interviewer might make a recording error, such as a transposition in writing the age of a 24-year-old person as 42, or the person answering an interview question might misinterpret the question and provide an incorrect response.

Experienced data analysts take great care in collecting and recording data to ensure that errors are not made. Special procedures can be used to check for internal consistency of the data. For instance, such procedures would indicate that the analyst should review the accuracy of data for a respondent shown to be 22 years of age but reporting 20 years of work experience. Data analysts also review data with unusually large and small values, called outliers, which are candidates for possible data errors. In Chapter 3 we present some of the methods statisticians use to identify outliers.

Errors often occur during data acquisition. Blindly using any data that happen to be available or using data that were acquired with little care can result in misleading information and bad decisions. Thus, taking steps to acquire accurate data can help ensure reliable and valuable decision-making information.

1.4 Descriptive Statistics

Most of the statistical information in the media, company reports, and other publications consists of data that are summarized and presented in a form that is easy for the reader to understand. Such summaries of data, which may be tabular, graphical, or numerical, are referred to as **descriptive statistics**.

Refer to the data set in Table 1.1 showing data for 60 nations that participate in the World Trade Organization. Methods of descriptive statistics can be used to summarize these data. For example, consider the variable Fitch Outlook, which indicates the direction the nation's credit rating is likely to move over the next two years. The Fitch Outlook is recorded as being negative, stable, or positive. A tabular summary of the data showing the number of nations with each of the Fitch Outlook ratings is shown in Table 1.4. A graphical summary of the same data, called a bar chart, is shown in Figure 1.4. These types of summaries make the data

TABLE 1.4	Frequencies and Percent Frequencies for the Fitch Credit Rating Outlook of 60 Nations	
Fitch Outlook	**Frequency**	**Percent Frequency (%)**
Positive	4	6.7
Stable	44	73.2
Negative	12	20.0

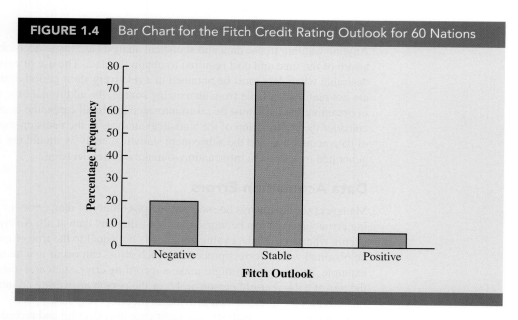

FIGURE 1.4   Bar Chart for the Fitch Credit Rating Outlook for 60 Nations

easier to interpret. Referring to Table 1.4 and Figure 1.4, we can see that the majority of Fitch Outlook credit ratings are stable, with 73.3% of the nations having this rating. More nations have a negative outlook (20%) than a positive outlook (6.7%).

A graphical summary of the data for the quantitative variable Per Capita GDP in Table 1.1, called a histogram, is provided in Figure 1.5. Using the histogram, it is easy to see that

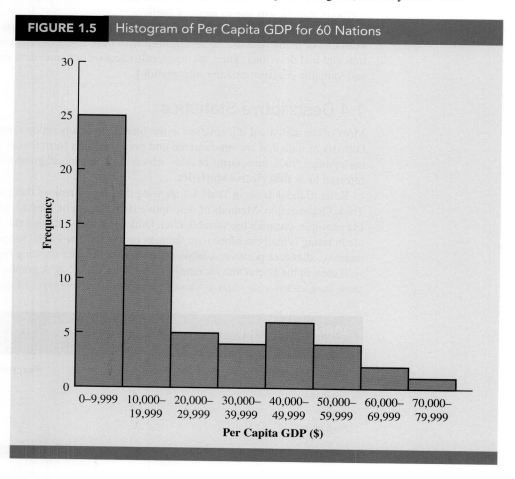

FIGURE 1.5   Histogram of Per Capita GDP for 60 Nations

Per Capita GDP for the 60 nations ranges from $0 to $80,000, with the highest concentration between $0 and $10,000. Only one nation had a Per Capita GDP exceeding $70,000.

In addition to tabular and graphical displays, numerical descriptive statistics are used to summarize data. The most common numerical measure is the average, or mean. Using the data on Per Capita GDP for the 60 nations in Table 1.1, we can compute the average by adding Per Capita GDP for all 60 nations and dividing the total by 60. Doing so provides an average Per Capita GDP of $21,279. This average provides a measure of the central tendency, or central location of the data.

Chapters 2 and 3 devote attention to the tabular, graphical, and numerical methods of descriptive statistics.

There is a great deal of interest in effective methods for developing and presenting descriptive statistics.

1.5 Statistical Inference

Many situations require information about a large group of elements (individuals, companies, voters, households, products, customers, and so on). But, because of time, cost, and other considerations, data can be collected from only a small portion of the group. The larger group of elements in a particular study is called the **population**, and the smaller group is called the **sample**. Formally, we use the following definitions.

> **POPULATION**
>
> A population is the set of all elements of interest in a particular study.

> **SAMPLE**
>
> A sample is a subset of the population.

The U.S. government conducts a census every 10 years. Market research firms conduct sample surveys every day.

The process of conducting a survey to collect data for the entire population is called a **census**. The process of conducting a survey to collect data for a sample is called a **sample survey**. As one of its major contributions, statistics uses data from a sample to make estimates and test hypotheses about the characteristics of a population through a process referred to as **statistical inference**.

As an example of statistical inference, let us consider the study conducted by Rogers Industries. Rogers manufactures lithium batteries used in rechargeable electronics such as laptop computers and tablets. In an attempt to increase battery life for its products, Rogers has developed a new solid-state lithium battery that should last longer and be safer to use. In this case, the population is defined as all lithium batteries that could be produced using the new solid-state technology. To evaluate the advantages of the new battery, a sample of 200 batteries manufactured with the new solid-state technology were tested. Data collected from this sample showed the number of hours each battery lasted before needing to be recharged under controlled conditions. See Table 1.5.

Suppose Rogers wants to use the sample data to make an inference about the average hours of battery life for the population of all batteries that could be produced with the new solid-state technology. Adding the 200 values in Table 1.5 and dividing the total by 200 provides the sample average battery life: 18.84 hours. We can use this sample result to estimate that the average lifetime for the batteries in the population is 18.84 hours. Figure 1.6 provides a graphical summary of the statistical inference process for Rogers Industries.

Whenever statisticians use a sample to estimate a population characteristic of interest, they usually provide a statement of the quality, or precision, associated with the estimate. For the Rogers Industries example, the statistician might state that the point estimate of the average battery life is 18.84 hours $\pm.68$ hours. Thus, an interval estimate of the average battery life is 18.16 to 19.52 hours. The statistician can also state how confident he or she is that the interval from 18.16 to 19.52 hours contains the population average.

TABLE 1.5	Hours Until Recharge for a Sample of 200 Batteries for the Rogers Industries Example

Rogers

Battery Life (hours)

19.49	18.18	18.65	19.45	19.89	18.94	17.72	18.35	18.66	18.23
19.08	19.92	19.01	18.84	17.73	19.70	18.37	18.69	19.98	18.80
19.11	18.26	19.05	17.89	19.61	18.52	18.10	19.08	18.27	18.29
19.55	18.81	18.68	17.43	20.34	17.73	17.66	18.52	19.90	19.33
18.81	19.12	18.39	19.27	19.43	19.29	19.11	18.96	19.65	18.20
19.18	20.07	18.54	18.37	18.13	18.29	19.11	20.22	18.07	18.91
18.44	19.04	18.88	19.51	18.84	20.98	18.82	19.40	19.00	17.53
18.74	19.04	18.35	19.01	17.54	18.14	19.82	19.23	19.20	20.02
20.14	17.75	18.50	19.85	18.93	19.07	18.83	18.54	17.85	18.51
18.74	18.74	19.06	19.00	18.77	19.12	19.58	18.75	18.67	20.71
18.35	19.42	19.42	19.41	19.85	18.23	18.31	18.44	17.61	19.21
17.71	18.04	19.53	18.87	19.11	19.28	18.55	18.58	17.33	18.75
18.52	19.06	18.54	18.41	19.86	17.24	18.32	19.27	18.34	18.89
18.78	18.88	18.67	18.19	19.07	20.12	17.69	17.92	19.49	19.52
19.91	18.46	18.98	19.18	19.01	18.79	17.90	18.43	18.35	19.02
18.06	19.11	19.40	18.71	18.91	18.95	18.51	19.27	20.39	19.72
17.48	17.49	19.29	18.49	17.93	19.42	19.19	19.46	18.56	18.41
18.24	17.83	18.28	19.51	18.17	18.64	18.57	18.65	18.61	17.97
18.73	19.32	19.37	18.60	19.16	19.44	18.28	19.20	17.88	18.90
19.66	19.00	18.43	19.54	19.15	18.62	19.64	18.87	18.31	19.54

FIGURE 1.6	The Process of Statistical Inference for the Norris Electronics Example

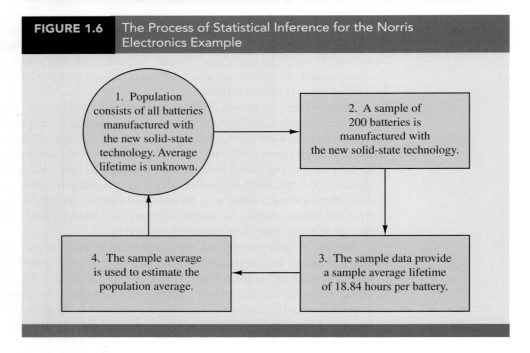

1.6 Analytics

Because of the dramatic increase in available data, more cost-effective data storage, faster computer processing, and recognition by managers that data can be extremely valuable for understanding customers and business operations, there has been a dramatic increase in data-driven decision making. The broad range of techniques that may be used to support data-driven decisions comprise what has become known as analytics.

We adopt the definition of analytics developed by the Institute for Operations Research and the Management Sciences (INFORMS).

Analytics is the scientific process of transforming data into insight for making better decisions. Analytics is used for data-driven or fact-based decision making, which is often seen as more objective than alternative approaches to decision making. The tools of analytics can aid decision making by creating insights from data, improving our ability to more accurately forecast for planning, helping us quantify risk, and yielding better alternatives through analysis.

Analytics can involve a variety of techniques from simple reports to the most advanced optimization techniques (algorithms for finding the best course of action). Analytics is now generally thought to comprise three broad categories of techniques. These categories are descriptive analytics, predictive analytics, and prescriptive analytics.

Descriptive analytics encompasses the set of analytical techniques that describe what has happened in the past. Examples of these types of techniques are data queries, reports, descriptive statistics, data visualization, data dash boards, and basic what-if spreadsheet models.

Predictive analytics consists of analytical techniques that use models constructed from past data to predict the future or to assess the impact of one variable on another. For example, past data on sales of a product may be used to construct a mathematical model that predicts future sales. Such a model can account for factors such as the growth trajectory and seasonality of the product's sales based on past growth and seasonal patterns. Point-of-sale scanner data from retail outlets may be used by a packaged food manufacturer to help estimate the lift in unit sales associated with coupons or sales events. Survey data and past purchase behavior may be used to help predict the market share of a new product. Each of these is an example of predictive analytics. Linear regression, time series analysis, and forecasting models fall into the category of predictive analytics; these techniques are discussed later in this text. Simulation, which is the use of probability and statistical computer models to better understand risk, also falls under the category of predictive analytics.

Prescriptive analytics differs greatly from descriptive or predictive analytics. What distinguishes prescriptive analytics is that prescriptive models yield a best course of action to take. That is, the output of a prescriptive model is a best decision. Hence, **prescriptive analytics** is the set of analytical techniques that yield a best course of action. Optimization models, which generate solutions that maximize or minimize some objective subject to a set of constraints, fall into the category of prescriptive models. The airline industry's use of revenue management is an example of a prescriptive model. The airline industry uses past purchasing data as inputs into a model that recommends the pricing strategy across all flights that will maximize revenue for the company.

How does the study of statistics relate to analytics? Most of the techniques in descriptive and predictive analytics come from probability and statistics. These include descriptive statistics, data visualization, probability and probability distributions, sampling, and predictive modeling, including regression analysis and time series forecasting. Each of these techniques is discussed in this text. The increased use of analytics for data-driven decision making makes it more important than ever for analysts and managers to understand statistics and data analysis. Companies are increasingly seeking data savvy managers who know how to use descriptive and predictive models to make data-driven decisions.

At the beginning of this section, we mentioned the increased availability of data as one of the drivers of the interest in analytics. In the next section we discuss this explosion in available data and how it relates to the study of statistics.

1.7 Big Data and Data Mining

With the aid of magnetic card readers, bar code scanners, and point-of-sale terminals, most organizations obtain large amounts of data on a daily basis. And, even for a small local restaurant that uses touch screen monitors to enter orders and handle billing, the amount of data collected can be substantial. For large retail companies, the sheer volume of data collected is hard to conceptualize, and figuring out how to effectively use these data to improve profitability is a challenge. Mass retailers such as Walmart and Amazon capture data on 20 to 30 million transactions every day, telecommunication companies such as Orange S.A. and AT&T generate over 300 million call records per day, and Visa processes 6800 payment transactions per second or approximately 600 million transactions per day.

In addition to the sheer volume and speed with which companies now collect data, more complicated types of data are now available and are proving to be of great value to businesses. Text data are collected by monitoring what is being said about a company's products or services on social media such as Twitter. Audio data are collected from service calls (on a service call, you will often hear "this call may be monitored for quality control"). Video data are collected by in-store video cameras to analyze shopping behavior. Analyzing information generated by these nontraditional sources is more complicated because of the complex process of transforming the information into data that can be analyzed.

Larger and more complex data sets are now often referred to as **big data**. Although there does not seem to be a universally accepted definition of *big data*, many think if it as a set of data that cannot be managed, processed, or analyzed with commonly available software in a reasonable amount of time. Many data analysts define *big data* by referring to the three v's of data: volume, velocity, and variety. *Volume* refers to the amount of available data (the typical unit of measure for is now a terabyte, which is 10^{12} bytes); *velocity* refers to the speed at which data is collected and processed; and *variety* refers to the different data types.

The term *data warehousing* is used to refer to the process of capturing, storing, and maintaining the data. Computing power and data collection tools have reached the point where it is now feasible to store and retrieve extremely large quantities of data in seconds. Analysis of the data in the warehouse may result in decisions that will lead to new strategies and higher profits for the organization. For example, General Electric (GE) captures a large amount of data from sensors on its aircraft engines each time a plane takes off or lands. Capturing these data allows GE to offer an important service to its customers; GE monitors the engine performance and can alert its customer when service is needed or a problem is likely to occur.

The subject of **data mining** deals with methods for developing useful decision-making information from large databases. Using a combination of procedures from statistics, mathematics, and computer science, analysts "mine the data" in the warehouse to convert it into useful information, hence the name *data mining*. Dr. Kurt Thearling, a leading practitioner in the field, defines data mining as "the automated extraction of predictive information from (large) databases." The two key words in Dr. Thearling's definition are "automated" and "predictive." Data mining systems that are the most effective use automated procedures to extract information from the data using only the most general or even vague queries by the user. And data mining software automates the process of uncovering hidden predictive information that in the past required hands-on analysis.

The major applications of data mining have been made by companies with a strong consumer focus, such as retail businesses, financial organizations, and communication companies. Data mining has been successfully used to help retailers such as Amazon determine one or more related products that customers who have already purchased a specific product are also likely to purchase. Then, when a customer logs on to the company's website and purchases a product, the website uses pop-ups to alert the customer about additional products that the customer is likely to purchase. In another application, data mining may be used to identify customers who are likely to spend more than $20 on a particular shopping trip. These customers may then be identified as the ones to receive special email or regular mail discount offers to encourage them to make their next shopping trip before the discount termination date.

Data mining is a technology that relies heavily on statistical methodology such as multiple regression, logistic regression, and correlation. But it takes a creative integration of all these methods and computer science technologies involving artificial

Statistical methods play an important role in data mining, both in terms of discovering relationships in the data and predicting future outcomes. However, a thorough coverage of data mining and the use of statistics in data mining is outside the scope of this text.

intelligence and machine learning to make data mining effective. A substantial investment in time and money is required to implement commercial data mining software packages developed by firms such as Oracle, Teradata, and SAS. The statistical concepts introduced in this text will be helpful in understanding the statistical methodology used by data mining software packages and enable you to better understand the statistical information that is developed.

Because statistical models play an important role in developing predictive models in data mining, many of the concerns that statisticians deal with in developing statistical models are also applicable. For instance, a concern in any statistical study involves the issue of model reliability. Finding a statistical model that works well for a particular sample of data does not necessarily mean that it can be reliably applied to other data. One of the common statistical approaches to evaluating model reliability is to divide the sample data set into two parts: a training data set and a test data set. If the model developed using the training data is able to accurately predict values in the test data, we say that the model is reliable. One advantage that data mining has over classical statistics is that the enormous amount of data available allows the data mining software to partition the data set so that a model developed for the training data set may be tested for reliability on other data. In this sense, the partitioning of the data set allows data mining to develop models and relationships and then quickly observe if they are repeatable and valid with new and different data. On the other hand, a warning for data mining applications is that with so much data available, there is a danger of overfitting the model to the point that misleading associations and cause/effect conclusions appear to exist. Careful interpretation of data mining results and additional testing will help avoid this pitfall.

1.8 Computers and Statistical Analysis

For students unfamiliar with Microsoft Excel, Appendix E provides an introduction to Excel 2016 and the tools available for statistical analysis.

Statisticians use computer software to perform statistical computations and analyses. For example, computing the average time until recharge for the 200 batteries in the Rogers Industries example (see Table 1.5) would be quite tedious without a computer. End-of-chapter appendixes cover the step-by-step procedures for using Microsoft Excel and the statistical package JMP to implement the statistical techniques presented in the chapter.

Special data manipulation and analysis tools are needed for big data, which was described in the previous section. Open-source software for distributed processing of large data sets such as Hadoop, open-source programming languages such as R and Python, and commercially available packages such as SAS and SPSS are used in practice for big data.

1.9 Ethical Guidelines for Statistical Practice

Ethical behavior is something we should strive for in all that we do. Ethical issues arise in statistics because of the important role statistics plays in the collection, analysis, presentation, and interpretation of data. In a statistical study, unethical behavior can take a variety of forms including improper sampling, inappropriate analysis of the data, development of misleading graphs, use of inappropriate summary statistics, and/or a biased interpretation of the statistical results.

As you begin to do your own statistical work, we encourage you to be fair, thorough, objective, and neutral as you collect data, conduct analyses, make oral presentations, and present written reports containing information developed. As a consumer of statistics, you should also be aware of the possibility of unethical statistical behavior by others. When you see statistics in the media, it is a good idea to view the information with some skepticism, always being aware of the source as well as the purpose and objectivity of the statistics provided.

The American Statistical Association, the nation's leading professional organization for statistics and statisticians, developed the report "Ethical Guidelines for Statistical

Practice"[2] to help statistical practitioners make and communicate ethical decisions and assist students in learning how to perform statistical work responsibly. The report contains 52 guidelines organized into eight topic areas: Professional Integrity and Accountability; Integrity of Data and Methods; Responsibilities to Science/Public/Funder/Client; Responsibilities to Research Subjects; Responsibilities to Research Team Colleagues; Responsibilities to Other Statisticians or Statistics Practitioners; Responsibilities Regarding Allegations of Misconduct; and Responsibilities of Employers Including Organizations, Individuals, Attorneys, or Other Clients Employing Statistical Practitioners.

One of the ethical guidelines in the Professional Integrity and Accountability area addresses the issue of running multiple tests until a desired result is obtained. Let us consider an example. In Section 1.5 we discussed a statistical study conducted by Rogers Industries involving a sample of 200 lithium batteries manufactured with a new solid-state technology. The average battery life for the sample, 18.84 hours, provided an estimate of the average lifetime for all lithium batteries produced with the new solid-state technology. However, since Rogers selected a sample of batteries, it is reasonable to assume that another sample would have provided a different average battery life.

Suppose Rogers's management had hoped the sample results would enable them to claim that the average time until recharge for the new batteries was 20 hours or more. Suppose further that Rogers's management decides to continue the study by manufacturing and testing repeated samples of 200 batteries with the new solid-state technology until a sample mean of 20 hours or more is obtained. If the study is repeated enough times, a sample may eventually be obtained—by chance alone—that would provide the desired result and enable Rogers to make such a claim. In this case, consumers would be misled into thinking the new product is better than it actually is. Clearly, this type of behavior is unethical and represents a gross misuse of statistics in practice.

Several ethical guidelines in the responsibilities and publications and testimony area deal with issues involving the handling of data. For instance, a statistician must account for all data considered in a study and explain the sample(s) actually used. In the Rogers Industries study the average battery life for the 200 batteries in the original sample is 18.84 hours; this is less than the 20 hours or more that management hoped to obtain. Suppose now that after reviewing the results showing a 18.84 hour average battery life, Rogers discards all the observations with 18 or less hours until recharge, allegedly because these batteries contain imperfections caused by startup problems in the manufacturing process. After discarding these batteries, the average lifetime for the remaining batteries in the sample turns out to be 22 hours. Would you be suspicious of Rogers's claim that the battery life for its new solid-state batteries is 22 hours?

If the Rogers batteries showing 18 or less hours until recharge were discarded to simply provide an average lifetime of 22 hours, there is no question that discarding the batteries with 18 or fewer hours until recharge is unethical. But, even if the discarded batteries contain imperfections due to startup problems in the manufacturing process—and, as a result, should not have been included in the analysis—the statistician who conducted the study must account for all the data that were considered and explain how the sample actually used was obtained. To do otherwise is potentially misleading and would constitute unethical behavior on the part of both the company and the statistician.

A guideline in the shared values section of the American Statistical Association report states that statistical practitioners should avoid any tendency to slant statistical work toward predetermined outcomes. This type of unethical practice is often observed when unrepresentative samples are used to make claims. For instance, in many areas of the country smoking is not permitted in restaurants. Suppose, however, a lobbyist for the tobacco industry interviews people in restaurants where smoking is permitted in order to estimate the percentage of people who are in favor of allowing smoking in restaurants. The sample results show that 90% of the people interviewed are in favor of allowing smoking

---

[2]American Statistical Association, "Ethical Guidelines for Statistical Practice," April 2018.

in restaurants. Based upon these sample results, the lobbyist claims that 90% of all people who eat in restaurants are in favor of permitting smoking in restaurants. In this case we would argue that only sampling persons eating in restaurants that allow smoking has biased the results. If only the final results of such a study are reported, readers unfamiliar with the details of the study (i.e., that the sample was collected only in restaurants allowing smoking) can be misled.

The scope of the American Statistical Association's report is broad and includes ethical guidelines that are appropriate not only for a statistician, but also for consumers of statistical information. We encourage you to read the report to obtain a better perspective of ethical issues as you continue your study of statistics and to gain the background for determining how to ensure that ethical standards are met when you start to use statistics in practice.

SUMMARY

Statistics is the art and science of collecting, analyzing, presenting, and interpreting data. Nearly every college student majoring in business or economics is required to take a course in statistics. We began the chapter by describing typical statistical applications for business and economics.

Data consist of the facts and figures that are collected and analyzed. Four scales of measurement used to obtain data on a particular variable include nominal, ordinal, interval, and ratio. The scale of measurement for a variable is nominal when the data are labels or names used to identify an attribute of an element. The scale is ordinal if the data demonstrate the properties of nominal data and the order or rank of the data is meaningful. The scale is interval if the data demonstrate the properties of ordinal data and the interval between values is expressed in terms of a fixed unit of measure. Finally, the scale of measurement is ratio if the data show all the properties of interval data and the ratio of two values is meaningful.

For purposes of statistical analysis, data can be classified as categorical or quantitative. Categorical data use labels or names to identify an attribute of each element. Categorical data use either the nominal or ordinal scale of measurement and may be nonnumeric or numeric. Quantitative data are numeric values that indicate how much or how many. Quantitative data use either the interval or ratio scale of measurement. Ordinary arithmetic operations are meaningful only if the data are quantitative. Therefore, statistical computations used for quantitative data are not always appropriate for categorical data.

In Sections 1.4 and 1.5 we introduced the topics of descriptive statistics and statistical inference. Descriptive statistics are the tabular, graphical, and numerical methods used to summarize data. The process of statistical inference uses data obtained from a sample to make estimates or test hypotheses about the characteristics of a population. The last four sections of the chapter provide an introduction to the relatively new fields of analytics, data mining and big data, information on the role of computers in statistical analysis, and a summary of ethical guidelines for statistical practice.

GLOSSARY

Analytics The scientific process of transforming data into insight for making better decisions.

Big Data A set of data that cannot be managed, processed, or analyzed with commonly available software in a reasonable amount of time. Big data are characterized by great volume (a large amount of data), high velocity (fast collection and processing), or wide variety (could include nontraditional data such as video, audio, and text).

Categorical data Labels or names used to identify an attribute of each element. Categorical data use either the nominal or ordinal scale of measurement and may be nonnumeric or numeric.

Categorical variable A variable with categorical data.

Census A survey to collect data on the entire population.

Cross-sectional data Data collected at the same or approximately the same point in time.

Data The facts and figures collected, analyzed, and summarized for presentation and interpretation.

Data mining The process of using procedures from statistics and computer science to extract useful information from extremely large databases.

Data set All the data collected in a particular study.

Descriptive Analytics The set of analytical techniques that describe what has happened in the past.

Descriptive statistics Tabular, graphical, and numerical summaries of data.

Elements The entities on which data are collected.

Interval scale The scale of measurement for a variable if the data demonstrate the properties of ordinal data and the interval between values is expressed in terms of a fixed unit of measure. Interval data are always numeric.

Nominal scale The scale of measurement for a variable when the data are labels or names used to identify an attribute of an element. Nominal data may be nonnumeric or numeric.

Observation The set of measurements obtained for a particular element.

Ordinal scale The scale of measurement for a variable if the data exhibit the properties of nominal data and the order or rank of the data is meaningful. Ordinal data may be nonnumeric or numeric.

Population The set of all elements of interest in a particular study.

Predictive Analytics The set of analytical techniques that use models constructed from past data to predict the future or assess the impact of one variable on another.

Prescriptive Analytics The set of analytical techniques that yield a best course of action.

Quantitative data Numeric values that indicate how much or how many of something. Quantitative data are obtained using either the interval or ratio scale of measurement.

Quantitative variable A variable with quantitative data.

Ratio scale The scale of measurement for a variable if the data demonstrate all the properties of interval data and the ratio of two values is meaningful. Ratio data are always numeric.

Sample A subset of the population.

Sample survey A survey to collect data on a sample.

Statistical inference The process of using data obtained from a sample to make estimates or test hypotheses about the characteristics of a population.

Statistics The art and science of collecting, analyzing, presenting, and interpreting data.

Time series data Data collected over several time periods.

Variable A characteristic of interest for the elements.

SUPPLEMENTARY EXERCISES

1. Discuss the differences between statistics as numerical facts and statistics as a discipline or field of study.

2. **Comparing Tablet Computers.** Tablet PC Comparison provides a wide variety of information about tablet computers. The company's website enables consumers to easily compare different tablets using factors such as cost, type of operating system, display size, battery life, and CPU manufacturer. A sample of 10 tablet computers is shown in Table 1.6 (Tablet PC Comparison website).
   a. How many elements are in this data set?
   b. How many variables are in this data set?
   c. Which variables are categorical and which variables are quantitative?
   d. What type of measurement scale is used for each of the variables?

3. **Tablet PCs: Cost, CPU, and Operating System.** Refer to Table 1.6.
   a. What is the average cost for the tablets?
   b. Compare the average cost of tablets with a Windows operating system to the average cost of tablets with an Android operating system.
   c. What percentage of tablets use a CPU manufactured by TI OMAP?
   d. What percentage of tablets use an Android operating system?

TABLE 1.6 Product Information for 10 Tablet Computers

Tablet	Cost ($)	Operating System	Display Size (inches)	Battery Life (hours)	CPU Manufacturer
Acer Iconia W510	599	Windows	10.1	8.5	Intel
Amazon Kindle Fire HD	299	Android	8.9	9	TI OMAP
Apple iPad 4	499	iOS	9.7	11	Apple
HP Envy X2	860	Windows	11.6	8	Intel
Lenovo ThinkPad Tablet	668	Windows	10.1	10.5	Intel
Microsoft Surface Pro	899	Windows	10.6	4	Intel
Motorola Droid XYboard	530	Android	10.1	9	TI OMAP
Samsung Ativ Smart PC	590	Windows	11.6	7	Intel
Samsung Galaxy Tab	525	Android	10.1	10	Nvidia
Sony Tablet S	360	Android	9.4	8	Nvidia

4. **Comparing Phones.** Table 1.7 shows data for eight phones (*Consumer Reports*). The Overall Score, a measure of the overall quality for the phone, ranges from 0 to 100. Voice Quality has possible ratings of poor, fair, good, very good, and excellent. Talk Time is the manufacturer's claim of how long the phone can be used when it is fully charged.
   a. How many elements are in this data set?
   b. For the variables Price, Overall Score, Voice Quality, and Talk Time, which variables are categorical and which variables are quantitative?
   c. What scale of measurement is used for each variable?
5. **Summarizing Phone Data.** Refer to the data set in Table 1.7.
   a. What is the average price for the phones?
   b. What is the average talk time for the phones?
   c. What percentage of the phones have a voice quality of excellent?
6. **New Automobile Owners Survey.** J.D. Power and Associates surveys new automobile owners to learn about the quality of recently purchased vehicles. The following questions were asked in a J.D. Power Initial Quality Survey.
   a. Did you purchase or lease the vehicle?
   b. What price did you pay?
   c. What is the overall attractiveness of your vehicle's exterior? (Unacceptable, Average, Outstanding, or Truly Exceptional)
   d. What is your average miles per gallon?

TABLE 1.7 Data for Eight Phones

Brand	Model	Price ($)	Overall Score	Voice Quality	Talk Time (hours)
AT&T	CL84100	60	73	Excellent	7
AT&T	TL92271	80	70	Very Good	7
Panasonic	4773B	100	78	Very Good	13
Panasonic	6592T	70	72	Very Good	13
Uniden	D2997	45	70	Very Good	10
Uniden	D1788	80	73	Very Good	7
Vtech	DS6521	60	72	Excellent	7
Vtech	CS6649	50	72	Very Good	7

    e. What is your overall rating of your new vehicle? (1- to 10-point scale with 1 Unacceptable and 10 Truly Exceptional)

Comment on whether each question provides categorical or quantitative data.

7. **Airline Customer Satisfaction.** Many service companies collect data via a follow-up survey of their customers. For example, to ascertain customer sentiment, Delta Air Lines sends an email to customers immediately following a flight. Among other questions, Delta asks:

How likely are you to recommend Delta Air Lines to others?

The possible responses are:

Definitely Will	Probably Will	May or May Not	Probably Will Not	Definitely Will Not
○	○	○	○	○

    a. Are the data collected by Delta in this example quantitative or categorical?
    b. What measurement scale is used?

8. **Readership Poll.** *The Tennessean*, an online newspaper located in Nashville, Tennessee, conducts a daily poll to obtain reader opinions on a variety of current issues. In a recent poll, 762 readers responded to the following question: "If a constitutional amendment to ban a state income tax is placed on the ballot in Tennessee, would you want it to pass?" Possible responses were Yes, No, or Not Sure (*The Tennessean* website).
    a. What was the sample size for this poll?
    b. Are the data categorical or quantitative?
    c. Would it make more sense to use averages or percentages as a summary of the data for this question?
    d. Of the respondents, 67% said Yes, they would want it to pass. How many individuals provided this response?

9. **College-Educated Workers.** Based on data from the U.S. Census Bureau, a Pew Research study showed that the percentage of employed individuals ages 25–29 who are college educated is at an all-time high. The study showed that the percentage of employed individuals aged 25–29 with at least a bachelor's degree in 2016 was 40%. In the year 2000, this percentage was 32%, in 1985 it was 25%, and in 1964 it was only 16% (Pew Research website).
    a. What is the population being studied in each of the four years in which Pew has data?
    b. What question was posed to each respondent?
    c. Do responses to the question provide categorical or quantitative data?

10. **Driving with Cell Phones.** The Bureau of Transportation Statistics Omnibus Household Survey is conducted annually and serves as an information source for the U.S. Department of Transportation. In one part of the survey the person being interviewed was asked to respond to the following statement: "Drivers of motor vehicles should be allowed to talk on a hand-held cell phone while driving." Possible responses were strongly agree, somewhat agree, somewhat disagree, and strongly disagree. Forty-four respondents said that they strongly agree with this statement, 130 said that they somewhat agree, 165 said they somewhat disagree, and 741 said they strongly disagree with this statement (Bureau of Transportation website).
    a. Do the responses for this statement provide categorical or quantitative data?
    b. Would it make more sense to use averages or percentages as a summary of the responses for this statement?
    c. What percentage of respondents strongly agree with allowing drivers of motor vehicles to talk on a hand-held cell phone while driving?
    d. Do the results indicate general support for or against allowing drivers of motor vehicles to talk on a hand-held cell phone while driving?

11. **Driverless Cars Expected Soon.** A Gallup Poll utilizing a random sample of 1,503 adults ages 18 or older was conducted in April 2018. The survey indicated a majority of Americans (53%) say driverless cars will be common in the next 10 years (Gallup,

FIGURE 1.7 Histogram of Survey Results on Driverless Cars

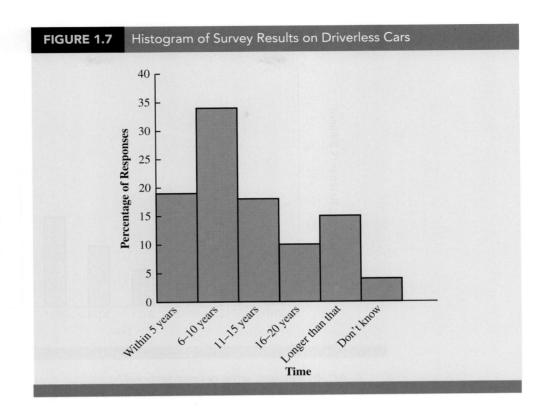

https://news.gallup.com/poll/234152/americans-expect-driverless-cars-common-next-decade.aspx). The question asked was:

> Thinking about fully automated, "driverless cars," cars that use technology to drive and do not need a human driver, based on what you have heard or read, how soon do you think driverless cars will be commonly used in the [United States]?

Figure 1.7 shows a summary of results of the survey in a histogram indicating the percentage of the total responses in different time intervals.

a. Are the responses to the survey question quantitative or categorical?
b. How many of the respondents said that they expect driverless cars to be common in the next 10 years?
c. How many respondents answered in the range 16–20 years?

12. **Hawaii Visitors Poll.** The Hawaii Visitors Bureau collects data on visitors to Hawaii. The following questions were among 16 asked in a questionnaire handed out to passengers during incoming airline flights.

- This trip to Hawaii is my: 1st, 2nd, 3rd, 4th, etc.
- The primary reason for this trip is: (10 categories, including vacation, convention, honeymoon)
- Where I plan to stay: (11 categories, including hotel, apartment, relatives, camping)
- Total days in Hawaii

a. What is the population being studied?
b. Is the use of a questionnaire a good way to reach the population of passengers on incoming airline flights?
c. Comment on each of the four questions in terms of whether it will provide categorical or quantitative data.

13. **Facebook Advertising Revenue.** Figure 1.8 provides a bar chart showing the annual advertising revenue for Facebook from 2010 to 2017 (Facebook Annual Reports).

a. What is the variable of interest?
b. Are the data categorical or quantitative?

| FIGURE 1.8 | Facebook Worldwide Advertising Revenue |

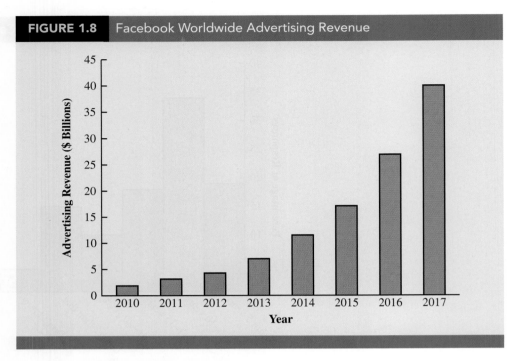

c. Are the data time series or cross-sectional?

d. Comment on the trend in Facebook's annual advertising revenue over time.

14. **Rental Car Fleet Size.** The following data show the number of rental cars in service (in thousands) for three rental car companies: Hertz, Avis, and Dollar over a three-year period (*Auto Rental News* website).

Company	Cars in Service (1000s)			
	Year 1	Year 2	Year 3	Year 4
Hertz	327	311	286	290
Dollar	167	140	106	108
Avis	204	220	300	270

a. Construct a time series graph for the years 2007 to 2010 showing the number of rental cars in service for each company. Show the time series for all three companies on the same graph.

b. Comment on who appears to be the market share leader and how the market shares are changing over time.

c. Construct a bar chart showing rental cars in service for 2010. Is this chart based on cross-sectional or time series data?

15. **Jewelry Sales.** The U.S. Census Bureau tracks sales per month for various products and services through its *Monthly Retail Trade Survey*. Figure 1.9 shows monthly jewelry sales in millions of dollars for 2016.

a. Are the data quantitative or categorical?

b. Are the data cross-sectional or time series?

c. Which four months have the highest sales?

d. Why do you think the answers to part c might be the highest four months?

16. **Athletic Shoe Sales.** Skechers U.S.A., Inc., is a performance footwear company headquartered in Manhattan Beach, California. The sales revenue for Skechers over a four-year period are as follows:

a. Are these cross-sectional or time-series data?

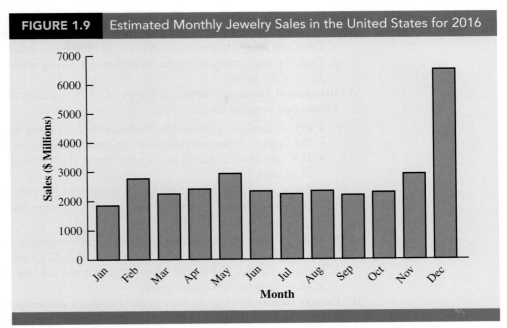

FIGURE 1.9 Estimated Monthly Jewelry Sales in the United States for 2016

Source: *The U.S. Census Bureau tracks sales per month for various products and services through its Monthly Retail Trade Survey (https://www.census.gov/retail/mrts/historic_releases.html)*

    b. Construct a bar graph similar to Figure 1.2 B.

    c. What can you say about how Skecher's sales are changing over these four years?

Year 1	Sales ($ Billion)
Year 1	2.30
Year 2	3.15
Year 3	3.56
Year 4	4.16

17. **Deciding on a Salary Increase.** A manager of a large corporation recommends a $10,000 raise be given to keep a valued subordinate from moving to another company. What internal and external sources of data might be used to decide whether such a salary increase is appropriate?

18. **Tax Survey.** A random telephone survey of 1021 adults (aged 18 and older) was conducted by Opinion Research Corporation on behalf of CompleteTax, an online tax preparation and e-filing service. The survey results showed that 684 of those surveyed planned to file their taxes electronically (CompleteTax Tax Prep Survey).

    a. Develop a descriptive statistic that can be used to estimate the percentage of all tax-payers who file electronically.

    b. The survey reported that the most frequently used method for preparing the tax return is to hire an accountant or professional tax preparer. If 60% of the people surveyed had their tax return prepared this way, how many people used an accountant or professional tax preparer?

    c. Other methods that the person filing the return often used include manual preparation, use of an online tax service, and use of a software tax program. Would the data for the method for preparing the tax return be considered categorical or quantitative?

19. **Magazine Subscriber Survey.** A *Bloomberg Businessweek* North American subscriber study collected data from a sample of 2861 subscribers. Fifty-nine percent of the respondents indicated an annual income of $75,000 or more, and 50% reported having an American Express credit card.

    a. What is the population of interest in this study?

    b. Is annual income a categorical or quantitative variable?

    c. Is ownership of an American Express card a categorical or quantitative variable?

    d. Does this study involve cross-sectional or time series data?

    e. Describe any statistical inferences *Bloomberg Businessweek* might make on the basis of the survey.

20. **Investment Manager Survey.** A survey of 131 investment managers in *Barron's* Big Money poll revealed the following:

- 43% of managers classified themselves as bullish or very bullish on the stock market.
- The average expected return over the next 12 months for equities was 11.2%.
- 21% selected health care as the sector most likely to lead the market in the next 12 months.
- When asked to estimate how long it would take for technology and telecom stocks to resume sustainable growth, the managers' average response was 2.5 years.

    a. Cite two descriptive statistics.

    b. Make an inference about the population of all investment managers concerning the average return expected on equities over the next 12 months.

    c. Make an inference about the length of time it will take for technology and telecom stocks to resume sustainable growth.

21. **Cancer Research.** A seven-year medical research study reported that women whose mothers took the drug diethylstilbestrol (DES) during pregnancy were twice as likely to develop tissue abnormalities that might lead to cancer as were women whose mothers did not take the drug.

    a. This study compared two populations. What were the populations?

    b. Do you suppose the data were obtained in a survey or an experiment?

    c. For the population of women whose mothers took the drug DES during pregnancy, a sample of 3980 women showed that 63 developed tissue abnormalities that might lead to cancer. Provide a descriptive statistic that could be used to estimate the number of women out of 1000 in this population who have tissue abnormalities.

    d. For the population of women whose mothers did not take the drug DES during pregnancy, what is the estimate of the number of women out of 1000 who would be expected to have tissue abnormalities?

    e. Medical studies often use a relatively large sample (in this case, 3980). Why?

22. **Why People Move.** A survey conducted by Better Homes and Gardens Real Estate LLC showed that one in five U.S. homeowners has either moved from their home or would like to move because their neighborhood or community isn't ideal for their lifestyle (Better Homes and Gardens Real Estate website). The top lifestyle priorities of respondents when searching for their next home include ease of commuting by car, access to health and safety services, family-friendly neighborhood, availability of retail stores, access to cultural activities, public transportation access, and nightlife and restaurant access. Suppose a real estate agency in Denver, Colorado, hired you to conduct a similar study to determine the top lifestyle priorities for clients that currently have a home listed for sale with the agency or have hired the agency to help them locate a new home.

    a. What is the population for the survey you will be conducting?

    b. How would you collect the data for this study?

23. **Teenage Cell Phone Use.** Pew Research Center is a nonpartisan polling organization that provides information about issues, attitudes, and trends shaping America. In a poll, Pew researchers found that 73% of teens aged 13–17 have a smartphone, 15% have a basic phone and 12% have no phone. The study also asked the respondents how they communicated with their closest friend. Of those with a smartphone, 58% responded texting, 17% social media and 10% phone calls. Of those with no smartphone, 25% responded texting, 29% social media and 21% phone calls (Pew Research Center website, October 2015).

    a. One statistic (58%) concerned the use of texting to contact his/her closest friend, if the teen owns a smartphone. To what population is that applicable?

b. Another statistic (25%) concerned the use of texting by those who do not own a smartphone. To what population is that applicable?

c. Do you think the Pew researchers conducted a census or a sample survey to obtain their results? Why?

24. **Midterm Grades.** A sample of midterm grades for five students showed the following results: 72, 65, 82, 90, 76. Which of the following statements are correct, and which should be challenged as being too generalized?

a. The average midterm grade for the sample of five students is 77.

b. The average midterm grade for all students who took the exam is 77.

c. An estimate of the average midterm grade for all students who took the exam is 77.

d. More than half of the students who take this exam will score between 70 and 85.

e. If five other students are included in the sample, their grades will be between 65 and 90.

25. **Comparing Compact SUVs.** *Consumer Reports* evaluates products for consumers. The file *CompactSUV* contains the data shown in Table 1.8 for 15 compact sports utility vehicles (SUVs) from the 2018 model line (*Consumer Reports* website):

Make—manufacturer

Model—name of the model

Overall score—awarded based on a variety of measures, including those in this data set

Recommended—*Consumer Reports* recommends the vehicle or not

Owner satisfaction—satisfaction on a five-point scale based on the percentage of owners who would purchase the vehicle again $(--, -, 0, +, ++)$.

Overall miles per gallon—miles per gallon achieved in a 150-mile test trip

Acceleration (0–60 sec)—time in seconds it takes vehicle to reach 60 miles per hour from a standstill with the engine idling

a. How many variables are in the data set?

b. Which of the variables are categorical, and which are quantitative?

c. What percentage of these 15 vehicles are recommended?

d. What is the average of the overall miles per gallon across all 15 vehicles?

e. For owner satisfaction, construct a bar chart similar to Figure 1.4.

f. Show the frequency distribution for acceleration using the following intervals: 7.0–7.9, 8.0–8.9, 9.0–9.9, and 10.0–10.9. Construct a histogram similar to Figure 1.5.

DATA *file*

CompactSUV

TABLE 1.8   *Consumer Reports* Data Set for 15 Compact Sports Utility Vichicles

Make	Model	Overall Score	Recommended	Owner Satisfaction	Overall Miles Per Gallon	Acceleration (0–60) Sec
Subaru	Forester	84	Yes	+	26	8.7
Honda	CRV	83	Yes	++	27	8.6
Toyota	Rav4	81	Yes	++	24	9.3
Nissan	Rogue	73	Yes	+	24	9.5
Mazda	CX-5	71	Yes	++	24	8.6
Kia	Sportage	71	Yes	+	23	9.6
Ford	Escape	69	Yes	0	23	10.1
Volkswagen	Tiguan Limited	67	No	0	21	8.5
Volkswagen	Tiguan	65	No	+	25	10.3
Mitsubishi	Outlander	63	No	0	24	10.0
Chevrolet	Equinox	63	No	0	31	10.1
Hyundai	Tucson	57	No	0	26	8.4
GMC	Terrain	57	No	0	22	7.2
Jeep	Cherokee	55	No	–	22	10.9
Jeep	Compass	50	No	0	24	9.8

Chapter 1 Appendix

Appendix 1.1 Opening and Saving DATA Files and Converting to Stacked form with JMP

In this appendix we show how to open a data file and how to save a JMP file as an Excel file in JMP. We also discuss how to convert a data file to stacked form.

Opening DATA files in JMP

The files for this textbook are provided as both Microsoft Excel (.xlsx) and comma-separated values (.csv) files. Therefore, we begin by showing how to open these file types in JMP. For example, the following steps indicate how to open the Excel file *Nations.xlsx* in JMP.

Step 1. From the **JMP Home Window** Ribbon, click **File** and select **Open…**

Step 2. Navigate to the directory where the *Nations.xlsx* file is located [if after navigating to the appropriate directory, you do not see Excel files, select **Excel Files (*.xls, *.xlsx, *.xlsm)** from the drop-down menu to the right of the **File name:** box]

Step 3. Select the file *Nation* and it will appear in the **File name:** box
Click **Open**

Step 4. When the **Excel Import Wizard** dialog box appears, select **Worksheet contains column headers** in the **Individual Worksheet Setting area**
Click **Import**

The Data window appears as shown in Figure JMP 1.1. The steps above have imported the data from the Excel file into JMP. Note that if you wish to open a comma-separated values (CSV) file in JMP, you would follow the instructions above, but you should select **Text Files (*.txt,*.csv,*.dat,*.tsv,*.xml)** rather than Excel Files (*.xls,*.xlsx,*.xlsm) in Step 2. Step 3 will then open the CSV file in JMP.

Note that the middle left-hand window labeled **Columns (5/0)** lists the five variables. The red bar chart icon ![icon] indicates that JMP has interpreted Nation, WTO Status, Fitch Rating and Fitch Outlook as being measured on a nominal scale. The blue triangle ![icon] next to Per Capita GDP ($) indicates that the varibale is measured on a continous scale. Clicking on the icon next to any variable allows you to change the scale of measure for a variable. The possible settings are Continuous, Ordinal, Nominal, and None.

Saving JMP Files as Excel or CSV Files

You can also save a JMP file as an Excel or CSV file. Use the following steps to save a file from JMP to Excel.

Step 1. From the **Data** window, click **File** and select **Save As…**

Step 2. When the **Save JMP File As** dialog box appears, navigate to the directory where you wish to save the file

Step 3. From the **Save as type:** drop-down menu, select **Excel Workbook (*.xlsx, *.xls)**

Step 4. Enter the name you wish to give the file in the **File name:** box
Click **Save**

JMP can also save the file as a comma-separated values (CSV) file. To save as a CSV file, follow the steps above by in the **Save as type:** menu in Step 3, you should select **CSV (Comma delimited) (*.csv).**

FIGURE JMP 1.1   The Data Window for the Audit Time Data

Converting to Stacked Form

Most statistical software assumes that each row of a data set is an observation. However, occasionally you may receive a file where a row contains information for multiple observations. Consider the file *Chemitech,* which we have opened according to the steps previously outlined in this appendix and as shown in Figure JMP 1.2. Each row corresponds to three different observations, one from each of three assembly methods being tested. The data are the number of filtration systems assembled under each assembly method. To analyze these data in JMP, we need to convert it to stacked form.

The following steps enable us to convert the data to stacked form.

DATA *file*

Chemitech

Step 1. From the **Data** window, select **Tables** and then select **Stack**

Step 2. In the **Select Columns** area, select **Method A** and click **Stack Columns**

In the **Select Columns** area, select **Method B** and click **Stack Columns**

In the **Select Columns** area, select **Method C** and click **Stack Columns**

Step 3. In the **Output table name:** box enter *ChemitechStacked*

Step 4. Under **New Column Names** enter *Number of Systems Assembled* in the box next to **Stacked Data Column**

Under **New Column Names,** enter *Method* in the box next to **Source Label Column**

Step 5. Select **Stack By Row**

Step 6. In the **Action** area, click **OK**

The stacked data set appears in Figure JMP 1.3.

FIGURE JMP 1.2   The *Chemitech* Data Set

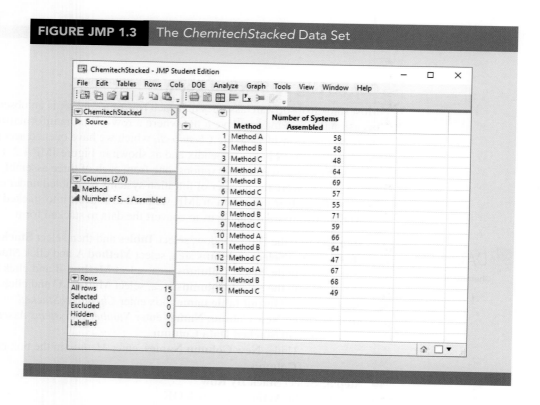

FIGURE JMP 1.3   The *ChemitechStacked* Data Set

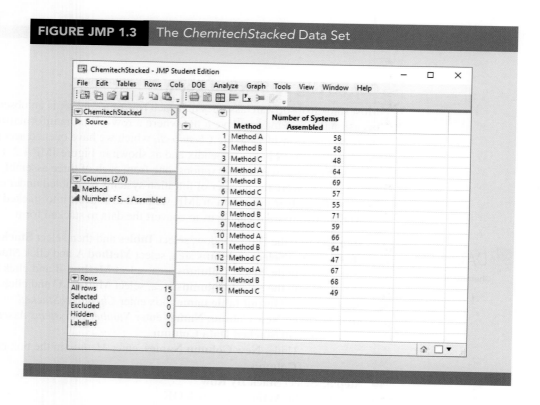

Chapter 2

Descriptive Statistics: Tabular and Graphical Displays

CONTENTS

APPENDIXES
APPENDIX 2.1: CREATING TABULAR AND GRAPHICAL PRESENTATIONS
WITH JMP
APPENDIX 2.2: CREATING TABULAR AND GRAPHICAL PRESENTATIONS
WITH EXCEL

STATISTICS IN PRACTICE

Colgate-Palmolive Company*

NEW YORK, NEW YORK

The Colgate-Palmolive Company started as a small soap and candle shop in New York City in 1806. Today, Colgate-Palmolive employs more than 38,000 people working in more than 200 countries and territories around the world. Although best known for its brand names of Colgate, Palmolive, and Fabuloso, the company also markets Irish Spring, and Ajax products.

The Colgate-Palmolive Company uses statistics in its quality assurance program for home laundry detergent products. One concern is customer satisfaction with the quantity of detergent in a carton. Every carton in each size category is filled with the same amount of detergent by weight, but the volume of detergent is affected by the density of the detergent powder. For instance, if the powder density is on the heavy side, a smaller volume of detergent is needed to reach the carton's specified weight. As a result, the carton may appear to be under-filled when opened by the consumer.

To control the problem of heavy detergent powder, limits are placed on the acceptable range of powder density. Statistical samples are taken periodically, and the density of each powder sample is measured. Data summaries are then provided for operating personnel so that corrective action can be taken if necessary to keep the density within the desired quality specifications.

A frequency distribution for the densities of 150 samples taken over a one-week period and a histogram are shown in the accompanying table and figure. Density levels above .40 are unacceptably high. The frequency distribution and histogram show that the operation is meeting its quality guidelines with all of the densities less than or equal to .40. Managers viewing these statistical summaries would be pleased with the quality of the detergent production process.

In this chapter, you will learn about tabular and graphical methods of descriptive statistics such as frequency distributions, bar charts, histograms, stem-and-leaf displays, crosstabulations, and others. The goal

The Colgate-Palmolive Company uses statistical summaries to help maintain the quality of its products.
Kurt Brady/Alamy Stock Photo

of these methods is to summarize data so that the data can be easily understood and interpreted.

Frequency Distribution of Density Data

Density	Frequency
.29–.30	30
.31–.32	75
.33–.34	32
.35–.36	9
.37–.38	3
.39–.40	1
Total	150

Histogram of Density Data

*The authors are indebted to William R. Fowle, Manager of Quality Assurance, Colgate-Palmolive Company, for providing the context for this Statistics in Practice.

Data can be classified as either categorical or quantitative. **Categorical data** use labels or names to identify categories of like items, and **quantitative data** are numerical values that indicate how much or how many. This chapter introduces the use of tabular and graphical displays for summarizing both categorical and quantitative data. Tabular and graphical displays can be found in annual reports, newspaper articles, and research studies. Everyone is exposed to these types of presentations. Hence, it is important to understand how they are constructed and how they should be interpreted.

We begin with a discussion of the use of tabular and graphical displays to summarize the data for a single variable. This is followed by a discussion of the use of tabular and graphical displays to summarize the data for two variables in a way that reveals the relationship between the two variables. **Data visualization** is a term often used to describe the use of graphical displays to summarize and present information about a data set. The last section of this chapter provides an introduction to data visualization and provides guidelines for creating effective graphical displays.

Modern statistical software packages provide extensive capabilities for summarizing data and preparing visual presentations. In the chapter appendixes, we show how some widely available statistical software packages can be used to summarize data and create graphical displays.

2.1 Summarizing Data for a Categorical Variable

Frequency Distribution

We begin the discussion of how tabular and graphical displays can be used to summarize categorical data with the definition of a **frequency distribution**.

> **FREQUENCY DISTRIBUTION**
>
> A frequency distribution is a tabular summary of data showing the number (frequency) of observations in each of several nonoverlapping categories or classes.

Let us use the following example to demonstrate the construction and interpretation of a frequency distribution for categorical data. Coca-Cola, Diet Coke, Dr. Pepper, Pepsi, and Sprite are five popular soft drinks. Assume that the data in Table 2.1 show the soft drink selected in a sample of 50 soft drink purchases.

To develop a frequency distribution for these data, we count the number of times each soft drink appears in Table 2.1. Coca-Cola appears 19 times, Diet Coke appears 8 times, Dr. Pepper appears 5 times, Pepsi appears 13 times, and Sprite appears 5 times. These counts are summarized in the frequency distribution in Table 2.2.

This frequency distribution provides a summary of how the 50 soft drink purchases are distributed across the five soft drinks. This summary offers more insight than the

DATAfile

SoftDrink

TABLE 2.1	Data from a Sample of 50 Soft Drink Purchases			
Coca-Cola	Coca-Cola	Coca-Cola	Sprite	Coca-Cola
Diet Coke	Dr. Pepper	Diet Coke	Dr. Pepper	Diet Coke
Pepsi	Sprite	Coca-Cola	Pepsi	Pepsi
Diet Coke	Coca-Cola	Sprite	Diet Coke	Pepsi
Coca-Cola	Diet Coke	Pepsi	Pepsi	Pepsi
Coca-Cola	Coca-Cola	Coca-Cola	Coca-Cola	Pepsi
Dr. Pepper	Coca-Cola	Coca-Cola	Coca-Cola	Coca-Cola
Diet Coke	Sprite	Coca-Cola	Coca-Cola	Dr. Pepper
Pepsi	Coca-Cola	Pepsi	Pepsi	Pepsi
Pepsi	Diet Coke	Coca-Cola	Dr. Pepper	Sprite

TABLE 2.2	Frequency Distribution of Soft Drink Purchases

Soft Drink	Frequency
Coca-Cola	19
Diet Coke	8
Dr. Pepper	5
Pepsi	13
Sprite	5
Total	50

original data shown in Table 2.1. Viewing the frequency distribution, we see that Coca-Cola is the leader, Pepsi is second, Diet Coke is third, and Sprite and Dr. Pepper are tied for fourth. The frequency distribution summarizes information about the popularity of the five soft drinks.

Relative Frequency and Percent Frequency Distributions

A frequency distribution shows the number (frequency) of observations in each of several nonoverlapping classes. However, we are often interested in the proportion, or percentage, of observations in each class. The *relative frequency* of a class equals the fraction or proportion of observations belonging to a class. For a data set with n observations, the relative frequency of each class can be determined as follows:

RELATIVE FREQUENCY

$$\text{Relative frequency of a class} = \frac{\text{Frequency of the class}}{n} \tag{2.1}$$

The *percent frequency* of a class is the relative frequency multiplied by 100.

A **relative frequency distribution** gives a tabular summary of data showing the relative frequency for each class. A **percent frequency distribution** summarizes the percent frequency of the data for each class. Table 2.3 shows a relative frequency distribution and a percent frequency distribution for the soft drink data. In Table 2.3 we see that the relative frequency for Coca-Cola is 19/50 = .38, the relative frequency for Diet Coke is 8/50 = .16, and so on. From the percent frequency distribution, we see that 38% of the purchases were Coca-Cola, 16% of the purchases were Diet Coke, and so on. We can also note that 38% + 26% + 16% = 80% of the purchases were for the top three soft drinks.

TABLE 2.3	Relative Frequency and Percent Frequency Distributions of Soft Drink Purchases	

Soft Drink	Relative Frequency	Percent Frequency
Coca-Cola	.38	38
Diet Coke	.16	16
Dr. Pepper	.10	10
Pepsi	.26	26
Sprite	.10	10
Total	1.00	100

Bar Charts and Pie Charts

A **bar chart** is a graphical display for depicting categorical data summarized in a frequency, relative frequency, or percent frequency distribution. On one axis of the chart (usually the horizontal axis), we specify the labels that are used for the classes (categories). A frequency, relative frequency, or percent frequency scale can be used for the other axis of the chart (usually the vertical axis). Then, using a bar of fixed width drawn above each class label, we extend the length of the bar until we reach the frequency, relative frequency, or percent frequency of the class. For categorical data, the bars should be separated to emphasize the fact that each category is separate. Figure 2.1 shows a bar chart of the frequency distribution for the 50 soft drink purchases. Note how the graphical display shows Coca-Cola, Pepsi, and Diet Coke to be the most preferred brands. We can make the brand preferences even more obvious by creating a sorted bar chart as shown in Figure 2.2. Here, we sort the soft drink categories: highest frequency on the left and lowest frequency on the right.

The **pie chart** provides another graphical display for presenting relative frequency and percent frequency distributions for categorical data. To construct a pie chart, we first draw a circle to represent all the data. Then we use the relative frequencies to subdivide the circle into sectors, or parts, that correspond to the relative frequency for each class. For example,

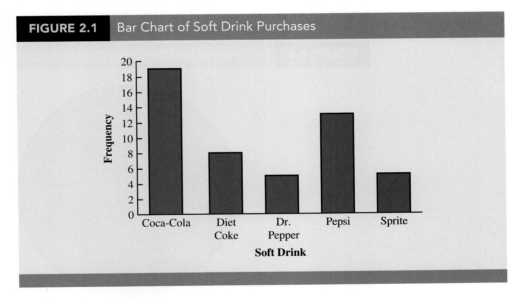

FIGURE 2.1 Bar Chart of Soft Drink Purchases

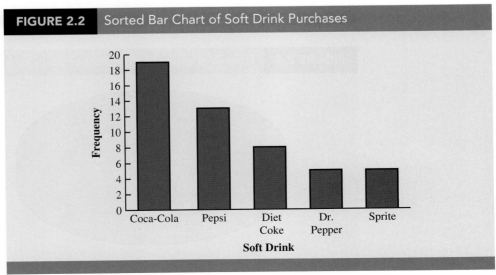

FIGURE 2.2 Sorted Bar Chart of Soft Drink Purchases

because a circle contains 360 degrees and Coca-Cola shows a relative frequency of .38, the sector of the pie chart labeled Coca-Cola consists of .38(360) = 136.8 degrees. The sector of the pie chart labeled Diet Coke consists of .16(360) = 57.6 degrees. Similar calculations for the other classes yield the pie chart in Figure 2.3. The numerical values shown for each sector can be frequencies, relative frequencies, or percent frequencies. Although pie charts are common ways of visualizing data, many data visualization experts do not recommend their use because people have difficulty perceiving differences in area. In most cases, a bar chart is superior to a pie chart for displaying categorical data.

Numerous options involving the use of colors, shading, legends, text font, and three-dimensional perspectives are available to enhance the visual appearance of bar and pie charts. However, one must be careful not to overuse these options because they may not enhance the usefulness of the chart. For instance, consider the three-dimensional pie chart for the soft drink data shown in Figure 2.4. Compare it to the charts shown in Figures 2.1–2.3. The three-dimensional perspective shown in Figure 2.4 adds no new understanding. The use of a legend in Figure 2.4 also forces your eyes to shift back and forth between the key and the chart. Most readers find the sorted bar chart in Figure 2.2 much easier to interpret because it is obvious which soft drinks have the highest frequencies.

In general, pie charts are not the best way to present percentages for comparison. In Section 2.5 we provide additional guidelines for creating effective visual displays.

FIGURE 2.3   Pie Chart of Soft Drink Purchases

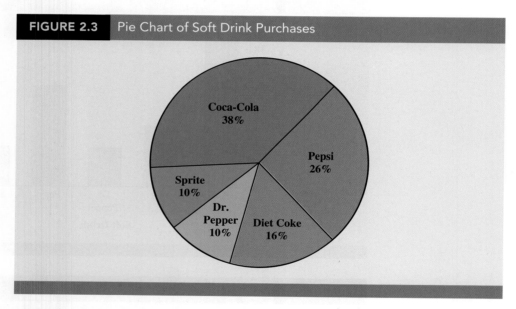

FIGURE 2.4   Three-Dimensional Pie Chart of Soft Drink Purchases

1. Often the number of classes in a frequency distribution is the same as the number of categories found in the data, as is the case for the soft drink purchase data in this section. The data involve only five soft drinks, and a separate frequency distribution class was defined for each one. Data that included all soft drinks would require many categories, most of which would have a small number of purchases. Most statisticians recommend that classes with smaller frequencies be grouped into an aggregate class called "other." Classes with frequencies of 5% or less would most often be treated in this fashion.

2. The sum of the frequencies in any frequency distribution always equals the number of observations. The sum of the relative frequencies in any relative frequency distribution always equals 1.00, and the sum of the percentages in a percent frequency distribution always equals 100.

E X E R C I S E S

Methods

1. The response to a question has three alternatives: A, B, and C. A sample of 120 responses provides 60 A, 24 B, and 36 C. Show the frequency and relative frequency distributions.

2. A partial relative frequency distribution is given.
   a. What is the relative frequency of class D?
   b. The total sample size is 200. What is the frequency of class D?
   c. Show the frequency distribution.
   d. Show the percent frequency distribution.

Class	Relative Frequency
A	.22
B	.18
C	.40
D	

3. A questionnaire provides 58 Yes, 42 No, and 20 no-opinion answers.
   a. In the construction of a pie chart, how many degrees would be in the section of the pie showing the Yes answers?
   b. How many degrees would be in the section of the pie showing the No answers?
   c. Construct a pie chart.
   d. Construct a bar chart.

Websites

Applications

4. **Most Visited Websites.** In a recent report, the top five most-visited English-language websites were google.com (GOOG), facebook.com (FB), youtube.com (YT), yahoo.com (YAH), and wikipedia.com (WIKI). The most-visited websites for a sample of 50 Internet users are shown in the following table:

YAH	WIKI	YT	WIKI	GOOG
YT	YAH	GOOG	GOOG	GOOG
WIKI	GOOG	YAH	YAH	YAH
YAH	YT	GOOG	YT	YAH
GOOG	FB	FB	WIKI	GOOG
GOOG	GOOG	FB	FB	WIKI
FB	YAH	YT	YAH	YAH
YT	GOOG	YAH	FB	FB
WIKI	GOOG	YAH	WIKI	WIKI
YAH	YT	GOOG	GOOG	WIKI

   a. Are these data categorical or quantitative?
   b. Provide frequency and percent frequency distributions.
   c. On the basis of the sample, which website is most frequently visited website for Internet users? Which is second?

5. **Most Popular Last Names.** In alphabetical order, the six most common last names in the United States in 2018 are Brown, Garcia, Johnson, Jones, Smith, and Williams (United States Census Bureau website). Assume that a sample of 50 individuals with one of these last names provided the following data:

DATA*file*

Names2018

Brown	Williams	Williams	Williams	Brown
Smith	Jones	Smith	Johnson	Smith
Garcia	Smith	Brown	Williams	Johnson
Johnson	Smith	Smith	Johnson	Brown
Williams	Garcia	Johnson	Williams	Johnson
Williams	Johnson	Jones	Smith	Brown
Johnson	Smith	Smith	Brown	Jones
Jones	Jones	Smith	Smith	Garcia
Garcia	Jones	Williams	Garcia	Smith
Jones	Johnson	Brown	Johnson	Garcia

Summarize the data by constructing the following:
   a. Relative and percent frequency distributions
   b. A bar chart
   c. A sorted bar chart
   d. A pie chart
   e. Based on these data, what are the three most common last names? Which type of chart makes this most apparent?

6. **Top Rated Television Show Networks.** Nielsen Media Research tracks the top-rated television shows. The following data show the television network that produced each of the 25 top-rated shows in the history of television.

DATA*file*

Networks2012

CBS	CBS	NBC	FOX	CBS
CBS	NBC	NBC	NBC	ABC
ABC	NBC	ABC	ABC	NBC
CBS	NBC	CBS	ABC	NBC
NBC	CBS	CBS	ABC	CBS

   a. Construct a frequency distribution, percent frequency distribution, and bar chart for the data.
   b. Which networks have done the best in terms of presenting top-rated television shows? Compare the performance of ABC, CBS, and NBC.

7. **Airline Customer Satisfaction Survey.** Many airlines use surveys to collect data on customer satisfaction related to flight experiences. Completing a flight, customers receive an email asking them to rate a variety of factors, including the reservation process, the check-in process, luggage policy, cleanliness of gate area, service by flight attendants, food/beverage selection, on-time arrival, and so on. Suppose that a five-point scale, with Excellent (E), Very Good (V), Good (G), Fair (F), and Poor (P), is used to record customer ratings. Assume that passengers on a Delta Airlines flight from Myrtle Beach, South Carolina, to Atlanta, Georgia, provided the following ratings for the question, "Please rate the airline based on your overall experience with this flight." The sample ratings are shown below.

DATA*file*

AirSurvey

E	E	G	V	V	E	V	V	V	E
E	G	V	E	E	V	E	E	E	V
V	V	V	F	V	E	V	E	G	E
G	E	V	E	V	E	V	V	V	V
E	E	V	V	E	P	E	V	P	V

a. Use a percent frequency distribution and a bar chart to summarize these data. What do these summaries indicate about the overall customer satisfaction with the Delta flight?

b. The online survey questionnaire enabled respondents to explain any aspect of the flight that failed to meet expectations. Would this be helpful information to a manager looking for ways to improve the overall customer satisfaction on Delta flights? Explain.

8. **Baseball Hall of Fame Positions.** Data for a sample of 55 members of the Baseball Hall of Fame in Cooperstown, New York, are shown here. Each observation indicates the primary position played by the Hall of Famers: pitcher (P), catcher (H), 1st base (1), 2nd base (2), 3rd base (3), shortstop (S), left field (L), center field (C), and right field (R).

BaseballHall

L	P	C	H	2	P	R	1	S	S	1	L	P	R	P
P	P	P	R	C	S	L	R	P	C	C	P	P	R	P
2	3	P	H	L	P	1	C	P	P	P	S	1	L	R
R	1	2	H	S	3	H	2	L	P					

a. Construct frequency and relative frequency distributions to summarize the data.

b. What position provides the most Hall of Famers?

c. What position provides the fewest Hall of Famers?

d. What outfield position (L, C, or R) provides the most Hall of Famers?

e. Compare infielders (1, 2, 3, and S) to outfielders (L, C, and R).

9. **Degrees Awarded Annually.** Nearly 1.9 million bachelor's degrees and over 758,000 master's degrees are awarded annually by U.S. postsecondary institutions as of 2018 (National Center for Education Statistics website). The Department of Education tracks the field of study for these graduates in the following categories: Business (B), Computer Sciences and Engineering (CSE), Education (E), Humanities (H), Natural Sciences and Mathematics (NSM), Social and Behavioral Sciences (SBS), and Other (O). Consider the following samples of 100 graduates:

Bachelor's Degree Field of Study

Majors

SBS	H	H	H	E	B	O	SBS	NSM	CSE
O	B	B	O	O	H	B	O	SBS	O
H	CSE	CSE	O	CSE	B	H	O	O	SBS
SBS	SBS	B	H	NSM	B	B	O	SBS	SBS
B	H	SBS	O	B	B	O	O	B	O
O	H	SBS	H	CSE	CSE	B	E	CSE	SBS
SBS	NSM	NSM	CSE	H	H	E	E	SBS	CSE
NSM	NSM	SBS	O	H	H	B	SBS	SBS	NSM
H	B	B	O	O	O	NSM	H	E	B
E	B	O	B	B	B	O	O	O	O

Master's Degree Field of Study

O	O	B	O	B	E	B	H	E	B
O	E	SBS	B	CSE	H	B	E	E	O
O	B	B	O	E	CSE	NSM	O	B	E
H	H	B	E	SBS	E	E	B	O	E
SBS	B	B	CSE	H	B	B	CSE	SBS	B
CSE	B	E	CSE	B	E	CSE	O	E	O
B	O	E	O	B	NSM	H	E	B	E
B	E	B	O	E	E	H	O	O	O
CSE	O	O	H	B	O	B	E	CSE	O
E	O	SBS	E	E	O	SBS	B	B	O

a. Provide a percent frequency distribution of field of study for each degree.
b. Construct a bar chart for field of study for each degree.
c. What is the lowest percentage field of study for each degree?
d. What is the highest percentage field of study for each degree?
e. Which field of study has the largest increase in percentage from bachelor's to masters'?

HotelRatings

10. **Online Hotel Ratings.** TripAdvisor is one of many online websites that provides ratings for hotels throughout the world. Ratings provided by 649 guests at the Lakeview Hotel can be found in the file *HotelRatings*. Possible responses were Excellent, Very Good, Average, Poor, and Terrible.
   a. Construct a frequency distribution.
   b. Construct a percent frequency distribution.
   c. Construct a bar chart for the percent frequency distribution.
   d. Comment on how guests rate their stay at the Sheraton Anaheim Hotel.
   e. Suppose that results for 1679 guests who stayed at the Timber Hotel provided the following frequency distribution.

Rating	Frequency
Excellent	807
Very Good	521
Average	200
Poor	107
Terrible	44

Compare the ratings for the Timber Hotel with the results obtained for the Lakeview Lodge.

2.2 Summarizing Data for a Quantitative Variable

Frequency Distribution

As defined in Section 2.1, a frequency distribution is a tabular summary of data showing the number (frequency) of observations in each of several nonoverlapping categories or classes. This definition holds for quantitative as well as categorical data. However, with quantitative data we must be more careful in defining the nonoverlapping classes to be used in the frequency distribution.

For example, consider the quantitative data in Table 2.4. These data show the time in days required to complete year-end audits for a sample of 20 clients of Sanderson and Clifford, a small public accounting firm. The three steps necessary to define the classes for a frequency distribution with quantitative data are

1. Determine the number of nonoverlapping classes.
2. Determine the width of each class.
3. Determine the class limits.

Audit

TABLE 2.4	Year-End Audit Times (In Days)		
12	14	19	18
15	15	18	17
20	27	22	23
22	21	33	28
14	18	16	13

Let us demonstrate these steps by developing a frequency distribution for the audit time data in Table 2.4.

Number of Classes   Classes are formed by specifying ranges that will be used to group the data. As a general guideline, we recommend using between 5 and 20 classes. For a small number of data items, as few as five or six classes may be used to summarize the data. For a larger number of data items, a larger number of classes are usually required. The goal is to use enough classes to show the variation in the data, but not so many classes that some contain only a few data items. Because the number of data items in Table 2.4 is relatively small ($n = 20$), we chose to develop a frequency distribution with five classes.

Width of the Classes   The second step in constructing a frequency distribution for quantitative data is to choose a width for the classes. As a general guideline, we recommend that the width be the same for each class. Thus the choices of the number of classes and the width of classes are not independent decisions. A larger number of classes means a smaller class width, and vice versa. To determine an approximate class width, we begin by identifying the largest and smallest data values. Then, with the desired number of classes specified, we can use the following expression to determine the approximate class width.

Making the classes the same width reduces the chance of inappropriate interpretations by the user.

$$\text{Approximate class width} = \frac{\text{Largest data value} - \text{Smallest data value}}{\text{Number of classes}} \qquad \textbf{(2.2)}$$

The approximate class width given by equation (2.2) can be rounded to a more convenient value based on the preference of the person developing the frequency distribution. For example, an approximate class width of 9.28 might be rounded to 10 simply because 10 is a more convenient class width to use in presenting a frequency distribution.

For the data involving the year-end audit times, the largest data value is 33 and the smallest data value is 12. Because we decided to summarize the data with five classes, using equation (2.2) provides an approximate class width of $(33 - 12)/5 = 4.2$. We therefore decided to round up and use a class width of five days in the frequency distribution.

No single frequency distribution is best for a data set. Different people may construct different, but equally acceptable, frequency distributions. The goal is to reveal the natural grouping and variation in the data.

In practice, the number of classes and the appropriate class width are determined by trial and error. Once a possible number of classes is chosen, equation (2.2) is used to find the approximate class width. The process can be repeated for a different number of classes. Ultimately, the analyst uses judgment to determine the combination of the number of classes and class width that provides the best frequency distribution for summarizing the data.

For the audit time data in Table 2.4, after deciding to use five classes, each with a width of five days, the next task is to specify the class limits for each of the classes.

Class limits   Class limits must be chosen so that each data item belongs to one and only one class. The *lower class limit* identifies the smallest possible data value assigned to the class. The *upper class limit* identifies the largest possible data value assigned to the class. In developing frequency distributions for categorical data, we did not need to specify class limits because each data item naturally fell into a separate class. But with quantitative data, such as the audit times in Table 2.4, class limits are necessary to determine where each data value belongs.

Using the audit time data in Table 2.4, we selected 10 days as the lower class limit and 14 days as the upper class limit for the first class. This class is denoted 10–14 in Table 2.5. The smallest data value, 12, is included in the 10–14 class. We then selected 15 days as the lower class limit and 19 days as the upper class limit of the next class. We continued defining the lower and upper class limits to obtain a total of five classes: 10–14, 15–19, 20–24, 25–29, and 30–34. The largest data value, 33, is included in the 30–34 class. The difference between the lower class limits of adjacent classes is the class width. Using the first two lower class limits of 10 and 15, we see that the class width is $15 - 10 = 5$.

With the number of classes, class width, and class limits determined, a frequency distribution can be obtained by counting the number of data values belonging to each class. For

TABLE 2.5	Frequency Distribution for the Audit Time Data

Audit Time (days)	Frequency
10–14	4
15–19	8
20–24	5
25–29	2
30–34	1
Total	20

example, the data in Table 2.4 show that four values—12, 14, 14, and 13—belong to the 10–14 class. Thus, the frequency for the 10–14 class is 4. Continuing this counting process for the 15–19, 20–24, 25–29, and 30–34 classes provides the frequency distribution in Table 2.5. Using this frequency distribution, we can observe the following:

1. The most frequently occurring audit times are in the class of 15–19 days. Eight of the 20 audit times belong to this class.
2. Only one audit required 30 or more days.

Other conclusions are possible, depending on the interests of the person viewing the frequency distribution. The value of a frequency distribution is that it provides insights about the data that are not easily obtained by viewing the data in their original unorganized form.

Class Midpoint   In some applications, we want to know the midpoints of the classes in a frequency distribution for quantitative data. The **class midpoint** is the value halfway between the lower and upper class limits. For the audit time data, the five class midpoints are 12, 17, 22, 27, and 32.

Relative Frequency and Percent Frequency Distributions

We define the relative frequency and percent frequency distributions for quantitative data in the same manner as for categorical data. First, recall that the relative frequency is the proportion of the observations belonging to a class. With n observations,

$$\text{Relative frequency of class} = \frac{\text{Frequency of the class}}{n}$$

The percent frequency of a class is the relative frequency multiplied by 100.

Based on the class frequencies in Table 2.5 and with $n = 20$, Table 2.6 shows the relative frequency distribution and percent frequency distribution for the audit time data. Note that .40

TABLE 2.6	Relative Frequency and Percent Frequency Distributions for the Audit Time Data

Audit Time (days)	Relative Frequency	Percent Frequency
10–14	.20	20
15–19	.40	40
20–24	.25	25
25–29	.10	10
30–34	.05	5
Total	1.00	100

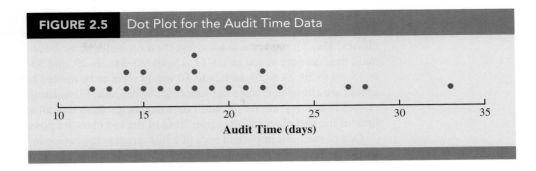

FIGURE 2.5   Dot Plot for the Audit Time Data

of the audits, or 40%, required from 15 to 19 days. Only .05 of the audits, or 5%, required 30 or more days. Again, additional interpretations and insights can be obtained by using Table 2.6.

Dot Plot

One of the simplest graphical summaries of data is a **dot plot**. A horizontal axis shows the range for the data. Each data value is represented by a dot placed above the axis. Figure 2.5 is the dot plot for the audit time data in Table 2.4. The three dots located above 18 on the horizontal axis indicate that an audit time of 18 days occurred three times. Dot plots show the details of the data and are useful for comparing the distribution of the data for two or more variables.

Histogram

A common graphical display of quantitative data is a **histogram**. This graphical display can be prepared for data previously summarized in either a frequency, relative frequency, or percent frequency distribution. A histogram is constructed by placing the variable of interest on the horizontal axis and the frequency, relative frequency, or percent frequency on the vertical axis. The frequency, relative frequency, or percent frequency of each class is shown by drawing a rectangle whose base is determined by the class limits on the horizontal axis and whose height is the corresponding frequency, relative frequency, or percent frequency.

Figure 2.6 is a histogram for the audit time data. Note that the class with the greatest frequency is shown by the rectangle appearing above the class of 15–19 days. The height of the rectangle shows that the frequency of this class is 8. A histogram for the relative or percent frequency distribution of these data would look the same as the histogram in Figure 2.6 with the exception that the vertical axis would be labeled with relative or percent frequency values.

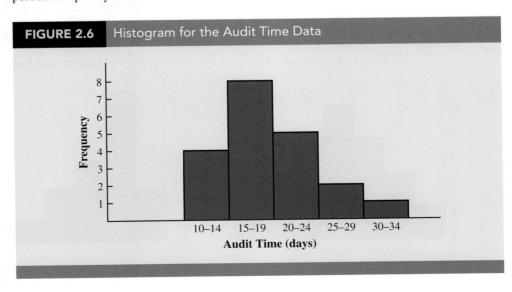

FIGURE 2.6   Histogram for the Audit Time Data

As Figure 2.6 shows, the adjacent rectangles of a histogram touch one another. Unlike a bar graph, a histogram contains no natural separation between the rectangles of adjacent classes. This format is the usual convention for histograms. Because the classes for the audit time data are stated as 10–14, 15–19, 20–24, 25–29, and 30–34, one-unit spaces of 14 to 15, 19 to 20, 24 to 25, and 29 to 30 would seem to be needed between the classes. These spaces are eliminated when constructing a histogram. Eliminating the spaces between classes in a histogram for the audit time data helps show that all values between the lower limit of the first class and the upper limit of the last class are possible.

One of the most important uses of a histogram is to provide information about the shape, or form, of a distribution. Figure 2.7 contains four histograms constructed from relative frequency distributions. Panel A shows the histogram for a set of data moderately skewed to the left. A histogram is said to be skewed to the left if its tail extends farther to the left. This histogram is typical for exam scores, with no scores above 100%, most of the scores above 70%, and only a few really low scores. Panel B shows the histogram for a set of data moderately skewed to the right. A histogram is said to be skewed to the right if its tail extends farther to the right. An example of this type of histogram would be for data such as housing prices; a few expensive houses create the skewness in the right tail.

Panel C shows a symmetric histogram. In a symmetric histogram, the left tail mirrors the shape of the right tail. Histograms for data found in applications are never perfectly symmetric, but the histogram for many applications may be roughly symmetric. Data for SAT scores, heights and weights of people, and so on lead to histograms that are roughly

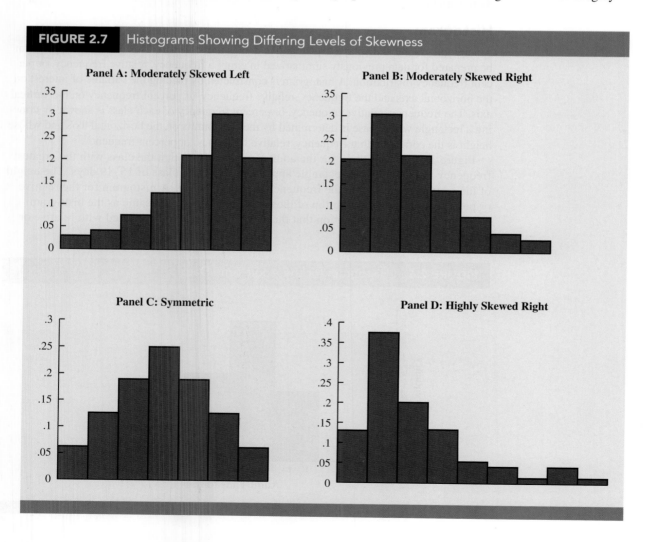

FIGURE 2.7   Histograms Showing Differing Levels of Skewness

symmetric. Panel D shows a histogram highly skewed to the right. This histogram was constructed from data on the amount of customer purchases over one day at a women's apparel store. Data from applications in business and economics often lead to histograms that are skewed to the right. For instance, data on housing prices, salaries, purchase amounts, and so on often result in histograms skewed to the right.

Cumulative Distributions

A variation of the frequency distribution that provides another tabular summary of quantitative data is the **cumulative frequency distribution**. The cumulative frequency distribution uses the number of classes, class widths, and class limits developed for the frequency distribution. However, rather than showing the frequency of each class, the cumulative frequency distribution shows the number of data items with values *less than or equal to the upper class limit* of each class. The first two columns of Table 2.7 provide the cumulative frequency distribution for the audit time data.

To understand how the cumulative frequencies are determined, consider the class with the description "less than or equal to 24." The cumulative frequency for this class is simply the sum of the frequencies for all classes with data values less than or equal to 24. For the frequency distribution in Table 2.5, the sum of the frequencies for classes 10–14, 15–19, and 20–24 indicates that $4 + 8 + 5 = 17$ data values are less than or equal to 24. Hence, the cumulative frequency for this class is 17. In addition, the cumulative frequency distribution in Table 2.7 shows that four audits were completed in 14 days or less and 19 audits were completed in 29 days or less.

As a final point, we note that a **cumulative relative frequency distribution** shows the proportion of data items, and a **cumulative percent frequency distribution** shows the percentage of data items with values less than or equal to the upper limit of each class. The cumulative relative frequency distribution can be computed either by summing the relative frequencies in the relative frequency distribution or by dividing the cumulative frequencies by the total number of items. Using the latter approach, we found the cumulative relative frequencies in column 3 of Table 2.7 by dividing the cumulative frequencies in column 2 by the total number of items ($n = 20$). The cumulative percent frequencies were again computed by multiplying the relative frequencies by 100. The cumulative relative and percent frequency distributions show that .85 of the audits, or 85%, were completed in 24 days or less, .95 of the audits, or 95%, were completed in 29 days or less, and so on.

Stem-and-Leaf Display

A **stem-and-leaf display** is a graphical display used to show simultaneously the rank order and shape of a distribution of data. To illustrate the use of a stem-and-leaf display, consider the data in Table 2.8. These data result from a 150-question aptitude test given to

TABLE 2.7	Cumulative Frequency, Cumulative Relative Frequency, and Cumulative Percent Frequency Distributions for the Audit Time Data		
Audit Time (days)	**Cumulative Frequency**	**Cumulative Relative Frequency**	**Cumulative Percent Frequency**
Less than or equal to 14	4	.20	20
Less than or equal to 19	12	.60	60
Less than or equal to 24	17	.85	85
Less than or equal to 29	19	.95	95
Less than or equal to 34	20	1.00	100

TABLE 2.8	Number of Questions Answered Correctly on an Aptitude Test			
112	72	69	97	107
73	92	76	86	73
126	128	118	127	124
82	104	132	134	83
92	108	96	100	92
115	76	91	102	81
95	141	81	80	106
84	119	113	98	75
68	98	115	106	95
100	85	94	106	119

DATA *file*

AptitudeTest

50 individuals recently interviewed for a position at Haskens Manufacturing. The data indicate the number of questions answered correctly.

To develop a stem-and-leaf display, we first arrange the leading digits of each data value to the left of a vertical line. To the right of the vertical line, we record the last digit for each data value. Based on the top row of data in Table 2.8 (112, 72, 69, 97, and 107), the first five entries in constructing a stem-and-leaf display would be as follows:

```
 6 | 9
 7 | 2
 8 |
 9 | 7
10 | 7
11 | 2
12 |
13 |
14 |
```

For example, the data value 112 shows the leading digits 11 to the left of the line and the last digit 2 to the right of the line. Similarly, the data value 72 shows the leading digit 7 to the left of the line and last digit 2 to the right of the line. Continuing to place the last digit of each data value on the line corresponding to its leading digit(s) provides the following:

```
 6 | 9  8
 7 | 2  3  6  3  6  5
 8 | 6  2  3  1  1  0  4  5
 9 | 7  2  2  6  2  1  5  8  8  5  4
10 | 7  4  8  0  2  6  6  0  6
11 | 2  8  5  9  3  5  9
12 | 6  8  7  4
13 | 2  4
14 | 1
```

With this organization of the data, sorting the digits on each line into rank order is simple. Doing so provides the stem-and-leaf display shown here.

```
 6 | 8  9
 7 | 2  3  3  5  6  6
 8 | 0  1  1  2  3  4  5  6
 9 | 1  2  2  2  4  5  5  6  7  8  8
10 | 0  0  2  4  6  6  6  7  8
11 | 2  3  5  5  8  9  9
12 | 4  6  7  8
13 | 2  4
14 | 1
```

The numbers to the left of the vertical line (6, 7, 8, 9, 10, 11, 12, 13, and 14) form the *stem,* and each digit to the right of the vertical line is a *leaf.* For example, consider the first row with a stem value of 6 and leaves of 8 and 9.

$$6 \mid 8 \quad 9$$

This row indicates that two data values have a first digit of 6. The leaves show that the data values are 68 and 69. Similarly, the second row

$$7 \mid 2 \quad 3 \quad 3 \quad 5 \quad 6 \quad 6$$

indicates that six data values have a first digit of 7. The leaves show that the data values are 72, 73, 73, 75, 76, and 76.

To focus on the shape indicated by the stem-and-leaf display, let us use a rectangle to contain the leaves of each stem. Doing so, we obtain the following:

```
 6 | 8  9
 7 | 2  3  3  5  6  6
 8 | 0  1  1  2  3  4  5  6
 9 | 1  2  2  2  4  5  5  6  7  8  8
10 | 0  0  2  4  6  6  6  7  8
11 | 2  3  5  5  8  9  9
12 | 4  6  7  8
13 | 2  4
14 | 1
```

Rotating this page counterclockwise onto its side provides a picture of the data that is similar to a histogram with classes of 60–69, 70–79, 80–89, and so on.

Although the stem-and-leaf display may appear to offer the same information as a histogram, it has two primary advantages.

1. The stem-and-leaf display is easier to construct by hand.
2. Within a class interval, the stem-and-leaf display provides more information than the histogram because the stem-and-leaf shows the actual data.

Just as a frequency distribution or histogram has no absolute number of classes, neither does a stem-and-leaf display have an absolute number of rows or stems. If we believe that our original stem-and-leaf display condensed the data too much, we can easily stretch the display by using two or more stems for each leading digit. For example, to use two stems for each leading digit, we would place all data values ending in 0, 1, 2, 3, and 4 in one row and all values ending in 5, 6, 7, 8, and 9 in a second row. The following stretched stem-and-leaf display illustrates this approach.

```
 6 | 8  9
 7 | 2  3  3
 7 | 5  6  6
 8 | 0  1  1  2  3  4
 8 | 5  6
 9 | 1  2  2  2  4
 9 | 5  5  6  7  8  8
10 | 0  0  2  4
10 | 6  6  6  7  8
11 | 2  3
11 | 5  5  8  9  9
12 | 4
12 | 6  7  8
13 | 2  4
13 |
14 | 1
```

In a stretched stem-and-leaf display, whenever a stem value is stated twice, the first value corresponds to leaf values of 0–4, and the second value corresponds to leaf values of 5–9.

Note that values 72, 73, and 73 have leaves in the 0–4 range and are shown with the first stem value of 7. The values 75, 76, and 76 have leaves in the 5–9 range and are shown with the second stem value of 7. This stretched stem-and-leaf display is similar to a frequency distribution with intervals of 65–69, 70–74, 75–79, and so on.

The preceding example showed a stem-and-leaf display for data with as many as three digits. Stem-and-leaf displays for data with more than three digits are possible. For example, consider the following data on the number of hamburgers sold by a fast-food restaurant for each of 15 weeks.

| 1565 | 1852 | 1644 | 1766 | 1888 | 1912 | 2044 | 1812 |
| 1790 | 1679 | 2008 | 1852 | 1967 | 1954 | 1733 | |

A stem-and-leaf display of these data follows.

Leaf unit = 10

```
15 | 6
16 | 4  7
17 | 3  6  9
18 | 1  5  5  8
19 | 1  5  6
20 | 0  4
```

A single digit is used to define each leaf in a stem-and-leaf display. The leaf unit indicates how to multiply the stem-and-leaf numbers in order to approximate the original data. Leaf units may be 100, 10, 1, .1, and so on.

Note that a single digit is used to define each leaf and that only the first three digits of each data value have been used to construct the display. At the top of the display we have specified Leaf unit = 10. To illustrate how to interpret the values in the display, consider the first stem, 15, and its associated leaf, 6. Combining these numbers, we obtain 156. To reconstruct an approximation of the original data value, we must multiply this number by 10, the value of the *leaf unit*. Thus, $156 \times 10 = 1560$ is an approximation of the original data value used to construct the stem-and-leaf display. Although it is not possible to reconstruct the exact data value from this stem-and-leaf display, the convention of using a single digit for each leaf enables stem-and-leaf displays to be constructed for data having a large number of digits. For stem-and-leaf displays where the leaf unit is not shown, the leaf unit is assumed to equal 1.

NOTES + COMMENTS

1. A bar chart and a histogram are essentially the same thing; both are graphical presentations of the data in a frequency distribution. A histogram is just a bar chart with no separation between bars. For some discrete quantitative data, a separation between bars is also appropriate. Consider, for example, the number of classes in which a college student is enrolled. The data may only assume integer values. Intermediate values such as 1.5, 2.73, and so on are not possible. With continuous quantitative data, however, such as the audit times in Table 2.4, a separation between bars is not appropriate.

2. The appropriate values for the class limits with quantitative data depend on the level of accuracy of the data. For instance, with the audit time data of Table 2.4 the limits used were integer values. If the data were rounded to the nearest tenth of a day (e.g., 12.3, 14.4, and so on), then the limits would be stated in tenths of days. For instance, the first class would be 10.0–14.9. If the data were recorded to the nearest hundredth of a day (e.g., 12.34, 14.45, and so

on), the limits would be stated in hundredths of days. For instance, the first class would be 10.00–14.99.

3. An *open-end* class requires only a lower class limit or an upper class limit. For example, in the audit time data of Table 2.4, suppose two of the audits had taken 58 and 65 days. Rather than continue with the classes of width 5 with classes 35–39, 40–44, 45–49, and so on, we could simplify the frequency distribution to show an open-end class of "35 or more." This class would have a frequency of 2. Most often the open-end class appears at the upper end of the distribution. Sometimes an open-end class appears at the lower end of the distribution, and occasionally such classes appear at both ends.

4. The last entry in a cumulative frequency distribution always equals the total number of observations. The last entry in a cumulative relative frequency distribution always equals 1.00 and the last entry in a cumulative percent frequency distribution always equals 100.

EXERCISES

Methods

11. Consider the following data.

Frequency

14	21	23	21	16
19	22	25	16	16
24	24	25	19	16
19	18	19	21	12
16	17	18	23	25
20	23	16	20	19
24	26	15	22	24
20	22	24	22	20

    a. Develop a frequency distribution using classes of 12–14, 15–17, 18–20, 21–23, and 24–26.

    b. Develop a relative frequency distribution and a percent frequency distribution using the classes in part (a).

12. Consider the following frequency distribution.

Class	Frequency
10–19	10
20–29	14
30–39	17
40–49	7
50–59	2

Construct a cumulative frequency distribution and a cumulative relative frequency distribution.

13. Construct a histogram for the data in exercise 12.

14. Consider the following data.

8.9	10.2	11.5	7.8	10.0	12.2	13.5	14.1	10.0	12.2
6.8	9.5	11.5	11.2	14.9	7.5	10.0	6.0	15.8	11.5

   a. Construct a dot plot.
   b. Construct a frequency distribution.
   c. Construct a percent frequency distribution.

15. Construct a stem-and-leaf display for the following data.

11.3	9.6	10.4	7.5	8.3	10.5	10.0
9.3	8.1	7.7	7.5	8.4	6.3	8.8

16. Construct a stem-and-leaf display for the following data. Use a leaf unit of 10.

1161	1206	1478	1300	1604	1725	1361	1422
1221	1378	1623	1426	1557	1730	1706	1689

Applications

17. **Patient Waiting Times.** A doctor's office staff studied the waiting times for patients who arrive at the office with a request for emergency service. The following data with waiting times in minutes were collected over a one-month period.

   2   5   10   12   4   4   5   17   11   8   9   8   12   21   6   8   7   13   18   3

   Use classes of 0–4, 5–9, and so on in the following:
   a. Show the frequency distribution.
   b. Show the relative frequency distribution.
   c. Show the cumulative frequency distribution.
   d. Show the cumulative relative frequency distribution.
   e. What proportion of patients needing emergency service wait 9 minutes or less?

18. **NBA Total Player Ratings.** CBSSports.com developed the Total Player Ratings system to rate players in the National Basketball Association (NBA) based upon various offensive and defensive statistics. The following data show the average number of points scored per game (PPG) for 50 players with the highest ratings for a portion of an NBA season (CBSSports.com website).

NBAPlayerPts

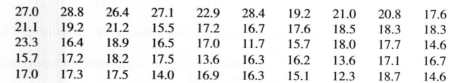

27.0	28.8	26.4	27.1	22.9	28.4	19.2	21.0	20.8	17.6
21.1	19.2	21.2	15.5	17.2	16.7	17.6	18.5	18.3	18.3
23.3	16.4	18.9	16.5	17.0	11.7	15.7	18.0	17.7	14.6
15.7	17.2	18.2	17.5	13.6	16.3	16.2	13.6	17.1	16.7
17.0	17.3	17.5	14.0	16.9	16.3	15.1	12.3	18.7	14.6

   Use classes starting at 10 and ending at 30 in increments of 2 for PPG in the following.
   a. Show the frequency distribution.
   b. Show the relative frequency distribution.
   c. Show the cumulative percent frequency distribution.
   d. Develop a histogram for the average number of points scored per game.
   e. Do the data appear to be skewed? Explain.
   f. What percentage of the players averaged at least 20 points per game?

19. **Busiest North American Airports.** Based on the total passenger traffic, the airports in the following list are the 20 busiest airports in North America in 2018 (*The World Almanac*).

Airport (Airport Code)	Total Passengers (Million)
Boston Logan (BOS)	36.3
Charlotte Douglas (CLT)	44.4
Chicago O'Hare (ORD)	78
Dallas/Ft. Worth (DFW)	65.7
Denver (DEN)	58.3
Detroit Metropolitan (DTW)	34.4
Hartsfield-Jackson Atlanta (ATL)	104.2
Houston George Bush (IAH)	41.6
Las Vegas McCarran (LAS)	47.5
Los Angeles (LAX)	80.9
Miami (MIA)	44.6
Minneapolis/St. Paul (MSP)	37.4
New York John F. Kennedy (JFK)	59.1
Newark Liberty (EWR)	40.6
Orlando (MCO)	41.9
Philadelphia (PHL)	36.4
Phoenix Sky Harbor (PHX)	43.3
San Francisco (SFO)	53.1
Seattle-Tacoma (SEA)	45.7
Toronto Pearson (YYZ)	44.3

Airports

a. Which is busiest airport in terms of total passenger traffic? Which is the least busy airport in terms of total passenger traffic?
b. Using a class width of 10, develop a frequency distribution of the data starting with 30–39.9, 40–49.9, 50–59.9, and so on.
c. Prepare a histogram. Interpret the histogram.

20. **CEO Time in Meetings.** The London School of Economics and the Harvard Business School have conducted studies of how chief executive officers (CEOs) spend their time. These studies have found that CEOs spend many hours per week in meetings that include conference calls, business meals, and public events. Suppose that the data below show the time spent per week in meetings (hours) for a sample of 25 CEOs.

CEOTime

14	15	18	23	15
19	20	13	15	23
23	21	15	20	21
16	15	18	18	19
19	22	23	21	12

a. What is the least amount of time spent per week on meetings? The highest?
b. Use a class width of two hours to prepare a frequency distribution and a percent frequency distribution for the data.
c. Prepare a histogram and comment on the shape of the distribution.

21. **Largest University Endowments.** University endowments are financial assets that are donated by supporters to be used to provide income to universities. There is a large discrepancy in the size of university endowments. The following table provides a listing of many of the universities that have the largest endowments as reported by the National Association of College and University Business Officers in 2017.

DATA *file*

Endowments

University	Endowment Amount ($ Billion)	University	Endowment Amount ($ Billion)
Amherst College	2.2	Smith College	1.8
Boston College	2.3	Stanford University	24.8
Boston University	2.0	Swarthmore College	2.0
Brown University	3.2	Texas A&M University	11.6
California Institute of Technology	2.6	Tufts University	1.7
		University of California	9.8
Carnegie Mellon University	2.2	University of California, Berkeley	1.8
Case Western Reserve University	1.8	University of California, Los Angeles	2.1
Columbia University	10.0	University of Chicago	7.5
Cornell University	6.8	University of Illinois	2.6
Dartmouth College	5.0	University of Michigan	10.9
Duke University	7.9	University of Minnesota	3.5
Emory University	6.9	University of North Carolina at Chapel Hill	3.0
George Washington University	1.7	University of Notre Dame	9.4
Georgetown University	1.7	University of Oklahoma	1.6
Georgia Institute of Technology	2.0	University of Pennsylvania	12.2
Grinnell College	1.9	University of Pittsburgh	3.9
Harvard University	36.0	University of Richmond	2.4
Indiana University	2.2	University of Rochester	2.1
Johns Hopkins University	3.8	University of Southern California	5.1
Massachusetts Institute of Technology	15.0	University of Texas	26.5
Michigan State University	2.7	University of Virginia	8.6
New York University	4.0	University of Washington	2.5
Northwestern University	10.4	University of Wisconsin–Madison	2.7
Ohio State University	4.3	Vanderbilt University	4.1
Pennsylvania State University	4.0	Virginia Commonwealth University	1.8
Pomona College	2.2	Washington University in St. Louis	7.9
Princeton University	23.8	Wellesley College	1.9
Purdue University	2.4	Williams College	2.5
Rice University	5.8	Yale University	27.2
Rockefeller University	2.0		

Summarize the data by constructing the following:

a. A frequency distribution (classes 0–1.9, 2.0–3.9, 4.0–5.9, 6.0–7.9, and so on).

b. A relative frequency distribution.

c. A cumulative frequency distribution.

d. A cumulative relative frequency distribution.

e. What do these distributions tell you about the endowments of universities?

f. Show a histogram. Comment on the shape of the distribution.

g. What is the largest university endowment and which university holds it?

22. **Top U.S. Franchises.** *Entrepreneur* magazine ranks franchises using performance measures such as growth rate, number of locations, startup costs, and financial stability. The number of locations for 20 U.S. franchises follows (*The World Almanac*).

Franchise	No. U.S. Locations	Franchise	No. U.S. Locations
Hampton Inn	1864	Jan-Pro Franchising Intl. Inc.	12,394
ampm	3183	Hardee's	1901
McDonald's	32,805	Pizza Hut Inc.	13,281
7-Eleven Inc.	37,496	Kumon Math & Reading Centers	25,199
Supercuts	2130	Dunkin' Donuts	9947
Days Inn	1877	KFC Corp.	16,224
Vanguard Cleaning Systems	2155	Jazzercise Inc.	7683
Servpro	1572	Anytime Fitness	1618
Subway	34,871	Matco Tools	1431
Denny's Inc.	1668	Stratus Building Solutions	5018

DATA *file*

Franchise

Use classes 0–4999, 5000–9999, 10,000–14,999 and so forth to answer the following questions.

a. Construct a frequency distribution and a percent frequency distribution of the number of U.S. locations for these top-ranked franchises.

b. Construct a histogram of these data.

c. Comment on the shape of the distribution.

23. **Percent Change in Stock Market Indexes.** The following data show the year to date percent change (YTD % Change) for 30 stock-market indexes from around the world (*The Wall Street Journal*).

Country	Index	YTD % Change
Australia	S&P/ASX200	10.2
Belgium	Bel-20	12.6
Brazil	São Paulo Bovespa	−14.4
Canada	S&P/TSX Comp	2.6
Chile	Santiago IPSA	−16.3
China	Shanghai Composite	−9.3
Eurozone	EURO Stoxx	10.0
France	CAC 40	11.8
Germany	DAX	10.6
Hong Kong	Hang Seng	−3.5
India	S&P BSE Sensex	−4.7
Israel	Tel Aviv	1.3
Italy	FTSE MIB	6.6
Japan	Nikkei	31.4
Mexico	IPC All-Share	−6.4
Netherlands	AEX	9.3
Singapore	Straits Times	−2.5
South Korea	Kospi	−6.4
Spain	IBEX 35	6.4
Sweden	SX All Share	13.8
Switzerland	Swiss Market	17.4
Taiwan	Weighted	2.3
U.K.	FTSE 100	10.1
U.S.	S&P 500	16.6
U.S.	DJIA	14.5
U.S.	Dow Jones Utility	6.6
U.S.	Nasdaq 100	17.4
U.S.	Nasdaq Composite	21.1
World	DJ Global ex U.S.	4.2
World	DJ Global Index	9.9

DATA *file*

MarketIndexes

a. What index has the largest positive YTD % Change?
b. Using a class width of 5 beginning with −20 and going to 40, develop a frequency distribution for the data.
c. Prepare a histogram. Interpret the histogram, including a discussion of the general shape of the histogram.
d. Use *The Wall Street Journal* or another media source to find the current percent changes for these stock market indexes in the current year. What index has had the largest percent increase? What index has had the smallest percent decrease? Prepare a summary of the data.

DATAfile
EngineeringSalary

24. **Engineering School Graduate Salaries.** The file *EngineeringSalary* contains the median starting salary and median mid-career salary (measured 10 years after graduation) for graduates from 19 engineering schools (*The Wall Street Journal*). Develop a stem-and-leaf display for both the median starting salary and the median mid-career salary. Comment on any differences you observe.

25. **Best Paying College Degrees.** Each year America.EDU ranks the best paying college degrees in America. The following data show the median starting salary, the mid-career salary, and the percentage increase from starting salary to mid-career salary for the 20 college degrees with the hi ghest mid-career salary (America.EDU website).

DATAfile
BestPayingDegrees

Degree	Starting Salary	Mid-Career Salary	% Increase
Aerospace engineering	59,400	108,000	82
Applied mathematics	56,400	101,000	79
Biomedical engineering	54,800	101,000	84
Chemical engineering	64,800	108,000	67
Civil engineering	53,500	93,400	75
Computer engineering	61,200	87,700	43
Computer science	56,200	97,700	74
Construction management	50,400	87,000	73
Economics	48,800	97,800	100
Electrical engineering	60,800	104,000	71
Finance	47,500	91,500	93
Government	41,500	88,300	113
Information systems	49,300	87,100	77
Management info. systems	50,900	90,300	77
Mathematics	46,400	88,300	90
Nuclear engineering	63,900	104,000	63
Petroleum engineering	93,000	157,000	69
Physics	50,700	99,600	96
Software engineering	56,700	91,300	61
Statistics	50,000	93,400	87

a. Using a class width of 10, construct a histogram for the percentage increase in the starting salary.
b. Comment on the shape of the distribution.
c. Develop a stem-and-leaf display for the percentage increase in the starting salary.
d. What are the primary advantages of the stem-and-leaf display as compared to the histogram?

26. **Marathon Runner Ages.** The Flying Pig is a marathon (26.2 mile long) running race held every year in Cincinnati, Ohio. Suppose that the following data show the ages for a sample of 40 marathon runners.

Marathon

49	33	40	37	56
44	46	57	55	32
50	52	43	64	40
46	24	30	37	43
31	43	50	36	61
27	44	35	31	43
52	43	66	31	50
72	26	59	21	47

a. Construct a stretched stem-and-leaf display.
b. Which age group had the largest number of runners?
c. Which age occurred most frequently?

2.3 Summarizing Data for Two Variables Using Tables

Thus far in this chapter, we have focused on using tabular and graphical displays to summarize the data for a single categorical or quantitative variable. Often a manager or decision maker needs to summarize the data for two variables in order to reveal the relationship—if any—between the variables. In this section, we show how to construct a tabular summary of the data for two variables.

Crosstabulation

A **crosstabulation** is a tabular summary of data for two variables. Although both variables can be either categorical or quantitative, crosstabulations in which one variable is categorical and the other variable is quantitative are just as common. We will illustrate this latter case by considering the following application based on data from Zagat's Restaurant Review. Data showing the quality rating and the typical meal price were collected for a sample of 300 restaurants in the Los Angeles area. Table 2.9 shows the data for the first 10 restaurants. Quality rating is a categorical variable with rating categories of good, very good, and excellent. Meal price is a quantitative variable that ranges from $10 to $49.

A crosstabulation of the data for this application is shown in Table 2.10. The labels shown in the margins of the table define the categories (classes) for the two variables. In

Grouping the data for a quantitative variable enables us to treat the quantitative variable as if it were a categorical variable when creating a crosstabulation.

TABLE 2.9	Quality Rating and Meal Price Data for 300 Los Angeles Restaurants

Restaurant

Restaurant	Quality Rating	Meal Price ($)
1	Good	18
2	Very Good	22
3	Good	28
4	Excellent	38
5	Very Good	33
6	Good	28
7	Very Good	19
8	Very Good	11
9	Very Good	23
10	Good	13
.	.	.
.	.	.
.	.	.

TABLE 2.10	Crosstabulation of Quality Rating and Meal Price Data for 300 Los Angeles Restaurants				

| | Meal Price | | | | |
Quality Rating	$10–19	$20–29	$30–39	$40–49	Total
Good	42	40	2	0	84
Very Good	34	64	46	6	150
Excellent	2	14	28	22	66
Total	78	118	76	28	300

the left margin, the row labels (good, very good, and excellent) correspond to the three rating categories for the quality rating variable. In the top margin, the column labels ($10–19, $20–29, $30–39, and $40–49) show that the meal price data have been grouped into four classes. Because each restaurant in the sample provides a quality rating and a meal price, each restaurant is associated with a cell appearing in one of the rows and one of the columns of the crosstabulation. For example, Table 2.9 shows restaurant 5 as having a very good quality rating and a meal price of $33. This restaurant belongs to the cell in row 2 and column 3 of the crosstabulation shown in Table 2.10. In constructing a crosstabulation, we simply count the number of restaurants that belong to each of the cells.

Although four classes of the meal price variable were used to construct the crosstabulation shown in Table 2.10, the crosstabulation of quality rating and meal price could have been developed using fewer or more classes for the meal price variable. The issues involved in deciding how to group the data for a quantitative variable in a crosstabulation are similar to the issues involved in deciding the number of classes to use when constructing a frequency distribution for a quantitative variable. For this application, four classes of meal price were considered a reasonable number of classes to reveal any relationship between quality rating and meal price.

In reviewing Table 2.10, we see that the greatest number of restaurants in the sample (64) have a very good rating and a meal price in the $20–29 range. Only two restaurants have an excellent rating and a meal price in the $10–19 range. Similar interpretations of the other frequencies can be made. In addition, note that the right and bottom margins of the crosstabulation provide the frequency distributions for quality rating and meal price separately. From the frequency distribution in the right margin, we see that data on quality ratings show 84 restaurants with a good quality rating, 150 restaurants with a very good quality rating, and 66 restaurants with an excellent quality rating. Similarly, the bottom margin shows the frequency distribution for the meal price variable.

Dividing the totals in the right margin of the crosstabulation by the total for that column provides a relative and percent frequency distribution for the quality rating variable.

Quality Rating	Relative Frequency	Percent Frequency
Good	.28	28
Very Good	.50	50
Excellent	.22	22
Total	1.00	100

From the percent frequency distribution we see that 28% of the restaurants were rated good, 50% were rated very good, and 22% were rated excellent.

Dividing the totals in the bottom row of the crosstabulation by the total for that row provides a relative and percent frequency distribution for the meal price variable.

Meal Price	Relative Frequency	Percent Frequency
$10–19	.26	26
$20–29	.39	39
$30–39	.25	25
$40–49	.09	9
Total	1.00	100

Note that the values in the relative frequency column do not add exactly to 1.00 and the values in the percent frequency distribution do not add exactly to 100; the reason is that the values being summed are rounded. From the percent frequency distribution we see that 26% of the meal prices are in the lowest price class ($10–19), 39% are in the next higher class, and so on.

The frequency and relative frequency distributions constructed from the margins of a crosstabulation provide information about each of the variables individually, but they do not shed any light on the relationship between the variables. The primary value of a crosstabulation lies in the insight it offers about the relationship between the variables. A review of the crosstabulation in Table 2.10 reveals that restaurants with higher meal prices received higher quality ratings than restaurants with lower meal prices.

Converting the entries in a crosstabulation into row percentages or column percentages can provide more insight into the relationship between the two variables. For row percentages, the results of dividing each frequency in Table 2.10 by its corresponding row total are shown in Table 2.11. Each row of Table 2.11 is a percent frequency distribution of meal price for one of the quality rating categories. Of the restaurants with the lowest quality rating (good), we see that the greatest percentages are for the less expensive restaurants (50% have $10–19 meal prices and 47.6% have $20–29 meal prices). Of the restaurants with the highest quality rating (excellent), we see that the greatest percentages are for the more expensive restaurants (42.4% have $30–39 meal prices and 33.4% have $40–49 meal prices). Thus, we continue to see that restaurants with higher meal prices received higher quality ratings.

Crosstabulations are widely used to investigate the relationship between two variables. In practice, the final reports for many statistical studies include a large number of crosstabulations. In the Los Angeles restaurant survey, the crosstabulation is based on one categorical variable (quality rating) and one quantitative variable (meal price). Crosstabulations can also be developed when both variables are categorical and when both variables are quantitative. When quantitative variables are used, however, we must first create classes for the values of the variable. For instance, in the restaurant example we grouped the meal prices into four classes ($10–19, $20–29, $30–39, and $40–49).

Simpson's Paradox

The data in two or more crosstabulations are often combined or aggregated to produce a summary crosstabulation showing how two variables are related. In such cases, conclusions drawn from two or more separate crosstabulations can be reversed when the data are aggregated into a single crosstabulation. The reversal of conclusions based on aggregate and unaggregated data

TABLE 2.11 Row Percentages for Each Quality Rating Category

Quality Rating	Meal Price				Total
	$10–19	$20–29	$30–39	$40–49	
Good	50.0	47.6	2.4	.0	100
Very Good	22.7	42.7	30.6	4.0	100
Excellent	3.0	21.2	42.4	33.4	100

is called **Simpson's paradox**. To provide an illustration of Simpson's paradox we consider an example involving the analysis of verdicts for two judges in two different courts.

Judges Ron Luckett and Dennis Kendall presided over cases in Common Pleas Court and Municipal Court during the past three years. Some of the verdicts they rendered were appealed. In most of these cases the appeals court upheld the original verdicts, but in some cases those verdicts were reversed. For each judge a crosstabulation was developed based upon two variables: Verdict (upheld or reversed) and Type of Court (Common Pleas and Municipal). Suppose that the two crosstabulations were then combined by aggregating the type of court data. The resulting aggregated crosstabulation contains two variables: Verdict (upheld or reversed) and Judge (Luckett or Kendall). This crosstabulation shows the number of appeals in which the verdict was upheld and the number in which the verdict was reversed for both judges. The following crosstabulation shows these results along with the column percentages in parentheses next to each value.

Verdict	Judge		
	Luckett	Kendall	Total
Upheld	129 (86%)	110 (88%)	239
Reversed	21 (14%)	15 (12%)	36
Total (%)	150 (100%)	125 (100%)	275

A review of the column percentages shows that 86% of the verdicts were upheld for Judge Luckett, while 88% of the verdicts were upheld for Judge Kendall. From this aggregated crosstabulation, we conclude that Judge Kendall is doing the better job because a greater percentage of Judge Kendall's verdicts are being upheld.

The following unaggregated crosstabulations show the cases tried by Judge Luckett and Judge Kendall in each court; column percentages are shown in parentheses next to each value.

Judge Luckett

Verdict	Common Pleas	Municipal Court	Total
Upheld	29 (91%)	100 (85%)	129
Reversed	3 (9%)	18 (15%)	21
Total (%)	32 (100%)	118 (100%)	150

Judge Kendall

Verdict	Common Pleas	Municipal Court	Total
Upheld	90 (90%)	20 (80%)	110
Reversed	10 (10%)	5 (20%)	15
Total (%)	100 (100%)	25 (100%)	125

From the crosstabulation and column percentages for Judge Luckett, we see that the verdicts were upheld in 91% of the Common Pleas Court cases and in 85% of the Municipal Court cases. From the crosstabulation and column percentages for Judge Kendall, we see that the verdicts were upheld in 90% of the Common Pleas Court cases and in 80% of the Municipal Court cases. Thus, when we unaggregate the data, we see that Judge Luckett has a better record because a greater percentage of Judge Luckett's verdicts are being upheld in both courts. This result contradicts the conclusion we reached with the aggregated data crosstabulation that showed Judge Kendall had the better record. This reversal of conclusions based on aggregated and unaggregated data illustrates Simpson's paradox.

The original crosstabulation was obtained by aggregating the data in the separate crosstabulations for the two courts. Note that for both judges the percentage of appeals that resulted in reversals was much higher in Municipal Court than in Common Pleas Court. Because Judge Luckett tried a much higher percentage of his cases in Municipal Court, the aggregated data favored Judge Kendall. When we look at the crosstabulations for the two courts separately, however, Judge Luckett shows the better record. Thus, for the original crosstabulation, we see that the *type of court* is a hidden variable that cannot be ignored when evaluating the records of the two judges.

Because of the possibility of Simpson's paradox, realize that the conclusion or interpretation may be reversed depending upon whether you are viewing unaggregated or aggregated crosstabulation data. Before drawing a conclusion, you may want to investigate whether the aggregated or unaggregated form of the crosstabulation provides the better insight and conclusion. Especially when the crosstabulation involves aggregated data, you should investigate whether a hidden variable could affect the results such that separate or unaggregated crosstabulations provide a different and possibly better insight and conclusion.

EXERCISES

Methods

27. The following data are for 30 observations involving two categorical variables, x and y. The categories for x are A, B, and C; the categories for y are 1 and 2.

DATA *file*

Crosstab

Observation	x	y	Observation	x	y
1	A	1	16	B	2
2	B	1	17	C	1
3	B	1	18	B	1
4	C	2	19	C	1
5	B	1	20	B	1
6	C	2	21	C	2
7	B	1	22	B	1
8	C	2	23	C	2
9	A	1	24	A	1
10	B	1	25	B	1
11	A	1	26	C	2
12	B	1	27	C	2
13	C	2	28	A	1
14	C	2	29	B	1
15	C	2	30	B	2

a. Develop a crosstabulation for the data, with x as the row variable and y as the column variable.
b. Compute the row percentages.
c. Compute the column percentages.
d. What is the relationship, if any, between x and y?

28. The following observations are for two quantitative variables, x and y.

DATA *file*

Crosstab2

Observation	x	y	Observation	x	y
1	28	72	11	13	98
2	17	99	12	84	21
3	52	58	13	59	32
4	79	34	14	17	81
5	37	60	15	70	34
6	71	22	16	47	64
7	37	77	17	35	68
8	27	85	18	62	67
9	64	45	19	30	39
10	53	47	20	43	28

a. Develop a crosstabulation for the data, with x as the row variable and y as the column variable. For x use classes of 10–29, 30–49, and so on; for y use classes of 40–59, 60–79, and so on.

b. Compute the row percentages.

c. Compute the column percentages.

d. What is the relationship, if any, between x and y?

Applications

29. **Daytona 500 Automobile Makes Average Speeds.** The Daytona 500 is a 500-mile automobile race held annually at the Daytona International Speedway in Daytona Beach, Florida. The following crosstabulation shows the automobile make by average speed of the 25 winners over a 25 year period (*The World Almanac*).

	Average Speed in Miles per Hour					
Make	130–139.9	140–149.9	150–159.9	160–169.9	170–179.9	Total
Buick	1					1
Chevrolet	3	5	4	3	1	16
Dodge		2				2
Ford	2	1	2	1		6
Total	6	8	6	4	1	25

a. Compute the row percentages.

b. What percentage of winners driving a Chevrolet won with an average speed of at least 150 miles per hour?

c. Compute the column percentages.

d. What percentage of winning average speeds 160–169.9 miles per hour were Chevrolets?

30. **Daytona 500 Average Speeds of Winners.** The following crosstabulation shows the average speed of the 25 winners by year of the Daytona 500 automobile race (*The World Almanac*).

	Year					
Average Speed	1988–1992	1993–1997	1998–2002	2003–2007	2008–2012	Total
130–139.9	1			2	3	6
140–149.9	2	2	1	2	1	8
150–159.9		3	1	1	1	6
160–169.9	2		2			4
170–179.9			1			1
Total	5	5	5	5	5	25

a. Calculate the row percentages.

b. What is the apparent relationship between average winning speed and year? What might be the cause of this apparent relationship?

31. **Golf Course Complaints.** Recently, management at Oak Tree Golf Course received a few complaints about the condition of the greens. Several players complained that the greens are too fast. Rather than react to the comments of just a few, the Golf Association conducted a survey of 100 male and 100 female golfers. The survey results are summarized here.

Male Golfers				Female Golfers		
	Greens Condition				Greens Condition	
Handicap	Too Fast	Fine		Handicap	Too Fast	Fine
Under 15	10	40		Under 15	1	9
15 or more	25	25		15 or more	39	51

a. Combine these two crosstabulations into one with Male and Female as the row labels and Too Fast and Fine as the column labels. Which group shows the highest percentage saying that the greens are too fast?
  b. Refer to the initial crosstabulations. For those players with low handicaps (better players), which group (male or female) shows the higher percentage saying the greens are too fast?
  c. Refer to the initial crosstabulations. For those players with higher handicaps, which group (male or female) shows the higher percentage saying the greens are too fast?
  d. What conclusions can you draw about the preferences of men and women concerning the speed of the greens? Are the conclusions you draw from part (a) as compared with parts (b) and (c) consistent? Explain any apparent inconsistencies.

32. **Household Income Levels.** The following crosstabulation shows the number of households (1000s) in each of the four regions of the United States and the number of households at each income level (U.S. Census Bureau website, https://www.census.gov/data/tables/time-series/demo/income-poverty/cps-hinc.html).

				Income Level of Household				
Region	Under $15,000	$15,000 to $24,999	$25,000 to $34,999	$35,000 to $49,999	$50,000 to $74,999	$75,000 to $99,999	$100,000 and over	Number of Households (1000s)
Northeast	2733	2244	2264	2807	3699	2486	5246	21,479
Midwest	3273	3326	3056	3767	5044	3183	4742	26,391
South	6235	5657	5038	6476	7730	4813	7660	43,609
West	3086	2796	2644	3557	4804	3066	6104	26,057
Total	15,327	14,023	13,002	16,607	21,277	13,548	23,752	117,536

a. Compute the row percentages and identify the percent frequency distributions of income for households in each region.
  b. What percentage of households in the West region have an income level of $50,000 or more? What percentage of households in the South region have an income level of $50,000 or more?
  c. Construct percent frequency histograms for each region of households. Do any relationships between regions and income level appear to be evident in your findings?
  d. Compute the column percentages. What information do the column percentages provide?
  e. What percent of households with a household income of $100,000 and over are from the South region? What percentage of households from the South region have a household income of $100,000 and over? Why are these two percentages different?

33. **Values of World's Most Valuable Brands.** Each year *Forbes* ranks the world's most valuable brands. A portion of the data for 82 of the brands in the 2013 *Forbes* list is shown in Table 2.12 (*Forbes* website). The data set includes the following variables:

Brand: The name of the brand.

Industry: The type of industry associated with the brand, labeled Automotive & Luxury, Consumer Packaged Goods, Financial Services, Other, Technology.

Brand Value ($ billions):   A measure of the brand's value in billions of dollars developed by Forbes based on a variety of financial information about the brand.

1-Yr Value Change (%):   The percentage change in the value of the brand over the previous year.

Brand Revenue ($ billions):   The total revenue in billions of dollars for the brand.

a. Prepare a crosstabulation of the data on Industry (rows) and Brand Value ($ billions). Use classes of 0–10, 10–20, 20–30, 30–40, 40–50, and 50–60 for Brand Value ($ billions).
  b. Prepare a frequency distribution for the data on Industry.
  c. Prepare a frequency distribution for the data on Brand Value ($ billions).

TABLE 2.12　Data for 82 of the Most Valuable Brands

BrandValue

Brand	Industry	Brand Value ($ billions)	1-Yr Value Change (%)	Brand Revenue ($ billions)
Accenture	Other	9.7	10	30.4
Adidas	Other	8.4	23	14.5
Allianz	Financial Services	6.9	5	130.8
Amazon.Com	Technology	14.7	44	60.6
.	.	.	.	.
.	.	.	.	.
.	.	.	.	.
Heinz	Consumer Packaged Goods	5.6	2	4.4
Hermès	Automotive & Luxury	9.3	20	4.5
.	.	.	.	.
.	.	.	.	.
.	.	.	.	.
Wells Fargo	Financial Services	9	−14	91.2
Zara	Other	9.4	11	13.5

Source: *Data from Forbes, 2014.*

　　d. How has the crosstabulation helped in preparing the frequency distributions in parts (b) and (c)?

　　e. What conclusions can you draw about the type of industry and the brand value?

34. **Revenue of World's Most Valuable Brands.** Refer to Table 2.12.

　　a. Prepare a crosstabulation of the data on Industry (rows) and Brand Revenue ($ billions). Use class intervals of 25 starting at 0 for Brand Revenue ($ billions).

　　b. Prepare a frequency distribution for the data on Brand Revenue ($ billions).

　　c. What conclusions can you draw about the type of industry and the brand revenue?

　　d. Prepare a crosstabulation of the data on Industry (rows) and the 1-Yr Value Change (%). Use class intervals of 20 starting at −60 for 1-Yr Value Change (%).

　　e. Prepare a frequency distribution for the data on 1-Yr Value Change (%).

　　f. What conclusions can you draw about the type of industry and the 1-year change in value?

35. **Car Fuel Efficiencies.** The U.S. Department of Energy's Fuel Economy Guide provides fuel efficiency data for cars and trucks (Fuel Economy website). A portion of the data from 2018 for 341 compact, midsize, and large cars is shown in Table 2.13. The data set contains the following variables:

　　Size:　Compact, Midsize, and Large

　　Displacement:　Engine size in liters

　　Cylinders:　Number of cylinders in the engine

　　Drive:　All wheel (A), front wheel (F), and rear wheel (R)

　　Fuel Type:　Premium (P) or regular (R) fuel

　　City MPG:　Fuel efficiency rating for city driving in terms of miles per gallon

　　Hwy MPG:　Fuel efficiency rating for highway driving in terms of miles per gallon

　　The complete data set is contained in the file *FuelData2018*.

　　a. Prepare a crosstabulation of the data on Size (rows) and Hwy MPG (columns). Use classes of 20–24, 25–29, 30–34, 35–39, and 40–44 for Hwy MPG.

　　b. Comment on the relationship between Size and Hwy MPG.

　　c. Prepare a crosstabulation of the data on Drive (rows) and City MPG (columns). Use classes of 10–14, 15–19, 20–24, 25–29, and 30–34 for City MPG.

　　d. Comment on the relationship between Drive and City MPG.

　　e. Prepare a crosstabulation of the data on Fuel Type (rows) and City MPG (columns). Use classes of 10–14, 15–19, 20–24, 25–29, and 30–34 for City MPG.

　　f. Comment on the relationship between Fuel Type and City MPG.

TABLE 2.13	Fuel Efficiency Data for 341 Cars						
Car	Size	Displacement	Cylinders	Drive	Fuel Type	City MPG	Hwy MPG
1	Compact	1.4	4	F	R	27	40
2	Compact	1.4	4	F	R	27	35
3	Compact	1.4	4	F	R	28	38
.	.	.	.	.	.	.	.
.	.	.	.	.	.	.	.
.	.	.	.	.	.	.	.
190	Compact	2.5	4	F	R	27	36
191	Large	2.5	4	F	R	22	30
192	Midsize	2.5	4	F	R	21	32
.	.		.	.	.	.	.
.	.			.	.	.	.
.	.			.	.	.	.
339	Large	6.0	12	R	P	13	21
340	Large	6.0	12	R	P	13	22
341	Large	6.0	12	R	P	13	20

DATA *file*

FuelData2018

2.4 Summarizing Data for Two Variables Using Graphical Displays

In the previous section we showed how a crosstabulation can be used to summarize the data for two variables and help reveal the relationship between the variables. In most cases, a graphical display is more useful for recognizing patterns and trends in the data.

In this section, we introduce a variety of graphical displays for exploring the relationships between two variables. Displaying data in creative ways can lead to powerful insights and allow us to make "common-sense inferences" based on our ability to visually compare, contrast, and recognize patterns. We begin with a discussion of scatter diagrams and trendlines.

Scatter Diagram and Trendline

A **scatter diagram** is a graphical display of the relationship between two quantitative variables, and a **trendline** is a line that provides an approximation of the relationship. As an illustration, consider the advertising/sales relationship for an electronics store in San Francisco. On 10 occasions during the past three months, the store used weekend television commercials to promote sales at its stores. The managers want to investigate whether a relationship exists between the number of commercials shown and sales at the store during the following week. Sample data for the 10 weeks with sales in hundreds of dollars are shown in Table 2.14.

Figure 2.8 shows the scatter diagram and the trendline[1] for the data in Table 2.14. The number of commercials (x) is shown on the horizontal axis and the sales (y) are shown on the vertical axis. For week 1, $x = 2$ and $y = 50$. A point with those coordinates is plotted on the scatter diagram. Similar points are plotted for the other nine weeks. Note that during two of the weeks one commercial was shown, during two of the weeks two commercials were shown, and so on.

The scatter diagram in Figure 2.8 indicates a positive relationship between the number of commercials and sales. Higher sales are associated with a higher number of commercials. The relationship is not perfect in that all points are not on a straight line. However, the general pattern of the points and the trendline suggest that the overall relationship is positive.

Some general scatter diagram patterns and the types of relationships they suggest are shown in Figure 2.9. The top left panel depicts a positive relationship similar to the one for the number of commercials and sales example. In the top right panel, the scatter diagram

---

[1]The equation of the trendline is $y = 36.15 + 4.95x$. The slope of the trendline is 4.95 and the y-intercept (the point where the trendline intersects the y-axis) is 36.15. We will discuss in detail the interpretation of the slope and y-intercept for a linear trendline in Chapter 14 when we study simple linear regression.

DATA *file*

Electronics

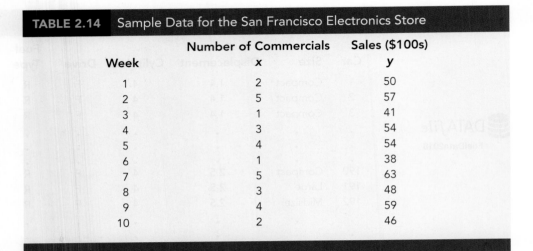

	Number of Commercials	**Sales ($100s)**
Week	**x**	**y**
1	2	50
2	5	57
3	1	41
4	3	54
5	4	54
6	1	38
7	5	63
8	3	48
9	4	59
10	2	46

TABLE 2.14   Sample Data for the San Francisco Electronics Store

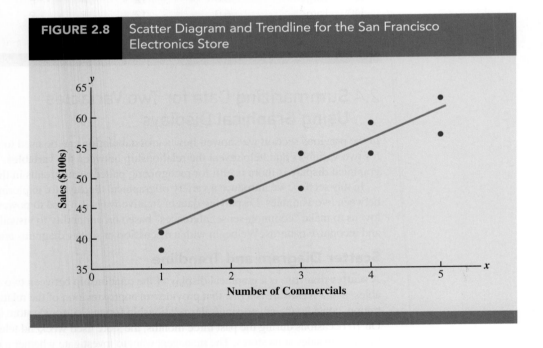

FIGURE 2.8   Scatter Diagram and Trendline for the San Francisco Electronics Store

shows no apparent relationship between the variables. The bottom panel depicts a negative relationship where *y* tends to decrease as *x* increases.

Side-by-Side and Stacked Bar Charts

In Section 2.1 we said that a bar chart is a graphical display for depicting categorical data summarized in a frequency, relative frequency, or percent frequency distribution. Side-by-side bar charts and stacked bar charts are extensions of basic bar charts that are used to display and compare two variables. By displaying two variables on the same chart, we may better understand the relationship between the variables.

A **side-by-side bar chart** is a graphical display for depicting multiple bar charts on the same display. To illustrate the construction of a side-by-side chart, recall the application involving the quality rating and meal price data for a sample of 300 restaurants located in the Los Angeles area. Quality rating is a categorical variable with rating categories of good, very good, and excellent. Meal price is a quantitative variable that ranges from $10 to $49. The crosstabulation displayed

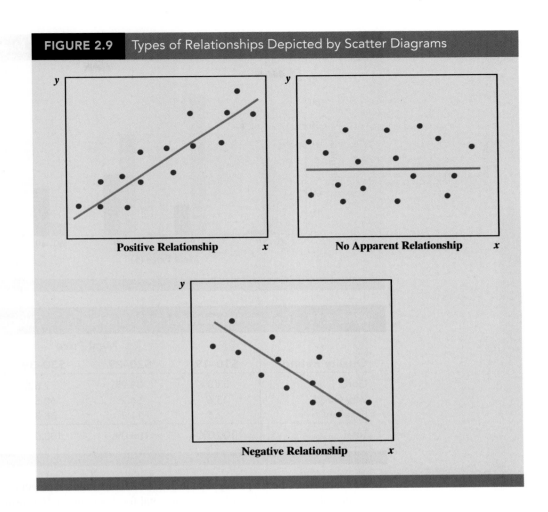

FIGURE 2.9   Types of Relationships Depicted by Scatter Diagrams

in Table 2.10 shows that the data for meal price were grouped into four classes: $10–19, $20–29, $30–39, and $40–49. We will use these classes to construct a side-by-side bar chart.

Figure 2.10 shows a side-by-side chart for the restaurant data. The color of each bar indicates the quality rating (light blue = good, medium blue = very good, and dark blue = excellent). Each bar is constructed by extending the bar to the point on the vertical axis that represents the frequency with which that quality rating occurred for each of the meal price categories. Placing each meal price category's quality rating frequency adjacent to one another allows us to quickly determine how a particular meal price category is rated. We see that the lowest meal price category ($10–$19) received mostly good and very good ratings, but very few excellent ratings. The highest price category ($40–49), however, shows a much different result. This meal price category received mostly excellent ratings, some very good ratings, but no good ratings.

Figure 2.10 also provides a good sense of the relationship between meal price and quality rating. Notice that as the price increases (left to right), the height of the light blue bars decreases and the height of the dark blue bars generally increases. This indicates that as price increases, the quality rating tends to be better. The very good rating, as expected, tends to be more prominent in the middle price categories as indicated by the dominance of the middle bar in the moderate price ranges of the chart.

Stacked bar charts are another way to display and compare two variables on the same display. A **stacked bar chart** is a bar chart in which each bar is broken into rectangular segments of a different color showing the relative frequency of each class in a manner similar to a pie chart. To illustrate a stacked bar chart we will use the quality rating and meal price data summarized in the crosstabulation shown in Table 2.10.

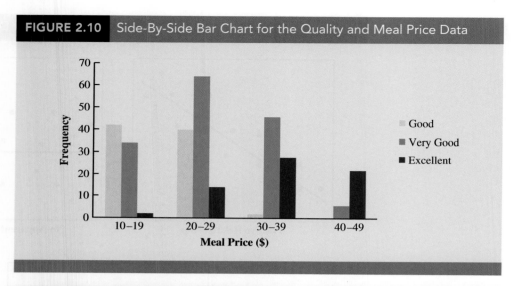

FIGURE 2.10   Side-By-Side Bar Chart for the Quality and Meal Price Data

TABLE 2.15   Column Percentages for each Meal Price Category

Quality Rating	Meal Price			
	$10–19	**$20–29**	**$30–39**	**$40–49**
Good	53.8%	33.9%	2.6%	.0%
Very Good	43.6	54.2	60.5	21.4
Excellent	2.6	11.9	36.8	78.6
Total	100.0%	100.0%	100.0%	100.0%

We can convert the frequency data in Table 2.10 into column percentages by dividing each element in a particular column by the total for that column. For instance, 42 of the 78 restaurants with a meal price in the $10–19 range had a good quality rating. In other words, (42/78)100 or 53.8% of the 78 restaurants had a good rating. Table 2.15 shows the column percentages for each meal price category. Using the data in Table 2.15 we constructed the stacked bar chart shown in Figure 2.11. Because the stacked bar chart is based on percentages, Figure 2.11 shows even more clearly than Figure 2.10 the relationship between the variables. As we move from the low price category ($10–19) to the high price category ($40–49), the length of the light blue bars decreases and the length of the dark blue bars increases.

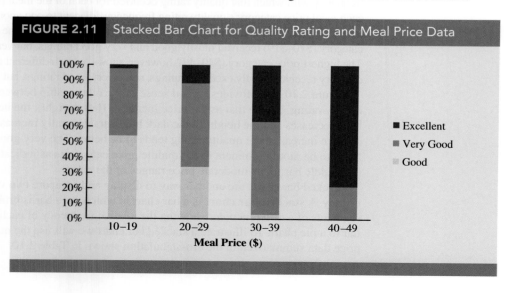

FIGURE 2.11   Stacked Bar Chart for Quality Rating and Meal Price Data

N O T E S   +   C O M M E N T S

1. A time series is a sequence of observations on a variable measured at successive points in time or over successive periods of time. A scatter diagram in which the value of time is shown on the horizontal axis and the time series values are shown on the vertical axis is referred to in time series analysis as a time series plot. We will discuss time series plots and how to analyze time series data in Chapter 17.

2. A stacked bar chart can also be used to display frequencies rather than percentage frequencies. In this case, the different color segments of each bar represent the contribution to the total for that bar, rather than the percentage contribution.

E X E R C I S E S

Methods

36. The following 20 observations are for two quantitative variables, *x* and *y*.

Scatter

Observation	x	y	Observation	x	y
1	−22	22	11	−37	48
2	−33	49	12	34	−29
3	2	8	13	9	−18
4	29	−16	14	−33	31
5	−13	10	15	20	−16
6	21	−28	16	−3	14
7	−13	27	17	−15	18
8	−23	35	18	12	17
9	14	−5	19	−20	−11
10	3	−3	20	−7	−22

   a. Develop a scatter diagram for the relationship between *x* and *y*.
   b. What is the relationship, if any, between *x* and *y*?

37. Consider the following data on two categorical variables. The first variable, *x*, can take on values A, B, C, or D. The second variable, *y*, can take on values I or II. The following table gives the frequency with which each combination occurs.

x	I	II
A	143	857
B	200	800
C	321	679
D	420	580

   a. Construct a side-by-side bar chart with *x* on the horizontal axis.
   b. Comment on the relationship between *x* and *y*.

38. The following crosstabulation summarizes the data for two categorical variables, *x* and *y*. The variable *x* can take on values low, medium, or high and the variable *y* can take on values yes or no.

x	Yes	No	Total
Low	20	10	30
Medium	15	35	50
High	20	5	25
Total	55	50	105

a. Compute the row percentages.

b. Construct a stacked percent frequency bar chart with x on the horizontal axis.

Applications

MPG

39. **Driving Speed and Fuel Efficiency.** A study on driving speed (miles per hour) and fuel efficiency (miles per gallon) for midsize automobiles resulted in the following data:

Driving Speed	30	50	40	55	30	25	60	25	50	55
Fuel Efficiency	28	25	25	23	30	32	21	35	26	25

a. Construct a scatter diagram with driving speed on the horizontal axis and fuel efficiency on the vertical axis.

b. Comment on any apparent relationship between these two variables.

Snow

40. **Low Temperatures and Snowfall.** The file *Snow* contains temperature and snowfall data for 51 major U.S. cities over 30 years. For example, the average low temperature for Columbus, Ohio, is 44 degrees and the average annual snowfall is 27.5 inches.

a. Construct a scatter diagram with the average annual low temperature on the horizontal axis and the average annual snowfall on the vertical axis.

b. Does there appear to be any relationship between these two variables?

c. Based on the scatter diagram, comment on any data points that seem to be unusual.

41. **Hypertension and Heart Disease.** People often wait until middle age to worry about having a healthy heart. However, many studies have shown that earlier monitoring of risk factors such as blood pressure can be very beneficial (*The Wall Street Journal*). Having higher than normal blood pressure, a condition known as hypertension, is a major risk factor for heart disease. Suppose a large sample of individuals of various ages and gender was selected and that each individual's blood pressure was measured to determine if they have hypertension. For the sample data, the following table shows the percentage of individuals with hypertension.

Hypertension

Age	Male	Female
20–34	11.00%	9.00%
35–44	24.00%	19.00%
45–54	39.00%	37.00%
55–64	57.00%	56.00%
65–74	62.00%	64.00%
75+	73.30%	79.00%

a. Develop a side-by-side bar chart with age on the horizontal axis, the percentage of individuals with hypertension on the vertical axis, and side-by-side bars based on gender.

b. What does the display you developed in part (a) indicate about hypertension and age?

c. Comment on differences by gender.

42. **Smartphone Ownership.** Consider the following survey results that show smartphone ownership by age.

Smartphones

Age Category	Smartphone (%)	Other Cell Phone (%)	No Cell Phone (%)
18–24	49	46	5
25–34	58	35	7
35–44	44	45	11
45–54	28	58	14
55–64	22	59	19
65+	11	45	44

a. Construct a stacked bar chart to display the above survey data on type of mobile phone ownership. Use age category as the variable on the horizontal axis.
b. Comment on the relationship between age and smartphone ownership.
c. How would you expect the results of this survey to be different if conducted 10 years from now?

43. **Store Managers Time Study.** The Northwest regional manager of an outdoor equipment retailer conducted a study to determine how managers at three store locations are using their time. A summary of the results are shown in the following table.

DATA *file*

ManagerTime

	Percentage of Manager's Work Week Spent on			
Store Location	Meetings	Reports	Customers	Idle
Bend	18	11	52	19
Portland	52	11	24	13
Seattle	32	17	37	14

a. Create a stacked bar chart with store location on the horizontal axis and percentage of time spent on each task on the vertical axis.
b. Create a side-by-side bar chart with store location on the horizontal axis and side-by-side bars of the percentage of time spent on each task.
c. Which type of bar chart (stacked or side-by-side) do you prefer for these data? Why?

2.5 Data Visualization: Best Practices in Creating Effective Graphical Displays

Data visualization is a term used to describe the use of graphical displays to summarize and present information about a data set. The goal of data visualization is to communicate as effectively and clearly as possible, the key information about the data. In this section, we provide guidelines for creating an effective graphical display, discuss how to select an appropriate type of display given the purpose of the study, illustrate the use of data dashboards, and show how the Cincinnati Zoo and Botanical Garden uses data visualization techniques to improve decision making.

Creating Effective Graphical Displays

The data presented in Table 2.16 show the forecasted or planned value of sales ($1000s) and the actual value of sales ($1000s) by sales region in the United States for Gustin Chemical for the past year. Note that there are two quantitative variables (planned sales and actual sales) and one categorical variable (sales region). Suppose we would like to develop a graphical display that would enable management of Gustin Chemical to visualize how each sales region did relative to planned sales and simultaneously enable management to visualize sales performance across regions.

TABLE 2.16	Planned and Actual Sales by Sales Region ($1000s)	
Sales Region	Planned Sales ($1000s)	Actual Sales ($1000s)
Northeast	540	447
Northwest	420	447
Southeast	575	556
Southwest	360	341

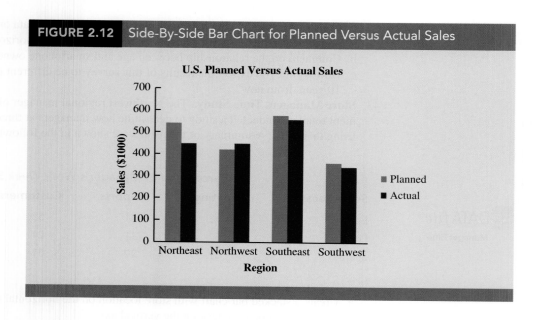

FIGURE 2.12   Side-By-Side Bar Chart for Planned Versus Actual Sales

Figure 2.12 shows a side-by-side bar chart of the planned versus actual sales data. Note how this bar chart makes it very easy to compare the planned versus actual sales in a region, as well as across regions. This graphical display is simple, contains a title, is well labeled, and uses distinct colors to represent the two types of sales. Note also that the scale of the vertical axis begins at zero. The four sales regions are separated by space so that it is clear that they are distinct, whereas the planned versus actual sales values are side-by-side for easy comparison within each region. The side-by-side bar chart in Figure 2.12 makes it easy to see that the Southwest region is the lowest in both planned and actual sales and that the Northwest region slightly exceeded its planned sales.

Creating an effective graphical display is as much art as it is science. By following the general guidelines listed below you can increase the likelihood that your display will effectively convey the key information in the data.

- Give the display a clear and concise title.
- Keep the display simple. Do not use three dimensions when two dimensions are sufficient.
- Clearly label each axis and provide the units of measure.
- If color is used to distinguish categories, make sure the colors are distinct.
- If multiple colors or line types are used, use a legend to define how they are used and place the legend close to the representation of the data.

Choosing the Type of Graphical Display

In this chapter we discussed a variety of graphical displays, including bar charts, pie charts, dot plots, histograms, stem-and-leaf plots, scatter diagrams, side-by-side bar charts, and stacked bar charts. Each of these types of displays was developed for a specific purpose. In order to provide guidelines for choosing the appropriate type of graphical display, we now provide a summary of the types of graphical displays categorized by their purpose. We note that some types of graphical displays may be used effectively for multiple purposes.

Displays Used to Show the Distribution of Data

- Bar Chart—Used to show the frequency distribution and relative frequency distribution for categorical data
- Pie Chart—Used to show the relative frequency and percent frequency for categorical data; generally not preferred to the use of a bar chart
- Dot Plot—Used to show the distribution for quantitative data over the entire range of the data
- Histogram—Used to show the frequency distribution for quantitative data over a set of class intervals
- Stem-and-Leaf Display—Used to show both the rank order and shape of the distribution for quantitative data

Displays Used to Make Comparisons

- Side-by-Side Bar Chart—Used to compare two variables
- Stacked Bar Charts—Used to compare the relative frequency or percent frequency of two categorical variables

Displays Used to Show Relationships

- Scatter diagram—Used to show the relationship between two quantitative variables
- Trendline—Used to approximate the relationship of data in a scatter diagram

Data Dashboards

Data dashboards are also referred to as digital dashboards.

One of the most widely used data visualization tools is a **data dashboard**. If you drive a car, you are already familiar with the concept of a data dashboard. In an automobile, the car's dashboard contains gauges and other visual displays that provide the key information that is important when operating the vehicle. For example, the gauges used to display the car's speed, fuel level, engine temperature, and oil level are critical to ensure safe and efficient operation of the automobile. In some new vehicles, this information is even displayed visually on the windshield to provide an even more effective display for the driver. Data dashboards play a similar role for managerial decision making.

Key performance indicators are sometimes referred to as key performance metrics (KPMs).

A data dashboard is a set of visual displays that organizes and presents information that is used to monitor the performance of a company or organization in a manner that is easy to read, understand, and interpret. Just as a car's speed, fuel level, engine temperature, and oil level are important information to monitor in a car, every business has key performance indicators (KPIs) that need to be monitored to assess how a company is performing. Examples of KPIs are inventory on hand, daily sales, percentage of on-time deliveries, and sales revenue per quarter. A data dashboard should provide timely summary information (potentially from various sources) on KPIs that is important to the user, and it should do so in a manner that informs rather than overwhelms its user.

To illustrate the use of a data dashboard in decision making, we will discuss an application involving the Grogan Oil Company. Grogan has offices located in three cities in Texas: Austin (its headquarters), Houston, and Dallas. Grogan's Information Technology (IT) call center, located in the Austin office, handles calls from employees regarding computer-related problems involving software, Internet, and email issues. For example, if a Grogan employee in Dallas has a computer software problem, the employee can call the IT call center for assistance.

The data dashboard shown in Figure 2.13 was developed to monitor the performance of the call center. This data dashboard combines several displays to monitor the call

FIGURE 2.13   Grogan Oil Information Technology Call Center Data Dashboard

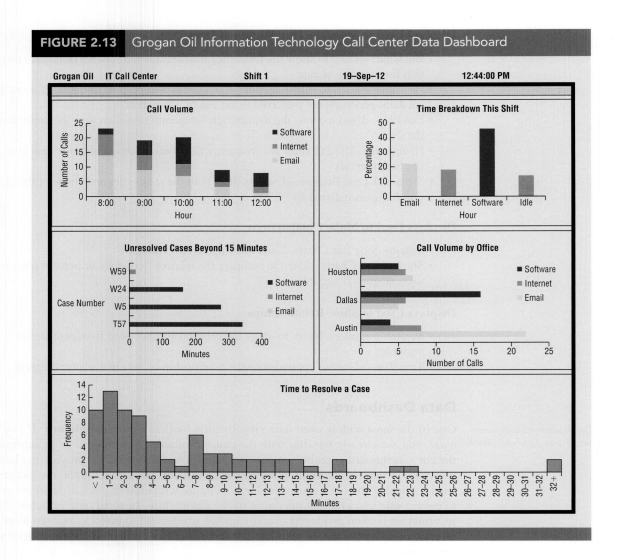

Grogan Oil   IT Call Center   Shift 1   19–Sep–12   12:44:00 PM

center's KPIs. The data presented are for the current shift, which started at 8:00 a.m. The stacked bar chart in the upper left-hand corner shows the call volume for each type of problem (software, Internet, or email) over time. This chart shows that call volume is heavier during the first few hours of the shift, calls concerning email issues appear to decrease over time, and volume of calls regarding software issues are highest at midmorning.

The bar chart in the upper right-hand corner of the dashboard shows the percentage of time that call center employees spent on each type of problem or were idle (not working on a call). These top two charts are important displays in determining optimal staffing levels. For instance, knowing the call mix and how stressed the system is, as measured by percentage of idle time, can help the IT manager make sure that enough call center employees are available with the right level of expertise.

The side-by-side bar chart titled "Call Volume by Office" shows the call volume by type of problem for each of Grogan's offices. This allows the IT manager to quickly identify if there is a particular type of problem by location. For example, it appears that the office in Austin is reporting a relatively high number of issues with email. If the source of the problem can be identified quickly, then the problem for many might be resolved quickly. Also, note that a relatively high number of software problems are coming from the Dallas office. The higher call volume in this case was simply due to the fact that the Dallas office is currently installing new software, and this has resulted in more calls to the IT call center. Because the IT manager was alerted to this by the Dallas office last week, the IT manager knew there would be an increase in calls coming from the Dallas office and was able to increase staffing levels to handle the expected increase in calls.

For each unresolved case that was received more than 15 minutes ago, the bar chart shown in the middle left-hand side of the data dashboard displays the length of time that each of these cases has been unresolved. This chart enables Grogan to quickly monitor the key problem cases and decide whether additional resources may be needed to resolve them. The worst case, T57, has been unresolved for over 300 minutes and is actually left over from the previous shift. Finally, the histogram at the bottom shows the distribution of the time to resolve the problem for all resolved cases for the current shift.

The Grogan Oil data dashboard illustrates the use of a dashboard at the operational level. The data dashboard is updated in real time and used for operational decisions such as staffing levels. Data dashboards may also be used at the tactical and strategic levels of management. For example, a logistics manager might monitor KPIs for on-time performance and cost for its third-party carriers. This could assist in tactical decisions such as transportation mode and carrier selection. At the highest level, a more strategic dashboard would allow upper management to quickly assess the financial health of the company by monitoring more aggregate financial, service level, and capacity utilization information.

The guidelines for good data visualization discussed previously apply to the individual charts in a data dashboard, as well as to the entire dashboard. In addition to those guidelines, it is important to minimize the need for screen scrolling, avoid unnecessary use of color or three-dimensional displays, and use borders between charts to improve readability. As with individual charts, simpler is almost always better.

Data Visualization in Practice: Cincinnati Zoo and Botanical Garden[2]

The Cincinnati Zoo and Botanical Garden, located in Cincinnati, Ohio, is the second oldest zoo in the world. In order to improve decision making by becoming more data-driven, management decided they needed to link together the different facets of their business and provide nontechnical managers and executives with an intuitive way to better understand their data. A complicating factor is that when the zoo is busy, managers are expected to be on the grounds interacting with guests, checking on operations, and anticipating issues as they arise or before they become an issue. Therefore, being able to monitor what is happening on a real-time basis was a key factor in deciding what to do. Zoo management concluded that a data visualization strategy was needed to address the problem.

Because of its ease of use, real-time updating capability, and iPad compatibility, the Cincinnati Zoo decided to implement its data visualization strategy using IBM's Cognos advanced data visualization software. Using this software, the Cincinnati Zoo developed the data dashboard shown in Figure 2.14 to enable zoo management to track the following key performance indicators:

- Item Analysis (sales volumes and sales dollars by location within the zoo)
- Geo Analytics (using maps and displays of where the day's visitors are spending their time at the zoo)

---

[2]The authors are indebted to John Lucas of the Cincinnati Zoo and Botanical Garden for providing this application.

FIGURE 2.14   Data Dashboard for the Cincinnati Zoo

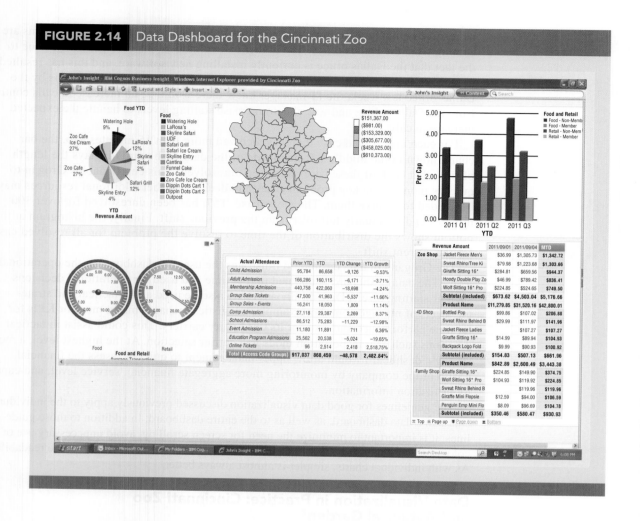

- Customer Spending
- Cashier Sales Performance
- Sales and Attendance Data versus Weather Patterns
- Performance of the Zoo's Loyalty Rewards Program

An iPad mobile application was also developed to enable the zoo's managers to be out on the grounds and still see and anticipate what is occurring on a real-time basis. The Cincinnati Zoo's iPad data dashboard, shown in Figure 2.15, provides managers with access to the following information:

- Real-time attendance data, including what "types" of guests are coming to the zoo
- Real-time analysis showing which items are selling the fastest inside the zoo
- Real-time geographical representation of where the zoo's visitors live

Having access to the data shown in Figures 2.14 and 2.15 allows the zoo managers to make better decisions on staffing levels within the zoo, which items to stock based upon weather and other conditions, and how to better target its advertising based on geodemographics.

The impact that data visualization has had on the zoo has been significant. Within the first year of use, the system has been directly responsible for revenue growth of over $500,000, increased visitation to the zoo, enhanced customer service, and reduced marketing costs.

FIGURE 2.15 The Cincinnati Zoo iPad Data Dashboard

NOTES + COMMENTS

1. A variety of software options are available for data visualization. Among the more popular packages are Excel, JMP, R, SAS Visual Analytics, Spotfire, and Tableau.

2. A very powerful tool for visualizing geographic data is a Geographic Information System (GIS). A GIS uses color, symbols, and text on a map to help you understand how variables are distributed geographically. For example, a company interested in trying to locate a new distribution center might wish to better understand how the demand for its product varies throughout the United States. A GIS can be used to map the demand where red regions indicate high demand, blue lower demand, and no color for regions where the product is not sold. Locations closer to red (high-demand) regions might be good candidate sites for further consideration.

SUMMARY

A set of data, even if modest in size, is often difficult to interpret directly in the form in which it is gathered. Tabular and graphical displays can be used to summarize and present data so that patterns are revealed and the data are more easily interpreted. Frequency distributions, relative frequency distributions, percent frequency distributions, bar charts, and pie charts were presented as tabular and graphical displays for summarizing the data for a single categorical variable. Frequency distributions, relative frequency distributions, percent frequency distributions, histograms, cumulative frequency distributions, cumulative relative frequency distributions, cumulative percent frequency distributions, and stem-and-leaf displays were presented as ways of summarizing the data for a single quantitative variable.

FIGURE 2.16   Tabular and Graphical Displays for Summarizing Data

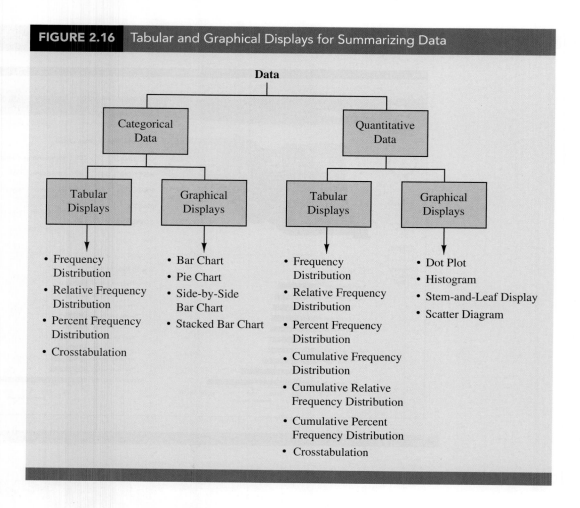

A crosstabulation was presented as a tabular display for summarizing the data for two variables and a scatter diagram was introduced as a graphical display for summarizing the data for two quantitative variables. We also showed that side-by-side bar charts and stacked bar charts are just extensions of basic bar charts that can be used to display and compare two categorical variables. Guidelines for creating effective graphical displays and how to choose the most appropriate type of display were discussed. Data dashboards were introduced to illustrate how a set of visual displays can be developed that organizes and presents information that is used to monitor a company's performance in a manner that is easy to read, understand, and interpret. Figure 2.16 provides a summary of the tabular and graphical methods presented in this chapter.

With large data sets, computer software packages are essential in constructing tabular and graphical summaries of data. In the chapter appendixes, we show how JMP and Excel can be used for this purpose.

GLOSSARY

Bar chart A graphical device for depicting categorical data that have been summarized in a frequency, relative frequency, or percent frequency distribution.

Categorical data Labels or names used to identify categories of like items.

Class midpoint The value halfway between the lower and upper class limits.

Crosstabulation A tabular summary of data for two variables. The classes for one variable are represented by the rows; the classes for the other variable are represented by the columns.

Cumulative frequency distribution A tabular summary of quantitative data showing the number of data values that are less than or equal to the upper class limit of each class.

Cumulative percent frequency distribution A tabular summary of quantitative data showing the percentage of data values that are less than or equal to the upper class limit of each class.

Cumulative relative frequency distribution A tabular summary of quantitative data showing the fraction or proportion of data values that are less than or equal to the upper class limit of each class.

Data dashboard A set of visual displays that organizes and presents information that is used to monitor the performance of a company or organization in a manner that is easy to read, understand, and interpret.

Data visualization A term used to describe the use of graphical displays to summarize and present information about a data set.

Dot plot A graphical device that summarizes data by the number of dots above each data value on the horizontal axis.

Frequency distribution A tabular summary of data showing the number (frequency) of observations in each of several nonoverlapping categories or classes.

Histogram A graphical display of a frequency distribution, relative frequency distribution, or percent frequency distribution of quantitative data constructed by placing the class intervals on the horizontal axis and the frequencies, relative frequencies, or percent frequencies on the vertical axis.

Percent frequency distribution A tabular summary of data showing the percentage of observations in each of several nonoverlapping classes.

Pie chart A graphical device for presenting data summaries based on subdivision of a circle into sectors that correspond to the relative frequency for each class.

Quantitative data Numerical values that indicate how much or how many.

Relative frequency distribution A tabular summary of data showing the fraction or proportion of observations in each of several nonoverlapping categories or classes.

Scatter diagram A graphical display of the relationship between two quantitative variables. One variable is shown on the horizontal axis and the other variable is shown on the vertical axis.

Side-by-side bar chart A graphical display for depicting multiple bar charts on the same display.

Simpson's paradox Conclusions drawn from two or more separate crosstabulations that can be reversed when the data are aggregated into a single crosstabulation.

Stacked bar chart A bar chart in which each bar is broken into rectangular segments of a different color showing the relative frequency of each class in a manner similar to a pie chart.

Stem-and-leaf display A graphical display used to show simultaneously the rank order and shape of a distribution of data.

Trendline A line that provides an approximation of the relationship between two variables.

KEY FORMULAS

Relative Frequency

$$\frac{\text{Frequency of the class}}{n} \tag{2.1}$$

Approximate Class Width

$$\frac{\text{Largest data value} - \text{Smallest data value}}{\text{Number of classes}} \tag{2.2}$$

SUPPLEMENTARY EXERCISES

44. **SAT Scores.** The SAT is a standardized test used by many colleges and universities in their admission decisions. More than one million high school students take the SAT each year. The current version of the SAT includes three parts: reading comprehension, mathematics, and writing. A perfect combined score for all three parts is 2400. A sample of SAT scores for the combined three-part SAT are as follows:

DATA *file*
NewSAT

1665	1525	1355	1645	1780
1275	2135	1280	1060	1585
1650	1560	1150	1485	1990
1590	1880	1420	1755	1375
1475	1680	1440	1260	1730
1490	1560	940	1390	1175

a. Show a frequency distribution and histogram. Begin with the first class starting at 800 and use a class width of 200.
b. Comment on the shape of the distribution.
c. What other observations can be made about the SAT scores based on the tabular and graphical summaries?

45. **Median Household Incomes.** The file *MedianHousehold* contains the median household income for a family with two earners for each of the fifty states (American Community Survey).

DATA *file*
MedianHousehold

a. Construct a frequency and a percent frequency distribution of median household income. Begin the first class at 65.0 and use a class width of 5.
b. Construct a histogram.
c. Comment on the shape of the distribution.
d. Which state has the highest median income for two-earner households?
e. Which state has the lowest median income for two-earner households?

46. **State Populations.** Data showing the population by state in millions of people follow (*The World Almanac*).

DATA *file*
Population2012

State	Population	State	Population	State	Population
Alabama	4.8	Louisiana	4.5	Ohio	11.5
Alaska	.7	Maine	1.3	Oklahoma	3.8
Arizona	6.4	Maryland	5.8	Oregon	4.3
Arkansas	2.9	Massachusetts	6.5	Pennsylvania	12.7
California	37.3	Michigan	9.9	Rhode Island	1.0
Colorado	5.0	Minnesota	5.3	South Carolina	4.6
Connecticut	3.6	Mississippi	3.0	South Dakota	.8
Delaware	.9	Missouri	6.0	Tennessee	6.3
Florida	18.8	Montana	.9	Texas	25.1
Georgia	9.7	Nebraska	1.8	Utah	2.8
Hawaii	1.4	Nevada	2.7	Vermont	.6
Idaho	1.6	New Hampshire	1.3	Virginia	8.0
Illinois	12.8	New Jersey	8.8	Washington	6.7
Indiana	6.5	New Mexico	2.0	West Virginia	1.9
Iowa	3.0	New York	19.4	Wisconsin	5.7
Kansas	2.9	North Carolina	9.5	Wyoming	.6
Kentucky	4.3	North Dakota	.7		

a. Develop a frequency distribution, a percent frequency distribution, and a histogram. Use a class width of 2.5 million.
b. Does there appear to be any skewness in the distribution? Explain.
c. What observations can you make about the population of the 50 states?

StartUps

47. **Startup Company Funds.** According to the *Wall Street Journal,* a startup company's ability to gain funding is a key to success. The funds raised (in millions of dollars) by 50 startup companies appear below.

81	61	103	166	168
80	51	130	77	78
69	119	81	60	20
73	50	110	21	60
192	18	54	49	63
91	272	58	54	40
47	24	57	78	78
154	72	38	131	52
48	118	40	49	55
54	112	129	156	31

a. Construct a stem-and-leaf display.

b. Comment on the display.

BBB

48. **Complaints Reported to BBB.** Consumer complaints are frequently reported to the Better Business Bureau (BBB). Some industries against whom the most complaints are reported to the BBB are banks; cable and satellite television companies; collection agencies; cellular phone providers; and new car dealerships (*USA Today*). The results for a sample of 200 complaints are contained in the file *BBB*.

a. Show the frequency and percent frequency of complaints by industry.

b. Construct a bar chart of the percent frequency distribution.

c. Which industry had the highest number of complaints?

d. Comment on the percentage frequency distribution for complaints.

49. **Stock Price Volatility.** The term "beta" refers to a measure of a stock's price volatility relative to the stock market as a whole. A beta of 1 means the stock's price moves exactly with the market. A beta of 1.6 means the stock's price would increase by 1.6% for an increase of 1% in the stock market. A larger beta means the stock price is more volatile. The beta values for the stocks of the companies that make up the Dow Jones Industrial Average are shown in Table 2.17 (*Yahoo Finance*).

a. Construct a frequency distribution and percent frequency distribution.

b. Construct a histogram.

c. Comment on the shape of the distribution.

d. Which stock has the highest beta? Which has the lowest beta?

50. **Education Level and Household Income.** The U.S. Census Bureau serves as the leading source of quantitative data about the nation's people and economy. The

DATA *file*

StocksBeta

TABLE 2.17	Betas for Dow Jones Industrial Average Companies		
Company	**Beta**	**Company**	**Beta**
American Express Company	1.24	3M Company	1.23
The Boeing Company	.99	Merck & Co. Inc.	.56
Caterpillar Inc.	1.2	Microsoft Corporation	.69
Cisco Systems, Inc.	1.36	Nike, Inc.	.47
Chevron Corporation	1.11	Pfizer Inc.	.72
E. I. du Pont de Nemours and Company	1.36	The Procter & Gamble Company	.73
The Walt Disney Company	.97	AT&T, Inc.	.18
The Goldman Sachs Group, Inc.	1.79	The Travelers Companies, Inc.	.86
The Home Depot, Inc.	1.22	UnitedHealth Group Incorporated	.88
International Business Machines Corporation	.92	United Technologies Corporation	1.22
Intel Corporation	.9	Visa Inc.	.82
Johnson & Johnson	.84	Verizon Communications Inc.	.04
JPMorgan Chase & Co.	1.84	Walgreens Boots Alliance	.81
The Coca-Cola Company	.68	Walmart Stores Inc.	.26
McDonald's Corp.	.62	Exxon Mobil Corporation	1.1

following crosstabulation shows the number of households (1000s) and the household income by the level of education for heads of household having received a high school degree or more education (U.S. Census Bureau website, https://www.census.gov/data/tables/time-series/demo/income-poverty/cps-hinc.html).

	Household Income				
Level of Education	Under $25,000	$25,000 to $49,999	$50,000 to $99,999	$100,000 and Over	Total
High School Graduate	9880	9970	9441	3482	32,773
Bachelor's Degree	2484	4164	7666	7817	22,131
Master's Degree	685	1205	3019	4094	9003
Doctoral Degree	79	160	422	1076	1737
Total	13,128	15,499	20,548	16,469	65,644

a. Construct a percent frequency distribution for the level of education variable. What percentage of heads of households have a master's or doctoral degree?
b. Construct a percent frequency distribution for the household income variable. What percentage of households have an income of $50,000 or more?
c. Convert the entries in the crosstabulation into column percentages. Compare the level of education of households with a household income of under $25,000 to the level of education of households with a household income of $100,000 or more. Comment on any other items of interest when reviewing the crosstabulation showing column percentages.

51. **Softball Players Batting Averages.** Western University has only one women's softball scholarship remaining for the coming year. The final two players that Western is considering are Allison Fealey and Emily Janson. The coaching staff has concluded that the speed and defensive skills are virtually identical for the two players, and that the final decision will be based on which player has the best batting average. Crosstabulations of each player's batting performance in their junior and senior years of high school are as follows:

	Allison Fealey			Emily Janson	
Outcome	Junior	Senior	Outcome	Junior	Senior
Hit	15	75	Hit	70	35
No Hit	25	175	No Hit	130	85
Total At-Bats	40	250	Total At Bats	200	120

A player's batting average is computed by dividing the number of hits a player has by the total number of at-bats. Batting averages are represented as a decimal number with three places after the decimal.

a. Calculate the batting average for each player in her junior year. Then calculate the batting average of each player in her senior year. Using this analysis, which player should be awarded the scholarship? Explain.
b. Combine or aggregate the data for the junior and senior years into one crosstabulation as follows:

	Player	
Outcome	Fealey	Janson
Hit		
No Hit		
Total At-Bats		

Calculate each player's batting average for the combined two years. Using this analysis, which player should be awarded the scholarship? Explain.

  c. Are the recommendations you made in parts (a) and (b) consistent? Explain any apparent inconsistencies.

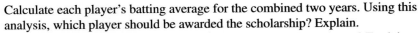

52. **Best Places to Work.** *Fortune* magazine publishes an annual survey of the 100 best companies to work for. The data in the file *FortuneBest100* shows the rank, company name, the size of the company, and the percentage job growth for full-time employees for 98 of the *Fortune* 100 companies for which percentage job growth data were available (*Fortune* magazine website). The column labeled "Rank" shows the rank of the company in the *Fortune* 100 list; the column labeled "Size" indicates whether the company is a small company (less than 2500 employees), a midsized company (2500 to 10,000 employees), or a large company (more than 10,000 employees); and the column labeled "Growth Rate (%)" shows the percentage growth rate for full-time employees.

  a. Construct a crosstabulation with Job Growth (%) as the row variable and Size as the column variable. Use classes starting at −10 and ending at 70 in increments of 10 for Growth Rate (%).

  b. Show the frequency distribution for Job Growth (%) and the frequency distribution for Size.

  c. Using the crosstabulation constructed in part (a), develop a crosstabulation showing column percentages.

  d. Using the crosstabulation constructed in part (a), develop a crosstabulation showing row percentages.

  e. Comment on the relationship between the percentage job growth for full-time employees and the size of the company.

53. **Colleges' Year Founded and Cost.** Table 2.18 shows a portion of the data for a sample of 103 private colleges and universities. The complete data set is contained in the file *Colleges*. The data include the name of the college or university, the year the institution was founded, the tuition and fees (not including room and board) for the most recent academic year, and the percentage of full time, first-time bachelor's degree-seeking undergraduate students who obtain their degree in six years or less (*The World Almanac*).

  a. Construct a crosstabulation with Year Founded as the row variable and Tuition & Fees as the column variable. Use classes starting with 1600 and ending with 2000 in increments of 50 for Year Founded. For Tuition & Fees, use classes starting with 1 and ending 45000 in increments of 5000.

  b. Compute the row percentages for the crosstabulation in part (a).

  c. What relationship, if any, do you notice between Year Founded and Tuition & Fees?

54. **Colleges' Year Founded and Percent Graduated.** Refer to the data set in Table 2.18.

TABLE 2.18	Data for a Sample of Private Colleges and Universities		
School	**Year Founded**	**Tuition & Fees**	**% Graduate**
American University	1893	$36,697	79.00
Baylor University	1845	$29,754	70.00
Belmont University	1951	$23,680	68.00
.	.	.	.
.	.	.	.
.	.	.	.
Wofford College	1854	$31,710	82.00
Xavier University	1831	$29,970	79.00
Yale University	1701	$38,300	98.00

DATA *file*

Colleges

a. Construct a crosstabulation with Year Founded as the row variable and % Graduate as the column variable. Use classes starting with 1600 and ending with 2000 in increments of 50 for Year Founded. For % Graduate, use classes starting with 35% and ending with 100% in increments of 5%.

b. Compute the row percentages for your crosstabulation in part (a).

c. Comment on any relationship between the variables.

55. **Colleges' Year Founded and Cost.** Refer to the data set in Table 2.18.

a. Construct a scatter diagram to show the relationship between Year Founded and Tuition & Fees.

b. Comment on any relationship between the variables.

56. **Colleges' Cost and Percent Graduated.** Refer to the data set in Table 2.18.

a. Prepare a scatter diagram to show the relationship between Tuition & Fees and % Graduate.

b. Comment on any relationship between the variables.

57. **Electric Vehicle Sales.** Electric plug-in vehicle sales have been increasing worldwide. The table below displays data collected by the U.S. Department of Energy on electric plug-in vehicle sales in the words top markets in 2013 and 2015. (Data compiled by Argonne National Laboratory, U.S. Department of Energy website, https://www.energy.gov/eere/vehicles/fact-918-march-28-2016 -global-plug-light-vehicle-sales-increased-about-80-2015)

DATA_file_

ElectricVehicles

Region	2013	2015
China	15,004	214,283
Western Europe	71,233	184,500
United States	97,102	115,262
Japan	28,716	46,339
Canada	931	5,284

a. Construct a side-by-side bar chart with year as the variable on the horizontal axis. Comment on any trend in the display.

b. Convert the above table to percentage allocation for each year. Construct a stacked bar chart with year as the variable on the horizontal axis.

c. Is the display in part (a) or part (b) more insightful? Explain.

58. **Zoo Member Types and Attendance.** A zoo has categorized its visitors into three categories: member, school, and general. The member category refers to visitors who pay an annual fee to support the zoo. Members receive certain benefits such as discounts on merchandise and trips planned by the zoo. The school category includes faculty and students from day care and elementary and secondary schools; these visitors generally receive a discounted rate. The general category includes all other visitors. The zoo has been concerned about a recent drop in attendance. To help better understand attendance and membership, a zoo staff member has collected the following data:

DATA_file_

Zoo

| Visitor Category | Attendance | | | |
	Year 1	Year 2	Year 3	Year 4
General	153,713	158,704	163,433	169,106
Member	115,523	104,795	98,437	81,217
School	82,885	79,876	81,970	81,290
Total	352,121	343,375	343,840	331,613

a. Construct a bar chart of total attendance over time. Comment on any trend in the data.
b. Construct a side-by-side bar chart showing attendance by visitor category with year as the variable on the horizontal axis.
c. Comment on what is happening to zoo attendance based on the charts from parts (a) and (b).

CASE PROBLEM 1: PELICAN STORES

Pelican Stores, a division of National Clothing, is a chain of women's apparel stores operating throughout the country. The chain recently ran a promotion in which discount coupons were sent to customers of other National Clothing stores. Data collected for a sample of 100 in-store credit card transactions at Pelican Stores during one day while the promotion was running are contained in the file named PelicanStores. Table 2.19 shows a portion of the data set. The Proprietary Card method of payment refers to charges made using a National Clothing charge card. Customers who made a purchase using a discount coupon are referred to as promotional customers and customers who made a purchase but did not use a discount coupon are referred to as regular customers. Because the promotional coupons were not sent to regular Pelican Stores customers, management considers the sales made to people presenting the promotional coupons as sales it would not otherwise make. Of course, Pelican also hopes that the promotional customers will continue to shop at its stores.

Most of the variables shown in Table 2.19 are self-explanatory, but two of the variables require some clarification.

| Items | The total number of items purchased |
| Net Sales | The total amount ($) charged to the credit card |

Pelican's management would like to use this sample data to learn about its customer base and to evaluate the promotion involving discount coupons.

DATAfile

PelicanStores

TABLE 2.19 Data for a Sample of 100 Credit Card Purchases at Pelican Stores

Customer	Type of Customer	Items	Net Sales	Method of Payment	Gender	Marital Status	Age
1	Regular	1	39.50	Discover	Male	Married	32
2	Promotional	1	102.40	Proprietary Card	Female	Married	36
3	Regular	1	22.50	Proprietary Card	Female	Married	32
4	Promotional	5	100.40	Proprietary Card	Female	Married	28
5	Regular	2	54.00	MasterCard	Female	Married	34
.	.	.	.	.	.	.	.
.	.	.	.	.	.	.	.
.	.	.	.	.	.	.	.
96	Regular	1	39.50	MasterCard	Female	Married	44
97	Promotional	9	253.00	Proprietary Card	Female	Married	30
98	Promotional	10	287.59	Proprietary Card	Female	Married	52
99	Promotional	2	47.60	Proprietary Card	Female	Married	30
100	Promotional	1	28.44	Proprietary Card	Female	Married	44

Managerial Report

Use the tabular and graphical methods of descriptive statistics to help management develop a customer profile and to evaluate the promotional campaign. At a minimum, your report should include the following:

1. Percent frequency distribution for key variables.
2. A bar chart or pie chart showing the number of customer purchases attributable to the method of payment.
3. A crosstabulation of type of customer (regular or promotional) versus net sales. Comment on any similarities or differences present.
4. A scatter diagram to explore the relationship between net sales and customer age.

CASE PROBLEM 2: MOVIE THEATER RELEASES

The movie industry is a competitive business. More than 50 studios produce hundreds of new movies for theater release each year, and the financial success of each movie varies considerably. The opening weekend gross sales ($ millions), the total gross sales ($ millions), the number of theaters the movie was shown in, and the number of weeks the movie was in release are common variables used to measure the success of a movie released to theaters. Data collected for the top 100 theater movies released in 2016 are contained in the file *Movies2016* (Box Office Mojo website). Table 2.20 shows the data for the first 10 movies in this file.

Managerial Report

Use the tabular and graphical methods of descriptive statistics to learn how these variables contribute to the success of a motion picture. Include the following in your report.

1. Tabular and graphical summaries for each of the four variables along with a discussion of what each summary tells us about the movies that are released to theaters.
2. A scatter diagram to explore the relationship between Total Gross Sales and Opening Weekend Gross Sales. Discuss.

DATA*file*

Movies2016

TABLE 2.20	Performance Data for Ten 2016 Movies Released to Theaters			
Movie Title	Opening Gross Sales ($ Million)	Total Gross Sales ($ Million)	Number of Theaters	Weeks in Release
Rogue One: A Star Wars Story	155.08	532.18	4,157	20
Finding Dory	135.06	486.30	4,305	25
Captain America: Civil War	179.14	408.08	4,226	20
The Secret Life of Pets	104.35	368.38	4,381	25
The Jungle Book	103.26	364.00	4,144	24
Deadpool	132.43	363.07	3,856	18
Zootopia	75.06	341.27	3,959	22
Batman v Superman: Dawn of Justice	166.01	330.36	4,256	12
Suicide Squad	133.68	325.10	4,255	14
Sing	35.26	270.40	4,029	20

3. A scatter diagram to explore the relationship between Total Gross Sales and Number of Theaters. Discuss.
4. A scatter diagram to explore the relationship between Total Gross Sales and Number of Weeks in Release. Discuss.

CASE PROBLEM 3: QUEEN CITY

Cincinnati, Ohio, also known as the Queen City, has a population of approximately 298,000 and is the third largest city in the state of Ohio. The Cincinnati metropolitan area has a population of about 2.2 million. The city is governed by a mayor and a nine-member city council. The city manager, who is responsible for the day-to-day operation of the city, reports to the mayor and city council. The city manager recently created the Office of Performance and Data Analytics with the goal of improving the efficiency of city operations. One of the first tasks of this new office is to review the previous year's expenditures. The file *QueenCity* contains data on the previous year's expenditures, including the following:

DATA *file*

QueenCity

Department: The number of the department incurring the expenditure
Department Description: The name of the department incurring the description
Category: The category of the expenditure
Fund: The fund to which the expenditure was charged
Expenditure: The dollar amount of the expense

Table 2.21 shows the first four entries of the 5427 expenditures for the year. The city manager would like to use this data to better understand how the city's budget is being spent.

Manageri al Report

Use tabular and graphical methods of descriptive statistics to help the city manager get a better understanding of how the city is spending its funding. Your report should include the following:

1. Tables and/or graphical displays that show the amount of expenditures by category and percentage of total expenditures by category.
2. A table that shows the amount of expenditures by department and the percentage of total expenditures by department. Combine any department with less than 1% into a category named "Other."
3. A table that shows the amount of expenditures by fund and the percentage of total expenditures by fund. Combine any fund with less than 1% into a category named "Other."

TABLE 2.21	Annual Expenditures for Queen City (First Four Entries)			
Department	**Department Description**	**Category**	**Fund**	**Expenditure**
121	Department of Human Resources	Fringe Benefits	050 - General Fund	$ 7,085.21
121	Department of Human Resources	Fringe Benefits	050 - General Fund	$102,678.64
121	Department of Human Resources	Fringe Benefits	050 - General Fund	$ 79,112.85
121	Department of Human Resources	Contractual Services	050 - General Fund	$ 3,572.50

CASE PROBLEM 4: CUT-RATE MACHINING, INC.

Jon Weideman, first shift foreman for Cut-Rate Machining, Inc., is attempting to decide on a vendor from whom to purchase a drilling machine. He narrows his alternatives to four vendors: The Hole-Maker, Inc. (HM); Shafts & Slips, Inc. (SS); Judge's Jigs (JJ); and Drill-for-Bits, Inc. (DB). Each of these vendors is offering machines of similar capabilities at similar prices, so the effectiveness of the machines is the only selection criteria that Mr. Weideman can use. He invites each vendor to ship one machine to his Richmond, Indiana manufacturing facility for a test. He starts all four machines at 8:00 A.M. and lets them warm up for two hours before starting to use any of the machines. After the warmup period, one of his employees will use each of the shipped machines to drill 3-centimeter-diameter holes in 25-centimeter-thick stainless-steel sheets for two hours. The widths of holes drilled with each machine are then measured and recorded. The results of Mr. Weideman's data collection are shown in Table 2.22.

TABLE 2.22	Data Collected for Drill-For-Bits, Inc Vendor Selection			
Shift	**Time Period**	**Employee**	**Vendor**	**Measured Width (cm)**
1	10:00 A.M. – noon	Ms. Arnes	HM	3.50
1	10:00 A.M. – noon	Ms. Arnes	HM	3.13
1	10:00 A.M. – noon	Ms. Arnes	HM	3.39
1	10:00 A.M. – noon	Ms. Arnes	HM	3.08
1	10:00 A.M. – noon	Ms. Arnes	HM	3.22
1	10:00 A.M. – noon	Ms. Arnes	HM	3.45
1	10:00 A.M. – noon	Ms. Arnes	HM	3.32
1	10:00 A.M. – noon	Ms. Arnes	HM	3.61
1	10:00 A.M. – noon	Ms. Arnes	HM	3.10
1	10:00 A.M. – noon	Ms. Arnes	HM	3.03
1	10:00 A.M. – noon	Ms. Arnes	HM	3.67
1	10:00 A.M. – noon	Ms. Arnes	HM	3.59
1	10:00 A.M. – noon	Ms. Arnes	HM	3.33
1	10:00 A.M. – noon	Ms. Arnes	HM	3.02
1	10:00 A.M. – noon	Ms. Arnes	HM	3.55
1	10:00 A.M. – noon	Ms. Arnes	HM	3.00
1	noon – 2:00 P.M.	Ms. Arnes	SS	2.48
1	noon – 2:00 P.M.	Ms. Arnes	SS	2.72
1	noon – 2:00 P.M.	Ms. Arnes	SS	2.99
1	noon – 2:00 P.M.	Ms. Arnes	SS	2.68
1	noon – 2:00 P.M.	Ms. Arnes	SS	2.75
1	noon – 2:00 P.M.	Ms. Arnes	SS	2.42
1	noon – 2:00 P.M.	Ms. Arnes	SS	2.92
1	noon – 2:00 P.M.	Ms. Arnes	SS	2.68
1	noon – 2:00 P.M.	Ms. Arnes	SS	2.98
1	noon – 2:00 P.M.	Ms. Arnes	SS	2.50
1	noon – 2:00 P.M.	Ms. Arnes	SS	2.45
1	noon – 2:00 P.M.	Ms. Arnes	SS	2.99
1	noon – 2:00 P.M.	Ms. Arnes	SS	2.31
1	noon – 2:00 P.M.	Ms. Arnes	SS	2.42
1	noon – 2:00 P.M.	Ms. Arnes	SS	2.91
1	noon – 2:00 P.M.	Ms. Arnes	SS	2.83

1	2:00 P.M. – 4:00 P.M.	Ms. Arnes	JJ	2.66
1	2:00 P.M. – 4:00 P.M.	Ms. Arnes	JJ	2.54
1	2:00 P.M. – 4:00 P.M.	Ms. Arnes	JJ	2.61
1	2:00 P.M. – 4:00 P.M.	Ms. Arnes	JJ	2.57
1	2:00 P.M. – 4:00 P.M.	Ms. Arnes	JJ	2.71
1	2:00 P.M. – 4:00 P.M.	Ms. Arnes	JJ	2.55
1	2:00 P.M. – 4:00 P.M.	Ms. Arnes	JJ	2.59
1	2:00 P.M. – 4:00 P.M.	Ms. Arnes	JJ	2.69
1	2:00 P.M. – 4:00 P.M.	Ms. Arnes	JJ	2.52
1	2:00 P.M. – 4:00 P.M.	Ms. Arnes	JJ	2.57
1	2:00 P.M. – 4:00 P.M.	Ms. Arnes	JJ	2.63
1	2:00 P.M. – 4:00 P.M.	Ms. Arnes	JJ	2.60
1	2:00 P.M. – 4:00 P.M.	Ms. Arnes	JJ	2.58
1	2:00 P.M. – 4:00 P.M.	Ms. Arnes	JJ	2.61
1	2:00 P.M. – 4:00 P.M.	Ms. Arnes	JJ	2.55
1	2:00 P.M. – 4:00 P.M.	Ms. Arnes	JJ	2.62
2	4:00 P.M. – 6:00 P.M.	Ms. Silver	DB	4.22
2	4:00 P.M. – 6:00 P.M.	Ms. Silver	DB	2.68
2	4:00 P.M. – 6:00 P.M.	Ms. Silver	DB	2.45
2	4:00 P.M. – 6:00 P.M.	Ms. Silver	DB	1.84
2	4:00 P.M. – 6:00 P.M.	Ms. Silver	DB	2.11
2	4:00 P.M. – 6:00 P.M.	Ms. Silver	DB	3.95
2	4:00 P.M. – 6:00 P.M.	Ms. Silver	DB	2.46
2	4:00 P.M. – 6:00 P.M.	Ms. Silver	DB	3.79
2	4:00 P.M. – 6:00 P.M.	Ms. Silver	DB	3.91
2	4:00 P.M. – 6:00 P.M.	Ms. Silver	DB	2.22
2	4:00 P.M. – 6:00 P.M.	Ms. Silver	DB	2.42
2	4:00 P.M. – 6:00 P.M.	Ms. Silver	DB	2.09
2	4:00 P.M. – 6:00 P.M.	Ms. Silver	DB	3.33
2	4:00 P.M. – 6:00 P.M.	Ms. Silver	DB	4.07
2	4:00 P.M. – 6:00 P.M.	Ms. Silver	DB	2.54
2	4:00 P.M. – 6:00 P.M.	Ms. Silver	DB	3.96

Based on these results, from which vendor would you suggest Mr. Weideman purchase his new machine?

DATA *file*

CutRate

Managerial Report

Use graphical methods of descriptive statistics to investigate the effectiveness of each vendor. Include the following in your report:

1. Scatter plots of the measured width of each hole (cm).
2. Based on the scatter plots, a discussion of the effectiveness of each vendor and under which conditions (if any) that vendor would be acceptable.
3. A discussion of possible sources of error in the approach taken to assess these vendors.

Chapter 2 Appendix

Appendix 2.1 Creating Tabular and Graphical Presentations with JMP

The Student Edition of JMP offers extensive capabilities for constructing tabular and graphical summaries of data. In this appendix we show how JMP can be used to construct several graphical summaries of data. The graphical methods presented include the histogram, bar charts, the stem-and-leaf display, and the scatter diagram. We also show how JMP can be used to create a frequency distribution for categorical data.

Histogram

We show how to construct a histogram with frequencies on the vertical axis using the audit time data in Table 2.4.

DATA *file*

Audit

Step 1. Open the file *Audit* with JMP using the steps provided in Appendix 1.1
Step 2. From the **Data** window containing the audit time data, click **Analyze** and select **Distribution**
Step 3. When the **Distribution** window appears:
        Drag **Audit Time** from the **Select Columns** area to the **Y**
        Columns box in the **Cast Selected Columns into Roles** area
        Click **OK** in the **Action** area

Box plots and summary statistics are discussed in Chapter 3.

These steps will produce the histogram in JMP shown in Figure JMP 2.1. Note that JMP also generated a box plot (shown above the histogram) and a table of summary statistics.

FIGURE JMP 2.1   Histogram Created in JMP for the Audit Time Data

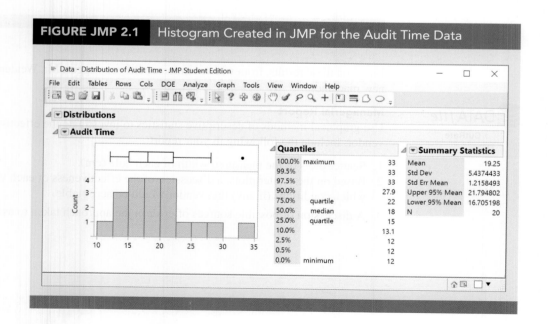

Stem-and-Leaf Display

We use the aptitude test data in Table 2.8 to demonstrate the construction of a stem-and-leaf display in JMP. To create a stem-and-leaf display in JMP, we first create a histogram as we did in the previous section and then modify the output to include a stem-and-leaf display. This is explained in the following directions.

DATA *file*

AptitudeTest

Step 1. Open the file *AptitudeTest* with JMP using the steps provided in Appendix 1.1
Step 2. From the **Data** window containing the aptitude test data, click **Analyze** and select **Distribution**
Step 3. When the **Distribution** window appears:
    Drag **Audit Time** from the **Select Columns** area to the **Y, Columns** box in the **Cast Selected Columns into Roles** area
    Click **OK** in the **Action** area
Step 4. Click the red triangle ▾ next to **Correct** and select **Stem and Leaf**

This will add a stem-and-leaf display to the Data—Distribution of Correct window as shown in Figure JMP 2.2.

Frequency Distribution and Bar Chart for Categorical Data

JMP can also be used to create bar charts and frequency distributions from categorical data. The following steps provide an example of this using the soft drink data from Table 2.1.

DATA *file*

SoftDrink

Step 1. Open the file *SoftDrink* with JMP using the steps provided in Appendix 1.1
Step 2. From the **Data** window containing the soft drink data, click **Analyze** and select **Distribution**

FIGURE JMP 2.2   Stem-and-Leaf Display Created in JMP for Aptitude Test Data

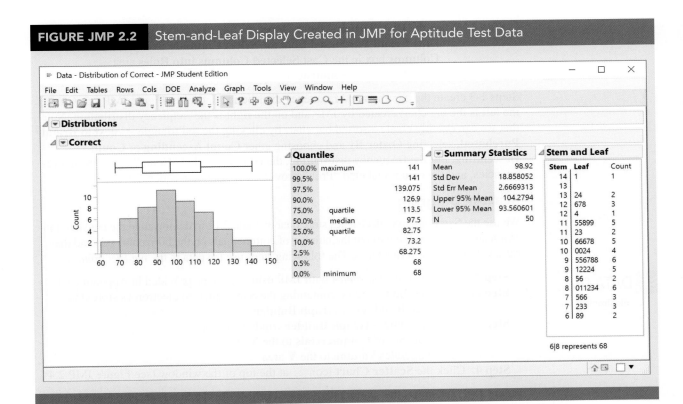

FIGURE JMP 2.3   Bar Chart and Frequency Distribution Created in JMP for Soft Drink Data

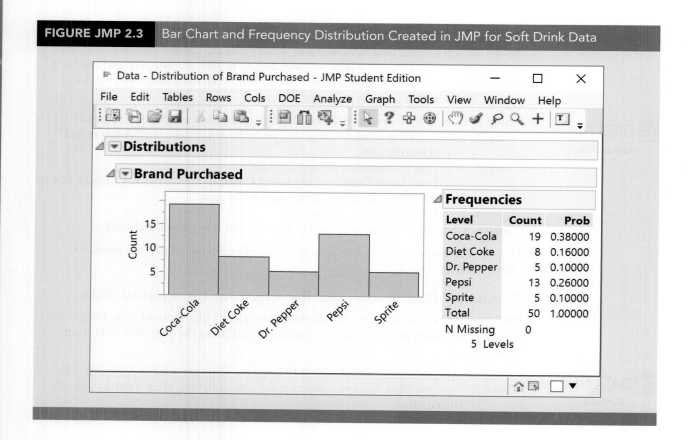

Step 3. When the **Distribution** window appears:
Drag **Brand Purchased** from the **Select Columns** area to the **Y Columns** box in the **Cast Selected Columns into Roles** area
Click **OK** in the **Action** area

Steps 1-3 create the bar chart and frequency distribution shown in Figure JMP 2.3. On the left is the bar chart created by JMP and on the right is the frequency distribution. Note that we can quickly create a sorted bar chart by clicking the red triangle ⬇ next to **Brand Purchased,** selecting **Order By** and choosing ether **Count Ascending** or **Count Descending.** For the frequency distribution, the column labeled "Count" provides the frequencies, and the column labeled "Prob" provides the relative frequencies.

Scatter Diagram

We use the San Francisco electronics store data in Table 2.12 to demonstrate the construction of a scatter diagram. We will put the number of commercials on the horizontal axis and the sales volume on the vertical axis. The following steps use the data in the file *Electronics*.

Electronics

Step 1. Open the file *Electronics* with JMP using the steps provided in Appendix 1.1
Step 2. From the **Data** window containing the San Francisco electronics store data, click **Graph** and select **Graph Builder**
Step 3. When the **Data—Graph Builder** window appears:
Drag **No. of Commercials** to the **X** area
Drag **Sales Volume** to the **Y** area
Step 4. Click the **Scatter Chart** icon ⠿ at the top of the window (see Figure JMP 2.4)

Figure JMP 2.4 shows the scatter chart created in JMP for the San Francisco electronics store data. If a linear trendline is desired on the scatter diagram, click the **Scatter Chart with Linear Fit** icon ⟋ at the top of the window

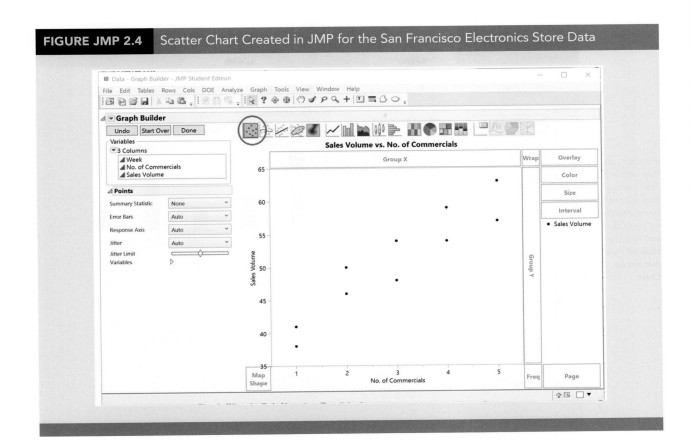

FIGURE JMP 2.4 Scatter Chart Created in JMP for the San Francisco Electronics Store Data

Appendix 2.2 Creating Tabular and Graphical Presentations with Excel

Excel offers extensive capabilities for constructing tabular and graphical summaries of data. In this appendix, we show how Excel can be used to construct a frequency distribution, bar chart, pie chart, histogram, scatter diagram, and crosstabulation. We will demonstrate three of Excel's most powerful tools for data analysis: chart tools, PivotChart Report, and PivotTable Report.

Opening Files in Excel

Launch Excel and use the following steps to open the files for this text.

> **Step 1.** Click the **File** tab on the Ribbon
> **Step 2.** Select **Open**
> **Step 3.** Select **Browse**
> **Step 4.** When the **Open** dialog box appears, navigate to the folder containing the desired file, select the file, and click **Open**

Excel will also display a list of recently used files from the **Open** *menu.*

Frequency Distribution and Bar Chart for Categorical Data

In this section we show how Excel can be used to construct a frequency distribution and a bar chart for categorical data using Excel's Recommended Charts tool. We illustrate each using the data on soft drink purchases in Table 2.1, and contained in the file *SoftDrink*.

DATA*file*

SoftDrink

> **Step 1.** Select any cell in the data set (cells A1:A51)
> **Step 2.** Click the **Insert** tab on the Ribbon

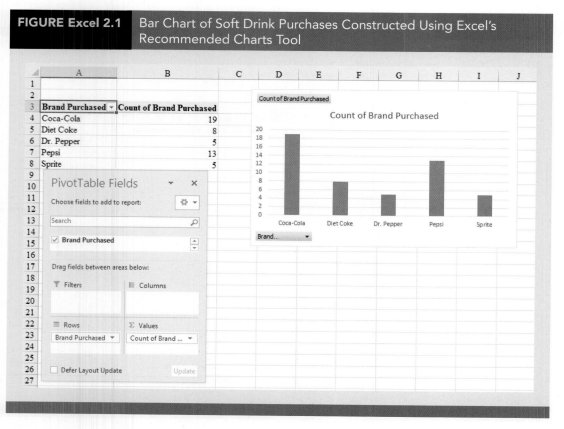

FIGURE Excel 2.1 Bar Chart of Soft Drink Purchases Constructed Using Excel's Recommended Charts Tool

*If desired, you may remove the Field Buttons from the chart by right-clicking on any button and selecting **Hide All Field Buttons on Chart.***

Step 3. In the **Charts** group click **Recommended Charts**; a preview showing the bar chart appears

Step 4. Click **OK**; the bar chart will appear in a new worksheet

The worksheet in Figure Excel 2.1 shows the bar chart for the 50 soft drink purchases created using these steps. Also shown are the frequency distribution and PivotTable fields dialog box that were created by Excel in order to construct the bar chart. Thus, using Excel's Recommended Charts tool, you can construct a bar chart and a frequency distribution at the same time.

You can easily edit the bar chart to display a different chart title and add axis titles. For instance, suppose you would like to use "Bar Chart of Soft Drink Purchases" as the chart title and insert "Soft Drink" for the horizontal axis title and "Frequency" for the vertical axis title.

Step 1. Click the **Chart Title** and replace it with *Bar Chart of Soft Drink Purchases*

Step 2. Click the **Chart Elements** button ⊞ (located next to the top right corner of the chart)

Step 3. When the list of chart elements appears:

Select the check box for **Axis Titles** (creates placeholders for the axis titles)

Step 4. Click the horizontal **Axis Title** placeholder and replace it with *Soft Drink*

Step 5. Click the vertical **Axis Title** placeholder and replace it with *Frequency*

The edited bar chart is shown in Figure Excel 2.2.

To display a different type of chart, select the bar chart (by clicking anywhere in the chart) to display three tabs (**Analyze**, **Design**, and **Format**) located on the Ribbon under the heading **PivotChart Tools**. Click the **Design** tab and choose the **Change Chart Type** option to display the **Change Chart Type** dialog box. This dialog box will allow you to change to many different charts, including line charts and scatter charts.

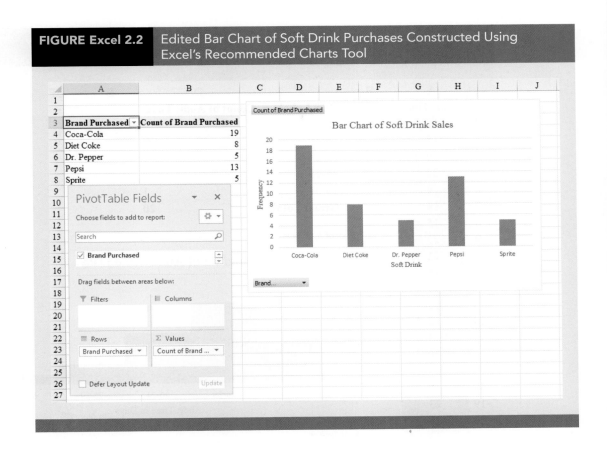

FIGURE Excel 2.2 Edited Bar Chart of Soft Drink Purchases Constructed Using Excel's Recommended Charts Tool

Frequency Distribution and Histogram for Quantitative Data

In a later section of this appendix we describe how to use Excel's PivotTable Report to construct a crosstabulation.

Excel's PivotTable Report is an interactive tool that allows you to quickly summarize data in a variety of ways, including developing a frequency distribution for quantitative data. Once a frequency distribution is created using the PivotTable Report, Excel's chart tools can then be used to construct the corresponding histogram. But, using Excel's PivotChart Report, we can construct a frequency distribution and a histogram simultaneously. We will illustrate this procedure using the audit time data in Table 2.4. The label "Audit Time" and the 20 audit time values are entered into cells A1:A21 of an Excel worksheet. The following steps describe how to use Excel's PivotChart Report to construct a frequency distribution and a histogram for the audit time data. Refer to Figure Excel 2.3 as we describe the steps involved.

DATA *file*

Audit

Step 1. Click the **Insert** tab on the Ribbon

Step 2. In the **Charts** group, click **PivotChart**

Step 3. Select **PivotChart** from the list of options that appears

Step 4. When the Create PivotChart dialog box appears,
Choose **Select a table or range**
Enter *A1:A21* in the **Table/Range** box
Choose **Existing Worksheet** as the location for the PivotChart
Enter *C1* in the **Location** box
Click **OK**

Step 5. In the **PivotChart Fields List**, go to **Choose Fields to add to report**
Drag the **Audit Time** field to the **Axis (Categories)** area
Drag the **Audit Time** field to the **Values** area

Step 6. Click **Sum of Audit Time** in the **Values** area

Step 7. Select **Value Field Settings** from the list of options that appears

FIGURE Excel 2.3 Using Excel's PivotChart report to Construct a Frequency Distribution and Histogram for the Audit Time Data

Step 8. When the **Value Field Settings** dialog box appears,
   Under **Summarize value field by**, choose **Count**
   Click **OK**
Step 9. Close the **PivotChart Fields List** by clicking on the × in the upper right hand corner
Step 10. Right-click cell C2 or any other cell in the PivotTable report containing an audit time
Step 11. Choose **Group** from the list of options that appears
Step 12. When the **Grouping** dialog box appears,
   Enter *10* in the **Starting at:** box
   Enter *34* in the **Ending at:** box
   Enter *5* in the **By:** box
   Click **OK** (a PivotChart will appear)
Step 13. Click inside the resulting PivotChart
Step 14. Click the **Design** tab on the Ribbon under **PivotChart Tools**
   In the **Chart Layouts** group, click the **Quick Layout** button
   Choose **Layout 8**
Step 15. Click the horizontal **Axis Title** placeholder and replace it with *Audit Time in Days*
Step 16. Click the vertical **Axis Title** placeholder and replace it with *Frequency*
Step 17. Click the **Chart Title** and replace it with *Histogram of Audit Time Data*

Figure Excel 2.3 shows the resulting PivotTable and PivotChart. We see that the PivotTable report provides the frequency distribution for the audit time data and the

PivotChart provides the corresponding histogram. If desired, we can change the labels in any cell in the frequency distribution by selecting the cell and typing in the new label.

Excel provides other ways of creating histograms. The Data Analysis ToolPak in Excel provides many different tools that can be used to analyze data in Excel, including histograms. The Data Analysis ToolPak is provided as a standard component of Excel but may not be enabled. To enable the Data Analysis ToolPak Add-in in Excel, follow the steps below.

Step 1. Click the **File** tab on the Ribbon and select **Options**
Step 2. When the **Excel Options** dialog box opens, click **Add-ins**
At the bottom of the **Excel Options** dialog box, where it says, **Manage: Excel Add-ins** click **Go...**
Select the check box for **Analysis ToolPak**
Click **OK**

The following steps explain how to use the Data Analysis ToolPak to create a histogram for the audit time data.

Step 1. Click the **Data** tab in the **Ribbon**
Step 2. Click **Data Analysis** in the **Analyze** group
Step 3. When the **Data Analysis** dialog box opens, choose **Histogram** from the list of **Analysis Tools,** and click **OK**
In the **Input Range:** box, enter *A2:D6*
In the **Bin Range:** box, enter *A10:A14*
Under **Output Options:**, select **New Worksheet Ply:**
Select the check box for **Chart Output** (see Figure Excel 2.4)
Click **OK**

The histogram created by Excel for these data is shown in Figure Excel 2.5. We have modified the bin ranges in column A by typing the values shown in cells A2:A6 of Figure Excel 2.5 so that the chart created by Excel shows both the lower and upper limits for each bin. We have also removed the gaps between the columns in the histogram in Excel to

FIGURE Excel 2.4 Using Excel's Data Analysis ToolPak to Construct a Frequency Distribution and Histogram in Excel

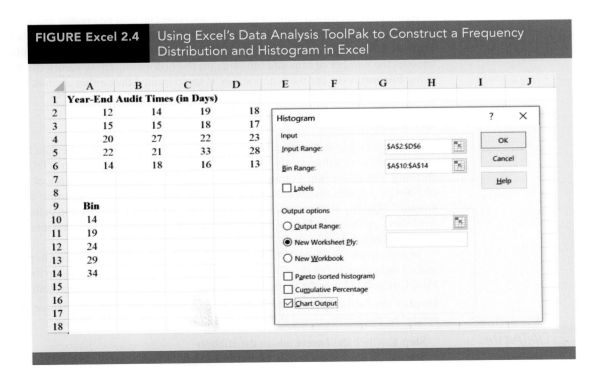

FIGURE Excel 2.5	Completed Histogram and Frequency Distribution for the Audit Time Data Created Using the Data Analysis ToolPak in Excel

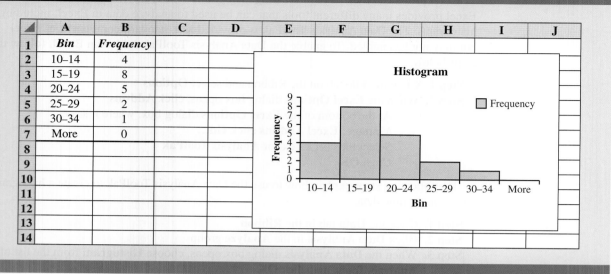

▲	A	B	C	D	E	F	G	H	I	J
1	*Bin*	*Frequency*								
2	10–14	4								
3	15–19	8								
4	20–24	5								
5	25–29	2								
6	30–34	1								
7	More	0								
8										
9										
10										
11										
12										
13										
14										

The text "10-14" in cell A2 can be entered in Excel as '10-14. The single quote indicates to Excel that this should be treated as text rather than a numerical or date value.

match the traditional format of histograms. To remove the gaps between the columns in the histogram created by Excel, follow these steps:

Step 1. Right-click on one of the columns in the histogram
Select **Format Data Series…**

Step 2. When the **Format Data Series** task pane opens, click the **Series Options** button,
Set the **Gap Width** to **0%**

In the most recent versions of Excel, histograms can also be created using the new histogram chart, which can be found by clicking on the **Insert** tab in the ribbon, clicking **Insert Statistic Chart** in the **Charts** group and selecting **Histogram.** Excel automatically chooses the number of bins and bin sizes for the histogram. These values can be changed using **Format Axis,** but the functionality is more limited than either approach we use above to create histograms in Excel.

Crosstabulation

Excel's PivotTable Report provides an excellent way to summarize the data for two or more variables simultaneously. We will illustrate the use of Excel's PivotTable Report by showing how to develop a crosstabulation of quality ratings and meal prices for the sample of 300 Los Angeles restaurants. We will use the data in the file *Restaurant;* the labels "Restaurant," "Quality Rating," and "Meal Price ($)" have been entered into cells A1:C1 of the worksheet as shown in Figure Excel 2.6. The data for each of the restaurants in the sample have been entered into cells B2:C301.

In order to use the PivotTable Report to create a crosstabulation, we need to perform three tasks: Display the Initial PivotTable Field List and PivotTable Report; Set Up the PivotTable Field List; and Finalize the PivotTable Report. These tasks are described as follows.

Display the Initial PivotTable Field List and PivotTable Report: Three steps are needed to display the initial PivotTable Field List and PivotTable Report.

DATA *file*

Restaurant

Step 1. Click the **Insert** tab on the Ribbon

Step 2. In the **Tables** group, click **PivotTable**

FIGURE Excel 2.6	Excel Worksheet Containing Restaurant Data

	A	B	C
1	Restaurant	Quality Rating	Meal Price ($)
2	1	Good	18
3	2	Very Good	22
4	3	Good	28
5	4	Excellent	38
6	5	Very Good	33
7	6	Good	28
8	7	Very Good	19
9	8	Very Good	11
10	9	Very Good	23
11	10	Good	13
292	291	Very Good	23
293	292	Very Good	24
294	293	Excellent	45
295	294	Good	14
296	295	Good	18
297	296	Good	17
298	297	Good	16
299	298	Good	15
300	299	Very Good	38
301	300	Very Good	31

Note: Rows 12–291 are hidden.

Step 3. When the **Create PivotTable** dialog box appears,
         Choose **Select a table or range**
         Enter *A1:C301* in the **Table/Range:** box
         Choose **New Worksheet** as the location for the PivotTable Report
         Click **OK**

The resulting initial PivotTable Field List and PivotTable Report are shown in Figure Excel 2.7.

Set Up the PivotTable Field List: Each of the three columns in Figure Excel 2.6 (labeled Restaurant, Quality Rating, and Meal Price ($)) is considered a field by Excel. Fields may be chosen to represent rows, columns, or values in the body of the PivotTable Report. The following steps show how to use Excel's PivotTable Field List to assign the Quality Rating field to the rows, the Meal Price ($) field to the columns, and the Restaurant field to the body of the PivotTable Report.

Step 4. In the **PivotTable Fields** task pane, go to **Drag fields between areas below**
         Drag the **Quality Rating** field to the **ROWS** area
         Drag the **Meal Price ($)** field to the **COLUMNS** area
         Drag the **Restaurant** field to the **VALUES** area
Step 5. Click on **Sum of Restaurant** in the **VALUES** area
Step 6. Click **Value Field Settings** from the list of options that appear
Step 7. When the **Value Field Settings** dialog box appears,
         Under **Summarize value field by,** select **Count**
         Click **OK**

Figure Excel 2.8 shows the completed PivotTable Field List and a portion of the PivotTable worksheet as it now appears.

FIGURE Excel 2.7   Initial PivotTable Field List and PivotTable Field Report for the Restaurant Data

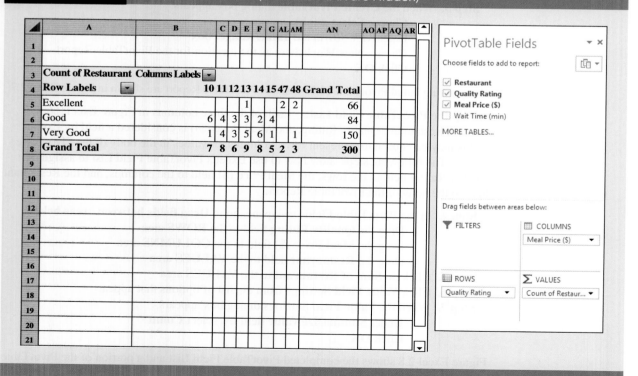

FIGURE Excel 2.8   Completed PivotTable Field List and a Portion of the PivotTable Report for the Restaurant Data (Columns H:AK are Hidden)

Finalize the PivotTable Report: To complete the PivotTable Report we need to group the columns representing meal prices and place the row labels for quality rating in the proper order. The following steps accomplish this.

Step 8. Right-click in cell B4 or any cell containing a meal price column label
Step 9. Select **Group** from the list of options
Step 10. When the **Grouping** dialog box appears,

> Enter *10* in the **Starting at:** box
> Enter *49* in the **Ending at:** box
> Enter *10* in the **By:** box
> Click **OK**

Step 11. Right-click on **Excellent** in cell A5
Step 12. Choose **Move** and click **Move "Excellent" to End**

The final PivotTable Report is shown in Figure Excel 2.9. Note that it provides the same information as the crosstabulation shown in Table 2.10.

Scatter Diagram

We can use Excel's chart tools to construct a scatter diagram and a trend line for the San Francisco electronics store data presented in Table 2.12. Refer to Figures Excel 2.10 and

FIGURE Excel 2.9 Final PivotTable Report for the Restaurant Data

	A	B	C	D	E	F	G
1							
2							
3	**Count of Restaurant**	**Column Labels** ▾					
4	**Row Labels** ▾	**10-19**	**20-29**	**30-39**	**40-49**	**Grand Total**	
5	Good		42	40	2		84
6	Very Good		34	64	46	6	150
7	Excellent		2	14	28	22	66
8	**Grand Total**		**78**	**118**	**76**	**28**	**300**

PivotTable Fields ▾ ✕

Choose fields to add to report: ⚙ ▾

Search 🔍

☑ Restaurant
☑ Quality Rating
☑ Meal Price ($)

Drag fields between areas below:

▼ FILTERS | ▥ COLUMNS
| Meal Price ($) ▾

▤ ROWS | Σ VALUES
Quality Rating ▾ | Count of Restaurant ▾

☐ Defer Layout Update | UPDATE

FIGURE Excel 2.10   Scatter Diagram for the San Francisco Electronics Store Using Excel's Chart Tools

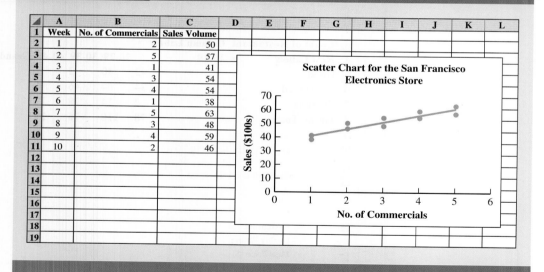

FIGURE Excel 2.11   Scatter Diagram and Trendline for the San Francisco Electronics Store Using Excel's Chart Tools

Excel 2.11 as we describe the steps involved. We will use the data in the file *Electronics*. The labels "Week", "No. of Commercials", and "Sales Volume" have been entered into cells A1:C1 of the worksheet. The data for each of the 10 weeks are entered into cells B2:C11. The following steps describe how to use Excel's chart tools to produce a scatter diagram for the data.

DATA *file*

Electronics

Step 1. Select cells B1:C11
Step 2. Click the **Insert** tab on the Ribbon
Step 3. In the **Charts** group, click **Insert Scatter (X,Y) or Bubble Chart**
Step 4. When the list of scatter diagram subtypes appears, click **Scatter** (the chart in the upper left corner)

The worksheet in Figure Excel 2.10 shows the scatter diagram produced using these steps.

You can easily edit the scatter diagram to display a different chart title, add axis titles, and display the trendline. For instance, suppose you would like to use "Scatter Diagram for the San Francisco Electronics Store" as the chart title and insert "Number of Commercials" for the horizontal axis title and "Sales ($100s)" for the vertical axis title.

Step 1. Click the **Chart Title** and replace it with *Scatter Diagram for the Stereo and Sound Equipment Store*

Step 2. Click the **Chart Elements** button ⊕ (located next to the top right corner of the chart)

Step 3. When the list of chart elements appears:
Click **Axis Titles** (creates placeholders for the axis titles)
Click **Gridlines** (to deselect the Gridlines option)
Click **Trendline**

Step 4. Click the horizontal **Axis Title** placeholder and replace it with *Number of Commercials*

Step 5. Click the vertical **Axis Title** placeholder and replace it with *Sales ($100s)*

Step 6. To change the trendline from a dashed line to a solid line, right-click on the trendline and choose the **Format Trendline** option

Step 7. When the **Format Trendline** dialog box appears,
Select the **Fill & Line** option
In the **Dash type** box, select **Solid**
Close the **Format Trendline** dialog box

The edited scatter diagram and trendline are shown in Figure Excel 2.11.

The **Chart Buttons** in Excel allow users to quickly modify and format charts. Three buttons appear next to a chart whenever you click on a chart to make it active. Clicking on the **Chart Elements** button ⊕ brings up a list of check boxes to quickly add and remove axes, axis titles, chart titles, data labels, trendlines, and more. Clicking on the **Chart Styles** button 🖌 allows the user to quickly choose from many preformatted styles to change the look of the chart. Clicking on the **Chart Filter** button 🔽 allows the user to select the data to be included in the chart. The Chart Filter button is especially useful for performing additional data analysis.

Side-by-Side Bar Chart

We can use Excel's Recommended Charts tool to construct a side-by-side bar chart for the restaurant data shown in Table 2.9. The data can be found in the file *Restaurant*. We assume that a pivot table has been constructed as shown in Figure Excel 2.9. The following steps can be used to construct a side-by-side bar chart of the pivot table results.

DATA *file*
Restaurant

Step 1. Select any cell in the pivot table
Step 2. Click the **Insert** tab on the Ribbon
Step 3. In the **Charts** group, click **Recommended Charts**
Step 4. When the chart appears you can choose the recommended chart type by clicking **OK** (alternatively, you can preview a different chart type by selecting one of the other chart types listed on the left side of the **Insert Chart** dialog box)

The default chart produced by Excel uses bright colors that some readers can find distracting. Therefore, to produce the chart shown in Figure Excel 2.12, we right-click on each bar and change the **Fill** to the desired color. The worksheet in Figure Excel 2.12 shows the side-by-side bar chart produced using these steps. Note that this is not the same chart shown in Figure 2.10, since the horizontal axis is quality rating rather than meal price. However, we can easily change this to match the chart in Figure 2.10 using the following steps.

Step 1. Click on the chart
Step 2. Click the **Design** tab on the Ribbon under the heading **PivotChart Tools**
Step 3. In the **Data** group, click **Switch Row/Column**

FIGURE Excel 2.12   Side-By-Side Bar Chart for the Restaurant Data

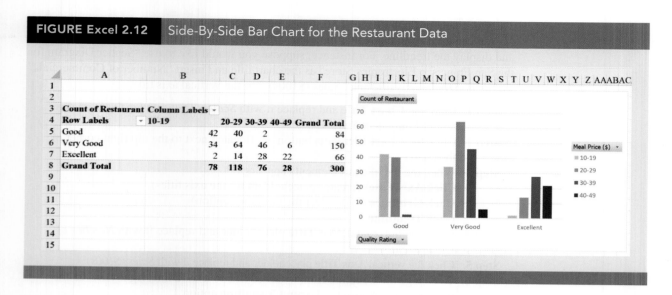

FIGURE Excel 2.13   Edited Side-By-Side Bar Chart for the Restaurant Data

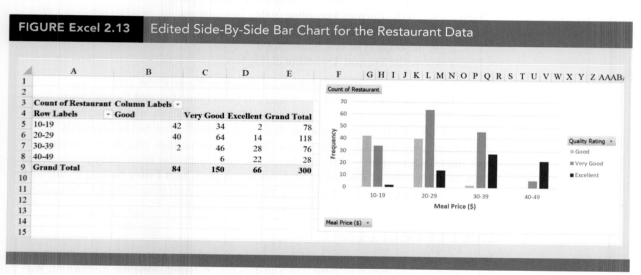

The new chart appears as shown in Figure Excel 2.13 after we modify the colors of the bars to change their colors. You can easily edit the side-by-side bar chart to display axis titles as shown in Figure Excel 2.13 using the following steps.

Step 1. Click on the chart
Step 2. Click the **Chart Elements** button ⊞ (located next to the top right corner of the chart)
Step 3. When the list of chart elements appears:
Click **Axis Titles** (creates placeholders for the axis titles)
Step 4. Click the horizontal **Axis Title** placeholder and replace it with *Meal Price ($)*
Step 5. Click the vertical **Axis Title** placeholder and replace it with *Frequency*

Note that the colors of the bars may be changed by right clicking on the bar and choosing the desired color from the **Fill** option.

Stacked Bar Chart

We can use Excel's Recommended Charts tool to construct a stacked bar chart for the restaurant data shown in Table 2.9. The data can be found in the file *Restaurant*. The following steps show how to construct a pivot chart that is based on percentage of column total as shown in Table 2.15. We assume that a pivot table has been constructed as shown in Figure Excel 2.9.

DATA *file*

Restaurant

Step 1. Select any cell in the pivot table
Step 2. Right-click and select **Show Values As**
Step 3. From the **Show Values As** drop down menu, choose **% of Column Total**

The worksheet in Figure Excel 2.14 shows new pivot table that gives percentages by column total.

The following steps allow us to create a stacked bar chart of the elements of this pivot table.

Step 1. Select any cell in the pivot table
Step 2. Click the **Insert** tab on the Ribbon
Step 3. In the **Charts** group, click **Recommended Charts**
Step 4. When the bar chart appears, choose the third option of the bar charts shown **(100% Stacked Column)** and click **OK**

The worksheet in Figure Excel 2.14 shows the resulting stacked bar chart. Note that this is not the same chart shown in Figure 2.11, since the horizontal axis is quality rating rather than meal price. However, we can easily change this to match the chart in Figure 2.11 using the following steps.

Step 1. Click on the chart
Step 2. Click the **Design** tab on the Ribbon under **PivotChart Tools**
Step 3. In the **Data** group, click **Switch Row/Column**

Once we edit the bar chart colors by right-clicking on each portion of the stacked bar and changing the color to a shade of blue, the new chart appears as shown in Figure Excel 2.15. Also, you can easily edit the stacked bar chart to display the horizontal axis title as shown in Figure Excel 2.15 using the following steps.

Step 1. Click on the chart
Step 2. Click the **Chart Elements** button ➕ (located next to the top right corner of the chart)
Step 3. When the list of chart elements appears:
         Click **Axis Titles** (creates placeholders for the axis titles)
Step 4. Click the horizontal **Axis Title** placeholder and replace it with *Restaurant Quality*
Step 5. Click the vertical **Axis Title** placeholder and press the **Delete** key

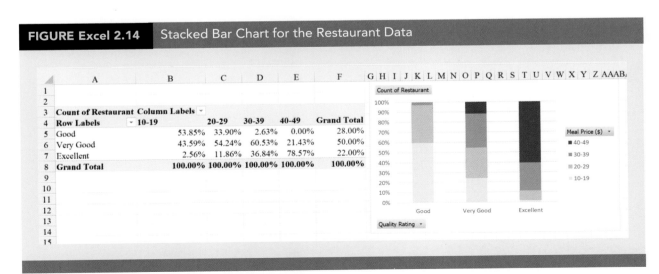

FIGURE Excel 2.14   Stacked Bar Chart for the Restaurant Data

FIGURE Excel 2.15   Edited Stacked Bar Chart for the Restaurant Data

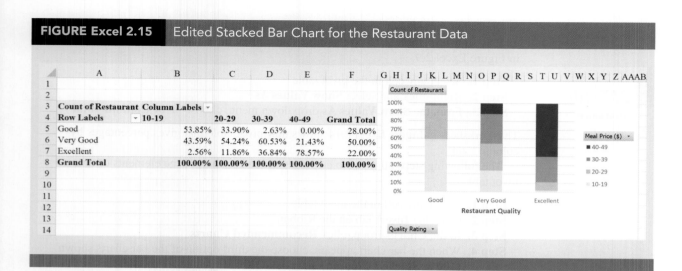

Chapter 3

Descriptive Statistics: Numerical Measures

CONTENTS

STATISTICS IN PRACTICE: *SMALL FRY DESIGN*

STATISTICS IN PRACTICE

Small Fry Design*

SANTA ANA, CALIFORNIA

Founded in 1997, Small Fry Design is a toy and accessory company that designs and imports products for infants. The company's product line includes teddy bears, mobiles, musical toys, rattles, and security blankets and features high-quality soft toy designs with an emphasis on color, texture, and sound. The products are designed in the United States and manufactured in China.

Small Fry Design uses independent representatives to sell the products to infant furnishing retailers, children's accessory and apparel stores, gift shops, upscale department stores, and major catalog companies. Currently, Small Fry Design products are distributed in more than 1000 retail outlets throughout the United States.

Cash flow management is one of the most critical activities in the day-to-day operation of this company. Ensuring sufficient incoming cash to meet both current and ongoing debt obligations can mean the difference between business success and failure. A critical factor in cash flow management is the analysis and control of accounts receivable. By measuring the average age and dollar value of outstanding invoices, management can predict cash availability and monitor changes in the status of accounts receivable. The company set the following goals: The average age for outstanding invoices should not exceed 45 days, and the dollar value of invoices more than 60 days old should not exceed 5% of the dollar value of all accounts receivable.

In a recent summary of accounts receivable status, the following descriptive statistics were provided for the age of outstanding invoices:

Mean	40 days
Median	35 days
Mode	31 days

Small Fry Design uses descriptive statistics to monitor its accounts receivable and incoming cash flow.
Source: Robert Dant/Alamy Stock Photo

Interpretation of these statistics shows that the mean or average age of an invoice is 40 days. The median shows that half of the invoices remain outstanding 35 days or more. The mode of 31 days, the most frequent invoice age, indicates that the most common length of time an invoice is outstanding is 31 days. The statistical summary also showed that only 3% of the dollar value of all accounts receivable was more than 60 days old. Based on the statistical information, management was satisfied that accounts receivable and incoming cash flow were under control.

In this chapter, you will learn how to compute and interpret some of the statistical measures used by Small Fry Design. In addition to the mean, median, and mode, you will learn about other descriptive statistics such as the range, variance, standard deviation, percentiles, and correlation. These numerical measures will assist in the understanding and interpretation of data.

*The authors are indebted to John A. McCarthy, President of Small Fry Design, for providing the context for this Statistics in Practice.

In Chapter 2 we discussed tabular and graphical presentations used to summarize data. In this chapter, we present several numerical measures that provide additional alternatives for summarizing data.

We start by developing numerical summary measures for data sets consisting of a single variable. When a data set contains more than one variable, the same numerical measures can be computed separately for each variable. However, in the two-variable case, we will also develop measures of the relationship between the variables.

Numerical measures of location, dispersion, shape, and association are introduced. If the measures are computed for data from a sample, they are called **sample statistics**. If the measures are computed for data from a population, they are called **population parameters**. In statistical inference, a sample statistic is referred to as the **point estimator** of the corresponding population parameter.

We discuss the process of point estimation in more detail in Chapter 7.

In the chapter appendixes we show how statistical software can be used to compute the numerical measures described in the chapter.

3.1 Measures of Location

Mean

The mean is sometimes referred to as the arithmetic mean.

Perhaps the most important measure of location is the **mean**, or average value, for a variable. The mean provides a measure of central location for the data. If the data are for a sample, the mean is denoted by $\bar{x}$; if the data are for a population, the mean is denoted by the Greek letter μ.

In statistical formulas, it is customary to denote the value of variable x for the first observation by x_1, the value of variable x for the second observation by x_2, and so on. In general, the value of variable x for the ith observation is denoted by x_i. For a sample with n observations, the formula for the sample mean is as follows.

The sample mean $\bar{x}$ is a sample statistic.

SAMPLE MEAN

$$\bar{x} = \frac{\Sigma x_i}{n} \tag{3.1}$$

In the preceding formula, the numerator is the sum of the values of the n observations. That is,

The Greek letter Σ is the summation sign.

$$\Sigma x_i = x_1 + x_2 + \cdots + x_n$$

To illustrate the computation of a sample mean, let us consider the following class size data for a sample of five college classes.

$$46 \quad 54 \quad 42 \quad 46 \quad 32$$

We use the notation x_1, x_2, x_3, x_4, x_5 to represent the number of students in each of the five classes.

$$x_1 = 46 \qquad x_2 = 54 \qquad x_3 = 42 \qquad x_4 = 46 \qquad x_5 = 32$$

Hence, to compute the sample mean, we can write

$$\bar{x} = \frac{\Sigma x_i}{n} = \frac{x_1 + x_2 + x_3 + x_4 + x_5}{5} = \frac{46 + 54 + 42 + 46 + 32}{5} = 44$$

The sample mean class size is 44 students.

To provide a visual perspective of the mean and to show how it can be influenced by extreme values, consider the dot plot for the class size data shown in Figure 3.1. Treating the horizontal axis used to create the dot plot as a long narrow board in which each of the dots has the same fixed weight, the mean is the point at which we would place a fulcrum or pivot point under the board in order to balance the dot plot. This is the same principle by which a see-saw on a playground works, the only difference being that the see-saw is pivoted in the middle so that as one end goes up, the other end goes down. In the dot plot we are locating the pivot point based

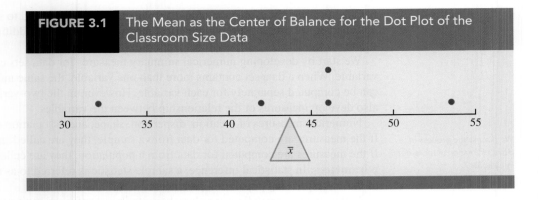

FIGURE 3.1   The Mean as the Center of Balance for the Dot Plot of the Classroom Size Data

upon the location of the dots. Now consider what happens to the balance if we increase the largest value from 54 to 114. We will have to move the fulcrum under the new dot plot in a positive direction in order to reestablish balance. To determine how far we would have to shift the fulcrum, we simply compute the sample mean for the revised class size data.

$$\bar{x} = \frac{\Sigma x_i}{n} = \frac{x_1 + x_2 + x_3 + x_4 + x_5}{5} = \frac{46 + 114 + 42 + 46 + 32}{5} = \frac{280}{5} = 56$$

Thus, the mean for the revised class size data is 56, an increase of 12 students. In other words, we have to shift the balance point 12 units to the right to establish balance under the new dot plot.

Another illustration of the computation of a sample mean is given in the following situation. Suppose that a college placement office sent a questionnaire to a sample of business school graduates requesting information on monthly starting salaries. Table 3.1 shows the collected data. The mean monthly starting salary for the sample of 12 business college graduates is computed as

$$\bar{x} = \frac{\Sigma x_i}{n} = \frac{x_1 + x_2 + \cdots + x_{12}}{12}$$
$$= \frac{5850 + 5950 + \cdots + 5880}{12}$$
$$= \frac{71{,}280}{12} = 5940$$

Equation (3.1) shows how the mean is computed for a sample with n observations. The formula for computing the mean of a population remains the same, but we use different notation to indicate that we are working with the entire population. The

TABLE 3.1   Monthly Starting Salaries for a Sample of 12 Business School Graduates

Graduate	Monthly Starting Salary ($)	Graduate	Monthly Starting Salary ($)
1	5850	7	5890
2	5950	8	6130
3	6050	9	5940
4	5880	10	6325
5	5755	11	5920
6	5710	12	5880

DATA_file_

StartingSalaries

number of observations in a population is denoted by N and the symbol for a population mean is μ.

The sample mean $\bar{x}$ is a point estimator of the population mean μ.

POPULATION MEAN

$$\mu = \frac{\Sigma x_i}{N} \tag{3.2}$$

Weighted Mean

In the formulas for the sample mean and population mean, each x_i is given equal importance or weight. For instance, the formula for the sample mean can be written as follows:

$$\bar{x} = \frac{\Sigma x_i}{n} = \frac{1}{n}\left(\Sigma x_i\right) = \frac{1}{n}(x_1 + x_2 + \cdots + x_n) = \frac{1}{n}(x_1) + \frac{1}{n}(x_2) + \cdots + \frac{1}{n}(x_n)$$

This shows that each observation in the sample is given a weight of $1/n$. Although this practice is most common, in some instances the mean is computed by giving each observation a weight that reflects its relative importance. A mean computed in this manner is referred to as a **weighted mean**. The weighted mean is computed as follows:

WEIGHTED MEAN

$$\bar{x} = \frac{\Sigma w_i x_i}{\Sigma w_i} \tag{3.3}$$

where

$$w_i = \text{weight for observation } i$$

When the data are from a sample, equation (3.3) provides the weighted sample mean. If the data are from a population, μ replaces $\bar{x}$ and equation (3.3) provides the weighted population mean.

As an example of the need for a weighted mean, consider the following sample of five purchases of a raw material over the past three months.

Purchase	Cost per Pound ($)	Number of Pounds
1	3.00	1200
2	3.40	500
3	2.80	2750
4	2.90	1000
5	3.25	800

Note that the cost per pound varies from $2.80 to $3.40, and the quantity purchased varies from 500 to 2750 pounds. Suppose that a manager wanted to know the mean cost per pound of the raw material. Because the quantities ordered vary, we must use the formula for a weighted mean. The five cost-per-pound data values are $x_1 = 3.00$, $x_2 = 3.40$, $x_3 = 2.80$, $x_4 = 2.90$, and $x_5 = 3.25$. The weighted mean cost per pound is found by weighting each cost by its corresponding quantity. For this example, the weights are $w_1 = 1200$, $w_2 = 500$, $w_3 = 2750$, $w_4 = 1000$, and $w_5 = 800$. Based on equation (3.3), the weighted mean is calculated as follows:

$$\bar{x} = \frac{1200(3.00) + 500(3.40) + 2750(2.80) + 1000(2.90) + 800(3.25)}{1200 + 500 + 2750 + 1000 + 800}$$

$$= \frac{18,500}{6250} = 2.96$$

Thus, the weighted mean computation shows that the mean cost per pound for the raw material is $2.96. Note that using equation (3.1) rather than the weighted mean formula in equation (3.3) would provide misleading results. In this case, the sample mean of the five cost-per-pound values is $(3.00 + 3.40 + 2.80 + 2.90 + 3.25)/5 = 15.35/5 = \$3.07$, which overstates the actual mean cost per pound purchased.

The choice of weights for a particular weighted mean computation depends upon the application. An example that is well known to college students is the computation of a grade point average (GPA). In this computation, the data values generally used are 4 for an A grade, 3 for a B grade, 2 for a C grade, 1 for a D grade, and 0 for an F grade. The weights are the number of credit hours earned for each grade. In other weighted mean computations, quantities such as pounds, dollars, or volume are frequently used as weights. In any case, when observations vary in importance, the analyst must choose the weight that best reflects the importance of each observation in the determination of the mean.

Exercise 16 at the end of this section provides an example of a weighted mean computation for GPA.

Median

The **median** is another measure of central location. The median is the value in the middle when the data are arranged in ascending order (smallest value to largest value). With an odd number of observations, the median is the middle value. An even number of observations has no single middle value. In this case, we follow convention and define the median as the average of the values for the middle two observations. For convenience the definition of the median is restated as follows.

> **MEDIAN**
>
> Arrange the data in ascending order (smallest value to largest value).
>
> **(a)** For an odd number of observations, the median is the middle value.
> **(b)** For an even number of observations, the median is the average of the two middle values.

Let us apply this definition to compute the median class size for the sample of five college classes. Arranging the data in ascending order provides the following list.

$$32 \quad 42 \quad 46 \quad 46 \quad 54$$

Because $n = 5$ is odd, the median is the middle value. Thus the median class size is 46 students. Even though this data set contains two observations with values of 46, each observation is treated separately when we arrange the data in ascending order.

Suppose we also compute the median starting salary for the 12 business college graduates in Table 3.1. We first arrange the data in ascending order.

$$5710 \quad 5755 \quad 5850 \quad 5880 \quad 5880 \quad \underbrace{5890 \quad 5920}_{\text{Middle Two Values}} \quad 5940 \quad 5950 \quad 6050 \quad 6130 \quad 6325$$

Because $n = 12$ is even, we identify the middle two values: 5890 and 5920. The median is the average of these values.

$$\text{Median} = \frac{5890 + 5920}{2} = 5905$$

The procedure we used to compute the median depends upon whether there is an odd number of observations or an even number of observations. Let us now describe a more conceptual and visual approach using the monthly starting salary for the 12 business college graduates. As before, we begin by arranging the data in ascending order.

$$5710 \quad 5755 \quad 5850 \quad 5880 \quad 5880 \quad 5890 \quad 5920 \quad 5940 \quad 5950 \quad 6050 \quad 6130 \quad 6325$$

Once the data are in ascending order, we trim pairs of extreme high and low values until no further pairs of values can be trimmed without completely eliminating all the data. For instance, after trimming the lowest observation (5710) and the highest observation (6325) we obtain a new data set with 10 observations.

~~5710~~   5755   5850   5880   5880   5890   5920   5940   5950   6050   6130   ~~6325~~

We then trim the next lowest remaining value (5755) and the next highest remaining value (6130) to produce a new data set with eight observations.

~~5710~~   ~~5755~~   5850   5880   5880   5890   5920   5940   5950   6050   ~~6130~~   ~~6325~~

Continuing this process, we obtain the following results.

~~5710~~   ~~5755~~   ~~5850~~   5880   5880   5890   5920   5940   5950   ~~6050~~   ~~6130~~   ~~6325~~

~~5710~~   ~~5755~~   ~~5850~~   ~~5880~~   5880   5890   5920   5940   ~~5950~~   ~~6050~~   ~~6130~~   ~~6325~~

~~5710~~   ~~5755~~   ~~5850~~   ~~5880~~   ~~5880~~   5890   5920   ~~5940~~   ~~5950~~   ~~6050~~   ~~6130~~   ~~6325~~

At this point no further trimming is possible without eliminating all the data. So, the median is just the average of the remaining two values. When there is an even number of observations, the trimming process will always result in two remaining values, and the average of these values will be the median. When there is an odd number of observations, the trimming process will always result in one final value, and this value will be the median. Thus, this method works whether the number of observations is odd or even.

The median is the measure of location most often reported for annual income and property value data because a few extremely large incomes or property values can inflate the mean. In such cases, the median is the preferred measure of central location.

   Although the mean is the more commonly used measure of central location, in some situations the median is preferred. The mean is influenced by extremely small and large data values. For instance, suppose that the highest paid graduate (see Table 3.1) had a starting salary of $15,000 per month. If we change the highest monthly starting salary in Table 3.1 from $6325 to $15,000 and recompute the mean, the sample mean changes from $5940 to $6663. The median of $5905, however, is unchanged, because $5890 and $5920 are still the middle two values. With the extremely high starting salary included, the median provides a better measure of central location than the mean. We can generalize to say that whenever a data set contains extreme values, the median is often the preferred measure of central location.

Geometric Mean

The **geometric mean** is a measure of location that is calculated by finding the nth root of the product of n values. The general formula for the geometric mean, denoted $\bar{x}_g$, follows.

GEOMETRIC MEAN

$$\bar{x}_g = \sqrt[n]{(x_1)(x_2) \cdots (x_n)} = [(x_1)(x_2) \cdots (x_n)]^{1/n} \qquad (3.4)$$

The geometric mean is often used in analyzing growth rates in financial data. In these types of situations the arithmetic mean or average value will provide misleading results.

   To illustrate the use of the geometric mean, consider Table 3.2, which shows the percentage annual returns, or growth rates, for a mutual fund over the past 10 years. Suppose we want to compute how much $100 invested in the fund at the beginning of year 1 would be worth at the end of year 10. Let's start by computing the balance in the fund at the end of year 1. Because the percentage annual return for year 1 was -22.1%, the balance in the fund at the end of year 1 would be

The growth factor for each year is 1 plus .01 times the percentage return. A growth factor less than 1 indicates negative growth, while a growth factor greater than 1 indicates positive growth. The growth factor cannot be less than zero.

$$\$100 - .221(\$100) = \$100(1 - .221) = \$100(.779) = \$77.90$$

We refer to .779 as the **growth factor** for year 1 in Table 3.2. We can compute the balance at the end of year 1 by multiplying the value invested in the fund at the beginning of year 1 times the growth factor for year 1: $100(.779) = $77.90.

TABLE 3.2	Percentage Annual Returns and Growth Factors for the Mutual Fund Data	
Year	**Return (%)**	**Growth Factor**
1	−22.1	.779
2	28.7	1.287
3	10.9	1.109
4	4.9	1.049
5	15.8	1.158
6	5.5	1.055
7	−37.0	.630
8	26.5	1.265
9	15.1	1.151
10	2.1	1.021

DATA *file*

MutualFund

The balance in the fund at the end of year 1, $77.90, now becomes the beginning balance in year 2. So, with a percentage annual return for year 2 of 28.7%, the balance at the end of year 2 would be

$$\$77.90 + .287(\$77.90) = \$77.90(1 + .287) = \$77.90(1.287) = \$100.2573$$

Note that 1.287 is the growth factor for year 2. And, by substituting $100(.779) for $77.90 we see that the balance in the fund at the end of year 2 is

$$\$100(.779)(1.287) = \$100.2573$$

In other words, the balance at the end of year 2 is just the initial investment at the beginning of year 1 times the product of the first two growth factors. This result can be generalized to show that the balance at the end of year 10 is the initial investment times the product of all 10 growth factors.

$$\$100[(.779)(1.287)(1.109)(1.049)(1.158)(1.055)(.630)(1.265)(1.151)(1.021)] =$$

$$\$100(1.334493) = \$133.4493$$

The nth root can be computed using most calculators or by using the POWER function in Excel. For instance, using Excel, the 10th root of 1.334493 =POWER(1.334493,1/10) or 1.029275.

So, a $100 investment in the fund at the beginning of year 1 would be worth $133.4493 at the end of year 10. Note that the product of the 10 growth factors is 1.334493. Thus, we can compute the balance at the end of year 10 for any amount of money invested at the beginning of year 1 by multiplying the value of the initial investment times 1.334493. For instance, an initial investment of $2500 at the beginning of year 1 would be worth $2500(1.334493) or approximately $3336 at the end of year 10.

What was the mean percentage annual return or mean rate of growth for this investment over the 10-year period? The geometric mean of the 10 growth factors can be used to answer to this question. Because the product of the 10 growth factors is 1.334493, the geometric mean is the 10th root of 1.334493 or

$$\bar{x}_g = \sqrt[10]{1.334493} = 1.029275$$

Excel can calculate the geometric mean directly from a series of growth factors using the function GEOMEAN.

The geometric mean tells us that annual returns grew at an average annual rate of $(1.029275 - 1)100\%$ or 2.9275%. In other words, with an average annual growth rate of 2.9275%, a $100 investment in the fund at the beginning of year 1 would grow to $\$100(1.029275)^{10} = \$133.4493$ at the end of 10 years.

It is important to understand that the arithmetic mean of the percentage annual returns does not provide the mean annual growth rate for this investment. The sum of the 10 annual percentage returns in Table 3.2 is 50.4. Thus, the arithmetic mean of the 10 percentage annual returns is 50.4/10 = 5.04%. A broker might try to convince you to invest in this fund by stating that the mean annual percentage return was 5.04%. Such a statement is not only misleading, it is inaccurate. A mean annual percentage return of 5.04% corresponds to an average growth factor of 1.0504. So, if the average growth factor were really 1.0504, $100 invested in the fund at the beginning of year 1 would have grown to $100(1.0504)^{10} = $163.51 at the end of 10 years. But, using the 10 annual percentage returns in Table 3.2, we showed that an initial $100 investment is worth $133.45 at the end of 10 years. The broker's claim that the mean annual percentage return is 5.04% grossly overstates the true growth for this mutual fund. The problem is that the sample mean is only appropriate for an additive process. For a multiplicative process, such as applications involving growth rates, the geometric mean is the appropriate measure of location.

While the applications of the geometric mean to problems in finance, investments, and banking are particularly common, the geometric mean should be applied any time you want to determine the mean rate of change over several successive periods. Other common applications include changes in populations of species, crop yields, pollution levels, and birth and death rates. Also note that the geometric mean can be applied to changes that occur over any number of successive periods of any length. In addition to annual changes, the geometric mean is often applied to find the mean rate of change over quarters, months, weeks, and even days.

Mode

Another measure of location is the **mode**. The mode is defined as follows.

> **MODE**
>
> The mode is the value that occurs with greatest frequency.

To illustrate the identification of the mode, consider the sample of five class sizes. The only value that occurs more than once is 46. Because this value, occurring with a frequency of 2, has the greatest frequency, it is the mode. As another illustration, consider the sample of starting salaries for the business school graduates. The only monthly starting salary that occurs more than once is $5880. Because this value has the greatest frequency, it is the mode.

Situations can arise for which the greatest frequency occurs at two or more different values. In these instances more than one mode exist. If the data contain exactly two modes, we say that the data are *bimodal*. If data contain more than two modes, we say that the data are *multimodal*. In multimodal cases the mode is almost never reported because listing three or more modes would not be particularly helpful in describing a location for the data.

Percentiles

A **percentile** provides information about how the data are spread over the interval from the smallest value to the largest value. For a data set containing n observations, the **pth percentile** divides the data into two parts: approximately $p\%$ of the observations are less than the pth percentile, and approximately $(100 - p)\%$ of the observations are greater than the pth percentile.

Colleges and universities frequently report admission test scores in terms of percentiles. For instance, suppose an applicant obtains a score of 630 on the math portion of an admission test. How this applicant performed in relation to others taking the same test may not be readily apparent from this score. However, if the score of 630 corresponds to the 82nd percentile, we know that approximately that 82% of the applicants scored lower than this individual and approximately 18% of the applicants scored higher than this individual.

To calculate the pth percentile for a data set containing n observations, we must first arrange the data in ascending order (smallest value to largest value). The smallest value is in position 1, the next smallest value is in position 2, and so on. The location of the *p*th percentile, denoted L_p, is computed using the following equation:

Several procedures can be used to compute the location of the pth percentile using sample data. All provide similar values, especially for large data sets. The procedure we show here is the procedure used by Excel's PERCENTILE.EXC function as well as several other statistical software packages.

LOCATION OF THE *P*TH PERCENTILE

$$L_p = \frac{p}{100}(n + 1) \qquad\qquad (3.5)$$

Once we find the position of the value of the *p*th percentile, we have the information we need to calculate the *p*th percentile.

To illustrate the computation of the *p*th percentile, let us compute the 80th percentile for the starting salary data in Table 3.1. We begin by arranging the sample of 12 starting salaries in ascending order.

5710	5755	5850	5880	5880	5890	5920	5940	5950	6050	6130	6325
Position 1	2	3	4	5	6	7	8	9	10	11	12

The position of each observation in the sorted data is shown directly below its value. For instance, the smallest value (5710) is in position 1, the next smallest value (5755) is in position 2, and so on. Using equation (3.5) with $p = 80$ and $n = 12$, the location of the 80th percentile is

$$L_{80} = \frac{p}{100}(n + 1) = \left(\frac{80}{100}\right)(12 + 1) = 10.4$$

The interpretation of $L_{80} = 10.4$ is that the 80th percentile is 40% of the way between the value in position 10 and the value in position 11. In other words, the 80th percentile is the value in position 10 (6050) plus .4 times the difference between the value in position 11 (6130) and the value in position 10 (6050). Thus, the 80th percentile is

$$\text{80th percentile} = 6050 + .4(6130 - 6050) = 6050 + .4(80) = 6082$$

Let us now compute the 50th percentile for the starting salary data. With $p = 50$ and $n = 12$, the location of the 50th percentile is

$$L_{50} = \frac{p}{100}(n + 1) = \left(\frac{50}{100}\right)(12 + 1) = 6.5$$

With $L_{50} = 6.5$, we see that the 50th percentile is 50% of the way between the value in position 6 (5890) and the value in position 7 (5920). Thus, the 50th percentile is

$$\text{50th percentile} = 5890 + .5(5920 - 5890) = 5890 + .5(30) = 5905$$

Note that the *50th percentile is also the median.*

Quartiles

Quartiles are just specific percentiles; thus, the steps for computing percentiles can be applied directly in the computation of quartiles.

It is often desirable to divide a data set into four parts, with each part containing approximately one-fourth, or 25%, of the observations. These division points are referred to as the **quartiles** and are defined as follows.

Q_1 = first quartile, or 25th percentile

Q_2 = second quartile, or 50th percentile (also the median)

Q_3 = third quartile, or 75th percentile

Because quartiles are specific percentiles, the procedure for computing percentiles can be used to compute the quartiles.

To illustrate the computation of the quartiles for a data set consisting of *n* observations, we will compute the quartiles for the starting salary data in Table 3.1. Previously we showed that the 50th percentile for the starting salary data is 5905; thus, the second quartile (median) is $Q_2 = 5905$. To compute the first and third quartiles, we must find the 25th and 75th percentiles. The calculations follow.

The method of computing quartiles explained here matches the method used in the Excel function QUARTILE.EXC.

For Q_1,

$$L_{25} = \frac{p}{100}(n + 1) = \left(\frac{25}{100}\right)(12 + 1) = 3.25$$

The first quartile, or 25th percentile, is .25 of the way between the value in position 3 (5850) and the value in position 4 (5880). Thus,

$$Q_1 = 5850 + .25(5880 - 5850) = 5850 + .25(30) = 5857.5$$

For Q_3,

$$L_{75} = \frac{p}{100}(n + 1) = \left(\frac{75}{100}\right)(12 + 1) = 9.75$$

The third quartile, or 75th percentile, is .75 of the way between the value in position 9 (5950) and the value in position 10 (6050). Thus,

$$Q_3 = 5950 + .75(6050 - 5950) = 5950 + .75(100) = 6025$$

The quartiles divide the starting salary data into four parts, with each part containing 25% of the observations.

25% of the data			25% of the data			25% of the data			25% of the data		
5710	5755	5850	5880	5880	5890	5920	5940	5950	6050	6130	6325

$Q_1 = 5857.5 \qquad Q_2 = 5905$ (Median) $\qquad Q_3 = 6025$

We defined the quartiles as the 25th, 50th, and 75th percentiles and then we computed the quartiles in the same way as percentiles. However, other conventions are sometimes used to compute quartiles, and the actual values reported for quartiles may vary slightly depending on the convention used. Nevertheless, the objective of all procedures for computing quartiles is to divide the data into four parts that contain equal numbers of observations.

N O T E S + C O M M E N T S

1. It is better to use the median than the mean as a measure of central location when a data set contains extreme values. Another measure that is sometimes used when extreme values are present is the trimmed mean. The trimmed mean is obtained by deleting a percentage of the smallest and largest values from a data set and then computing the mean of the remaining values. For example, the 5% trimmed mean is obtained by removing the smallest 5% and the largest 5% of the data values and then computing the mean of the remaining values. Using the sample with $n = 12$ starting salaries, .05(12) = .6. Rounding this value to 1 indicates that the 5% trimmed mean is obtained by removing the smallest data value and the largest data value and then computing the mean of the remaining 10 values. For the starting salary data, the 5% trimmed mean is 5924.50.

2. Other commonly used percentiles are the quintiles (the 20th, 40th, 60th, and 80th percentiles) and the deciles (the 10th, 20th, 30th, 40th, 50th, 60th, 70th, 80th, and 90th percentiles).

E X E R C I S E S

Methods
1. Consider a sample with data values of 10, 20, 12, 17, and 16. Compute the mean and median.
2. Consider a sample with data values of 10, 20, 21, 17, 16, and 12. Compute the mean and median.
3. Consider the following data and corresponding weights.

x_i	Weight (w_i)
3.2	6
2.0	3
2.5	2
5.0	8

a. Compute the weighted mean.
b. Compute the sample mean of the four data values without weighting. Note the difference in the results provided by the two computations.

4. Consider the following data.

Period	Rate of Return (%)
1	−6.0
2	−8.0
3	−4.0
4	2.0
5	5.4

What is the mean growth rate over these five periods?

5. Consider a sample with data values of 27, 25, 20, 15, 30, 34, 28, and 25. Compute the 20th, 25th, 65th, and 75th percentiles.

6. Consider a sample with data values of 53, 55, 70, 58, 64, 57, 53, 69, 57, 68, and 53. Compute the mean, median, and mode.

Applications

7. **eICU Waiting Times.** There is a severe shortage of critical care doctors and nurses to provide intensive-care services in hospitals. To offset this shortage, many hospitals, such as Emory Hospital in Atlanta, are using electronic intensive-care units (eICUs) to help provide this care to patients (Emory University News Center). eICUs use electronic monitoring tools and two-way communication through video and audio so that a centralized staff of specially trained doctors and nurses—who can be located as far away as Australia—can provide critical care services to patients located in remote hospitals without fully staffed ICUs. One of the most important metrics tracked by these eICUs is the time that a patient must wait for the first video interaction between the patient and the eICU staff. Consider the following sample of 40 patient waiting times until their first video interaction with the eICU staff.

DATA *file*

eICU

Wait Time (minutes)	Wait Time (minutes)	Wait Time (minutes)	Wait Time (minutes)
40	46	49	44
45	45	38	51
42	46	41	45
49	41	48	42
49	40	42	43
43	42	41	41
55	43	42	40
42	40	49	43
44	45	61	37
40	37	39	43

a. Compute the mean waiting time for these 40 patients.
b. Compare the mean waiting time.
c. Compute the mode.
d. Compute the first and third quartiles.

8. **Middle-Level Manager Salaries.** Suppose that an independent study of middle-level managers employed at companies located in Atlanta, Georgia, was conducted to compare the salaries of managers working at firms in Atlanta to the salaries of middle-level managers across the nation. The following data show the salary, in thousands of dollars, for a sample of 15 middle-level managers employed at companies in the Atlanta area.

108   83   106   73   53   85   80   63   67   75   124   55   93   118   77

   a. Compute the median salary for the sample of 15 middle-level managers. Suppose the median salary of middle-level managers employed at companies located across the nation is $85,000. How does the median salary for middle-level managers in the Atlanta area compare to the median for managers across the nation?
   b. Compute the mean annual salary for managers in the Atlanta area and discuss how and why it differs from the median computed in part (a) for Atlanta area managers.
   c. Compute the first and third quartiles for the salaries of middle-level managers in the Atlanta area.

DATA*file*

AdvertisingSpend

9. **Advertising Spending.** Which companies spend the most money on advertising? *Business Insider* maintains a list of the top-spending companies. In 2014, Procter & Gamble spent more than any other company, a whopping $5 billion. In second place was Comcast, which spent $3.08 billion (*Business Insider* website). The top 12 companies and the amount each spent on advertising in billions of dollars are as follows.

Company	Advertising ($billions)	Company	Advertising ($billions)
Procter & Gamble	$5.00	American Express	$2.19
Comcast	3.08	General Motors	2.15
AT&T	2.91	Toyota	2.09
Ford	2.56	Fiat Chrysler	1.97
Verizon	2.44	Walt Disney Company	1.96
L'Oreal	2.34	J.P. Morgan	1.88

   a. What is the mean amount spent on advertising?
   b. What is the median amount spent on advertising?
   c. What are the first and third quartiles?

DATA*file*

JacketRatings

10. **Hardshell Jacket Ratings.** OutdoorGearLab is an organization that tests outdoor gear used for climbing, camping, mountaineering, and backpacking. Suppose that the following data show the ratings of hardshell jackets based on the breathability, durability, versatility, features, mobility, and weight of each jacket. The ratings range from 0 (lowest) to 100 (highest).

42	66	67	71	78	62	61	76	71	67
61	64	61	54	83	63	68	69	81	53

   a. Compute the mean, median, and mode.
   b. Compute the first and third quartiles.
   c. Compute and interpret the 90th percentile.

11. **Time Spent Watching Traditional TV.** Nielsen tracks the amount of time that people spend consuming media content across different platforms (digital, audio, television) in the United States. Nielsen has found that traditional television viewing habits vary based on the age of the consumer as an increasing number of people consume media through streaming devices (Nielsen website). The following data represent the weekly traditional TV viewing hours in 2016 for a sample of 14 people aged 18–34 and 12 people aged 35–49.

Viewers aged   18–34: 24.2, 21.0, 17.8, 19.6, 23.4, 19.1, 14.6, 27.1, 19.2, 18.3, 22.9, 23.4, 17.3, 20.5

Viewers aged   35–49: 24.9, 34.9, 35.8, 31.9, 35.4, 29.9, 30.9, 36.7, 36.2, 33.8, 29.5, 30.8

DATA *file*

TelevisionViewing

a. Compute the mean and median weekly hours of traditional TV viewed by those aged 18–34.

b. Compute the mean and median weekly hours of traditional TV viewed by those aged 35–49.

c. Compare the mean and median viewing hours for each age group. Which group watches more traditional TV per week?

12. **Online Multiplayer Game Downloads.** The creator of a new online multiplayer survival game has been tracking the monthly downloads of the newest game. The following table shows the monthly downloads (in thousands) for each month of the current and previous year.

DATA *file*

OnlineGame

Month (previous year)	Downloads (thousands)	Month (current year)	Downloads (thousands)
February	33.0	January	37.0
March	34.0	February	37.0
April	34.0	March	37.0
May	32.0	April	38.0
June	32.0	May	37.0
July	35.0	June	36.0
August	34.0	July	37.0
September	37.0	August	35.0
October	37.0	September	33.0
November	35.0	October	32.0
December	33.0		

a. Compute the mean, median, and mode for number of downloads in the previous year.

b. Compute the mean, median, and mode for number of downloads in the current year.

c. Compute the first and third quartiles for downloads in the previous year.

d. Compute the first and third quartiles for downloads in the current year.

e. Compare the values calculated in parts a through d for the previous and current years. What does this tell you about the downloads of the game in the current year compared to the previous year?

13. **Automobile Fuel Efficiencies.** In automobile mileage and gasoline-consumption testing, 13 automobiles were road tested for 300 miles in both city and highway driving conditions. The following data were recorded for miles-per-gallon performance.

City: 16.2   16.7   15.9   14.4   13.2   15.3   16.8   16.0   16.1   15.3   15.2   15.3   16.2

Highway: 19.4   20.6   18.3   18.6   19.2   17.4   17.2   18.6   19.0   21.1   19.4   18.5   18.7

Use the mean, median, and mode to make a statement about the difference in performance for city and highway driving.

14. **Unemployment Rates by State.** The U.S. Bureau of Labor Statistics collects data on unemployment rates in each state. The data contained in the file *UnemploymentRates* show the unemployment rate for every state and the District of Columbia over two consecutive years. To compare unemployment rates for the previous year with unemployment rates for the current year, compute the first quartile, the median, and the third quartile for the previous year unemployment data and the current year unemployment data. What do these statistics suggest about the change in unemployment rates across the states over these two years?

DATA *file*

UnemploymentRates

15. **Motor Oil Prices.** Martinez Auto Supplies has retail stores located in eight cities in California. The price they charge for a particular product in each city varies because of differing competitive conditions. For instance, the price they charge for a case of a popular brand of motor oil in each city follows. Also shown are the number of cases that Martinez Auto sold last quarter in each city.

City	Price ($)	Sales (cases)
Bakersfield	34.99	501
Los Angeles	38.99	1425
Modesto	36.00	294
Oakland	33.59	882
Sacramento	40.99	715
San Diego	38.59	1088
San Francisco	39.59	1644
San Jose	37.99	819

Compute the average sales price per case for this product during the last quarter.

16. **Calculating Grade Point Averages.** The grade point average for college students is based on a weighted mean computation. For most colleges, the grades are given the following data values: A (4), B (3), C (2), D (1), and F (0). After 60 credit hours of course work, a student at State University earned 9 credit hours of A, 15 credit hours of B, 33 credit hours of C, and 3 credit hours of D.
    a. Compute the student's grade point average.
    b. Students at State University must maintain a 2.5 grade point average for their first 60 credit hours of course work in order to be admitted to the business college. Will this student be admitted?

17. **Mutual Fund Rate of Return.** The following table shows the total return and the number of funds for four categories of mutual funds.

Type of Fund	Number of Funds	Total Return (%)
Domestic Equity	9191	4.65
International Equity	2621	18.15
Specialty Stock	1419	11.36
Hybrid	2900	6.75

   a. Using the number of funds as weights, compute the weighted average total return for these mutual funds.
   b. Is there any difficulty associated with using the "number of funds" as the weights in computing the weighted average total return in part (a)? Discuss. What else might be used for weights?
   c. Suppose you invested $10,000 in this group of mutual funds and diversified the investment by placing $2000 in Domestic Equity funds, $4000 in International Equity funds, $3000 in Specialty Stock funds, and $1000 in Hybrid funds. What is the expected return on the portfolio?

18. **Business School Ranking.** Based on a survey of master's programs in business adminis-tration, magazines such as *U.S. News & World Report* rank U.S. business schools. These types of rankings are based in part on surveys of business school deans and corporate recruiters. Each survey respondent is asked to rate the overall academic quality of the master's program on a scale from 1 "marginal" to 5 "outstanding." Use the sample of responses shown below to compute the weighted mean score for the business school deans and the corporate recruiters. Discuss.

Quality Assessment	Business School Deans	Corporate Recruiters
5	44	31
4	66	34
3	60	43
2	10	12
1	0	0

19. **Revenue Growth Rate.** Annual revenue for Corning Supplies grew by 5.5% in 2014, 1.1% in 2015, −3.5% in 2016, −1.1% in 2017, and 1.8% in 2018. What is the mean growth annual rate over this period?

20. **Mutual Fund Comparison.** Suppose that at the beginning of Year 1 you invested $10,000 in the Stivers mutual fund and $5000 in the Trippi mutual fund. The value of each investment at the end of each subsequent year is provided in the table below. Which mutual fund performed better?

Year	Stivers	Trippi
1	11,000	5,600
2	12,000	6,300
3	13,000	6,900
4	14,000	7,600
5	15,000	8,500
6	16,000	9,200
7	17,000	9,900
8	18,000	10,600

21. **Asset Growth Rate.** If an asset declines in value from $5000 to $3500 over nine years, what is the mean annual growth rate in the asset's value over these nine years?

22. **Company Value Growth Rate.** The current value of a company is $25 million. If the value of the company six year ago was $10 million, what is the company's mean annual growth rate over the past six years?

3.2 Measures of Variability

In addition to measures of location, it is often desirable to consider measures of variability, or dispersion. For example, suppose that you are a purchasing agent for a large manufacturing firm and that you regularly place orders with two different suppliers. After several months of operation, you find that the mean number of days required to fill orders is 10 days for both of the suppliers. The histograms summarizing the number of working days required to fill orders from the suppliers are shown in Figure 3.2. Although the mean number of days is 10 for both suppliers, do the two suppliers demonstrate the same degree of reliability in terms of making deliveries on schedule? Note the dispersion, or variability, in delivery times indicated by the histograms. Which supplier would you prefer?

The variability in the delivery time creates uncertainty for production scheduling. Methods in this section help measure and understand variability.

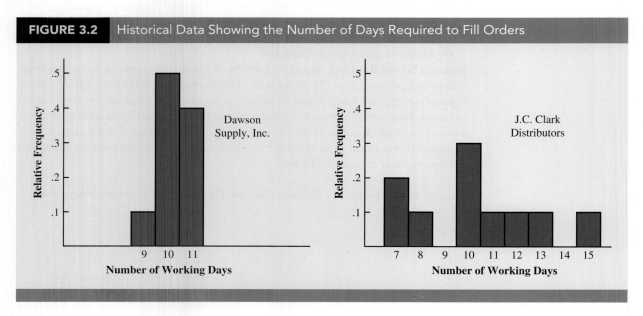

FIGURE 3.2   Historical Data Showing the Number of Days Required to Fill Orders

For most firms, receiving materials and supplies on schedule is important. The 7- or 8-day deliveries shown for J.C. Clark Distributors might be viewed favorably; however, a few of the slow 13- to 15-day deliveries could be disastrous in terms of keeping a work-force busy and production on schedule. This example illustrates a situation in which the variability in the delivery times may be an overriding consideration in selecting a supplier. For most purchasing agents, the lower variability shown for Dawson Supply, Inc., would make Dawson the preferred supplier.

We turn now to a discussion of some commonly used measures of variability.

Range

The simplest measure of variability is the **range**.

> **RANGE**
>
> $$\text{Range} = \text{Largest value} - \text{Smallest value}$$

Let us refer to the data on starting salaries for business school graduates in Table 3.1. The largest starting salary is 6325 and the smallest is 5710. The range is $6325 - 5710 = 615$.

Although the range is the easiest of the measures of variability to compute, it is seldom used as the only measure. The reason is that the range is based on only two of the observations and thus is highly influenced by extreme values. Suppose the highest paid graduate received a starting salary of \$15,000 per month. In this case, the range would be $15,000 - 5710 = 9290$ rather than 615. This large value for the range would not be especially descriptive of the variability in the data because 11 of the 12 starting salaries are closely grouped between 5710 and 6130.

Interquartile Range

A measure of variability that overcomes the dependency on extreme values is the **interquartile range (IQR)**. This measure of variability is the difference between the third quartile, Q_3, and the first quartile, Q_1. In other words, the interquartile range is the range for the middle 50% of the data.

> **INTERQUARTILE RANGE**
>
> $$\text{IQR} = Q_3 - Q_1 \tag{3.6}$$

For the data on monthly starting salaries, the quartiles are $Q_3 = 6000$ and $Q_1 = 5865$. Thus, the interquartile range is $6000 - 5865 = 135$.

Variance

The **variance** is a measure of variability that utilizes all the data. The variance is based on the difference between the value of each observation (x_i) and the mean. The difference between each x_i and the mean ($\bar{x}$ for a sample, μ for a population) is called a *deviation about the mean*. For a sample, a deviation about the mean is written ($x_i - \bar{x}$); for a population, it is written ($x_i - \mu$). In the computation of the variance, the deviations about the mean are *squared*.

If the data are for a population, the average of the squared deviations is called the *population variance*. The population variance is denoted by the Greek symbol σ^2. For a population of N observations and with μ denoting the population mean, the definition of the population variance is as follows.

POPULATION VARIANCE

$$\sigma^2 = \frac{\Sigma(x_i - \mu)^2}{N} \tag{3.7}$$

In most statistical applications, the data being analyzed are for a sample. When we compute a sample variance, we are often interested in using it to estimate the population variance σ^2. Although a detailed explanation is beyond the scope of this text, it can be shown that if the sum of the squared deviations about the sample mean is divided by $n - 1$, and not n, the resulting sample variance provides an unbiased estimate of the population variance. For this reason, the *sample variance,* denoted by s^2, is defined as follows.

The sample variance s^2 is a point estimator of the population variance σ^2.

SAMPLE VARIANCE

$$s^2 = \frac{\Sigma(x_i - \bar{x})^2}{n - 1} \tag{3.8}$$

To illustrate the computation of the sample variance, we will use the data on class size for the sample of five college classes as presented in Section 3.1. A summary of the data, including the computation of the deviations about the mean and the squared deviations about the mean, is shown in Table 3.3. The sum of squared deviations about the mean is $\Sigma(x_i - \bar{x})^2 = 256$. Hence, with $n - 1 = 4$, the sample variance is

$$s^2 = \frac{\Sigma(x_i - \bar{x})^2}{n - 1} = \frac{256}{4} = 64$$

Before moving on, let us note that the units associated with the sample variance often cause confusion. Because the values being summed in the variance calculation, $(x_i - \bar{x})^2$, are squared, the units associated with the sample variance are also *squared*. For instance, the sample variance for the class size data is $s^2 = 64$ (students)^2. The squared units associated with variance make it difficult to develop an intuitive understanding and interpretation of the numerical value of the variance. We recommend that you think of the variance as a measure useful in comparing the amount of variability for two or more variables. In a comparison of the variables, the one with the largest variance shows the most variability. Further interpretation of the value of the variance may not be necessary.

The variance is useful in comparing the variability of two or more variables.

TABLE 3.3	Computation of Deviations and Squared Deviations About the Mean for the Class Size Data		
Number of Students in Class (x_i)	Mean Class Size ($\bar{x}$)	Deviation About the Mean ($x_i - \bar{x}$)	Squared Deviation About the Mean ($x_i - \bar{x})^2$
46	44	2	4
54	44	10	100
42	44	−2	4
46	44	2	4
32	44	−12	144
		0	256
		$\Sigma(x_i - \bar{x})$	$\Sigma(x_i - \bar{x})^2$

TABLE 3.4	Computation of the Sample Variance for the Starting Salary Data		

Monthly Salary (x_i)	Sample Mean ($\bar{x}$)	Deviation About the Mean ($x_i - \bar{x}$)	Squared Deviation About the Mean ($x_i - \bar{x}$)^2
5850	5940	−90	8100
5950	5940	10	100
6050	5940	110	12,100
5880	5940	−60	3600
5755	5940	−185	34,225
5710	5940	−230	52,900
5890	5940	−50	2500
6130	5940	190	36,100
5940	5940	0	0
6325	5940	385	148,225
5920	5940	−20	400
5880	5940	−60	3600
		0	301,850
		$\Sigma(x_i - \bar{x})$	$\Sigma(x_i - \bar{x})^2$

Using equation (3.8),

$$s^2 = \frac{\Sigma(x_i - \bar{x})^2}{n - 1} = \frac{301,850}{11} = 27,440.91$$

As another illustration of computing a sample variance, consider the starting salaries listed in Table 3.1 for the 12 business school graduates. In Section 3.1, we showed that the sample mean starting salary was 5940. The computation of the sample variance ($s^2 = 27,440.91$) is shown in Table 3.4.

In Tables 3.3 and 3.4 we show both the sum of the deviations about the mean and the sum of the squared deviations about the mean. For any data set, the sum of the deviations about the mean will *always equal zero*. Note that in Tables 3.3 and 3.4, $\Sigma(x_i - \bar{x}) = 0$. The positive deviations and negative deviations cancel each other, causing the sum of the deviations about the mean to equal zero.

Standard Deviation

The **standard deviation** is defined to be the positive square root of the variance. Following the notation we adopted for a sample variance and a population variance, we use s to denote the sample standard deviation and σ to denote the population standard deviation. The standard deviation is derived from the variance in the following way.

The sample standard deviation s is a point estimator of the population standard deviation σ.

STANDARD DEVIATION

$$\text{Sample standard deviation} = s = \sqrt{s^2} \tag{3.9}$$

$$\text{Population standard deviation} = \sigma = \sqrt{\sigma^2} \tag{3.10}$$

Recall that the sample variance for the sample of class sizes in five college classes is $s^2 = 64$. Thus, the sample standard deviation is $s = \sqrt{64} = 8$. For the data on starting salaries, the sample standard deviation is $s = \sqrt{27,440.91} = 165.65$.

The standard deviation is easier to interpret than the variance because the standard deviation is measured in the same units as the data.

What is gained by converting the variance to its corresponding standard deviation? Recall that the units associated with the variance are squared. For example, the sample variance for the starting salary data of business school graduates is $s^2 = 27,440.91$ (dollars).[2] Because the standard deviation is the square root of the variance, the units of the variance, dollars squared, are converted to dollars in the standard deviation. Thus, the standard deviation of the starting salary data is $165.65. In other words, the standard deviation is measured in the same units as the original data. For this reason the standard deviation is more easily compared to the mean and other statistics that are measured in the same units as the original data.

Coefficient of Variation

The coefficient of variation is a relative measure of variability; it measures the standard deviation relative to the mean.

In some situations we may be interested in a descriptive statistic that indicates how large the standard deviation is relative to the mean. This measure is called the **coefficient of variation** and is usually expressed as a percentage.

COEFFICIENT OF VARIATION

$$\left(\frac{\text{Standard deviation}}{\text{Mean}} \times 100 \right)\% \tag{3.11}$$

For the class size data, we found a sample mean of 44 and a sample standard deviation of 8. The coefficient of variation is $[(8/44) \times 100]\% = 18.2\%$. In words, the coefficient of variation tells us that the sample standard deviation is 18.2% of the value of the sample mean. For the starting salary data with a sample mean of 3940 and a sample standard deviation of 165.65, the coefficient of variation, $[(165.65/5940) \times 100]\% = 2.8\%$, tells us the sample standard deviation is only 2.8% of the value of the sample mean. In general, the coefficient of variation is a useful statistic for comparing the variability of variables that have different standard deviations and different means.

N O T E S   +   C O M M E N T S

1. Statistical software packages and spreadsheets can be used to develop the descriptive statistics presented in this chapter. After the data are entered into a worksheet, a few simple commands can be used to generate the desired output. In two chapter-ending appendixes we show how JMP and Excel can be used to develop descriptive statistics.

2. The standard deviation is a commonly used measure of the risk associated with investing in stock and stock funds. It provides a measure of how monthly returns fluctuate around the long-run average return.

3. Rounding the value of the sample mean $\bar{x}$ and the values of the squared deviations $(x_i - \bar{x})^2$ may introduce errors when calculating the computation of the variance and standard deviation. To reduce rounding errors, we recommend carrying at least six significant digits during intermediate calculations. The resulting variance or standard deviation can then be rounded to fewer digits.

4. An alternative formula for the computation of the sample variance is

$$s^2 = \frac{\sum x_i^2 - n\bar{x}^2}{n - 1}$$

where $\sum x_i^2 = x_1^2 + x_2^2 + \cdots + x_n^2$.

5. The mean absolute error (MAE) is another measure of variability that is computed by summing the absolute values of the deviations of the observations about the mean and dividing this sum by the number of observations. For a sample of size n, the MAE is computed as follows:

$$\text{MAE} = \frac{\sum |x_i - \bar{x}|}{n}$$

For the class size data presented in Section 3.1, $\bar{x} = 44$, $\sum |x_i - \bar{x}| = 28$, and the MAE = $28/5 = 5.6$. We discuss more about the MAE and other measures of variability in Chapter 17.

EXERCISES

Methods

23. Consider a sample with data values of 10, 20, 12, 17, and 16. Compute the range and interquartile range.
24. Consider a sample with data values of 10, 20, 12, 17, and 16. Compute the variance and standard deviation.
25. Consider a sample with data values of 27, 25, 20, 15, 30, 34, 28, and 25. Compute the range, interquartile range, variance, and standard deviation.

Applications

26. **Price of Unleaded Gasoline.** Data collected by the Oil Price Information Service from more than 90,000 gasoline and convenience stores throughout the U.S. showed that the average price for a gallon of unleaded gasoline was $3.28 (MSN Auto website). The following data show the price per gallon ($) for a sample of 20 gasoline and convenience stores located in San Francisco.

SFGasPrices

| 3.59 | 3.59 | 4.79 | 3.56 | 3.55 | 3.71 | 3.65 | 3.60 | 3.75 | 3.56 |
| 3.57 | 3.59 | 3.55 | 3.99 | 4.15 | 3.66 | 3.63 | 3.73 | 3.61 | 3.57 |

   a. Use the sample data to estimate the mean price for a gallon of unleaded gasoline in San Francisco.
   b. Compute the sample standard deviation.
   c. Compare the mean price per gallon for the sample data to the national average price. What conclusions can you draw about the cost living in San Francisco?

27. **Round-Trip Flight Prices.** The following table displays round-trip flight prices from 14 major U.S. cities to Atlanta and Salt Lake City.

Flights

Departure City	Round-Trip Cost ($)	
	Atlanta	Salt Lake City
Cincinnati	340.10	570.10
New York	321.60	354.60
Chicago	291.60	465.60
Denver	339.60	219.60
Los Angeles	359.60	311.60
Seattle	384.60	297.60
Detroit	309.60	471.60
Philadelphia	415.60	618.40
Washington, D.C.	293.60	513.60
Miami	249.60	523.20
San Francisco	539.60	381.60
Las Vegas	455.60	159.60
Phoenix	359.60	267.60
Dallas	333.90	458.60

   a. Compute the mean price for a round-trip flight into Atlanta and the mean price for a round-trip flight into Salt Lake City. Is Atlanta less expensive to fly into than Salt Lake City? If so, what could explain this difference?
   b. Compute the range, variance, and standard deviation for the two samples. What does this information tell you about the prices for flights into these two cities?

28. **Annual Sales Amounts.** Varatta Enterprises sells industrial plumbing valves. The following table lists the annual sales amounts for the different salespeople in the organization for the most recent fiscal year.

DATA*file*

VarattaSales

Salesperson	Sales Amount ($1000)	Salesperson	Sales Amount ($1000)
Joseph	147	Wei	465
Jennifer	232	Samantha	410
Phillip	547	Erin	298
Stanley	328	Dominic	321
Luke	295	Charlie	190
Lexie	194	Amol	211
Margaret	368	Lenisa	413

a. Compute the mean, variance, and standard deviation for these annual sales values.
b. In the previous fiscal year, the average annual sales amount was $300,000 with a standard deviation of $95,000. Discuss any differences you observe between the annual sales amount in the most recent and previous fiscal years.

29. **Air Quality Index**. The *Los Angeles Times* regularly reports the air quality index for various areas of Southern California. A sample of air quality index values for Pomona provided the following data: 28, 42, 58, 48, 45, 55, 60, 49, and 50.
a. Compute the range and interquartile range.
b. Compute the sample variance and sample standard deviation.
c. A sample of air quality index readings for Anaheim provided a sample mean of 48.5, a sample variance of 136, and a sample standard deviation of 11.66. What comparisons can you make between the air quality in Pomona and that in Anaheim on the basis of these descriptive statistics?

30. **Reliability of Delivery Service.** The following data were used to construct the histograms of the number of days required to fill orders for Dawson Supply, Inc., and J.C. Clark Distributors (see Figure 3.2).

Dawson Supply Days for Delivery: 11   10   9   10   11   11   10   11   10   10
Clark Distributors Days for Delivery: 8   10   13   7   10   11   10   7   15   12

Use the range and standard deviation to support the previous observation that Dawson Supply provides the more consistent and reliable delivery times.

31. **Cellular Phone Spending.** According to the 2016 Consumer Expenditure Survey, Americans spend an average of $1124 on cellular phone service annually (U.S. Bureau of Labor Statistics website). Suppose that we wish to determine if there are differences in cellular phone expenditures by age group. Therefore, samples of 10 consumers were selected for three age groups (18–34, 35–44, 45 and older). The annual expenditure for each person in the sample is provided in the table below.

DATA*file*

CellPhoneExpenses

18–34	35–44	45 and Older
1355	969	1135
115	434	956
1456	1792	400
2045	1500	1374
1621	1277	1244
994	1056	825
1937	1922	763
1200	1350	1192
1567	1586	1305
1390	1415	1510

a. Compute the mean, variance, and standard deviation for the each of these three samples.
b. What observations can be made based on these data?

Advertising

32. **Advertising Spend by Companies.** *Advertising Age* annually compiles a list of the 100 companies that spend the most on advertising. Consumer-goods company Procter & Gamble has often topped the list, spending billions of dollars annually. Consider the data found in the file *Advertising*. It contains annual advertising expenditures for a sample of 20 companies in the automotive sector and 20 companies in the department store sector.
    a. What is the mean advertising spent for each sector?
    b. What is the standard deviation for each sector?
    c. What is the range of advertising spent for each sector?
    d. What is the interquartile range for each sector?
    e. Based on this sample and your answers to parts (a) to (d), comment on any differences in the advertising spending in the automotive companies versus the department store companies.

33. **Amateur Golfer Scores.** Scores turned in by an amateur golfer at the Bonita Fairways Golf Course in Bonita Springs, Florida, during 2017 and 2018 are as follows:

2017 Season:	74	78	79	77	75	73	75	77
2018 Season:	71	70	75	77	85	80	71	79

a. Use the mean and standard deviation to evaluate the golfer's performance over the two-year period.
b. What is the primary difference in performance between 2017 and 2018? What improvement, if any, can be seen in the 2018 scores?

34. **Consistency of Running Times.** The following times were recorded by the quarter-mile and mile runners of a university track team (times are in minutes).

Quarter-Mile Times:	.92	.98	1.04	.90	.99
Mile Times:	4.52	4.35	4.60	4.70	4.50

After viewing this sample of running times, one of the coaches commented that the quarter-milers turned in the more consistent times. Use the standard deviation and the coefficient of variation to summarize the variability in the data. Does the use of the coefficient of variation indicate that the coach's statement should be qualified?

3.3 Measures of Distribution Shape, Relative Location, and Detecting Outliers

We have described several measures of location and variability for data. In addition, it is often important to have a measure of the shape of a distribution. In Chapter 2 we noted that a histogram provides a graphical display showing the shape of a distribution. An important numerical measure of the shape of a distribution is called **skewness**.

Distribution Shape

Figure 3.3 shows four histograms constructed from relative frequency distributions. The histograms in Panels A and B are moderately skewed. The one in Panel A is skewed to the left; its skewness is $-.85$. The histogram in Panel B is skewed to the right; its skewness is $+.85$. The histogram in Panel C is symmetric; its skewness is zero. The histogram in Panel D is highly skewed to the right; its skewness is 1.62. The formula used to compute skewness is somewhat complex.[1] However, the skewness can easily

---
[1]The formula for the skewness of sample data:

$$\text{Skewness} = \frac{n}{(n-1)(n-2)} \sum \left(\frac{x_i - \bar{x}}{s} \right)^3$$

FIGURE 3.3   Histograms Showing the Skewness for Four Distributions

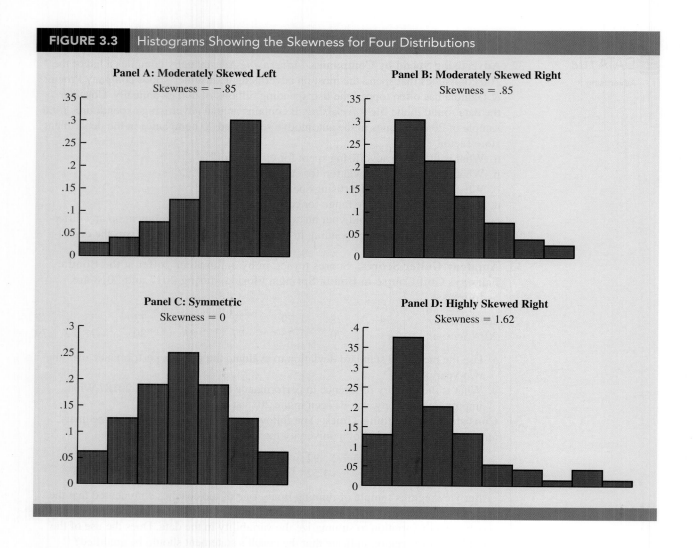

be computed using statistical software. For data skewed to the left, the skewness is negative; for data skewed to the right, the skewness is positive. If the data are symmetric, the skewness is zero.

For a symmetric distribution, the mean and the median are equal. When the data are positively skewed, the mean will usually be greater than the median; when the data are negatively skewed, the mean will usually be less than the median. The data used to construct the histogram in Panel D are customer purchases at a women's apparel store. The mean purchase amount is $77.60 and the median purchase amount is $59.70. The relatively few large purchase amounts tend to increase the mean, while the median remains unaffected by the large purchase amounts. The median provides the preferred measure of location when the data are highly skewed.

z-Scores

In addition to measures of location, variability, and shape, we are also interested in the relative location of values within a data set. Measures of relative location help us determine how far a particular value is from the mean.

By using both the mean and standard deviation, we can determine the relative location of any observation. Suppose we have a sample of n observations, with the values denoted by $x_1, x_2, \ldots, x_n$. In addition, assume that the sample mean, $\bar{x}$, and the sample standard deviation, s, are already computed. Associated with each value, x_i, is another value called its **z-score**. Equation (3.12) shows how the z-score is computed for each x_i.

---

z-SCORE

$$z_i = \frac{x_i - \bar{x}}{s}$$
(3.12)

where

$$z_i = \text{the z-score for } x_i$$
$$\bar{x} = \text{the sample mean}$$
$$s = \text{the sample standard deviation}$$

The z-score is often called the *standardized value*. The z-score, z_i, can be interpreted as the *number of standard deviations x_i is from the mean $\bar{x}$*. For example, $z_1 = 1.2$ would indicate that x_1 is 1.2 standard deviations greater than the sample mean. Similarly, $z_2 = -.5$ would indicate that x_2 is .5, or 1/2, standard deviation less than the sample mean. A z-score greater than zero occurs for observations with a value greater than the mean, and a z-score less than zero occurs for observations with a value less than the mean. A z-score of zero indicates that the value of the observation is equal to the mean.

The z-score for any observation can be interpreted as a measure of the relative location of the observation in a data set. Thus, observations in two different data sets with the same z-score can be said to have the same relative location in terms of being the same number of standard deviations from the mean.

The z-scores for the class size data from Section 3.1 are computed in Table 3.5. Recall the previously computed sample mean, $\bar{x} = 44$, and sample standard deviation, $s = 8$. The z-score of -1.50 for the fifth observation shows it is farthest from the mean; it is 1.50 standard deviations below the mean. Figure 3.4 provides a dot plot of the class size data with a graphical representation of the associated z-scores on the axis below.

Chebyshev's Theorem

Chebyshev's theorem enables us to make statements about the proportion of data values that must be within a specified number of standard deviations of the mean.

CHEBYSHEV'S THEOREM

At least $(1 - 1/z^2)$ of the data values must be within z standard deviations of the mean, where z is any value greater than 1.

TABLE 3.5	z-Scores for the Class Size Data	
Number of Students in Class (x_i)	**Deviation About the Mean ($x_i - \bar{x}$)**	**z-Score $\left(\dfrac{x_i - \bar{x}}{s}\right)$**
46	2	2/8 = .25
54	10	10/8 = 1.25
42	−2	−2/8 = −.25
46	2	2/8 = .25
32	−12	−12/8 = −1.50

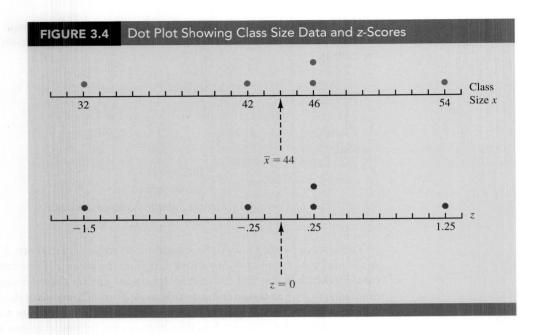

FIGURE 3.4   Dot Plot Showing Class Size Data and z-Scores

Some of the implications of this theorem, with $z = 2, 3,$ and 4 standard deviations, follow.

- At least .75, or 75%, of the data values must be within $z = 2$ standard deviations of the mean.
- At least .89, or 89%, of the data values must be within $z = 3$ standard deviations of the mean.
- At least .94, or 94%, of the data values must be within $z = 4$ standard deviations of the mean.

For an example using Chebyshev's theorem, suppose that the midterm test scores for 100 students in a college business statistics course had a mean of 70 and a standard deviation of 5. How many students had test scores between 60 and 80? How many students had test scores between 58 and 82?

For the test scores between 60 and 80, we note that 60 is two standard deviations below the mean and 80 is two standard deviations above the mean. Using Chebyshev's theorem, we see that at least .75, or at least 75%, of the observations must have values within two standard deviations of the mean. Thus, at least 75% of the students must have scored between 60 and 80.

Chebyshev's theorem requires $z > 1$; but z need not be an integer.

For the test scores between 58 and 82, we see that $(58 - 70)/5 = -2.4$ indicates 58 is 2.4 standard deviations below the mean and that $(82 - 70)/5 = +2.4$ indicates 82 is 2.4 standard deviations above the mean. Applying Chebyshev's theorem with $z = 2.4$, we have

$$\left(1 - \frac{1}{z^2}\right) = \left(1 - \frac{1}{(2.4)^2}\right) = .826$$

At least 82.6% of the students must have test scores between 58 and 82.

Empirical Rule

One of the advantages of Chebyshev's theorem is that it applies to any data set regardless of the shape of the distribution of the data. Indeed, it could be used with any of the distributions in Figure 3.3. In many practical applications, however, data sets exhibit a symmetric mound-shaped or bell-shaped distribution like the one shown in blue in Figure 3.5. When the data are believed to approximate this distribution, the **empirical rule** can be used to determine the percentage of data values that must be within a specified number of standard deviations of the mean.

FIGURE 3.5   A Bell-Shaped Distribution of Detergent Carton Weights with Percentage of Data Values Within 1, 2, and 3 Standard Deviations

The empirical rule is based on the normal probability distribution, which will be discussed in Chapter 6. The normal distribution is used extensively throughout the text.

EMPIRICAL RULE

For data having a bell-shaped distribution:

- Approximately 68% of the data values will be within one standard deviation of the mean.
- Approximately 95% of the data values will be within two standard deviations of the mean.
- Almost all of the data values will be within three standard deviations of the mean.

For example, liquid detergent cartons are filled automatically on a production line. Filling weights frequently have a bell-shaped distribution. If the mean filling weight is 16 ounces and the standard deviation is .25 ounces, we can use the empirical rule to draw the following conclusions.

- Approximately 68% of the filled cartons will have weights between 15.75 and 16.25 ounces (within one standard deviation of the mean).
- Approximately 95% of the filled cartons will have weights between 15.50 and 16.50 ounces (within two standard deviations of the mean).
- Almost all filled cartons will have weights between 15.25 and 16.75 ounces (within three standard deviations of the mean).

Use Figure 3.5 to help you answer these four questions.

Can we use this information to say anything about how many filled cartons will:

- weigh between 16 and 16.25 ounces?
- weigh between 15.50 and 16 ounces?
- weigh less than 15.50 ounces?
- weigh between 15.50 and 16.25 ounces?

If we recognize that the normal distribution is symmetric about its mean, we can answer each of the questions in the previous list, and we will be able to determine the following:

- Since the percentage of filled cartons that will weigh between 15.75 and 16.25 is approximately 68% and the mean 16 is at the midpoint between 15.75 and 16.25, the percentage of filled cartons that will weigh between 16 and 16.25 ounces is approximately (68%)/2 or approximately 34%.
- Since the percentage of filled cartons that will weigh between 15.50 and 16.50 is approximately 95% and the mean 16 is at the midpoint between 15.50 and 16.50, the percentage of filled cartons that will weigh between 15.50 and 16 ounces is approximately (95%)/2 or approximately 47.5%.
- We just determined that the percentage of filled cartons that will weigh between 15.50 and 16 ounces is approximately 47.5%. Since the distribution is symmetric about its mean, we also know that 50% of the filled cartons will weigh below 16 ounces. Therefore, the percentage of filled cartons with weights less than 15.50 ounces is approximately 50% − 47.5% or approximately 2.5%.
- We just determined that approximately 47.5% of the filled cartons will weigh between 15.50 and 16 ounces, and we earlier determined that approximately 34% of the filled cartons will weigh between 16 and 16.25 ounces. Therefore, the percentage of filled cartons that will weigh between 15.50 and 16.25 ounces is approximately 47.5% + 34% or approximately 81.5%.

In Chapter 6 we will learn to work with noninteger values of z to answer a much broader range of these types of questions.

Detecting Outliers

Sometimes a data set will have one or more observations with unusually large or unusually small values. These extreme values are called **outliers**. Experienced statisticians take steps to identify outliers and then review each one carefully. An outlier may be a data value that has been incorrectly recorded. If so, it can be corrected before further analysis. An outlier may also be from an observation that was incorrectly included in the data set; if so, it can be removed. Finally, an outlier may be an unusual data value that has been recorded correctly and belongs in the data set. In such cases it should remain.

Standardized values (z-scores) can be used to identify outliers. Recall that the empirical rule allows us to conclude that for data with a bell-shaped distribution, almost all the data values will be within three standard deviations of the mean. Hence, in using z-scores to identify outliers, we recommend treating any data value with a z-score less than -3 or greater than $+3$ as an outlier. Such data values can then be reviewed for accuracy and to determine whether they belong in the data set.

Refer to the z-scores for the class size data in Table 3.5. The z-score of -1.50 shows the fifth class size is farthest from the mean. However, this standardized value is well within the -3 to $+3$ guideline for outliers. Thus, the z-scores do not indicate that outliers are present in the class size data.

Another approach to identifying outliers is based upon the values of the first and third quartiles (Q_1 and Q_3) and the interquartile range (IQR). Using this method, we first compute the following lower and upper limits:

$$\text{Lower Limit} = Q_1 - 1.5(\text{IQR})$$
$$\text{Upper Limit} = Q_3 + 1.5(\text{IQR})$$

The approach that uses the first and third quartiles and the IQR to identify outliers does not necessarily provide the same results as the approach based upon a z-score less than −3 or greater than +3. Either or both procedures may be used.

An observation is classified as an outlier if its value is less than the lower limit or greater than the upper limit. For the monthly starting salary data shown in Table 3.1, $Q_1 = 5857.5$, $Q_3 = 6025$, IQR $= 167.5$, and the lower and upper limits are

$$\text{Lower Limit} = Q_1 - 1.5(\text{IQR}) = 5857.5 - 1.5(167.5) = 5606.25$$
$$\text{Upper Limit} = Q_3 + 1.5(\text{IQR}) = 6025 + 1.5(167.5) = 6276.25$$

Looking at the data in Table 3.1, we see that there are no observations with a starting salary less than the lower limit of 5606.25. But, there is one starting salary, 6325, that is greater than the upper limit of 6276.25. Thus, 6325 is considered to be an outlier using this alternate approach to identifying outliers.

NOTES + COMMENTS

1. Chebyshev's theorem is applicable for any data set and can be used to state the minimum number of data values that will be within a certain number of standard deviations of the mean. If the data are known to be approximately bell-shaped, more can be said. For instance, the empirical rule allows us to say that *approximately* 95% of the data values will be within two standard deviations of the mean;

   Chebyshev's theorem allows us to conclude only that at least 75% of the data values will be in that interval.

2. Before analyzing a data set, statisticians usually make a variety of checks to ensure the validity of data. In a large study it is not uncommon for errors to be made in recording data values or in entering the values into a computer. Identifying outliers is one tool used to check the validity of the data.

EXERCISES

Methods

35. Consider a sample with data values of 10, 20, 12, 17, and 16. Compute the z-score for each of the five observations.
36. Consider a sample with a mean of 500 and a standard deviation of 100. What are the z-scores for the following data values: 520, 650, 500, 450, and 280?
37. Consider a sample with a mean of 30 and a standard deviation of 5. Use Chebyshev's theorem to determine the percentage of the data within each of the following ranges:
    a. 20 to 40
    b. 15 to 45
    c. 22 to 38
    d. 18 to 42
    e. 12 to 48
38. Suppose the data have a bell-shaped distribution with a mean of 30 and a standard deviation of 5. Use the empirical rule to determine the percentage of data within each of the following ranges:
    a. 20 to 40
    b. 15 to 45
    c. 25 to 35

Applications

39. **Amount of Sleep per Night.** The results of a national survey showed that on average, adults sleep 6.9 hours per night. Suppose that the standard deviation is 1.2 hours.
    a. Use Chebyshev's theorem to calculate the percentage of individuals who sleep between 4.5 and 9.3 hours.
    b. Use Chebyshev's theorem to calculate the percentage of individuals who sleep between 3.9 and 9.9 hours.
    c. Assume that the number of hours of sleep follows a bell-shaped distribution. Use the empirical rule to calculate the percentage of individuals who sleep between 4.5 and 9.3 hours per day. How does this result compare to the value that you obtained using Chebyshev's theorem in part (a)?
40. **Price per Gallon of Gasoline.** Suppose that the mean retail price per gallon of regular grade gasoline in the United States is $3.43 with a standard deviation of $.10 and that the retail price per gallon has a bell-shaped distribution.

    a. What percentage of regular grade gasoline sold between $3.33 and $3.53 per gallon?

    b. What percentage of regular grade gasoline sold between $3.33 and $3.63 per gallon?

    c. What percentage of regular grade gasoline sold for more than $3.63 per gallon?

41. **GMAT Exam Scores.** The Graduate Management Admission Test (GMAT) is a standardized exam used by many universities as part of the assessment for admission to graduate study in business. The average GMAT score is 547 (*Magoosh* website). Assume that GMAT scores are bell-shaped with a standard deviation of 100.

    a. What percentage of GMAT scores are 647 or higher?

    b. What percentage of GMAT scores are 747 or higher?

    c. What percentage of GMAT scores are between 447 and 547?

    d. What percentage of GMAT scores are between 347 and 647?

42. **Cost of Backyard Structure.** Many families in California are using backyard structures for home offices, art studios, and hobby areas as well as for additional storage. Suppose that the mean price for a customized wooden, shingled backyard structure is $3100. Assume that the standard deviation is $1200.

    a. What is the z-score for a backyard structure costing $2300?

    b. What is the z-score for a backyard structure costing $4900?

    c. Interpret the z-scores in parts (a) and (b). Comment on whether either should be considered an outlier.

    d. If the cost for a backyard shed-office combination built in Albany, California, is $13,000, should this structure be considered an outlier? Explain.

43. **Best Places to Live.** Each year *Money* magazine publishes a list of "Best Places to Live in the United States." These listings are based on affordability, educational performance, convenience, safety, and livability. The list below shows the median household income of *Money* magazine's top city in each U.S. state for 2017 (*Money* magazine website).

DATAfile

BestCities

City	Median Household Income ($)	City	Median Household Income ($)
Pelham, AL	66,772	Bozeman, MT	49,303
Juneau, AK	84,101	Papillion, NE	79,131
Paradise Valley, AZ	138,192	Sparks, NV	54,230
Fayetteville, AR	40,835	Nashua, NH	66,872
Monterey Park, CA	57,419	North Arlington, NJ	73,885
Lone Tree, CO	116,761	Rio Rancho, NM	58,982
Manchester, CT	64,828	Valley Stream, NY	88,693
Hockessin, DE	115,124	Concord, NC	54,579
St. Augustine, FL	47,748	Dickinson, ND	71,866
Vinings, GA	73,103	Wooster, OH	43,054
Kapaa, HI	62,546	Mustang, OK	66,714
Meridian, ID	62,899	Beaverton, OR	58,785
Schaumburg, IL	73,824	Lower Merion, PA	117,438
Fishers, IN	87,043	Warwick, RI	63,414
Council Bluffs, IA	46,844	Mauldin, SC	57,480
Lenexa, KS	76,505	Rapid City, SD	47,788
Georgetown, KY	58,709	Franklin, TN	82,334
Bossier City, LA	47,051	Allen, TX	104,524
South Portland, ME	56,472	Orem, UT	54,515
Rockville, MD	100,158	Colchester, VT	69,181
Waltham, MA	75,106	Reston, VA	112,722
Farmington Hills, MI	71,154	Mercer Island, WA	128,484
Woodbury, MN	99,657	Morgantown, WV	38,060
Olive Branch, MS	62,958	New Berlin, WI	74,983
St. Peters, MO	57,728	Cheyenne, WY	56,593

a. Compute the mean and median for these household income data.
b. Compare the mean and median values for these data. What does this indicate about the distribution of household income data?
c. Compute the range and standard deviation for these household income data.
d. Compute the first and third quartiles for these household income data.
e. Are there any outliers in these data? What does this suggest about the data?

44. **NCAA Basketball Game Scores.** A sample of 10 NCAA college basketball game scores provided the following data.

DATAfile

NCAA

Winning Team	Points	Losing Team	Points	Winning Margin
Arizona	90	Oregon	66	24
Duke	85	Georgetown	66	19
Florida State	75	Wake Forest	70	5
Kansas	78	Colorado	57	21
Kentucky	71	Notre Dame	63	8
Louisville	65	Tennessee	62	3
Oklahoma State	72	Texas	66	6
Purdue	76	Michigan State	70	6
Stanford	77	Southern Cal	67	10
Wisconsin	76	Illinois	56	20

a. Compute the mean and standard deviation for the points scored by the winning teams.
b. Assume that the points scored by the winning teams for all NCAA games follow a bell-shaped distribution. Using the mean and standard deviation found in part (a), estimate the percentage of all NCAA games in which the winning team scores 84 or more points. Estimate the percentage of NCAA games in which the winning team scores more than 90 points.
c. Compute the mean and standard deviation for the winning margin. Do the data contain outliers? Explain.

45. **Apple iPads in Schools.** *The New York Times* reported that Apple has unveiled a new iPad marketed specifically to school districts for use by students (*The New York Times* website). The 9.7-inch iPads will have faster processors and a cheaper price point in an effort to take market share away from Google Chromebooks in public school districts. Suppose that the following data represent the percentages of students currently using Apple iPads for a sample of 18 U.S. public school districts.

15   22   12   21   26   18   42   29   64   20   15   22   18   24   27
24   26   19

DATAfile

iPads

a. Compute the mean and median percentage of students currently using Apple iPads.
b. Compare the first and third quartiles for these data.
c. Compute the range and interquartile range for these data.
d. Compute the variance and standard deviation for these data.
e. Are there any outliers in these data?
f. Based on your calculated values, what can we say about the percentage of students using iPads in public school districts?

3.4 Five-Number Summaries and Boxplots

Summary statistics and easy-to-draw graphs based on summary statistics can be used to quickly summarize large quantities of data. In this section we show how five-number summaries and boxplots can be developed to identify several characteristics of a data set.

Five-Number Summary

In a **five-number summary**, five numbers are used to summarize the data:

1. Smallest value
2. First quartile (Q_1)
3. Median (Q_2)
4. Third quartile (Q_3)
5. Largest value

To illustrate the development of a five-number summary, we will use the monthly starting salary data shown in Table 3.1. Arranging the data in ascending order, we obtain the following results.

5710 5755 5850 5880 5880 5890 5920 5940 5950 6050 6130 6325

The smallest value is 5710 and the largest value is 6325. We showed how to compute the quartiles ($Q_1 = 5857.5$; $Q_2 = 5905$; and $Q_3 = 6025$) in Section 3.1. Thus, the five-number summary for the monthly starting salary data is

5710   5857.5   5905   6025   6325

The five-number summary indicates that the starting salaries in the sample are between 5710 and 6325 and that the median or middle value is 5905; and, the first and third quartiles show that approximately 50% of the starting salaries are between 5857.5 and 6025.

Boxplot

A boxplot is a graphical display of data based on a five-number summary. A key to the development of a boxplot is the computation of the interquartile range, $IQR = Q_3 - Q_1$. Figure 3.6 shows a boxplot for the monthly starting salary data. The steps used to construct the boxplot follow.

Boxplots provide another way to identify outliers. But they do not necessarily identify the same values as those with a z-score less than −3 or greater than +3. Either or both procedures may be used.

1. A box is drawn with the ends of the box located at the first and third quartiles. For the salary data, $Q_1 = 5857.5$ and $Q_2 = 6025$. This box contains the middle 50% of the data.
2. A vertical line is drawn in the box at the location of the median (5905 for the salary data).
3. By using the interquartile range, $IQR = Q_3 - Q_1$, *limits* are located at 1.5(IQR) below Q_1 and 1.5(IQR) above Q_3. For the salary data, $IQR = Q_3 - Q_1 = 6025 - 5857.5 = 167.5$. Thus, the limits are $5857.5 - 1.5(167.5) = 5606.25$ and $6025 + 1.5(167.5) = 6276.25$. Data outside these limits are considered *outliers*.
4. The horizontal lines extending from each end of the box in Figure 3.6 are called *whiskers*. The whiskers are drawn from the ends of the box to the smallest and largest values *inside* the *limits* computed in step 3. Thus, the whiskers end at salary values of 5710 and 6130.

FIGURE 3.6   Boxplot of the Monthly Starting Salary Data with Lines Showing the Lower and Upper Limits

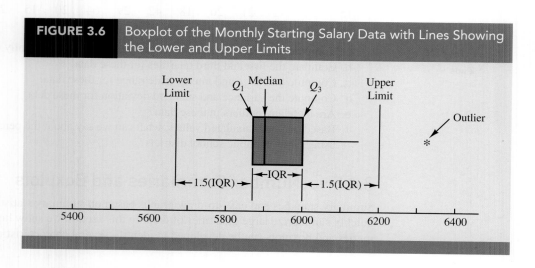

5. Finally, the location of each outlier is shown with a small asterisk. In Figure 3.6 we see one outlier, 6325.

In Figure 3.6 we included lines showing the location of the upper and lower limits. These lines were drawn to show how the limits are computed and where they are located. Although the limits are always computed, generally they are not drawn on the boxplots. Figure 3.7 shows the usual appearance of a boxplot for the starting salary data.

Comparative Analysis Using Boxplots

Boxplots can also be used to provide a graphical summary of two or more groups and facilitate visual comparisons among the groups. For example, suppose the placement office decided to conduct a follow-up study to compare monthly starting salaries by the graduate's major: accounting, finance, information systems, management, and marketing. The major and starting salary data for a new sample of 111 recent business school graduates are shown in the data set in the file *MajorSalaries,* and Figure 3.8 shows the boxplots corresponding to each major. Note that major is shown on the horizontal axis, and each boxplot is shown vertically above the corresponding major. Displaying boxplots in this manner is an excellent graphical technique for making comparisons among two or more groups.

We show how to create box plots using JMP and Excel in the end-of-chapter appendixes.

What interpretations can you make from the boxplots in Figure 3.8? Specifically, we note the following:

- The higher salaries are in accounting; the lower salaries are in management and marketing.

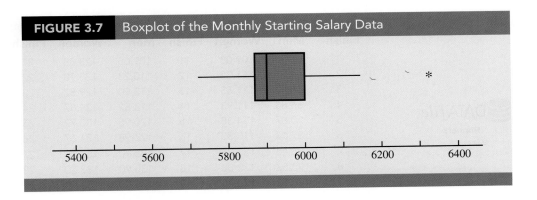

FIGURE 3.7 Boxplot of the Monthly Starting Salary Data

DATAfile

MajorSalaries

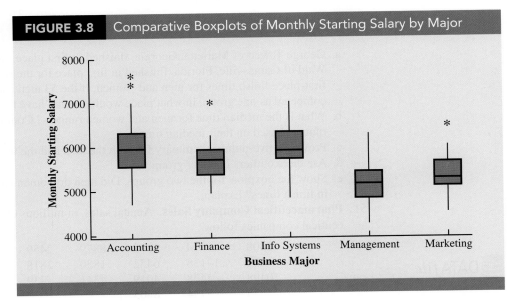

FIGURE 3.8 Comparative Boxplots of Monthly Starting Salary by Major

- Based on the medians, accounting and information systems have similar and higher median salaries. Finance is next, with management and marketing showing lower median salaries.
- High salary outliers exist for accounting, finance, and marketing majors.

Can you think of additional interpretations based on these boxplots?

EXERCISES

Methods

46. Consider a sample with data values of 27, 25, 20, 15, 30, 34, 28, and 25. Provide the five-number summary for the data.
47. Show the boxplot for the data in exercise 46.
48. Show the five-number summary and the boxplot for the following data: 5, 15, 18, 10, 8, 12, 16, 10, 6.
49. A data set has a first quartile of 42 and a third quartile of 50. Compute the lower and upper limits for the corresponding boxplot. Should a data value of 65 be considered an outlier?

Applications

50. **Naples Half-Marathon Times.** Naples, Florida, hosts a half-marathon (13.1-mile race) in January each year. The event attracts top runners from throughout the United States as well as from around the world. In the race results shown below 22 men and 31 women entered the 19–24 age class. Finish times in minutes are as follows. Times are shown in order of finish.

DATAfile
Runners

Finish	Men	Women	Finish	Men	Women	Finish	Men	Women
1	65.30	109.03	11	109.05	123.88	21	143.83	136.75
2	66.27	111.22	12	110.23	125.78	22	148.70	138.20
3	66.52	111.65	13	112.90	129.52	23		139.00
4	66.85	111.93	14	113.52	129.87	24		147.18
5	70.87	114.38	15	120.95	130.72	25		147.35
6	87.18	118.33	16	127.98	131.67	26		147.50
7	96.45	121.25	17	128.40	132.03	27		147.75
8	98.52	122.08	18	130.90	133.20	28		153.88
9	100.52	122.48	19	131.80	133.50	29		154.83
10	108.18	122.62	20	138.63	136.57	30		189.27
						31		189.28

a. George Towett of Marietta, Georgia, finished in first place for the men and Lauren Wald of Gainesville, Florida, finished in first place for the women. Compare the first-place finish times for men and women. If the 53 men and women runners had competed as one group, in what place would Lauren have finished?
b. What is the median time for men and women runners? Compare men and women runners based on their median times.
c. Provide a five-number summary for both the men and the women.
d. Are there outliers in either group?
e. Show the boxplots for the two groups. Did men or women have the most variation in finish times? Explain.

51. **Pharmaceutical Company Sales.** Annual sales, in millions of dollars, for 21 pharmaceutical companies follow.

DATAfile
PharmacySales

8408	1374	1872	8879	2459	11413
608	14138	6452	1850	2818	1356
10498	7478	4019	4341	739	2127
3653	5794	8305			

a. Provide a five-number summary.
b. Compute the lower and upper limits.
c. Do the data contain any outliers?
d. Johnson & Johnson's sales are the largest on the list at $14,138 million. Suppose a data entry error (a transposition) had been made and the sales had been entered as $41,138 million. Would the method of detecting outliers in part (c) identify this problem and allow for correction of the data entry error?
e. Show a boxplot.

52. **Cell Phone Companies Customer Satisfaction.** *Consumer Reports* provides overall customer satisfaction scores for AT&T, Sprint, T-Mobile, and Verizon cell-phone services in major metropolitan areas throughout the United States. The rating for each service reflects the overall customer satisfaction considering a variety of factors such as cost, connectivity problems, dropped calls, static interference, and customer support. A satisfaction scale from 0 to 100 is used with 0 indicating completely dissatisfied and 100 indicating completely satisfied. Suppose that the ratings for the four cell-phone services in 20 metropolitan areas are as shown below.

CellService

Metropolitan Area	AT&T	Sprint	T-Mobile	Verizon
Atlanta	70	66	71	79
Boston	69	64	74	76
Chicago	71	65	70	77
Dallas	75	65	74	78
Denver	71	67	73	77
Detroit	73	65	77	79
Jacksonville	73	64	75	81
Las Vegas	72	68	74	81
Los Angeles	66	65	68	78
Miami	68	69	73	80
Minneapolis	68	66	75	77
Philadelphia	72	66	71	78
Phoenix	68	66	76	81
San Antonio	75	65	75	80
San Diego	69	68	72	79
San Francisco	66	69	73	75
Seattle	68	67	74	77
St. Louis	74	66	74	79
Tampa	73	63	73	79
Washington	72	68	71	76

a. Consider T-Mobile first. What is the median rating?
b. Develop a five-number summary for the T-Mobile service.
c. Are there outliers for T-Mobile? Explain.
d. Repeat parts (b) and (c) for the other three cell-phone services.
e. Show the boxplots for the four cell-phone services on one graph. Discuss what a comparison of the boxplots tells about the four services. Which service does *Consumer Reports* recommend as being best in terms of overall customer satisfaction?

53. **Most Admired Companies.** *Fortune* magazine's list of the world's most admired companies for 2014 is provided in the data contained in the file *AdmiredCompanies* (*Fortune* magazine website). The data in the column labeled "Return" shows the one-year total return (%) for the top ranked 50 companies. For the same time period the S&P average return was 18.4%.
a. Compute the median return for the top ranked 50 companies.
b. What percentage of the top-ranked 50 companies had a one-year return greater than the S&P average return?

AdmiredCompanies

BorderCrossings

c. Develop the five-number summary for the data.

d. Are there any outliers?

e. Develop a boxplot for the one-year total return.

54. **U.S. Border Crossings.** The Bureau of Transportation Statistics keeps track of all border crossings through ports of entry along the U.S.-Canadian and U.S.-Mexican borders. The data contained in the file *BorderCrossings* show the most recently published figures for the number of personal vehicle crossings (rounded to the nearest 1000) at the 50 busiest ports of entry during the month of August (U.S. Department of Transportation website).

a. What are the mean and median numbers of crossings for these ports of entry?

b. What are the first and third quartiles?

c. Provide a five-number summary.

d. Do the data contain any outliers? Show a boxplot.

3.5 Measures of Association Between Two Variables

Thus far we have examined numerical methods used to summarize the data for *one variable at a time*. Often a manager or decision maker is interested in the *relationship between two variables*. In this section we present covariance and correlation as descriptive measures of the relationship between two variables.

We begin by reconsidering the application concerning an electronics store in San Francisco as presented in Section 2.4. The store's manager wants to determine the relationship between the number of weekend television commercials shown and the sales at the store during the following week. Sample data with sales expressed in hundreds of dollars are provided in Table 3.6. It shows 10 observations ($n = 10$), one for each week. The scatter diagram in Figure 3.9 shows a positive relationship, with higher sales (y) associated with a greater number of commercials (x). In fact, the scatter diagram suggests that a straight line could be used as an approximation of the relationship. In the following discussion, we introduce **covariance** as a descriptive measure of the linear association between two variables.

Covariance

For a sample of size n with the observations (x_1, y_1), (x_2, y_2), and so on, the sample covariance is defined as follows:

SAMPLE COVARIANCE

$$s_{xy} = \frac{\Sigma(x_i - \bar{x})(y_i - \bar{y})}{n - 1}$$

(3.13)

Electronics

TABLE 3.6	Sample Data for the San Francisco Electronics Store	
Week	**Number of Commercials x**	**Sales Volume ($100s) y**
1	2	50
2	5	57
3	1	41
4	3	54
5	4	54
6	1	38
7	5	63
8	3	48
9	4	59
10	2	46

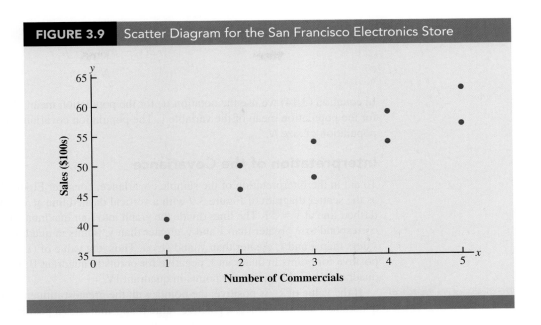

FIGURE 3.9 Scatter Diagram for the San Francisco Electronics Store

This formula pairs each x_i with a y_i. We then sum the products obtained by multiplying the deviation of each x_i from its sample mean $\bar{x}$ by the deviation of the corresponding y_i from its sample mean $\bar{y}$; this sum is then divided by $n-1$.

To measure the strength of the linear relationship between the number of commercials x and the sales volume y in the San Francisco electronics store problem, we use equation (3.13) to compute the sample covariance. The calculations in Table 3.7 show the computation of $\Sigma(x_i - \bar{x})(y_i - \bar{y})$. Note that $\bar{x} = 30/10 = 3$ and $\bar{y} = 510/10 = 51$. Using equation (3.13), we obtain a sample covariance of

$$s_{xy} = \frac{\Sigma(x_i - \bar{x})(y_i - \bar{y})}{n-1} = \frac{99}{9} = 11$$

The formula for computing the covariance of a population of size N is similar to equation (3.13), but we use different notation to indicate that we are working with the entire population.

TABLE 3.7 Calculations for the Sample Covariance

x_i	y_i	$x_i - \bar{x}$	$y_i - \bar{y}$	$(x_i - \bar{x})(y_i - \bar{y})$
2	50	−1	−1	1
5	57	2	6	12
1	41	−2	−10	20
3	54	0	3	0
4	54	1	3	3
1	38	−2	−13	26
5	63	2	12	24
3	48	0	−3	0
4	59	1	8	8
2	46	−1	−5	5
Totals 30	510	0	0	99

$$s_{xy} = \frac{\Sigma(x_i - \bar{x})(y_i - \bar{y})}{n-1} = \frac{99}{10-1} = 11$$

POPULATION COVARIANCE

$$\sigma_{xy} = \frac{\Sigma(x_i - \mu_x)(y_i - \mu_y)}{N} \tag{3.14}$$

In equation (3.14) we use the notation μ_x for the population mean of the variable x and μ_y for the population mean of the variable y. The population covariance σ_{xy} is defined for a population of size N.

Interpretation of the Covariance

To aid in the interpretation of the sample covariance, consider Figure 3.10. It is the same as the scatter diagram of Figure 3.9 with a vertical dashed line at $\bar{x} = 3$ and a horizontal dashed line at $\bar{y} = 51$. The lines divide the graph into four quadrants. Points in quadrant I correspond to x_i greater than $\bar{x}$ and y_i greater than $\bar{y}$, points in quadrant II correspond to x_i less than $\bar{x}$ and y_i greater than $\bar{y}$, and so on. Thus, the value of $(x_i - \bar{x})(y_i - \bar{y})$ must be positive for points in quadrant I, negative for points in quadrant II, positive for points in quadrant III, and negative for points in quadrant IV.

The covariance is a measure of the linear association between two variables.

If the value of s_{xy} is positive, the points with the greatest influence on s_{xy} must be in quadrants I and III. Hence, a positive value for s_{xy} indicates a positive linear association between x and y; that is, as the value of x increases, the value of y increases. If the value of s_{xy} is negative, however, the points with the greatest influence on s_{xy} are in quadrants II and IV. Hence, a negative value for s_{xy} indicates a negative linear association between x and y; that is, as the value of x increases, the value of y decreases. Finally, if the points are evenly distributed across all four quadrants, the value of s_{xy} will be close to zero, indicating no linear association between x and y. Figure 3.11 shows the values of s_{xy} that can be expected with three different types of scatter diagrams.

Referring again to Figure 3.10, we see that the scatter diagram for the San Francisco electronics store follows the pattern in the top panel of Figure 3.11. As we should expect, the value of the sample covariance indicates a positive linear relationship with $s_{xy} = 11$.

From the preceding discussion, it might appear that a large positive value for the covariance indicates a strong positive linear relationship and that a large negative value indicates a strong negative linear relationship. However, one problem with using covariance as a measure of the strength of the linear relationship is that the value of the covariance depends on the units of

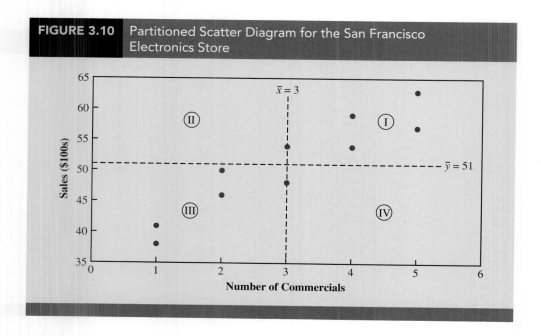

FIGURE 3.10 Partitioned Scatter Diagram for the San Francisco Electronics Store

FIGURE 3.11 Interpretation of Sample Covariance

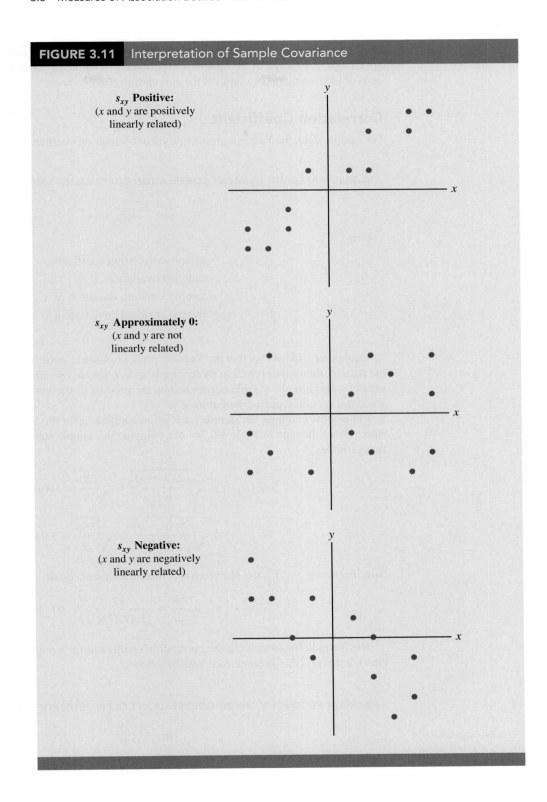

measurement for x and y. For example, suppose we are interested in the relationship between height x and weight y for individuals. Clearly the strength of the relationship should be the same whether we measure height in feet or inches. Measuring the height in inches, however, gives us much larger numerical values for $(x_i - \bar{x})$ than when we measure height in feet. Thus, with height measured in inches, we would obtain a larger value for the numerator $\Sigma(x_i - \bar{x})$

$(y_i - \bar{y})$ in equation (3.13)—and hence a larger covariance—when in fact the relationship does not change. A measure of the relationship between two variables that is not affected by the units of measurement for x and y is the **correlation coefficient**.

Correlation Coefficient

For sample data, the Pearson product moment correlation coefficient is defined as follows.

PEARSON PRODUCT MOMENT CORRELATION COEFFICIENT: SAMPLE DATA

$$r_{xy} = \frac{s_{xy}}{s_x s_y}$$

(3.15)

where

r_{xy} = sample correlation coefficient
s_{xy} = sample covariance
s_x = sample standard deviation of x
s_y = sample standard deviation of y

Equation (3.15) shows that the Pearson product moment correlation coefficient for sample data (commonly referred to more simply as the *sample correlation coefficient*) is computed by dividing the sample covariance by the product of the sample standard deviation of x and the sample standard deviation of y.

Let us now compute the sample correlation coefficient for the San Francisco electronics store. Using the data in Table 3.6, we can compute the sample standard deviations for the two variables:

$$s_x = \sqrt{\frac{\Sigma(x_i - \bar{x})^2}{n - 1}} = \sqrt{\frac{20}{9}} = 1.49$$

$$s_y = \sqrt{\frac{\Sigma(y_i - \bar{y})^2}{n - 1}} = \sqrt{\frac{566}{9}} = 7.93$$

Now, because $s_{xy} = 11$, the sample correlation coefficient equals

$$r_{xy} = \frac{s_{xy}}{s_x s_y} = \frac{11}{(1.49)(7.93)} = .93$$

The formula for computing the correlation coefficient for a population, denoted by the Greek letter ρ_{xy} (rho, pronounced "row"), follows.

PEARSON PRODUCT MOMENT CORRELATION COEFFICIENT: POPULATION DATA

The sample correlation coefficient r_{xy} is a point estimator of the population correlation coefficient ρ_{xy}

$$\rho_{xy} = \frac{\sigma_{xy}}{\sigma_x \sigma_y}$$

(3.16)

where

ρ_{xy} = population correlation coefficient
σ_{xy} = population covariance
σ_x = population standard deviation for x
σ_y = population standard deviation for y

The sample correlation coefficient r_{xy} provides an estimate of the population correlation coefficient ρ_{xy}.

Interpretation of the Correlation Coefficient

First let us consider a simple example that illustrates the concept of a perfect positive linear relationship. The scatter diagram in Figure 3.12 depicts the relationship between x and y based on the following sample data.

x_i	y_i
5	10
10	30
15	50

The straight line drawn through each of the three points shows a perfect linear relationship between x and y. In order to apply equation (3.15) to compute the sample correlation we must first compute s_{xy}, s_x, and s_y. Some of the computations are shown in Table 3.8. Using the results in this table, we find

$$s_{xy} = \frac{\Sigma(x_i - \bar{x})(y_i - \bar{y})}{n - 1} = \frac{200}{2} = 100$$

$$s_x = \sqrt{\frac{\Sigma(x_i - \bar{x})^2}{n - 1}} = \sqrt{\frac{50}{2}} = 5$$

$$s_y = \sqrt{\frac{\Sigma(y_i - \bar{y})^2}{n - 1}} = \sqrt{\frac{800}{2}} = 20$$

$$r_{xy} = \frac{s_{xy}}{s_x s_y} = \frac{100}{5(20)} = 1$$

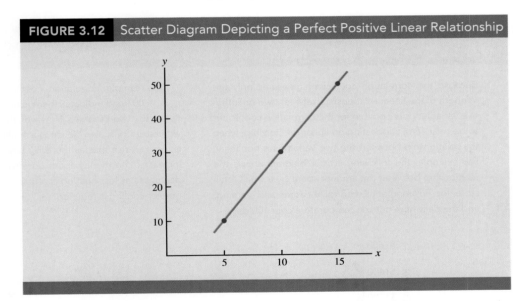

FIGURE 3.12 Scatter Diagram Depicting a Perfect Positive Linear Relationship

TABLE 3.8 Computations Used in Calculating the Sample Correlation Coefficient

	x_i	y_i	$x_i - \bar{x}$	$(x_i - \bar{x})^2$	$y_i - \bar{y}$	$(y_i - \bar{y})^2$	$(x_i - \bar{x})(y_i - \bar{y})$
	5	10	−5	25	−20	400	100
	10	30	0	0	0	0	0
	15	50	5	25	20	400	100
Totals	30	90	0	50	0	800	200

$\bar{x} = 10$ $\bar{y} = 30$

The correlation coefficient ranges from −1 to +1. Values close to −1 or +1 indicate a strong linear relationship. The closer the correlation is to zero, the weaker the relationship.

Thus, we see that the value of the sample correlation coefficient is 1.

In general, it can be shown that if all the points in a data set fall on a positively sloped straight line, the value of the sample correlation coefficient is +1; that is, a sample correlation coefficient of +1 corresponds to a perfect positive linear relationship between x and y. Moreover, if the points in the data set fall on a straight line having negative slope, the value of the sample correlation coefficient is −1; that is, a sample correlation coefficient of −1 corresponds to a perfect negative linear relationship between x and y.

Let us now suppose that a certain data set indicates a positive linear relationship between x and y but that the relationship is not perfect. The value of r_{xy} will be less than 1, indicating that the points in the scatter diagram are not all on a straight line. As the points deviate more and more from a perfect positive linear relationship, the value of r_{xy} becomes smaller and smaller. A value of r_{xy} equal to zero indicates no linear relationship between x and y, and values of r_{xy} near zero indicate a weak linear relationship.

For the data involving the San Francisco electronics store, $r_{xy} = .93$. Therefore, we conclude that a strong positive linear relationship occurs between the number of commercials and sales. More specifically, an increase in the number of commercials is associated with an increase in sales.

In closing, we note that correlation provides a measure of linear association and not necessarily causation. A high correlation between two variables does not mean that changes in one variable will cause changes in the other variable. For example, we may find that the quality rating and the typical meal price of restaurants are positively correlated. However, simply increasing the meal price at a restaurant will not cause the quality rating to increase.

NOTES + COMMENTS

1. Because the correlation coefficient measures only the strength of the linear relationship between two quantitative variables, it is possible for the correlation coefficient to be near zero, suggesting no linear relationship, when the relationship between the two variables is nonlinear. For example, the following scatter diagram shows the relationship between the amount spent by a small retail store for environmental control (heating and cooling) and the daily high outside temperature over 100 days.

The sample correlation coefficient for these data is $r_{xy} = -.007$ and indicates there is no linear relationship between the two variables. However, the scatter diagram provides strong visual evidence of a nonlinear relationship. That is, we can see that as the daily high outside temperature increases, the money spent on environmental control first decreases as less heating is required and then increases as greater cooling is required.

2. While the correlation coefficient is useful in assessing the relationship between two quantitative variables, other measures—such as the Spearman rank-correlation coefficient—can be used to assess a relationship between two variables when at least one of the variables is nominal or ordinal. We discuss the use of the Spearman rank-correlation coefficient in Chapter 18.

EXERCISES

Methods

55. Five observations taken for two variables follow.

x_i	4	6	11	3	16
y_i	50	50	40	60	30

   a. Develop a scatter diagram with x on the horizontal axis.
   b. What does the scatter diagram developed in part (a) indicate about the relationship between the two variables?
   c. Compute and interpret the sample covariance.
   d. Compute and interpret the sample correlation coefficient.

56. Five observations taken for two variables follow.

x_i	6	11	15	21	27
y_i	6	9	6	17	12

   a. Develop a scatter diagram for these data.
   b. What does the scatter diagram indicate about a relationship between x and y?
   c. Compute and interpret the sample covariance.
   d. Compute and interpret the sample correlation coefficient.

Applications

DATA *file*
StockComparison

57. **Stock Price Comparison.** The file *StockComparison* contains monthly adjusted stock prices for technology company Apple, Inc., and consumer-goods company Procter & Gamble (P&G) from 2013–2018.
   a. Develop a scatter diagram with Apple stock price on the horizontal axis and P&G stock price on the vertical axis.
   b. What appears to be the relationship between these two stock prices?
   c. Compute and interpret the sample covariance.
   d. Compute the sample correlation coefficient. What does this value indicate about the relationship between the stock price of Apple and the stock price of P&G?

58. **Driving Speed and Fuel Efficiency.** A department of transportation's study on driving speed and miles per gallon for midsize automobiles resulted in the following data:

Speed (Miles per Hour)	30	50	40	55	30	25	60	25	50	55
Miles per Gallon	28	25	25	23	30	32	21	35	26	25

Compute and interpret the sample correlation coefficient.

DATA *file*
SmokeDetectors

59. **Smoke Detector Use and Death Rates.** Over the past 40 years, the percentage of homes in the United States with smoke detectors has risen steadily and has plateaued at about 96% as of 2015 (*National Fire Protection Association* website). With this increase in the use of home smoke detectors, what has happened to the death rate from home fires? The file *SmokeDetectors* contains 17 years of data on the estimated percentage of homes with smoke detectors and the estimated home fire deaths per million of population.
   a. Do you expect a positive or negative relationship between smoke detector use and deaths from home fires? Why or why not?
   b. Compute and report the correlation coefficient. Is there a positive or negative correlation between smoke detector use and deaths from home fires? Comment.

Russell

BestPrivateColleges

c. Show a scatter plot of the death rate per million of population and the percentage of homes with smoke detectors.

60. **Stock Market Indexes Comparison.** The Russell 1000 is a stock market index consisting of the largest U.S. companies. The Dow Jones Industrial Average is based on 30 large companies. The file *Russell* gives the annual percentage returns for each of these stock indexes for the years 1988 to 2012 (1Stock1 website).
    a. Plot these percentage returns using a scatter plot.
    b. Compute the sample mean and standard deviation for each index.
    c. Compute the sample correlation.
    d. Discuss similarities and differences in these two indexes.

61. **Best Private Colleges.** A random sample of 30 colleges from Kiplinger's list of the best values in private college provided the data shown in the file *BestPrivateColleges* (Kiplinger website). The variable named Admit Rate (%) shows the percentage of students that applied to the college and were admitted, and the variable named 4-yr Grad. Rate (%) shows the percentage of students that were admitted and graduated in four years.
    a. Develop a scatter diagram with Admit Rate (%) as the independent variable. What does the scatter diagram indicate about the relationship between the two variables?
    b. Compute the sample correlation coefficient. What does the value of the sample correlation coefficient indicate about the relationship between the Admit Rate (%) and the 4-yr Grad. Rate (%)?

3.6 Data Dashboards: Adding Numerical Measures to Improve Effectiveness

In Section 2.5 we provided an introduction to data visualization, a term used to describe the use of graphical displays to summarize and present information about a data set. The goal of data visualization is to communicate key information about the data as effectively and clearly as possible. One of the most widely used data visualization tools is a data dashboard, a set of visual displays that organizes and presents information that is used to monitor the performance of a company or organization in a manner that is easy to read, understand, and interpret. In this section we extend the discussion of data dashboards to show how the addition of numerical measures can improve the overall effectiveness of the display.

The addition of numerical measures, such as the mean and standard deviation of key performance indicators (KPIs) to a data dashboard is critical because numerical measures often provide benchmarks or goals by which KPIs are evaluated. In addition, graphical displays that include numerical measures as components of the display are also frequently included in data dashboards. We must keep in mind that the purpose of a data dashboard is to provide information on the KPIs in a manner that is easy to read, understand, and interpret. Adding numerical measures and graphs that utilize numerical measures can help us accomplish these objectives.

To illustrate the use of numerical measures in a data dashboard, recall the Grogan Oil Company application that we used in Section 2.5 to introduce the concept of a data dashboard. Grogan Oil has offices located in three Texas cities: Austin (its headquarters), Houston, and Dallas. Grogan's Information Technology (IT) call center, located in the Austin office, handles calls regarding computer-related problems (software, Internet, and email) from employees in the three offices. Figure 3.13 shows the data dashboard that Grogan developed to monitor the performance of the call center. The key components of this dashboard are as follows:

- The stacked bar chart in the upper left corner of the dashboard shows the call volume for each type of problem (software, Internet, or email) over time.
- The bar chart in the upper right-hand corner of the dashboard shows the percentage of time that call center employees spent on each type of problem or were idle (not working on a call).

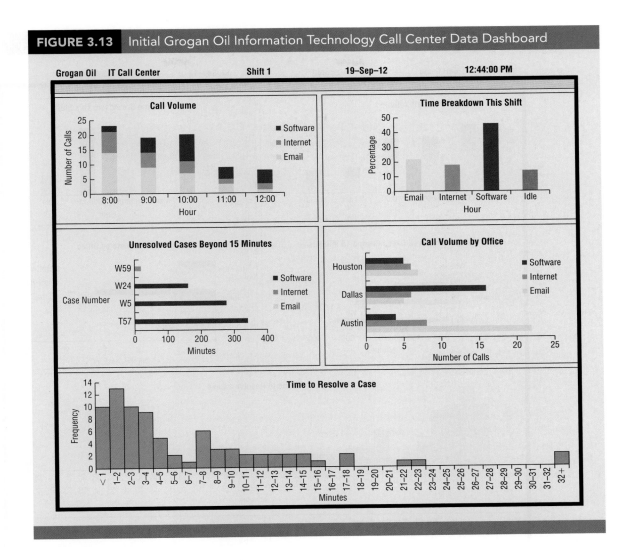

FIGURE 3.13   Initial Grogan Oil Information Technology Call Center Data Dashboard

- For each unresolved case that was received more than 15 minutes ago, the bar chart shown in the middle left portion of the dashboard shows the length of time that each of these cases has been unresolved.
- The bar chart in the middle right portion of the dashboard shows the call volume by office (Houston, Dallas, and Austin) for each type of problem.
- The histogram at the bottom of the dashboard shows the distribution of the time to resolve a case for all resolved cases for the current shift.

In order to gain additional insight into the performance of the call center, Grogan's IT manager has decided to expand the current dashboard by adding boxplots for the time required to resolve calls received for each type of problem (email, Internet, and software). In addition, a graph showing the time to resolve individual cases has been added in the lower left portion of the dashboard. Finally, the IT manager added a display of summary statistics for each type of problem and summary statistics for each of the first few hours of the shift. The updated dashboard is shown in Figure 3.14.

The IT call center has set a target performance level or benchmark of 10 minutes for the mean time to resolve a case. Furthermore, the center has decided it is undesirable for the time to resolve a case to exceed 15 minutes. To reflect these benchmarks, a black horizontal line at the mean target value of 10 minutes and a red horizontal line at the maximum acceptable level of 15 minutes have been added to both the graph showing

FIGURE 3.14   Updated Grogan Oil Information Technology Call Center Data Dashboard

Grogan Oil   IT Call Center   Shift 1   19–Sep–12   12:44:00 PM

Summary Statistics - Resolved Cases

Type of Case	Cases	Mean	Median	Std. Dev		Hour	Cases	Mean	Median	Std. Dev
Email	34	5.8	3.5	5.4		8:00	22	3.5	2.0	3.7
Internet	19	3.0	1.0	4.0		9:00	19	5.8	3.0	6.6
Software	23	5.4	4.0	5.0		10:00	19	5.3	4.0	4.8
						11:00	9	6.9	6.0	5.1
						12:00	6	4.8	3.5	3.9

the time to resolve cases and the boxplots of the time required to resolve calls received for each type of problem.

The summary statistics in the dashboard in Figure 3.21 show that the mean time to resolve an email case is 5.8 minutes, the mean time to resolve an Internet case is 3.0 minutes, and the mean time to resolve a software case is 5.4 minutes. Thus, the mean time to resolve each type of case is better than the target mean (10 minutes).

Reviewing the boxplots, we see that the box associated with the email cases is "larger" than the boxes associated with the other two types of cases. The summary statistics also show that the standard deviation of the time to resolve email cases is larger than the standard deviations of the times to resolve the other types of cases. This leads us to take a closer look at the email cases in the two new graphs. The boxplot for the email cases has a whisker that extends beyond 15 minutes and an outlier well beyond 15 minutes. The graph of the time to resolve individual cases (in the lower left position of the dashboard) shows that this is because of two calls on email cases during the 9:00 hour that took longer than the target maximum time (15 minutes) to resolve. This analysis may lead the IT call center manager to further investigate why resolution times are more variable for email cases than for Internet or software cases. Based on this analysis, the IT manager may also decide to investigate the circumstances that led to inordinately long resolution times for the two email cases that took longer than 15 minutes to resolve.

The graph of the time to resolve individual cases shows that most calls received during the first hour of the shift were resolved relatively quickly; the graph also shows that the time to resolve cases increased gradually throughout the morning. This could be due to a tendency for complex problems to arise later in the shift or possibly to the backlog of calls that accumulates over time. Although the summary statistics suggest that cases submitted during the 9:00 hour take the longest to resolve, the graph of time to resolve individual cases shows that two time-consuming email cases and one time-consuming software case were reported during that hour, and this may explain why the mean time to resolve cases during the 9:00 hour is larger than during any other hour of the shift. Overall, reported cases have generally been resolved in 15 minutes or less during this shift.

Drilling down refers to functionality in interactive data dashboards that allows the user to access information and analyses at an increasingly detailed level.

Dashboards such as the Grogan Oil data dashboard are often interactive. For instance, when a manager uses a mouse or a touch screen monitor to position the cursor over the display or point to something on the display, additional information, such as the time to resolve the problem, the time the call was received, and the individual and/or the location that reported the problem, may appear. Clicking on the individual item may also take the user to a new level of analysis at the individual case level.

S U M M A R Y

In this chapter we introduced several descriptive statistics that can be used to summarize the location, variability, and shape of a data distribution. Unlike the tabular and graphical displays introduced in Chapter 2, the measures introduced in this chapter summarize the data in terms of numerical values. When the numerical values obtained are for a sample, they are called sample statistics. When the numerical values obtained are for a population, they are called population parameters. Some of the notation used for sample statistics and population parameters follow.

In statistical inference, a sample statistic is referred to as a point estimator of the population parameter.

	Sample Statistic	Population Parameter
Mean	$\bar{x}$	μ
Variance	s^2	σ^2
Standard deviation	s	σ
Covariance	s_{xy}	σ_{xy}
Correlation	r_{xy}	ρ_{xy}

As measures of location, we defined the mean, median, mode, weighted mean, geometric mean, percentiles, and quartiles. Next, we presented the range, interquartile range, variance, standard deviation, and coefficient of variation as measures of variability or dispersion. Our primary measure of the shape of a data distribution was the skewness. Negative values of skewness indicate a data distribution skewed to the left, and positive values of skewness indicate a data distribution skewed to the right. We then described how the mean and standard deviation could be used, applying Chebyshev's theorem and the empirical rule, to provide more information about the distribution of data and to identify outliers.

In Section 3.4 we showed how to develop a five-number summary and a boxplot to provide simultaneous information about the location, variability, and shape of the distribution. In Section 3.5 we introduced covariance and the correlation coefficient as measures of association between two variables. In the final section, we showed how adding numerical measures can improve the effectiveness of data dashboards.

The descriptive statistics we discussed can be developed using statistical software packages and spreadsheets. In the chapter-ending appendixes we show how to use JMP and Excel to develop the descriptive statistics introduced in this chapter.

GLOSSARY

Boxplot A graphical summary of data based on a five-number summary.

Chebyshev's theorem A theorem that can be used to make statements about the proportion of data values that must be within a specified number of standard deviations of the mean.

Coefficient of variation A measure of relative variability computed by dividing the standard deviation by the mean and multiplying by 100.

Correlation coefficient A measure of linear association between two variables that takes on values between -1 and $+1$. Values near $+1$ indicate a strong positive linear relationship; values near -1 indicate a strong negative linear relationship; and values near zero indicate the lack of a linear relationship.

Covariance A measure of linear association between two variables. Positive values indicate a positive relationship; negative values indicate a negative relationship.

Empirical rule A rule that can be used to compute the percentage of data values that must be within one, two, and three standard deviations of the mean for data that exhibit a bell-shaped distribution.

Five-number summary A technique that uses five numbers to summarize the data: smallest value, first quartile, median, third quartile, and largest value.

Geometric mean A measure of location that is calculated by finding the nth root of the product of n values.

Growth Factor One plus the percentage increase over a period of time. A growth factor less than 1 indicates negative growth, whereas a growth factor greater than 1 indicates positive growth. The growth factor cannot be less than 0.

Interquartile range (IQR) A measure of variability, defined to be the difference between the third and first quartiles.

Mean A measure of central location computed by summing the data values and dividing by the number of observations.

Median A measure of central location provided by the value in the middle when the data are arranged in ascending order.

Mode A measure of location, defined as the value that occurs with greatest frequency.

Outlier An unusually small or unusually large data value.

Percentile A value such that at least p percent of the observations are less than or equal to this value and at least $(100 - p)$ percent of the observations are greater than or equal to this value. The 50th percentile is the median.

Point estimator A sample statistic, such as $\bar{x}$, s^2, and s, used to estimate the corresponding population parameter.

Population parameter A numerical value used as a summary measure for a population (e.g., the population mean, μ, the population variance, σ^2, and the population standard deviation, σ).

Quartiles The 25th, 50th, and 75th percentiles, referred to as the first quartile, the second quartile (median), and third quartile, respectively. The quartiles can be used to divide a data set into four parts, with each part containing approximately 25% of the data.

Range A measure of variability, defined to be the largest value minus the smallest value.

Sample statistic A numerical value used as a summary measure for a sample (e.g., the sample mean, $\bar{x}$, the sample variance, s^2, and the sample standard deviation, s).

Skewness A measure of the shape of a data distribution. Data skewed to the left result in negative skewness; a symmetric data distribution results in zero skewness; and data skewed to the right result in positive skewness.

Standard deviation A measure of variability computed by taking the positive square root of the variance.

Variance A measure of variability based on the squared deviations of the data values about the mean.

Weighted mean The mean obtained by assigning each observation a weight that reflects its importance.

z-score A value computed by dividing the deviation about the mean ($x_i - \bar{x}$) by the standard deviation s. A z-score is referred to as a standardized value and denotes the number of standard deviations x_i is from the mean.

KEY FORMULAS

Sample Mean

$$\bar{x} = \frac{\Sigma x_i}{n} \tag{3.1}$$

Population Mean

$$\mu = \frac{\Sigma x_i}{N} \tag{3.2}$$

Weighted Mean

$$\bar{x} = \frac{\Sigma w_i x_i}{\Sigma w_i} \tag{3.3}$$

Geometric Mean

$$\bar{x}_g = \sqrt[n]{(x_1)(x_2) \cdots (x_n)} = [(x_1)(x_2) \cdots (x_n)]^{1/n} \tag{3.4}$$

Location of the pth Percentile

$$L_p = \frac{p}{100}(n + 1) \tag{3.5}$$

Interquartile Range

$$\text{IQR} = Q_3 - Q_1 \tag{3.6}$$

Population Variance

$$\sigma^2 = \frac{\Sigma(x_i - \mu)^2}{N} \tag{3.7}$$

Sample Variance

$$s^2 = \frac{\Sigma(x_i - \bar{x})^2}{n - 1} \tag{3.8}$$

Standard Deviation

$$\text{Sample standard deviation} = s = \sqrt{s^2} \qquad (3.9)$$

$$\text{Population standard deviation} = \sigma = \sqrt{\sigma^2} \qquad (3.10)$$

Coefficient of Variation

$$\left(\frac{\text{Standard deviation}}{\text{Mean}} \times 100\right)\% \qquad (3.11)$$

z-Score

$$z_i = \frac{x_i - \bar{x}}{s} \qquad (3.12)$$

Sample Covariance

$$s_{xy} = \frac{\Sigma(x_i - \bar{x})(y_i - \bar{y})}{n - 1} \qquad (3.13)$$

Population Covariance

$$\sigma_{xy} = \frac{\Sigma(x_i - \mu_x)(y_i - \mu_y)}{N} \qquad (3.14)$$

Pearson Product Moment Correlation Coefficient: Sample Data

$$r_{xy} = \frac{s_{xy}}{s_x s_y} \qquad (3.15)$$

Pearson Product Moment Correlation Coefficient: Population Data

$$\rho_{xy} = \frac{\sigma_{xy}}{\sigma_x \sigma_y} \qquad (3.16)$$

SUPPLEMENTARY EXERCISES

62. **Americans Dining Out.** Americans tend to dine out multiple times per week. The number of times a sample of 20 families dined out last week provides the following data.

6	1	5	3	7	3	0	3	1	3
4	1	2	4	1	0	5	6	3	1

    a. Compute the mean and median.
    b. Compute the first and third quartiles.
    c. Compute the range and interquartile range.
    d. Compute the variance and standard deviation.
    e. The skewness measure for these data is .34. Comment on the shape of this distribution. Is it the shape you would expect? Why or why not?
    f. Do the data contain outliers?

Coaches

63. **NCAA Football Coaches Salaries.** A 2017 *USA Today* article reports that NCAA football coaches' salaries have continued to increase in recent years (*USA Today*). The annual base salaries for the previous head football coach and the new head football coach at 23 schools are given in the file *Coaches*.

    a. Determine the median annual salary for a previous head football coach and a new head football coach.
    b. Compute the range for salaries for both previous and new head football coaches.
    c. Compute the standard deviation for salaries for both previous and new head football coaches.
    d. Based on your answers to (a) to (c), comment on any differences between the annual base salary a school pays a new head football coach compared to what it paid its previous head football coach.

64. **Physician Office Waiting Times.** The average waiting time for a patient at an El Paso physician's office is just over 29 minutes, well above the national average of 21 minutes. In order to address the issue of long patient wait times, some physician's offices are using wait tracking systems to notify patients of expected wait times. Patients can adjust their arrival times based on this information and spend less time in waiting rooms. The following data show wait times (minutes) for a sample of patients at offices that do not have an office tracking system and wait times for a sample of patients at offices with an office tracking system.

DATA *file*
WaitTracking

Without Wait Tracking System	With Wait Tracking System
24	31
67	11
17	14
20	18
31	12
44	37
12	9
23	13
16	12
37	15

a. What are the mean and median patient wait times for offices with a wait tracking system? What are the mean and median patient wait times for offices without a wait tracking system?
b. What are the variance and standard deviation of patient wait times for offices with a wait tracking system? What are the variance and standard deviation of patient wait times for visits to offices without a wait tracking system?
c. Do offices with a wait tracking system have shorter patient wait times than offices without a wait tracking system? Explain.
d. Considering only offices without a wait tracking system, what is the z-score for the tenth patient in the sample?
e. Considering only offices with a wait tracking system, what is the z-score for the sixth patient in the sample? How does this z-score compare with the z-score you calculated for part (d)?
f. Based on z-scores, do the data for offices without a wait tracking system contain any outliers? Based on z-scores, do the data for offices with a wait tracking system contain any outliers?

DATA *file*
Sleep

65. **Worker Productivity and Insomnia.** U.S. companies lose $63.2 billion per year from workers with insomnia. Accordign to a 2013 article in the *Wall Street Journal*, workers lose an average of 7.8 days of productivity per year due to lack of sleep. The following data show the number of hours of sleep attained during a recent night for a sample of 20 workers.

6	5	10	5	6	9	9	5	9	5
8	7	8	6	9	8	9	6	10	8

a. What is the mean number of hours of sleep for this sample?
b. What is the variance? Standard deviation?

DATA *file*
Smartphone

66. **Smartphone Use.** Smartphones have become ubiquitous for most people and have become the predominant means of communication among people. Consider the following data indicating the number of minutes in a month spent interacting with others via a smartphone for a sample of 50 smartphone users.

353	458	404	394	416
437	430	369	448	430
431	469	446	387	445
354	468	422	402	360
444	424	441	357	435
461	407	470	413	351
464	374	417	460	352
445	387	468	368	430
384	367	436	390	464
405	372	401	388	367

a. What is the mean number of minutes spent interacting with others for this sample? How does it compare to the mean reported in the study?

b. What is the standard deviation for this sample?

c. Are there any outliers in this sample?

67. **Work Commuting Methods.** Public transportation and the automobile are two methods an employee can use to get to work each day. Samples of times recorded for each method are shown. Times are in minutes.

Transportation

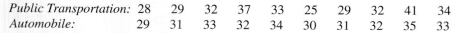

Public Transportation:	28	29	32	37	33	25	29	32	41	34
Automobile:		29	31	33	32	34	30	31	32	35	33

a. Compute the sample mean time to get to work for each method.

b. Compute the sample standard deviation for each method.

c. On the basis of your results from parts (a) and (b), which method of transportation should be preferred? Explain.

d. Develop a boxplot for each method. Does a comparison of the boxplots support your conclusion in part (c)?

68. **Household Incomes.** The following data represent a sample of 14 household incomes ($1000s). Answer the following questions based on this sample.

49.4	52.4	53.4	51.3	52.1	48.7	52.1
52.2	64.5	51.6	46.5	52.9	52.5	51.2

a. What is the median household income for these sample data?

b. According to a previous survey, the median annual household income five years ago was $55,000. Based on the sample data above, estimate the percentage change in the median household income from five years ago to today.

c. Compute the first and third quartiles.

d. Provide a five-number summary.

e. Using the z-score approach, do the data contain any outliers? Does the approach that uses the values of the first and third quartiles and the interquartile range to detect outliers provide the same results?

69. **Restaurant Chains' Sales per Store.** The data contained in the file *FoodIndustry* show the company/chain name, the average sales per store ($1000s), and the food segment industry for 47 restaurant chains (*Quick Service Restaurant Magazine* website).

FoodIndustry

a. What was the mean U.S. sales per store for the 47 restaurant chains?

b. What are the first and third quartiles? What is your interpretation of the quartiles?

c. Show a boxplot for the level of sales and discuss if there are any outliers in terms of sales that would skew the results.

d. Develop a frequency distribution showing the average sales per store for each segment. Comment on the results obtained.

70. **Best Hotels.** *Travel + Leisure* magazine provides an annual list of the 500 best hotels in the world. The magazine provides a rating for each hotel along with a brief description that includes the size of the hotel, amenities, and the cost per night for a double room. A sample of 12 of the top-rated hotels in the United States follows.

Hotel	Location	Rooms	Cost/Night
Boulders Resort & Spa	Phoenix, AZ	220	499
Disney's Wilderness Lodge	Orlando, FL	727	340
Four Seasons Hotel Beverly Hills	Los Angeles, CA	285	585
Four Seasons Hotel	Boston, MA	273	495
Hay-Adams	Washington, DC	145	495
Inn on Biltmore Estate	Asheville, NC	213	279
Loews Ventana Canyon Resort	Phoenix, AZ	398	279
Mauna Lani Bay Hotel	Island of Hawaii	343	455
Montage Laguna Beach	Laguna Beach, CA	250	595
Sofitel Water Tower	Chicago, IL	414	367
St. Regis Monarch Beach	Dana Point, CA	400	675
The Broadmoor	Colorado Springs, CO	700	420

DATA *file*

Travel

a. What is the mean number of rooms?
b. What is the mean cost per night for a double room?
c. Develop a scatter diagram with the number of rooms on the horizontal axis and the cost per night on the vertical axis. Does there appear to be a relationship between the number of rooms and the cost per night? Discuss.
d. What is the sample correlation coefficient? What does it tell you about the relationship between the number of rooms and the cost per night for a double room? Does this appear reasonable? Discuss.

71. **NFL Teams Worth.** In 2014, the 32 teams in the National Football League (NFL) were worth, on average, $1.17 billion, 5% more than in 2013. The following data show the annual revenue ($ millions) and the estimated team value ($ millions) for the 32 NFL teams in 2014 (*Forbes* website).

Team	Revenue ($ millions)	Current Value ($ millions)
Arizona Cardinals	253	961
Atlanta Falcons	252	933
Baltimore Ravens	292	1227
Buffalo Bills	256	870
Carolina Panthers	271	1057
Chicago Bears	298	1252
Cincinnati Bengals	250	924
Cleveland Browns	264	1005
Dallas Cowboys	539	2300
Denver Broncos	283	1161
Detroit Lions	248	900
Green Bay Packers	282	1183
Houston Texans	320	1450
Indianapolis Colts	276	1200
Jacksonville Jaguars	260	840
Kansas City Chiefs	245	1009
Miami Dolphins	268	1074
Minnesota Vikings	234	1007
New England Patriots	408	1800
New Orleans Saints	276	1004
New York Giants	338	1550
New York Jets	321	1380
Oakland Raiders	229	825
Philadelphia Eagles	306	1314
Pittsburgh Steelers	266	1118

DATA *file*

NFLTeamValue

(continued)

Team	Revenue ($ millions)	Current Value ($ millions)
San Diego Chargers	250	949
San Francisco 49ers	255	1224
Seattle Seahawks	270	1081
St. Louis Rams	239	875
Tampa Bay Buccaneers	267	1067
Tennessee Titans	270	1055
Washington Redskins	381	1700

a. Develop a scatter diagram with Revenue on the horizontal axis and Value on the vertical axis. Does there appear that there is any relationship between the two variables?

b. What is the sample correlation coefficient? What can you say about the strength of the relationship between Revenue and Value?

72. **MLB Team Winning Percentages.** Does a major league baseball team's record during spring training indicate how the team will play during the regular season? Over a six-year period, the correlation coefficient between a team's winning percentage in spring training and its winning percentage in the regular season is .18. Shown are the winning percentages for the 14 American League teams during a previous season.

DATAfile
SpringTraining

Team	Spring Training	Regular Season	Team	Spring Training	Regular Season
Baltimore Orioles	.407	.422	Minnesota Twins	.500	.540
Boston Red Sox	.429	.586	New York Yankees	.577	.549
Chicago White Sox	.417	.546	Oakland A's	.692	.466
Cleveland Indians	.569	.500	Seattle Mariners	.500	.377
Detroit Tigers	.569	.457	Tampa Bay Rays	.731	.599
Kansas City Royals	.533	.463	Texas Rangers	.643	.488
Los Angeles Angels	.724	.617	Toronto Blue Jays	.448	.531

a. What is the correlation coefficient between the spring training and the regular season winning percentages?

b. What is your conclusion about a team's record during spring training indicating how the team will play during the regular season? What are some of the reasons why this occurs? Discuss.

73. **Money Market Funds Days to Maturity.** The days to maturity for a sample of five money market funds are shown here. The dollar amounts invested in the funds are provided. Use the weighted mean to determine the mean number of days to maturity for dollars invested in these five money market funds.

Days to Maturity	Dollar Value ($ millions)
20	20
12	30
7	10
5	15
6	10

74. **Automobile Speeds.** Automobiles traveling on a road with a posted speed limit of 55 miles per hour are checked for speed by a state police radar system. Following is a frequency distribution of speeds.

Speed (miles per hour)	Frequency
45–49	10
50–54	40
55–59	150
60–64	175
65–69	75
70–74	15
75–79	10
Total	475

a. What is the mean speed of the automobiles traveling on this road?
b. Compute the variance and the standard deviation.

75. **Annual Returns for Panama Railroad Company Stock.** The Panama Railroad Company was established in 1850 to construct a railroad across the isthmus that would allow fast and easy access between the Atlantic and Pacific Oceans. The following table provides annual returns for Panama Railroad stock from 1853 through 1880.

DATAfile
PanamaRailroad

Year	Return on Panama Railroad Company Stock (%)
1853	−1
1854	−9
1855	19
1856	2
1857	3
1858	36
1859	21
1860	16
1861	−5
1862	43
1863	44
1864	48
1865	7
1866	11
1867	23
1868	20
1869	−11
1870	−51
1871	−42
1872	39
1873	42
1874	12
1875	26
1876	9
1877	−6
1878	25
1879	31
1880	30

a. Create a graph of the annual returns on the stock. The New York Stock Exchange earned an annual average return of 8.4% from 1853 through 1880. Can you tell from the graph if the Panama Railroad Company stock outperformed the New York Stock Exchange?

b. Calculate the mean annual return on Panama Railroad Company stock from 1853 through 1880. Did the stock outperform the New York Stock Exchange over the same period?

CASE PROBLEM 1: PELICAN STORES

Pelican Stores, a division of National Clothing, is a chain of women's apparel stores operating throughout the country. The chain recently ran a promotion in which discount coupons were sent to customers of other National Clothing stores. Data collected for a sample of 100 in-store credit card transactions at Pelican Stores during one day while the promotion was running are contained in the file named PelicanStores. Table 3.9 shows a portion of the data set. The proprietary card method of payment refers to charges made using a National Clothing charge card. Customers who made a purchase using a discount coupon are referred to as promotional customers and customers who made a purchase but did not use a discount coupon are referred to as regular customers. Because the promotional coupons were not sent to regular Pelican Stores customers, management considers the sales made to people presenting the promotional coupons as sales it would not otherwise make. Of course, Pelican also hopes that the promotional customers will continue to shop at its stores.

Most of the variables shown in Table 3.9 are self-explanatory, but two of the variables require some clarification.

Items   The total number of items purchased
Net Sales   The total amount ($) charged to the credit card

PelicanStores

TABLE 3.9   Sample of 100 Credit Card Purchases at Pelican Stores

Customer	Type of Customer	Items	Net Sales	Method of Payment	Gender	Marital Status	Age
1	Regular	1	39.50	Discover	Male	Married	32
2	Promotional	1	102.40	Proprietary Card	Female	Married	36
3	Regular	1	22.50	Proprietary Card	Female	Married	32
4	Promotional	5	100.40	Proprietary Card	Female	Married	28
5	Regular	2	54.00	MasterCard	Female	Married	34
6	Regular	1	44.50	MasterCard	Female	Married	44
7	Promotional	2	78.00	Proprietary Card	Female	Married	30
8	Regular	1	22.50	Visa	Female	Married	40
9	Promotional	2	56.52	Proprietary Card	Female	Married	46
10	Regular	1	44.50	Proprietary Card	Female	Married	36
.	.	.	.	.	.	.	.
.	.	.	.	.	.	.	.
96	Regular	1	39.50	MasterCard	Female	Married	44
97	Promotional	9	253.00	Proprietary Card	Female	Married	30
98	Promotional	10	287.59	Proprietary Card	Female	Married	52
99	Promotional	2	47.60	Proprietary Card	Female	Married	30
100	Promotional	1	28.44	Proprietary Card	Female	Married	44

Pelican's management would like to use this sample data to learn about its customer base and to evaluate the promotion involving discount coupons.

Managerial Report

Use the methods of descriptive statistics presented in this chapter to summarize the data and comment on your findings. At a minimum, your report should include the following:

1. Descriptive statistics on net sales and descriptive statistics on net sales by various classifications of customers.
2. Descriptive statistics concerning the relationship between age and net sales.

CASE PROBLEM 2: MOVIE THEATER RELEASES

The movie industry is a competitive business. More than 50 studios produce hundreds of new movies for theater release each year, and the financial success of each movie varies considerably. The opening weekend gross sales ($ millions), the total gross sales ($ millions), the number of theaters the movie was shown in, and the number of weeks the movie was in release are common variables used to measure the success of a movie. Data on the top 100 grossing movies released in 2016 (Box Office Mojo website) are contained in the file *Movies2016*. Table 3.10 shows the data for the first 10 movies in this file.

Managerial Report

Use the numerical methods of descriptive statistics presented in this chapter to learn how these variables contribute to the success of a movie. Include the following in your report:

1. Descriptive statistics for each of the four variables along with a discussion of what the descriptive statistics tell us about the movie industry.
2. What movies, if any, should be considered high-performance outliers? Explain.
3. Descriptive statistics showing the relationship between total gross sales and each of the other variables. Discuss.

DATA *file*

Movies2016

TABLE 3.10	Performance Data for Ten 2016 Movies Released to Theaters			
Movie Title	**Opening Gross Sales ($ Million)**	**Total Gross Sales ($ Million)**	**Number of Theaters**	**Weeks in Release**
Rogue One: A Star Wars Story	155.08	532.18	4,157	20
Finding Dory	135.06	486.30	4,305	25
Captain America: Civil War	179.14	408.08	4,226	20
The Secret Life of Pets	104.35	368.38	4,381	25
The Jungle Book	103.26	364.00	4,144	24
Deadpool	132.43	363.07	3,856	18
Zootopia	75.06	341.27	3,959	22
Batman v Superman: Dawn of Justice	166.01	330.36	4,256	12
Suicide Squad	133.68	325.10	4,255	14
Sing	35.26	270.40	4,029	20

CASE PROBLEM 3: BUSINESS SCHOOLS OF ASIA-PACIFIC

The pursuit of a higher education degree in business is now international. A survey shows that more and more Asians choose the master of business administration (MBA) degree route to corporate success. As a result, the number of applicants for MBA courses at Asia-Pacific schools continues to increase.

Across the region, thousands of Asians show an increasing willingness to temporarily shelve their careers and spend two years in pursuit of a theoretical business qualification. Courses in these schools are notoriously tough and include economics, banking, marketing, behavioral sciences, labor relations, decision making, strategic thinking, business law, and more. The data set in Table 3.11 shows some of the characteristics of the leading Asia-Pacific business schools.

Managerial Report

Use the methods of descriptive statistics to summarize the data in Table 3.11. Discuss your findings.

1. Include a summary for each variable in the data set. Make comments and interpretations based on maximums and minimums, as well as the appropriate means and proportions. What new insights do these descriptive statistics provide concerning Asia-Pacific business schools?
2. Summarize the data to compare the following:
   a. Any difference between local and foreign tuition costs.
   b. Any difference between mean starting salaries for schools requiring and not requiring work experience.
   c. Any difference between starting salaries for schools requiring and not requiring English tests.
3. Do starting salaries appear to be related to tuition?
4. Present any additional graphical and numerical summaries that will be beneficial in communicating the data in Table 3.11 to others.

CASE PROBLEM 4: HEAVENLY CHOCOLATES WEBSITE TRANSACTIONS

Heavenly Chocolates manufactures and sells quality chocolate products at its plant and retail store located in Saratoga Springs, New York. Two years ago the company developed a website and began selling its products over the Internet. Website sales have exceeded the company's expectations, and management is now considering strategies to increase sales even further. To learn more about the website customers, a sample of 50 Heavenly Chocolate transactions was selected from the previous month's sales. Data showing the day of the week each transaction was made, the type of browser the customer used, the time spent on the website, the number of website pages viewed, and the amount spent by each of the 50 customers are contained in the file *HeavenlyChocolates*. A portion of the data are shown in Table 3.12.

Heavenly Chocolates would like to use the sample data to determine if online shoppers who spend more time and view more pages also spend more money during their visit to the website. The company would also like to investigate the effect that the day of the week and the type of browser have on sales.

Managerial Report

Use the methods of descriptive statistics to learn about the customers who visit the Heavenly Chocolates website. Include the following in your report.

1. Graphical and numerical summaries for the length of time the shopper spends on the website, the number of pages viewed, and the mean amount spent per transaction.

TABLE 3.11 Data for 25 Asia-Pacific Business Schools

Business School ww	Full-Time Enrollment	Students per Faculty	Local Tuition ($)	Foreign Tuition ($)	Age	%Foreign	GMAT	English Test	Work Experience	Starting Salary ($)
Melbourne Business School	200	5	24,420	29,600	28	47	Yes	No	Yes	71,400
University of New South Wales (Sydney)	228	4	19,993	32,582	29	28	Yes	No	Yes	65,200
Indian Institute of Management (Ahmedabad)	392	5	4,300	4,300	22	0	No	No	No	7,100
Chinese University of Hong Kong	90	5	11,140	11,140	29	10	Yes	No	No	31,000
International University of Japan (Niigata)	126	4	33,060	33,060	28	60	Yes	Yes	No	87,000
Asian Institute of Management (Manila)	389	5	7,562	9,000	25	50	Yes	No	Yes	22,800
Indian Institute of Management (Bangalore)	380	5	3,935	16,000	23	1	Yes	No	No	7,500
National University of Singapore	147	6	6,146	7,170	29	51	Yes	Yes	Yes	43,300
Indian Institute of Management (Calcutta)	463	8	2,880	16,000	23	0	No	No	No	7,400
Australian National University (Canberra)	42	2	20,300	20,300	30	80	Yes	Yes	Yes	46,600
Nanyang Technological University (Singapore)	50	5	8,500	8,500	32	20	Yes	No	Yes	49,300
University of Queensland (Brisbane)	138	17	16,000	22,800	32	26	No	No	Yes	49,600
Hong Kong University of Science and Technology	60	2	11,513	11,513	26	37	Yes	No	Yes	34,000
Macquarie Graduate School of Management (Sydney)	12	8	17,172	19,778	34	27	No	No	Yes	60,100
Chulalongkorn University (Bangkok)	200	7	17,355	17,355	25	6	Yes	No	Yes	17,600
Monash Mt. Eliza Business School (Melbourne)	350	13	16,200	22,500	30	30	Yes	Yes	Yes	52,500
Asian Institute of Management (Bangkok)	300	10	18,200	18,200	29	90	No	Yes	Yes	25,000
University of Adelaide	20	19	16,426	23,100	30	10	No	No	Yes	66,000
Massey University (Palmerston North, New Zealand)	30	15	13,106	21,625	37	35	No	Yes	Yes	41,400
Royal Melbourne Institute of Technology Business Graduate School	30	7	13,880	17,765	32	30	No	Yes	Yes	48,900
Jamnalal Bajaj Institute of Management Studies (Mumbai)	240	9	1,000	1,000	24	0	No	No	Yes	7,000
Curtin Institute of Technology (Perth)	98	15	9,475	19,097	29	43	Yes	No	Yes	55,000
Lahore University of Management Sciences	70	14	11,250	26,300	23	2.5	No	No	No	7,500
Universiti Sains Malaysia (Penang)	30	5	2,260	2,260	32	15	No	Yes	Yes	16,000
De La Salle University (Manila)	44	17	3,300	3,600	28	3.5	Yes	No	Yes	13,100

| TABLE 3.12 | A Sample of 50 Heavenly Chocolates Website Transactions |

Customer	Day	Browser	Time (min)	Pages Viewed	Amount Spent ($)
1	Mon	Chrome	12.0	4	54.52
2	Wed	Other	19.5	6	94.90
3	Mon	Chrome	8.5	4	26.68
4	Tue	Firefox	11.4	2	44.73
5	Wed	Chrome	11.3	4	66.27
6	Sat	Firefox	10.5	6	67.80
7	Sun	Chrome	11.4	2	36.04
.	.	.	.	.	.
.	.	.	.	.	.
.	.	.	.	.	.
48	Fri	Chrome	9.7	5	103.15
49	Mon	Other	7.3	6	52.15
50	Fri	Chrome	13.4	3	98.75

DATA*file*

HeavenlyChocolates

Discuss what you learn about Heavenly Chocolates' online shoppers from these numerical summaries.

2. Summarize the frequency, the total dollars spent, and the mean amount spent per transaction for each day of week. What observations can you make about Heavenly Chocolates' business based on the day of the week?

3. Summarize the frequency, the total dollars spent, and the mean amount spent per transaction for each type of browser. What observations can you make about Heavenly Chocolate's business based on the type of browser?

4. Develop a scatter diagram and compute the sample correlation coefficient to explore the relationship between the time spent on the website and the dollar amount spent. Use the horizontal axis for the time spent on the website. Discuss your findings.

5. Develop a scatter diagram and compute the sample correlation coefficient to explore the relationship between the number of website pages viewed and the amount spent. Use the horizontal axis for the number of website pages viewed. Discuss your findings.

6. Develop a scatter diagram and compute the sample correlation coefficient to explore the relationship between the time spent on the website and the number of pages viewed. Use the horizontal axis to represent the number of pages viewed. Discuss your findings.

CASE PROBLEM 5: AFRICAN ELEPHANT POPULATIONS

Although millions of elephants once roamed across Africa, by the mid-1980s elephant populations in African nations had been devastated by poaching. Elephants are important to African ecosystems. In tropical forests, elephants create clearings in the canopy that encourage new tree growth. In savannas, elephants reduce bush cover to create an environment that is favorable to browsing and grazing animals. In addition, the seeds of many plant species depend on passing through an elephant's digestive tract before germination.

The status of the elephant now varies greatly across the continent. In some nations, strong measures have been taken to effectively protect elephant populations; for example, Kenya has destroyed over five tons of elephant ivory confiscated from poachers in an attempt to deter the growth of illegal ivory trade (Associated Press, July 20, 2011). In other nations the elephant populations remain in danger due to poaching for meat and ivory, loss of habitat,

TABLE 3.13	Elephant Populations for Several African Nations in 1979, 1989, 2007, and 2012

Elephant Population

Country	1979	1989	2007	2012
Angola	12,400	12,400	2,530	2,530
Botswana	20,000	51,000	175,487	175,454
Cameroon	16,200	21,200	15,387	14,049
Cen African Rep	63,000	19,000	3,334	2,285
Chad	15,000	3,100	6,435	3,004
Congo	10,800	70,000	22,102	49,248
Dem Rep of Congo	377,700	85,000	23,714	13,674
Gabon	13,400	76,000	70,637	77,252
Kenya	65,000	19,000	31,636	36,260
Mozambique	54,800	18,600	26,088	26,513
Somalia	24,300	6,000	70	70
Tanzania	316,300	80,000	167,003	117,456
Zambia	150,000	41,000	29,231	21,589
Zimbabwe	30,000	43,000	99,107	100,291

DATA*file*

AfricanElephants

and conflict with humans. Table 3.13 shows elephant populations for several African nations in 1979, 1989, 2007, and 2012 (ElephantDatabase.org website).

The David Sheldrick Wildlife Trust was established in 1977 to honor the memory of naturalist David Leslie William Sheldrick, who founded Warden of Tsavo East National Park in Kenya and headed the Planning Unit of the Wildlife Conservation and Management Department in that country. Management of the Sheldrick Trust would like to know what these data indicate about elephant populations in various African countries since 1979.

Managerial Report

Use methods of descriptive statistics to summarize the data and comment on changes in elephant populations in African nations since 1979. At a minimum your report should include the following.

1. The mean annual change in elephant population for each country in the 10 years from 1979 to 1989, and a discussion of which countries saw the largest changes in elephant population over this 10-year period.
2. The mean annual change in elephant population for each country from 1989 to 2007, and a discussion of which countries saw the largest changes in elephant population over this 18-year period.
3. The mean annual change in elephant population for each country from 2007 to 2012, and a discussion of which countries saw the largest changes in elephant population over this 5-year period.
4. A comparison of your results from parts 1, 2, and 3, and a discussion of the conclusions you can draw from this comparison.

Chapter 3 Appendix

Appendix 3.1 Descriptive Statistics with JMP

In this appendix we describe how JMP can be used to compute a variety of descriptive statistics and display box plots. We then show how JMP can be used to obtain covariance and correlation measures for two variables.

Descriptive Statistics

Table 3.1 provides the starting monthly salaries for the 12 business school graduates. These data are in the file *StartingSalaries*. The following steps can be used to generate descriptive statistics for the starting salary data.

DATA *file*

StartingSalaries

Step 1. Open the file *StartingSalaries* with JMP using the steps provided in Appendix 1.1

Step 2. From the **Data** window containing the starting salaries data, click **Analyze** and select **Distribution**

Step 3. When the **Distribution** window appears:
Drag **Monthly Starting Salary ($)** from the **Select Columns** area to the **Y, Columns** box in the **Cast Selected Columns into Roles** area
Click **OK** in the **Action** area

These steps produce the JMP output shown in Figure JMP 3.1. On the left of Figure JMP 3.1 is the histogram and box plot for the monthly starting salaries data. On the right is a table of summary statistics that includes the mean and standard deviation. In

FIGURE JMP 3.1 Descriptive Statistics Created in JMP for the Starting Salaries Data

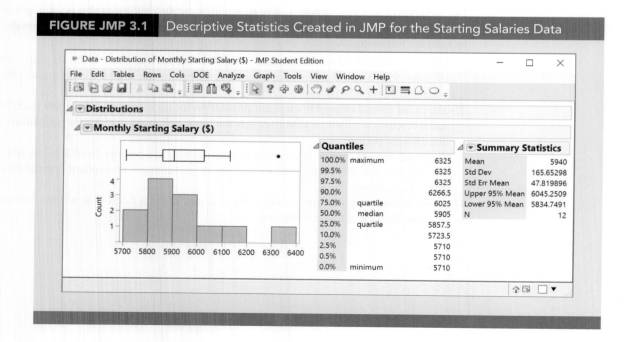

FIGURE JMP 3.2   Descriptive Statistics Including Mode Created in JMP for the Starting Salaries Data

The interpretation and use of the standard error of the mean are discussed in Chapter 7 when we introduce the topics of sampling and sampling distributions.

the middle of Figure JMP 3.1 we see a table labeled "Quantiles" that shows the percentiles and quartiles of the data as well as the median.

Note that the summary statistics provided by JMP also includes the "Std Err Mean," which refers to the *standard error of the mean*. This value is computed by dividing the standard deviation by the square root of the number of data values.

JMP can also calculate the modes for a data set. To add this to the output, click the red triangle ▼ next to **Summary Statistics** and choose **Show All Modes.** This will add the information shown in Figure JMP 3.2 under **All Modes.** This output indicates that the mode for these data is 5880 and that this value occurs twice in the data set.

Box Plots

We see in Figure JMP 3.1 that JMP creates a box plot automatically as part of its distribution analysis. This is quite useful when examining a single variable. However, JMP can also be used to create comparative box plots. We will use the data from the file *MajorSalaries* to illustrate how this is done using the following steps.

MajorSalaries

Step 1. Open the file *MajorSalaries* with JMP using the steps provided in Appendix 1.1

Step 2. From the **Data** window containing the salary data by major:
Click **Graph** and select **Graph Builder**

Step 3. When the **Data—Graph Builder** window appears:
Click the **Boxplots** ▯▯▯ icon at the top of the window
Drag **Major** from the **Variables** area to the **Group X** box
Drag **Monthly Starting Salary ($)** from the **Variables** area to the **Y** box

These steps produce the comparative box plots shown in Figure JMP 3.3. These box plots match those shown in Figure 3.8.

FIGURE JMP 3.3   Comparative Box Plots Created in JMP for the Starting Salaries by Major Data

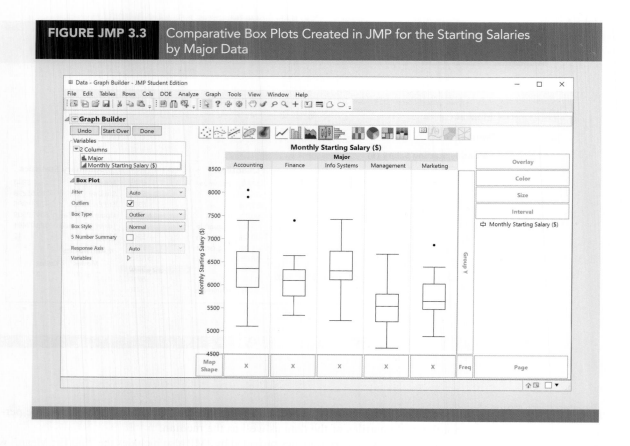

Covariance and Correlation

Table 3.6 provided the number of commercials and the sales volume for an electronics store in San Francisco. These data are in the file *Electronics*. The following steps show how JMP can be used to compute the covariance and correlation of the variables number of commercials and sales volume.

DATA *file*

Electronics

Step 1. Open the file *Electronics* with JMP using the steps provided in Appendix 1.1

Step 2. From the **Data** window containing the San Francisco electronics store data:
Click **Analyze** and select **Fit Y by X**

Step 3. When the **Fit Y by X—Contextual** window appears:
Drag **No. of Commercials** from the **Select Columns** area to the **X, Factor** box
Drag **Sales Volume** from the **Select Columns** area to the **Y, Response** box
Click **OK** in the **Action** area

Step 4. When the **Data—Fit Y by X of Sales Volume by No. of Commercials** window appears:
Click the red triangle next to **Bivariate Fit of Sales Volume By No. of Commercials** and select **Summary Statistics**

These steps produce the output shown in Figure JMP 3.4. The values in the Summary Statistics table contain both the covariance and the correlation values. From Figure JMP 3.4 we see that the covariance is 11 and the correlation is .930491. These values match those found in Section 3.5 for the San Francisco electronics store data.

FIGURE JMP 3.4   Covariance and Correlation Values Calculated in JMP for the San Fran-cisco Electronics Store Data

Appendix 3.2 Descriptive Statistics with Excel

Excel can be used to generate the descriptive statistics discussed in this chapter. We show how Excel can be used to generate several measures of location and variability for a single variable and to generate the covariance and correlation coefficient as measures of associa-tion between two variables.

Using Excel Functions

DATA*file*

StartingSalaries

Excel provides functions for computing the mean, median, mode, sample variance, and sample standard deviation. We illustrate the use of these Excel functions by computing the mean, median, mode, sample variance, and sample standard deviation for the starting salary data in Table 3.1 using the file *StartingSalaries*. Refer to Figure Excel 3.1 as we describe the steps involved.

Excel's AVERAGE function can be used to compute the mean by entering the following formula into cell E1:

$$=AVERAGE(B2:B13)$$

FIGURE Excel 3.1 Using Excel Functions for Computing the Mean, Median, Mode, Variance, and Standard Deviation

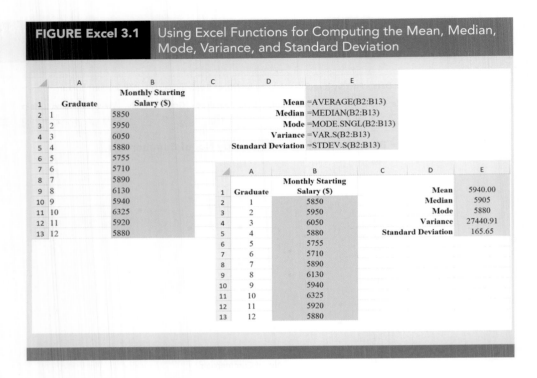

To find the variance, standard deviation, and covariance for population data, follow the same steps but use the VAR.P, STDEV.P, and COV.P functions.

Similarly, the formulas =MEDIAN(B2:B13), =MODE.SNGL(B2:B13), =VAR.S(B2:B13), and =STDEV.S(B2:B13) are entered into cells E2:E5, respectively, to compute the median, mode, variance, and standard deviation for this sample. The worksheet in the foreground shows that the values computed using the Excel functions are the same as we computed earlier in the chapter.

Excel also provides functions that can be used to compute the sample covariance and the sample correlation coefficient. We show here how these functions can be used to compute the sample covariance and the sample correlation coefficient for the stereo and sound equipment store data in Table 3.6. Refer to Figure Excel 3.2 as we present the steps involved.

Excel's sample covariance function, COVARIANCE.S, can be used to compute the sample covariance by entering the following formula into cell F1:

DATA *file*

Electronics

$$=\text{COVARIANCE.S(B2:B11,C2:C11)}$$

FIGURE Excel 3.2 Using Excel Functions for Computing the Covariance and Correlation

	A	B	C	D	E	F	G
1	Week	Commercials	Sales Volume		Sample Covariance	=COVARIANCE.S(B2:B11,C2:C11)	
2	1	2	50		Sample Correlation	=CORREL(B2:B11,C2:C11)	
3	2	5	57				
4	3	1	41				
5	4	3	54				
6	5	4	54				
7	6	1	38				
8	7	5	63				
9	8	3	48				
10	9	4	59				
11	10	2	46				
12							

	A	B	C	D	E	F	G
1	Week	Commercials	Sales Volume		Sample Covariance	11	
2	1	2	50		Sample Correlation	0.9305	
3	2	5	57				
4	3	1	41				
5	4	3	54				
6	5	4	54				
7	6	1	38				
8	7	5	63				
9	8	3	48				
10	9	4	59				
11	10	2	46				
12							

Similarly, the formula =CORREL(B2:B11,C2:C11) is entered into cell F2 to compute the sample correlation coefficient. The worksheet in the foreground shows the values computed using the Excel functions. Note that the value of the sample covariance (11) is the same as computed using equation (3.13). And the value of the sample correlation coefficient (.93) is the same as computed using equation (3.15).

Using Excel's Descriptive Statistics Tool

We used Excel's Data Analysis ToolPak in Appendix 2.2 to produce histograms.

As we already demonstrated, Excel provides statistical functions to compute descriptive statistics for a data set. These functions can be used to compute one statistic at a time (e.g., mean, variance, etc.). Excel also provides a variety of functionality in its Data Analysis ToolPak. The Data Analysis ToolPak provides many different tools that can be used to analyze data in Excel. To enable the Data Analysis ToolPak add-in in Excel, follow the steps below.

Step 1. Click the **File** tab on the Ribbon and select **Options**
Step 2. When the **Excel Options** dialog box opens, click **Add-ins:**
  At the bottom of the **Excel Options** dialog box, where it says, **Manage: Excel Add-ins** click **Go…**
  Select the check box for **Analysis ToolPak**
  Click **OK**

One of the tools included in Excel's Data Analysis ToolPak is called Descriptive Statistics which allows the user to compute a variety of descriptive statistics at once. We show here how it can be used to compute descriptive statistics for the starting salary data in Table 3.1.

Step 1. Click the **Data** tab on the Ribbon
Step 2. In the **Analyze** group, click **Data Analysis**
Step 3. When the **Data Analysis** dialog box appears:
  Choose **Descriptive Statistics**
  Click **OK**
Step 4. When the **Descriptive Statistics** dialog box appears:
  Enter *B1:B13* in the **Input Range:** box
  Select **Columns** for **Grouped By:**
  Select the check box for **Labels in first row**
  In the **Output options** area, select **Output Range,** type *D1* in the **Output Range:** box and select the check box for **Summary statistics**
  Click **OK**

Cells D1:E15 of Figure Excel 3.3 show the descriptive statistics provided by Excel. The descriptive statistics provided by Excel include all of those we covered in this chapter. We note that the output of the Descriptive Statistics tool is static. For example, referring to Figure Excel 3.3, if a value of the data in the range B2:B13 would change, the Descriptive Statistics output in cells E3:E15 would not change. One would have to re-run the Descriptive Statistics tool.

Boxplots

We can use Excel's Insert Statistic Chart to construct a boxplot of the monthly starting salary data contained in the file *StartingSalaries* using the steps below. The data are in cells B2:B13.

In Excel, a boxplot is referred to as a box and whisker plot. Also, boxplots in Excel are vertical rather than horizontal.

The following steps describe how to use Excel's Insert Statistic Chart to construct a histogram of the audit time data.

Step 1. Select cells in the data set (B2:B13)
Step 2. Click the **Insert** tab on the Ribbon
Step 3. In the **Charts** group click **Insert Statistic Chart** and then click **Box and Whisker**

StartingSalaries

The boxplot appears in Figure Excel 3.4. The following steps may be used to edit the boxplot.

Step 1. Click on **Chart Title** and press the **Delete** key
Step 2. Click on the **1** under the horizontal axis and press the **Delete** key

FIGURE Excel 3.3   Excel's Descriptive Statistics Tool Output

	A	B	C	D	E
1	**Graduate**	**Monthly Starting Salary ($)**		*Monthly Starting Salary ($)*	
2	1	5850			
3	2	5950		Mean	5940
4	3	6050		Standard Error	47.8199
5	4	5880		Median	5905
6	5	5755		Mode	5880
7	6	5710		Standard Deviation	165.65
8	7	5890		Sample Variance	27440.9
9	8	6130		Kurtosis	1.72
10	9	5940		Skewness	1.09
11	10	6325		Range	615
12	11	5920		Minimum	5710
13	12	5880		Maximum	6325
14				Sum	71280
15				Count	12

FIGURE Excel 3.4   A Boxplot Created in Excel for the Monthly Starting Salary Data

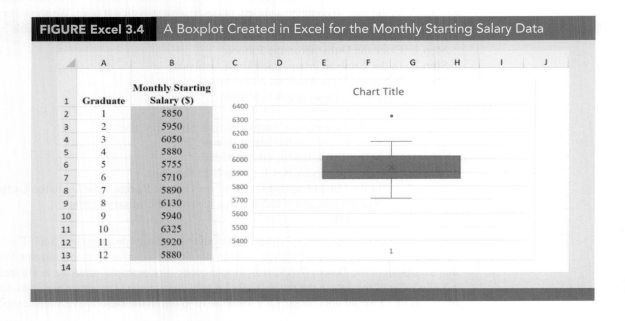

Step 3. Click on the **Chart Elements** button ⊞ (located next to the top right corner of the chart)

Step 4. When the list of chart elements appears:
   Click **Axis Titles** to create placeholders for the axis titles
   Click on the horizontal **Axis Title** and press the **Delete** key
   Click on the vertical **Axis Title** placeholder and replace it with *Monthly Starting Salary ($)*

Step 5. Click on a horizontal line in the chart and press the **Delete** key

Step 6. Right-click on the vertical axis, select **Format Axis…**

Step 7. In the **Format Axis** task pane, select **Tick Marks**, and from the drop-down **Major type** menu select **Inside**

Figure Excel 3.5 shows the resulting boxplot.

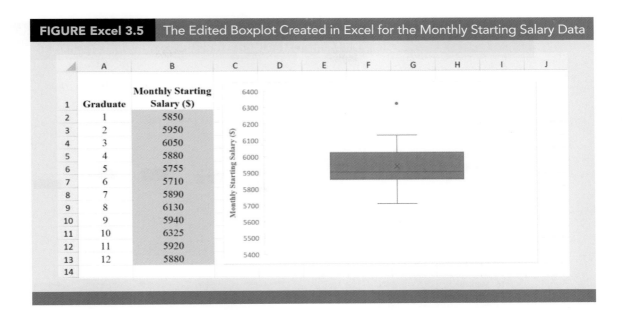

FIGURE Excel 3.5   The Edited Boxplot Created in Excel for the Monthly Starting Salary Data

There are several other options available for Excel's Box and Whisker chart. To invoke these options, right-click on the box part of the chart, select **Format Data Series**…, and the **Format Data Series** task pane will appear. This allows you to control what appears in the chart; for example, whether or not to show the mean marker, markers for outliers, and markers for all points.

Comparative Boxplots

We can use Excel's Insert Statistic Chart to construct a comparative boxplot using the data in the file *MajorSalaries.*

The following steps describe how to use Excel's Insert Statistical Chart to construct boxplots of monthly salary by major.

DATA *file*

MajorSalaries

Step 1. Select cells in the data set (A2:B112)
Step 2. Click the **Insert** tab on the Ribbon
Step 3. In the **Charts** group click **Insert Statistic Chart** and then click **Box and Whisker**

The resulting comparative boxplot is shown in Figure Excel 3.6. The following steps may be used to edit the comparative boxplot.

Step 1. Click on **Chart Title** and replace it with *Comparative Analysis of Monthly Starting Salary by Major.*
Step 2. To put the majors in alphabetical order from left to right:
   Select cells in the data set (A1:B112)
   Click the **Data** tab on the Ribbon
   Select **Sort** from the **Sort & Filter** group
   From the **Sort by** drop down menu in the **Sort** dialog box, select **Major**
   From the **Order** drop down menu in the **Sort** dialog box, select **A to Z**
   Click **OK**
Step 3. Click anywhere in the chart
   Click on the **Chart Elements** button ➕ (located next to the top right corner of the chart)
Step 4. When the list of chart elements appears:
   Click **Axis Titles** to create placeholders for the axis titles
   Click on the horizontal **Axis Title** placeholder and replace it with *Major*

FIGURE Excel 3.6   Comparative Boxplots Created in Excel for the Monthly Starting Salary by Major Data Using Excel's Box and Whisker Chart Tool

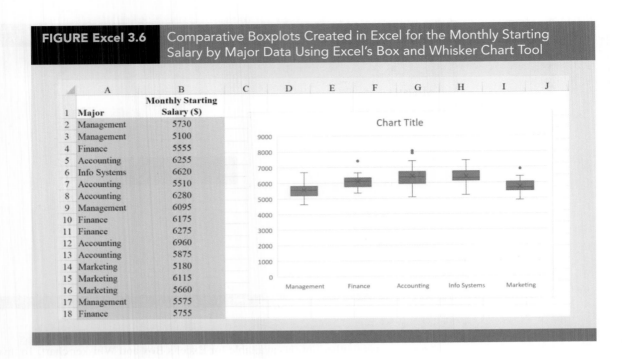

Click on the vertical **Axis Title** placeholder and replace it with *Monthly Starting Salary ($)*

Step 5.   Click on a horizontal line in the chart and press the **Delete** key

Step 6.   Right-click on the vertical axis and select **Format Axis…**

Step 7.   In the **Format Axis** task pane

Select **Axis Options** and enter *4000* for **Minimum**

Select **Tick Marks,** and from the drop-down **Major type** select **Inside**

Figure Excel 3.7 shows the resulting comparative boxplot analysis.

FIGURE Excel 3.7   The Edited Comparative Boxplots Created in Excel for the Monthly Starting Salary by Major Data

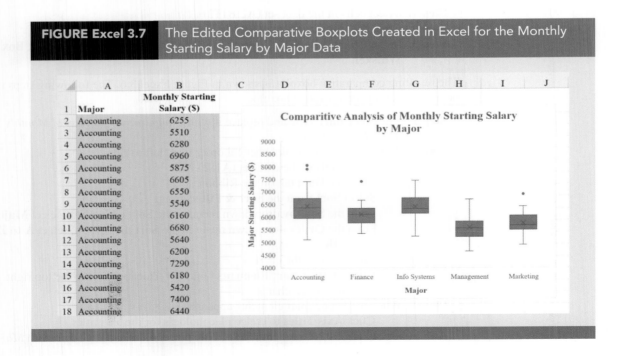

Chapter 4

Introduction to Probability

CONTENTS

STATISTICS IN PRACTICE

National Aeronautics and Space Administration*

WASHINGTON, D.C.

The National Aeronautics and Space Administration (NASA) is the agency of the United States government that is responsible for the U.S. civilian space program and aeronautics and aerospace research. NASA is best known for its manned space exploration; its mission statement is to "pioneer the future in space exploration, scientific discovery and aeronautics research." NASA, with its 18,800 employees, is currently working on the design of a new Space Launch System that will take the astronauts farther into space than ever before and provide the cornerstone for future human space exploration.

Although NASA's primary mission is space exploration, its expertise has been called upon to assist countries and organizations throughout the world. In one such situation, the San José copper and gold mine in Copiapó, Chile, caved in, trapping 33 men more than 2000 feet underground. While it was important to bring the men safely to the surface as quickly as possible, it was imperative that the rescue effort be carefully designed and implemented to save as many miners as possible. The Chilean government asked NASA to provide assistance in developing a rescue method. In response, NASA sent a four-person team consisting of an engineer, two physicians, and a psychologist with expertise in vehicle design and issues of long-term confinement.

The probability of success and failure of various rescue methods was prominent in the thoughts of everyone involved. Since there were no historical data available that applied to this unique rescue situation, NASA scientists developed subjective probability estimates for the success

NASA scientists based probabilities on similar circumstances experienced during space flights.
Source: JUAN MABROMATA/AFP/Getty Images

and failure of various rescue methods based on similar circumstances experienced by astronauts returning from short- and long-term space missions. The probability estimates provided by NASA guided officials in the selection of a rescue method and provided insight as to how the miners would survive the ascent in a rescue cage.

The rescue method designed by the Chilean officials in consultation with the NASA team resulted in the construction of 13-foot-long, 924-pound steel rescue capsule that would be used to bring up the miners one at a time. All miners were rescued, with the last miner emerging 68 days after the cave-in occurred.

In this chapter you will learn about probability as well as how to compute and interpret probabilities for a variety of situations. In addition to subjective probabilities, you will learn about classical and relative frequency methods for assigning probabilities. The basic relationships of probability, conditional probability, and Bayes' theorem will be covered.

*The authors are indebted to Dr. Michael Duncan and Clinton Cragg at NASA for providing the context for this Statistics in Practice.

Managers often base their decisions on an analysis of uncertainties such as the following:

1. What are the chances that sales will decrease if we increase prices?
2. What is the likelihood a new assembly method will increase productivity?
3. How likely is it that the project will be finished on time?
4. What is the chance that a new investment will be profitable?

Probability is a numerical measure of the likelihood that an event will occur. Thus, probabilities can be used as measures of the degree of uncertainty associated with the four events previously listed. If probabilities are available, we can determine the likelihood of each event occurring.

Some of the earliest work on probability originated in a series of letters between Pierre de Fermat and Blaise Pascal in the 1650s.

Probability values are always assigned on a scale from 0 to 1. A probability near zero indicates an event is unlikely to occur; a probability near 1 indicates an event is almost certain to occur. Other probabilities between 0 and 1 represent degrees of likelihood that

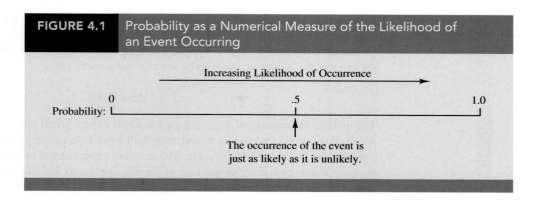

FIGURE 4.1 Probability as a Numerical Measure of the Likelihood of an Event Occurring

an event will occur. For example, if we consider the event "rain tomorrow," we understand that when the weather report indicates "a near-zero probability of rain," it means almost no chance of rain. However, if a .90 probability of rain is reported, we know that rain is likely to occur. A .50 probability indicates that rain is just as likely to occur as not. Figure 4.1 depicts the view of probability as a numerical measure of the likelihood of an event occurring.

4.1 Random Experiments, Counting Rules, and Assigning Probabilities

In discussing probability, we deal with experiments that have the following characteristics:

1. The experimental outcomes are well defined, and in many cases can even be listed prior to conducting the experiment.
2. On any single repetition or *trial* of the experiment, one and only one of the possible experimental outcomes will occur.
3. The experimental outcome that occurs on any trial is determined solely by chance.

We refer to these types of experiments as **random experiments**.

RANDOM EXPERIMENT

A random experiment is a process that generates well-defined experimental outcomes. On any single repetition or trial, the outcome that occurs is determined completely by chance.

To illustrate the key features associated with a random experiment, consider the process of tossing a coin. Referring to one face of the coin as the head and to the other face as the tail, after tossing the coin the upward face will be either a head or a tail. Thus, there are two possible experimental outcomes: head or tail. On an any single repetition or *trial* of this experiment, only one of the two possible experimental outcomes will occur; in other words, each time we toss the coin we will either observe a head or a tail. And, the outcome that occurs on any trial is determined solely by chance or random variability. As a result, the process of tossing a coin is considered a random experiment.

By specifying all the possible experimental outcomes, we identify the **sample space** for a random experiment.

SAMPLE SPACE

The sample space for a random experiment is the set of all experimental outcomes.

An experimental outcome is also called a **sample point** to identify it as an element of the sample space.

Consider the random experiment of tossing a coin. If we let S denote the sample space, we can use the following notation to describe the sample space.

$$S = \{\text{Head, Tail}\}$$

The random experiment of tossing a coin has two experimental outcomes (sample points). As an illustration of a random experiment with more than two experimental outcomes, consider the process of rolling a die. The possible experimental outcomes, defined as the number of dots appearing on the face of the die, are the six sample points in the sample space for this random experiment,

$$S = \{1, 2, 3, 4, 5, 6\}$$

Counting Rules, Combinations, and Permutations

Being able to identify and count the experimental outcomes is a necessary step in assigning probabilities. We now discuss three useful counting rules.

Multiple-Step Experiments The first counting rule applies to **multiple-step experiments**. Consider the experiment of tossing two coins. Let the experimental outcomes be defined in terms of the pattern of heads and tails appearing on the upward faces of the two coins. How many experimental outcomes are possible for this experiment? The experiment of tossing two coins can be thought of as a two-step experiment in which step 1 is the tossing of the first coin and step 2 is the tossing of the second coin. If we use H to denote a head and T to denote a tail, (H, H) indicates the experimental outcome with a head on the first coin and a head on the second coin. Continuing this notation, we can describe the sample space (S) for this coin-tossing experiment as follows:

$$S = \{(H, H), (H, T), (T, H), (T, T)\}$$

Thus, we see that four experimental outcomes are possible. In this case, we can easily list all the experimental outcomes.

The counting rule for multiple-step experiments makes it possible to determine the number of experimental outcomes without listing them.

COUNTING RULE FOR MULTIPLE-STEP EXPERIMENTS

If an experiment can be described as a sequence of k steps with n_1 possible outcomes on the first step, n_2 possible outcomes on the second step, and so on, then the total number of experimental outcomes is given by $(n_1) (n_2) \ldots (n_k)$.

Viewing the experiment of tossing two coins as a sequence of first tossing one coin ($n_1 = 2$) and then tossing the other coin ($n_2 = 2$), we can see from the counting rule that $(2)(2) = 4$ distinct experimental outcomes are possible. As shown, they are $S = \{(H, H), (H, T), (T, H), (T, T)\}$. The number of experimental outcomes in an experiment involving tossing six coins is $(2)(2)(2)(2)(2)(2) = 64$.

A **tree diagram** is a graphical representation that helps in visualizing a multiple-step experiment. Figure 4.2 shows a tree diagram for the experiment of tossing two coins. The sequence of steps moves from left to right through the tree. Step 1 corresponds to tossing the first coin, and step 2 corresponds to tossing the second coin. For each step, the two possible outcomes are head or tail. Note that for each possible outcome at step 1

FIGURE 4.2	Tree Diagram for the Experiment of Tossing Two Coins

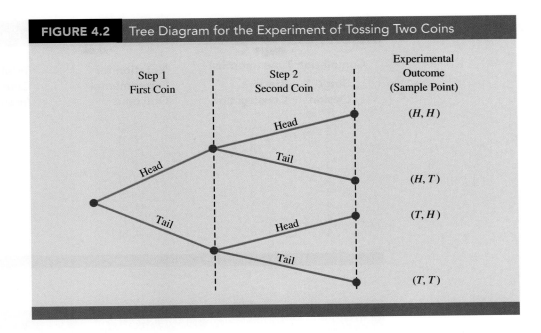

two branches correspond to the two possible outcomes at step 2. Each of the points on the right end of the tree corresponds to an experimental outcome. Each path through the tree from the leftmost node to one of the nodes at the right side of the tree corresponds to a unique sequence of outcomes.

Let us now see how the counting rule for multiple-step experiments can be used in the analysis of a capacity expansion project for the Kentucky Power & Light Company (KP&L). KP&L is starting a project designed to increase the generating capacity of one of its plants in northern Kentucky. The project is divided into two sequential stages or steps: stage 1 (design) and stage 2 (construction). Even though each stage will be scheduled and controlled as closely as possible, management cannot predict beforehand the exact time required to complete each stage of the project. An analysis of similar construction projects revealed possible completion times for the design stage of 2, 3, or 4 months and possible completion times for the construction stage of 6, 7, or 8 months. In addition, because of the critical need for additional electrical power, management set a goal of 10 months for the completion of the entire project.

Because this project has three possible completion times for the design stage (step 1) and three possible completion times for the construction stage (step 2), the counting rule for multiple-step experiments can be applied here to determine a total of (3)(3) = 9 experimental outcomes. To describe the experimental outcomes, we use a two-number notation; for instance, (2, 6) indicates that the design stage is completed in 2 months and the construction stage is completed in 6 months. This experimental outcome results in a total of 2 + 6 = 8 months to complete the entire project. Table 4.1 summarizes the nine experimental outcomes for the KP&L problem. The tree diagram in Figure 4.3 shows how the nine outcomes (sample points) occur.

The counting rule and tree diagram help the project manager identify the experimental outcomes and determine the possible project completion times. From the information in Figure 4.3, we see that the project will be completed in 8 to 12 months, with six of the nine experimental outcomes providing the desired completion time of 10 months or less. Even though identifying the experimental outcomes may be helpful, we need to consider how probability values can be assigned to the experimental outcomes before making an assessment of the probability that the project will be completed within the desired 10 months.

TABLE 4.1	Experimental Outcomes (Sample Points) for the KP&L Project		
Completion Time (months)		**Notation for Experimental Outcome**	**Total Project Completion Time (months)**
Stage 1 Design	**Stage 2 Construction**		
2	6	(2, 6)	8
2	7	(2, 7)	9
2	8	(2, 8)	10
3	6	(3, 6)	9
3	7	(3, 7)	10
3	8	(3, 8)	11
4	6	(4, 6)	10
4	7	(4, 7)	11
4	8	(4, 8)	12

FIGURE 4.3	Tree Diagram for the KP&L Project

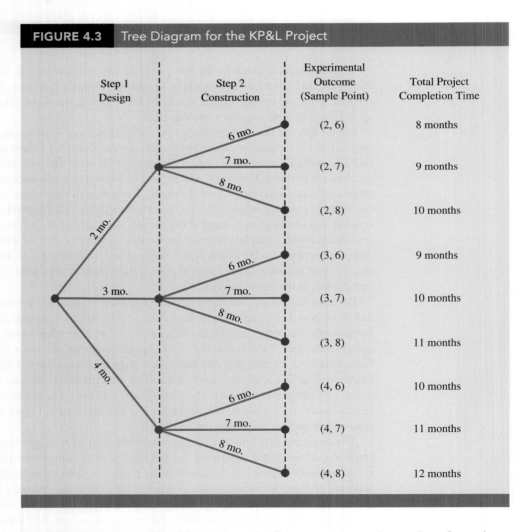

Combinations A second useful counting rule allows one to count the number of experimental outcomes when the experiment involves selecting n objects from a set of N objects. It is called the counting rule for **combinations**.

COUNTING RULE FOR COMBINATIONS

The number of combinations of N objects taken n at a time is

$$C_n^N = \binom{N}{n} = \frac{N!}{n!(N-n)!} \tag{4.1}$$

The notation ! means factorial; for example, 5 factorial is 5! = (5)(4)(3)(2)(1) = 120.

where

$$N! = N(N-1)(N-2)\cdots(2)(1)$$
$$n! = n(n-1)(n-2)\cdots(2)(1)$$

and, by definition, $$0! = 1$$

As an illustration of the counting rule for combinations, consider a quality control procedure in which an inspector randomly selects two of five parts to test for defects. In a group of five parts, how many combinations of two parts can be selected? The counting rule in equation (4.1) shows that with $N = 5$ and $n = 2$, we have

$$C_2^5 = \binom{5}{2} = \frac{5!}{2!(5-2)!} = \frac{(5)(4)(3)(2)(1)}{(2)(1)(3)(2)(1)} = \frac{120}{12} = 10$$

In sampling from a finite population of size N, the counting rule for combinations is used to find the number of different samples of size n that can be selected.

Thus, 10 outcomes are possible for the experiment of randomly selecting two parts from a group of five. If we label the five parts as A, B, C, D, and E, the 10 combinations or experimental outcomes can be identified as AB, AC, AD, AE, BC, BD, BE, CD, CE, and DE.

As another example, consider that the Florida Lotto lottery system uses the random selection of 6 integers from a group of 53 to determine the weekly winner. The counting rule for combinations, equation (4.1), can be used to determine the number of ways 6 different integers can be selected from a group of 53.

$$\binom{53}{6} = \frac{53!}{6!(53-6)!} = \frac{53!}{6!47!} = \frac{(53)(52)(51)(50)(49)(48)}{(6)(5)(4)(3)(2)(1)} = 22{,}957{,}480$$

The counting rule for combinations tells us that almost 23 million experimental outcomes are possible in the lottery drawing. An individual who buys a lottery ticket has 1 chance in 22,957,480 of winning.

Permutations A third counting rule that is sometimes useful is the counting rule for **permutations**. It allows one to compute the number of experimental outcomes when n objects are to be selected from a set of N objects where the order of selection is important. The same n objects selected in a different order are considered a different experimental outcome.

COUNTING RULE FOR PERMUTATIONS

The number of permutations of N objects taken n at a time is given by

$$P_n^N = n!\binom{N}{n} = \frac{N!}{(N-n)!} \tag{4.2}$$

The counting rule for permutations closely relates to the one for combinations; however, an experiment results in more permutations than combinations for the same number of objects because every selection of n objects can be ordered in $n!$ different ways.

As an example, consider again the quality control process in which an inspector selects two of five parts to inspect for defects. How many permutations may be selected? The counting rule in equation (4.2) shows that with $N = 5$ and $n = 2$, we have

$$P_2^5 = 2!\frac{5!}{2!(5-2)!} = \frac{5!}{(5-2)!} = \frac{5!}{3!} = \frac{(5)(4)(3)(2)(1)}{(3)(2)(1)} = \frac{120}{6} = 20$$

Thus, 20 outcomes are possible for the experiment of randomly selecting two parts from a group of five when the order of selection must be taken into account. If we label the parts A, B, C, D, and E, the 20 permutations are AB, BA, AC, CA, AD, DA, AE, EA, BC, CB, BD, DB, BE, EB, CD, DC, CE, EC, DE, and ED.

Assigning Probabilities

Now let us see how probabilities can be assigned to experimental outcomes. The three approaches most frequently used are the classical, relative frequency, and subjective methods. Regardless of the method used, two **basic requirements for assigning probabilities** must be met.

BASIC REQUIREMENTS FOR ASSIGNING PROBABILITIES

1. The probability assigned to each experimental outcome must be between 0 and 1, inclusively. If we let E_i denote the ith experimental outcome and $P(E_i)$ its probability, then this requirement can be written as

$$0 \le P(E_i) \le 1 \text{ for all } i \tag{4.3}$$

2. The sum of the probabilities for all the experimental outcomes must equal 1.0. For n experimental outcomes, this requirement can be written as

$$P(E_1) + P(E_2) + \cdots + P(E_n) = 1 \tag{4.4}$$

The **classical method** of assigning probabilities is appropriate when all the experimental outcomes are equally likely. If n experimental outcomes are possible, a probability of $1/n$ is assigned to each experimental outcome. When using this approach, the two basic requirements for assigning probabilities are automatically satisfied.

For an example, consider the experiment of tossing a fair coin; the two experimental outcomes—head and tail—are equally likely. Because one of the two equally likely outcomes is a head, the probability of observing a head is 1/2, or .50. Similarly, the probability of observing a tail is also 1/2, or .50.

As another example, consider the experiment of rolling a die. It would seem reasonable to conclude that the six possible outcomes are equally likely, and hence each outcome is assigned a probability of 1/6. If $P(1)$ denotes the probability that one dot appears on the upward face of the die, then $P(1) = 1/6$. Similarly, $P(2) = 1/6$, $P(3) = 1/6$, $P(4) = 1/6$, $P(5) = 1/6$, and $P(6) = 1/6$. Note that these probabilities satisfy the two basic requirements of equations (4.3) and (4.4) because each of the probabilities is greater than or equal to zero and they sum to 1.0.

The **relative frequency method** of assigning probabilities is appropriate when data are available to estimate the proportion of the time the experimental outcome will occur if the experiment is repeated a large number of times. As an example, consider a study of waiting times in the X-ray department for a local hospital. A clerk recorded the number of patients waiting for service at 9:00 A.M. on 20 successive days and obtained the following results.

Number Waiting	Number of Days Outcome Occurred
0	2
1	5
2	6
3	4
4	3
Total	20

These data show that on 2 of the 20 days, zero patients were waiting for service; on 5 of the days, one patient was waiting for service; and so on. Using the relative frequency method, we would assign a probability of 2/20 = .10 to the experimental outcome of zero patients waiting for service, 5/20 = .25 to the experimental outcome of one patient waiting, 6/20 = .30 to two patients waiting, 4/20 = .20 to three patients waiting, and 3/20 = .15 to four patients waiting. As with the classical method, using the relative frequency method automatically satisfies the two basic requirements of equations (4.3) and (4.4).

The **subjective method** of assigning probabilities is most appropriate when one cannot realistically assume that the experimental outcomes are equally likely and when little relevant data are available. When the subjective method is used to assign probabilities to the experimental outcomes, we may use any information available, such as our experience or intuition. After considering all available information, a probability value that expresses our *degree of belief* (on a scale from 0 to 1) that the experimental outcome will occur is specified. Because subjective probability expresses a person's degree of belief, it is personal. Using the subjective method, different people can be expected to assign different probabilities to the same experimental outcome.

The subjective method requires extra care to ensure that the two basic requirements of equations (4.3) and (4.4) are satisfied. Regardless of a person's degree of belief, the probability value assigned to each experimental outcome must be between 0 and 1, inclusive, and the sum of all the probabilities for the experimental outcomes must equal 1.0.

Consider the case in which Tom and Judy Elsbernd make an offer to purchase a house. Two outcomes are possible:

$$E_1 = \text{their offer is accepted}$$
$$E_2 = \text{their offer is rejected}$$

Judy believes that the probability their offer will be accepted is .8; thus, Judy would set $P(E_1) = .8$ and $P(E_2) = .2$. Tom, however, believes that the probability that their offer will be accepted is .6; hence, Tom would set $P(E_1) = .6$ and $P(E_2) = .4$. Note that Tom's probability estimate for E_1 reflects a greater pessimism that their offer will be accepted.

Bayes' theorem (see Section 4.5) provides a means for combining subjectively determined prior probabilities with probabilities obtained by other means to obtain revised, or posterior, probabilities.

Both Judy and Tom assigned probabilities that satisfy the two basic requirements. The fact that their probability estimates are different emphasizes the personal nature of the subjective method.

Even in business situations where either the classical or the relative frequency approach can be applied, managers may want to provide subjective probability estimates. In such cases, the best probability estimates often are obtained by combining the estimates from the classical or relative frequency approach with subjective probability estimates.

Probabilities for the KP&L Project

To perform further analysis on the KP&L project, we must develop probabilities for each of the nine experimental outcomes listed in Table 4.1. On the basis of experience and judgment, management concluded that the experimental outcomes were not equally likely. Hence, the classical method of assigning probabilities could not be used. Management then decided to conduct a study of the completion times for similar projects undertaken by

TABLE 4.2	Completion Results for 40 KP&L Projects

Completion Time (months)			Number of Past Projects Having These Completion Times
Stage 1 Design	Stage 2 Construction	Sample Point	
2	6	(2, 6)	6
2	7	(2, 7)	6
2	8	(2, 8)	2
3	6	(3, 6)	4
3	7	(3, 7)	8
3	8	(3, 8)	2
4	6	(4, 6)	2
4	7	(4, 7)	4
4	8	(4, 8)	6
		Total	40

KP&L over the past three years. The results of a study of 40 similar projects are summarized in Table 4.2.

After reviewing the results of the study, management decided to employ the relative frequency method of assigning probabilities. Management could have provided subjective probability estimates but felt that the current project was quite similar to the 40 previous projects. Thus, the relative frequency method was judged best.

In using the data in Table 4.2 to compute probabilities, we note that outcome (2, 6)—stage 1 completed in 2 months and stage 2 completed in 6 months—occurred six times in the 40 projects. We can use the relative frequency method to assign a probability of 6/40 = .15 to this outcome. Similarly, outcome (2, 7) also occurred in six of the 40 projects, providing a 6/40 = .15 probability. Continuing in this manner, we obtain the probability assignments for the sample points of the KP&L project shown in Table 4.3. Note that $P(2, 6)$ represents the probability of the sample point (2, 6), $P(2, 7)$ represents the probability of the sample point (2, 7), and so on.

TABLE 4.3	Probability Assignments for the KP&L Project Based on the Relative Frequency Method

Sample Point	Project Completion Time	Probability of Sample Point
(2, 6)	8 months	$P(2, 6) = 6/40 = .15$
(2, 7)	9 months	$P(2, 7) = 6/40 = .15$
(2, 8)	10 months	$P(2, 8) = 2/40 = .05$
(3, 6)	9 months	$P(3, 6) = 4/40 = .10$
(3, 7)	10 months	$P(3, 7) = 8/40 = .20$
(3, 8)	11 months	$P(3, 8) = 2/40 = .05$
(4, 6)	10 months	$P(4, 6) = 2/40 = .05$
(4, 7)	11 months	$P(4, 7) = 4/40 = .10$
(4, 8)	12 months	$P(4, 8) = 6/40 = .15$
		Total 1.00

1. In statistics, the notion of an experiment differs somewhat from the notion of an experiment in the physical sciences. In the physical sciences, researchers usually conduct an experiment in a laboratory or a controlled environment in order to learn about cause and effect. In statistical experiments, probability determines outcomes. Even though the experiment is repeated in exactly the same way, an entirely different outcome may occur. Because of this influence of probability on the outcome, the experiments of statistics are sometimes called *random experiments*.

2. When drawing a random sample without replacement from a population of size N, the counting rule for combinations is used to find the number of different samples of size n that can be selected.

E X E R C I S E S

Methods

1. An experiment has three steps with three outcomes possible for the first step, two outcomes possible for the second step, and four outcomes possible for the third step. How many experimental outcomes exist for the entire experiment?

2. How many ways can three items be selected from a group of six items? Use the letters A, B, C, D, E, and F to identify the items, and list each of the different combinations of three items.

3. How many permutations of three items can be selected from a group of six? Use the letters A, B, C, D, E, and F to identify the items, and list each of the permutations of items B, D, and F.

4. Consider the experiment of tossing a coin three times.
   a. Develop a tree diagram for the experiment.
   b. List the experimental outcomes.
   c. What is the probability for each experimental outcome?

5. Suppose an experiment has five equally likely outcomes: E_1, E_2, E_3, E_4, E_5. Assign probabilities to each outcome and show that the requirements in equations (4.3) and (4.4) are satisfied. What method did you use?

6. An experiment with three outcomes has been repeated 50 times, and it was learned that E_1 occurred 20 times, E_2 occurred 13 times, and E_3 occurred 17 times. Assign probabilities to the outcomes. What method did you use?

7. A decision maker subjectively assigned the following probabilities to the four outcomes of an experiment: $P(E_1) = .10$, $P(E_2) = .15$, $P(E_3) = .40$, and $P(E_4) = .20$. Are these probability assignments valid? Explain.

Applications

8. **Zoning Changes.** In the city of Milford, applications for zoning changes go through a two-step process: a review by the planning commission and a final decision by the city council. At step 1 the planning commission reviews the zoning change request and makes a positive or negative recommendation concerning the change. At step 2 the city council reviews the planning commission's recommendation and then votes to approve or to disapprove the zoning change. Suppose the developer of an apartment complex submits an application for a zoning change. Consider the application process as an experiment.
   a. How many sample points are there for this experiment? List the sample points.
   b. Construct a tree diagram for the experiment.

9. **Sampling Bank Accounts.** Simple random sampling uses a sample of size n from a population of size N to obtain data that can be used to make inferences about the characteristics of a population. Suppose that, from a population of 50 bank accounts, we want to take a random sample of four accounts in order to learn about the population. How many different random samples of four accounts are possible?

DATA *file*

CodeChurn

10. **Code Churn.** Code Churn is a common metric used to measure the efficiency and productivity of software engineers and computer programmers. It's usually measured as the percentage of a programmer's code that must be edited over a short period of time. Programmers with higher rates of code churn must rewrite code more often because of errors and inefficient programming techniques. The following table displays sample information for 10 computer programmers.

Programmer	Total Lines of Code Written	Number of Lines of Code Requiring Edits
Liwei	23,789	4,589
Andrew	17,962	2,780
Jaime	31,025	12,080
Sherae	26,050	3,780
Binny	19,586	1,890
Roger	24,786	4,005
Dong-Gil	24,030	5,785
Alex	14,780	1,052
Jay	30,875	3,872
Vivek	21,546	4,125

a. Use the data in the table above and the relative frequency method to determine probabilities that a randomly selected line of code will need to be edited for each programmer.
b. If you randomly select a line of code from Liwei, what is the probability that the line of code will require editing?
c. If you randomly select a line of code from Sherae, what is the probability that the line of code will *not* require editing?
d. Which programmer has the lowest probability of a randomly selected line of code requiring editing? Which programmer has the highest probability of a randomly selected line of code requiring editing?

11. **Tri-State Smokers.** A Gallup Poll of U.S. adults indicated that Kentucky is the state with the highest percentage of smokers (Gallup website). Consider the following example data from the Tri-State region, an area that comprises northern Kentucky, southeastern Indiana, and southwestern Ohio.

State	Smoker	Non-Smoker
Kentucky	47	176
Indiana	32	134
Ohio	39	182
Total:	118	492

a. Use the data to compute the probability that an adult in the Tri-State region smokes.
b. What is the probability of an adult in each state of the Tri-State region being a smoker? Which state in the Tri-State region has the lowest probability of an adult being a smoker?

12. **Toothpaste Package Designs.** A company that manufactures toothpaste is studying five different package designs. Assuming that one design is just as likely to be selected

by a consumer as any other design, what selection probability would you assign to each of the package designs? In an actual experiment, 100 consumers were asked to pick the design they preferred. The following data were obtained. Do the data confirm the belief that one design is just as likely to be selected as another? Explain.

Design	Number of Times Preferred
1	5
2	15
3	30
4	40
5	10

13. **Powerball Lottery.** The Powerball lottery is played twice each week in 44 states, the District of Columbia, and the Virgin Islands. To play Powerball, a participant must purchase a $2 ticket, select five numbers from the digits 1 through 69, and then select a Powerball number from the digits 1 through 26. To determine the winning numbers for each game, lottery officials draw 5 white balls out a drum of 69 white balls numbered 1 through 69 and 1 red ball out of a drum of 26 red balls numbered 1 through 26. To win the Powerball jackpot, a participant's numbers must match the numbers on the 5 white balls in any order and must also match the number on the red Powerball. The numbers 4–8–19–27–34 with a Powerball number of 10 provided the record jackpot of $1.586 billion (Powerball website).
    a. How many Powerball lottery outcomes are possible? (*Hint:* Consider this a two-step random experiment. Select the 5 white ball numbers and then select the 1 red Powerball number.)
    b. What is the probability that a $2 lottery ticket wins the Powerball lottery?

4.2 Events and Their Probabilities

In the introduction to this chapter we used the term *event* much as it would be used in everyday language. Then, in Section 4.1 we introduced the concept of an experiment and its associated experimental outcomes or sample points. Sample points and events provide the foundation for the study of probability. As a result, we must now introduce the formal definition of an **event** as it relates to sample points. Doing so will provide the basis for determining the probability of an event.

> **EVENT**
>
> An event is a collection of sample points.

For an example, let us return to the KP&L project and assume that the project manager is interested in the event that the entire project can be completed in 10 months or less. Referring to Table 4.3, we see that six sample points—(2, 6), (2, 7), (2, 8), (3, 6), (3, 7), and (4, 6)—provide a project completion time of 10 months or less. Let C denote the event that the project is completed in 10 months or less; we write

$$C = \{(2, 6), (2, 7), (2, 8), (3, 6), (3, 7), (4, 6)\}$$

Event C is said to occur if *any one* of these six sample points appears as the experimental outcome.

Other events that might be of interest to KP&L management include the following.

L = The event that the project is completed in *less* than 10 months

M = The event that the project is completed in *more* than 10 months

Using the information in Table 4.3, we see that these events consist of the following sample points.

$$L = \{(2, 6), (2, 7), (3, 6)\}$$
$$M = \{(3, 8), (4, 7), (4, 8)\}$$

A variety of additional events can be defined for the KP&L project, but in each case the event must be identified as a collection of sample points for the experiment.

Given the probabilities of the sample points shown in Table 4.3, we can use the following definition to compute the probability of any event that KP&L management might want to consider.

PROBABILITY OF AN EVENT

The probability of any event is equal to the sum of the probabilities of the sample points in the event.

Using this definition, we calculate the probability of a particular event by adding the probabilities of the sample points (experimental outcomes) that make up the event. We can now compute the probability that the project will take 10 months or less to complete. Because this event is given by $C = \{(2, 6), (2, 7), (2, 8), (3, 6), (3, 7), (4, 6)\}$, the probability of event C, denoted $P(C)$, is given by

$$P(C) = P(2, 6) + P(2, 7) + P(2, 8) + P(3, 6) + P(3, 7) + P(4, 6)$$

Refer to the sample point probabilities in Table 4.3; we have

$$P(C) = .15 + .15 + .05 + .10 + .20 + .05 = .70$$

Similarly, because the event that the project is completed in less than 10 months is given by $L = \{(2, 6), (2, 7), (3, 6)\}$, the probability of this event is given by

$$P(L) = P(2, 6) + P(2, 7) + P(3, 6)$$
$$= .15 + .15 + .10 = .40$$

Finally, for the event that the project is completed in more than 10 months, we have $M = \{(3, 8), (4, 7), (4, 8)\}$ and thus

$$P(M) = P(3, 8) + P(4, 7) + P(4, 8)$$
$$= .05 + .10 + .15 = .30$$

Using these probability results, we can now tell KP&L management that there is a .70 probability that the project will be completed in 10 months or less, a .40 probability that the project will be completed in less than 10 months, and a .30 probability that the project will be completed in more than 10 months. This procedure of computing event probabilities can be repeated for any event of interest to the KP&L management.

Any time that we can identify all the sample points of an experiment and assign probabilities to each, we can compute the probability of an event using the definition. However, in many experiments the large number of sample points makes the identification of the sample points, as well as the determination of their associated probabilities, extremely cumbersome, if not impossible. In the remaining sections of this chapter, we present some basic probability relationships that can be used to compute the probability of an event without knowledge of all the sample point probabilities.

N O T E S + C O M M E N T S

1. The sample space, S, is an event. Because it contains all the experimental outcomes, it has a probability of 1; that is, $P(S) = 1$.
2. When the classical method is used to assign probabilities, the assumption is that the experimental outcomes are equally likely. In such cases, the probability of an event can be computed by counting the number of experimental outcomes in the event and dividing the result by the total number of experimental outcomes.

E X E R C I S E S

Methods

14. An experiment has four equally likely outcomes: E_1, E_2, E_3, and E_4.
    a. What is the probability that E_2 occurs?
    b. What is the probability that any two of the outcomes occur (e.g., E_1 or E_3)?
    c. What is the probability that any three of the outcomes occur (e.g., E_1 or E_2 or E_4)?
15. Consider the experiment of selecting a playing card from a deck of 52 playing cards. Each card corresponds to a sample point with a 1/52 probability.
    a. List the sample points in the event an ace is selected.
    b. List the sample points in the event a club is selected.
    c. List the sample points in the event a face card (jack, queen, or king) is selected.
    d. Find the probabilities associated with each of the events in parts (a), (b), and (c).
16. Consider the experiment of rolling a pair of dice. Suppose that we are interested in the sum of the face values showing on the dice.
    a. How many sample points are possible? (*Hint:* Use the counting rule for multiple-step experiments.)
    b. List the sample points.
    c. What is the probability of obtaining a value of 7?
    d. What is the probability of obtaining a value of 9 or greater?
    e. Because each roll has six possible even values (2, 4, 6, 8, 10, and 12) and only five possible odd values (3, 5, 7, 9, and 11), the dice should show even values more often than odd values. Do you agree with this statement? Explain.
    f. What method did you use to assign the probabilities requested?

Applications

17. **KP&L Project Over Budget.** Refer to the KP&L sample points and sample point probabilities in Tables 4.2 and 4.3.
    a. The design stage (stage 1) will run over budget if it takes 4 months to complete. List the sample points in the event the design stage is over budget.
    b. What is the probability that the design stage is over budget?
    c. The construction stage (stage 2) will run over budget if it takes 8 months to complete. List the sample points in the event the construction stage is over budget.
    d. What is the probability that the construction stage is over budget?
    e. What is the probability that both stages are over budget?
18. **Corporate Headquarters Locations.** Each year *Fortune* magazine publishes an annual list of the 500 largest companies in the United States. The corporate headquarters for the 500 companies are located in 38 different states. The following table shows the 8 states with the largest number of *Fortune* 500 companies (*Money*/CNN website).

State	Number of Companies	State	Number of Companies
California	53	Ohio	28
Illinois	32	Pennsylvania	23
New Jersey	21	Texas	52
New York	50	Virginia	24

Suppose one of the 500 companies is selected at random for a follow-up questionnaire.

a. What is the probability that the company selected has its corporate headquarters in California?

b. What is the probability that the company selected has its corporate headquarters in California, New York, or Texas?

c. What is the probability that the company selected has its corporate headquarters in one of the eight states listed above?

19. **Impact of Global Warming.** Do you think global warming will have an impact on you during your lifetime? A 2014 CBS News/*New York Times* poll of 1000 adults in the United States asked this question (CBS News website). Consider the responses by age groups shown below.

Response	Age	
	18–29	30+
Yes	134	293
No	131	432
Unsure	2	8

a. What is the probability that a respondent 18–29 years of age thinks that global warming will not pose a serious threat during his/her lifetime?

b. What is the probability that a respondent 30+ years of age thinks that global warming will not pose a serious threat during his/her lifetime?

c. For a randomly selected respondent, what is the probability that a respondent answers yes?

d. Based on the survey results, does there appear to be a difference between ages 18–29 and 30+ regarding concern over global warming?

20. **Age of Financial Independence.** Suppose that the following table represents a sample of 944 teenagers' responses to the question, "When do you think you will become financially independent?"

Age of Financially Independent	Number of Responses
16 to 20	191
21 to 24	467
25 to 27	244
28 or older	42

Consider the experiment of randomly selecting a teenager from the population of teenagers aged 14 to 18.

a. Compute the probability of being financially independent for each of the four age categories.

b. What is the probability of being financially independent before the age of 25?

c. What is the probability of being financially independent after the age of 24?

d. Do the probabilities suggest that the teenagers may be somewhat unrealistic in their expectations about when they will become financially independent?

21. **Fatal Collisions with a Fixed Object.** The National Highway Traffic Safety Administration (NHTSA) collects traffic safety-related data for the U.S. Department of Transportation. According to NHTSA's data, 10,426 fatal collisions in 2016 were the result of collisions with fixed objects (NHTSA website, https://www.careforcrashvictims.com/wp-content/uploads/2018/07/Traffic-Safety-Facts-2016_-Motor-Vehicle-Crash-Data-from-the-Fatality-Analysis-Reporting-System-FARS-and-the-General-Estimates-System-GES.pdf). The following table provides more information on these collisions.

Fixed Object Involved in Collision	Number of Collisions
Pole/post	1,416
Culvert/curb/ditch	2,516
Shrubbery/tree	2,585
Guardrail	896
Embankment	947
Bridge	231
Other/unknown	1,835

Assume that a collision will be randomly chosen from this population.

a. What is the probability of a fatal collision with a pole or post?

b. What is the probability of a fatal collision with a guardrail?

c. What type of fixed object is least likely to be involved in a fatal collision? What is the probability associated with this type of fatal collision?

d. What type of object is most likely to be involved in a fatal collision? What is the probability associated with this type of fatal collision?

4.3 Some Basic Relationships of Probability

Complement of an Event

Given an event A, the **complement of A** is defined to be the event consisting of all sample points that are *not* in A. The complement of A is denoted by A^c. Figure 4.4 is a diagram, known as a **Venn diagram**, which illustrates the concept of a complement. The rectangular area represents the sample space for the experiment and as such contains all possible sample points. The circle represents event A and contains only the sample points that belong to A. The shaded region of the rectangle contains all sample points not in event A and is by definition the complement of A.

In any probability application, either event A or its complement A^c must occur. Therefore, we have

$$P(A) + P(A^c) = 1$$

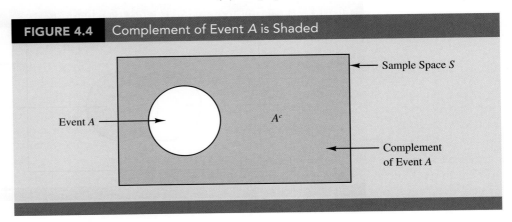

FIGURE 4.4   Complement of Event A is Shaded

Solving for $P(A)$, we obtain the following result.

COMPUTING PROBABILITY USING THE COMPLEMENT

$$P(A) = 1 - P(A^c) \tag{4.5}$$

Equation (4.5) shows that the probability of an event A can be computed easily if the probability of its complement, $P(A^c)$, is known.

As an example, consider the case of a sales manager who, after reviewing sales reports, states that 80% of new customer contacts result in no sale. By allowing A to denote the event of a sale and A^c to denote the event of no sale, the manager is stating that $P(A^c) = .80$. Using equation (4.5), we see that

$$P(A) = 1 - P(A^c) = 1 - .80 = .20$$

We can conclude that a new customer contact has a .20 probability of resulting in a sale.

In another example, a purchasing agent states a .90 probability that a supplier will send a shipment that is free of defective parts. Using the complement, we can conclude that there is a $1 - .90 = .10$ probability that the shipment will contain defective parts.

Addition Law

The addition law is helpful when we are interested in knowing the probability that at least one of two events occurs. That is, with events A and B we are interested in knowing the probability that event A or event B or both occur.

Before we present the addition law, we need to discuss two concepts related to the combination of events: the *union* of events and the *intersection* of events. Given two events A and B, the **union of A and B** is defined as follows.

UNION OF TWO EVENTS

The *union* of A and B is the event containing *all* sample points belonging to A or B or *both*. The union is denoted by $A \cup B$.

The Venn diagram in Figure 4.5 depicts the union of events A and B. Note that the two circles contain all the sample points in event A as well as all the sample points in event B. The fact that the circles overlap indicates that some sample points are contained in both A and B.

FIGURE 4.5   Union of Events A and B is Shaded

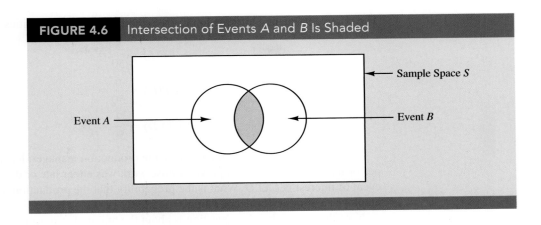

FIGURE 4.6   Intersection of Events *A* and *B* Is Shaded

The definition of the **intersection of** *A* **and** *B* follows.

INTERSECTION OF TWO EVENTS

Given two events *A* and *B*, the *intersection* of *A* and *B* is the event containing the sample points belonging to *both A and B*. The intersection is denoted by $A \cap B$.

The Venn diagram depicting the intersection of events *A* and *B* is shown in Figure 4.6. The area where the two circles overlap is the intersection; it contains the sample points that are in both *A* and *B*.

Let us now continue with a discussion of the addition law. The **addition law** provides a way to compute the probability that event *A* or event *B* or both occur. In other words, the addition law is used to compute the probability of the union of two events. The addition law is written as follows.

ADDITION LAW

$$P(A \cup B) = P(A) + P(B) - P(A \cap B) \qquad (4.6)$$

To understand the addition law intuitively, note that the first two terms in the addition law, $P(A) + P(B)$, account for all the sample points in $A \cup B$. However, because the sample points in the intersection $A \cap B$ are in both *A* and *B*, when we compute $P(A) + P(B)$, we are in effect counting each of the sample points in $A \cap B$ twice. We correct for this overcounting by subtracting $P(A \cap B)$.

As an example of an application of the addition law, let us consider the case of a small assembly plant with 50 employees. Each worker is expected to complete work assignments on time and in such a way that the assembled product will pass a final inspection. On occasion, some of the workers fail to meet the performance standards by completing work late or assembling a defective product. At the end of a performance evaluation period, the production manager found that 5 of the 50 workers completed work late, 6 of the 50 workers assembled a defective product, and 2 of the 50 workers both completed work late *and* assembled a defective product.

Let

$L =$ the event that the work is completed late

$D =$ the event that the assembled product is defective

The relative frequency information leads to the following probabilities.

$$P(L) = \frac{5}{50} = .10$$

$$P(D) = \frac{6}{50} = .12$$

$$P(L \cap D) = \frac{2}{50} = .04$$

After reviewing the performance data, the production manager decided to assign a poor performance rating to any employee whose work was either late or defective; thus the event of interest is $L \cup D$. What is the probability that the production manager assigned an employee a poor performance rating?

Note that the probability question is about the union of two events. Specifically, we want to know $P(L \cup D)$. Using equation (4.6), we have

$$P(L \cup D) = P(L) + P(D) - P(L \cap D)$$

Knowing values for the three probabilities on the right side of this expression, we can write

$$P(L \cup D) = .10 + .12 - .04 = .18$$

This calculation tells us that there is a .18 probability that a randomly selected employee received a poor performance rating.

As another example of the addition law, consider a recent study conducted by the personnel manager of a major computer software company. The study showed that 30% of the employees who left the firm within two years did so primarily because they were dissatisfied with their salary, 20% left because they were dissatisfied with their work assignments, and 12% of the former employees indicated dissatisfaction with *both* their salary and their work assignments. What is the probability that an employee who leaves within two years does so because of dissatisfaction with salary, dissatisfaction with the work assignment, or both?

Let

S = the event that the employee leaves because of salary
W = the event that the employee leaves because of work assignment

We have $P(S) = .30$, $P(W) = .20$, and $P(S \cap W) = .12$. Using equation (4.6), the addition law, we have

$$P(S \cup W) = P(S) + P(W) - P(S \cap W) = .30 + .20 - .12 = .38.$$

We find a .38 probability that an employee leaves for salary or work assignment reasons.

Before we conclude our discussion of the addition law, let us consider a special case that arises for **mutually exclusive events**.

MUTUALLY EXCLUSIVE EVENTS

Two events are said to be mutually exclusive if the events have no sample points in common.

Events A and B are mutually exclusive if, when one event occurs, the other cannot occur. Thus, a requirement for A and B to be mutually exclusive is that their intersection must contain no sample points. The Venn diagram depicting two mutually exclusive events A and B is shown in Figure 4.7. In this case $P(A \cap B) = 0$ and the addition law can be written as follows.

ADDITION LAW FOR MUTUALLY EXCLUSIVE EVENTS

$$P(A \cup B) = P(A) + P(B)$$

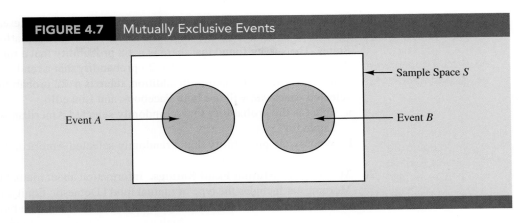

FIGURE 4.7   Mutually Exclusive Events

EXERCISES

Methods

22. Suppose that we have a sample space with five equally likely experimental outcomes: E_1, E_2, E_3, E_4, E_5. Let

$$A = \{E_1, E_2\}$$
$$B = \{E_3, E_4\}$$
$$C = \{E_2, E_3, E_5\}$$

   a. Find $P(A)$, $P(B)$, and $P(C)$.
   b. Find $P(A \cup B)$. Are A and B mutually exclusive?
   c. Find A^c, C^c, $P(A^c)$, and $P(C^c)$.
   d. Find $A \cup B^c$ and $P(A \cup B^c)$.
   e. Find $P(B \cup C)$.

23. Suppose that we have a sample space $S = \{E_1, E_2, E_3, E_4, E_5, E_6, E_7\}$, where $E_1, E_2, \ldots, E_7$ denote the sample points. The following probability assignments apply: $P(E_1) = .05$, $P(E_2) = .20$, $P(E_3) = .20$, $P(E_4) = .25$, $P(E_5) = .15$, $P(E_6) = .10$, and $P(E_7) = .05$. Let

$$A = \{E_1, E_4, E_6\}$$
$$B = \{E_2, E_4, E_7\}$$
$$C = \{E_2, E_3, E_5, E_7\}$$

   a. Find $P(A)$, $P(B)$, and $P(C)$.
   b. Find $A \cup B$ and $P(A \cup B)$.
   c. Find $A \cap B$ and $P(A \cap B)$.
   d. Are events A and C mutually exclusive?
   e. Find B^c and $P(B^c)$.

Applications

24. **Clarkson University Alumni Survey.** Clarkson University surveyed alumni to learn more about what they think of Clarkson. One part of the survey asked respondents to indicate whether their overall experience at Clarkson fell short of expectations, met expectations, or surpassed expectations. The results showed that 4% of the respondents did not provide a response, 26% said that their experience fell short of expectations, and 65% of the respondents said that their experience met expectations.
   a. If we chose an alumnus at random, what is the probability that the alumnus would say their experience *surpassed* expectations?
   b. If we chose an alumnus at random, what is the probability that the alumnus would say their experience met or surpassed expectations?

25. **Americans Using Facebook and LinkedIn.** A 2018 Pew Research Center survey (Pew Research website) examined the use of social media platforms in the United States. The survey found that there is a .68 probability that a randomly selected American will use Facebook and a .25 probability that a randomly selected American will use LinkedIn. In addition, there is a .22 probability that a randomly selected American will use both Facebook and LinkedIn.

    a. What is the probability that a randomly selected American will use Facebook or LinkedIn?

    b. What is the probability that a randomly selected American will not use either social media platform?

26. **Morningstar Mutual Fund Ratings.** Information about mutual funds provided by Morningstar includes the type of mutual fund (Domestic Equity, International Equity, or Fixed Income) and the Morningstar rating for the fund. The rating is expressed from 1-star (lowest rating) to 5-star (highest rating). Suppose a sample of 25 mutual funds provided the following counts:

    • Sixteen mutual funds were Domestic Equity funds.
    • Thirteen mutual funds were rated 3-star or less.
    • Seven of the Domestic Equity funds were rated 4-star.
    • Two of the Domestic Equity funds were rated 5-star.

    Assume that one of these 25 mutual funds will be randomly selected in order to learn more about the mutual fund and its investment strategy.

    a. What is the probability of selecting a Domestic Equity fund?

    b. What is the probability of selecting a fund with a 4-star or 5-star rating?

    c. What is the probability of selecting a fund that is both a Domestic Equity fund *and* a fund with a 4-star or 5-star rating?

    d. What is the probability of selecting a fund that is a Domestic Equity fund *or* a fund with a 4-star or 5-star rating?

27. **Social Media Use.** A marketing firm would like to test-market the name of a new energy drink targeted at 18- to 29-year-olds via social media. A study by the Pew Research Center found that 35% of U.S. adults (18 and older) do not use social media (*Pew Research Center* website, October 2015). The percentage of U.S. young adults age 30 and older is 78%. Suppose that the percentage of the U.S. adult population that is either age 18–29 or uses social media is 67.2%.

    a. What is the probability that a randomly selected U.S. adult uses social media?

    b. What is the probability that a randomly selected U.S. adult is aged 18–29?

    c. What is the probability that a randomly selected U.S. adult is 18–29 and a user of social media?

28. **Survey on Car Rentals.** A survey of magazine subscribers showed that 45.8% rented a car during the past 12 months for business reasons, 54% rented a car during the past 12 months for personal reasons, and 30% rented a car during the past 12 months for both business and personal reasons.

    a. What is the probability that a subscriber rented a car during the past 12 months for business or personal reasons?

    b. What is the probability that a subscriber did not rent a car during the past 12 months for either business or personal reasons?

29. **Ivy League Admissions.** High school seniors with strong academic records apply to the nation's most selective colleges in greater numbers each year. Because the number of slots remains relatively stable, some colleges reject more early applicants. Suppose that for a recent admissions class, an Ivy League college received 2851 applications for early admission. Of this group, it admitted 1033 students early, rejected 854 outright, and deferred 964 to the regular admission pool for further consideration. In the past, this school has admitted 18% of the deferred early admission applicants during the regular admission process. Counting the students admitted early and the students admitted during the regular admission process, the

total class size was 2375. Let E, R, and D represent the events that a student who applies for early admission is admitted early, rejected outright, or deferred to the regular admissions pool.

a. Use the data to estimate $P(E)$, $P(R)$, and $P(D)$.

b. Are events E and D mutually exclusive? Find $P(E \cap D)$.

c. For the 2375 students who were admitted, what is the probability that a randomly selected student was accepted during early admission?

d. Suppose a student applies for early admission. What is the probability that the student will be admitted for early admission or be deferred and later admitted during the regular admission process?

4.4 Conditional Probability

Often, the probability of an event is influenced by whether a related event already occurred. Suppose we have an event A with probability $P(A)$. If we obtain new information and learn that a related event, denoted by B, already occurred, we will want to take advantage of this information by calculating a new probability for event A. This new probability of event A is called a **conditional probability** and is written $P(A \mid B)$. We use the notation $\mid$ to indicate that we are considering the probability of event A *given* the condition that event B has occurred. Hence, the notation $P(A \mid B)$ reads "the probability of A given B."

As an illustration of the application of conditional probability, consider the situation of the promotion status of male and female officers of a major metropolitan police force in the eastern United States. The police force consists of 1200 officers, 960 men and 240 women. Over the past two years, 324 officers on the police force received promotions. The specific breakdown of promotions for male and female officers is shown in Table 4.4.

After reviewing the promotion record, a committee of female officers raised a discrimination case on the basis that 288 male officers had received promotions, but only 36 female officers had received promotions. The police administration argued that the relatively low number of promotions for female officers was due not to discrimination, but to the fact that relatively few females are members of the police force. Let us show how conditional probability could be used to analyze the discrimination charge.

Let

$$M = \text{event an officer is a man}$$
$$W = \text{event an officer is a woman}$$
$$A = \text{event an officer is promoted}$$
$$A^c = \text{event an officer is not promoted}$$

Dividing the data values in Table 4.4 by the total of 1200 officers enables us to summarize the available information with the following probability values.

TABLE 4.4	Promotion Status of Police Officers Over the Past Two Years		
	Men	**Women**	**Total**
Promoted	288	36	324
Not Promoted	672	204	876
Total	960	240	1200

TABLE 4.5   Joint Probability Table for Promotions

Joint probabilities appear in the body of the table.	Men (M)	Women (W)	Total
Promoted (A)	.24	.03	.27
Not Promoted (A^c)	.56	.17	.73
Total	.80	.20	1.00

Marginal probabilities appear in the margins of the table.

$P(M \cap A) = 288/1200 = .24$ probability that a randomly selected officer is a man *and* is promoted

$P(M \cap A^c) = 672/1200 = .56$ probability that a randomly selected officer is a man *and* is not promoted

$P(W \cap A) = 36/1200 = .03$ probability that a randomly selected officer is a woman *and* is promoted

$P(W \cap A^c) = 204/1200 = .17$ probability that a randomly selected officer is a woman *and* is not promoted

Because each of these values gives the probability of the intersection of two events, the probabilities are called **joint probabilities**. Table 4.5, which provides a summary of the probability information for the police officer promotion situation, is referred to as a *joint probability table.*

The values in the margins of the joint probability table provide the probabilities of each event separately. That is, $P(M) = .80$, $P(W) = .20$, $P(A) = .27$, and $P(A^c) = .73$. These probabilities are referred to as **marginal probabilities** because of their location in the margins of the joint probability table. We note that the marginal probabilities are found by summing the joint probabilities in the corresponding row or column of the joint probability table. For instance, the marginal probability of being promoted is $P(A) = P(M \cap A) + P(W \cap A) = .24 + .03 = .27$. From the marginal probabilities, we see that 80% of the force is male, 20% of the force is female, 27% of all officers received promotions, and 73% were not promoted.

Let us begin the conditional probability analysis by computing the probability that an officer is promoted given that the officer is a man. In conditional probability notation, we are attempting to determine $P(A \mid M)$. To calculate $P(A \mid M)$, we first realize that this notation simply means that we are considering the probability of the event A (promotion) given that the condition designated as event M (the officer is a man) is known to exist. Thus $P(A \mid M)$ tells us that we are now concerned only with the promotion status of the 960 male officers. Because 288 of the 960 male officers received promotions, the probability of being promoted given that the officer is a man is $288/960 = .30$. In other words, given that an officer is a man, that officer had a 30% chance of receiving a promotion over the past two years.

This procedure was easy to apply because the values in Table 4.4 show the number of officers in each category. We now want to demonstrate how conditional probabilities such as $P(A \mid M)$ can be computed directly from related event probabilities rather than the frequency data of Table 4.4.

We have shown that $P(A \mid M) = 288/960 = .30$. Let us now divide both the numerator and denominator of this fraction by 1200, the total number of officers in the study.

$$P(A \mid M) = \frac{288}{960} = \frac{288/1200}{960/1200} = \frac{.24}{.80} = .30$$

We now see that the conditional probability $P(A \mid M)$ can be computed as .24/.80. Refer to the joint probability table (Table 4.5). Note in particular that .24 is the joint probability of A and M; that is, $P(A \cap M) = .24$. Also note that .80 is the marginal probability that a randomly selected officer is a man; that is, $P(M) = .80$. Thus, the conditional probability $P(A \mid M)$ can be computed as the ratio of the joint probability $P(A \cap M)$ to the marginal probability $P(M)$.

$$P(A \mid M) = \frac{P(A \cap M)}{P(M)} = \frac{.24}{.80} = .30$$

The fact that conditional probabilities can be computed as the ratio of a joint probability to a marginal probability provides the following general formula for conditional probability calculations for two events A and B.

CONDITIONAL PROBABILITY

$$P(A \mid B) = \frac{P(A \cap B)}{P(B)} \tag{4.7}$$

or

$$P(B \mid A) = \frac{P(A \cap B)}{P(A)} \tag{4.8}$$

The Venn diagram in Figure 4.8 is helpful in obtaining an intuitive understanding of conditional probability. The circle on the right shows that event B has occurred; the portion of the circle that overlaps with event A denotes the event $(A \cap B)$. We know that once event B has occurred, the only way that we can also observe event A is for the event $(A \cap B)$ to occur. Thus, the ratio $P(A \cap B)/P(B)$ provides the conditional probability that we will observe event A given that event B has already occurred.

Let us return to the issue of discrimination against the female officers. The marginal probability in row 1 of Table 4.5 shows that the probability of promotion of an officer is $P(A) = .27$ (regardless of whether that officer is male or female). However, the critical issue in the discrimination case involves the two conditional probabilities $P(A \mid M)$ and $P(A \mid W)$. That is, what is the probability of a promotion *given* that the officer is a man, and what is the probability of a promotion *given* that the officer is a woman? If these two

FIGURE 4.8   Conditional Probability $P(A \mid B) = P(A \cap B)/P(B)$

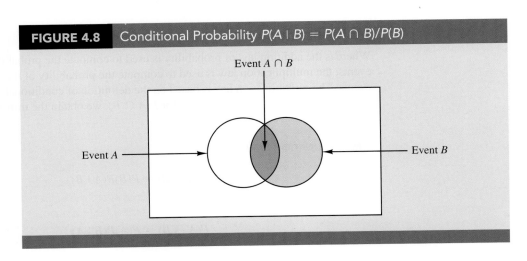

probabilities are equal, a discrimination argument has no basis because the chances of a promotion are the same for male and female officers. However, a difference in the two conditional probabilities will support the position that male and female officers are treated differently in promotion decisions.

We already determined that $P(A \mid M) = .30$. Let us now use the probability values in Table 4.5 and the basic relationship of conditional probability in equation (4.7) to compute the probability that an officer is promoted given that the officer is a woman; that is, $P(A \mid W)$. Using equation (4.7), with W replacing B, we obtain

$$P(A \mid W) = \frac{P(A \cap W)}{P(W)} = \frac{.03}{.20} = .15$$

What conclusion do you draw? The probability of a promotion given that the officer is a man is .30, twice the .15 probability of a promotion given that the officer is a woman. Although the use of conditional probability does not in itself prove that discrimination exists in this case, the conditional probability values support the argument presented by the female officers.

Independent Events

In the preceding illustration, $P(A) = .27$, $P(A \mid M) = .30$, and $P(A \mid W) = .15$. We see that the probability of a promotion (event A) is affected or influenced by whether the officer is a man or a woman. Particularly, because $P(A \mid M) \neq P(A)$, we would say that events A and M are dependent events. That is, the probability of event A (promotion) is altered or affected by knowing that event M (the officer is a man) exists. Similarly, with $P(A \mid W) \neq P(A)$, we would say that events A and W are *dependent events*. However, if the probability of event A is not changed by the existence of event M—that is, $P(A \mid M) = P(A)$—we would say that events A and M are **independent events**. This situation leads to the following definition of the independence of two events.

INDEPENDENT EVENTS

Two events A and B are independent if

$$P(A \mid B) = P(A) \tag{4.9}$$

or

$$P(B \mid A) = P(B) \tag{4.10}$$

Otherwise, the events are dependent.

Multiplication Law

Whereas the addition law of probability is used to compute the probability of a union of two events, the multiplication law is used to compute the probability of the intersection of two events. The multiplication law is based on the definition of conditional probability. Using equations (4.7) and (4.8) and solving for $P(A \cap B)$, we obtain the **multiplication law**.

MULTIPLICATION LAW

$$P(A \cap B) = P(B)P(A \mid B) \tag{4.11}$$

or

$$P(A \cap B) = P(A)P(B \mid A) \tag{4.12}$$

To illustrate the use of the multiplication law, consider a telecommunications company that offers services such as high-speed Internet, cable television, and telephone services. For a particular city, it is known that 84% of the households subscribe to high-speed Internet service. If we let H denote the event that a household subscribes to high-speed Internet service, $P(H) = .84$. In addition, it is known that the probability that a household that already subscribes to high-speed Internet service also subscribes to cable television service (event C) is .75; that is, $P(C \mid H) = .75$. What is the probability that a household subscribes to both high-speed Internet and cable television services? Using the multiplication law, we compute the desired $P(C \cap H)$ as

$$P(C \cap H) = P(H)P(C \mid H) = .84(.75) = .63$$

We now know that 63% of the households subscribe to both high-speed Internet and cable television services.

Before concluding this section, let us consider the special case of the multiplication law when the events involved are independent. Recall that events A and B are independent whenever $P(A \mid B) = P(A)$ or $P(B \mid A) = P(B)$. Hence, using equations (4.11) and (4.12) for the special case of independent events, we obtain the following multiplication law.

MULTIPLICATION LAW FOR INDEPENDENT EVENTS

$$P(A \cap B) = P(A)P(B) \tag{4.13}$$

To compute the probability of the intersection of two independent events, we simply multiply the corresponding probabilities. Note that the multiplication law for independent events provides another way to determine whether A and B are independent. That is, if $P(A \cap B) = P(A)P(B)$, then A and B are independent; if $P(A \cap B) \neq P(A)P(B)$, then A and B are dependent.

As an application of the multiplication law for independent events, consider the situation of a service station manager who knows from past experience that 80% of the customers use a credit card when they purchase gasoline. What is the probability that the next two customers purchasing gasoline will each use a credit card? If we let

$$A = \text{the event that the first customer uses a credit card}$$
$$B = \text{the event that the second customer uses a credit card}$$

then the event of interest is $A \cap B$. Given no other information, we can reasonably assume that A and B are independent events. Thus,

$$P(A \cap B) = P(A)P(B) = (.80)(.80) = .64$$

To summarize this section, we note that our interest in conditional probability is motivated by the fact that events are often related. In such cases, we say the events are dependent and the conditional probability formulas in equations (4.7) and (4.8) must be used to compute the event probabilities. If two events are not related, they are independent; in this case neither event's probability is affected by whether the other event occurred.

NOTES + COMMENTS

Do not confuse the notion of mutually exclusive events with that of independent events. Two events with nonzero probabilities cannot be both mutually exclusive and independent. If one mutually exclusive event is known to occur, the other cannot occur; thus, the probability of the other event occurring is reduced to zero. They are therefore dependent.

EXERCISES

Methods

30. Suppose that we have two events, A and B, with $P(A) = .50$, $P(B) = .60$, and $P(A \cap B) = .40$.
   a. Find $P(A \mid B)$.
   b. Find $P(B \mid A)$.
   c. Are A and B independent? Why or why not?

31. Assume that we have two events, A and B, that are mutually exclusive. Assume further that we know $P(A) = .30$ and $P(B) = .40$.
   a. What is $P(A \cap B)$?
   b. What is $P(A \mid B)$?
   c. A student in statistics argues that the concepts of mutually exclusive events and independent events are really the same, and that if events are mutually exclusive they must be independent. Do you agree with this statement? Use the probability information in this problem to justify your answer.
   d. What general conclusion would you make about mutually exclusive and independent events given the results of this problem?

Applications

32. **Living with Family.** Consider the following example survey results of 18- to 34-year-olds in the United States, in response to the question "Are you currently living with your family?"

	Yes	No	Totals
Men	106	141	247
Women	92	161	253
Totals	198	302	500

   a. Develop the joint probability table for these data and use it to answer the following questions.
   b. What are the marginal probabilities?
   c. What is the probability of living with family given you are an 18- to 34-year-old man in the United States?
   d. What is the probability of living with family given you are an 18- to 34-year-old woman in the United States?
   e. What is the probability of an 18- to 34-year-old in the United States living with family?
   f. If, in the United States, 49.4% of 18- to 34-year-olds are male, do you consider this a good representative sample? Why?

33. **Intent to Pursue MBA.** Students taking the Graduate Management Admissions Test (GMAT) were asked about their undergraduate major and intent to pursue their MBA as a full-time or part-time student. A summary of their responses follows.

		Undergraduate Major			
		Business	Engineering	Other	Totals
Intended	Full-Time	352	197	251	800
Enrollment	Part-Time	150	161	194	505
Status	Totals	502	358	445	1305

a. Develop a joint probability table for these data.
b. Use the marginal probabilities of undergraduate major (business, engineering, or other) to comment on which undergraduate major produces the most potential MBA students.
c. If a student intends to attend classes full-time in pursuit of an MBA degree, what is the probability that the student was an undergraduate engineering major?
d. If a student was an undergraduate business major, what is the probability that the student intends to attend classes full-time in pursuit of an MBA degree?
e. Let A denote the event that the student intends to attend classes full-time in pursuit of an MBA degree, and let B denote the event that the student was an undergraduate business major. Are events A and B independent? Justify your answer.

34. **On-Time Performance of Airlines.** The Bureau of Transportation Statistics reports on-time performance for airlines at major U.S. airports. JetBlue, United, and US Airways share terminal C at Boston's Logan Airport. Suppose that the percentage of on-time flights reported was 76.8% for JetBlue, 71.5% for United, and 82.2% for US Airways. Assume that 30% of the flights arriving at terminal C are JetBlue flights, 32% are United flights, and 38% are US Airways flights.
    a. Develop a joint probability table with three rows (the airlines) and two columns (on-time and late).
    b. An announcement is made that Flight 1382 will be arriving at gate 20 of terminal C. What is the probability that Flight 1382 will arrive on time?
    c. What is the most likely airline for Flight 1382? What is the probability that Flight 1382 is by this airline?
    d. Suppose that an announcement is made saying that Flight 1382 will now be arriving late. What is the most likely airline for this flight? What is the probability that Flight 1382 is by this airline?

35. **Better at Getting Deals.** To better understand how husbands and wives feel about their finances, *Money* magazine conducted a national poll of 1010 married adults age 25 and older with household incomes of $50,000 or more (*Money* website). Consider the following example set of responses to the question, "Who is better at getting deals?"

	Who Is Better?		
Respondent	**I Am**	**My Spouse**	**We Are Equal**
Husband	278	127	102
Wife	290	111	102

a. Develop a joint probability table and use it to answer the following questions.
b. Construct the marginal probabilities for Who Is Better (I Am, My Spouse, We Are Equal). Comment.
c. Given that the respondent is a husband, what is the probability that he feels he is better at getting deals than his wife?
d. Given that the respondent is a wife, what is the probability that she feels she is better at getting deals than her husband?
e. Given a response "My spouse" is better at getting deals, what is the probability that the response came from a husband?
f. Given a response "We are equal," what is the probability that the response came from a husband? What is the probability that the response came from a wife?

36. **NBA Free Throws.** Suppose that a particular NBA player makes 93% of his free throws. Assume that late in a basketball game, this player is fouled and is awarded two shots.

a. What is the probability that he will make both shots?

b. What is the probability that he will make at least one shot?

c. What is the probability that he will miss both shots?

d. Late in a basketball game, a team often intentionally fouls an opposing player in order to stop the game clock. The usual strategy is to intentionally foul the other team's worst free-throw shooter. Assume that the the team's worst free-throw shooter makes 58% of his free-throw shots. Calculate the probabilities for this player as shown in parts (a), (b), and (c), and show that intentionally fouling this player who makes 58% of his free throws is a better strategy than intentionally fouling the player who makes 93% of his free throws. Assume as in parts (a), (b), and (c) that two shots will be awarded.

37. **Giving Up Electronics.** A 2018 Pew Research Center survey found that more Americans believe they could give up their televisions than could give up their cell phones (Pew Research website). Assume that the following table represents the joint probabilities of Americans who could give up their television or cell phone.

		Could Give Up Television		
		Yes	No	
Could Give Up	Yes	.31	.17	.48
Cellphone	No	.38	.14	.52
		.69	.31	

a. What is the probability that a person could give up her cell phone?

b. What is the probability that a person who could give up her cell phone could also give up television?

c. What is the probability that a person who could not give up her cell phone could give up television?

d. Is the probability a person could give up television higher if the person could not give up a cell phone or if the person could give up a cell phone?

38. **Payback of Student Loans.** The Institute for Higher Education Policy, a Washington, D.C.-based research firm, studied the payback of student loans for 1.8 million college students who had student loans that began to become due six years ago (*The Wall Street Journal*). The study found that 50% of the student loans were being paid back in a satisfactory fashion, whereas 50% of the student loans were delinquent. The following joint probability table shows the probabilities of the student loan status and whether or not the student had received a college degree.

		College Degree		
		Yes	No	
Loan	Satisfactory	.26	.24	.50
Status	Delinquent	.16	.34	.50
		.42	.58	

a. What is the probability that a student with a student loan had received a college degree?

b. What is the probability that a student with a student loan had not received a college degree?

c. Given the student had received a college degree, what is the probability that the student has a delinquent loan?

d. Given the student had not received a college degree, what is the probability that the student has a delinquent loan?

e. What is the impact of dropping out of college without a degree for students who have a student loan?

4.5 Bayes' Theorem

In the discussion of conditional probability, we indicated that revising probabilities when new information is obtained is an important phase of probability analysis. Often, we begin the analysis with initial or **prior probability** estimates for specific events of interest. Then, from sources such as a sample, a special report, or a product test, we obtain additional information about the events. Given this new information, we update the prior probability values by calculating revised probabilities, referred to as **posterior probabilities. Bayes' theorem** provides a means for making these probability calculations. The steps in this probability revision process are shown in Figure 4.9.

As an application of Bayes' theorem, consider a manufacturing firm that receives shipments of parts from two different suppliers. Let A_1 denote the event that a part is from supplier 1 and A_2 denote the event that a part is from supplier 2. Currently, 65% of the parts purchased by the company are from supplier 1 and the remaining 35% are from supplier 2. Hence, if a part is selected at random, we would assign the prior probabilities $P(A_1) = .65$ and $P(A_2) = .35$.

The quality of the purchased parts varies with the source of supply. Historical data suggest that the quality ratings of the two suppliers are as shown in Table 4.6. If we let G denote the event that a part is good and B denote the event that a part is bad, the information in Table 4.6 provides the following conditional probability values.

$$P(G \mid A_1) = .98 \quad P(B \mid A_1) = .02$$
$$P(G \mid A_2) = .95 \quad P(B \mid A_2) = .05$$

The tree diagram in Figure 4.10 depicts the process of the firm receiving a part from one of the two suppliers and then discovering that the part is good or bad as a two-step

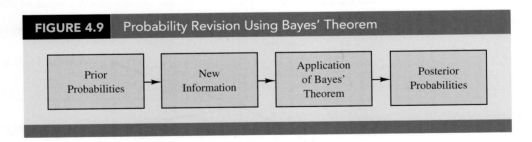

FIGURE 4.9 Probability Revision Using Bayes' Theorem

Prior Probabilities	→	New Information	→	Application of Bayes' Theorem	→	Posterior Probabilities

TABLE 4.6 Historical Quality Levels of Two Suppliers

	Percentage Good Parts	Percentage Bad Parts
Supplier 1	98	2
Supplier 2	95	5

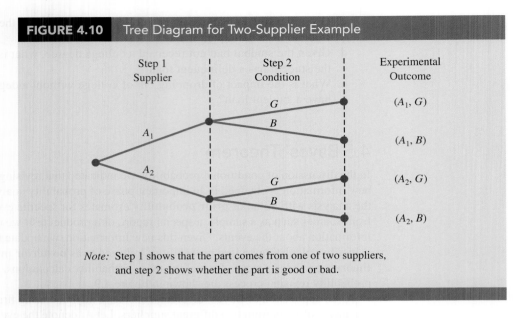

FIGURE 4.10   Tree Diagram for Two-Supplier Example

Note: Step 1 shows that the part comes from one of two suppliers, and step 2 shows whether the part is good or bad.

experiment. We see that four experimental outcomes are possible; two correspond to the part being good and two correspond to the part being bad.

Each of the experimental outcomes is the intersection of two events, so we can use the multiplication rule to compute the probabilities. For instance,

$$P(A_1, G) = P(A_1 \cap G) = P(A_1)P(G \mid A_1)$$

The process of computing these joint probabilities can be depicted in what is called a probability tree (see Figure 4.11). From left to right through the tree, the probabilities for each branch at step 1 are prior probabilities and the probabilities for each branch at step 2 are conditional probabilities. To find the probabilities of each experimental outcome, we simply multiply the probabilities on the branches leading to the outcome. Each of these joint probabilities is shown in Figure 4.11 along with the known probabilities for each branch.

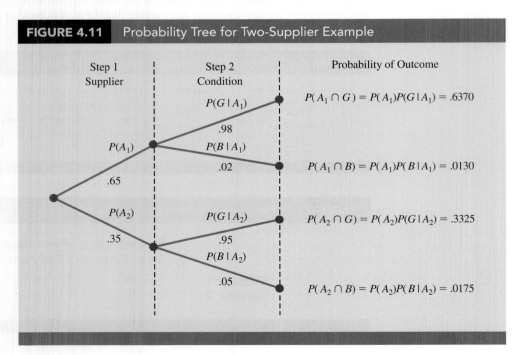

FIGURE 4.11   Probability Tree for Two-Supplier Example

Suppose now that the parts from the two suppliers are used in the firm's manufacturing process and that a machine breaks down because it attempts to process a bad part. Given the information that the part is bad, what is the probability that it came from supplier 1 and what is the probability that it came from supplier 2? With the information in the probability tree (Figure 4.11), Bayes' theorem can be used to answer these questions.

Letting B denote the event that the part is bad, we are looking for the posterior probabilities $P(A_1 \mid B)$ and $P(A_2 \mid B)$. From the law of conditional probability, we know that

$$P(A_1 \mid B) = \frac{P(A_1 \cap B)}{P(B)} \qquad \textbf{(4.14)}$$

Referring to the probability tree, we see that

$$P(A_1 \cap B) = P(A_1)P(B \mid A_1) \qquad \textbf{(4.15)}$$

To find $P(B)$, we note that event B can occur in only two ways: $(A_1 \cap B)$ and $(A_2 \cap B)$. Therefore, we have

$$\begin{aligned} P(B) &= P(A_1 \cap B) + P(A_2 \cap B) \\ &= P(A_1)P(B \mid A_1) + P(A_2)P(B \mid A_2) \end{aligned} \qquad \textbf{(4.16)}$$

Substituting from equations (4.15) and (4.16) into equation (4.14) and writing a similar result for $P(A_2 \mid B)$, we obtain Bayes' theorem for the case of two events.

The Reverend Thomas Bayes (1702–1761), a Presbyterian minister, is credited with the original work leading to the version of Bayes' theorem in use today.

BAYES' THEOREM (TWO-EVENT CASE)

$$P(A_1 \mid B) = \frac{P(A_1)P(B \mid A_1)}{P(A_1)P(B \mid A_1) + P(A_2)P(B \mid A_2)} \qquad \textbf{(4.17)}$$

$$P(A_2 \mid B) = \frac{P(A_2)P(B \mid A_2)}{P(A_1)P(B \mid A_1) + P(A_2)P(B \mid A_2)} \qquad \textbf{(4.18)}$$

Using equation (4.17) and the probability values provided in the example, we have

$$\begin{aligned} P(A_1 \mid B) &= \frac{P(A_1)P(B \mid A_1)}{P(A_1)P(B \mid A_1) + P(A_2)P(B \mid A_2)} \\[2mm] &= \frac{(.65)(.02)}{(.65)(.02) + (.35)(.05)} = \frac{.0130}{.0130 + .0175} \\[2mm] &= \frac{.0130}{.0305} = .4262 \end{aligned}$$

In addition, using equation (4.18), we find $P(A_2 \mid B)$.

$$\begin{aligned} P(A_2 \mid B) &= \frac{(.35)(.05)}{(.65)(.02) + (.35)(.05)} \\[2mm] &= \frac{.0175}{.0130 + .0175} = \frac{.0175}{.0305} = .5738 \end{aligned}$$

Note that in this application we started with a probability of .65 that a part selected at random was from supplier 1. However, given information that the part is bad, the probability that the part is from supplier 1 drops to .4262. In fact, if the part is bad, it has better than a 50–50 chance that it came from supplier 2; that is, $P(A_2 \mid B) = .5738$.

Bayes' theorem is applicable when the events for which we want to compute posterior probabilities are mutually exclusive and their union is the entire sample space.[1] For the case of n mutually exclusive events $A_1, A_2, \ldots, A_n$, whose union is the entire sample space, Bayes' theorem can be used to compute any posterior probability $P(A_i \mid B)$ as shown here.

BAYES' THEOREM

$$P(A_i \mid B) = \frac{P(A_i)P(B \mid A_i)}{P(A_1)P(B \mid A_1) + P(A_2)P(B \mid A_2) + \cdots + P(A_n)P(B \mid A_n)} \qquad (4.19)$$

With prior probabilities $P(A_1), P(A_2), \ldots, P(A_n)$ and the appropriate conditional probabilities $P(B \mid A_1), P(B \mid A_2), \ldots, P(B \mid A_n)$, equation (4.19) can be used to compute the posterior probability of the events $A_1, A_2, \ldots, A_n$.

Tabular Approach

A tabular approach is helpful in conducting the Bayes' theorem calculations. Such an approach is shown in Table 4.7 for the parts supplier problem. The computations shown there are done in the following steps.

Step 1. Prepare the following three columns:

Column 1—The mutually exclusive events A_i for which posterior probabilities are desired

Column 2—The prior probabilities $P(A_i)$ for the events

Column 3—The conditional probabilities $P(B \mid A_i)$ of the new information B given each event

Step 2. In column 4, compute the joint probabilities $P(A_i \cap B)$ for each event and the new information B by using the multiplication law. These joint probabilities are found by multiplying the prior probabilities in column 2 by the corresponding conditional probabilities in column 3; that is, $P(A_i \cap B) = P(A_i)P(B \mid A_i)$.

Step 3. Sum the joint probabilities in column 4. The sum is the probability of the new information, $P(B)$. Thus we see in Table 4.7 that there is a .0130 probability that the part came from supplier 1 and is bad and a .0175 probability that the part came from supplier 2 and is bad. Because these are the only two ways in which a bad part can be obtained, the sum .0130 + .0175 shows an overall probability of .0305 of finding a bad part from the combined shipments of the two suppliers.

TABLE 4.7	Tabular Approach to Bayes' Theorem Calculations for the Two-Supplier Problem			
(1) **Events** A_i	**(2)** **Prior Probabilities** $P(A_i)$	**(3)** **Conditional Probabilities** $P(B \mid A_i)$	**(4)** **Joint Probabilities** $P(A_i \cap B)$	**(5)** **Posterior Probabilities** $P(A_i \mid B)$
A_1	.65	.02	.0130	.0130/.0305 = .4262
A_2	.35	.05	.0175	.0175/.0305 = .5738
	1.00		$P(B) = $ .0305	1.0000

[1]If the union of events is the entire sample space, the events are said to be collectively exhaustive.

Step 4. In column 5, compute the posterior probabilities using the basic relationship of conditional probability.

$$P(A_i \mid B) = \frac{P(A_i \cap B)}{P(B)}$$

Note that the joint probabilities $P(A_i \cap B)$ are in column 4 and the probability $P(B)$ is the sum of column 4.

NOTES + COMMENTS

1. Bayes' theorem is used extensively in decision analysis. The prior probabilities are often subjective estimates provided by a decision maker. Sample information is obtained and posterior probabilities are computed for use in choosing the best decision.

2. An event and its complement are mutually exclusive, and their union is the entire sample space. Thus, Bayes' theorem is always applicable for computing posterior probabilities of an event and its complement.

EXERCISES

Methods

39. The prior probabilities for events A_1 and A_2 are $P(A_1) = .40$ and $P(A_2) = .60$. It is also known that $P(A_1 \cap A_2) = 0$. Suppose $P(B \mid A_1) = .20$ and $P(B \mid A_2) = .05$.
    a. Are A_1 and A_2 mutually exclusive? Explain.
    b. Compute $P(A_1 \cap B)$ and $P(A_2 \cap B)$.
    c. Compute $P(B)$.
    d. Apply Bayes' theorem to compute $P(A_1 \mid B)$ and $P(A_2 \mid B)$.
40. The prior probabilities for events A_1, A_2, and A_3 are $P(A_1) = .20$, $P(A_2) = .50$, and $P(A_3) = .30$. The conditional probabilities of event B given A_1, A_2, and A_3 are $P(B \mid A_1) = .50$, $P(B \mid A_2) = .40$, and $P(B \mid A_3) = .30$.
    a. Compute $P(B \cap A_1)$, $P(B \cap A_2)$, and $P(B \cap A_3)$.
    b. Apply Bayes' theorem, equation (4.19), to compute the posterior probability $P(A_2 \mid B)$.
    c. Use the tabular approach to applying Bayes' theorem to compute $P(A_1 \mid B)$, $P(A_2 \mid B)$, and $P(A_3 \mid B)$.

Applications

41. **Consulting Firm Bids.** A consulting firm submitted a bid for a large research project. The firm's management initially felt they had a 50–50 chance of getting the project. However, the agency to which the bid was submitted subsequently requested additional information on the bid. Past experience indicates that for 75% of the successful bids and 40% of the unsuccessful bids the agency requested additional information.
    a. What is the prior probability of the bid being successful (that is, prior to the request for additional information)?
    b. What is the conditional probability of a request for additional information given that the bid will ultimately be successful?
    c. Compute the posterior probability that the bid will be successful given a request for additional information.
42. **Credit Card Defaults.** A local bank reviewed its credit card policy with the intention of recalling some of its credit cards. In the past approximately 5% of cardholders defaulted, leaving the bank unable to collect the outstanding balance. Hence, management established a prior probability of .05 that any particular cardholder will default. The bank also found that the probability of missing a monthly payment

is .20 for customers who do not default. Of course, the probability of missing a monthly payment for those who default is 1.

   a. Given that a customer missed one or more monthly payments, compute the posterior probability that the customer will default.

   b. The bank would like to recall its card if the probability that a customer will default is greater than .20. Should the bank recall its card if the customer misses a monthly payment? Why or why not?

43. **Prostate Cancer Screening.** According to a 2018 article in *Esquire* magazine, approximately 70% of males over age 70 will develop cancerous cells in their prostate. Prostate cancer is second only to skin cancer as the most common form of cancer for males in the United States. One of the most common tests for the detection of prostate cancer is the prostate-specific antigen (PSA) test. However, this test is known to have a high false-positive rate (tests that come back positive for cancer when no cancer is present). Suppose there is a .02 probability that a male patient has prostate cancer before testing. The probability of a false-positive test is .75, and the probability of a false-negative (no indication of cancer when cancer is actually present) is .20.

   a. What is the probability that the male patient has prostate cancer if the PSA test comes back positive?

   b. What is the probability that the male patient has prostate cancer if the PSA test comes back negative?

   c. For older men, the prior probability of having cancer increases. Suppose that the prior probability of the male patient is .3 rather than .02. What is the probability that the male patient has prostate cancer if the PSA test comes back positive? What is the probability that the male patient has prostate cancer if the PSA test comes back negative?

   d. What can you infer about the PSA test from the results of parts (a), (b), and (c)?

44. **Golf Equipment Website Visitors.** ParFore created a website to market golf equipment and golf apparel. Management would like a special pop-up offer to appear for female website visitors and a different special pop-up offer to appear for male website visitors. From a sample of past website visitors, ParFore's management learned that 60% of the visitors are male and 40% are female.

   a. What is the probability that a current visitor to the website is female?

   b. Suppose 30% of ParFore's female visitors previously visited the Dillard's department store website and 10% of ParFore's male visitors previously visited the Dillard's department store website. If the current visitor to ParFore's website previously visited the Dillard's website, what is the revised probability that the current visitor is female? Should the ParFore's website display the special offer that appeals to female visitors or the special offer that appeals to male visitors?

45. **Americans Without Health Insurance.** The National Center for Health Statistics, housed within the U.S. Centers for Disease Control and Prevention (CDC), tracks the number of adults in the United States who have health insurance. According to this agency, the uninsured rates for Americans in 2018 are as follows: 5.1% of those under the age of 18, 12.4% of those ages 18–64, and 1.1% of those 65 and older do not have health insurance (CDC website). Approximately 22.8% of Americans are under age 18, and 61.4% of Americans are ages 18–64.

   a. What is the probability that a randomly selected person in the United States is 65 or older?

   b. Given that the person is an uninsured American, what is the probability that the person is 65 or older?

SUMMARY

In this chapter we introduced basic probability concepts and illustrated how probability analysis can be used to provide helpful information for decision making. We described how probability can be interpreted as a numerical measure of the likelihood that an event will occur. In addition, we saw that the probability of an event can be computed either by summing the probabilities of the experimental outcomes (sample points) comprising the event or by using the relationships established by the addition, conditional probability, and multiplication laws of probability. For cases in which additional information is available, we showed how Bayes' theorem can be used to obtain revised or posterior probabilities.

GLOSSARY

Addition law A probability law used to compute the probability of the union of two events. It is $P(A \cup B) = P(A) + P(B) - P(A \cap B)$. For mutually exclusive events, $P(A \cap B) = 0$; in this case the addition law reduces to $P(A \cup B) = P(A) + P(B)$.

Basic requirements for assigning probabilities Two requirements that restrict the manner in which probability assignments can be made: (1) for each experimental outcome E_i we must have $0 \leq P(E_i) \leq 1$; (2) considering all experimental outcomes, we must have $P(E_1) + P(E_2) + \ldots + P(E_n) = 1.0$.

Bayes' theorem A method used to compute posterior probabilities.

Classical method A method of assigning probabilities that is appropriate when all the experimental outcomes are equally likely.

Combination In an experiment we may be interested in determining the number of ways n objects may be selected from among N objects without regard to the *order in which the n objects are selected*. Each selection of n objects is called a combination and the total number of combinations of N objects taken n at a time is $C_n^N = \binom{N}{n} = \dfrac{N!}{n!(N-n)!}$ for $n = 0, 1, 2, \ldots, N$.

Complement of A The event consisting of all sample points that are not in A.

Conditional probability The probability of an event given that another event already occurred. The conditional probability of A given B is $P(A \mid B) = P(A \cap B)/P(B)$.

Event A collection of sample points.

Experiment A process that generates well-defined outcomes.

Independent events Two events A and B where $P(A \mid B) = P(A)$ or $P(B \mid A) = P(B)$; that is, the events have no influence on each other.

Intersection of A and B The event containing the sample points belonging to both A and B. The intersection is denoted $A \cap B$.

Joint probability The probability of two events both occurring; that is, the probability of the intersection of two events.

Marginal probability The values in the margins of a joint probability table that provide the probabilities of each event separately.

Multiple-step experiment An experiment that can be described as a sequence of steps. If a multiple-step experiment has k steps with n_1 possible outcomes on the first step, n_2 possible outcomes on the second step, and so on, the total number of experimental outcomes is given by $(n_1)(n_2) \ldots (n_k)$.

Multiplication law A probability law used to compute the probability of the intersection of two events. It is $P(A \cap B) = P(B)P(A \mid B)$ or $P(A \cap B) = P(A)P(B \mid A)$. For independent events it reduces to $P(A \cap B) = P(A)P(B)$.

Mutually exclusive events Events that have no sample points in common; that is, $A \cap B$ is empty and $P(A \cap B) = 0$.

Permutation In an experiment we may be interested in determining the number of ways n objects may be selected from among N objects when the *order in which the n objects are selected* is important. Each ordering of n objects is called a permutation and the total number of permutations of N objects taken n at a time is $P_n^N = n!\binom{N}{n} = \dfrac{N!}{(N-n)!}$ for $n = 0, 1, 2, \ldots, N$.

Posterior probabilities Revised probabilities of events based on additional information.

Prior probabilities Initial estimates of the probabilities of events.

Probability A numerical measure of the likelihood that an event will occur.

Relative frequency method A method of assigning probabilities that is appropriate when data are available to estimate the proportion of the time the experimental outcome will occur if the experiment is repeated a large number of times.

Sample point An element of the sample space. A sample point represents an experimental outcome.

Sample space The set of all experimental outcomes.

Subjective method A method of assigning probabilities on the basis of judgment.

Tree diagram A graphical representation that helps in visualizing a multiple-step experiment.

Union of A and B The event containing all sample points belonging to A or B or both. The union is denoted $A \cup B$.

Venn diagram A graphical representation for showing symbolically the sample space and operations involving events in which the sample space is represented by a rectangle and events are represented as circles within the sample space.

KEY FORMULAS

Counting Rule for Combinations

$$C_n^N = \binom{N}{n} = \frac{N!}{n!(N-n)!} \tag{4.1}$$

Counting Rule for Permutations

$$P_n^N = n!\binom{N}{n} = \frac{N!}{(N-n)!} \tag{4.2}$$

Computing Probability Using the Complement

$$P(A) = 1 - P(A^c) \tag{4.5}$$

Addition Law

$$P(A \cup B) = P(A) + P(B) - P(A \cap B) \tag{4.6}$$

Conditional Probability

$$P(A \mid B) = \frac{P(A \cap B)}{P(B)} \tag{4.7}$$

$$P(B \mid A) = \frac{P(A \cap B)}{P(A)} \tag{4.8}$$

Multiplication Law

$$P(A \cap B) = P(B)P(A \mid B) \tag{4.11}$$

$$P(A \cap B) = P(A)P(B \mid A) \tag{4.12}$$

Multiplication Law for Independent Events

$$P(A \cap B) = P(A)P(B) \tag{4.13}$$

Bayes' Theorem

$$P(A_i \mid B) = \frac{P(A_i)P(B \mid A_i)}{P(A_1)P(B \mid A_1) + P(A_2)P(B \mid A_2) + \cdots + P(A_n)P(B \mid A_n)} \tag{4.19}$$

SUPPLEMENTARY EXERCISES

46. **Time in Vacation Until Relaxed.** A *USA Today* survey of adults aged 18 and older conducted by Princess Cruises asked how many days into your vacation does it take until you feel truly relaxed. The responses were as follows: 422—a day or less; 181—2 days; 80—3 days; 121—4 or more days; and 201—never feel relaxed.

a. How many adults participated in the Princess Cruises survey?
b. What response has the highest probability? What is the probability of this response?
c. What is the probability a respondent never feels truly relaxed on a vacation?
d. What is the probability it takes a respondent 2 or more days to feel truly relaxed?

47. **Financial Manager Investments.** A financial manager made two new investments—one in the oil industry and one in municipal bonds. After a one-year period, each of the investments will be classified as either successful or unsuccessful. Consider the making of the two investments as a random experiment.
    a. How many sample points exist for this experiment?
    b. Show a tree diagram and list the sample points.
    c. Let O = the event that the oil industry investment is successful and M = the event that the municipal bond investment is successful. List the sample points in O and in M.
    d. List the sample points in the union of the events ($O \cup M$).
    e. List the sample points in the intersection of the events ($O \cap M$).
    f. Are events O and M mutually exclusive? Explain.

48. **Opinions About Television Programs.** Below are the results of a survey of 1364 individuals who were asked if they use social media and other websites to voice their opinions about television programs.

	Uses Social Media and Other Websites to Voice Opinions About Television Programs	Doesn't Use Social Media and Other Websites to Voice Opinions About Television Programs
Female	395	291
Male	323	355

a. What is the probability a respondent is female?
b. What is the conditional probability a respondent uses social media and other websites to voice opinions about television programs given the respondent is female?
c. Let F denote the event that the respondent is female and A denote the event that the respondent uses social media and other websites to voice opinions about television programs. Are events F and A independent?

49. **Treatment-Caused Injuries.** A study of 31,000 hospital admissions in New York State found that 4% of the admissions led to treatment-caused injuries. One-seventh of these treatment-caused injuries resulted in death, and one-fourth were caused by negligence. Malpractice claims were filed in one out of 7.5 cases involving negligence, and payments were made in one out of every two claims.
    a. What is the probability a person admitted to the hospital will suffer a treatment-caused injury due to negligence?
    b. What is the probability a person admitted to the hospital will die from a treatment-caused injury?
    c. In the case of a negligent treatment-caused injury, what is the probability a malpractice claim will be paid?

50. **Viewer Responses to New Television Show.** A survey to determine viewer response to a new television show obtained the following data.

Rating	Frequency
Poor	4
Below average	8
Average	11
Above average	14
Excellent	13

a. What is the probability that a randomly selected viewer will rate the new show as average or better?

b. What is the probability that a randomly selected viewer will rate the new show below average or worse?

51. **Highest Level of Education and Household Income.** The U.S. Census Bureau serves as the leading source of quantitative data about the nation's people and economy. The following crosstabulation shows the number of households (1000s) and the household income by the highest level of education for the head of household (U.S. Census Bureau website, https://www.census.gov/library/publications/2017/acs/acsbr16-02.html). Only households in which the head has a high school diploma or more are included.

| | Household Income | | | | |
Highest Level of Education	Under $25,000	$25,000 to $49,999	$50,000 to $99,999	$100,000 and Over	Total
High school graduate	9880	9970	9441	3482	32,773
Bachelor's degree	2484	4164	7666	7817	22,131
Master's degree	685	1205	3019	4094	9003
Doctoral degree	79	160	422	1076	1737
Total	13,128	15,499	20,548	16,469	65,644

a. Develop a joint probability table.

b. What is the probability of the head of one of these households having a master's degree or more education?

c. What is the probability of a household headed by someone with a high school diploma earning $100,000 or more?

d. What is the probability of one of these households having an income below $25,000?

e. What is the probability of a household headed by someone with a bachelor's degree earning less than $25,000?

f. Is household income independent of educational level?

52. **MBA New-Matriculants Survey.** An MBA new-matriculants survey provided the following data for 2018 students.

		Applied to More Than One School	
		Yes	No
	23 and under	207	201
Age	24–26	299	379
Group	27–30	185	268
	31–35	66	193
	36 and over	51	169

a. For a randomly selected MBA student, prepare a joint probability table for the experiment consisting of observing the student's age and whether the student applied to one or more schools.

b. What is the probability that a randomly selected applicant is 23 or under?

c. What is the probability that a randomly selected applicant is older than 26?

d. What is the probability that a randomly selected applicant applied to more than one school?

53. **MBA New-Matriculants Survey** Refer again to the data from the MBA new-matriculants survey in exercise 52.

a. Given that a person applied to more than one school, what is the probability that the person is 24–26 years old?

b. Given that a person is in the 36-and-over age group, what is the probability that the person applied to more than one school?

c. What is the probability that a person is 24–26 years old or applied to more than one school?

d. Suppose a person is known to have applied to only one school. What is the probability that the person is 31 or more years old?

e. Is the number of schools applied to independent of age? Explain.

54. **Internet Sites Collecting User Information.** The Pew Internet & American Life project conducted a survey that included several questions about how Internet users feel about search engines and other websites collecting information about them and using this information either to shape search results or target advertising to them. In one question, participants were asked, "If a search engine kept track of what you search for, and then used that information to personalize your future search results, how would you feel about that?" Respondents could indicate either "Would *not* be okay with it because you feel it is an invasion of your privacy" or "Would be *okay* with it, even if it means they are gathering information about you." Frequencies of responses by age group are summarized in the following table.

Age	Not Okay	Okay
18–29	.1485	.0604
30–49	.2273	.0907
50+	.4008	.0723

a. What is the probability a survey respondent will say she or he is *not okay* with this practice?

b. Given a respondent is 30–49 years old, what is the probability the respondent will say she or he is *okay* with this practice?

c. Given a respondent says she or he is *not okay* with this practice, what is the probability the respondent is 50+ years old?

d. Is the attitude about this practice independent of the age of the respondent? Why or why not?

e. Do attitudes toward this practice for respondents who are 18–29 years old and respondents who are 50+ years old differ?

55. **Advertisements and Product Purchases.** A large consumer goods company ran a television advertisement for one of its soap products. On the basis of a survey that was conducted, probabilities were assigned to the following events.

$$B = \text{individual purchased the product}$$
$$S = \text{individual recalls seeing the advertisement}$$
$$B \cap S = \text{individual purchased the product and recalls seeing the advertisement}$$

The probabilities assigned were $P(B) = .20$, $P(S) = .40$, and $P(B \cap S) = .12$.

a. What is the probability of an individual's purchasing the product given that the individual recalls seeing the advertisement? Does seeing the advertisement increase the probability that the individual will purchase the product? As a decision maker, would you recommend continuing the advertisement (assuming that the cost is reasonable)?

b. Assume that individuals who do not purchase the company's soap product buy from its competitors. What would be your estimate of the company's market share? Would you expect that continuing the advertisement will increase the company's market share? Why or why not?

c. The company also tested another advertisement and assigned it values of $P(S) = .30$ and $P(B \cap S) = .10$. What is $P(B \mid S)$ for this other advertisement? Which advertisement seems to have had the bigger effect on customer purchases?

56. **Days Listed Until Sold.** Cooper Realty is a small real estate company located in Albany, New York, specializing primarily in residential listings. They recently became interested

in determining the likelihood of one of their listings being sold within a certain number of days. An analysis of company sales of 800 homes in previous years produced the following data.

		Days Listed Until Sold			
		Under 30	31–90	Over 90	Total
Initial Asking Price	**Under $150,000**	50	40	10	100
	$150,000–$199,999	20	150	80	250
	$200,000–$250,000	20	280	100	400
	Over $250,000	10	30	10	50
	Total	100	500	200	800

a. If A is defined as the event that a home is listed for more than 90 days before being sold, estimate the probability of A.
b. If B is defined as the event that the initial asking price is under $150,000, estimate the probability of B.
c. What is the probability of $A \cap B$?
d. Assuming that a contract was just signed to list a home with an initial asking price of less than $150,000, what is the probability that the home will take Cooper Realty more than 90 days to sell?
e. Are events A and B independent?

57. **Lost-Time Accidents.** A company studied the number of lost-time accidents occurring at its Brownsville, Texas, plant. Historical records show that 6% of the employees suffered lost-time accidents last year. Management believes that a special safety program will reduce such accidents to 5% during the current year. In addition, it estimates that 15% of employees who had lost-time accidents last year will experience a lost-time accident during the current year.
a. What percentage of the employees will experience lost-time accidents in both years?
b. What percentage of the employees will suffer at least one lost-time accident over the two-year period?

58. **Students Studying Abroad.** Many undergraduate students in the U.S. study abroad as part of their education. Assume that 60% of the undergraduate students who study abroad are female and that 49% of the undergraduate students who do not study abroad are female.
a. Given a female undergraduate student, what is the probability that she studies abroad?
b. Given a male undergraduate student, what is the probability that he studies abroad?
c. What is the overall percentage of full-time female undergraduate students? What is the overall percentage of full-time male undergraduate students?

59. **Finding Oil in Alaska.** An oil company purchased an option on land in Alaska. Preliminary geologic studies assigned the following prior probabilities.

$$P(\text{high-quality oil}) = .50$$
$$P(\text{medium-quality oil}) = .20$$
$$P(\text{no oil}) = .30$$

a. What is the probability of finding oil?
b. After 200 feet of drilling on the first well, a soil test is taken. The probabilities of finding the particular type of soil identified by the test follow.

$$P(\text{soil} \mid \text{high-quality oil}) = .20$$
$$P(\text{soil} \mid \text{medium-quality oil}) = .80$$
$$P(\text{soil} \mid \text{no oil}) = .20$$

How should the firm interpret the soil test? What are the revised probabilities, and what is the new probability of finding oil?

60. **Spam Email Filters.** A study by *Forbes* indicated that the five most common words appearing in spam emails are *shipping!, today!, here!, available,* and *fingertips!*. Many spam filters separate spam from ham (email not considered to be spam) through application of Bayes' theorem. Suppose that for one email account, 1 in every 10 messages is spam and the proportions of spam messages that have the five most common words in spam email are given below.

shipping!	.051
today!	.045
here!	.034
available	.014
fingertips!	.014

Also suppose that the proportions of ham messages that have these words are

shipping!	.0015
today!	.0022
here!	.0022
available	.0041
fingertips!	.0011

a. If a message includes the word *shipping!,* what is the probability the message is spam? If a message includes the word *shipping!,* what is the probability the message is ham? Should messages that include the word *shipping!* be flagged as spam?
b. If a message includes the word *today!,* what is the probability the message is spam? If a message includes the word *here!,* what is the probability the message is spam? Which of these two words is a stronger indicator that a message is spam? Why?
c. If a message includes the word *available,* what is the probability the message is spam? If a message includes the word *fingertips!,* what is the probability the message is spam? Which of these two words is a stronger indicator that a message is spam? Why?
d. What insights do the results of parts (b) and (c) yield about what enables a spam filter that uses Bayes' theorem to work effectively?

CASE PROBLEM 1: HAMILTON COUNTY JUDGES

Hamilton County judges try thousands of cases per year. In an overwhelming majority of the cases disposed, the verdict stands as rendered. However, some cases are appealed, and of those appealed, some of the cases are reversed. Kristen DelGuzzi of *The Cincinnati Enquirer* conducted a study of cases handled by Hamilton County judges over a three-year period. Shown in Table 4.8 are the results for 182,908 cases handled (disposed) by 38 judges in Common Pleas Court, Domestic Relations Court, and Municipal Court. Two of the judges (Dinkelacker and Hogan) did not serve in the same court for the entire three-year period.

The purpose of the newspaper's study was to evaluate the performance of the judges. Appeals are often the result of mistakes made by judges, and the newspaper wanted to know which judges were doing a good job and which were making too many mistakes. You are called in to assist in the data analysis. Use your knowledge of probability and conditional probability to help with the ranking of the judges. You also may be able to analyze the likelihood of appeal and reversal for cases handled by different courts.

Managerial Report

Prepare a report with your rankings of the judges. Also, include an analysis of the likelihood of appeal and case reversal in the three courts. At a minimum, your report should include the following:

1. The probability of cases being appealed and reversed in the three different courts.
2. The probability of a case being appealed for each judge.
3. The probability of a case being reversed for each judge.
4. The probability of reversal given an appeal for each judge.
5. Rank the judges within each court. State the criteria you used and provide a rationale for your choice.

Judge

TABLE 4.8	Total Cases Disposed, Appealed, and Reversed in Hamilton County Courts

Common Pleas Court

Judge	Total Cases Disposed	Appealed Cases	Reversed Cases
Fred Cartolano	3037	137	12
Thomas Crush	3372	119	10
Patrick Dinkelacker	1258	44	8
Timothy Hogan	1954	60	7
Robert Kraft	3138	127	7
William Mathews	2264	91	18
William Morrissey	3032	121	22
Norbert Nadel	2959	131	20
Arthur Ney, Jr.	3219	125	14
Richard Niehaus	3353	137	16
Thomas Nurre	3000	121	6
John O'Connor	2969	129	12
Robert Ruehlman	3205	145	18
J. Howard Sundermann	955	60	10
Ann Marie Tracey	3141	127	13
Ralph Winkler	3089	88	6
Total	43,945	1762	199

Domestic Relations Court

Judge	Total Cases Disposed	Appealed Cases	Reversed Cases
Penelope Cunningham	2729	7	1
Patrick Dinkelacker	6001	19	4
Deborah Gaines	8799	48	9
Ronald Panioto	12,970	32	3
Total	30,499	106	17

Municipal Court

Judge	Total Cases Disposed	Appealed Cases	Reversed Cases
Mike Allen	6149	43	4
Nadine Allen	7812	34	6
Timothy Black	7954	41	6
David Davis	7736	43	5
Leslie Isaiah Gaines	5282	35	13
Karla Grady	5253	6	0
Deidra Hair	2532	5	0
Dennis Helmick	7900	29	5
Timothy Hogan	2308	13	2
James Patrick Kenney	2798	6	1
Joseph Luebbers	4698	25	8
William Mallory	8277	38	9
Melba Marsh	8219	34	7
Beth Mattingly	2971	13	1
Albert Mestemaker	4975	28	9
Mark Painter	2239	7	3
Jack Rosen	7790	41	13
Mark Schweikert	5403	33	6
David Stockdale	5371	22	4
John A. West	2797	4	2
Total	108,464	500	104

CASE PROBLEM 2: ROB'S MARKET

Rob's Market (RM) is a regional food store chain in the southwest United States. David White, Director of Business Intelligence for RM, would like to initiate a study of the purchase behavior of customers who use the RM loyalty card (a card that customers scan at checkout to qualify for discounted prices). The use of the loyalty card allows RM to capture what is known as "point-of-sale" data, that is, a list of products purchased by customers as they check out of the market. David feels that better understanding of which products tend to be purchased together could lead to insights for better pricing and display strategies as well as a better understanding of sales and the potential impact of different levels of coupon discounts. This type of analysis is known as *market basket analysis,* as it is a study of what different customers have in their shopping baskets as they check out of the store.

MarketBasket

As a prototype study, David wants to investigate customer buying behavior with regard to bread, jelly, and peanut butter. RM's Information Technology (IT) group, at David's request, has provided a data set of purchases by 1000 customers over a one-week period. The data set is in the file *MarketBasket,* and it contains the following variables for each customer:

- Bread—wheat, white, or none
- Jelly—grape, strawberry, or none
- Peanut butter—creamy, natural, or none

The variables appear in the above order from left to right in the data set, where each row is a customer. For example, the first record of the data set is

> white   grape   none

which means that customer 1 purchased white bread, grape jelly, and no peanut butter. The second record is

> white   strawberry   none

which means that customer 2 purchased white bread, strawberry jelly, and no peanut butter. The sixth record in the data set is

> none   none   none

which means that the sixth customer did not purchase bread, jelly, or peanut butter.

Other records are interpreted in a similar fashion.

David would like you to do an initial study of the data to get a better understanding of RM customer behavior with regard to these three products.

Managerial Report

Prepare a report that gives insight into the purchase behavior of customers who use the RM loyalty card. At a minimum your report should include estimates of the following:

1. The probability that a random customer does not purchase any of the three products (bread, jelly, or peanut butter).
2. The probability that a random customer purchases white bread.
3. The probability that a random customer purchases wheat bread.
4. The probability that a random customer purchases grape jelly given that he or she purchases white bread.
5. The probability that a random customer purchases strawberry jelly given that he or she purchases white bread.
6. The probability that a random customer purchases creamy peanut butter given that he or she purchases white bread.
7. The probability that a random customer purchases natural peanut butter given that he or she purchases white bread.
8. The probability that a random customer purchases creamy peanut butter given that he or she purchases wheat bread.
9. The probability that a random customer purchases natural peanut butter given that he or she purchases wheat bread.
10. The probability that a random customer purchases white bread, grape jelly, and creamy peanut butter.

Chapter 5

Discrete Probability Distributions

CONTENTS

STATISTICS IN PRACTICE

Voter Waiting Times in Elections*

Most people in the United States who vote during an election do so by arriving to a specific location known as a *precinct polling location* and casting a ballot in person. Although voting by mail is becoming more common and is the standard mechanism for voting in the state of Oregon, most voters outside Oregon still cast their ballot in person. In recent elections, some voters have experienced extremely long waiting times to cast their ballots. This has been a cause of some concern because it could potentially disenfranchise voters who cannot wait in line to cast their ballots.

Statisticians have developed models for elections that estimate the arrivals to precinct polling locations and wait times for voters. These models use mathematical equations from the field of queueing theory to estimate wait times for voters. The wait time depends on many factors, including how many voting machines or voting booths are available at the polling precinct location, the length of the election ballot, and the arrival rate of voters.

Data collected on voter arrivals show that voter arrivals follow a probability distribution known as the *Poisson distribution*. Using the properties of the Poisson distribution, statisticians can compute the probabilities for the number of voters arriving during any time period. For example, let *x* = the number of

voters arriving to a particular precinct polling location during a one-minute period. Assuming that this location has a mean arrival rate of two voters per minute, the following table shows the probabilities for the number of voters arriving during a one-minute period.

x	Probability
0	.1353
1	.2707
2	.2707
3	.1804
4	.0902
5 or more	.0527

Using these probabilities as inputs into their models, the statisticians use queueing theory to estimate voter wait times at each precinct polling location. The statisticians can then make recommendations on how many voting machines or voting booths to place at each precinct polling location to control voter waiting times.

Discrete probability distributions, such as the Poisson distribution used to model voter arrivals to precinct polling locations, are the topic of this chapter. In addition to the Poisson distribution, you will learn about the binomial and the hypergeometric distributions and how they can be used to provide helpful probability information.

*This Statistics in Practice is based on research done by Muer Yang, Michael J. Fry, Ted Allen, and W. David Kelton.

In this chapter we extend the study of probability by introducing the concepts of random variables and probability distributions. Random variables and probability distributions are models for populations of data. The values of what are called random variables represent the values of the data and the probability distribution provides either the probability of each data value or a rule for computing the probability of each data value or a set of data values. The focus of this chapter is on probability distributions for discrete data, that is, discrete probability distributions.

We will introduce two types of discrete probability distributions. The first type is a table with one column for the values of the random variable and a second column for the associated probabilities. We will see that the rules for assigning probabilities to experimental outcomes introduced in Chapter 4 are used to assign probabilities for such a distribution. The second type of discrete probability distribution uses a special mathematical function to compute the probabilities for each value of the random variable. We present three probability distributions of this type that are widely used in practice: the binomial, Poisson, and hypergeometric distributions.

5.1 Random Variables

The concept of an experiment and its associated experimental outcomes are discussed in Chapter 4.

A random variable provides a means for describing experimental outcomes using numerical values. Random variables must assume numerical values.

> **RANDOM VARIABLE**
>
> A **random variable** is a numerical description of the outcome of an experiment.

In effect, a random variable associates a numerical value with each possible experimental outcome. The particular numerical value of the random variable depends on the outcome of the experiment. A random variable can be classified as being either *discrete* or *continuous* depending on the numerical values it assumes.

Discrete Random Variables

A random variable that may assume either a finite number of values or an infinite sequence of values such as 0, 1, 2, . . . is referred to as a **discrete random variable**. For example, consider the experiment of an accountant taking the certified public accountant (CPA) examination. The examination has four parts. We can define a random variable as $x =$ the number of parts of the CPA examination passed. It is a discrete random variable because it may assume the finite number of values 0, 1, 2, 3, or 4.

As another example of a discrete random variable, consider the experiment of cars arriving at a tollbooth. The random variable of interest is $x =$ the number of cars arriving during a one-day period. The possible values for x come from the sequence of integers 0, 1, 2, and so on. Hence, x is a discrete random variable assuming one of the values in this infinite sequence.

Although the outcomes of many experiments can naturally be described by numerical values, others cannot. For example, a survey question might ask an individual to recall the message in a recent television commercial. This experiment would have two possible outcomes: The individual cannot recall the message and the individual can recall the message. We can still describe these experimental outcomes numerically by defining the discrete random variable x as follows: let $x = 0$ if the individual cannot recall the message and $x = 1$ if the individual can recall the message. The numerical values for this random variable are arbitrary (we could use 5 and 10), but they are acceptable in terms of the definition of a random variable—namely, x is a random variable because it provides a numerical description of the outcome of the experiment.

Table 5.1 provides some additional examples of discrete random variables. Note that in each example the discrete random variable assumes a finite number of values or an infinite sequence of values such as 0, 1, 2, ... These types of discrete random variables are discussed in detail in this chapter.

Continuous Random Variables

A random variable that may assume any numerical value in an interval or collection of intervals is called a **continuous random variable**. Experimental outcomes based on measurement scales such as time, weight, distance, and temperature can be described by continuous random variables. For example, consider an experiment of monitoring incoming telephone calls to the claims office of a major insurance company. Suppose the random variable of interest is $x =$ the time between consecutive incoming calls in minutes. This random variable may assume any value in the interval $x \geq 0$. Actually, an infinite number of values are possible for x, including values such as 1.26 minutes, 2.751 minutes, 4.3333 minutes, and so on. As another example, consider a 90-mile section of interstate highway I-75 north of Atlanta, Georgia. For an emergency ambulance service located in Atlanta, we might

TABLE 5.1	Examples of Discrete Random Variables	

Random Experiment	Random Variable (x)	Possible Values for the Random Variable
Flip a coin	Face of coin showing	1 if heads; 0 if tails
Roll a die	Number of dots showing on top of die	1, 2, 3, 4, 5, 6
Contact five customers	Number of customers who place an order	0, 1, 2, 3, 4, 5
Operate a health care clinic for one day	Number of patients who arrive	0, 1, 2, 3, . . .
Offer a customer the choice of two products	Product chosen by customer	0 if none; 1 if choose product A; 2 if choose product B

define the random variable as $x =$ number of miles to the location of the next traffic accident along this section of I-75. In this case, x would be a continuous random variable assuming any value in the interval $0 \leq x \leq 90$. Additional examples of continuous random variables are listed in Table 5.2. Note that each example describes a random variable that may assume any value in an interval of values. Continuous random variables and their probability distributions will be the topic of Chapter 6.

TABLE 5.2	Examples of Continuous Random Variables	

Random Experiment	Random Variable (x)	Possible Values for the Random Variable
Customer visits a web page	Time customer spends on web page in minutes	$x \geq 0$
Fill a soft drink can (max capacity = 12.1 ounces)	Number of ounces	$0 \leq x \leq 12.1$
Test a new chemical process	Temperature when the desired reaction takes place (min temperature = 150°F; max temperature = 212°F)	$150 \leq x \leq 212$
Invest $10,000 in the stock market	Value of investment after one year	$x \geq 0$

NOTES + COMMENTS

One way to determine whether a random variable is discrete or continuous is to think of the values of the random variable as points on a line segment. Choose two points representing values of the random variable. If the entire line segment between the two points also represents possible values for the random variable, then the random variable is continuous.

EXERCISES

Methods

1. Consider the experiment of tossing a coin twice.
   a. List the experimental outcomes.
   b. Define a random variable that represents the number of heads occurring on the two tosses.
   c. Show what value the random variable would assume for each of the experimental outcomes.
   d. Is this random variable discrete or continuous?

2. Consider the experiment of a worker assembling a product.
   a. Define a random variable that represents the time in minutes required to assemble the product.
   b. What values may the random variable assume?
   c. Is the random variable discrete or continuous?

Applications

3. **Interviews at Brookwood Institute.** Three students scheduled interviews for summer employment at the Brookwood Institute. In each case the interview results in either an offer for a position or no offer. Experimental outcomes are defined in terms of the results of the three interviews.
   a. List the experimental outcomes.
   b. Define a random variable that represents the number of offers made. Is the random variable continuous?
   c. Show the value of the random variable for each of the experimental outcomes.

4. **Unemployment in Northeastern States.** The Census Bureau includes nine states in what it defines as the Northeast region of the United States. Assume that the government is interested in tracking unemployment in these nine states and that the random variable of interest is the number of Northeastern states with an unemployment rate that is less than 8.3%. What values may this random variable assume?

5. **Blood Test Analysis.** To perform a certain type of blood analysis, lab technicians must perform two procedures. The first procedure requires either one or two separate steps, and the second procedure requires either one, two, or three steps.
   a. List the experimental outcomes associated with performing the blood analysis.
   b. If the random variable of interest is the total number of steps required to do the complete analysis (both procedures), show what value the random variable will assume for each of the experimental outcomes.

6. **Types of Random Variables.** Listed below is a series of experiments and associated random variables. In each case, identify the values that the random variable can assume and state whether the random variable is discrete or continuous.

Experiment	Random Variable (x)
a. Take a 20-question examination	Number of questions answered correctly
b. Observe cars arriving at a tollbooth for 1 hour	Number of cars arriving at tollbooth
c. Audit 50 tax returns	Number of returns containing errors
d. Observe an employee's work	Number of nonproductive hours in an eight-hour workday
e. Weigh a shipment of goods	Number of pounds

5.2 Developing Discrete Probability Distributions

The **probability distribution** for a random variable describes how probabilities are distributed over the values of the random variable. For a discrete random variable x, a **probability function**, denoted by $f(x)$, provides the probability for each value of the random variable. The classical, subjective, and relative frequency methods of assigning probabilities can be used to develop discrete probability distributions. Application of this methodology leads to what we call tabular discrete probability distributions; that is, probability distributions that are presented in a table.

The classical, subjective and relative frequency methods were introduced in Chapter 4.

The classical method of assigning probabilities to values of a random variable is applicable when the experimental outcomes generate values of the random variable that are equally likely. For instance, consider the experiment of rolling a die and observing the number on the upward face. It must be one of the numbers 1, 2, 3, 4, 5, or 6 and each of these outcomes is equally likely. Thus, if we let $x =$ number obtained on one roll of a die and $f(x) =$ the probability of x, the probability distribution of x is given in Table 5.3.

The subjective method of assigning probabilities can also lead to a table of values of the random variable together with the associated probabilities. With the subjective method the individual developing the probability distribution uses their best judgment to assign each probability. So, unlike probability distributions developed using the classical method, different people can be expected to obtain different probability distributions.

The relative frequency method of assigning probabilities to values of a random variable is applicable when reasonably large amounts of data are available. We then treat the data as if they were the population and use the relative frequency method to assign probabilities to the experimental outcomes. The use of the relative frequency method to develop discrete probability distributions leads to what is called an **empirical discrete distribution**. With the large amounts of data available today (e.g., scanner data, credit card data), this type of probability distribution is becoming more widely used in practice. Let us illustrate by considering the sale of automobiles at a dealership.

We will use the relative frequency method to develop a probability distribution for the number of cars sold per day at DiCarlo Motors in Saratoga, New York. Over the past 300 days, DiCarlo has experienced 54 days with no automobiles sold, 117 days with 1 automobile sold, 72 days with 2 automobiles sold, 42 days with 3 automobiles sold, 12 days with 4 automobiles sold, and 3 days with 5 automobiles sold. Suppose we consider the experiment of observing a day of operations at DiCarlo Motors and define the random variable of interest as $x =$ the number of automobiles sold during a day. Using the relative frequencies to assign probabilities to the values of the random variable x, we can develop the probability distribution for x.

TABLE 5.3	Probability Distribution for Number Obtained on One Roll of a Die
Number Obtained x	**Probability of x** $f(x)$
1	1/6
2	1/6
3	1/6
4	1/6
5	1/6
6	1/6

TABLE 5.4	Probability Distribution for the Number of Automobiles Sold During a Day at Dicarlo Motors

x	f(x)
0	.18
1	.39
2	.24
3	.14
4	.04
5	.01
Total	1.00

In probability function notation, $f(0)$ provides the probability of 0 automobiles sold, $f(1)$ provides the probability of 1 automobile sold, and so on. Because historical data show 54 of 300 days with 0 automobiles sold, we assign the relative frequency $54/300 = .18$ to $f(0)$, indicating that the probability of 0 automobiles being sold during a day is .18. Similarly, because 117 of 300 days had 1 automobile sold, we assign the relative frequency $117/300 = .39$ to $f(1)$, indicating that the probability of exactly 1 automobile being sold during a day is .39. Continuing in this way for the other values of the random variable, we compute the values for $f(2), f(3), f(4)$, and $f(5)$ as shown in Table 5.4.

A primary advantage of defining a random variable and its probability distribution is that once the probability distribution is known, it is relatively easy to determine the probability of a variety of events that may be of interest to a decision maker. For example, using the probability distribution for DiCarlo Motors as shown in Table 5.4, we see that the most probable number of automobiles sold during a day is 1 with a probability of $f(1) = .39$. In addition, there is an $f(3) + f(4) + f(5) = .14 + .04 + .01 = .19$ probability of selling 3 or more automobiles during a day. These probabilities, plus others the decision maker may ask about, provide information that can help the decision maker understand the process of selling automobiles at DiCarlo Motors.

In the development of a probability function for any discrete random variable, the following two conditions must be satisfied.

These conditions are the ana-logs to the two basic require-ments for assigning probabili-ties to experimental outcomes presented in Chapter 4.

REQUIRED CONDITIONS FOR A DISCRETE PROBABILITY FUNCTION

$$f(x) \geq 0 \tag{5.1}$$

$$\Sigma f(x) = 1 \tag{5.2}$$

Table 5.4 shows that the probabilities for the random variable x satisfy equation (5.1); $f(x)$ is greater than or equal to 0 for all values of x. In addition, because the probabilities sum to 1, equation (5.2) is satisfied. Thus, the DiCarlo Motors probability function is a valid discrete probability function.

We can also show the DiCarlo Motors probability distribution graphically. In Figure 5.1 the values of the random variable x for DiCarlo Motors are shown on the horizontal axis and the probability associated with these values is shown on the vertical axis.

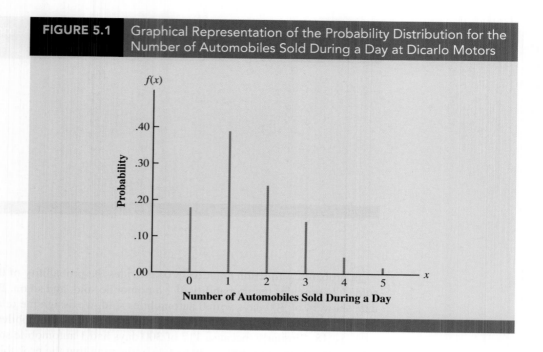

FIGURE 5.1   Graphical Representation of the Probability Distribution for the Number of Automobiles Sold During a Day at Dicarlo Motors

In addition to the probability distributions shown in tables, a formula that gives the probability function, $f(x)$, for every value of x is often used to describe probability distributions. The simplest example of a discrete probability distribution given by a formula is the **discrete uniform probability distribution**. Its probability function is defined by equation (5.3).

DISCRETE UNIFORM PROBABILITY FUNCTION

$$f(x) = 1/n \qquad \text{(5.3)}$$

where

$$n = \text{the number of values the random variable may assume}$$

For example, consider again the experiment of rolling a die. We define the random variable x to be the number of dots on the upward face. For this experiment, $n = 6$ values are possible for the random variable; $x = 1, 2, 3, 4, 5, 6$. We showed earlier how the probability distribution for this experiment can be expressed as a table. Since the probabilities are equally likely, the discrete uniform probability function can also be used. The probability function for this discrete uniform random variable is

$$f(x) = 1/6 \qquad x = 1, 2, 3, 4, 5, 6$$

Several widely used discrete probability distributions are specified by formulas. Three important cases are the binomial, Poisson, and hypergeometric distributions; these distributions are discussed later in the chapter.

EXERCISES

Methods

7. The probability distribution for the random variable x follows.

x	f(x)
20	.20
25	.15
30	.25
35	.40

   a. Is this probability distribution valid? Explain.
   b. What is the probability that $x = 30$?
   c. What is the probability that x is less than or equal to 25?
   d. What is the probability that x is greater than 30?

Applications

8. **Operating Room Use.** The following data were collected by counting the number of operating rooms in use at Tampa General Hospital over a 20-day period: On three of the days only one operating room was used, on five of the days two were used, on eight of the days three were used, and on four days all four of the hospital's operating rooms were used.
   a. Use the relative frequency approach to construct an empirical discrete probability distribution for the number of operating rooms in use on any given day.
   b. Draw a graph of the probability distribution.
   c. Show that your probability distribution satisfies the required conditions for a valid discrete probability distribution.

9. **Employee Retention.** Employee retention is a major concern for many companies. A survey of Americans asked how long they have worked for their current employer (Bureau of Labor Statistics website). Consider the following example of sample data of 2000 college graduates who graduated five years ago.

Time with Current Employer (years)	Number
1	506
2	390
3	310
4	218
5	576

   Let x be the random variable indicating the number of years the respondent has worked for her/his current employer.
   a. Use the data to develop an empirical discrete probability distribution for x.
   b. Show that your probability distribution satisfies the conditions for a valid discrete probability distribution.
   c. What is the probability that a respondent has been at her/his current place of employment for more than 3 years?

10. **Job Satisfaction of IS Managers.** The percent frequency distributions of job satisfaction scores for a sample of information systems (IS) senior executives and middle managers are as follows. The scores range from a low of 1 (very dissatisfied) to a high of 5 (very satisfied).

Job Satisfaction Score	IS Senior Executives (%)	IS Middle Managers (%)
1	5	4
2	9	10
3	3	12
4	42	46
5	41	28

a. Develop a probability distribution for the job satisfaction score of a senior executive.
b. Develop a probability distribution for the job satisfaction score of a middle manager.
c. What is the probability a senior executive will report a job satisfaction score of 4 or 5?
d. What is the probability a middle manager is very satisfied?
e. Compare the overall job satisfaction of senior executives and middle managers.

11. **Mailing Machine Malfunctions.** A technician services mailing machines at companies in the Phoenix area. Depending on the type of malfunction, the service call can take 1, 2, 3, or 4 hours. The different types of malfunctions occur at about the same frequency.
a. Develop a probability distribution for the duration of a service call.
b. Draw a graph of the probability distribution.
c. Show that your probability distribution satisfies the conditions required for a discrete probability function.
d. What is the probability a service call will take three hours?
e. A service call has just come in, but the type of malfunction is unknown. It is 3:00 P.M. and service technicians usually get off at 5:00 P.M. What is the probability the service technician will have to work overtime to fix the machine today?

12. **New Cable Subscribers.** Spectrum provides cable television and Internet service to millions of customers. Suppose that the management of Spectrum subjectively assesses a probability distribution for the number of new subscribers next year in the state of New York as follows.

x	f(x)
100,000	.10
200,000	.20
300,000	.25
400,000	.30
500,000	.10
600,000	.05

a. Is this probability distribution valid? Explain.
b. What is the probability Spectrum will obtain more than 400,000 new subscribers?
c. What is the probability Spectrum will obtain fewer than 200,000 new subscribers?

13. **Establishing Patient Trust.** A psychologist determined that the number of sessions required to obtain the trust of a new patient is either 1, 2, or 3. Let x be a

random variable indicating the number of sessions required to gain the patient's trust. The following probability function has been proposed.

$$f(x) = \frac{x}{6} \qquad \text{for } x = 1, 2, \text{ or } 3$$

a. Is this probability function valid? Explain.
b. What is the probability that it takes exactly 2 sessions to gain the patient's trust?
c. What is the probability that it takes at least 2 sessions to gain the patient's trust?

14. **MRA Company Projected Profits.** The following table is a partial probability distribution for the MRA Company's projected profits (x = profit in $1000s) for the first year of operation (the negative value denotes a loss).

x	f(x)
−100	.10
0	.20
50	.30
100	.25
150	.10
200	

a. What is the proper value for $f(200)$? What is your interpretation of this value?
b. What is the probability that MRA will be profitable?
c. What is the probability that MRA will make at least $100,000?

5.3 Expected Value and Variance

Expected Value

The **expected value**, or mean, of a random variable is a measure of the central location for the random variable. The formula for the expected value of a discrete random variable x follows.

The expected value is a weighted average of the values of the random variable where the weights are the probabilities.

EXPECTED VALUE OF A DISCRETE RANDOM VARIABLE

$$E(x) = \mu = \Sigma x f(x) \qquad \text{(5.4)}$$

Both the notations $E(x)$ and μ are used to denote the expected value of a random variable.

Equation (5.4) shows that to compute the expected value of a discrete random variable, we must multiply each value of the random variable by the corresponding probability $f(x)$ and then add the resulting products. Using the DiCarlo Motors automobile sales example from Section 5.2, we show the calculation of the expected value for the number of automobiles sold during a day in Table 5.5. The sum of the entries in the $xf(x)$ column shows that the expected value is 1.50 automobiles per day. We therefore know that although sales of 0, 1, 2, 3, 4, or 5 automobiles are possible on any one day, over time DiCarlo can anticipate selling an average of 1.50 automobiles per day. Assuming 30 days of operation during a month, we can use the expected value of 1.50 to forecast average monthly sales of $30(1.50) = 45$ automobiles.

The expected value does not have to be a value the random variable can assume.

Variance

The expected value provides a measure of central tendency for a random variable, but we often also want a measure of variability, or dispersion. Just as we used the variance in Chapter 3 to summarize the variability in data, we now use **variance** to summarize the variability in the values of a random variable. The formula for the variance of a discrete random variable follows.

TABLE 5.5	Calculation of the Expected Value for the Number of Automobiles Sold During a Day at Dicarlo Motors	

x	$f(x)$	$xf(x)$
0	.18	0(.18) = .00
1	.39	1(.39) = .39
2	.24	2(.24) = .48
3	.14	3(.14) = .42
4	.04	4(.04) = .16
5	.01	5(.01) = .05
		1.50

$$E(x) = \mu = \Sigma xf(x)$$

The variance is a weighted average of the squared deviations of a random variable from its mean. The weights are the probabilities.

VARIANCE OF A DISCRETE RANDOM VARIABLE

$$Var(x) = \sigma^2 = \Sigma(x - \mu)^2 f(x) \tag{5.5}$$

As equation (5.5) shows, an essential part of the variance formula is the deviation, $x - \mu$, which measures how far a particular value of the random variable is from the expected value, or mean, μ. In computing the variance of a random variable, the deviations are squared and then weighted by the corresponding value of the probability function. The sum of these weighted squared deviations for all values of the random variable is referred to as the *variance*. The notations $Var(x)$ and σ^2 are both used to denote the variance of a random variable.

The calculation of the variance for the probability distribution of the number of automobiles sold during a day at DiCarlo Motors is summarized in Table 5.6. We see that the variance is 1.25. The **standard deviation**, σ, is defined as the positive square root of the variance. Thus, the standard deviation for the number of automobiles sold during a day is

$$\sigma = \sqrt{1.25} = 1.118$$

The standard deviation is measured in the same units as the random variable ($\sigma = 1.118$ automobiles) and therefore is often preferred in describing the variability of a random variable. The variance σ^2 is measured in squared units and is thus more difficult to interpret.

TABLE 5.6	Calculation of the Variance for the Number of Automobiles Sold During a Day at Dicarlo Motors			

x	$x - \mu$	$(x - \mu)^2$	$f(x)$	$(x - \mu)^2 f(x)$
0	0 − 1.50 = −1.50	2.25	.18	2.25(.18) = .4050
1	1 − 1.50 = −.50	.25	.39	.25(.39) = .0975
2	2 − 1.50 = .50	.25	.24	.25(.24) = .0600
3	3 − 1.50 = 1.50	2.25	.14	2.25(.14) = .3150
4	4 − 1.50 = 2.50	6.25	.04	6.25(.04) = .2500
5	5 − 1.50 = 3.50	12.25	.01	12.25(.01) = .1225
				1.2500

$$\sigma^2 = \Sigma(x - \mu)^2 f(x)$$

EXERCISES

Methods

15. The following table provides a probability distribution for the random variable x.

x	$f(x)$
3	.25
6	.50
9	.25

    a. Compute $E(x)$, the expected value of x.
    b. Compute σ^2, the variance of x.
    c. Compute σ, the standard deviation of x.

16. The following table provides a probability distribution for the random variable y.

y	$f(y)$
2	.20
4	.30
7	.40
8	.10

    a. Compute $E(y)$.
    b. Compute $Var(y)$ and σ.

Applications

Coldstream12

17. **Golf Scores.** During the summer of 2018, Coldstream Country Club in Cincinnati, Ohio, collected data on 443 rounds of golf played from its white tees. The data for each golfer's score on the twelfth hole are contained in the DATAfile *Coldstream12*.
    a. Construct an empirical discrete probability distribution for the player scores on the twelfth hole.
    b. A *par* is the score that a good golfer is expected to get for the hole. For hole number 12, par is four. What is the probability of a player scoring less than or equal to par on hole number 12?
    c. What is the expected score for hole number 12?
    d. What is the variance for hole number 12?
    e. What is the standard deviation for hole number 12?

18. **Water Supply Stoppages.** The following data has been collected on the number of times that owner-occupied and renter-occupied units had a water supply stoppage lasting 6 or more hours in the past 3 months.

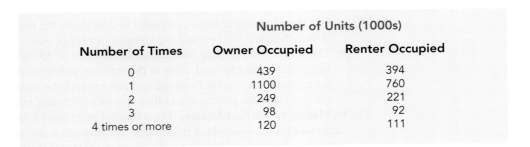

| | Number of Units (1000s) | |
Number of Times	Owner Occupied	Renter Occupied
0	439	394
1	1100	760
2	249	221
3	98	92
4 times or more	120	111

a. Define a random variable x = number of times that owner-occupied units had a water supply stoppage lasting 6 or more hours in the past 3 months and develop a probability distribution for the random variable. (Let $x = 4$ represent 4 or more times.)

b. Compute the expected value and variance for x.

c. Define a random variable y = number of times that renter-occupied units had a water supply stoppage lasting 6 or more hours in the past 3 months and develop a probability distribution for the random variable. (Let $y = 4$ represent 4 or more times.)

d. Compute the expected value and variance for y.

e. What observations can you make from a comparison of the number of water supply stoppages reported by owner-occupied units versus renter-occupied units?

19. **New Tax Accounting Clients.** New legislation passed in 2017 by the U.S. Congress changed tax laws that affect how many people file their taxes in 2018 and beyond. These tax law changes will likely lead many people to seek tax advice from their accountants (*The New York Times*). Backen and Hayes LLC is an accounting firm in New York state. The accounting firm believes that it may have to hire additional accountants to assist with the increased demand in tax advice for the upcoming tax season. Backen and Hayes LLC has developed the following probability distribution for x = number of new clients seeking tax advice.

x	f(x)
20	.05
25	.20
30	.25
35	.15
40	.15
45	.10
50	.10

a. Is this a valid probability distribution? Explain.

b. What is the probability that Backen and Hayes LLC will obtain 40 or more new clients?

c. What is the probability that Backen and Hayes LLC will obtain fewer than 35 new clients?

d. Compute the expected value, variance, and standard deviation of x.

20. **Automobile Insurance Damage Claims.** The probability distribution for damage claims paid by the Newton Automobile Insurance Company on collision insurance follows.

Payment ($)	Probability
0	.85
500	.04
1000	.04
3000	.03
5000	.02
8000	.01
10000	.01

a. Use the expected collision payment to determine the collision insurance premium that would enable the company to break even.

b. The insurance company charges an annual rate of $520 for the collision coverage. What is the expected value of the collision policy for a policyholder? (*Hint:* It is the expected payments from the company minus the cost of coverage.) Why does the policyholder purchase a collision policy with this expected value?

21. **IS Managers Job Satisfaction.** The following probability distributions of job satisfaction scores for a sample of information systems (IS) senior executives and middle managers range from a low of 1 (very dissatisfied) to a high of 5 (very satisfied).

	Probability	
Job Satisfaction Score	IS Senior Executives	IS Middle Managers
1	.05	.04
2	.09	.10
3	.03	.12
4	.42	.46
5	.41	.28

a. What is the expected value of the job satisfaction score for senior executives?
b. What is the expected value of the job satisfaction score for middle managers?
c. Compute the variance of job satisfaction scores for executives and middle managers.
d. Compute the standard deviation of job satisfaction scores for both probability distributions.
e. Compare the overall job satisfaction of senior executives and middle managers.

22. **Carolina Industries Product Demand.** The demand for a product of Carolina Industries varies greatly from month to month. The probability distribution in the following table, based on the past two years of data, shows the company's monthly demand.

Unit Demand	Probability
300	.20
400	.30
500	.35
600	.15

a. If the company bases monthly orders on the expected value of the monthly demand, what should Carolina's monthly order quantity be for this product?
b. Assume that each unit demanded generates $70 in revenue and that each unit ordered costs $50. How much will the company gain or lose in a month if it places an order based on your answer to part (a) and the actual demand for the item is 300 units?

23. **Coffee Consumption.** In Gallup's Annual Consumption Habits Poll, telephone interviews were conducted for a random sample of 1014 adults aged 18 and over. One of the questions was, "How many cups of coffee, if any, do you drink on an average day?" The following table shows the results obtained (Gallup website).

Number of Cups per Day	Number of Responses
0	365
1	264
2	193
3	91
4 or more	101

Define a random variable x = number of cups of coffee consumed on an average day. Let $x = 4$ represent four or more cups.
a. Develop a probability distribution for x.
b. Compute the expected value of x.
c. Compute the variance of x.
d. Suppose we are only interested in adults who drink at least one cup of coffee on an average day. For this group, let y = the number of cups of coffee consumed on an average day. Compute the expected value of y and compare it to the expected value of x.

24. **Computer Company Plant Expansion.** The J. R. Ryland Computer Company is considering a plant expansion to enable the company to begin production of a new computer product. The company's president must determine whether to make the expansion a medium- or large-scale project. Demand for the new product is uncertain, which for planning purposes may be low demand, medium demand, or high demand. The probability estimates for demand are .20, .50, and .30, respectively. Letting x and y indicate the annual profit in thousands of dollars, the firm's planners developed the following profit forecasts for the medium- and large-scale expansion projects.

		Medium-Scale Expansion Profit		Large-Scale Expansion Profit	
		x	$f(x)$	y	$f(y)$
Demand	Low	50	.20	0	.20
	Medium	150	.50	100	.50
	High	200	.30	300	.30

   a. Compute the expected value for the profit associated with the two expansion alternatives. Which decision is preferred for the objective of maximizing the expected profit?
   b. Compute the variance for the profit associated with the two expansion alternatives. Which decision is preferred for the objective of minimizing the risk or uncertainty?

5.4 Bivariate Distributions, Covariance, and Financial Portfolios

A probability distribution involving two random variables is called a **bivariate probability distribution**. In discussing bivariate probability distributions, it is useful to think of a bivariate experiment. Each outcome for a bivariate experiment consists of two values, one for each random variable. For example, consider the bivariate experiment of rolling a pair of dice. The outcome consists of two values, the number obtained with the first die and the number obtained with the second die. As another example, consider the experiment of observing the financial markets for a year and recording the percentage gain for a stock fund and a bond fund. Again, the experimental outcome provides a value for two random variables, the percent gain in the stock fund and the percent gain in the bond fund. When dealing with bivariate probability distributions, we are often interested in the relationship between the random variables. In this section, we introduce bivariate distributions and show how the covariance and correlation coefficient can be used as a measure of linear association between the random variables. We shall also see how bivariate probability distributions can be used to construct and analyze financial portfolios.

A Bivariate Empirical Discrete Probability Distribution

Recall that in Section 5.2 we developed an empirical discrete distribution for daily sales at the DiCarlo Motors automobile dealership in Saratoga, New York. DiCarlo has another dealership in Geneva, New York. Table 5.7 shows the number of cars sold at each of the dealerships over a 300-day period. The numbers in the bottom (total) row are the frequencies we used to develop an empirical probability distribution for daily sales at DiCarlo's Saratoga dealership in Section 5.2. The numbers in the right-most (total) column are the frequencies of daily sales for the Geneva dealership. Entries in the body of the table give the number of days the Geneva dealership had a level of sales indicated by the row, when the Saratoga dealership had the level of sales indicated by the column. For example, the entry of 33 in the Geneva dealership row labeled 1 and the Saratoga column labeled 2 indicates that for 33 days out of the 300, the Geneva dealership sold 1 car and the Saratoga dealership sold 2 cars.

TABLE 5.7	Number of Automobiles Sold at DiCarlo's Saratoga and Geneva Dealerships Over 300 Days

	Saratoga Dealership						
Geneva Dealership	0	1	2	3	4	5	Total
0	21	30	24	9	2	0	86
1	21	36	33	18	2	1	111
2	9	42	9	12	3	2	77
3	3	9	6	3	5	0	26
Total	54	117	72	42	12	3	300

Suppose we consider the bivariate experiment of observing a day of operations at DiCarlo Motors and recording the number of cars sold. Let us define x = number of cars sold at the Geneva dealership and y = the number of cars sold at the Saratoga dealership. We can now divide all of the frequencies in Table 5.7 by the number of observations (300) to develop a bivariate empirical discrete probability distribution for automobile sales at the two DiCarlo dealerships. Table 5.8 shows this bivariate discrete probability distribution. The probabilities in the lower margin provide the marginal distribution for the DiCarlo Motors Saratoga dealership. The probabilities in the right margin provide the marginal distribution for the DiCarlo Motors Geneva dealership.

The probabilities in the body of the table provide the bivariate probability distribution for sales at both dealerships. Bivariate probabilities are often called joint probabilities. We see that the joint probability of selling 0 automobiles at Geneva and 1 automobile at Saratoga on a typical day is $f(0, 1) = .1000$, the joint probability of selling 1 automobile at Geneva and 4 automobiles at Saratoga on a typical day is .0067, and so on. Note that there is one bivariate probability for each experimental outcome. With 4 possible values for x and 6 possible values for y, there are 24 experimental outcomes and bivariate probabilities.

Suppose we would like to know the probability distribution for total sales at both DiCarlo dealerships and the expected value and variance of total sales. We can define $s = x + y$ as total sales for DiCarlo Motors. Working with the bivariate probabilities in Table 5.8, we see that $f(s = 0) = .0700, f(s = 1) = .0700 + .1000 = .1700, f(s = 2) = .0300 + .1200 + .0800 = .2300$, and so on. We show the complete probability distribution for $s = x + y$ along with the computation of the expected value and variance in Table 5.9. The expected value is $E(s) = 2.6433$ and the variance is $Var(s) = 2.3895$.

With bivariate probability distributions, we often want to know the relationship between the two random variables. The covariance and/or correlation coefficient are good measures

TABLE 5.8	Bivariate Empirical Discrete Probability Distribution for Daily Sales at DiCarlo Dealerships in Saratoga and Geneva, New York

	Saratoga Dealership						
Geneva Dealership	0	1	2	3	4	5	Total
0	.0700	.1000	.0800	.0300	.0067	.0000	.2867
1	.0700	.1200	.1100	.0600	.0067	.0033	.3700
2	.0300	.1400	.0300	.0400	.0100	.0067	.2567
3	.0100	.0300	.0200	.0100	.0167	.0000	.0867
Total	.18	.39	.24	.14	.04	.01	1.0000

TABLE 5.9	Calculation of the Expected Value and Variance for Total Daily Sales at DiCarlo Motors				
s	f(s)	sf(s)	s − E(s)	(s − E(s))²	(s − E(s))² f(s)
0	.0700	.0000	−2.6433	6.9872	.4891
1	.1700	.1700	−1.6433	2.7005	.4591
2	.2300	.4600	−.6433	.4139	.0952
3	.2900	.8700	.3567	.1272	.0369
4	.1267	.5067	1.3567	1.8405	.2331
5	.0667	.3333	2.3567	5.5539	.3703
6	.0233	.1400	3.3567	11.2672	.2629
7	.0233	.1633	4.3567	18.9805	.4429
8	.0000	.0000	5.3567	28.6939	.0000
		E(s) = 2.6433			**Var(s) = 2.3895**

Computing covariance and correlation coefficients for sample data are discussed in Chapter 3.

of association between two random variables. The formula we will use for computing the covariance between two random variables x and y is given below.

COVARIANCE OF RANDOM VARIABLES x AND y (see footnote 1)

$$\sigma_{xy} = [Var(x + y) - Var(x) - Var(y)]/2 \qquad (5.6)$$

We have already computed $Var(s) = Var(x + y)$ and, in Section 5.2, we computed $Var(y)$. Now we need to compute $Var(x)$ before we can use equation (5.6) to compute the covariance of x and y. Using the probability distribution for x (the right margin of Table 5.8), we compute $E(x)$ and $Var(x)$ in Table 5.10.

We can now use equation (5.6) to compute the covariance of the random variables x and y.

$$\sigma_{xy} = [Var(x + y) - Var(x) - Var(y)]/2 = (2.3895 - .8696 - 1.25)/2 = .1350$$

A covariance of .1350 indicates that daily sales at DiCarlo's two dealerships have a positive relationship. To get a better sense of the strength of the relationship we can compute the correlation coefficient. The correlation coefficient for the two random variables x and y is given by equation (5.7).

TABLE 5.10	Calculation of the Expected Value and Variance of Daily Automobile Sales at DiCarlo Motors' Geneva Dealership				
x	f(x)	xf(x)	x − E(x)	[(x − E(x)]²	[x − E(x)]² f(x)
0	.2867	.0000	−1.1435	1.3076	.3749
1	.3700	.3700	−.1435	.0206	.0076
2	.2567	.5134	.8565	.7336	.1883
3	.0867	.2601	1.8565	3.447	.2988
		E(x) = 1.1435			**Var(x) = .8696**

---

[1]Another formula is often used to compute the covariance of x and y when $Var(x + y)$ is not known. It is
$\sigma_{xy} = \sum_{i,j} [x_i - E(x_i)][y_j - E(y_j)] f(x_i, y_j)$.

From equation (5.7), we see that the correlation coefficient for two random variables is the covariance divided by the product of the standard deviations for the two random variables.

Let us compute the correlation coefficient between daily sales at the two DiCarlo dealerships. First we compute the standard deviations for sales at the Saratoga and Geneva dealerships by taking the square root of the variance.

$$\sigma_x = \sqrt{.8696} = .9325$$

$$\sigma_y = \sqrt{1.25} = 1.1180$$

Now we can compute the correlation coefficient as a measure of the linear association between the two random variables.

$$\rho_{xy} = \frac{\sigma_{xy}}{\sigma_x \sigma_y} = \frac{.1350}{(.9325)(1.1180)} = .1295$$

The correlation coefficient is a measure of the linear association between two variables. Values near $+1$ indicate a strong positive linear relationship; values near -1 indicate a strong negative linear relationship; and values near zero indicate a lack of a linear relationship. The correlation coefficient of .1295 indicates there is a weak positive relationship between the random variables representing daily sales at the two DiCarlo dealerships. If the correlation coefficient had equaled zero, we would have concluded that daily sales at the two dealerships were independent.

Financial Applications

Let us now see how what we have learned can be useful in constructing financial portfolios that provide a good balance of risk and return. A financial advisor is considering four possible economic scenarios for the coming year and has developed a probability distribution showing the percent return, x, for investing in a large-cap stock fund and the percent return, y, for investing in a long-term government bond fund given each of the scenarios. The bivariate probability distribution for x and y is shown in Table 5.11. Table 5.11 is simply a list with a separate row for each experimental outcome (economic scenario).

TABLE 5.11 Probability Distribution of Percent Returns for Investing in a Large-Cap Stock Fund, x, and Investing in a Long-Term Government Bond Fund, y

Economic Scenario	Probability $f(x, y)$	Large-Cap Stock Fund (x)	Long-Term Government Bond Fund (y)
Recession	.10	−40	30
Weak Growth	.25	5	5
Stable Growth	.50	15	4
Strong Growth	.15	30	2

Each row contains the joint probability for the experimental outcome and a value for each random variable. Since there are only four joint probabilities, the tabular form used in Table 5.11 is simpler than the one we used for DiCarlo Motors where there were $(4)(6) = 24$ joint probabilities.

Using the formula in Section 5.3 for computing the expected value of a single random variable, we can compute the expected percent return for investing in the stock fund, $E(x)$, and the expected percent return for investing in the bond fund, $E(y)$.

$$E(x) = .10(-40) + .25(5) + .5(15) + .15(30) = 9.25$$
$$E(y) = .10(30) + .25(5) + .5(4) + .15(2) = 6.55$$

Using this information, we might conclude that investing in the stock fund is a better investment. It has a higher expected return, 9.25%. But, financial analysts recommend that investors also consider the risk associated with an investment. The standard deviation of percent return is often used as a measure of risk. To compute the standard deviation, we must first compute the variance. Using the formula in Section 5.3 for computing the variance of a single random variable, we can compute the variance of the percent returns for the stock and bond fund investments.

$$Var(x) = .1(-40 - 9.25)^2 + .25(5 - 9.25)^2 + .50(15 - 9.25)^2 + .15(30 - 9.25)^2 = 328.1875$$
$$Var(y) = .1(30 - 6.55)^2 + .25(5 - 6.55)^2 + .50(4 - 6.55)^2 + .15(2 - 6.55)^2 = 61.9475$$

The standard deviation of the return from an investment in the stock fund is $\sigma_x = \sqrt{328.1875} = 18.1159\%$ and the standard deviation of the return from an investment in the bond fund is $\sigma_y = \sqrt{61.9475} = 7.8707\%$. So, we can conclude that investing in the bond fund is less risky. It has the smaller standard deviation. We have already seen that the stock fund offers a greater expected return, so if we want to choose between investing in either the stock fund or the bond fund it depends on our attitude toward risk and return. An aggressive investor might choose the stock fund because of the higher expected return; a conservative investor might choose the bond fund because of the lower risk. But, there are other options. What about the possibility of investing in a portfolio consisting of both an investment in the stock fund and an investment in the bond fund?

Suppose we would like to consider three alternatives: investing solely in the large-cap stock fund, investing solely in the long-term government bond fund, and splitting our funds equally between the stock fund and the bond fund (one-half in each). We have already computed the expected value and standard deviation for investing solely in the stock fund and the bond fund. Let us now evaluate the third alternative: constructing a portfolio by investing equal amounts in the large-cap stock fund and in the long-term government bond fund.

To evaluate this portfolio, we start by computing its expected return. We have previously defined x as the percent return from an investment in the stock fund and y as the percent return from an investment in the bond fund so the percent return for our portfolio is $r = .5x + .5y$. To find the expected return for a portfolio with one-half invested in the stock fund and one-half invested in the bond fund, we want to compute $E(r) = E(.5x + .5y)$. The expression $.5x + .5y$ is called a linear combination of the random variables x and y. Equation (5.8) provides an easy method for computing the expected value of a linear combination of the random variables x and y when we already know $E(x)$ and $E(y)$. In equation (5.8), a represents the coefficient of x and b represents the coefficient of y in the linear combination.

EXPECTED VALUE OF A LINEAR COMBINATION OF RANDOM VARIABLES x AND y

$$E(ax + by) = aE(x) + bE(y) \qquad \text{(5.8)}$$

Since we have already computed $E(x) = 9.25$ and $E(y) = 6.55$, we can use equation (5.8) to compute the expected value of our portfolio.

$$E(.5x + .5y) = .5E(x) + .5E(y) = .5(9.25) + .5(6.55) = 7.9$$

We see that the expected return for investing in the portfolio is 7.9%. With $100 invested, we would expect a return of $100(.079) = $7.90; with $1000 invested we would expect a return of $1000(.079) = $79.00; and so on. But, what about the risk? As mentioned previously, financial analysts often use the standard deviation as a measure of risk.

Our portfolio is a linear combination of two random variables, so we need to be able to compute the variance and standard deviation of a linear combination of two random variables in order to assess the portfolio risk. When the covariance between two random variables is known, the formula given by equation (5.9) can be used to compute the variance of a linear combination of two random variables.

VARIANCE OF A LINEAR COMBINATION OF TWO RANDOM VARIABLES

$$Var(ax + by) = a^2 Var(x) + b^2 Var(y) + 2ab\sigma_{xy} \qquad \text{(5.9)}$$

where σ_{xy} is the covariance of x and y.

From equation (5.9), we see that both the variance of each random variable individually and the covariance between the random variables are needed to compute the variance of a linear combination of two random variables and hence the variance of our portfolio.

We computed Var(x + y) = 119.46 the same way we did for DiCarlo Motors in the previous subsection.

We have already computed the variance of each random variable individually: $Var(x) = 328.1875$ and $Var(y) = 61.9475$. Also, it can be shown that $Var(x + y) = 119.46$. So, using equation (5.6), the covariance of the random variables x and y is

$$\sigma_{xy} = [Var(x + y) - Var(x) - Var(y)]/2 = [119.46 - 328.1875 - 61.9475]/2 = -135.3375$$

A negative covariance between x and y, such as this, means that when x tends to be above its mean, y tends to be below its mean and vice versa.

We can now use equation (5.9) to compute the variance of return for our portfolio.

$$Var(.5x + .5y) = .5^2(328.1875) + .5^2(61.9475) + 2(.5)(.5)(-135.3375) = 29.865$$

The standard deviation of our portfolio is then given by $\sigma_{.5x+.5y} = \sqrt{29.865} = 5.4650\%$. This is our measure of risk for the portfolio consisting of investing 50% in the stock fund and 50% in the bond fund.

Perhaps we would now like to compare the three investment alternatives: investing solely in the stock fund, investing solely in the bond fund, or creating a portfolio by dividing our investment amount equally between the stock and bond funds. Table 5.12 shows the expected returns, variances, and standard deviations for each of the three alternatives.

TABLE 5.12 Expected Values, Variances, and Standard Deviations for Three Investment Alternatives

Investment Alternative	Expected Return (%)	Variance of Return	Standard Deviation of Return (%)
100% in Stock Fund	9.25	328.1875	18.1159
100% in Bond Fund	6.55	61.9475	7.8707
Portfolio (50% in stock fund, 50% in bond fund)	7.90	29.865	5.4650

Which of these alternatives would you prefer? The expected return is highest for investing 100% in the stock fund, but the risk is also highest. The standard deviation is 18.1159%. Investing 100% in the bond fund has a lower expected return, but a significantly smaller risk. Investing 50% in the stock fund and 50% in the bond fund (the portfolio) has an expected return that is halfway between that of the stock fund alone and the bond fund alone. But note that it has less risk than investing 100% in either of the individual funds. Indeed, it has both a higher return and less risk (smaller standard deviation) than investing solely in the bond fund. So we would say that investing in the portfolio dominates the choice of investing solely in the bond fund.

Whether you would choose to invest in the stock fund or the portfolio depends on your attitude toward risk. The stock fund has a higher expected return. But the portfolio has significantly less risk and also provides a fairly good return. Many would choose it. It is the negative covariance between the stock and bond funds that has caused the portfolio risk to be so much smaller than the risk of investing solely in either of the individual funds.

The portfolio analysis we just performed was for investing 50% in the stock fund and the other 50% in the bond fund. How would you calculate the expected return and the variance for other portfolios? Equations (5.8) and (5.9) can be used to make these calculations easily.

Suppose we wish to create a portfolio by investing 25% in the stock fund and 75% in the bond fund? What are the expected value and variance of this portfolio? The percent return for this portfolio is $r = .25x + .75y$, so we can use equation (5.8) to get the expected value of this portfolio:

$$E(.25x + .75y) = .25E(x) + .75E(y) = .25(9.25) + .75(6.55) = 7.225$$

Likewise, we may calculate the variance of the portfolio using equation (5.9):

$$\begin{aligned} Var(.25x + .75y) &= (.25)^2 Var(x) + (.75)^2 \, Var(y) + 2(.25)(.75)\sigma_{xy} \\ &= .0625(328.1875) + (.5625)(61.9475) + (.375)(-135.3375) \\ &= 4.6056 \end{aligned}$$

The standard deviation of the new portfolio is $\sigma_{.25x+.75y} = \sqrt{4.6056} = 2.1461$.

Summary

We have introduced bivariate discrete probability distributions in this section. Since such distributions involve two random variables, we are often interested in a measure of association between the variables. The covariance and the correlation coefficient are the two measures we introduced and showed how to compute. A correlation coefficient near 1 or -1 indicates a strong correlation between the two random variables, a correlation coefficient near zero indicates a weak correlation between the variables. If two random variables are independent, the covariance and the correlation coefficient will equal zero.

We also showed how to compute the expected value and variance of linear combinations of random variables. From a statistical point of view, financial portfolios are linear combinations of random variables. They are actually a special kind of linear combination called a weighted average. The coefficients are nonnegative and add to 1. The portfolio example we presented showed how to compute the expected value and variance for a portfolio consisting of an investment in a stock fund and a bond fund. The same methodology can be used to compute the expected value and variance of a portfolio consisting of any two financial assets. It is the effect of covariance between the individual random variables on the variance of the portfolio that is the basis for much of the theory of reducing portfolio risk by diversifying across investment alternatives.

NOTES + COMMENTS

1. Equations (5.8) and (5.9), along with their extensions to three or more random variables, are key building blocks in financial portfolio construction and analysis.

2. Equations (5.8) and (5.9) for computing the expected value and variance of a linear combination of two random variables can be extended to three or more random variables. The extension of equation (5.8) is straightforward; one more term is added for each additional random variable. The extension of equation (5.9) is more complicated because a separate term is needed for the covariance between all pairs of random variables. We leave these extensions to more advanced books.

3. The covariance term of equation (5.9) shows why negatively correlated random variables (investment alternatives) reduce the variance and, hence, the risk of a portfolio.

EXERCISES

Methods

25. Given below is a bivariate distribution for the random variables x and y.

f(x, y)	x	y
.2	50	80
.5	30	50
.3	40	60

a. Compute the expected value and the variance for x and y.
b. Develop a probability distribution for $x + y$.
c. Using the result of part (b), compute $E(x + y)$ and $Var(x + y)$.
d. Compute the covariance and correlation for x and y. Are x and y positively related, negatively related, or unrelated?
e. Is the variance of the sum of x and y bigger, smaller, or the same as the sum of the individual variances? Why?

26. A person is interested in constructing a portfolio. Two stocks are being considered. Let x = percent return for an investment in stock 1, and y = percent return for an investment in stock 2. The expected return and variance for stock 1 are $E(x)$ = 8.45% and $Var(x)$ = 25. The expected return and variance for stock 2 are $E(y)$ = 3.20% and $Var(y)$ = 1. The covariance between the returns is σ_{xy} = −3.
a. What is the standard deviation for an investment in stock 1 and for an investment in stock 2? Using the standard deviation as a measure of risk, which of these stocks is the riskier investment?
b. What is the expected return and standard deviation, in dollars, for a person who invests $500 in stock 1?
c. What is the expected percent return and standard deviation for a person who constructs a portfolio by investing 50% in each stock?
d. What is the expected percent return and standard deviation for a person who constructs a portfolio by investing 70% in stock 1 and 30% in stock 2?
e. Compute the correlation coefficient for x and y and comment on the relationship between the returns for the two stocks.

Applications

27. **Canadian Restaurant Ratings.** The Chamber of Commerce in a Canadian city has conducted an evaluation of 300 restaurants in its metropolitan area. Each restaurant received a rating on a 3-point scale on typical meal price (1 least expensive to 3 most expensive) and quality (1 lowest quality to 3 greatest quality). A crosstabulation of the rating data is shown below. Forty-two of the restaurants

received a rating of 1 on quality and 1 on meal price, 39 of the restaurants received a rating of 1 on quality and 2 on meal price, and so on. Forty-eight of the restaurants received the highest rating of 3 on both quality and meal price.

Quality (x)	Meal Price (y)			Total
	1	2	3	
1	42	39	3	84
2	33	63	54	150
3	3	15	48	66
Total	78	117	105	300

a. Develop a bivariate probability distribution for quality and meal price of a randomly selected restaurant in this Canadian city. Let x = quality rating and y = meal price.
b. Compute the expected value and variance for quality rating, x.
c. Compute the expected value and variance for meal price, y.
d. The $Var(x + y) = 1.6691$. Compute the covariance of x and y. What can you say about the relationship between quality and meal price? Is this what you would expect?
e. Compute the correlation coefficient between quality and meal price. What is the strength of the relationship? Do you suppose it is likely to find a low-cost restaurant in this city that is also high quality? Why or why not?

28. **Printer Manufacturing Costs.** PortaCom has developed a design for a high-quality portable printer. The two key components of manufacturing cost are direct labor and parts. During a testing period, the company has developed prototypes and conducted extensive product tests with the new printer. PortaCom's engineers have developed the bivariate probability distribution shown below for the manufacturing costs. Parts cost (in dollars) per printer is represented by the random variable x and direct labor cost (in dollars) per printer is represented by the random variable y. Management would like to use this probability distribution to estimate manufacturing costs.

Parts (x)	Direct Labor (y)			Total
	43	45	48	
85	.05	.2	.2	.45
95	.25	.2	.1	.55
Total	.30	.4	.3	1.00

a. Show the marginal distribution of direct labor cost and compute its expected value, variance, and standard deviation.
b. Show the marginal distribution of parts cost and compute its expected value, variance, and standard deviation.
c. Total manufacturing cost per unit is the sum of direct labor cost and parts cost. Show the probability distribution for total manufacturing cost per unit.
d. Compute the expected value, variance, and standard deviation of total manufacturing cost per unit.
e. Are direct labor and parts costs independent? Why or why not? If you conclude that they are not, what is the relationship between direct labor and parts cost?
f. PortaCom produced 1500 printers for its product introduction. The total manufacturing cost was $198,350. Is that about what you would expect? If it is higher or lower, what do you think may have caused it?

29. **Investment Portfolio of Index Fund and Core Bonds Fund.** J.P. Morgan Asset Management publishes information about financial investments. Between 2002 and 2011, the expected return for the S&P 500 was 5.04% with a standard deviation of 19.45% and the expected return over that same period for a core bonds fund was 5.78% with a standard deviation of 2.13% (*J.P. Morgan Asset Management, Guide to the Markets*). The publication also reported that the correlation between the S&P 500 and core bonds is −.32. You are considering portfolio investments that are composed of an S&P 500 index fund and a core bonds fund.
    a. Using the information provided, determine the covariance between the S&P 500 and core bonds.
    b. Construct a portfolio that is 50% invested in an S&P 500 index fund and 50% in a core bonds fund. In percentage terms, what are the expected return and standard deviation for such a portfolio?
    c. Construct a portfolio that is 20% invested in an S&P 500 index fund and 80% invested in a core bonds fund. In percentage terms, what are the expected return and standard deviation for such a portfolio?
    d. Construct a portfolio that is 80% invested in an S&P 500 index fund and 20% invested in a core bonds fund. In percentage terms, what are the expected return and standard deviation for such a portfolio?
    e. Which of the portfolios in parts (b), (c), and (d) has the largest expected return? Which has the smallest standard deviation? Which of these portfolios is the best investment?
    f. Discuss the advantages and disadvantages of investing in the three portfolios in parts (b), (c), and (d). Would you prefer investing all your money in the S&P 500 index, the core bonds fund, or one of the three portfolios? Why?

30. **Investment Fund Including REITs.** In addition to the information in exercise 29 on the S&P 500 and core bonds, J.P. Morgan Asset Management reported that the expected return for real estate investment trusts (REITs) during the same time period was 13.07% with a standard deviation of 23.17% (*J.P. Morgan Asset Management, Guide to the Markets*). The correlation between the S&P 500 and REITs is .74 and the correlation between core bonds and REITs is −.04. You are considering portfolio investments that are composed of an S&P 500 index fund and REITs as well as portfolio investments composed of a core bonds fund and REITs.
    a. Using the information provided here and in exercise 29, determine the covariance between the S&P 500 and REITs and between core bonds and REITs.
    b. Construct a portfolio that is 50% invested in an S&P 500 fund and 50% invested in REITs. In percentage terms, what are the expected return and standard deviation for such a portfolio?
    c. Construct a portfolio that is 50% invested in a core bonds fund and 50% invested in REITs. In percentage terms, what are the expected return and standard deviation for such a portfolio?
    d. Construct a portfolio that is 80% invested in a core bonds fund and 20% invested in REITs. In percentage terms, what are the expected return and standard deviation for such a portfolio?
    e. Which of the portfolios in parts (b), (c), and (d) would you recommend to an aggressive investor? Which would you recommend to a conservative investor? Why?

5.5 Binomial Probability Distribution

The binomial probability distribution is a discrete probability distribution that has many applications. It is associated with a multiple-step experiment that we call the binomial experiment.

A Binomial Experiment

A **binomial experiment** exhibits the following four properties.

> **PROPERTIES OF A BINOMIAL EXPERIMENT**
> 1. The experiment consists of a sequence of n identical trials.
> 2. Two outcomes are possible on each trial. We refer to one outcome as a *success* and the other outcome as a *failure*.
> 3. The probability of a success, denoted by p, does not change from trial to trial. Consequently, the probability of a failure, denoted by $1 - p$, does not change from trial to trial.
> 4. The trials are independent.

Jakob Bernoulli (1654–1705), the first of the Bernoulli family of Swiss mathematicians, published a treatise on probability that contained the theory of permutations and combinations, as well as the binomial theorem.

If properties 2, 3, and 4 are present, we say the trials are generated by a Bernoulli process. If, in addition, property 1 is present, we say we have a binomial experiment. Figure 5.2 depicts one possible sequence of successes and failures for a binomial experiment involving eight trials.

In a binomial experiment, our interest is in the *number of successes occurring in the n trials*. If we let x denote the number of successes occurring in the n trials, we see that x can assume the values of 0, 1, 2, 3, . . . , n. Because the number of values is finite, x is a *discrete* random variable. The probability distribution associated with this random variable is called the **binomial probability distribution**. For example, consider the experiment of tossing a coin five times and on each toss observing whether the coin lands with a head or a tail on its upward face. Suppose we want to count the number of heads appearing over the five tosses. Does this experiment show the properties of a binomial experiment? What is the random variable of interest? Note that:

1. The experiment consists of five identical trials; each trial involves the tossing of one coin.
2. Two outcomes are possible for each trial: a head or a tail. We can designate head a success and tail a failure.
3. The probability of a head and the probability of a tail are the same for each trial, with $p = .5$ and $1 - p = .5$.
4. The trials or tosses are independent because the outcome on any one trial is not affected by what happens on other trials or tosses.

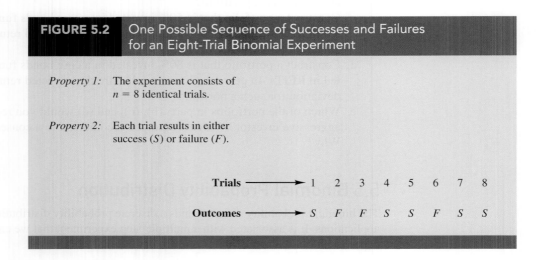

FIGURE 5.2   One Possible Sequence of Successes and Failures for an Eight-Trial Binomial Experiment

Property 1:   The experiment consists of $n = 8$ identical trials.

Property 2:   Each trial results in either success (S) or failure (F).

Trials ⟶   1   2   3   4   5   6   7   8

Outcomes ⟶ S F F S S F S S

Thus, the properties of a binomial experiment are satisfied. The random variable of interest is $x =$ the number of heads appearing in the five trials. In this case, x can assume the values of 0, 1, 2, 3, 4, or 5.

As another example, consider an insurance salesperson who visits 10 randomly selected families. The outcome associated with each visit is classified as a success if the family purchases an insurance policy and a failure if the family does not. From past experience, the salesperson knows the probability that a randomly selected family will purchase an insurance policy is .10. Checking the properties of a binomial experiment, we observe that:

1. The experiment consists of 10 identical trials; each trial involves contacting one family.
2. Two outcomes are possible on each trial: the family purchases a policy (success) or the family does not purchase a policy (failure).
3. The probabilities of a purchase and a nonpurchase are assumed to be the same for each sales call, with $p = .10$ and $1 - p = .90$.
4. The trials are independent because the families are randomly selected.

Because the four assumptions are satisfied, this example is a binomial experiment. The random variable of interest is the number of sales obtained in contacting the 10 families. In this case, x can assume the values of 0, 1, 2, 3, 4, 5, 6, 7, 8, 9, and 10.

Property 3 of the binomial experiment is called the *stationarity assumption* and is sometimes confused with property 4, independence of trials. To see how they differ, consider again the case of the salesperson calling on families to sell insurance policies. If, as the day wore on, the salesperson got tired and lost enthusiasm, the probability of success (selling a policy) might drop to .05, for example, by the tenth call. In such a case, property 3 (stationarity) would not be satisfied, and we would not have a binomial experiment. Even if property 4 held—that is, the purchase decisions of each family were made independently—it would not be a binomial experiment if property 3 was not satisfied.

In applications involving binomial experiments, a special mathematical formula, called the *binomial probability function,* can be used to compute the probability of x successes in the n trials. Using probability concepts introduced in Chapter 4, we will show in the context of an illustrative problem how the formula can be developed.

Martin Clothing Store Problem

Let us consider the purchase decisions of the next three customers who enter the Martin Clothing Store. On the basis of past experience, the store manager estimates the probability that any one customer will make a purchase is .30. What is the probability that two of the next three customers will make a purchase?

Using a tree diagram (Figure 5.3), we can see that the experiment of observing the three customers each making a purchase decision has eight possible outcomes. Using S to denote success (a purchase) and F to denote failure (no purchase), we are interested in experimental outcomes involving two successes in the three trials (purchase decisions). Next, let us verify that the experiment involving the sequence of three purchase decisions can be viewed as a binomial experiment. Checking the four requirements for a binomial experiment, we note that:

1. The experiment can be described as a sequence of three identical trials, one trial for each of the three customers who will enter the store.
2. Two outcomes—the customer makes a purchase (success) or the customer does not make a purchase (failure)—are possible for each trial.
3. The probability that the customer will make a purchase (.30) or will not make a purchase (.70) is assumed to be the same for all customers.
4. The purchase decision of each customer is independent of the decisions of the other customers.

FIGURE 5.3   Tree Diagram for the Martin Clothing Store Problem

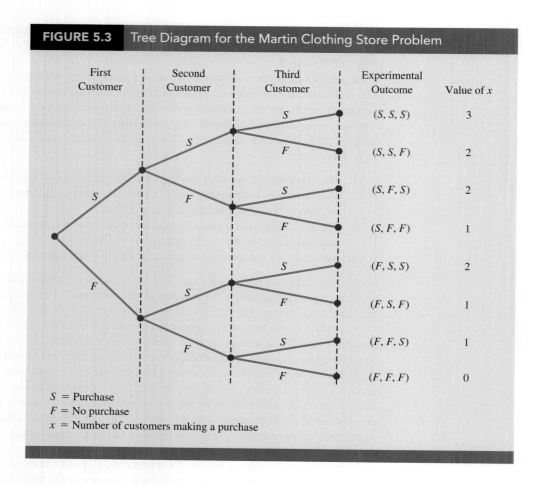

S = Purchase
F = No purchase
x = Number of customers making a purchase

Hence, the properties of a binomial experiment are present.

The number of experimental outcomes resulting in exactly *x* successes in *n* trials can be computed using the following formula.[2]

NUMBER OF EXPERIMENTAL OUTCOMES PROVIDING EXACTLY *x* SUCCESSES IN *n* TRIALS

$$\binom{n}{x} = \frac{n!}{x!(n-x)!} \tag{5.10}$$

where

$$n! = n(n-1)(n-2)\cdots(2)(1)$$

and, by definition,

$$0! = 1$$

Now let us return to the Martin Clothing Store experiment involving three customer purchase decisions. Equation (5.10) can be used to determine the number of experimental

[2]This formula, introduced in Chapter 4, determines the number of combinations of *n* objects selected *x* at a time. For the binomial experiment, this combinatorial formula provides the number of experimental outcomes (sequences of *n* trials) resulting in *x* successes.

outcomes involving two purchases; that is, the number of ways of obtaining $x = 2$ successes in the $n = 3$ trials. From equation (5.10) we have

$$\binom{n}{x} = \binom{3}{2} = \frac{3!}{2!(3-2)!} = \frac{(3)(2)(1)}{(2)(1)(1)} = \frac{6}{2} = 3$$

Equation (5.10) shows that three of the experimental outcomes yield two successes. From Figure 5.3 we see these three outcomes are denoted by (S, S, F), (S, F, S), and (F, S, S).

Using equation (5.10) to determine how many experimental outcomes have three successes (purchases) in the three trials, we obtain

$$\binom{n}{x} = \binom{3}{3} = \frac{3!}{3!(3-3)!} = \frac{3!}{3!0!} = \frac{(3)(2)(1)}{3(2)(1)(1)} = \frac{6}{6} = 1$$

From Figure 5.3 we see that the one experimental outcome with three successes is identified by (S, S, S).

We know that equation (5.10) can be used to determine the number of experimental outcomes that result in x successes in n trials. If we are to determine the probability of x successes in n trials, however, we must also know the probability associated with each of these experimental outcomes. Because the trials of a binomial experiment are independent, we can simply multiply the probabilities associated with each trial outcome to find the probability of a particular sequence of successes and failures.

The probability of purchases by the first two customers and no purchase by the third customer, denoted (S, S, F), is given by

$$pp(1-p)$$

With a .30 probability of a purchase on any one trial, the probability of a purchase on the first two trials and no purchase on the third is given by

$$(.30)(.30)(.70) = (.30)^2(.70) = .063$$

Two other experimental outcomes also result in two successes and one failure. The probabilities for all three experimental outcomes involving two successes follow.

Trial Outcomes				
1st Customer	2nd Customer	3rd Customer	Experimental Outcome	Probability of Experimental Outcome
Purchase	Purchase	No purchase	(S, S, F)	$pp(1-p) = p^2(1-p)$ $= (.30)^2(.70) = .063$
Purchase	No purchase	Purchase	(S, F, S)	$p(1-p)p = p^2(1-p)$ $= (.30)^2(.70) = .063$
No purchase	Purchase	Purchase	(F, S, S)	$(1-p)pp = p^2(1-p)$ $= (.30)^2(.70) = .063$

Observe that all three experimental outcomes with two successes have exactly the same probability. This observation holds in general. In any binomial experiment, all sequences of trial outcomes yielding x successes in n trials have the *same probability* of occurrence. The probability of each sequence of trials yielding x successes in n trials follows.

Probability of a particular
sequence of trial outcomes $= p^x(1 - p)^{(n-x)}$ **(5.11)**
with x successes in n trials

For the Martin Clothing Store, this formula shows that any experimental outcome with two successes has a probability of $p^2(1 - p)^{(3-2)} = p^2(1 - p)^1 = (.30)^2(.70)^1 = .063$.

Because equation (5.10) shows the number of outcomes in a binomial experiment with x successes and equation (5.11) gives the probability for each sequence involving x successes, we combine equations (5.10) and (5.11) to obtain the following **binomial probability function**.

BINOMIAL PROBABILITY FUNCTION

$$f(x) = \binom{n}{x} p^x(1 - p)^{(n-x)}$$ **(5.12)**

where

$x =$ the number of successes
$p =$ the probability of a success on one trial
$n =$ the number of trials
$f(x) =$ the probability of x successes in n trials
$\binom{n}{x} = \dfrac{n!}{x!(n - x)!}$

For the binomial probability distribution, x is a discrete random variable with the probability function $f(x)$ applicable for values of $x = 0, 1, 2, \ldots, n$.

In the Martin Clothing Store example, let us use equation (5.12) to compute the probability that no customer makes a purchase, exactly one customer makes a purchase, exactly two customers make a purchase, and all three customers make a purchase. The calculations are summarized in Table 5.13, which gives the probability distribution of the number of customers making a purchase. Figure 5.4 is a graph of this probability distribution.

The binomial probability function can be applied to *any* binomial experiment. If we are satisfied that a situation demonstrates the properties of a binomial experiment and if we know the values of n and p, we can use equation (5.12) to compute the probability of x successes in the n trials.

TABLE 5.13	Probability Distribution for the Number of Customers Making a Purchase

x	f(x)
0	$\dfrac{3!}{0!3!}(.30)^0(.70)^3 = .343$
1	$\dfrac{3!}{1!2!}(.30)^1(.70)^2 = .441$
2	$\dfrac{3!}{2!1!}(.30)^2(.70)^1 = .189$
3	$\dfrac{3!}{3!0!}(.30)^3(.70)^0 = \dfrac{.027}{1.000}$

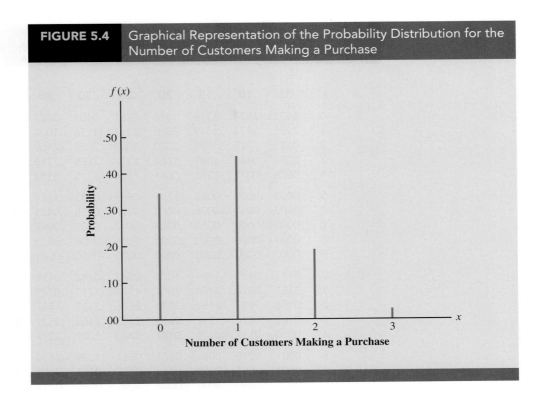

FIGURE 5.4   Graphical Representation of the Probability Distribution for the Number of Customers Making a Purchase

If we consider variations of the Martin experiment, such as 10 customers rather than three entering the store, the binomial probability function given by equation (5.12) is still applicable. Suppose we have a binomial experiment with $n = 10$, $x = 4$, and $p = .30$. The probability of making exactly four sales to 10 customers entering the store is

$$f(4) = \frac{10!}{4!6!}(.30)^4(.70)^6 = .2001$$

Using Tables of Binomial Probabilities

Tables have been developed that give the probability of x successes in n trials for a binomial experiment. The tables are generally easy to use and quicker than equation (5.12). Table 5 of Appendix B provides such a table of binomial probabilities. A portion of this table appears in Table 5.14. To use this table, we must specify the values of n, p, and x for the binomial experiment of interest. In the example at the top of Table 5.14, we see that the probability of $x = 3$ successes in a binomial experiment with $n = 10$ and $p = .40$ is .2150. You can use equation (5.12) to verify that you would obtain the same answer if you used the binomial probability function directly.

Now let us use Table 5.14 to verify the probability of 4 successes in 10 trials for the Martin Clothing Store problem. Note that the value of $f(4) = .2001$ can be read directly from the table of binomial probabilities, with $n = 10$, $x = 4$, and $p = .30$.

Even though the tables of binomial probabilities are relatively easy to use, it is impossible to have tables that show all possible values of n and p that might be encountered in a binomial experiment. However, with today's calculators, using equation (5.12) to calculate the desired probability is not difficult, especially if the number of trials is not large. In the exercises, you should practice using equation (5.12) to compute the binomial probabilities unless the problem specifically requests that you use the binomial probability table.

TABLE 5.14   Selected Values from the Binomial Probability Table
Example: $n = 10$, $x = 3$, $P = .40$; $f(3) = .2150$

n	x	.05	.10	.15	.20	p .25	.30	.35	.40	.45	.50
9	0	.6302	.3874	.2316	.1342	.0751	.0404	.0207	.0101	.0046	.0020
	1	.2985	.3874	.3679	.3020	.2253	.1556	.1004	.0605	.0339	.0176
	2	.0629	.1722	.2597	.3020	.3003	.2668	.2162	.1612	.1110	.0703
	3	.0077	.0446	.1069	.1762	.2336	.2668	.2716	.2508	.2119	.1641
	4	.0006	.0074	.0283	.0661	.1168	.1715	.2194	.2508	.2600	.2461
	5	.0000	.0008	.0050	.0165	.0389	.0735	.1181	.1672	.2128	.2461
	6	.0000	.0001	.0006	.0028	.0087	.0210	.0424	.0743	.1160	.1641
	7	.0000	.0000	.0000	.0003	.0012	.0039	.0098	.0212	.0407	.0703
	8	.0000	.0000	.0000	.0000	.0001	.0004	.0013	.0035	.0083	.0176
	9	.0000	.0000	.0000	.0000	.0000	.0000	.0001	.0003	.0008	.0020
10	0	.5987	.3487	.1969	.1074	.0563	.0282	.0135	.0060	.0025	.0010
	1	.3151	.3874	.3474	.2684	.1877	.1211	.0725	.0403	.0207	.0098
	2	.0746	.1937	.2759	.3020	.2816	.2335	.1757	.1209	.0763	.0439
	3	.0105	.0574	.1298	.2013	.2503	.2668	.2522	**.2150**	.1665	.1172
	4	.0010	.0112	.0401	.0881	.1460	.2001	.2377	.2508	.2384	.2051
	5	.0001	.0015	.0085	.0264	.0584	.1029	.1536	.2007	.2340	.2461
	6	.0000	.0001	.0012	.0055	.0162	.0368	.0689	.1115	.1596	.2051
	7	.0000	.0000	.0001	.0008	.0031	.0090	.0212	.0425	.0746	.1172
	8	.0000	.0000	.0000	.0001	.0004	.0014	.0043	.0106	.0229	.0439
	9	.0000	.0000	.0000	.0000	.0000	.0001	.0005	.0016	.0042	.0098
	10	.0000	.0000	.0000	.0000	.0000	.0000	.0000	.0001	.0003	.0010

Statistical software packages also provide a capability for computing binomial probabilities. Consider the Martin Clothing Store example with $n = 10$ and $p = .30$. Figure 5.5 shows the binomial probabilities generated by JMP for all possible values of x. Note that these values are the same as those found in the $p = .30$ column of Table 5.14. The chapter appendices contain step-by-step instructions for using widely available software packages to generate binomial probabilities.

Expected Value and Variance for the Binomial Distribution

In Section 5.3 we provided formulas for computing the expected value and variance of a discrete random variable. In the special case where the random variable has a binomial distribution with a known number of trials n and a known probability of success p, the general formulas for the expected value and variance can be simplified. The results follow.

EXPECTED VALUE AND VARIANCE FOR THE BINOMIAL DISTRIBUTION

$$E(x) = \mu = np \tag{5.13}$$

$$Var(x) = \sigma^2 = np(1 - p) \tag{5.14}$$

FIGURE 5.5	JMP Output Showing Binomial Probabilities for the Martin Clothing Store Problem

x	P(X = x)
0	.0282475249
1	.121060821
2	.2334744405
3	.266827932
4	.200120949
5	.1029193425
6	.036756909
7	.009001692
8	.0014467005
9	.000137781
10	.0000059049

For the Martin Clothing Store problem with three customers, we can use equation (5.13) to compute the expected number of customers who will make a purchase.

$$E(x) = np = 3(.30) = .9$$

Suppose that for the next month the Martin Clothing Store forecasts 1000 customers will enter the store. What is the expected number of customers who will make a purchase? The answer is $\mu = np = (1000)(.3) = 300$. Thus, to increase the expected number of purchases, Martin's must induce more customers to enter the store and/or somehow increase the probability that any individual customer will make a purchase after entering.

For the Martin Clothing Store problem with three customers, we see that the variance and standard deviation for the number of customers who will make a purchase are

$$\sigma^2 = np(1 - p) = 3(.3)(.7) = .63$$
$$\sigma = \sqrt{.63} = .79$$

For the next 1000 customers entering the store, the variance and standard deviation for the number of customers who will make a purchase are

$$\sigma^2 = np(1 - p) = 1000(.3)(.7) = 210$$
$$\sigma = \sqrt{210} = 14.49$$

NOTES + COMMENTS

1. The binomial table in Appendix B shows values of p up to and including $p = .95$. Some sources of the binomial table only show values of p up to and including $p = .50$. It would appear that such a table cannot be used when the probability of success exceeds $p = .50$. However, the table can be used by noting that the probability of $n - x$ failures is also the probability of x successes. Thus, when the probability of success is greater than $p = .50$, we can compute the probability of $n - x$ failures instead. The probability of failure, $1 - p$, will be less than .50 when $p > .50$.

2. Some sources present the binomial table in a cumulative form. In using such a table, one must subtract entries in the table to find the probability of exactly x success in n trials. For example, $f(2) = P(x \le 2) - P(x \le 1)$. The binomial table we provide in Appendix B provides $f(2)$ directly. To compute cumulative probabilities using the binomial table in Appendix B, sum the entries in the table. For example, to determine the cumulative probability $P(x \le 2)$, compute the sum $f(0) + f(1) + f(2)$.

EXERCISES

Methods

31. Consider a binomial experiment with two trials and $p = .4$.
    a. Draw a tree diagram for this experiment (see Figure 5.3).
    b. Compute the probability of one success, $f(1)$.
    c. Compute $f(0)$.
    d. Compute $f(2)$.
    e. Compute the probability of at least one success.
    f. Compute the expected value, variance, and standard deviation.

32. Consider a binomial experiment with $n = 10$ and $p = .10$.
    a. Compute $f(0)$.
    b. Compute $f(2)$.
    c. Compute $P(x \le 2)$.
    d. Compute $P(x \ge 1)$.
    e. Compute $E(x)$.
    f. Compute $Var(x)$ and σ.

33. Consider a binomial experiment with $n = 20$ and $p = .70$.
    a. Compute $f(12)$.
    b. Compute $f(16)$.
    c. Compute $P(x \ge 16)$.
    d. Compute $P(x \le 15)$.
    e. Compute $E(x)$.
    f. Compute $Var(x)$ and σ.

Applications

34. **How Teenagers Listen to Music.** For its Music 360 survey, Nielsen Co. asked teenagers and adults how each group has listened to music in the past 12 months. Nearly two-thirds of U.S. teenagers under the age of 18 say they use Google Inc.'s video-sharing site to listen to music and 35% of the teenagers said they use Pandora Media Inc.'s custom online radio service (*The Wall Street Journal*). Suppose 10 teenagers are selected randomly to be interviewed about how they listen to music.
    a. Is randomly selecting 10 teenagers and asking whether or not they use Pandora Media Inc.'s online service a binomial experiment?
    b. What is the probability that none of the 10 teenagers uses Pandora Media Inc.'s online radio service?
    c. What is the probability that 4 of the 10 teenagers use Pandora Media Inc.'s online radio service?
    d. What is the probability that at least 2 of the 10 teenagers use Pandora Media Inc.'s online radio service?

35. **Appeals for Medicare Service.** The Center for Medicare and Medical Services reported that there were 295,000 appeals for hospitalization and other Part A Medicare service. For this group, 40% of first-round appeals were successful (*The Wall Street Journal*). Suppose 10 first-round appeals have just been received by a Medicare appeals office.
    a. Compute the probability that none of the appeals will be successful.
    b. Compute the probability that exactly one of the appeals will be successful.
    c. What is the probability that at least two of the appeals will be successful?
    d. What is the probability that more than half of the appeals will be successful?

36. **Number of Defective Parts.** When a new machine is functioning properly, only 3% of the items produced are defective. Assume that we will randomly select two parts produced on the machine and that we are interested in the number of defective parts found.
    a. Describe the conditions under which this situation would be a binomial experiment.
    b. Draw a tree diagram similar to Figure 5.4 showing this problem as a two-trial experiment.
    c. How many experimental outcomes result in exactly one defect being found?

d. Compute the probabilities associated with finding no defects, exactly one defect, and two defects.

37. **Americans Saving for Retirement.** According to a 2018 survey by Bankrate.com, 20% of adults in the United States save nothing for retirement (CNBC website). Suppose that 15 adults in the United States are selected randomly.
   a. Is the selection of the 15 adults a binomial experiment? Explain.
   b. What is the probability that all of the selected adults save nothing for retirement?
   c. What is the probability that exactly five of the selected adults save nothing for retirement?
   d. What is the probability that at least one of the selected adults saves nothing for retirement?

38. **Detecting Missile Attacks.** Military radar and missile detection systems are designed to warn a country of an enemy attack. A reliability question is whether a detection system will be able to identify an attack and issue a warning. Assume that a particular detection system has a .90 probability of detecting a missile attack. Use the binomial probability distribution to answer the following questions.
   a. What is the probability that a single detection system will detect an attack?
   b. If two detection systems are installed in the same area and operate independently, what is the probability that at least one of the systems will detect the attack?
   c. If three systems are installed, what is the probability that at least one of the systems will detect the attack?
   d. Would you recommend that multiple detection systems be used? Explain.

39. **Web Browser Market Share.** Market-share-analysis company Net Applications monitors and reports on Internet browser usage. According to Net Applications, in the summer of 2014, Google's Chrome browser exceeded a 20% market share for the first time, with a 20.37% share of the browser market (*Forbes* website). For a randomly selected group of 20 Internet browser users, answer the following questions.
   a. Compute the probability that exactly 8 of the 20 Internet browser users use Chrome as their Internet browser.
   b. Compute the probability that at least 3 of the 20 Internet browser users use Chrome as their Internet browser.
   c. For the sample of 20 Internet browser users, compute the expected number of Chrome users.
   d. For the sample of 20 Internet browser users, compute the variance and standard deviation for the number of Chrome users.

40. **Contributing to Household Income.** Suppose that a random sample of fifteen 18- to 34-year-olds living with their parents is selected and asked if they contribute to household expenses.
   a. Is the selection of the fifteen 18- to 34-year-olds living with their parents a binomial experiment? Explain.
   b. If the sample shows that none of the fifteen 18- to 34-year-olds living with their parents contribute to household expenses, would you question the results of the Pew Research Study? Explain.
   c. What is the probability that at least 10 of the fifteen 18- to 34-year-olds living with their parents contribute to household expenses?

41. **Introductory Statistics Course Withdrawals.** A university found that 20% of its students withdraw without completing the introductory statistics course. Assume that 20 students registered for the course.
   a. Compute the probability that 2 or fewer will withdraw.
   b. Compute the probability that exactly 4 will withdraw.
   c. Compute the probability that more than 3 will withdraw.
   d. Compute the expected number of withdrawals.

42. **State of the Nation Survey.** Suppose a sample of 20 Americans is selected as part of a study of the state of the nation. The Americans in the sample are asked whether or not they are satisfied with the way things are going in the United States.

a. Compute the probability that exactly 4 of the 20 Americans surveyed are satisfied with the way things are going in the United States.
b. Compute the probability that at least 2 of the Americans surveyed are satisfied with the way things are going in the United States.
c. For the sample of 20 Americans, compute the expected number of Americans who are satisfied with the way things are going in the United States.
d. For the sample of 20 Americans, compute the variance and standard deviation of the number of Americans who are satisfied with the way things are going in the United States.

43. **Tracked Emails.** According to a 2017 *Wired* magazine article, 40% of emails that are received are tracked using software that can tell the email sender when, where, and on what type of device the email was opened (*Wired* magazine website). Suppose we randomly select 50 received emails.
a. What is the expected number of these emails that are tracked?
b. What are the variance and standard deviation for the number of these emails that are tracked?

5.6 Poisson Probability Distribution

In this section we consider a discrete random variable that is often useful in estimating the number of occurrences over a specified interval of time or space. For example, the random variable of interest might be the number of arrivals at a car wash in one hour, the number of repairs needed in 10 miles of highway, or the number of leaks in 100 miles of pipeline. If the following two properties are satisfied, the number of occurrences is a random variable described by the **Poisson probability distribution**.

The Poisson probability distribution is often used to model random arrivals in waiting line situations.

PROPERTIES OF A POISSON EXPERIMENT

1. The probability of an occurrence is the same for any two intervals of equal length.
2. The occurrence or nonoccurrence in any interval is independent of the occurrence or nonoccurrence in any other interval.

The **Poisson probability function** is defined by equation (5.15).

Siméon Poisson taught mathematics at the Ecole Polytechnique in Paris from 1802 to 1808. In 1837, he published a work entitled, "Researches on the Probability of Criminal and Civil Verdicts," which includes a discussion of what later became known as the Poisson distribution.

POISSON PROBABILITY FUNCTION

$$f(x) = \frac{\mu^x e^{-\mu}}{x!}$$ (5.15)

where

$f(x) =$ the probability of x occurrences in an interval

$\mu =$ expected value or mean number of occurrences in an interval

$e = 2.71828$

For the Poisson probability distribution, x is a discrete random variable indicating the number of occurrences in the interval. Since there is no stated upper limit for the number of occurrences, the probability function $f(x)$ is applicable for values $x = 0, 1, 2, \ldots$ without limit. In practical applications, x will eventually become large enough so that $f(x)$ is approximately zero and the probability of any larger values of x becomes negligible.

An Example Involving Time Intervals

Suppose that we are interested in the number of patients who arrive at the emergency room of a large hospital during a 15-minute period on weekday mornings. If we can assume that the probability of a patient arriving is the same for any two time periods of equal length and that the arrival or nonarrival of a patient in any time period is independent of the arrival or nonarrival in any other time period, the Poisson probability function is applicable. Suppose these assumptions are satisfied and an analysis of historical data shows that the average number of patients arriving in a 15-minute period of time is 10; in this case, the following probability function applies.

$$f(x) = \frac{10^x e^{-10}}{x!}$$

The random variable here is x = number of patients arriving in any 15-minute period.

If management wanted to know the probability of exactly five arrivals in 15 minutes, we would set $x = 5$ and thus obtain

$$\text{Probability of exactly} \atop \text{5 arrivals in 15 minutes} = f(5) = \frac{10^5 e^{-10}}{5!} = .0378$$

Although this probability was determined by evaluating the probability function with $\mu = 10$ and $x = 5$, it is often easier to refer to a table for the Poisson distribution. The table provides probabilities for specific values of x and μ. We included such a table as Table 7 of Appendix B. For convenience, we reproduced a portion of this table as Table 5.15. Note that

TABLE 5.15	Selected Values from the Poisson Probability Tables Example: $\mu = 10$, $x = 5$; $f(5) = .0378$

x	9.1	9.2	9.3	9.4	9.5	9.6	9.7	9.8	9.9	10
0	.0001	.0001	.0001	.0001	.0001	.0001	.0001	.0001	.0001	.0000
1	.0010	.0009	.0009	.0008	.0007	.0007	.0006	.0005	.0005	.0005
2	.0046	.0043	.0040	.0037	.0034	.0031	.0029	.0027	.0025	.0023
3	.0140	.0131	.0123	.0115	.0107	.0100	.0093	.0087	.0081	.0076
4	.0319	.0302	.0285	.0269	.0254	.0240	.0226	.0213	.0201	.0189
5	.0581	.0555	.0530	.0506	.0483	.0460	.0439	.0418	.0398	**.0378**
6	.0881	.0851	.0822	.0793	.0764	.0736	.0709	.0682	.0656	.0631
7	.1145	.1118	.1091	.1064	.1037	.1010	.0982	.0955	.0928	.0901
8	.1302	.1286	.1269	.1251	.1232	.1212	.1191	.1170	.1148	.1126
9	.1317	.1315	.1311	.1306	.1300	.1293	.1284	.1274	.1263	.1251
10	.1198	.1210	.1219	.1228	.1235	.1241	.1245	.1249	.1250	.1251
11	.0991	.1012	.1031	.1049	.1067	.1083	.1098	.1112	.1125	.1137
12	.0752	.0776	.0799	.0822	.0844	.0866	.0888	.0908	.0928	.0948
13	.0526	.0549	.0572	.0594	.0617	.0640	.0662	.0685	.0707	.0729
14	.0342	.0361	.0380	.0399	.0419	.0439	.0459	.0479	.0500	.0521
15	.0208	.0221	.0235	.0250	.0265	.0281	.0297	.0313	.0330	.0347
16	.0118	.0127	.0137	.0147	.0157	.0168	.0180	.0192	.0204	.0217
17	.0063	.0069	.0075	.0081	.0088	.0095	.0103	.0111	.0119	.0128
18	.0032	.0035	.0039	.0042	.0046	.0051	.0055	.0060	.0065	.0071
19	.0015	.0017	.0019	.0021	.0023	.0026	.0028	.0031	.0034	.0037
20	.0007	.0008	.0009	.0010	.0011	.0012	.0014	.0015	.0017	.0019
21	.0003	.0003	.0004	.0004	.0005	.0006	.0006	.0007	.0008	.0009
22	.0001	.0001	.0002	.0002	.0002	.0002	.0003	.0003	.0004	.0004
23	.0000	.0001	.0001	.0001	.0001	.0001	.0001	.0001	.0002	.0002
24	.0000	.0000	.0000	.0000	.0000	.0000	.0000	.0001	.0001	.0001

to use the table of Poisson probabilities, we need know only the values of x and μ. From Table 5.15 we see that the probability of five arrivals in a 15-minute period is found by locating the value in the row of the table corresponding to $x = 5$ and the column of the table corresponding to $\mu = 10$. Hence, we obtain $f(5) = .0378$.

A property of the Poisson distribution is that the mean and variance are equal.

In the preceding example, the mean of the Poisson distribution is $\mu = 10$ arrivals per 15-minute period. A property of the Poisson distribution is that the mean of the distribution and the variance of the distribution are *equal*. Thus, the variance for the number of arrivals during 15-minute periods is $\sigma^2 = 10$. The standard deviation is $\sigma = \sqrt{10} = 3.16$.

Our illustration involves a 15-minute period, but other time periods can be used. Suppose we want to compute the probability of one arrival in a 3-minute period. Because 10 is the expected number of arrivals in a 15-minute period, we see that $10/15 = 2/3$ is the expected number of arrivals in a 1-minute period and that $(2/3)(3 \text{ minutes}) = 2$ is the expected number of arrivals in a 3-minute period. Thus, the probability of x arrivals in a 3-minute time period with $\mu = 2$ is given by the following Poisson probability function:

$$f(x) = \frac{2^x e^{-2}}{x!}$$

The probability of one arrival in a 3-minute period is calculated as follows:

$$\begin{array}{c}\text{Probability of exactly}\\ \text{1 arrival in 3 minutes}\end{array} = f(1) = \frac{2^1 e^{-2}}{1!} = .2707$$

One might expect that because (5 arrivals)/5 = 1 arrival and (15 minutes)/5 = 3 minutes, we would get the same probability for one arrival during a 3-minute period as we do for five arrivals during a 15-minute period. Earlier we computed the probability of five arrivals in a 15-minute period to be .0378. However, note that the probability of one arrival in a three-minute period (.2707) is not the same. When computing a Poisson probability for a different time interval, we must first convert the mean arrival rate to the time period of interest and then compute the probability.

An Example Involving Length or Distance Intervals

Let us illustrate an application not involving time intervals in which the Poisson distribution is useful. Suppose we are concerned with the occurrence of major defects in a highway one month after resurfacing. We will assume that the probability of a defect is the same for any two highway intervals of equal length and that the occurrence or nonoccurrence of a defect in any one interval is independent of the occurrence or nonoccurrence of a defect in any other interval. Hence, the Poisson distribution can be applied.

Suppose we learn that major defects one month after resurfacing occur at the average rate of two per mile. Let us find the probability of no major defects in a particular three-mile section of the highway. Because we are interested in an interval with a length of three miles, $\mu = (2 \text{ defects/mile})(3 \text{ miles}) = 6$ represents the expected number of major defects over the three-mile section of highway. Using equation (5.15), the probability of no major defects is $f(0) = 6^0 e^{-6}/0! = .0025$. Thus, it is unlikely that no major defects will occur in the three-mile section. In fact, this example indicates a $1 - .0025 = .9975$ probability of at least one major defect in the three-mile highway section.

EXERCISES

Methods

44. Consider a Poisson distribution with $\mu = 3$.
    a. Write the appropriate Poisson probability function.
    b. Compute $f(2)$.
    c. Compute $f(1)$.
    d. Compute $P(x \geq 2)$.

45. Consider a Poisson distribution with a mean of two occurrences per time period.
    a. Write the appropriate Poisson probability function.
    b. What is the expected number of occurrences in three time periods?
    c. Write the appropriate Poisson probability function to determine the probability of x occurrences in three time periods.
    d. Compute the probability of two occurrences in one time period.
    e. Compute the probability of six occurrences in three time periods.
    f. Compute the probability of five occurrences in two time periods.

Applications

46. **Regional Airways Calls.** Phone calls arrive at the rate of 48 per hour at the reservation desk for Regional Airways.
    a. Compute the probability of receiving three calls in a 5-minute interval of time.
    b. Compute the probability of receiving exactly 10 calls in 15 minutes.
    c. Suppose no calls are currently on hold. If the agent takes 5 minutes to complete the current call, how many callers do you expect to be waiting by that time? What is the probability that none will be waiting?
    d. If no calls are currently being processed, what is the probability that the agent can take 3 minutes for personal time without being interrupted by a call?

47. **911 Calls.** Emergency 911 calls to a small municipality in Idaho come in at the rate of one every 2 minutes.
    a. What is the expected number of 911 calls in one hour?
    b. What is the probability of three 911 calls in five minutes?
    c. What is the probability of no 911 calls in a five-minute period?

48. **Motor Vehicle Accidents in New York City.** In a one-year period, New York City had a total of 11,232 motor vehicle accidents that occurred on Monday through Friday between the hours of 3 P.M. and 6 P.M. (New York State Department of Motor Vehicles website). This corresponds to mean of 14.4 accidents per hour.
    a. Compute the probability of no accidents in a 15-minute period.
    b. Compute the probability of at least one accident in a 15-minute period.
    c. Compute the probability of four or more accidents in a 15-minute period.

49. **Airport Passenger-Screening Facility.** Airline passengers arrive randomly and independently at the passenger-screening facility at a major international airport. The mean arrival rate is 10 passengers per minute.
    a. Compute the probability of no arrivals in a one-minute period.
    b. Compute the probability that three or fewer passengers arrive in a one-minute period.
    c. Compute the probability of no arrivals in a 15-second period.
    d. Compute the probability of at least one arrival in a 15-second period.

50. **Tornadoes in Colorado.** According to the National Oceanic and Atmospheric Administration (NOAA), the state of Colorado averages 18 tornadoes every June (NOAA website). (*Note*: There are 30 days in June.)
    a. Compute the mean number of tornadoes per day.
    b. Compute the probability of no tornadoes during a day.
    c. Compute the probability of exactly one tornado during a day.
    d. Compute the probability of more than one tornado during a day.

51. **Emails Received.** According to a 2017 survey conducted by the technology market research firm The Radicati Group, U.S. office workers receive an average of 121 emails per day (*Entrepreneur* magazine website). Assume the number of emails received per hour follows a Poisson distribution and that the average number of emails received per hour is five.
    a. What is the probability of receiving no emails during an hour?
    b. What is the probability of receiving at least three emails during an hour?
    c. What is the expected number of emails received during 15 minutes?
    d. What is the probability that no emails are received during 15 minutes?

5.7 Hypergeometric Probability Distribution

The **hypergeometric probability distribution** is closely related to the binomial distribution. The two probability distributions differ in two key ways. With the hypergeometric distribution, the trials are not independent; and the probability of success changes from trial to trial.

In the usual notation for the hypergeometric distribution, r denotes the number of elements in the population of size N labeled success, and $N - r$ denotes the number of elements in the population labeled failure. The **hypergeometric probability function** is used to compute the probability that in a random selection of n elements, selected without replacement, we obtain x elements labeled success and $n - x$ elements labeled failure. For this outcome to occur, we must obtain x successes from the r successes in the population and $n - x$ failures from the $N - r$ failures. The following hypergeometric probability function provides $f(x)$, the probability of obtaining x successes in n trials.

HYPERGEOMETRIC PROBABILITY FUNCTION

$$f(x) = \frac{\binom{r}{x}\binom{N-r}{n-x}}{\binom{N}{n}} \tag{5.16}$$

where

x = the number of successes

n = the number of trials

$f(x)$ = the probability of x successes in n trials

N = the number of elements in the population

r = the number of elements in the population labeled success

Note that $\binom{N}{n}$ represents the number of ways n elements can be selected from a population of size N; $\binom{r}{x}$ represents the number of ways that x successes can be selected from a total of r successes in the population; and $\binom{N-r}{n-x}$ represents the number of ways that $n - x$ failures can be selected from a total of $N - r$ failures in the population.

For the hypergeometric probability distribution, x is a discrete random variable and the probability function $f(x)$ given by equation (5.16) is usually applicable for values of $x = 0$, $1, 2, \ldots, n$. However, only values of x where the number of observed successes is *less than or equal* to the number of successes in the population ($x \leq r$) and where the number of observed failures is *less than or equal to* the number of failures in the population ($n - x \leq N - r$) are valid. If these two conditions do not hold for one or more values of x, the corresponding $f(x) = 0$ indicates that the probability of this value of x is zero.

To illustrate the computations involved in using equation (5.16), let us consider the following quality control application. Electric fuses produced by Ontario Electric are packaged in boxes of 12 units each. Suppose an inspector randomly selects three of the 12 fuses in a box for testing. If the box contains exactly five defective fuses, what is the probability that the inspector will find exactly one of the three fuses defective? In this application, $n = 3$ and $N = 12$. With $r = 5$ defective fuses in the box the probability of finding $x = 1$ defective fuse is

$$f(1) = \frac{\binom{5}{1}\binom{7}{2}}{\binom{12}{3}} = \frac{\left(\frac{5!}{1!4!}\right)\left(\frac{7!}{2!5!}\right)}{\left(\frac{12!}{3!9!}\right)} = \frac{(5)(21)}{220} = .4773$$

Now suppose that we wanted to know the probability of finding *at least* one defective fuse. The easiest way to answer this question is to first compute the probability that the inspector does not find any defective fuses. The probability of $x = 0$ is

$$f(0) = \frac{\binom{5}{0}\binom{7}{3}}{\binom{12}{3}} = \frac{\left(\frac{5!}{0!5!}\right)\left(\frac{7!}{3!4!}\right)}{\left(\frac{12!}{3!9!}\right)} = \frac{(1)(35)}{220} = .1591$$

With a probability of zero defective fuses $f(0) = .1591$, we conclude that the probability of finding at least 1 defective fuse must be $1 - .1591 = .8409$. Thus, there is a reasonably high probability that the inspector will find at least 1 defective fuse.

The mean and variance of a hypergeometric distribution are as follows.

$$E(x) = \mu = n\left(\frac{r}{N}\right) \tag{5.17}$$

$$Var(x) = \sigma^2 = n\left(\frac{r}{N}\right)\left(1 - \frac{r}{N}\right)\left(\frac{N-n}{N-1}\right) \tag{5.18}$$

In the preceding example $n = 3$, $r = 5$, and $N = 12$. Thus, the mean and variance for the number of defective fuses are

$$\mu = n\left(\frac{r}{N}\right) = 3\left(\frac{5}{12}\right) = 1.25$$

$$\sigma^2 = n\left(\frac{r}{N}\right)\left(1 - \frac{r}{N}\right)\left(\frac{N-n}{N-1}\right) = 3\left(\frac{5}{12}\right)\left(1 - \frac{5}{12}\right)\left(\frac{12-3}{12-1}\right) = .60$$

The standard deviation is $\sigma = \sqrt{.60} = .77$.

NOTES + COMMENTS

Consider a hypergeometric distribution with n trials. Let $p = (r/N)$ denote the probability of a success on the first trial. If the population size is large, the term $(N - n)/(N - 1)$ in equation (5.18) approaches 1. As a result, the expected value and variance can be written $E(x) = np$ and $Var(x) = np(1 - p)$. Note that these expressions are the same as the expressions used to compute the expected value and variance of a binomial distribution, as in equations (5.13) and (5.14). When the population size is large, a hypergeometric distribution can be approximated by a binomial distribution with n trials and a probability of success $p = (r/N)$.

EXERCISES

Methods

52. Suppose $N = 10$ and $r = 3$. Compute the hypergeometric probabilities for the following values of n and x.
    a. $n = 4$, $x = 1$.
    b. $n = 2$, $x = 2$.
    c. $n = 2$, $x = 0$.
    d. $n = 4$, $x = 2$.
    e. $n = 4$, $x = 4$.
53. Suppose $N = 15$ and $r = 4$. What is the probability of $x = 3$ for $n = 10$?

Applications

54. **Online Holiday Shopping.** More and more shoppers prefer to do their holiday shopping online from companies such as Amazon. Suppose we have a group of 10 shoppers; 7 prefer to do their holiday shopping online and 3 prefer to do their holiday shopping in stores. A random sample of 3 of these 10 shoppers is selected for a more in-depth study of how the economy has impacted their shopping behavior.
    a. What is the probability that exactly 2 prefer shopping online?
    b. What is the probability that the majority (either 2 or 3) prefer shopping online?

55. **Playing Blackjack.** Blackjack, or twenty-one as it is frequently called, is a popular gambling game played in casinos. A player is dealt two cards. Face cards (jacks, queens, and kings) and tens have a point value of 10. Aces have a point value of 1 or 11. A 52-card deck contains 16 cards with a point value of 10 (jacks, queens, kings, and tens) and four aces.
    a. What is the probability that both cards dealt are aces or 10-point cards?
    b. What is the probability that both of the cards are aces?
    c. What is the probability that both of the cards have a point value of 10?
    d. A blackjack is a 10-point card and an ace for a value of 21. Use your answers to parts (a), (b), and (c) to determine the probability that a player is dealt blackjack. (*Hint:* Part (d) is not a hypergeometric problem. Develop your own logical relationship as to how the hypergeometric probabilities from parts (a), (b), and (c) can be combined to answer this question.)

56. **Computer Company Benefits Questionnaire.** Axline Computers manufactures personal computers at two plants, one in Texas and the other in Hawaii. The Texas plant has 40 employees; the Hawaii plant has 20. A random sample of 10 employees is to be asked to fill out a benefits questionnaire.
    a. What is the probability that none of the employees in the sample works at the plant in Hawaii?
    b. What is the probability that one of the employees in the sample works at the plant in Hawaii?
    c. What is the probability that two or more of the employees in the sample work at the plant in Hawaii?
    d. What is the probability that 9 of the employees in the sample work at the plant in Texas?

57. **Business Meal Reimbursement.** The Zagat Restaurant Survey provides food, decor, and service ratings for some of the top restaurants across the United States. For 15 restaurants located in Boston, the average price of a dinner, including one drink and tip, was $48.60. You are leaving on a business trip to Boston and will eat dinner at three of these restaurants. Your company will reimburse you for a maximum of $50 per dinner. Business associates familiar with these restaurants have told you that the meal cost at one-third of these restaurants will exceed $50. Suppose that you randomly select three of these restaurants for dinner.
    a. What is the probability that none of the meals will exceed the cost covered by your company?
    b. What is the probability that one of the meals will exceed the cost covered by your company?
    c. What is the probability that two of the meals will exceed the cost covered by your company?
    d. What is the probability that all three of the meals will exceed the cost covered by your company?

58. **TARP Funds.** The Troubled Asset Relief Program (TARP), passed by the U.S. Congress in October 2008, provided $700 billion in assistance for the struggling U.S. economy. Over $200 billion was given to troubled financial institutions with the hope that there would be an increase in lending to help jump-start the economy. But three months later, a Federal Reserve survey found that two-thirds of the banks that had received TARP funds had tightened terms for business loans (*The Wall Street Journal*).

Of the 10 banks that were the biggest recipients of TARP funds, only 3 had actually increased lending during this period.

Increased Lending	Decreased Lending
BB&T	Bank of America
Sun Trust Banks	Capital One
U.S. Bancorp	Citigroup
	Fifth Third Bancorp
	J.P. Morgan Chase
	Regions Financial
	Wells Fargo

For the purposes of this exercise, assume that you will randomly select 3 of these 10 banks for a study that will continue to monitor bank lending practices. Let x be a random variable indicating the number of banks in the study that had increased lending.

a. What is $f(0)$? What is your interpretation of this value?
b. What is $f(3)$? What is your interpretation of this value?
c. Compute $f(1)$ and $f(2)$. Show the probability distribution for the number of banks in the study that had increased lending. What value of x has the highest probability?
d. What is the probability that the study will have at least one bank that had increased lending?
e. Compute the expected value, variance, and standard deviation for the random variable.

SUMMARY

A random variable provides a numerical description of the outcome of an experiment. The probability distribution for a random variable describes how the probabilities are distributed over the values the random variable can assume. For any discrete random variable x, the probability distribution is defined by a probability function, denoted by $f(x)$, which provides the probability associated with each value of the random variable.

We introduced two types of discrete probability distributions. One type involved providing a list of the values of the random variable and the associated probabilities in a table. We showed how the relative frequency method of assigning probabilities could be used to develop empirical discrete probability distributions of this type. Bivariate empirical distributions were also discussed. With bivariate distributions, interest focuses on the relationship between two random variables. We showed how to compute the covariance and correlation coefficient as measures of such a relationship. We also showed how bivariate distributions involving market returns on financial assets could be used to create financial portfolios.

The second type of discrete probability distribution we discussed involved the use of a mathematical function to provide the probabilities for the random variable. The binomial, Poisson, and hypergeometric distributions discussed were all of this type. The binomial distribution can be used to determine the probability of x successes in n trials whenever the experiment has the following properties:

1. The experiment consists of a sequence of n identical trials.
2. Two outcomes are possible on each trial, one called success and the other failure.
3. The probability of a success p does not change from trial to trial. Consequently, the probability of failure, $1 - p$, does not change from trial to trial.
4. The trials are independent.

When the four properties hold, the binomial probability function can be used to determine the probability of obtaining x successes in n trials. Formulas were also presented for the mean and variance of the binomial distribution.

The Poisson distribution is used when it is desirable to determine the probability of obtaining x occurrences over an interval of time or space. The following assumptions are necessary for the Poisson distribution to be applicable.

1. The probability of an occurrence of the event is the same for any two intervals of equal length.
2. The occurrence or nonoccurrence of the event in any interval is independent of the occurrence or nonoccurrence of the event in any other interval.

A third discrete probability distribution, the hypergeometric, was introduced in Section 5.7. Like the binomial, it is used to compute the probability of x successes in n trials. But, in contrast to the binomial, the probability of success changes from trial to trial.

GLOSSARY

Binomial experiment An experiment having the four properties stated at the beginning of Section 5.5.

Binomial probability distribution A probability distribution showing the probability of x successes in n trials of a binomial experiment.

Binomial probability function The function used to compute binomial probabilities.

Bivariate probability distribution A probability distribution involving two random variables. A discrete bivariate probability distribution provides a probability for each pair of values that may occur for the two random variables.

Continuous random variable A random variable that may assume any numerical value in an interval or collection of intervals.

Discrete random variable A random variable that may assume either a finite number of values or an infinite sequence of values.

Discrete uniform probability distribution A probability distribution for which each possible value of the random variable has the same probability.

Empirical discrete distribution A discrete probability distribution for which the relative frequency method is used to assign the probabilities.

Expected value A measure of the central location of a random variable.

Hypergeometric probability distribution A probability distribution showing the probability of x successes in n trials from a population with r successes and $N - r$ failures.

Hypergeometric probability function The function used to compute hypergeometric probabilities.

Poisson probability distribution A probability distribution showing the probability of x occurrences of an event over a specified interval of time or space.

Poisson probability function The function used to compute Poisson probabilities.

Probability distribution A description of how the probabilities are distributed over the values of the random variable.

Probability function A function, denoted by $f(x)$, that provides the probability that x assumes a particular value for a discrete random variable.

Random variable A numerical description of the outcome of an experiment.

Standard deviation The positive square root of the variance.

Variance A measure of the variability, or dispersion, of a random variable.

KEY FORMULAS

Discrete Uniform Probability Function

$$f(x) = 1/n \tag{5.3}$$

Expected Value of a Discrete Random Variable

$$E(x) = \mu = \Sigma x f(x) \tag{5.4}$$

Variance of a Discrete Random Variable

$$Var(x) = \sigma^2 = \Sigma (x - \mu)^2 f(x) \tag{5.5}$$

Covariance of Random Variables x and y

$$\sigma_{xy} = [Var(x + y) - Var(x) - Var(y)]/2 \qquad \textbf{(5.6)}$$

Correlation between Random Variables x and y

$$\rho_{xy} = \frac{\sigma_{xy}}{\sigma_x \sigma_y} \qquad \textbf{(5.7)}$$

Expected Value of a Linear Combination of Random Variables x and y

$$E(ax + by) = aE(x) + bE(y) \qquad \textbf{(5.8)}$$

Variance of a Linear Combination of Two Random Variables

$$Var(ax + by) = a^2 Var(x) + b^2 Var(y) + 2ab\sigma_{xy} \qquad \textbf{(5.9)}$$

where σ_{xy} is the covariance of x and y

Number of Experimental Outcomes Providing Exactly x Successes in n Trials

$$\binom{n}{x} = \frac{n!}{x!(n - x)!} \qquad \textbf{(5.10)}$$

Binomial Probability Function

$$f(x) = \binom{n}{x} p^x (1 - p)^{(n-x)} \qquad \textbf{(5.12)}$$

Expected Value for the Binomial Distribution

$$E(x) = \mu = np \qquad \textbf{(5.13)}$$

Variance for the Binomial Distribution

$$Var(x) = \sigma^2 = np(1 - p) \qquad \textbf{(5.14)}$$

Poisson Probability Function

$$f(x) = \frac{\mu^x e^{-\mu}}{x!} \qquad \textbf{(5.15)}$$

Hypergeometric Probability Function

$$f(x) = \frac{\binom{r}{x}\binom{N - r}{n - x}}{\binom{N}{n}} \qquad \textbf{(5.16)}$$

Expected Value for the Hypergeometric Distribution

$$E(x) = \mu = n\left(\frac{r}{N}\right) \qquad \textbf{(5.17)}$$

Variance for the Hypergeometric Distribution

$$Var(x) = \sigma^2 = n\left(\frac{r}{N}\right)\left(1 - \frac{r}{N}\right)\left(\frac{N - n}{N - 1}\right) \qquad \textbf{(5.18)}$$

SUPPLEMENTARY EXERCISES

59. **Wind Conditions and Boating Accidents.** The U.S. Coast Guard (USCG) provides a wide variety of information on boating accidents including the wind condition at the time of the accident. The following table shows the results obtained for 4401 accidents (USCG website, http://www.uscgboating.org/statistics/accident_statistics.php).

Wind Condition	Percentage of Accidents
None	9.6
Light	57.0
Moderate	23.8
Strong	7.7
Storm	1.9

Let x be a random variable reflecting the known wind condition at the time of each accident. Set $x = 0$ for none, $x = 1$ for light, $x = 2$ for moderate, $x = 3$ for strong, and $x = 4$ for storm.
a. Develop a probability distribution for x.
b. Compute the expected value of x.
c. Compute the variance and standard deviation for x.
d. Comment on what your results imply about the wind conditions during boating accidents.

60. **Wait Times at Car Repair Garages.** The Car Repair Ratings website provides consumer reviews and ratings for garages in the United States and Canada. The time customers wait for service to be completed is one of the categories rated. The following table provides a summary of the wait-time ratings (1 = Slow/Delays; 10 = Quick/On Time) for 40 randomly selected garages located in the province of Ontario, Canada.

Wait-Time Rating	Number of Garages
1	6
2	2
3	3
4	2
5	5
6	2
7	4
8	5
9	5
10	6

a. Develop a probability distribution for x = wait-time rating.
b. Any garage that receives a wait-time rating of at least 9 is considered to provide outstanding service. If a consumer randomly selects one of the 40 garages for their next car service, what is the probability the garage selected will provide outstanding wait-time service?
c. What is the expected value and variance for x?
d. Suppose that 7 of the 40 garages reviewed were new car dealerships. Of the 7 new car dealerships, two were rated as providing outstanding wait-time service. Compare the likelihood of a new car dealership achieving an outstanding wait-time service rating as compared to other types of service providers.

61. **Expense Forecasts.** The budgeting process for a midwestern college resulted in expense forecasts for the coming year (in $ millions) of $9, $10, $11, $12, and $13. Because the actual expenses are unknown, the following respective probabilities are assigned: .3, .2, .25, .05, and .2.
    a. Show the probability distribution for the expense forecast.
    b. What is the expected value of the expense forecast for the coming year?
    c. What is the variance of the expense forecast for the coming year?
    d. If income projections for the year are estimated at $12 million, comment on the financial position of the college.

62. **Bookstore Customer Purchases.** A bookstore at the Hartsfield-Jackson Airport in Atlanta sells reading materials (paper-back books, newspapers, magazines) as well as snacks (peanuts, pretzels, candy, etc.). A point-of-sale terminal collects a variety of information about customer purchases. Shown below is a table showing the number of snack items and the number of items of reading material purchased by the most recent 600 customers.

		Reading Material		
		0	1	2
	0	0	60	18
Snacks	1	240	90	30
	2	120	30	12

   a. Using the data in the table construct an empirical discrete bivariate probability distribution for x = number of snack items and y = number of reading materials in a randomly selected customer purchase. What is the probability of a customer purchase consisting of one item of reading materials and two snack items? What is the probability of a customer purchasing one snack item only? Why is the probability $f(x = 0, y = 0) = 0$?
   b. Show the marginal probability distribution for the number of snack items purchased. Compute the expected value and variance.
   c. What is the expected value and variance for the number of reading materials purchased by a customer?
   d. Show the probability distribution for t = total number of items in a customer purchase. Compute its expected value and variance.
   e. Compute the covariance and correlation coefficient between x and y. What is the relationship, if any, between the number of reading materials and number of snacks purchased on a customer visit?

63. **Creating a Diversified Investment Portfolio.** The Knowles/Armitage (KA) group at Merrill Lynch advises clients on how to create a diversified investment portfolio. One of the investment alternatives they make available to clients is the All World Fund composed of global stocks with good dividend yields. One of their clients is interested in a portfolio consisting of investment in the All World Fund and a treasury bond fund. The expected percent return of an investment in the All World Fund is 7.80% with a standard deviation of 18.90%. The expected percent return of an investment in a treasury bond fund is 5.50% and the standard deviation is 4.60%. The covariance of an investment in the All World Fund with an investment in a treasury bond fund is −12.4.
   a. Which of the funds would be considered the more risky? Why?
   b. If KA recommends that the client invest 75% in the All World Fund and 25% in the treasury bond fund, what is the expected percent return and standard deviation for such a portfolio? What would be the expected return and standard deviation, in dollars, for a client investing $10,000 in such a portfolio?
   c. If KA recommends that the client invest 25% in the All World Fund and 75% in the treasury bond fund, what is the expected return and standard deviation for such a portfolio? What would be the expected return and standard deviation, in dollars, for a client investing $10,000 in such a portfolio?

d. Which of the portfolios in parts (b) and (c) would you recommend for an aggressive investor? Which would you recommend for a conservative investor? Why?

64. **Giving up Technology.** A Pew Research Survey asked adults in the United States which technologies would be "very hard" to give up. The following responses were obtained: Internet 53%, smartphone 49%, email 36%, and land-line phone 28% (*USA Today* website).

   a. If 20 adult Internet users are surveyed, what is the probability that 3 users will report that it would be very hard to give it up?
   b. If 20 adults who own a land-line phone are surveyed, what is the probability that 5 or fewer will report that it would be very hard to give it up?
   c. If 2000 owners of smartphones were surveyed, what is the expected number that will report that it would be very hard to give it up?
   d. If 2000 users of email were surveyed, what is expected number that will report that it would be very hard to give it up? What is the variance and standard deviation?

65. **Investing in the Stock Market.** According to a 2017 Gallup survey, the percentage of individuals in the United States who are invested in the stock market by age is as shown in the following table (Gallup website).

Age Range	Percent of Individuals Invested in Stock Market
18 to 29	31
30 to 49	62
50 to 64	62
65+	54

Suppose Gallup wishes to complete a follow-up survey to find out more about the specific type of stocks people in the United States are purchasing.

   a. How many 18 to 29 year olds must be sampled to find at least 50 who invest in the stock market?
   b. How many people 65 years of age and older must be sampled to find at least 50 who invest in the stock market?
   c. If 1000 individuals are randomly sampled, what is the expected number of 18 to 29 year olds who invest in the stock market in this sample? What is the standard deviation of the number of 18 to 29 year olds who invest in the stock market?
   d. If 1000 individuals are randomly sampled, what is the expected number of those 65 and older who invest in the stock market in this sample? What is the standard deviation of the number of those 65 years of age and older who invest in the stock market?

66. **Acceptance Sampling.** Many companies use a quality control technique called acceptance sampling to monitor incoming shipments of parts, raw materials, and so on. In the electronics industry, component parts are commonly shipped from suppliers in large lots. Inspection of a sample of n components can be viewed as the n trials of a binomial experiment. The outcome for each component tested (trial) will be that the component is classified as good or defective. Reynolds Electronics accepts a lot from a particular supplier if the defective components in the lot do not exceed 1%. Suppose a random sample of five items from a recent shipment is tested.

   a. Assume that 1% of the shipment is defective. Compute the probability that no items in the sample are defective.
   b. Assume that 1% of the shipment is defective. Compute the probability that exactly one item in the sample is defective.
   c. What is the probability of observing one or more defective items in the sample if 1% of the shipment is defective?

    d. Would you feel comfortable accepting the shipment if one item was found to be defective? Why or why not?

67. **Americans with at Least a Two-Year Degree.** PBS *News Hour* reported in 2014 that 39.4% of Americans between the ages of 25 and 64 have at least a two-year college degree (PBS website). Assume that 50 Americans between the ages of 25 and 64 are selected randomly.

    a. What is the expected number of people with at least a two-year college degree?

    b. What are the variance and standard deviation for the number of people with at least a two-year college degree?

68. **Choosing a Home Builder.** Mahoney Custom Home Builders, Inc. of Canyon Lake, Texas, asked visitors to their website what is most important when choosing a home builder. Possible responses were quality, price, customer referral, years in business, and special features. Results showed that 23.5% of the respondents chose price as the most important factor (Mahoney Custom Homes website). Suppose a sample of 200 potential home buyers in the Canyon Lake area are selected.

    a. How many people would you expect to choose price as the most important factor when choosing a home builder?

    b. What is the standard deviation of the number of respondents who would choose price as the most important factor in selecting a home builder?

    c. What is the standard deviation of the number of respondents who do not list price as the most important factor in selecting a home builder?

69. **Arrivals to a Car Wash.** Cars arrive at a car wash randomly and independently; the probability of an arrival is the same for any two time intervals of equal length. The mean arrival rate is 15 cars per hour. What is the probability that 20 or more cars will arrive during any given hour of operation?

70. **Production Process Breakdowns.** A new automated production process averages 1.5 breakdowns per day. Because of the cost associated with a breakdown, management is concerned about the possibility of having three or more breakdowns during a day. Assume that breakdowns occur randomly, that the probability of a breakdown is the same for any two time intervals of equal length, and that breakdowns in one period are independent of breakdowns in other periods. What is the probability of having three or more breakdowns during a day?

71. **Small Business Failures.** A regional director responsible for business development in the state of Pennsylvania is concerned about the number of small business failures. If the mean number of small business failures per month is 10, what is the probability that exactly 4 small businesses will fail during a given month? Assume that the probability of a failure is the same for any two months and that the occurrence or nonoccurrence of a failure in any month is independent of failures in any other month.

72. **Bank Customer Arrivals.** Customer arrivals at a bank are random and independent; the probability of an arrival in any one-minute period is the same as the probability of an arrival in any other one-minute period. Answer the following questions, assuming a mean arrival rate of three customers per minute.

    a. What is the probability of exactly three arrivals in a one-minute period?

    b. What is the probability of at least three arrivals in a one-minute period?

73. **Poker Hands.** A deck of playing cards contains 52 cards, four of which are aces. What is the probability that the deal of a five-card poker hand provides

    a. A pair of aces?

    b. Exactly one ace?

    c. No aces?

    d. At least one ace?

74. **Business School Student GPAs.** According to *U.S. News & World Reports,* 7 of the top 10 graduate schools of business have students with an average undergraduate grade point average (GPA) of 3.50 or higher. Suppose that we randomly select 2 of the top 10 graduate schools of business.

a. What is the probability that exactly one school has students with an average undergraduate GPA of 3.50 or higher?

b. What is the probability that both schools have students with an average undergraduate GPA of 3.50 or higher?

c. What is the probability that neither school has students with an average undergraduate GPA of 3.50 or higher?

CASE PROBLEM 1: *GO BANANAS!* BREAKFAST CEREAL

Great Grasslands Grains, Inc. (GGG) manufactures and sells a wide variety of breakfast cereals. GGG's product development lab recently created a new cereal that consists of rice flakes and banana-flavored marshmallows. The company's marketing research department has tested the new cereal extensively and has found that consumers are enthusiastic about the cereal when 16-ounce boxes contain at least 1.6 ounces and no more than 2.4 ounces of the banana-flavored marshmallows.

As GGG prepares to begin producing and selling 16-ounce boxes of the new cereal, which it has named *Go Bananas!*, management is concerned about the amount of banana-flavored marshmallows. It wants to be careful not to include less than 1.6 ounces or more than 2.4 ounces of banana-flavored marshmallows in each 16-ounce box of *Go Bananas!* Tina Finkel, VP of Production for GGG, has suggested that the company measure the weight of banana-flavored marshmallows in a random sample of 25 boxes of *Go Bananas!* on a weekly basis. Each week, GGG can count the number of boxes out of the 25 boxes in the sample that contain less than 1.6 ounces or more than 2.4 ounces of banana-flavored marshmallows; if the number of boxes that fail to meet the standard weight of banana-flavored marshmallows is too high, production will be shut down and inspected.

Ms. Finkel and her staff have designed the production process so that only 8% of all 16-ounce boxes of *Go Bananas!* fail to meet the standard weight of banana-flavored marshmallows. After much debate, GGG management has decided to shut down production of *Go Bananas!* if at least five boxes in a weekly sample fail to meet the standard weight of banana-flavored marshmallows.

Managerial Report

Prepare a managerial report that addresses the following issues.

1. Calculate the probability that a weekly sample will result in a shutdown of production if the production process is working properly. Comment on GGG management's policy for deciding when to shut down production of *Go Bananas!*.

2. GGG management wants to shut down production of *Go Bananas!* no more than 1% of the time when the production process is working properly. Suggest the appropriate number of boxes in the weekly sample that must fail to meet the standard weight of banana-flavored marshmallows in order for production to be shut down if this goal is to be achieved.

3. Ms. Finkel has suggested that if given sufficient resources, she could redesign the production process to reduce the percentage of 16-ounce boxes of *Go Bananas!* that fail to meet the standard weight of banana-flavored marshmallows when the process is working properly. To what level must Ms. Finkel reduce the percentage of 16-ounce boxes of *Go Bananas!* that fail to meet the standard weight of banana-flavored marshmallows when the process is working properly in order for her to reduce the probability at least five of the sampled boxes fail to meet the standard to .01 or less?

CASE PROBLEM 2: McNEIL'S AUTO MALL

Harriet McNeil, proprietor of McNeil's Auto Mall, believes that it is good business for her atuomobile dealership to have more customers on the lot than can be served, as she believes this creates an impression that demand for the automobiles on her lot is high.

However, she also understands that if there are far more customers on the lot than can be served by her salespeople, her dealership may lose sales to customers who become frustrated and leave without making a purchase.

Ms. McNeil is primarily concerned about the staffing of salespeople on her lot on Saturday mornings (8:00 A.M. to noon), which are the busiest time of the week for McNeil's Auto Mall. On Saturday mornings, an average of 6.8 customers arrive per hour. The customers arrive randomly at a constant rate throughout the morning, and a salesperson spends an average of one hour with a customer. Ms. McNeil's experience has led her to conclude that if there are two more customers on her lot than can be served at any time on a Saturday morning, her automobile dealership achieves the optimal balance of creating an impression of high demand without losing too many customers who become frustrated and leave without making a purchase.

Ms. McNeil now wants to determine how many salespeople she should have on her lot on Saturday mornings in order to achieve her goal of having two more customers on her lot than can be served at any time. She understands that occasionally the number of customers on her lot will exceed the number of salespersons by more than two, and she is willing to accept such an occurrence no more than 10% of the time.

Managerial Report

Ms. McNeil has asked you to determine the number of salespersons she should have on her lot on Saturday mornings in order to satisfy her criteria. In answering Ms. McNeil's question, consider the following three quesitons:

1. How is the number of customers who arrive in the lot on a Saturday morning distributed?
2. Suppose Ms. McNeil currently uses five salespeople on her lot on Saturday morning. Using the probability distribution you identified in (1), what is the probability that the number of customers who arrive on her lot will exceed the number of salespersons by more than two? Does her current Saturday morning employment strategy satisfy her stated objective? Why or why not?
3. What is the minimum number of salespeople Ms. McNeil should have on her lot on Saturday mornings to achieve her objective?

CASE PROBLEM 3: GRIEVANCE COMMITTEE AT TUGLAR CORPORATION

Several years ago, management at Tuglar Corporation established a grievance committee composed of employees who volunteered to work toward the amicable resolution of disputes between Tuglar management and its employees. Each year management issue a call for volunteers to serve on the grievance committee, and 10 of the respondents are randomly selected to serve on the committee for the upcoming year.

Employees in the Accounting Department are distressed because no member of their department has served on the Tuglar grievance committee in the past five years. Management has assured its employees in the Accounting Department that the selections have been made randomly, but these assurances have not quelled suspicions that management has intentionally omitted accountants from the committee. The table below summarizes the total number of volunteers and the number of employees from the Accounting Department who have volunteered for the grievance committee in each of the past five years:

	Year 1	Year 2	Year 3	Year 4	Year 5
Total Number of Volunteers	29	31	23	26	28
Number of Volunteers from the Accounting Department	1	1	1	2	1

In its defense, management has provided these numbers to the Accounting Department. Given these numbers, is the lack of members of the Accounting Department on the grievance committee for the past five years suspicious (i.e., unlikely)?

Managerial Report

In addressing the issue of whether or not the committee selection process is random, consider the following questions:

1. How is the number of members of the Accounting Department who are selected to serve on the grievance committee distributed?
2. Using the probability distribution you identified in (1), what is the probability for each of these five years that no member of the Accounting Department has been selected to serve?
3. Using the probabilities you identified in (2), what is the probability that no member of the Accounting Department has been selected to serve during the past five years?
4. What is the cause of the lack of Accounting Department representation on the grievance committee over the past five years? What can be done to increase the probability that a member of the Accounting Department will be selected to serve on the grievance committee using the current selection method?

Chapter 5 Appendix

Appendix 5.1 Discrete Probability Distributions with JMP

Statistical packages such as JMP provide procedures for computing probabilities for discrete random variables. In this appendix, we show the step-by-step procedure for determining the binomial probabilities for the Martin Clothing Store problem in Section 5.5. Recall that the desired binomial probabilities are based on $n = 10$ and $p = .3$. Before beginning the procedure in JMP, we must first open a new Data Table, and then we must enter the desired values of the random variable into a column of the Data Table. The steps to obtain the desired binomial probabilities in JMP follow.

Step 1. Click **File** in the JMP ribbon
Select **New** and click **Data Table**

Step 2. Double-click **Column 1** in the Data Table

Step 3. When the **Column 1** dialog box appears (see Figure JMP 5.1):
Enter x in the **Column Name** box
Click **OK**

Step 4. Enter the values *0, 1, 2, 3, 4, 5, 6, 7, 8, 9, 10* in the first 11 rows of **Column x** of the Data Table (see Figure JMP 5.2)

Step 5. Right-click anywhere in the Data Table and select **New Columns…**

Step 6. When the **New Column** dialog box appears (see Figure JMP 5.3):
Enter *Pr(X = x)* in the **Column Name** box
Click on **Column Properties** and choose **Formula**

Step 7. When the **Pr(X = x)** dialog box appears:
From the left-hand side, click **Discrete Probability**
Select **Binomial Probability**
In the **Binomial Probability(p, n, k)** formula, click on **p** and enter *.3*

FIGURE JMP 5.1	Renaming Column 1 in JMP

FIGURE JMP 5.2   Creating Column for Binomial Probabilities in JMP

FIGURE JMP 5.3   Creating Binomial Probability Calculation Column in JMP

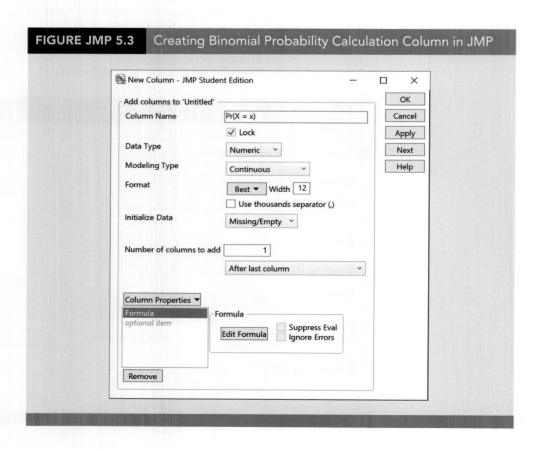

FIGURE JMP 5.4   Binomial Probability Function in JMP Before Entering Parameters

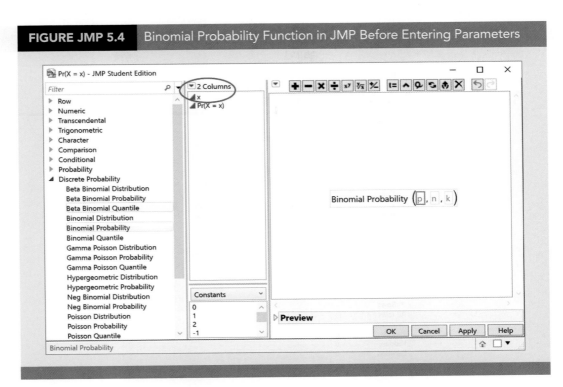

In the **Binomial Probability(p, n, k)** formula, click on **n** and enter *10*

In the **Binomial Probability(p, n, k)** formula, click on **k** and select **x** from the **2 Columns** area to the left of the formula (see circled area in Figure JMP 5.4)

Step 8. Click **OK** to close the **Pr(X = x)** dialog box

Step 9. Click **OK** to close the **New Column** dialog box

Figure JMP 5.4 shows the Pr(X = x) dialog box before the binomial probability distribution parameters are entered. Figure JMP 5.5 shows the completed binomial

FIGURE JMP 5.5   Completed Binomial Probability Function in JMP

FIGURE JMP 5.6   Binomial Probabilities Computed in JMP

		x	Pr(X = x)
1		0	0.0282475249
2		1	0.121060821
3		2	0.2334744405
4		3	0.266827932
5		4	0.200120949
6		5	0.1029193452
7		6	0.036756909
8		7	0.009001692
9		8	0.0014467005
10		9	0.000137781
11		10	0.0000059049

Columns (2/0)
- x
- Pr(X = x)

Rows
All rows	11
Selected	0
Excluded	0
Hidden	0
Labelled	0

Hovering the mouse pointer over the formula in JMP will bring up a ToolTip that can is helpful in understanding which parameters are needed for the probability formula.

probability distribution formula in JMP once all parameters have been entered. JMP provides the computed binomial probabilities in the Pr(X = x) column of the Data Table as shown in Figure JMP 5.6. JMP can compute probabilities for the Poisson and the hypergeometric distributions by selecting **Poisson Probability** and **Hypergeometric Probability** in Step 7, respectively, rather than Binomial Probability, and then entering the proper parameters for each type of distribution. For instance, for **Poisson Probability,** the mean number of occurrences in an interval is entered as **lambda**, and the number of occurrences of interest is entered as **k** in the JMP formula **Poisson Probability (lambda, k).**

Appendix 5.2 Discrete Probability Distributions with Excel

Excel provides functions for computing probabilities for the binomial, Poisson, and hypergeometric distributions introduced in this chapter. The Excel function for computing binomial probabilities is BINOM.DIST. It has four arguments: x (the number of successes), n (the number of trials), p (the probability of success), and cumulative. FALSE is used for the fourth argument (cumulative) if we want the probability of x successes, and TRUE is used for the fourth argument if we want the cumulative probability of x or fewer successes. Here we show how to compute the probabilities of 0 through 10 successes for the Martin Clothing Store problem in Section 5.4 (see Figure 5.5).

As we describe the worksheet development, refer to Figure Excel 5.1; the formula worksheet is set in the background, and the value worksheet appears in the foreground. We entered the number of trials (10) into cell B1, the probability of success into cell B2, and

FIGURE Excel 5.1	Excel Worksheet for Computing Binomial Probabilities

	A	B	C
1	**Number of Trials (*n*)**	10	
2	**Probability of Success (*p*)**	0.3	
3			
4		*x*	*f(x)*
5		0	=BINOM.DIST(B5,B1,B2,FALSE)
6		1	=BINOM.DIST(B6,B1,B2,FALSE)
7		2	=BINOM.DIST(B7,B1,B2,FALSE)
8		3	=BINOM.DIST(B8,B1,B2,FALSE)
9		4	=BINOM.DIST(B9,B1,B2,FALSE)
10		5	=BINOM.DIST(B10,B1,B2,FALSE)
11		6	=BINOM.DIST(B11,B1,B2,FALSE)
12		7	=BINOM.DIST(B12,B1,B2,FALSE)
13		8	=BINOM.DIST(B13,B1,B2,FALSE)
14		9	=BINOM.DIST(B14,B1,B2,FALSE)
15		10	=BINOM.DIST(B15,B1,B2,FALSE)

	A	B	C
1	**Number of Trials (*n*)**	10	
2	**Probability of Success (*p*)**	0.3	
3			
4		*x*	*f(x)*
5		0	0.0282
6		1	0.1211
7		2	0.2335
8		3	0.2668
9		4	0.2001
10		5	0.1029
11		6	0.0368
12		7	0.0090
13		8	0.0014
14		9	0.0001
15		10	0.0000

the values for the random variable into cells B5:B15. The following steps will generate the desired probabilities:

Step 1. Use the BINOM.DIST function to compute the probability of $x = 0$ by entering the following formula into cell C5:

$$=BINOM.DIST(B5,\$B\$1,\$B\$2,FALSE)$$

Step 2. Copy the formula in cell C5 into cells C6:C15

The value worksheet in Figure Excel 5.1 shows that the probabilities obtained are the same as in Figure 5.5. Poisson and hypergeometric probabilities can be computed in a similar fashion using the Excel functions POISSON.DIST and HYPGEOM.DIST, respectively. Excel's Insert Function dialog box can help the user in entering the proper arguments for these functions (see Appendix E).

Chapter 6

Continuous Probability Distributions

STATISTICS IN PRACTICE

Procter & Gamble*

CINCINNATI, OHIO

Procter & Gamble (P&G) produces and markets such products as detergents, disposable diapers, razors, toothpastes, soaps, mouthwashes, and paper towels. Worldwide, it has the leading brand in more categories than any other consumer products company.

As a leader in the application of statistical methods in decision making, P&G employs people with diverse academic backgrounds: engineering, statistics, operations research, analytics and business. The major quantitative technologies for which these people provide support are probabilistic decision and risk analysis, advanced simulation, quality improvement, and quantitative methods (e.g., linear programming, data analytics, probability analysis, machine learning).

The Industrial Chemicals Division of P&G is a major supplier of fatty alcohols derived from natural substances such as coconut oil and from petroleum-based derivatives. The division wanted to know the economic risks and opportunities of expanding its fatty-alcohol production facilities, so it called in P&G's experts in probabilistic decision and risk analysis to help. After structuring and modeling the problem, they determined that the key to profitability was the cost difference between the petroleum- and coconut-based raw materials. Future costs were unknown, but the analysts were able to approximate them with the following continuous random variables.

  x = the coconut oil price per pound of fatty alcohol

and

  y = the petroleum raw material price per pound of fatty alcohol

Because the key to profitability was the difference between these two random variables, a third random variable, $d = x - y$, was used in the analysis. Experts were interviewed to determine the probability distributions for x and y. In turn, this information was used to develop a probability distribution for the difference in prices d. This continuous probability distribution showed a .90 prob-

Procter & Gamble is a leader in the application of statistical methods in decision making.
Source: John Sommers II/Reuters

ability that the price difference would be \$.0655 or less and a .50 probability that the price difference would be \$.035 or less. In addition, there was only a .10 probability that the price difference would be \$.0045 or less.[†]

The Industrial Chemicals Division thought that being able to quantify the impact of raw material price differences was key to reaching a consensus. The probabilities obtained were used in a sensitivity analysis of the raw material price difference. The analysis yielded sufficient insight to form the basis for a recommendation to management.

The use of continuous random variables and their probability distributions was helpful to P&G in analyzing the economic risks associated with its fatty-alcohol production. In this chapter, you will gain an understanding of continuous random variables and their probability distributions, including one of the most important probability distributions in statistics, the normal distribution.

---

*The authors are indebted to Joel Kahn of Procter & Gamble for providing the context for this Statistics in Practice.

†The price differences stated here have been modified to protect proprietary data.

In the preceding chapter we discussed discrete random variables and their probability distributions. In this chapter we turn to the study of continuous random variables. Specifically, we discuss three continuous probability distributions: the uniform, the normal, and the exponential.

A fundamental difference separates discrete and continuous random variables in terms of how probabilities are computed. For a discrete random variable, the probability function $f(x)$ provides the probability that the random variable assumes a particular value. With continuous random variables, the counterpart of the probability function is the **probability density function**, also denoted by $f(x)$. The difference is that the probability density function does not directly provide probabilities. However, the area under the graph of $f(x)$ corresponding to a given interval does provide the probability that the continuous random variable x assumes a value in that interval. So when we compute probabilities for continuous random variables we are computing the probability that the random variable assumes any value in an interval.

Because the area under the graph of $f(x)$ at any particular point is zero, one of the implications of the definition of probability for continuous random variables is that the probability of any particular value of the random variable is zero. In Section 6.1 we demonstrate these concepts for a continuous random variable that has a uniform distribution.

Much of the chapter is devoted to describing and showing applications of the normal distribution. The normal distribution is of major importance because of its wide applicability and its extensive use in statistical inference. The chapter closes with a discussion of the exponential distribution. The exponential distribution is useful in applications involving such factors as waiting times and service times.

6.1 Uniform Probability Distribution

Consider the random variable x representing the flight time of an airplane traveling from Chicago to New York. Suppose the flight time can be any value in the interval from 120 minutes to 140 minutes. Because the random variable x can assume any value in that interval, x is a continuous rather than a discrete random variable. Let us assume that sufficient actual flight data are available to conclude that the probability of a flight time within any 1-minute interval is the same as the probability of a flight time within any other 1-minute interval contained in the larger interval from 120 to 140 minutes. With every 1-minute interval being equally likely, the random variable x is said to have a **uniform probability distribution**. The probability density function, which defines the uniform distribution for the flight-time random variable, is

Whenever the probability is proportional to the length of the interval, the random variable is uniformly distributed.

$$f(x) = \begin{cases} 1/20 & \text{for } 120 \leq x \leq 140 \\ 0 & \text{elsewhere} \end{cases}$$

Figure 6.1 is a graph of this probability density function. In general, the uniform probability density function for a random variable x is defined by the following formula.

UNIFORM PROBABILITY DENSITY FUNCTION

$$f(x) = \begin{cases} \dfrac{1}{b - a} & \text{for } a \leq x \leq b \\ 0 & \text{elsewhere} \end{cases} \tag{6.1}$$

For the flight-time random variable, $a = 120$ and $b = 140$.

As noted in the introduction, for a continuous random variable, we consider probability only in terms of the likelihood that a random variable assumes a value within a specified interval. In the flight time example, an acceptable probability question is: What is the probability that the flight time is between 120 and 130 minutes? That is, what is $P(120 \leq x \leq 130)$? Because the flight time must be between 120

FIGURE 6.1   Uniform Probability Distribution for Flight Time

and 140 minutes and because the probability is described as being uniform over this interval, we feel comfortable saying $P(120 \leq x \leq 130) = .50$. In the following subsection we show that this probability can be computed as the area under the graph of $f(x)$ from 120 to 130 (see Figure 6.2).

Area as a Measure of Probability

Let us make an observation about the graph in Figure 6.2. Consider the area under the graph of $f(x)$ in the interval from 120 to 130. The area is rectangular, and the area of a rectangle is simply the width multiplied by the height. With the width of the interval equal to $130 - 120 = 10$ and the height equal to the value of the probability density function $f(x) = 1/20$, we have area = width $\times$ height = $10(1/20) = 10/20 = .50$.

What observation can you make about the area under the graph of $f(x)$ and probability? They are identical! Indeed, this observation is valid for all continuous random variables. Once a probability density function $f(x)$ is identified, the probability that x takes a value between some lower value x_1 and some higher value x_2 can be found by computing the area under the graph of $f(x)$ over the interval from x_1 to x_2.

Given the uniform distribution for flight time and using the interpretation of area as probability, we can answer any number of probability questions about flight times. For example, what is the probability of a flight time between 128 and 136 minutes? The width of the interval is $136 - 128 = 8$. With the uniform height of $f(x) = 1/20$, we see that $P(128 \leq x \leq 136) = 8(1/20) = .40$.

FIGURE 6.2   Area Provides Probability of a Flight Time between 120 and 130 Minutes

Note that $P(120 \leq x \leq 140) = 20(1/20) = 1$; that is, the total area under the graph of $f(x)$ is equal to 1. This property holds for all continuous probability distributions and is the analog of the condition that the sum of the probabilities must equal 1 for a discrete probability function. For a continuous probability density function, we must also require that $f(x) \geq 0$ for all values of x. This requirement is the analog of the requirement that $f(x) \geq 0$ for discrete probability functions.

Two major differences stand out between the treatment of continuous random variables and the treatment of their discrete counterparts.

To see that the probability of any single point is 0, refer to Figure 6.2 and compute the probability of a single point, say, $x = 125$. $P(x = 125)$ $= P(125 \leq x \leq 125)$ $= 0(1/20) = 0$.

1. We no longer talk about the probability of the random variable assuming a particular value. Instead, we talk about the probability of the random variable assuming a value within some given interval.

2. The probability of a continuous random variable assuming a value within some given interval from x_1 to x_2 is defined to be the area under the graph of the probability density function between x_1 and x_2. Because a single point is an interval of zero width, this implies that the probability of a continuous random variable assuming any particular value exactly is zero. It also means that the probability of a continuous random variable assuming a value in any interval is the same whether or not the endpoints are included.

The calculation of the expected value and variance for a continuous random variable is analogous to that for a discrete random variable. However, because the computational procedure involves integral calculus, we leave the derivation of the appropriate formulas to more advanced texts.

For the uniform continuous probability distribution introduced in this section, the formulas for the expected value and variance are

$$E(x) = \frac{a + b}{2}$$

$$Var(x) = \frac{(b - a)^2}{12}$$

In these formulas, a is the smallest value and b is the largest value that the random variable may assume.

Applying these formulas to the uniform distribution for flight times from Chicago to New York, we obtain

$$E(x) = \frac{(120 + 140)}{2} = 130$$

$$Var(x) = \frac{(140 - 120)^2}{12} = 33.33$$

The standard deviation of flight times can be found by taking the square root of the variance. Thus, $\sigma = 5.77$ minutes.

NOTES + COMMENTS

To see more clearly why the height of a probability density function is not a probability, think about a random variable with the following uniform probability distribution.

$$f(x) = \begin{cases} 2 & \text{for } 0 \leq x \leq .5 \\ 0 & \text{elsewhere} \end{cases}$$

The height of the probability density function, $f(x)$, is 2 for values of x between 0 and .5. However, we know probabilities can never be greater than 1. Thus, we see that $f(x)$ cannot be interpreted as the probability of x.

EXERCISES

Methods

1. The random variable x is known to be uniformly distributed between 1.0 and 1.5.
   a. Show the graph of the probability density function.
   b. Compute $P(x = 1.25)$.
   c. Compute $P(1.0 \leq x \leq 1.25)$.
   d. Compute $P(1.20 < x < 1.5)$.
2. The random variable x is known to be uniformly distributed between 10 and 20.
   a. Show the graph of the probability density function.
   b. Compute $P(x < 15)$.
   c. Compute $P(12 \leq x \leq 18)$.
   d. Compute $E(x)$.
   e. Compute $Var(x)$.

Applications

3. **Cincinnati to Tampa Flight Time.** Delta Airlines quotes a flight time of 2 hours, 5 minutes for its flights from Cincinnati to Tampa. Suppose we believe that actual flight times are uniformly distributed between 2 hours and 2 hours, 20 minutes.
   a. Show the graph of the probability density function for flight time.
   b. What is the probability that the flight will be no more than 5 minutes late?
   c. What is the probability that the flight will be more than 10 minutes late?
   d. What is the expected flight time?
4. **Excel RAND Function.** Most computer languages include a function that can be used to generate random numbers. In Excel, the RAND function can be used to generate random numbers between 0 and 1. If we let x denote a random number generated using RAND, then x is a continuous random variable with the following probability density function.

$$f(x) = \begin{cases} 1 & \text{for } 0 \leq x \leq 1 \\ 0 & \text{elsewhere} \end{cases}$$

   a. Graph the probability density function.
   b. What is the probability of generating a random number between .25 and .75?
   c. What is the probability of generating a random number with a value less than or equal to .30?
   d. What is the probability of generating a random number with a value greater than .60?
   e. Generate 50 random numbers by entering =RAND() into 50 cells of an Excel worksheet.
   f. Compute the mean and standard deviation for the random numbers in part (e).
5. **Tesla Battery Recharge Time.** The electric-vehicle manufacturing company Tesla estimates that a driver who commutes 50 miles per day in a Model S will require a nightly charge time of around 1 hour and 45 minutes (105 minutes) to recharge the vehicle's battery (Tesla company website). Assume that the actual recharging time required is uniformly distributed between 90 and 120 minutes.
   a. Give a mathematical expression for the probability density function of battery recharging time for this scenario.
   b. What is the probability that the recharge time will be less than 110 minutes?
   c. What is the probability that the recharge time required is at least 100 minutes?
   d. What is the probability that the recharge time required is between 95 and 110 minutes?
6. **Daily Discretionary Spending.** A Gallup Daily Tracking Survey found that the mean daily discretionary spending by Americans earning over $90,000 per year was $136

per day. The discretionary spending excluded home purchases, vehicle purchases, and regular monthly bills. Let $x =$ the discretionary spending per day and assume that a uniform probability density function applies with $f(x) = .00625$ for $a \leq x \leq b$.
   a. Find the values of a and b for the probability density function.
   b. What is the probability that consumers in this group have daily discretionary spending between $100 and $200?
   c. What is the probability that consumers in this group have daily discretionary spending of $150 or more?
   d. What is the probability that consumers in this group have daily discretionary spending of $80 or less?

7. **Bidding on Land.** Suppose we are interested in bidding on a piece of land and we know one other bidder is interested.[1] The seller announced that the highest bid in excess of $10,000 will be accepted. Assume that the competitor's bid x is a random variable that is uniformly distributed between $10,000 and $15,000.
   a. Suppose you bid $12,000. What is the probability that your bid will be accepted?
   b. Suppose you bid $14,000. What is the probability that your bid will be accepted?
   c. What amount should you bid to maximize the probability that you get the property?
   d. Suppose you know someone who is willing to pay you $16,000 for the property. Would you consider bidding less than the amount in part (c)? Why or why not?

6.2 Normal Probability Distribution

The most commonly used probability distribution for describing a continuous random variable is the **normal probability distribution**. The normal distribution has been used in a wide variety of practical applications in which the random variables are heights and weights of people, test scores, scientific measurements, amounts of rainfall, and other similar values. It is also widely used in statistical inference, which is the major topic of the remainder of this book. In such applications, the normal distribution provides a description of the likely results obtained through sampling.

Abraham de Moivre, a French mathematician, published The Doctrine of Chances in 1733. He derived the normal distribution.

Normal Curve

The form, or shape, of the normal distribution is illustrated by the bell-shaped normal curve in Figure 6.3. The probability density function that defines the bell-shaped curve of the normal distribution follows.

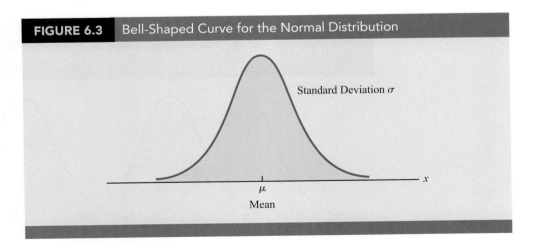

FIGURE 6.3   Bell-Shaped Curve for the Normal Distribution

---

[1]This exercise is based on a problem suggested to us by Professor Roger Myerson of Northwestern University.

NORMAL PROBABILITY DENSITY FUNCTION

$$f(x) = \frac{1}{\sigma\sqrt{2\pi}}\, e^{-\frac{1}{2}\left(\frac{x-\mu}{\sigma}\right)^2} \tag{6.2}$$

Both π (pi) and e (Euler's number) are irrational numbers, meaning that each has an infinite number of digits with no pattern or repetition to the right of the decimal point. Here we use an approximation to five decimal places for π and e.

where

μ = mean

σ = standard deviation

π = 3.14159

e = 2.71828

We make several observations about the characteristics of the normal distribution.

The normal curve has two parameters, μ and σ. They determine the location and shape of the normal distribution.

1. The entire family of normal distributions is differentiated by two parameters: the mean μ and the standard deviation σ.
2. The highest point on the normal curve is at the mean, which is also the median and mode of the distribution.
3. The mean of the distribution can be any numerical value: negative, zero, or positive. Three normal distributions with the same standard deviation but three different means (-10, 0, and 20) are shown in Figure 6.4.
4. The normal distribution is symmetric, with the shape of the normal curve to the left of the mean a mirror image of the shape of the normal curve to the right of the mean. The tails of the normal curve extend to infinity in both directions and theoretically never touch the horizontal axis. Because it is symmetric, the normal distribution is not skewed; its skewness measure is zero.
5. The standard deviation determines how flat and wide the normal curve is. Larger values of the standard deviation result in wider, flatter curves, showing more variability in the data. Two normal distributions with the same mean but with different standard deviations are shown in Figure 6.5.
6. Probabilities for the normal random variable are given by areas under the normal curve. The total area under the curve for the normal distribution is 1. Because the distribution is symmetric, the area under the curve to the left of the mean is .50 and the area under the curve to the right of the mean is .50.

FIGURE 6.4   Normal Distributions with Same Standard Deviation and Different Means

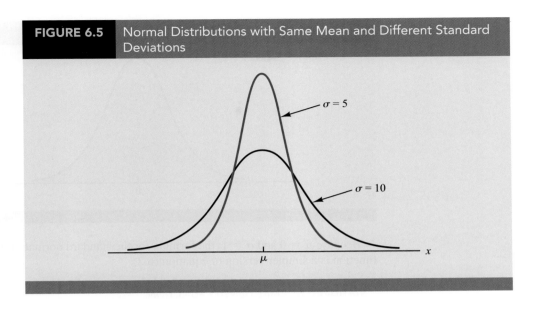

FIGURE 6.5   Normal Distributions with Same Mean and Different Standard Deviations

$\sigma = 5$

$\sigma = 10$

μ

x

7. The percentage of values in some commonly used intervals are
   a. 68.3% of the values of a normal random variable are within plus or minus one standard deviation of its mean.

   These percentages are the basis for the empirical rule introduced in Section 3.3.

   b. 95.4% of the values of a normal random variable are within plus or minus two standard deviations of its mean.
   c. 99.7% of the values of a normal random variable are within plus or minus three standard deviations of its mean.

   Figure 6.6 shows properties (a), (b), and (c) graphically.

Standard Normal Probability Distribution

A random variable that has a normal distribution with a mean of zero and a standard deviation of one is said to have a **standard normal probability distribution**. The letter z is commonly used to designate this particular normal random variable. Figure 6.7 is the graph of the standard normal distribution. It has the same general appearance as other normal distributions, but with the special properties of $\mu = 0$ and $\sigma = 1$.

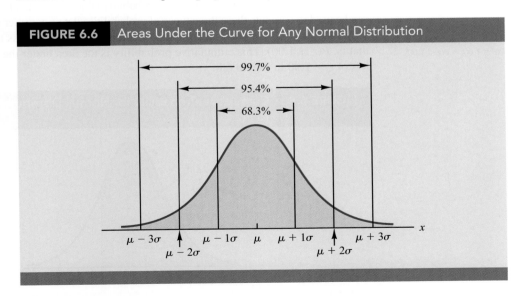

FIGURE 6.6   Areas Under the Curve for Any Normal Distribution

99.7%

95.4%

68.3%

$\mu - 3\sigma$ $\mu - 1\sigma$ μ $\mu + 1\sigma$ $\mu + 3\sigma$ x

$\mu - 2\sigma$ $\mu + 2\sigma$

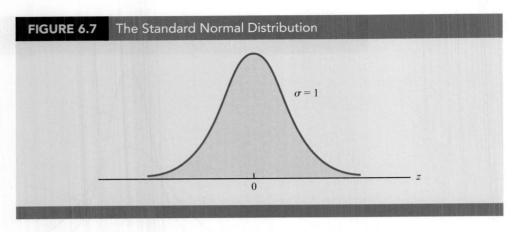

FIGURE 6.7   The Standard Normal Distribution

Because $\mu = 0$ and $\sigma = 1$, the formula for the standard normal probability density function is a simpler version of equation (6.2).

STANDARD NORMAL DENSITY FUNCTION

$$f(z) = \frac{1}{\sqrt{2\pi}} \, e^{-\frac{z^2}{2}}$$

For the normal probability density function, the height of the normal curve varies and more advanced mathematics is required to compute the areas that represent probability.

As with other continuous random variables, probability calculations with any normal distribution are made by computing areas under the graph of the probability density function. Thus, to find the probability that a normal random variable is within any specific interval, we must compute the area under the normal curve over that interval.

For the standard normal distribution, areas under the normal curve have been computed and are available in tables that can be used to compute probabilities. Such a table appears inside the front cover of the this text, and as part of Appendix B in the digital version. The table on the left-hand page contains areas, or cumulative probabilities, for z values less than or equal to the mean of zero. The table on the right-hand page contains areas, or cumulative probabilities, for z values greater than or equal to the mean of zero.

The three types of probabilities we need to compute include (1) the probability that the standard normal random variable z will be less than or equal to a given value; (2) the probability that z will be between two given values; and (3) the probability that z will be greater than or equal to a given value. To see how the cumulative probability table for the standard normal distribution can be used to compute these three types of probabilities, let us consider some examples.

Because the standard normal random variable is continuous, $P(z \leq 1.00) = P(z < 1.00)$.

We start by showing how to compute the probability that z is less than or equal to 1.00; that is, $P(z \leq 1.00)$. This cumulative probability is the area under the normal curve to the left of $z = 1.00$ in Figure 6.8.

FIGURE 6.8   Cumulative Probability for Normal Distribution Corresponding to $P(z \leq 1.00)$

The standard normal probability table is provided inside the front cover of the physical text, and as part of Appendix B at the end of the text.

Refer to the standard normal portability table. The cumulative probability corresponding to $z = 1.00$ is the table value located at the intersection of the row labeled 1.0 and the column labeled .00. First we find 1.0 in the left column of the table and then find .00 in the top row of the table. By looking in the body of the table, we find that the 1.0 row and the .00 column intersect at the value of .8413; thus, $P(z \le 1.00) = .8413$. The following excerpt from the probability table shows these steps.

z	.00	.01	.02
.			
.			
.			
.9	.8159	.8186	.8212
1.0	.8413	.8438	.8461
1.1	.8643	.8665	.8686
1.2	.8849	.8869	.8888
.			
.			

$P(z \le 1.00)$

To illustrate the second type of probability calculation we show how to compute the probability that z is in the interval between $-.50$ and 1.25; that is, $P(-.50 \le z \le 1.25)$. Figure 6.9 shows this area, or probability.

Three steps are required to compute this probability. First, we find the area under the normal curve to the left of $z = 1.25$. Second, we find the area under the normal curve to the left of $z = -.50$. Finally, we subtract the area to the left of $z = -.50$ from the area to the left of $z = 1.25$ to find $P(-.50 \le z \le 1.25)$.

To find the area under the normal curve to the left of $z = 1.25$, we first locate the 1.2 row in the standard normal probability table and then move across to the .05 column. Because the table value in the 1.2 row and the .05 column is .8944, $P(z \le 1.25) = .8944$. Similarly, to find the area under the curve to the left of $z = -.50$, we use the left-hand page of the table to locate the table value in the $-.5$ row and the .00 column; with a table value of .3085, $P(z \le -.50) = .3085$. Thus, $P(-.50 \le z \le 1.25) = P(z \le 1.25) - P(z \le -.50) = .8944 - .3085 = .5859$.

FIGURE 6.9 Cumulative Probability for Normal Distribution Corresponding to $P(-.50 \le z \le 1.25)$

$P(-.50 \le z \le 1.25)$

$P(z < -.50)$

FIGURE 6.10 Cumulative Probability for Normal Distribution Corresponding to $P(-1.00 \leq z \leq 1.00)$

Let us consider another example of computing the probability that z is in the interval between two given values. Often it is of interest to compute the probability that a normal random variable assumes a value within a certain number of standard deviations of the mean. Suppose we want to compute the probability that the standard normal random variable is within one standard deviation of the mean; that is, $P(-1.00 \leq z \leq 1.00)$. To compute this probability we must find the area under the curve between -1.00 and 1.00. Earlier we found that $P(z \leq 1.00) = .8413$. Referring again to the table inside the front cover of the book, we find that the area under the curve to the left of $z = -1.00$ is $.1587$, so $P(z \leq -1.00) = .1587$. Therefore, $P(-1.00 \leq z \leq 1.00) = P(z \leq 1.00) - P(z \leq -1.00) = .8413 - .1587 = .6826$. This probability is shown graphically in Figure 6.10.

To illustrate how to make the third type of probability computation, suppose we want to compute the probability of obtaining a z value of at least 1.58; that is, $P(z \geq 1.58)$. The value in the $z = 1.5$ row and the $.08$ column of the cumulative normal table is $.9429$; thus, $P(z < 1.58) = .9429$. However, because the total area under the normal curve is 1, $P(z \geq 1.58) = 1 - .9429 = .0571$. This probability is shown in Figure 6.11.

In the preceding illustrations, we showed how to compute probabilities given specified z values. In some situations, we are given a probability and are interested in working backward to find the corresponding z value. Suppose we want to find a z value such that the probability of obtaining a larger z value is $.10$. Figure 6.12 shows this situation graphically.

FIGURE 6.11 Cumulative Probability for Normal Distribution Corresponding to $P(z \geq 1.58)$

FIGURE 6.12   Finding z Value such that Probability of Obtaining a Larger z Value is .10

Probability = .10

z

−2   −1   0   +1   +2

What is this z value?

This problem is the inverse of those in the preceding examples. Previously, we specified the z value of interest and then found the corresponding probability, or area. In this example, we are given the probability, or area, and asked to find the corresponding z value. To do so, we use the standard normal probability table somewhat differently.

Recall that the standard normal probability table gives the area under the curve to the left of a particular z value. We have been given the information that the area in the upper tail of the curve is .10. Hence, the area under the curve to the left of the unknown z value must equal .9000. Scanning the body of the table, we find .8997 is the cumulative probability value closest to .9000. The section of the table providing this result follows.

Given a probability, we can use the standard normal table in an inverse fashion to find the corresponding z value.

z	.06	.07	.08	.09
.				
.				
.				
1.0	.8554	.8577	.8599	.8621
1.1	.8770	.8790	.8810	.8830
1.2	.8962	.8980	.8997	.9015
1.3	.9131	.9147	.9162	.9177
1.4	.9279	.9292	.9306	.9319
.				
.				
.				

Cumulative probability value closest to .9000

Reading the z value from the left-most column and the top row of the table, we find that the corresponding z value is 1.28. Thus, an area of approximately .9000 (actually .8997) will be to the left of z = 1.28.[2] In terms of the question originally asked, there is an approximately .10 probability of a z value larger than 1.28.

The examples illustrate that the table of cumulative probabilities for the standard normal probability distribution can be used to find probabilities associated with values of the standard normal random variable z. Two types of questions can be asked. The first type of question specifies a value, or values, for z and asks us to use the table to determine the

---

[2] We could use interpolation in the body of the table to get a better approximation of the z value that corresponds to an area of .9000. Doing so to provide one more decimal place of accuracy would yield a z value of 1.282. However, in most practical situations, sufficient accuracy is obtained by simply using the table value closest to the desired probability.

corresponding areas or probabilities. The second type of question provides an area, or probability, and asks us to use the table to determine the corresponding z value. Thus, we need to be flexible in using the standard normal probability table to answer the desired probability question. In most cases, sketching a graph of the standard normal probability distribution and shading the appropriate area will help to visualize the situation and aid in determining the correct answer.

Computing Probabilities for Any Normal Probability Distribution

The reason for discussing the standard normal distribution so extensively is that probabilities for all normal distributions can be computed using the standard normal distribution. That is, when we have a normal distribution with any mean μ and any standard deviation σ, we can answer probability questions about the distribution by first converting to the standard normal distribution. Then we can use the standard normal probability table and the appropriate z values to find the desired probabilities. The formula used to convert any normal random variable x with mean μ and standard deviation σ to the standard normal random variable z follows.

The formula for the standard normal random variable is similar to the formula we introduced in Chapter 3 for computing z-scores for a data set.

CONVERTING TO THE STANDARD NORMAL RANDOM VARIABLE

$$z = \frac{x - \mu}{\sigma} \tag{6.3}$$

A value of x equal to its mean μ results in $z = (\mu - \mu)/\sigma = 0$. Thus, we see that a value of x equal to its mean μ corresponds to $z = 0$. Now suppose that x is one standard deviation above its mean; that is, $x = \mu + \sigma$. Applying equation (6.3), we see that the corresponding z value is $z = [(\mu + \sigma) - \mu]/\sigma = \sigma/\sigma = 1$. Thus, an x value that is one standard deviation above its mean corresponds to $z = 1$. In other words, *we can interpret z as the number of standard deviations that the normal random variable x is from its mean μ.*

To see how this conversion enables us to compute probabilities for any normal distribution, suppose we have a normal distribution with $\mu = 10$ and $\sigma = 2$. What is the probability that the random variable x is between 10 and 14? Using equation (6.3), we see that at $x = 10$, $z = (x - \mu)/\sigma = (10 - 10)/2 = 0$ and that at $x = 14$, $z = (14 - 10)/2 = 4/2 = 2$. Thus, the answer to our question about the probability of x being between 10 and 14 is given by the equivalent probability that z is between 0 and 2 for the standard normal distribution. In other words, the probability that we are seeking is the probability that the random variable x is between its mean and two standard deviations above the mean. Using $z = 2.00$ and the standard normal probability table inside the front cover of the text, we see that $P(z \leq 2) = .9772$. Because $P(z \leq 0) = .5000$, we can compute $P(.00 \leq z \leq 2.00) = P(z \leq 2) - P(z \leq 0) = .9772 - .5000 = .4772$. Hence the probability that x is between 10 and 14 is .4772.

Grear Tire Company Problem

We turn now to an application of the normal probability distribution. Suppose the Grear Tire Company developed a new steel-belted radial tire to be sold through a national chain of discount stores. Because the tire is a new product, Grear's managers believe that the mileage guarantee offered with the tire will be an important factor in the acceptance of the product. Before finalizing the tire mileage guarantee policy, Grear's managers want probability information about $x =$ number of miles the tires will last.

From actual road tests with the tires, Grear's engineering group estimated that the mean tire mileage is $\mu = 36{,}500$ miles and that the standard deviation is $\sigma = 5000$. In addition, the data collected indicate that a normal distribution is a reasonable assumption. What

FIGURE 6.13   Grear Tire Company Mileage Distribution

percentage of the tires can be expected to last more than 40,000 miles? In other words, what is the probability that the tire mileage, x, will exceed 40,000? This question can be answered by finding the area of the darkly shaded region in Figure 6.13.

At $x = 40,000$, we have

$$z = \frac{x - \mu}{\sigma} = \frac{40,000 - 36,500}{5000} = \frac{3500}{5000} = .70$$

Refer now to the bottom of Figure 6.13. We see that a value of $x = 40,000$ on the Grear Tire normal distribution corresponds to a value of $z = .70$ on the standard normal distribution. Using the standard normal probability table, we see that the area under the standard normal curve to the left of $z = .70$ is .7580. Thus, $1.000 - .7580 = .2420$ is the probability that z will exceed .70 and hence x will exceed 40,000. We can conclude that about 24.2% of the tires will exceed 40,000 in mileage.

Let us now assume that Grear is considering a guarantee that will provide a discount on replacement tires if the original tires do not provide the guaranteed mileage. What should the guarantee mileage be if Grear wants no more than 10% of the tires to be eligible for the discount guarantee? This question is interpreted graphically in Figure 6.14.

FIGURE 6.14   Grear's Discount Guarantee

According to Figure 6.14, the area under the curve to the left of the unknown guarantee mileage must be .10. So, we must first find the z value that cuts off an area of .10 in the left tail of a standard normal distribution. Using the standard normal probability table, we see that $z = -1.28$ cuts off an area of .10 in the lower tail. Hence, $z = -1.28$ is the value of the standard normal random variable corresponding to the desired mileage guarantee on the Grear Tire normal distribution. To find the value of x corresponding to $z = -1.28$, we have

The guarantee mileage we need to find is 1.28 standard deviations below the mean. Thus, $x = \mu - 1.28\sigma$.

$$z = \frac{x - \mu}{\sigma} = -1.28$$

$$x - \mu = -1.28\sigma$$

$$x = \mu - 1.28\sigma$$

With $\mu = 36{,}500$ and $\sigma = 5000$,

$$x = 36{,}500 - 1.28(5000) = 30{,}100$$

With the guarantee set at 30,000 miles, the actual percentage eligible for the guarantee will be 9.68%.

Thus, a guarantee of 30,100 miles will meet the requirement that approximately 10% of the tires will be eligible for the guarantee. Perhaps, with this information, the firm will set its tire mileage guarantee at 30,000 miles.

Again, we see the important role that probability distributions play in providing decision-making information. Namely, once a probability distribution is established for a particular application, it can be used to obtain probability information about the problem. Probability does not make a decision recommendation directly, but it provides information that helps the decision maker better understand the risks and uncertainties associated with the problem. Ultimately, this information may assist the decision maker in reaching a good decision.

EXERCISES

Methods

8. Using Figure 6.6 as a guide, sketch a normal curve for a random variable x that has a mean of $\mu = 100$ and a standard deviation of $\sigma = 10$. Label the horizontal axis with values of 70, 80, 90, 100, 110, 120, and 130.

9. A random variable is normally distributed with a mean of $\mu = 50$ and a standard deviation of $\sigma = 5$.
   a. Sketch a normal curve for the probability density function. Label the horizontal axis with values of 35, 40, 45, 50, 55, 60, and 65. Figure 6.6 shows that the normal curve almost touches the horizontal axis at three standard deviations below and at three standard deviations above the mean (in this case at 35 and 65).
   b. What is the probability the random variable will assume a value between 45 and 55?
   c. What is the probability the random variable will assume a value between 40 and 60?

10. Draw a graph for the standard normal distribution. Label the horizontal axis at values of $-3, -2, -1, 0, 1, 2,$ and 3. Then use the table of probabilities for the standard normal distribution inside the front cover of the text to compute the following probabilities.
    a. $P(z \leq 1.5)$
    b. $P(z \leq 1)$
    c. $P(1 \leq z \leq 1.5)$
    d. $P(0 < z < 2.5)$

11. Given that z is a standard normal random variable, compute the following probabilities.
    a. $P(z \leq -1.0)$
    b. $P(z \geq -1)$
    c. $P(z \geq -1.5)$
    d. $P(-2.5 \leq z)$
    e. $P(-3 < z \leq 0)$

12. Given that z is a standard normal random variable, compute the following probabilities.
    a. $P(0 \leq z \leq .83)$
    b. $P(-1.57 \leq z \leq 0)$
    c. $P(z > .44)$
    d. $P(z \geq -.23)$
    e. $P(z < 1.20)$
    f. $P(z \leq -.71)$

13. Given that z is a standard normal random variable, compute the following probabilities.
    a. $P(-1.98 \leq z \leq .49)$
    b. $P(.52 \leq z \leq 1.22)$
    c. $P(-1.75 \leq z \leq -1.04)$

14. Given that z is a standard normal random variable, find z for each situation.
    a. The area to the left of z is .9750.
    b. The area between 0 and z is .4750.
    c. The area to the left of z is .7291.
    d. The area to the right of z is .1314.
    e. The area to the left of z is .6700.
    f. The area to the right of z is .3300.

15. Given that z is a standard normal random variable, find z for each situation.
    a. The area to the left of z is .2119.
    b. The area between $-z$ and z is .9030.
    c. The area between $-z$ and z is .2052.
    d. The area to the left of z is .9948.
    e. The area to the right of z is .6915.

16. Given that z is a standard normal random variable, find z for each situation.
    a. The area to the right of z is .01.
    b. The area to the right of z is .025.
    c. The area to the right of z is .05.
    d. The area to the right of z is .10.

Applications

17. **Height of Dutch Men.** Males in the Netherlands are the tallest, on average, in the world with an average height of 183 centimeters (cm) (BBC News website). Assume that the height of men in the Netherlands is normally distributed with a mean of 183 cm and standard deviation of 10.5 cm.
    a. What is the probability that a Dutch male is shorter than 175 cm?
    b. What is the probability that a Dutch male is taller than 195 cm?
    c. What is the probability that a Dutch male is between 173 and 193 cm?
    d. Out of a random sample of 1000 Dutch men, how many would we expect to be taller than 190 cm?

18. **Large-Cap Domestic Stock Fund.** The average return for large-cap domestic stock funds over the three years was 14.4%. Assume the three-year returns were normally distributed across funds with a standard deviation of 4.4%.
    a. What is the probability an individual large-cap domestic stock fund had a three-year return of at least 20%?

b. What is the probability an individual large-cap domestic stock fund had a three-year return of 10% or less?

c. How big does the return have to be to put a domestic stock fund in the top 10% for the three-year period?

19. **Automobile Repair Costs.** Automobile repair costs continue to rise with an average 2015 cost of $367 per repair (*U.S. News & World Report* website). Assume that the cost for an automobile repair is normally distributed with a standard deviation of $88. Answer the following questions about the cost of automobile repairs.
    a. What is the probability that the cost will be more than $450?
    b. What is the probability that the cost will be less than $250?
    c. What is the probability that the cost will be between $250 and $450?
    d. If the cost for your car repair is in the lower 5% of automobile repair charges, what is your cost?

20. **Gasoline Prices.** Suppose that the average price for a gallon of gasoline in the United States is $3.73 and in Russia is $3.40. Assume these averages are the population means in the two countries and that the probability distributions are normally distributed with a standard deviation of $.25 in the United States and a standard deviation of $.20 in Russia.
    a. What is the probability that a randomly selected gas station in the United States charges less than $3.50 per gallon?
    b. What percentage of the gas stations in Russia charge less than $3.50 per gallon?
    c. What is the probability that a randomly selected gas station in Russia charged more than the mean price in the United States?

21. **Mensa Membership.** A person must score in the upper 2% of the population on an IQ test to qualify for membership in Mensa, the international high-IQ society. If IQ scores are normally distributed with a mean of 100 and a standard deviation of 15, what score must a person have to qualify for Mensa?

22. **Television Viewing.** Suppose that the mean daily viewing time of television is 8.35 hours. Use a normal probability distribution with a standard deviation of 2.5 hours to answer the following questions about daily television viewing per household.
    a. What is the probability that a household views television between 5 and 10 hours a day?
    b. How many hours of television viewing must a household have in order to be in the top 3% of all television viewing households?
    c. What is the probability that a household views television more than 3 hours a day?

23. **Time to Complete Final Exam.** The time needed to complete a final examination in a particular college course is normally distributed with a mean of 80 minutes and a standard deviation of 10 minutes. Answer the following questions.
    a. What is the probability of completing the exam in one hour or less?
    b. What is the probability that a student will complete the exam in more than 60 minutes but less than 75 minutes?
    c. Assume that the class has 60 students and that the examination period is 90 minutes in length. How many students do you expect will be unable to complete the exam in the allotted time?

24. **Labor Day Travel Costs.** The American Automobile Association (AAA) reported that families planning to travel over the Labor Day weekend spend an average of $749. Assume that the amount spent is normally distributed with a standard deviation of $225.
    a. What is the probability of family expenses for the weekend being less that $400?
    b. What is the probability of family expenses for the weekend being $800 or more?
    c. What is the probability that family expenses for the weekend will be between $500 and $1000?
    d. What would the Labor Day weekend expenses have to be for the 5% of the families with the most expensive travel plans?

25. **Household Income in Maryland.** According to *Money* magazine, Maryland had the highest median annual household income of any state in 2018 at $75,847 (Time.com

website). Assume that annual household income in Maryland follows a normal distribution with a median of $75,847 and standard deviation of $33,800.

a. What is the probability that a household in Maryland has an annual income of $100,000 or more?
b. What is the probability that a household in Maryland has an annual income of $40,000 or less?
c. What is the probability that a household in Maryland has an annual income between $50,000 and $70,000?
d. What is the annual income of a household in the 90th percentile of annual household income in Maryland?

6.3 Normal Approximation of Binomial Probabilities

In Section 5.5 we presented the discrete binomial distribution. Recall that a binomial experiment consists of a sequence of n identical independent trials with each trial having two possible outcomes, a success or a failure. The probability of a success on a trial is the same for all trials and is denoted by p. The binomial random variable is the number of successes in the n trials, and probability questions pertain to the probability of x successes in the n trials.

When the number of trials becomes large, evaluating the binomial probability function by hand or with a calculator is difficult. In cases where $np \geq 5$, and $n(1 - p) \geq 5$, the normal distribution provides an easy-to-use approximation of binomial probabilities. When using the normal approximation to the binomial, we set $\mu = np$ and $\sigma = \sqrt{np(1 - p)}$ in the definition of the normal curve.

Let us illustrate the normal approximation to the binomial by supposing that a particular company has a history of making errors in 10% of its invoices. A sample of 100 invoices has been taken, and we want to compute the probability that 12 invoices contain errors. That is, we want to find the binomial probability of 12 successes in 100 trials. In applying the normal approximation in this case, we set $\mu = np = (100)(.1) = 10$ and $\sigma = \sqrt{np(1 - p)} = \sqrt{(100)(.1)(.9)} = 3$. A normal distribution with $\mu = 10$ and $\sigma = 3$ is shown in Figure 6.15.

Recall that, with a continuous probability distribution, probabilities are computed as areas under the probability density function. As a result, the probability of any single value for the random variable is zero. Thus to approximate the binomial probability of 12 successes, we compute the area under the corresponding normal curve between 11.5 and 12.5. The .5 that we add and subtract from 12 is called a **continuity correction factor**.

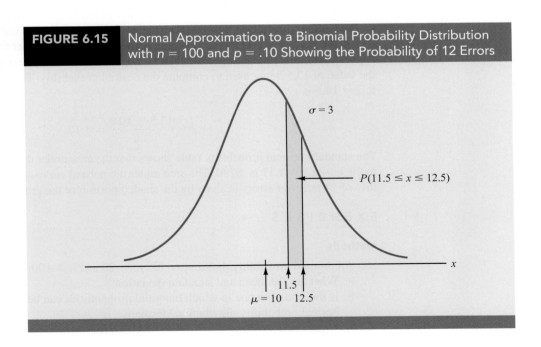

FIGURE 6.15   Normal Approximation to a Binomial Probability Distribution with $n = 100$ and $p = .10$ Showing the Probability of 12 Errors

$\sigma = 3$

$P(11.5 \leq x \leq 12.5)$

11.5

$\mu = 10$ 12.5

x

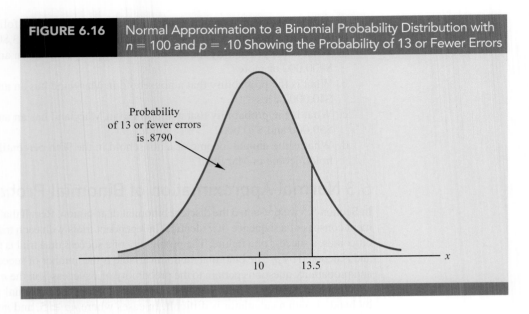

FIGURE 6.16   Normal Approximation to a Binomial Probability Distribution with $n = 100$ and $p = .10$ Showing the Probability of 13 or Fewer Errors

It is introduced because a continuous distribution is being used to approximate a discrete distribution. Thus, $P(x = 12)$ for the *discrete* binomial distribution is approximated by $P(11.5 \leq x \leq 12.5)$ for the *continuous* normal distribution.

Converting to the standard normal distribution to compute $P(11.5 \leq x \leq 12.5)$, we have

$$z = \frac{x - \mu}{\sigma} = \frac{12.5 - 10.0}{3} = .83 \qquad \text{at } x = 12.5$$

and

$$z = \frac{x - \mu}{\sigma} = \frac{11.5 - 10.0}{3} = .50 \qquad \text{at } x = 11.5$$

Using the standard normal probability table, we find that the area under the curve (in Figure 6.15) to the left of 12.5 is .7967. Similarly, the area under the curve to the left of 11.5 is .6915. Therefore, the area between 11.5 and 12.5 is .7967 − .6915 = .1052. The normal approximation to the probability of 12 successes in 100 trials is .1052.

For another illustration, suppose we want to compute the probability of 13 or fewer errors in the sample of 100 invoices. Figure 6.16 shows the area under the normal curve that approximates this probability. Note that the use of the continuity correction factor results in the value of 13.5 being used to compute the desired probability. The z value corresponding to $x = 13.5$ is

$$z = \frac{13.5 - 10.0}{3.0} = 1.17$$

The standard normal probability table shows that the area under the standard normal curve to the left of $z = 1.17$ is .8790. The area under the normal curve approximating the probability of 13 or fewer errors is given by the shaded portion of the graph in Figure 6.16.

EXERCISES

Methods

26. A binomial probability distribution has $p = .20$ and $n = 100$.
    a. What are the mean and standard deviation?
    b. Is this situation one in which binomial probabilities can be approximated by the normal probability distribution? Explain.

    c. What is the probability of exactly 24 successes?

    d. What is the probability of 18 to 22 successes?

    e. What is the probability of 15 or fewer successes?

27. Assume a binomial probability distribution has $p = .60$ and $n = 200$.

    a. What are the mean and standard deviation?

    b. Is this situation one in which binomial probabilities can be approximated by the normal probability distribution? Explain.

    c. What is the probability of 100 to 110 successes?

    d. What is the probability of 130 or more successes?

    e. What is the advantage of using the normal probability distribution to approximate the binomial probabilities? Use part (d) to explain the advantage.

Applications

28. **Adults Who Smoke.** Although studies continue to show smoking leads to significant health problems, 20% of adults in the United States smoke. Consider a group of 250 adults, and use the normal approximation of the binomial distribution to answer the questions below.

    a. What is the expected number of adults who smoke?

    b. What is the probability that fewer than 40 smoke?

    c. What is the probability that from 55 to 60 smoke?

    d. What is the probability that 70 or more smoke?

29. **Americans Who Believe Global Warming Is Occurring.** According to a Yale program on climate change communication survey, 71% of Americans think global warming is happening (American Psychological Association website).

    a. For a sample of 15 Americans, what is the probability that at least 12 believe global warming is occurring? Use the binomial distribution probability function discussed in Section 5.5 to answer this question.

    b. For a sample of 150 Americans, what is the probability that at least 100 believe global warming is occurring? Use the normal approximation of the binomial distribution to answer this question.

    c. As the number of trials in a binomial distribution application becomes large, what is the advantage of using the normal approximation of the binomial distribution to compute probabilities?

    d. When the number of trials for a binomial distribution application becomes large, would developers of statistical software packages prefer to use the binomial distribution probability function shown in Section 5.5 or the normal approximation of the binomial distribution discussed in Section 6.3? Explain.

30. **Playing Video Games.** Suppose that of those individuals who play video and computer games, 18% are under 18 years old, 53% are 18–59 years old, and 29% are over 59 years old. Use the normal approximation of the binomial distribution to answer the questions below.

    a. For a sample of 800 people who play these games, how many would you expect to be under 18 years of age?

    b. For a sample of 600 people who play these games, what is the probability that fewer than 100 will be under 18 years of age?

    c. For a sample of 800 people who play these games, what is the probability that 200 or more will be over 59 years of age?

31. **Visitors to Rocky Mountain National Park.** Rocky Mountain National Park is a popular park for outdoor recreation activities in Colorado. According to U.S. National Park Service statistics, 46.7% of visitors to Rocky Mountain National Park in 2018 entered through the Beaver Meadows park entrance, 24.3% of visitors entered through the Fall River park entrance, 6.3% of visitors entered through the Grand Lake park entrance, and 22.7% of visitors had no recorded point of entry to the park (U.S. National Park Service website). Consider a random sample of 175 Rocky Mountain

National Park visitors. Use the normal approximation of the binomial distribution to answer the following questions.

a. What is the probability that at least 75 visitors had a recorded entry through the Beaver Meadows park entrance?

b. What is the probability that at least 70 but less than 80 visitors had a recorded entry through the Beaver Meadows park entrance?

c. What is the probability that fewer than 10 visitors had a recorded entry through the Grand Lake park entrance?

d. What is the probability that more than 45 visitors have no recorded point of entry?

6.4 Exponential Probability Distribution

The **exponential probability distribution** may be used for random variables such as the time between arrivals at a hospital emergency room, the time required to load a truck, the distance between major defects in a highway, and so on. The exponential probability density function follows.

EXPONENTIAL PROBABILITY DENSITY FUNCTION

$$f(x) = \frac{1}{\mu} e^{-x/\mu} \qquad \text{for } x \geq 0 \qquad \textbf{(6.4)}$$

where μ = expected value or mean

As an example of the exponential distribution, suppose that x represents the loading time for a truck at the Schips loading dock and follows such a distribution. If the mean, or average, loading time is 15 minutes ($\mu = 15$), the appropriate probability density function for x is

$$f(x) = \frac{1}{15} e^{-x/15}$$

Figure 6.17 is the graph of this probability density function.

Computing Probabilities for the Exponential Distribution

In waiting line applications, the exponential distribution is often used for service time.

As with any continuous probability distribution, the area under the curve corresponding to an interval provides the probability that the random variable assumes a value in that interval. In the Schips loading dock example, the probability that loading a truck will take 6 minutes or less, $P(x \leq 6)$, is defined to be the area under the curve in Figure 6.17 from $x = 0$ to $x = 6$. Similarly, the probability that the loading time will be 18 minutes or less,

FIGURE 6.17 Exponential Distribution for the Schips Loading Dock Example

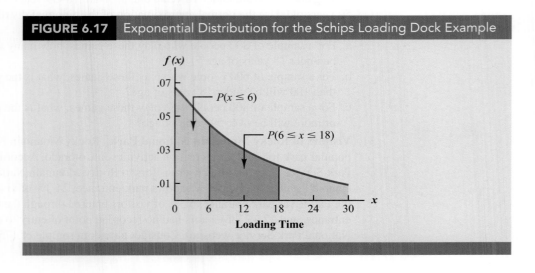

$P(x \leq 18)$, is the area under the curve from $x = 0$ to $x = 18$. Note also that the probability that the loading time will be between 6 minutes and 18 minutes, $P(6 \leq x \leq 18)$, is given by the area under the curve from $x = 6$ to $x = 18$.

To compute exponential probabilities such as those just described, we use the following formula. It provides the cumulative probability of obtaining a value for the exponential random variable of less than or equal to some specific value denoted by x_0.

EXPONENTIAL DISTRIBUTION: CUMULATIVE PROBABILITIES

$$P(x \leq x_0) = 1 - e^{-x_0/\mu} \qquad\qquad (6.5)$$

For the Schips loading dock example, $x =$ loading time in minutes and $\mu = 15$ minutes. Using equation (6.5),

$$P(x \leq x_0) = 1 - e^{-x_0/15}$$

Hence, the probability that loading a truck will take 6 minutes or less is

$$P(x \leq 6) = 1 - e^{-6/15} = .3297$$

Using equation (6.5), we calculate the probability of loading a truck in 18 minutes or less.

$$P(x \leq 18) = 1 - e^{-18/15} = .6988$$

Thus, the probability that loading a truck will take between 6 minutes and 18 minutes is equal to $.6988 - .3297 = .3691$. Probabilities for any other interval can be computed similarly.

A property of the exponential distribution is that the mean and standard deviation are equal.

In the preceding example, the mean time it takes to load a truck is $\mu = 15$ minutes. A property of the exponential distribution is that the mean of the distribution and the standard deviation of the distribution are *equal*. Thus, the standard deviation for the time it takes to load a truck is $\sigma = 15$ minutes. The variance is $\sigma^2 = (15)^2 = 225$.

Relationship Between the Poisson and Exponential Distributions

In Section 5.6 we introduced the Poisson distribution as a discrete probability distribution that is often useful in examining the number of occurrences of an event over a specified interval of time or space. Recall that the Poisson probability function is

$$f(x) = \frac{\mu^x e^{-\mu}}{x!}$$

where

$$\mu = \text{expected value or mean number of}$$
$$\text{occurrences over a specified interval}$$

If arrivals follow a Poisson distribution, the time between arrivals must follow an exponential distribution.

The continuous exponential probability distribution is related to the discrete Poisson distribution. If the Poisson distribution provides an appropriate description of the number of occurrences per interval, the exponential distribution provides a description of the length of the interval between occurrences.

To illustrate this relationship, suppose the number of patients who arrive at a hospital emergency room during one hour is described by a Poisson probability distribution with a mean of 10 patients per hour. The Poisson probability function that gives the probability of x arrivals per hour is

$$f(x) = \frac{10^x e^{-10}}{x!}$$

Because the average number of arrivals is 10 patients per hour, the average time between patients arriving is

$$\frac{1 \text{ hour}}{10 \text{ cars}} = .1 \text{ hour/patient}$$

Thus, the corresponding exponential distribution that describes the time between the arrivals has a mean of $\mu = .1$ hour per patient; as a result, the appropriate exponential probability density function is

$$f(x) = \frac{1}{.1} e^{-x/.1} = 10e^{-10x}$$

NOTES + COMMENTS

As we can see in Figure 6.17, the exponential distribution is skewed to the right. Indeed, the skewness measure for exponential distributions is 2. The exponential distribution gives us a good idea what a skewed distribution looks like.

EXERCISES

Methods

32. Consider the following exponential probability density function.

$$f(x) = \frac{1}{8} e^{-x/8} \qquad \text{for } x \geq 0$$

 a. Find $P(x \leq 6)$.
 b. Find $P(x \leq 4)$.
 c. Find $P(x \geq 6)$.
 d. Find $P(4 \leq x \leq 6)$.

33. Consider the following exponential probability density function.

$$f(x) = \frac{1}{3} e^{-x/3} \qquad \text{for } x \geq 0$$

 a. Write the formula for $P(x \leq x_0)$.
 b. Find $P(x \leq 2)$.
 c. Find $P(x \geq 3)$.
 d. Find $P(x \leq 5)$.
 e. Find $P(2 \leq x \leq 5)$.

Applications

34. **Phone Battery Life.** Battery life between charges for a certain mobile phone is 20 hours when the primary use is talk time, and drops to 7 hours when the phone is primarily used for Internet applications over a cellular network. Assume that the battery life in both cases follows an exponential distribution.
 a. Show the probability density function for battery life for this phone when its primary use is talk time.
 b. What is the probability that the battery charge for a randomly selected phone will last no more than 15 hours when its primary use is talk time?
 c. What is the probability that the battery charge for a randomly selected phone will last more than 20 hours when its primary use is talk time?
 d. What is the probability that the battery charge for a randomly selected phone will last no more than 5 hours when its primary use is Internet applications?

35. **Arrival of Vehicles at an Intersection.** The time between arrivals of vehicles at a particular intersection follows an exponential probability distribution with a mean of 12 seconds.
 a. Sketch this exponential probability distribution.
 b. What is the probability that the arrival time between vehicles is 12 seconds or less?

c. What is the probability that the arrival time between vehicles is 6 seconds or less?

d. What is the probability of 30 or more seconds between vehicle arrivals?

36. **Comcast Service Interruptions.** Comcast Corporation is a global telecommunications company headquartered in Philadelphia, PA. Generally known for reliable service, the company periodically experiences unexpected service interruptions. When service interruptions do occur, Comcast customers who call the office receive a message providing an estimate of when service will be restored. Suppose that for a particular outage, Comcast customers are told that service will be restored in two hours. Assume that two hours is the mean time to do the repair and that the repair time has an exponential probability distribution.

a. What is the probability that the cable service will be repaired in one hour or less?

b. What is the probability that the repair will take between one hour and two hours?

c. For a customer who calls the Comcast office at 1:00 P.M., what is the probability that the cable service will not be repaired by 5:00 P.M.?

37. **Patient Length of Stays in ICUs.** Intensive care units (ICUs) generally treat the sickest patients in a hospital. ICUs are often the most expensive department in a hospital because of the specialized equipment and extensive training required to be an ICU doctor or nurse. Therefore, it is important to use ICUs as efficiently as possible in a hospital. According to a 2017 large-scale study of elderly ICU patients, the average length of stay in the ICU is 3.4 days (*Critical Care Medicine* journal article). Assume that this length of stay in the ICU has an exponential distribution.

a. What is the probability that the length of stay in the ICU is one day or less?

b. What is the probability that the length of stay in the ICU is between two and three days?

c. What is the probability that the length of stay in the ICU is more than five days?

38. **Boston 911 Calls.** The Boston Fire Department receives 911 calls at a mean rate of 1.6 calls per hour (Mass.gov website). Suppose the number of calls per hour follows a Poisson probability distribution.

a. What is the mean time between 911 calls to the Boston Fire Department in minutes?

b. Using the mean in part (a), show the probability density function for the time between 911 calls in minutes.

c. What is the probability that there will be less than one hour between 911 calls?

d. What is the probability that there will be 30 minutes or more between 911 calls?

e. What is the probability that there will be more than 5 minutes, but less than 20 minutes between 911 calls?

SUMMARY

This chapter extended the discussion of probability distributions to the case of continuous random variables. The major conceptual difference between discrete and continuous probability distributions involves the method of computing probabilities. With discrete distributions, the probability function $f(x)$ provides the probability that the random variable x assumes various values. With continuous distributions, the probability density function $f(x)$ does not provide probability values directly. Instead, probabilities are given by areas under the curve or graph of the probability density function $f(x)$. Because the area under the curve above a single point is zero, we observe that the probability of any particular value is zero for a continuous random variable.

Three continuous probability distributions—the uniform, normal, and exponential distributions—were treated in detail. The normal distribution is used widely in statistical inference and will be used extensively throughout the remainder of the text.

GLOSSARY

Continuity correction factor A value of .5 that is added to or subtracted from a value of x when the continuous normal distribution is used to approximate the discrete binomial distribution.

Exponential probability distribution A continuous probability distribution that is useful in computing probabilities for the time it takes to complete a task.

Normal probability distribution A continuous probability distribution. Its probability density function is bell-shaped and determined by its mean μ and standard deviation σ.

Probability density function A function used to compute probabilities for a continuous random variable. The area under the graph of a probability density function over an interval represents probability.

Standard normal probability distribution A normal distribution with a mean of zero and a standard deviation of one.

Uniform probability distribution A continuous probability distribution for which the probability that the random variable will assume a value in any interval is the same for each interval of equal length.

KEY FORMULAS

Uniform Probability Density Function

$$f(x) = \begin{cases} \dfrac{1}{b-a} & \text{for } a \le x \le b \\ 0 & \text{elsewhere} \end{cases} \tag{6.1}$$

Normal Probability Density Function

$$f(x) = \frac{1}{\sigma\sqrt{2\pi}} e^{-\frac{1}{2}\left(\frac{x-\mu}{\sigma}\right)^2} \tag{6.2}$$

Converting to the Standard Normal Random Variable

$$z = \frac{x - \mu}{\sigma} \tag{6.3}$$

Exponential Probability Density Function

$$f(x) = \frac{1}{\mu} e^{-x/\mu} \qquad \text{for } x \ge 0 \tag{6.4}$$

Exponential Distribution: Cumulative Probabilities

$$P(x \le x_0) = 1 - e^{-x_0/\mu} \tag{6.5}$$

SUPPLEMENTARY EXERCISES

39. **Selling a House.** A business executive, transferred from Chicago to Atlanta, needs to sell her house in Chicago quickly. The executive's employer has offered to buy the house for $210,000, but the offer expires at the end of the week. The executive does not currently have a better offer but can afford to leave the house on the market for another month. From conversations with her realtor, the executive believes the price she will get by leaving the house on the market for another month is uniformly distributed between $200,000 and $225,000.
   a. If she leaves the house on the market for another month, what is the mathematical expression for the probability density function of the sales price?
   b. If she leaves it on the market for another month, what is the probability she will get at least $215,000 for the house?
   c. If she leaves it on the market for another month, what is the probability she will get less than $210,000?
   d. Should the executive leave the house on the market for another month? Why or why not?

40. **NCAA Scholarships.** The NCAA estimates that the yearly value of a full athletic scholarship at in-state public universities is $19,000. Assume the scholarship value is normally distributed with a standard deviation of $2100.
    a. For the 10% of athletic scholarships of least value, how much are they worth?
    b. What percentage of athletic scholarships are valued at $22,000 or more?
    c. For the 3% of athletic scholarships that are most valuable, how much are they worth?

41. **Production Defects.** Motorola used the normal distribution to determine the probability of defects and the number of defects expected in a production process. Assume a production process produces items with a mean weight of 10 ounces. Calculate the probability of a defect and the expected number of defects for a 1000-unit production run in the following situations.
    a. The process standard deviation is .15, and the process control is set at plus or minus one standard deviation. Units with weights less than 9.85 or greater than 10.15 ounces will be classified as defects.
    b. Through process design improvements, the process standard deviation can be reduced to .05. Assume the process control remains the same, with weights less than 9.85 or greater than 10.15 ounces being classified as defects.
    c. What is the advantage of reducing process variation, thereby causing process control limits to be at a greater number of standard deviations from the mean?

42. **Bringing Items to a Pawnshop.** One indicator of the level of economic hardship is the number of people who bring items to a pawnbroker. Assume that the number of people bringing items to a pawnshop per day in is normally distributed with a mean of 658.
    a. Suppose you learn that on 3% of the days, 610 or fewer people brought items to the pawnshop. What is the standard deviation of the number of people bringing items to the pawnshop per day?
    b. On any given day, what is the probability that between 600 and 700 people bring items to the pawnshop?
    c. How many people bring items to the pawnshop on the busiest 3% of days?

43. **Amazon Alexa App Downloads.** Alexa is the popular virtual assistant developed by Amazon. Alexa interacts with users using artificial intelligence and voice recognition. It can be used to perform daily tasks such as making to-do lists, reporting the news and weather, and interacting with other smart devices in the home. In 2018, the Amazon Alexa app was downloaded some 2800 times per day from the Google Play store (AppBrain website). Assume that the number of downloads per day of the Amazon Alexa app is normally distributed with a mean of 2800 and standard deviation of 860.
    a. What is the probability there are 2000 or fewer downloads of Amazon Alexa in a day?
    b. What is the probability there are between 1500 and 2500 downloads of Amazon Alexa in a day?
    c. What is the probability there are more than 3000 downloads of Amazon Alexa in a day?
    d. Assume that Google has designed its servers so there is probability .01 that the number of Amazon Alexa app downloads in a day exceeds the servers' capacity and more servers have to be brought online. How many Amazon Alexa app downloads per day are Google's servers designed to handle?

44. **Service Contract Offer.** Ward Doering Auto Sales is considering offering a special service contract that will cover the total cost of any service work required on leased vehicles. From experience, the company manager estimates that yearly service costs are approximately normally distributed, with a mean of $150 and a standard deviation of $25.
    a. If the company offers the service contract to customers for a yearly charge of $200, what is the probability that any one customer's service costs will exceed the contract price of $200?
    b. What is Ward's expected profit per service contract?

45. **Wedding Costs.** The XO Group Inc. conducted a 2015 survey of 13,000 brides and grooms married in the United States and found that the average cost of a wedding is $29,858 (XO Group website). Assume that the cost of a wedding is normally distributed with a mean of $29,858 and a standard deviation of $5600.
    a. What is the probability that a wedding costs less than $20,000?
    b. What is the probability that a wedding costs between $20,000 and $30,000?
    c. For a wedding to be among the 5% most expensive, how much would it have to cost?

46. **College Admissions Test Scores.** Assume that the test scores from a college admissions test are normally distributed, with a mean of 450 and a standard deviation of 100.
    a. What percentage of the people taking the test score between 400 and 500?
    b. Suppose someone receives a score of 630. What percentage of the people taking the test score better? What percentage score worse?
    c. If a particular university will not admit anyone scoring below 480, what percentage of the persons taking the test would be acceptable to the university?

47. **College Graduates Starting Salaries.** According to the National Association of Colleges and Employers, the 2015 mean starting salary for new college graduates in health sciences was $51,541. The mean 2015 starting salary for new college graduates in business was $53,901 (National Association of Colleges and Employers website). Assume that starting salaries are normally distributed and that the standard deviation for starting salaries for new college graduates in health sciences is $11,000. Assume that the standard deviation for starting salaries for new college graduates in business is $15,000.
    a. What is the probability that a new college graduate in business will earn a starting salary of at least $65,000?
    b. What is the probability that a new college graduate in health sciences will earn a starting salary of at least $65,000?
    c. What is the probability that a new college graduate in health sciences will earn a starting salary less than $40,000?
    d. How much would a new college graduate in business have to earn in order to have a starting salary higher than 99% of all starting salaries of new college graduates in the health sciences?

48. **Filling Weights.** A machine fills containers with a particular product. The standard deviation of filling weights is known from past data to be .6 ounce. If only 2% of the containers hold less than 18 ounces, what is the mean filling weight for the machine? That is, what must μ equal? Assume the filling weights have a normal distribution.

49. **Multiple-Choice Exam.** Consider a multiple-choice examination with 50 questions. Each question has four possible answers. Assume that a student who has done the homework and attended lectures has probability .75 of answering any question correctly.
    a. A student must answer 43 or more questions correctly to obtain a grade of A. What percentage of the students who have done their homework and attended lectures will obtain a grade of A on this multiple-choice examination?
    b. A student who answers 35 to 39 questions correctly will receive a grade of C. What percentage of students who have done their homework and attended lectures will obtain a grade of C on this multiple-choice examination?
    c. A student must answer 30 or more questions correctly to pass the examination. What percentage of the students who have done their homework and attended lectures will pass the examination?
    d. Assume that a student has not attended class and has not done the homework for the course. Furthermore, assume that the student will simply guess at the answer to each question. What is the probability that this student will answer 30 or more questions correctly and pass the examination?

50. **Playing Blackjack.** A blackjack player at a Las Vegas casino learned that the house will provide a free room if play is for four hours at an average bet of $50. The player's strategy provides a probability of .49 of winning on any one hand, and the player knows that there are 60 hands per hour. Suppose the player plays for four hours at a bet of $50 per hand.
    a. What is the player's expected payoff?
    b. What is the probability the player loses $1000 or more?
    c. What is the probability the player wins?
    d. Suppose the player starts with $1500. What is the probability of going broke?

51. **Mean Time Between Failures.** The mean time between failures (MTBF) is a common metric used to measure the performance of manufacturing systems. MTBF is the elapsed time between failures of a system during normal operations. The failures could be caused by broken machines or computer errors, among other failures. Suppose that the MTBF for a new automated manufacturing system follows an exponential distribution with a mean of 12.7 hours.
    a. What is the probability that the automated manufacturing system runs for more than 15 hours without a failure?
    b. What is the probability that the automated manufacturing system runs for eight or fewer hours before failure?
    c. What is the probability that the automated manufacturing system runs for more than six hours but less than 10 hours before a failure?

52. **Bed and Breakfast Inns Website.** The website for the Bed and Breakfast Inns of North America gets approximately seven visitors per minute. Suppose the number of website visitors per minute follows a Poisson probability distribution.
    a. What is the mean time between visits to the website?
    b. Show the exponential probability density function for the time between website visits.
    c. What is the probability no one will access the website in a 1-minute period?
    d. What is the probability no one will access the website in a 12-second period?

53. **Waiting in Line at Kroger.** Do you dislike waiting in line? Supermarket chain Kroger has used computer simulation and information technology to reduce the average waiting time for customers at 2300 stores. Using a new system called *Que-Vision*, which allows Kroger to better predict when shoppers will be checking out, the company was able to decrease average customer waiting time to just 26 seconds (*InformationWeek* website).
    a. Assume that Kroger waiting times are exponentially distributed. Show the probability density function of waiting time at Kroger.
    b. What is the probability that a customer will have to wait between 15 and 30 seconds?
    c. What is the probability that a customer will have to wait more than 2 minutes?

54. **Calls to Insurance Claims Office.** The time (in minutes) between telephone calls at an insurance claims office has the following exponential probability distribution.

$$f(x) = .50e^{-.50x} \qquad \text{for } x \geq 0$$

    a. What is the mean time between telephone calls?
    b. What is the probability of having 30 seconds or less between telephone calls?
    c. What is the probability of having 1 minute or less between telephone calls?
    d. What is the probability of having 5 or more minutes without a telephone call?

CASE PROBLEM 1: SPECIALTY TOYS

Specialty Toys, Inc., sells a variety of new and innovative children's toys. Management learned that the preholiday season is the best time to introduce a new toy, because many families use this time to look for new ideas for December holiday gifts. When Specialty discovers a new toy with good market potential, it chooses an October market entry date.

In order to get toys in its stores by October, Specialty places one-time orders with its manufacturers in June or July of each year. Demand for children's toys can be highly volatile. If a new toy catches on, a sense of shortage in the marketplace often increases the demand to high levels and large profits can be realized. However, new toys can also flop, leaving Specialty stuck with high levels of inventory that must be sold at reduced prices. The most important question the company faces is deciding how many units of a new toy should be purchased to meet anticipated sales demand. If too few are purchased, sales will be lost; if too many are purchased, profits will be reduced because of low prices realized in clearance sales.

For the coming season, Specialty plans to introduce a new product called Weather Teddy. This variation of a talking teddy bear is made by a company in Taiwan. When a child presses Teddy's hand, the bear begins to talk. A built-in barometer selects one of five responses that predict the weather conditions. The responses range from "It looks to be a very nice day! Have fun" to "I think it may rain today. Don't forget your umbrella." Tests with the product show that, even though it is not a perfect weather predictor, its predictions are surprisingly good. Several of Specialty's managers claimed Teddy gave predictions of the weather that were as good as many local television weather forecasters.

As with other products, Specialty faces the decision of how many Weather Teddy units to order for the coming holiday season. Members of the management team suggested order quantities of 15,000, 18,000, 24,000, or 28,000 units. The wide range of order quantities suggested indicates considerable disagreement concerning the market potential. The product management team asks you for an analysis of the stock-out probabilities for various order quantities, an estimate of the profit potential, and to help make an order quantity recommendation. Specialty expects to sell Weather Teddy for $24 based on a cost of $16 per unit. If inventory remains after the holiday season, Specialty will sell all surplus inventory for $5 per unit. After reviewing the sales history of similar products, Specialty's senior sales forecaster predicted an expected demand of 20,000 units with a .95 probability that demand would be between 10,000 units and 30,000 units.

Managerial Report

Prepare a managerial report that addresses the following issues and recommends an order quantity for the Weather Teddy product.

1. Use the sales forecaster's prediction to describe a normal probability distribution that can be used to approximate the demand distribution. Sketch the distribution and show its mean and standard deviation.
2. Compute the probability of a stock-out for the order quantities suggested by members of the management team.
3. Compute the projected profit for the order quantities suggested by the management team under three scenarios: worst case in which sales = 10,000 units, most likely case in which sales = 20,000 units, and best case in which sales = 30,000 units.
4. One of Specialty's managers felt that the profit potential was so great that the order quantity should have a 70% chance of meeting demand and only a 30% chance of any stock-outs. What quantity would be ordered under this policy, and what is the projected profit under the three sales scenarios?
5. Provide your own recommendation for an order quantity and note the associated profit projections. Provide a rationale for your recommendation.

CASE PROBLEM 2: GEBHARDT ELECTRONICS

Gebhardt Electronics produces a wide variety of transformers that it sells directly to manufacturers of electronics equipment. For one component used in several models of its transformers, Gebhardt uses a 3-foot length of .20 mm diameter solid wire made of pure Oxygen-Free Electronic (OFE) copper. A flaw in the wire reduces its conductivity and increases the likelihood it will break, and this critical component is difficult to reach and repair after a transformer has been constructed. Therefore, Gebhardt wants to use primarily flawless lengths of wire in making this component. The company is willing to accept no more than a 1 in 20 chance that a 3-foot length taken from a spool will be flawless. Gebhardt also occasionally uses smaller pieces of the same wire in the manufacture of other components, so the 3-foot segments to be used for this component are essentially taken randomly from a long spool of .20 mm diameter solid OFE copper wire.

Gebhardt is now considering a new supplier for copper wire. This supplier claims that its spools of .20 mm diameter solid OFE copper wire average 50 inches between flaws. Gebhardt now must determine whether the new supply will be satisfactory if the supplier's claim is valid.

Managerial Report

In making this assessment for Gebhardt Electronics, consider the following three questions:

1. If the new supplier does provide spools fo .20 mm solid OFE copper wire that average 50 inches between flaws, how is the length of wire between two consecutive flaws distributed?
2. Using the probability distribution you identified in (1), what is the probability that Gebhardt's criteria will be met (i.e., a 1 in 20 chance that a randomly selected 3-foot segment of wire provided by the new supplier will be flawless)?
3. In inches, what is the minimum mean length between consecutive flaws that would result in satisfaction of Gebhardt's criteria?
4. In inches, what is the minimum mean length between consecutive flaws that would result in a 1 in 100 chance that a randomly selected 3-foot segment of wire provided by the new supplier will be flawless?

Chapter 6 Appendix

Appendix 6.1 Continuous Probability Distributions with JMP

Statistical packages such as JMP provide procedures for computing continuous random variable probabilities. In this appendix, we demonstrate the JMP procedure for computing continuous probabilities by referring to the Grear Tire Company problem for which tire mileage was described by a normal distribution with $\mu = 36,500$ and $\sigma = 5,000$. Using JMP we will determine the probability that the tire mileage will exceed 40,000 miles.

For continuous probability distributions, JMP provides the cumulative probability that the random variable takes on a value less than or equal to a specified constant. For the Grear Tire mileage example, JMP can be used to determine the cumulative probability that the tire mileage will be less than or equal to 40,000 miles. After obtaining the cumulative probability, we must subtract it from 1 to determine the probability that the tire mileage will exceed 40,000 miles.

Before beginning the procedure in JMP, we must first open a new Data Table and then enter the specified constant into a column of the Data Table. The steps to obtain the desired cumulative probability in JMP follow.

Step 1. Click **File** in the JMP ribbon
        Select **New** and click **Data Table**
Step 2. Double-click **Column 1** in the Data Table
Step 3. When the **Column 1** dialog box appears (see Figure JMP 6.1):
        Enter *x (miles)* in the **Column Name** box
        Click **OK**
Step 4. Enter the value *40000* in the first row of **Column 1** of the Data Table
Step 5. Right-click anywhere in the Data Table and select **New Columns...**

FIGURE JMP 6.1　Renaming Column 1 in JMP

FIGURE JMP 6.2 Creating Normal Cumulative Probability Calculation Column in JMP

Step 6. When the **New Column** dialog box appears (see Figure JMP 6.2):
Enter $Pr(X \leq x)$ in the **Column Name** box
Click on **Column Properties** and select **Formula**
Step 7. When the **Pr(X ≤ x)** dialog box appears (see Figure JMP 6.3):
From the left-hand side, click **Probability**
Select **Normal Distribution**

FIGURE JMP 6.3 Normal Probability Distribution in JMP Before Entering Parameters

FIGURE JMP 6.4   Completed Normal Distribution Function in JMP

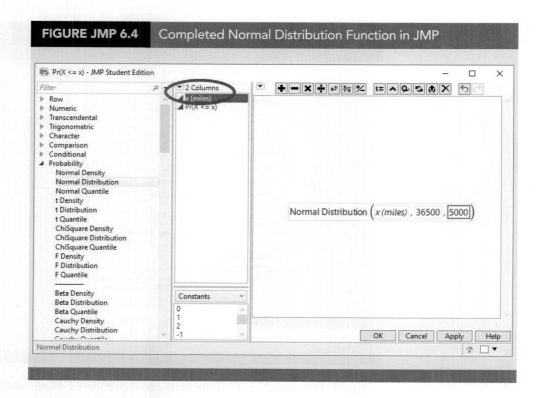

If you do not press the *Caret* button to change the mean and standard deviation values, JMP assumes that you are using a standard normal distribution with μ = 0 and σ = 1.

Click the **Caret** button ⌃ at the top of the formula area twice to add the extra formula fields for **mean** and **std dev** to the **Normal Distribution** formula (see Figure JMP 6.3)

In the **Normal Distribution (x, <mean=0>, <std dev=1>)** formula, click on **x** and select **x (miles)** from the **2 Columns** area to the left of the formula (see circled area in Figure JMP 6.4)

In the **Normal Distribution (x, <mean=0>, <std dev=1>)** formula, click on **<mean=0>** and enter *36500*

In the **Normal Distribution (x, <mean=0>, <std dev=1>)** formula, click on **<std dev=1>** and enter *5000*

Step 8. Click **OK** to close the **Pr(X ≤ x)** dialog box

Step 9. Click **OK** to close the **New Column** dialog box

Figure JMP 6.3 shows the Pr(X = x) dialog box before entering the normal probability distribution parameters. Figure JMP 6.4 shows the completed normal probability distribution formula in JMP once all parameters have been entered. JMP provides the normal cumulative probabilities in the Pr(X ≤ x) column of the Data Table as shown in Figure JMP 6.5. The calculation in JMP indicates that the probability of tire mileage being less than or equal to 40,000 miles is .7580. Therefore, the probability that tire mileage will exceed 40,000 miles is 1 − .7580 = .2420. Note that if we wanted to calculate the cumulative normal probabilities for mileages other than 40,000, we could enter other mileage values in the x (miles) column in Step 4 above and JMP would compute the cumulative probabilities for these mileages as well.

JMP can compute probabilities for the exponential distribution by selecting **Exp Distribution** in Step 7 rather than **Normal Distribution.** Pressing the **Caret** button ⌃ for the exponential distribution allows you to enter the mean of the exponential distribution, which JMP refers to as theta and by default sets to **<theta=1>.**

JMP also includes a Distribution Calculator that can be used to calculate and visualize continuous probability distributions. The following steps show how to use

FIGURE JMP 6.5 Cumulative Normal Probability Computed in JMP

JMP's Distribution Calculator to calculate the probability that tire mileage will exceed 40,000 miles.

Step 1. Click **Help** in the JMP ribbon

Step 2. Click **Teaching Demos** and select **Distribution Calculator**

Step 3. When the **JMP Distribution and Probability Calculator** dialog box appears:

Select **Normal** for **Distribution** under **Distribution Characteristics**

Step 4. In the **Parameters** area:

Enter *36500* in the **Mean** box

Enter *5000* in the **Std. Dev.** box

Step 5. For **Type of Calculation**, select **Input values and calculate probability**

Step 6. For **Probability Options** under **Calculations**:

Select **X ≤ q**

Enter *40000* in the **Value:** box of **Input**

*Note that we can calculate P(X > 40,000) directly by choosing **X > q** for Probability Options in Step 6.*

The output for the JMP Distribution Calculator is shown in Figure JMP 6.6. The output indicates that the P(X ≤ 40,000) = .7580. Therefore, the probability that tire mileage will exceed 40,000 miles is 1 − .7580 = .2420. Figure JMP 6.6 also visually shows this value as the area under the curve for the normal probability distribution.

We can also use the JMP Probability Distribution Calculator to find the *x* value corresponding to a given cumulative probability. For instance, suppose we want to find the guaranteed mileage Grear should offer so that no more than 10% of the tires will be eligible for the guarantee. The following steps show how to calculate this using the JMP Probability Distribution Calculator. Steps 1 through 4 are the same as previously.

Step 5. For **Type of Calculation**, select **Input probability and calculate values**

Step 6. For **Percentile Options** under **Calculations**:

Select **Left tail probability**

Enter *.1* in the **Probability:** box of **Input**

Figure JMP 6.7 shows the output from the JMP Probability Distribution Calculator. The output indicates that the probability of a tire lasting 30,092.24 miles or less is .1. Figure JMP 6.7 also shows us visually that we are using the area under the curve to the left of 30,092.24 because we chose Left tail probability in Step 6. If we had instead chosen **Right tail probability** in Step 6, JMP would give us the mileage such that 10% of the tires would last that many miles or more.

FIGURE JMP 6.6   Using JMP Probability Distribution Calculator to Calculate Cumulative Probability for Normal Distribution

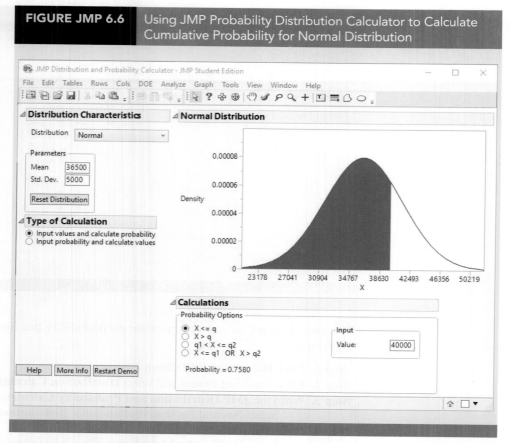

FIGURE JMP 6.7   Using JMP Probability Distribution Calculator to Calculate Inverse Normal Probability Value

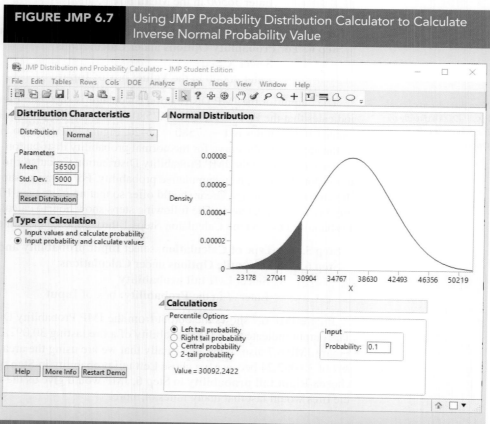

Appendix 6.2 Continuous Probability Distributions with Excel

Excel provides the capability for computing probabilities for several continuous probability distributions, including the normal and exponential probability distributions. In this appendix, we describe how Excel can be used to compute probabilities for any normal distribution. The procedures for the exponential and other continuous distributions are similar to the one we describe for the normal distribution.

Let us return to the Grear Tire Company problem where the tire mileage was described by a normal distribution with $\mu = 36{,}500$ and $\sigma = 5000$. Assume we are interested in the probability that tire mileage will exceed 40,000 miles.

Excel's NORM.DIST function can be used to compute cumulative probabilities for a normal distribution. The general form of the function is NORM.DIST(x, μ, σ, *cumulative*). For the fourth argument *(cumulative)*, TRUE is specified if a cumulative probability is desired. Thus, to compute the cumulative probability that the tire mileage will be less than or equal to 40,000 miles we would enter the following formula into any cell of an Excel worksheet:

$$=NORM.DIST(40000,36500,5000,TRUE)$$

At this point, .7580 will appear in the cell where the formula was entered, indicating that the probability of tire mileage being less than or equal to 40,000 miles is .7580. Therefore, the probability that tire mileage will exceed 40,000 miles is $1 - .7580 = .2420$.

Excel's NORM.INV function uses an inverse computation to find the x value corresponding to a given cumulative probability. For instance, suppose we want to find the guaranteed mileage Grear should offer so that no more than 10% of the tires will be eligible for the guarantee. We would enter the following formula into any cell of an Excel worksheet:

$$=NORM.INV(.1,36500,5000)$$

At this point, 30092 will appear in the cell where the formula was entered, indicating that the probability of a tire lasting 30,092 miles or less is .10.

The Excel function for computing exponential probabilities is EXPON.DIST. This function requires three inputs: x, the value of the variable; *lambda*, which is $1/\mu$, and TRUE if you would like the cumulative probability. For example, consider an exponential probability distribution with mean $\mu = 15$. The probability that the exponential variable is less than or equal to 6 can be computed by the Excel formula

$$=EXPON.DIST(6,1/15,TRUE)$$

At this point, .3297 will appear in the cell where the formula was entered, indicating that the probability the exponential variable will be less than or equal to 6 is .3297. If you need help inserting functions in a worksheet, Excel's Insert Function dialog box may be used (see Appendix E).

Chapter 7

Sampling and Sampling Distributions

CONTENTS

STATISTICS IN PRACTICE: *MEADWESTVACO CORPORATION*

STATISTICS IN PRACTICE

Meadwestvaco Corporation*

STAMFORD, CONNECTICUT

MeadWestvaco Corporation, a leading producer of pack-aging, coated and specialty papers, and specialty chem-icals, employs more than 17,000 people. It operates worldwide in 30 countries and serves customers located in approximately 100 countries. MeadWestvaco's internal consulting group uses sampling to provide a variety of information that enables the company to obtain signifi-cant productivity benefits and remain competitive.

For example, MeadWestvaco maintains large wood-land holdings, which supply the trees, or raw material, for many of the company's products. Managers need reliable and accurate information about the timberlands and for-ests to evaluate the company's ability to meet its future raw material needs. What is the present volume in the forests? What is the past growth of the forests? What is the projected future growth of the forests? With answers to these important questions MeadWestvaco's managers can develop plans for the future, including long-term planting and harvesting schedules for the trees.

How does MeadWestvaco obtain the information it needs about its vast forest holdings? Data collected from sample plots throughout the forests are the basis for learning about the population of trees owned by the company. To identify the sample plots, the timberland holdings are first divided into three sections based on location and types of trees. Using maps and random numbers, MeadWestvaco analysts identify random samples of 1/5- to 1/7-acre plots in each section of the forest. MeadWestvaco foresters collect data from these sample plots to learn about the forest population.

Random sampling of its forest holdings enables Mead-Westvaco Corporation to meet future raw material needs.
Source: Walter Hodges/CORBIS

Foresters throughout the organization participate in the field data collection process. Periodically, two-per-son teams gather information on each tree in every sam-ple plot. The sample data are entered into the company's continuous forest inventory (CFI) computer system. Re-ports from the CFI system include a number of frequency distribution summaries containing statistics on types of trees, present forest volume, past forest growth rates, and projected future forest growth and volume. Sampling and the associated statistical summaries of the sample data provide the reports essential for the effective manage-ment of MeadWestvaco's forests and timberlands.

In this chapter you will learn about simple random sampling and the sample selection process. In addition, you will learn how statistics such as the sample mean and sample proportion are used to estimate the popu-lation mean and population proportion. The important concept of a sampling distribution is also introduced.

*The authors are indebted to Dr. Edward P. Winkofsky for providing the context for this Statistics in Practice.

In Chapter 1 we presented the following definitions of an element, a population, and a sample.

- An *element* is the entity on which data are collected.
- A *population* is the collection of all the elements of interest.
- A *sample* is a subset of the population.

The reason we select a sample is to collect data to make an inference and answer research questions about a population.

Let us begin by citing two examples in which sampling was used to answer a research question about a population.

1. Members of a political party in Texas are considering supporting a particular candidate for election to the U.S. Senate, and party leaders want to estimate the proportion of registered voters in the state who favor the candidate. A sample of 400 registered voters in Texas is selected and 160 of the 400 sampled voters indicate a preference for the candidate. Thus, an estimate of the proportion of the population of registered voters favoring the candidate is 160/400 = .40.
2. A tire manufacturer is considering producing a new tire designed to provide an increase in mileage over the firm's current line of tires. To estimate the mean useful life of the new tires, the manufacturer produced a sample of 120 tires for testing. The test results provided a sample mean of 36,500 miles. Hence, an estimate of the mean useful life for the population of new tires was 36,500 miles.

A sample mean provides an estimate of a population mean, and a sample proportion provides an estimate of a population proportion. With estimates such as these, some estimation error can be expected. This chapter provides the basis for determining how large that error might be.

It is important to realize that sample results provide only *estimates* of the values of the corresponding population characteristics. We do not expect exactly .40, or 40%, of the population of registered voters to favor the candidate, nor do we expect the sample mean of 36,500 miles to exactly equal the mean mileage for the population of all new tires produced. The reason is simply that the sample contains only a portion of the population. Some sampling error is to be expected. With proper sampling methods, the sample results will provide "good" estimates of the population parameters. But how good can we expect the sample results to be? Fortunately, statistical procedures are available for answering this question.

Let us define some of the terms used in sampling. The **sampled population** is the population from which the sample is drawn, and a **frame** is a list of the elements that the sample will be selected from. In the first example, the sampled population is all registered voters in Texas, and the frame is a list of all the registered voters. Because the number of registered voters in Texas is a finite number, the first example is an illustration of sampling from a finite population. In Section 7.2, we discuss how a simple random sample can be selected when sampling from a finite population.

The sampled population for the tire mileage example is more difficult to define because the sample of 120 tires is obtained from a production process at a particular point in time. We can think of the sampled population as the conceptual population of all the tires that could have been made by the production process at that particular point in time. In this sense the sampled population is considered infinite, making it impossible to construct a frame to draw the sample from. In Section 7.2, we discuss how to select a random sample in such a situation.

In this chapter, we show how simple random sampling can be used to select a sample from a finite population and describe how a random sample can be taken from an infinite population that is generated by an ongoing process. We then show how data obtained from a sample can be used to compute estimates of a population mean, a population standard deviation, and a population proportion. In addition, we introduce the important concept of a sampling distribution. As we will show, knowledge of the appropriate sampling distribution enables us to make statements about how close the sample estimates are to the corresponding population parameters. The last two sections discuss some alternatives to simple random sampling that are often employed in practice and the ramifications of large samples on sampling distributions.

7.1 The Electronics Associates Sampling Problem

The director of personnel for Electronics Associates, Inc. (EAI), has been assigned the task of developing a profile of the company's 2500 managers. The characteristics to be identified include the mean annual salary for the managers and the proportion of managers having completed the company's management training program.

Using the 2500 managers as the population for this study, we can find the annual salary and the training program status for each individual by referring to the firm's personnel records. The data set containing this information for all 2500 managers in the population is in the file named EAI.

DATA *file*

EAI

Using the EAI data and the formulas presented in Chapter 3, we computed the population mean and the population standard deviation for the annual salary data.

$$\text{Population mean:}\quad \mu = \$71{,}800$$
$$\text{Population standard deviation:}\quad \sigma = \$4000$$

The data for the training program status show that 1500 of the 2500 managers completed the training program.

Numerical characteristics of a population are called **parameters**. Letting p denote the proportion of the population that completed the training program, we see that $p = 1500/2500 = .60$. The population mean annual salary ($\mu = \$71{,}800$), the population standard deviation of annual salary ($\sigma = \$4000$), and the population proportion that completed the training program ($p = .60$) are parameters of the population of EAI managers.

Now, suppose that the necessary information on all the EAI managers was not readily available in the company's database. The question we now consider is how the firm's director of personnel can obtain estimates of the population parameters by using a sample of managers rather than all 2500 managers in the population. Suppose that a sample of 30 managers will be used. Clearly, the time and the cost of developing a profile would be substantially less for 30 managers than for the entire population. If the personnel director could be assured that a sample of 30 managers would provide adequate information about the population of 2500 managers, working with a sample would be preferable to working with the entire population. Let us explore the possibility of using a sample for the EAI study by first considering how we can identify a sample of 30 managers.

Often the cost of collecting information from a sample is substantially less than from a population, especially when personal interviews must be conducted to collect the information.

7.2 Selecting a Sample

In this section we describe how to select a sample. We first describe how to sample from a finite population and then describe how to select a sample from an infinite population.

Sampling from a Finite Population

Statisticians recommend selecting a probability sample when sampling from a finite population because a probability sample allows them to make valid statistical inferences about the population. The simplest type of probability sample is one in which each sample of size n has the same probability of being selected. It is called a simple random sample. A simple random sample of size n from a finite population of size N is defined as follows.

Other methods of probability sampling are described in Section 7.8

SIMPLE RANDOM SAMPLE (FINITE POPULATION)

A **simple random sample** of size n from a finite population of size N is a sample selected such that each possible sample of size n has the same probability of being selected.

We describe how Excel and JMP can be used to generate a simple random sample in the chapter appendixes.

One procedure for selecting a simple random sample from a finite population is to use a table of random numbers to choose the elements for the sample one at a time in such a way that, at each step, each of the elements remaining in the population has the same probability of being selected. Sampling n elements in this way will satisfy the definition of a simple random sample from a finite population.

To select a simple random sample from the finite population of EAI managers, we first construct a frame by assigning each manager a number. For example, we can assign the managers the numbers 1 to 2500 in the order that their names appear in the EAI personnel file. Next, we refer to the table of random numbers shown in Table 7.1. Using the first row of the table, each digit, 6, 3, 2, . . . , is a random digit having an equal chance of occurring. Because the largest number in the population list of EAI managers, 2500, has four digits, we will select random numbers from the table in sets or groups of four digits. Even though

TABLE 7.1		Random Numbers							
63271	59986	71744	51102	15141	80714	58683	93108	13554	79945
88547	09896	95436	79115	08303	01041	20030	63754	08459	28364
55957	57243	83865	09911	19761	66535	40102	26646	60147	15702
46276	87453	44790	67122	45573	84358	21625	16999	13385	22782
55363	07449	34835	15290	76616	67191	12777	21861	68689	03263
69393	92785	49902	58447	42048	30378	87618	26933	40640	16281
13186	29431	88190	04588	38733	81290	89541	70290	40113	08243
17726	28652	56836	78351	47327	18518	92222	55201	27340	10493
36520	64465	05550	30157	82242	29520	69753	72602	23756	54935
81628	36100	39254	56835	37636	02421	98063	89641	64953	99337
84649	48968	75215	75498	49539	74240	03466	49292	36401	45525
63291	11618	12613	75055	43915	26488	41116	64531	56827	30825
70502	53225	03655	05915	37140	57051	48393	91322	25653	06543
06426	24771	59935	49801	11082	66762	94477	02494	88215	27191
20711	55609	29430	70165	45406	78484	31639	52009	18873	96927
41990	70538	77191	25860	55204	73417	83920	69468	74972	38712
72452	36618	76298	26678	89334	33938	95567	29380	75906	91807
37042	40318	57099	10528	09925	89773	41335	96244	29002	46453
53766	52875	15987	46962	67342	77592	57651	95508	80033	69828
90585	58955	53122	16025	84299	53310	67380	84249	25348	04332
32001	96293	37203	64516	51530	37069	40261	61374	05815	06714
62606	64324	46354	72157	67248	20135	49804	09226	64419	29457
10078	28073	85389	50324	14500	15562	64165	06125	71353	77669
91561	46145	24177	15294	10061	98124	75732	00815	83452	97355
13091	98112	53959	79607	52244	63303	10413	63839	74762	50289

The random numbers in the table are shown in groups of five for readability.

we may start the selection of random numbers anywhere in the table and move systematically in a direction of our choice, we will use the first row of Table 7.1 and move from left to right. The first 7 four-digit random numbers are

6327	1599	8671	7445	1102	1514	1807

Because the numbers in the table are random, these four-digit numbers are equally likely. We can now use these four-digit random numbers to give each manager in the population an equal chance of being included in the random sample. The first number, 6327, is greater than 2500. It does not correspond to one of the numbered managers in the population, and hence is discarded. The second number, 1599, is between 1 and 2500. Thus the first manager selected for the random sample is number 1599 on the list of EAI managers. Continuing this process, we ignore the numbers 8671 and 7445 before identifying managers number 1102, 1514, and 1807 to be included in the random sample. This process continues until the simple random sample of 30 EAI managers has been obtained.

In implementing this simple random sample selection process, it is possible that a random number used previously may appear again in the table before the complete sample of 30 EAI managers has been selected. Because we do not want to select a manager more than one time, any previously used random numbers are ignored because the corresponding manager is already included in the sample. Selecting a sample in this manner is referred to as **sampling without replacement**. If we selected a sample such that previously used random numbers are acceptable and specific managers could be included in the sample two or more times, we would be **sampling with replacement**. Sampling with replacement is a valid way of identifying a simple random sample. However, sampling without replacement is the sampling procedure used most often in practice. When we refer to simple random sampling, we will assume the sampling is without replacement.

Sampling from an Infinite Population

Sometimes we want to select a sample from a population, but the population is infinitely large or the elements of the population are being generated by an ongoing process for which there is no limit on the number of elements that can be generated. Thus, it is not possible to develop a list of all the elements in the population. This is considered the infinite population case. With an infinite population, we cannot select a simple random sample because we cannot construct a frame consisting of all the elements. In the infinite population case, statisticians recommend selecting what is called a random sample.

RANDOM SAMPLE (INFINITE POPULATION)

A **random sample** of size n from an infinite population is a sample selected such that the following conditions are satisfied.

1. Each element selected comes from the same population.
2. Each element is selected independently.

Care and judgment must be exercised in implementing the selection process for obtaining a random sample from an infinite population. Each case may require a different selection procedure. Let us consider two examples to see what we mean by the conditions (1) each element selected comes from the same population and (2) each element is selected independently.

A common quality control application involves a production process where there is no limit on the number of elements that can be produced. The conceptual population we are sampling from is all the elements that could be produced (not just the ones that are produced) by the ongoing production process. Because we cannot develop a list of all the elements that could be produced, the population is considered infinite. To be more specific, let us consider a production line designed to fill boxes of a breakfast cereal with a mean weight of 24 ounces of breakfast cereal per box. Samples of 12 boxes filled by this process are periodically selected by a quality control inspector to determine if the process is operating properly or if, perhaps, a machine malfunction has caused the process to begin underfilling or overfilling the boxes.

With a production operation such as this, the biggest concern in selecting a random sample is to make sure that condition 1, the sampled elements are selected from the same population, is satisfied. To ensure that this condition is satisfied, the boxes must be selected at approximately the same point in time. This way the inspector avoids the possibility of selecting some boxes when the process is operating properly and other boxes when the process is not operating properly and is underfilling or overfilling the boxes. With a production process such as this, the second condition, each element is selected independently, is satisfied by designing the production process so that each box of cereal is filled independently. With this assumption, the quality control inspector only needs to worry about satisfying the same population condition.

As another example of selecting a random sample from an infinite population, consider the population of customers arriving at a fast-food restaurant. Suppose an employee is asked to select and interview a sample of customers in order to develop a profile of customers who visit the restaurant. The customer arrival process is ongoing and there is no way to obtain a list of all customers in the population. So, for practical purposes, the population for this ongoing process is considered infinite. As long as a sampling procedure is designed so that all the elements in the sample are customers of the restaurant and they are selected independently, a random sample will be obtained. In this case, the employee collecting the sample needs to select the sample from people who come into the restaurant and make a purchase to ensure that the same population condition is satisfied. If, for instance, the employee selected someone for the sample who came into the restaurant just to use the restroom, that person would not be a customer and the same population condition would be violated. So, as long as the interviewer selects the sample from people making a purchase at the restaurant, condition 1 is satisfied. Ensuring that the customers are selected independently can be more difficult.

The purpose of the second condition of the random sample selection procedure (each element is selected independently) is to prevent selection bias. In this case, selection bias would occur if the interviewer were free to select customers for the sample arbitrarily. The interviewer might feel more comfortable selecting customers in a particular age group and might avoid customers in other age groups. Selection bias would also occur if the interviewer selected a group of five customers who entered the restaurant together and asked all of them to participate in the sample. Such a group of customers would be likely to exhibit similar characteristics, which might provide misleading information about the population of customers. Selection bias such as this can be avoided by ensuring that the selection of a particular customer does not influence the selection of any other customer. In other words, the elements (customers) are selected independently.

McDonald's, the fast-food restaurant leader, implemented a random sampling procedure for this situation. The sampling procedure was based on the fact that some customers presented discount coupons. Whenever a customer presented a discount coupon, the next customer served was asked to complete a customer profile questionnaire. Because arriving customers presented discount coupons randomly and independently of other customers, this sampling procedure ensured that customers were selected independently. As a result, the sample satisfied the requirements of a random sample from an infinite population.

Situations involving sampling from an infinite population are usually associated with a process that operates over time. Examples include parts being manufactured on a production line, repeated experimental trials in a laboratory, transactions occurring at a bank, telephone calls arriving at a technical support center, and customers entering a retail store. In each case, the situation may be viewed as a process that generates elements from an infinite population. As long as the sampled elements are selected from the same population and are selected independently, the sample is considered a random sample from an infinite population.

NOTES + COMMENTS

1. In this section we have been careful to define two types of samples: a simple random sample from a finite population and a random sample from an infinite population. In the remainder of the text, we will generally refer to both of these as either a *random sample* or simply a *sample*. We will not make a distinction of the sample being a "simple" random sample unless it is necessary for the exercise or discussion.

2. Statisticians who specialize in sample surveys from finite populations use sampling methods that provide probability samples. With a probability sample, each possible sample has a known probability of selection and a random process is used to select the elements for the sample. Simple random sampling is one of these methods. In Section 7.8, we describe some other probability sampling methods: stratified random sampling, cluster sampling, and systematic sampling. We use the term "simple" in simple random sampling to clarify that this is the probability sampling method that assures each sample of size n has the same probability of being selected.

3. The number of different simple random samples of size n that can be selected from a finite population of size N is

$$\frac{N!}{n!(N-n)!}$$

In this formula, $N!$ and $n!$ are the factorial formulas discussed in Chapter 4. For the EAI problem with $N = 2500$ and $n = 30$, this expression can be used to show that approximately 2.75×10^{69} different simple random samples of 30 EAI managers can be obtained.

EXERCISES

Methods

1. Consider a finite population with five elements labeled A, B, C, D, and E. Ten possible simple random samples of size 2 can be selected.
   a. List the 10 samples beginning with AB, AC, and so on.
   b. Using simple random sampling, what is the probability that each sample of size 2 is selected?
   c. Assume random number 1 corresponds to A, random number 2 corresponds to B, and so on. List the simple random sample of size 2 that will be selected by using the random digits 8 0 5 7 5 3 2.

2. Assume a finite population has 350 elements. Using the last three digits of each of the following five-digit random numbers (e.g., 601, 022, 448, . . .), determine the first four elements that will be selected for the simple random sample.

   98601   73022   83448   02147   34229   27553   84147   93289   14209

Applications

3. **Industrial Stock Performance.** *Fortune* publishes data on sales, profits, assets, stockholders' equity, market value, and earnings per share for the 500 largest U.S. industrial corporations every year. Assume that you want to select a simple random sample of 10 corporations from the *Fortune* 500 list. Use the last three digits in column 9 of Table 7.1, beginning with 554. Read down the column and identify the numbers of the 10 corporations that would be selected.

4. **Investigating Trading Practices.** The 10 most active stocks on the New York Stock Exchange for a given week, are shown here.

AT&T	Alcatel Lucent	Exxon Mobile	Petrobras	Vale SA
Pfizer	Verizon	Gen. Elect.	Citigroup	Ford

   Exchange authorities decided to investigate trading practices using a sample of three of these stocks.
   a. Beginning with the first random digit in column 6 of Table 7.1, read down the column to select a simple random sample of three stocks for the exchange authorities.
   b. Using the information in the third Note and Comment, determine how many different simple random samples of size 3 can be selected from the list of 10 stocks.

5. **Pass–Fail Grading.** A student government organization is interested in estimating the proportion of students who favor a mandatory "pass-fail" grading policy for elective courses. A list of names and addresses of the 645 students enrolled during the current quarter is available from the registrar's office. Using three-digit random numbers in row 10 of Table 7.1 and moving across the row from left to right, identify the first 10 students who would be selected using simple random sampling. The three-digit random numbers begin with 816, 283, and 610.

6. **Census Bureau County Data.** The *County and City Data Book,* published by the Census Bureau, lists information on 3139 counties throughout the United States. Assume that a national study will collect data from 30 randomly selected counties. Use four-digit random numbers from the last column of Table 7.1 to identify the numbers corresponding to the first five counties selected for the sample. Ignore the first digits and begin with the four-digit random numbers 9945, 8364, 5702, and so on.

7. **Sampling Doctors.** Assume that we want to identify a simple random sample of 12 of the 372 doctors practicing in a particular city. The doctors' names are available from a local medical organization. Use the eighth column of five-digit random numbers in Table 7.1 to identify the 12 doctors for the sample. Ignore the first two random digits in each five-digit grouping of the random numbers. This process begins with random number 108 and proceeds down the column of random numbers.

8. **DJIA Stocks.** The following stocks make up the Dow Jones Industrial Average.

1. 3M	11. Exxon Mobil	21. Microsoft
2. American Express	12. General Electric	22. Nike
3. Apple	13. Goldman Sachs	23. Pfizer
4. Boeing	14. Home Depot	24. Procter & Gamble
5. Caterpillar	15. IBM	25. Travelers Companies, Inc.
6. Chevron	16. Intel	26. United Technologies
7. Cisco	17. Johnson & Johnson	27. UnitedHealth
8. Coca-Cola	18. JP Morgan Chase	28. Verizon
9. Disney	19. McDonald's	29. Visa
10. DowDuPont, Inc.	20. Merck	30. Wal-Mart

Suppose you would like to select a sample of six of these companies to conduct an in-depth study of management practices. Use the first two digits in each row of the ninth column of Table 7.1 to select a simple random sample of six companies.

9. **Returns on Mutual Finds.** *The Wall Street Journal* provides the net asset value, the year-to-date percent return, and the three-year percent return for 882 mutual funds at the end of 2017. Assume that a simple random sample of 12 of the 882 mutual funds will be selected for a follow-up study on the size and performance of mutual funds. Use the fourth column of the random numbers in Table 7.1, beginning with 51102, to select the simple random sample of 12 mutual funds. Begin with mutual fund 102 and use the *last* three digits in each row of the fourth column for your selection process. What are the numbers of the 12 mutual funds in the simple random sample?

10. **Sampling from Infinite Populations.** Indicate which of the following situations involve sampling from a finite population and which involve sampling from an infinite population. In cases where the sampled population is finite, describe how you would construct a frame.
   a. Obtain a sample of licensed drivers in the state of New York.
   b. Obtain a sample of boxes of cereal produced by the Breakfast Choice company.
   c. Obtain a sample of cars crossing the Golden Gate Bridge on a typical weekday.
   d. Obtain a sample of students in a statistics course at Indiana University.
   e. Obtain a sample of the orders that are processed by a mail-order firm.

7.3 Point Estimation

Now that we have described how to select a simple random sample, let us return to the EAI problem. A simple random sample of 30 managers and the corresponding data on annual salary and management training program participation are as shown in Table 7.2. The notation x_1, x_2, and so on is used to denote the annual salary of the first manager in the sample, the annual salary of the second manager in the sample, and so on. Participation in the management training program is indicated by Yes in the management training program column.

To estimate the value of a population parameter, we compute a corresponding characteristic of the sample, referred to as a **sample statistic**. For example, to estimate the population mean μ and the population standard deviation σ for the annual salary of EAI managers, we use the data in Table 7.2 to calculate the corresponding sample statistics: the sample mean and the sample standard deviation s. Using the formulas for a sample mean and a sample standard deviation presented in Chapter 3, the sample mean is

$$\bar{x} = \frac{\Sigma x_i}{n} = \frac{2{,}154{,}420}{30} = \$71{,}814$$

TABLE 7.2	Annual Salary and Training Program Status for a Simple Random Sample of 30 EAI Managers		
Annual Salary ($)	**Management Training Program**	**Annual Salary ($)**	**Management Training Program**
$x_1 = 69,094.30$	Yes	$x_{16} = 71,766.00$	Yes
$x_2 = 73,263.90$	Yes	$x_{17} = 72,541.30$	No
$x_3 = 69,643.50$	Yes	$x_{18} = 64,980.00$	Yes
$x_4 = 69,894.90$	Yes	$x_{19} = 71,932.60$	Yes
$x_5 = 67,621.60$	No	$x_{20} = 72,973.00$	Yes
$x_6 = 75,924.00$	Yes	$x_{21} = 65,120.90$	Yes
$x_7 = 69,092.30$	Yes	$x_{22} = 71,753.00$	Yes
$x_8 = 71,404.40$	Yes	$x_{23} = 74,391.80$	No
$x_9 = 70,957.70$	Yes	$x_{24} = 70,164.20$	No
$x_{10} = 75,109.70$	Yes	$x_{25} = 72,973.60$	No
$x_{11} = 65,922.60$	Yes	$x_{26} = 70,241.30$	No
$x_{12} = 77,268.40$	No	$x_{27} = 72,793.90$	No
$x_{13} = 75,688.80$	Yes	$x_{28} = 70,979.40$	Yes
$x_{14} = 71,564.70$	No	$x_{29} = 75,860.90$	Yes
$x_{15} = 76,188.20$	No	$x_{30} = 77,309.10$	No

and the sample standard deviation is

$$s = \sqrt{\frac{\Sigma(x_i - \bar{x})^2}{n-1}} = \sqrt{\frac{325,009,260}{29}} = \$3348$$

To estimate p, the proportion of managers in the population who completed the management training program, we use the corresponding sample proportion $\bar{p}$. Let x denote the number of managers in the sample who completed the management training program. The data in Table 7.2 show that $x = 19$. Thus, with a sample size of $n = 30$, the sample proportion is

$$\bar{p} = \frac{x}{n} = \frac{19}{30} = .63$$

By making the preceding computations, we perform the statistical procedure called *point estimation*. We refer to the sample mean $\bar{x}$ as the **point estimator** of the population mean μ, the sample standard deviation s as the point estimator of the population standard deviation σ, and the sample proportion $\bar{p}$ as the point estimator of the population proportion p. The numerical value obtained for $\bar{x}$, s, or $\bar{p}$ is called the **point estimate**. Thus, for the simple random sample of 30 EAI managers shown in Table 7.2, \$71,814 is the point estimate of μ, \$3348 is the point estimate of σ, and .63 is the point estimate of p. Table 7.3 summarizes the sample results and compares the point estimates to the actual values of the population parameters.

As is evident from Table 7.3, the point estimates differ somewhat from the corresponding population parameters. This difference is to be expected because a sample, and not a census of the entire population, is being used to develop the point estimates. In the next chapter, we will show how to construct an interval estimate in order to provide information about how close the point estimate is to the population parameter.

TABLE 7.3	Summary of Point Estimates Obtained from a Simple Random Sample of 30 EAI Managers		
Population Parameter	**Parameter Value**	**Point Estimator**	**Point Estimate**
μ = Population mean annual salary	$71,800	$\bar{x}$ = Sample mean annual salary	$71,814
σ = Population standard deviation for annual salary	$4000	s = Sample standard deviation for annual salary	$3348
p = Population proportion having completed the management training program	.60	$\bar{p}$ = Sample proportion having completed the management training program	.63

Practical Advice

The subject matter of most of the rest of the book is concerned with statistical inference. Point estimation is a form of statistical inference. We use a sample statistic to make an inference about a population parameter. When making inferences about a population based on a sample, it is important to have a close correspondence between the sampled population and the target population. The **target population** is the population we want to make inferences about, while the sampled population is the population from which the sample is actually taken. In this section, we have described the process of drawing a simple random sample from the population of EAI managers and making point estimates of characteristics of that same population. So the sampled population and the target population are identical, which is the desired situation. But in other cases, it is not as easy to obtain a close correspondence between the sampled and target populations.

Consider the case of an amusement park selecting a sample of its customers to learn about characteristics such as age and time spent at the park. Suppose all the sample elements were selected on a day when park attendance was restricted to employees of a single company. Then the sampled population would be composed of employees of that company and members of their families. If the target population we wanted to make inferences about were typical park customers over a typical summer, then we might encounter a significant difference between the sampled population and the target population. In such a case, we would question the validity of the point estimates being made. Park management would be in the best position to know whether a sample taken on a particular day was likely to be representative of the target population.

In summary, whenever a sample is used to make inferences about a population, we should make sure that the study is designed so that the sampled population and the target population are in close agreement. Good judgment is a necessary ingredient of sound statistical practice.

EXERCISES

Methods

11. The following data are from a simple random sample.

    5   8   10   7   10   14

    a. What is the point estimate of the population mean?
    b. What is the point estimate of the population standard deviation?

12. A survey question for a sample of 150 individuals yielded 75 Yes responses, 55 No responses, and 20 No Opinions.
    a. What is the point estimate of the proportion in the population who respond Yes?
    b. What is the point estimate of the proportion in the population who respond No?

Applications

13. **Monthly Sales Data.** A sample of 5 months of sales data provided the following information:

Month:	1	2	3	4	5
Units Sold:	94	100	85	94	92

    a. Develop a point estimate of the population mean number of units sold per month.
    b. Develop a point estimate of the population standard deviation.

DATA *file*

Morningstar

14. **Morningstar Stock Data.** Morningstar publishes ratings data on 1208 company stocks. A sample of 40 of these stocks is contained in the file *Morningstar*. Use the Morningstar data set to answer the following questions.
    a. Develop a point estimate of the proportion of the stocks that receive Morningstar's highest rating of 5 Stars.
    b. Develop a point estimate of the proportion of the Morningstar stocks that are rated Above Average with respect to business risk.
    c. Develop a point estimate of the proportion of the Morningstar stocks that are rated 2 Stars or less.

15. **Rating Wines.** According to Wine-Searcher, wine critics generally use a wine-scoring scale to communicate their opinions on the relative quality of wines. Wine scores range from 0 to 100, with a score of 95–100 indicating a great wine, 90–94 indicating an outstanding wine, 85–89 indicating a very good wine, 80–84 indicating a good wine, 75–79 indicating a mediocre wine, and below 75 indicating that the wine is not recommended. Random ratings of a pinot noir recently produced by a newly established vineyard in 2018 follow:

87	91	86	82	72	91
60	77	80	79	83	96

    a. Develop a point estimate of mean wine score for this pinot noir.
    b. Develop a point estimate of the standard deviation for wine scores received by this pinot noir.

16. **AARP Survey.** In a sample of 426 U.S. adults age 50 and older, AARP asked how important a variety of issues were in choosing whom to vote for in the next presidential election.
    a. What is the sampled population for this study?
    b. Social Security and Medicare was cited as "very important" by 350 respondents. Estimate the proportion of the population of U.S. adults age 50 and over who believe this issue is very important.
    c. Education was cited as "very important" by 74% of the respondents. Estimate the number of respondents who believe this issue is very important.
    d. Job Growth was cited as "very important" by 354 respondents. Estimate the proportion of U.S. adults age 50 and over who believe job growth is very important.
    e. What is the target population for the inferences being made in parts (b) and (d)? Is it the same as the sampled population you identified in part (a)? Suppose you later learn that the sample was restricted to members of the American Association of Retired People (AARP). Would you still feel the inferences being made in parts (b) and (d) are valid? Why or why not?

17. **Attitudes Toward Automation.** The Pew American Trends Survey includes a series of questions on attitudes toward automation. The May 2018 results showed that 2977 of 4135 respondents are worried about a future in which robots and computers can do many human jobs, 2770 are worried about the development of algorithms that can evaluate and hire job candidates, and 2233 are worried about the development of driverless vehicles.

a. Develop a point estimate of the proportion of respondents who are worried about a future in which robots and computers can do many human jobs.
b. Develop a point estimate of the proportion of respondents who are worried about the development of algorithms that can evaluate and hire job candidates.
c. Develop a point estimate of the proportion of respondents who are worried about the development of driverless vehicles.

7.4 Introduction to Sampling Distributions

In the preceding section we said that the sample mean $\bar{x}$ is the point estimator of the population mean μ, and the sample proportion $\bar{p}$ is the point estimator of the population proportion p. For the simple random sample of 30 EAI managers shown in Table 7.2, the point estimate of μ is $\bar{x} = \$71,814$ and the point estimate of p is $\bar{p} = .63$. Suppose we select another simple random sample of 30 EAI managers and obtain the following point estimates:

$$\text{Sample mean: } \bar{x} = \$72,670$$
$$\text{Sample proportion: } \bar{p} = .70$$

Note that different values of $\bar{x}$ and $\bar{p}$ were obtained. Indeed, a second simple random sample of 30 EAI managers cannot be expected to provide the same point estimates as the first sample.

The ability to understand the material in subsequent chapters depends heavily on the ability to understand and use the sampling distributions presented in this chapter.

Now, suppose we repeat the process of selecting a simple random sample of 30 EAI managers over and over again, each time computing the values of $\bar{x}$ and $\bar{p}$. Table 7.4 contains a portion of the results obtained for 500 simple random samples, and Table 7.5 shows the frequency and relative frequency distributions for the 500 $\bar{x}$ values. Figure 7.1 shows the relative frequency histogram for the $\bar{x}$ values.

In Chapter 5 we defined a random variable as a numerical description of the outcome of an experiment. If we consider the process of selecting a simple random sample as an experiment, the sample mean $\bar{x}$ is the numerical description of the outcome of the experiment. Thus, the sample mean $\bar{x}$ is a random variable. As a result, just like other random variables, $\bar{x}$ has a mean or expected value, a standard deviation, and a probability distribution. Because the various possible values of $\bar{x}$ are the result of different simple random samples, the probability distribution of $\bar{x}$ is called the **sampling distribution** of $\bar{x}$. Knowledge of this sampling distribution and its properties will enable us to make probability statements about how close the sample mean $\bar{x}$ is to the population mean μ.

Let us return to Figure 7.1. We would need to enumerate every possible sample of 30 managers and compute each sample mean to completely determine the sampling distribution of $\bar{x}$. However, the histogram of 500 $\bar{x}$ values gives an approximation of this

TABLE 7.4	Values of $\bar{x}$ and $\bar{p}$ from 500 Simple Random Samples of 30 EAI Managers		
Sample Number		**Sample Mean ($\bar{x}$)**	**Sample Proportion ($\bar{p}$)**
1		71,814	.63
2		72,670	.70
3		71,780	.67
4		71,588	.53
.		.	.
.		.	.
.		.	.
500		71,752	.50

TABLE 7.5	Frequency and Relative Frequency Distributions of $\bar{x}$ from 500 Simple Random Samples of 30 EAI Managers

Mean Annual Salary ($)	Frequency	Relative Frequency
69,500.00–69,999.99	2	.004
70,000.00–70,499.99	16	.032
70,500.00–70,999.99	52	.104
71,000.00–71,499.99	101	.202
71,500.00–71,999.99	133	.266
72,000.00–72,499.99	110	.220
72,500.00–72,999.99	54	.108
73,000.00–73,499.99	26	.052
73,500.00–73,999.99	6	.012
Totals	500	1.000

FIGURE 7.1	Relative Frequency Histogram of $\bar{x}$ Values from 500 Simple Random Samples of Size 30 Each

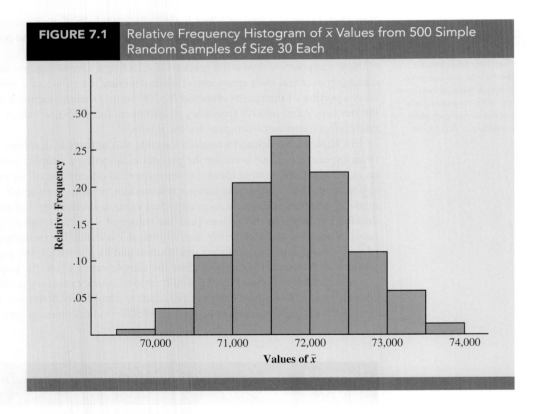

sampling distribution. From the approximation we observe the bell-shaped appearance of the distribution. We note that the largest concentration of the $\bar{x}$ values and the mean of the 500 $\bar{x}$ values are near the population mean $\mu = \$71,800$. We will describe the properties of the sampling distribution of $\bar{x}$ more fully in the next section.

The 500 values of the sample proportion $\bar{p}$ are summarized by the relative frequency histogram in Figure 7.2. As in the case of $\bar{x}$, $\bar{p}$ is a random variable. If every possible sample of size 30 were selected from the population and if a value of $\bar{p}$ were computed for each sample, the resulting probability distribution would be the sampling distribution of $\bar{p}$. The relative frequency histogram of the 500 sample values in Figure 7.2 provides a general idea of the appearance of the sampling distribution of $\bar{p}$.

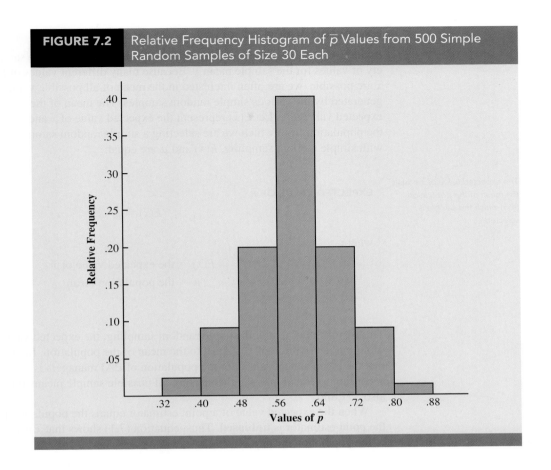

FIGURE 7.2 Relative Frequency Histogram of $\bar{p}$ Values from 500 Simple Random Samples of Size 30 Each

In practice, we select only one simple random sample from the population. We repeated the sampling process 500 times in this section simply to illustrate that many different samples are possible and that the different samples generate a variety of values for the sample statistics $\bar{x}$ and $\bar{p}$. The probability distribution of any particular sample statistic is called the sampling distribution of the statistic. In Section 7.5 we show the characteristics of the sampling distribution of $\bar{x}$. In Section 7.6 we show the characteristics of the sampling distribution of $\bar{p}$.

7.5 Sampling Distribution of $\bar{x}$

In the previous section we said that the sample mean $\bar{x}$ is a random variable and its probability distribution is called the sampling distribution of $\bar{x}$.

SAMPLING DISTRIBUTION OF $\bar{x}$

The sampling distribution of $\bar{x}$ is the probability distribution of all possible values of the sample mean $\bar{x}$.

This section describes the properties of the sampling distribution of $\bar{x}$. Just as with other probability distributions we studied, the sampling distribution of $\bar{x}$ has an expected value or mean, a standard deviation, and a characteristic shape or form. Let us begin by considering the mean of all possible $\bar{x}$ values, which is referred to as the expected value of $\bar{x}$.

Expected Value of $\bar{x}$

In the EAI sampling problem we saw that different simple random samples result in a variety of values for the sample mean $\bar{x}$. Because many different values of the random variable $\bar{x}$ are possible, we are often interested in the mean of all possible values of $\bar{x}$ that can be generated by the various simple random samples. The mean of the $\bar{x}$ random variable is the expected value of $\bar{x}$. Let $E(\bar{x})$ represent the expected value of $\bar{x}$ and μ represent the mean of the population from which we are selecting a simple random sample. It can be shown that with simple random sampling, $E(\bar{x})$ and μ are equal.

The expected value of $\bar{x}$ equals the mean of the population from which the sample is selected.

EXPECTED VALUE OF $\bar{x}$

$$E(\bar{x}) = \mu \tag{7.1}$$

where

$$E(\bar{x}) = \text{the expected value of } \bar{x}$$
$$\mu = \text{the population mean}$$

This result shows that with simple random sampling, the expected value or mean of the sampling distribution of $\bar{x}$ is equal to the mean of the population. In Section 7.1 we saw that the mean annual salary for the population of EAI managers is $\mu = \$71,800$. Thus, according to equation (7.1), the mean of all possible sample means for the EAI study is also $71,800.

When the expected value of a point estimator equals the population parameter, we say the point estimator is **unbiased**. Thus, equation (7.1) shows that $\bar{x}$ is an unbiased estimator of the population mean μ.

Standard Deviation of $\bar{x}$

Let us define the standard deviation of the sampling distribution of $\bar{x}$. We will use the following notation.

$$\sigma_{\bar{x}} = \text{the standard deviation of } \bar{x}$$
$$\sigma = \text{the standard deviation of the population}$$
$$n = \text{the sample size}$$
$$N = \text{the population size}$$

It can be shown that the formula for the standard deviation of $\bar{x}$ depends on whether the population is finite or infinite. The two formulas for the standard deviation of $\bar{x}$ follow.

STANDARD DEVIATION OF $\bar{x}$

Finite Population	*Infinite Population*	
$\sigma_{\bar{x}} = \sqrt{\dfrac{N-n}{N-1}}\left(\dfrac{\sigma}{\sqrt{n}}\right)$	$\sigma_{\bar{x}} = \dfrac{\sigma}{\sqrt{n}}$	(7.2)

In comparing the two formulas in (7.2), we see that the factor $\sqrt{(N-n)/(N-1)}$ is required for the finite population case but not for the infinite population case. This factor is commonly referred to as the **finite population correction factor**. In many practical sampling situations, we find that the population involved, although finite, is "large," whereas the sample size is relatively "small." In such cases the finite population correction factor $\sqrt{(N-n)/(N-1)}$ is close to 1. As a result, the difference between the values of the standard deviation of $\bar{x}$ for the finite and infinite population cases becomes negligible. Then, $\sigma_{\bar{x}} = \sigma/\sqrt{n}$ becomes a good approximation to the standard deviation of $\bar{x}$ even though the population is finite. This observation leads to the following general guideline, or rule of thumb, for computing the standard deviation of $\bar{x}$.

USE THE FOLLOWING EXPRESSION TO COMPUTE THE STANDARD DEVIATION OF $\bar{x}$

$$\sigma_{\bar{x}} = \frac{\sigma}{\sqrt{n}} \qquad (7.3)$$

whenever

1. The population is infinite; or
2. The population is finite *and* the sample size is less than or equal to 5% of the population size; that is, $n/N \leq .05$.

Problem 21 shows that when $n/N \leq .05$, the finite population correction factor has little effect on the value of $\sigma_{\bar{x}}$.

In cases where $n/N > .05$, the finite population version of formula (7.2) should be used in the computation of $\sigma_{\bar{x}}$. Unless otherwise noted, throughout the text we will assume that the population size is "large," $n/N \leq .05$, and expression (7.3) can be used to compute $\sigma_{\bar{x}}$.

To compute $\sigma_{\bar{x}}$, we need to know σ, the standard deviation of the population. To further emphasize the difference between $\sigma_{\bar{x}}$ and σ, we refer to the standard deviation of $\bar{x}$, $\sigma_{\bar{x}}$, as the **standard error** of the mean. In general, the term *standard error* refers to the standard deviation of a point estimator. Later we will see that the value of the standard error of the mean is helpful in determining how far the sample mean may be from the population mean. Let us now return to the EAI example and compute the standard error of the mean associated with simple random samples of 30 EAI managers.

The term standard error *is used throughout statistical inference to refer to the standard deviation of a point estimator.*

In Section 7.1 we saw that the standard deviation of annual salary for the population of 2500 EAI managers is $\sigma = 4000$. In this case, the population is finite, with $N = 2500$. However, with a sample size of 30, we have $n/N = 30/2500 = .012$. Because the sample size is less than 5% of the population size, we can ignore the finite population correction factor and use equation (7.3) to compute the standard error.

$$\sigma_{\bar{x}} = \frac{\sigma}{\sqrt{n}} = \frac{4000}{\sqrt{30}} = 730.3$$

Form of the Sampling Distribution of $\bar{x}$

The preceding results concerning the expected value and standard deviation for the sampling distribution of $\bar{x}$ are applicable for any population. The final step in identifying the characteristics of the sampling distribution of $\bar{x}$ is to determine the form or shape of the sampling distribution. We will consider two cases: (1) The population has a normal distribution; and (2) the population does not have a normal distribution.

Population has a Normal Distribution In many situations it is reasonable to assume that the population from which we are selecting a random sample has a normal, or nearly normal, distribution. When the population has a normal distribution, the sampling distribution of $\bar{x}$ is normally distributed for any sample size.

Population does not have a Normal Distribution When the population from which we are selecting a random sample does not have a normal distribution, the **central limit theorem** is helpful in identifying the shape of the sampling distribution of $\bar{x}$. A statement of the central limit theorem as it applies to the sampling distribution of $\bar{x}$ follows.

CENTRAL LIMIT THEOREM

In selecting random samples of size n from a population, the sampling distribution of the sample mean $\bar{x}$ can be approximated by a *normal distribution* as the sample size becomes large.

Figure 7.3 shows how the central limit theorem works for three different populations; each column refers to one of the populations. The top panel of the figure shows that none of the populations are normally distributed. Population I follows a uniform distribution. Population II is often called the rabbit-eared distribution. It is symmetric, but the more likely values fall in the tails of the distribution. Population III is shaped like the exponential distribution; it is skewed to the right.

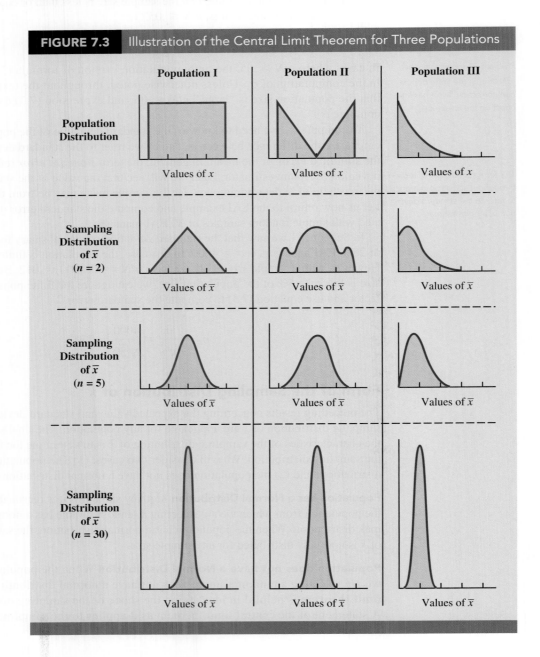

FIGURE 7.3 Illustration of the Central Limit Theorem for Three Populations

The bottom three panels of Figure 7.3 show the shape of the sampling distribution for samples of size $n = 2$, $n = 5$, and $n = 30$. When the sample size is 2, we see that the shape of each sampling distribution is different from the shape of the corresponding population distribution. For samples of size 5, we see that the shapes of the sampling distributions for populations I and II begin to look similar to the shape of a normal distribution. Even though the shape of the sampling distribution for population III begins to look similar to the shape of a normal distribution, some skewness to the right is still present. Finally, for samples of size 30, the shapes of each of the three sampling distributions are approximately normal.

From a practitioner standpoint, we often want to know how large the sample size needs to be before the central limit theorem applies and we can assume that the shape of the sampling distribution is approximately normal. Statistical researchers have investigated this question by studying the sampling distribution of $\bar{x}$ for a variety of populations and a variety of sample sizes. General statistical practice is to assume that, for most applications, the sampling distribution of $\bar{x}$ can be approximated by a normal distribution whenever the sample is size 30 or more. In cases where the population is highly skewed or outliers are present, samples of size 50 may be needed. Finally, if the population is discrete, the sample size needed for a normal approximation often depends on the population proportion. We say more about this issue when we discuss the sampling distribution of $\bar{p}$ in Section 7.6.

Sampling Distribution of $\bar{x}$ for the EAI Problem

Let us return to the EAI problem where we previously showed that $E(\bar{x}) = \$71,800$ and $\sigma_{\bar{x}} = 730.3$. At this point, we do not have any information about the population distribution; it may or may not be normally distributed. If the population has a normal distribution, the sampling distribution of $\bar{x}$ is normally distributed. If the population does not have a normal distribution, the simple random sample of 30 managers and the central limit theorem enable us to conclude that the sampling distribution of $\bar{x}$ can be approximated by a normal distribution. In either case, we are comfortable proceeding with the conclusion that the sampling distribution of $\bar{x}$ can be described by the normal distribution shown in Figure 7.4.

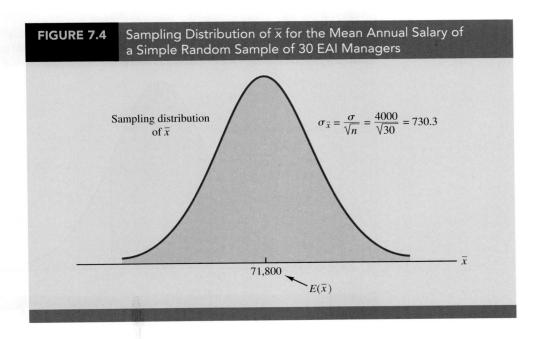

FIGURE 7.4   Sampling Distribution of $\bar{x}$ for the Mean Annual Salary of a Simple Random Sample of 30 EAI Managers

Sampling distribution of $\bar{x}$

$$\sigma_{\bar{x}} = \frac{\sigma}{\sqrt{n}} = \frac{4000}{\sqrt{30}} = 730.3$$

71,800

$E(\bar{x})$

Practical Value of the Sampling Distribution of $\bar{x}$

Whenever a simple random sample is selected and the value of the sample mean is used to estimate the value of the population mean μ, we cannot expect the sample mean to exactly equal the population mean. The practical reason we are interested in the sampling distribution of $\bar{x}$ is that it can be used to provide probability information about the difference between the sample mean and the population mean. To demonstrate this use, let us return to the EAI problem.

Suppose the personnel director believes the sample mean will be an acceptable estimate of the population mean if the sample mean is within $500 of the population mean. However, it is not possible to guarantee that the sample mean will be within $500 of the population mean. Indeed, Table 7.5 and Figure 7.1 show that some of the 500 sample means differed by more than $2000 from the population mean. So we must think of the personnel director's request in probability terms. That is, the personnel director is concerned with the following question: What is the probability that the sample mean computed using a simple random sample of 30 EAI managers will be within $500 of the population mean?

Because we have identified the properties of the sampling distribution of $\bar{x}$ (see Figure 7.4), we will use this distribution to answer the probability question. Refer to the sampling distribution of $\bar{x}$ shown again in Figure 7.5. With a population mean of $71,800, the personnel director wants to know the probability that $\bar{x}$ is between $71,300 and $72,300. This probability is given by the darkly shaded area of the sampling distribution shown in Figure 7.5. Because the sampling distribution is normally distributed, with mean 71,800 and standard error of the mean 730.3, we can use the standard normal probability table to find the area or probability.

We first calculate the z value at the upper endpoint of the interval (72,300) and use the table to find the area under the curve to the left of that point (left tail area). Then we compute the z value at the lower endpoint of the interval (71,300) and use the table to find the area under the curve to the left of that point (another left tail area). Subtracting the second tail area from the first gives us the desired probability.

At $\bar{x} = 72,300$, we have

$$z = \frac{72,300 - 71,800}{730.30} = .68$$

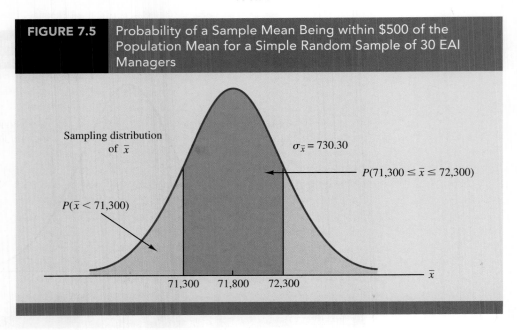

FIGURE 7.5   Probability of a Sample Mean Being within $500 of the Population Mean for a Simple Random Sample of 30 EAI Managers

Referring to the standard normal probability table, we find a cumulative probability (area to the left of $z = .68$) of .7517.

At $\bar{x} = 71,300$, we have

$$z = \frac{71,300 - 71,800}{730.30} = -.68$$

The area under the curve to the left of $z = -.68$ is .2483. Therefore, $P(71,300 \leq \bar{x} \leq 72,300) = P(z \leq .68) - P(z < -.68) = .7517 - .2483 = .5034$.

The sampling distribution of $\bar{x}$ can be used to provide probability information about how close the sample mean $\bar{x}$ is to the population mean μ.

The preceding computations show that a simple random sample of 30 EAI managers has a .5034 probability of providing a sample mean $\bar{x}$ that is within \$500 of the population mean. Thus, there is a $1 - .5034 = .4966$ probability that the difference between $\bar{x}$ and $\mu = \$71,800$ will be more than \$500. In other words, a simple random sample of 30 EAI managers has roughly a 50–50 chance of providing a sample mean within the allowable \$500. Perhaps a larger sample size should be considered. Let us explore this possibility by considering the relationship between the sample size and the sampling distribution of $\bar{x}$.

Relationship Between the Sample Size and the Sampling Distribution of $\bar{x}$

Suppose that in the EAI sampling problem we select a simple random sample of 100 EAI managers instead of the 30 originally considered. Intuitively, it would seem that with more data provided by the larger sample size, the sample mean based on $n = 100$ should provide a better estimate of the population mean than the sample mean based on $n = 30$. To see how much better, let us consider the relationship between the sample size and the sampling distribution of $\bar{x}$.

First note that $E(\bar{x}) = \mu$ regardless of the sample size. Thus, the mean of all possible values of $\bar{x}$ is equal to the population mean μ regardless of the sample size n. However, note that the standard error of the mean, $\sigma_{\bar{x}} = \sigma / \sqrt{n}$, is related to the square root of the sample size. Whenever the sample size is increased, the standard error of the mean $\sigma_{\bar{x}}$ decreases. With $n = 30$, the standard error of the mean for the EAI problem is 730.3. However, with the increase in the sample size to $n = 100$, the standard error of the mean is decreased to

$$\sigma_{\bar{x}} = \frac{\sigma}{\sqrt{n}} = \frac{4000}{\sqrt{100}} = 400$$

The sampling distributions of $\bar{x}$ with $n = 30$ and $n = 100$ are shown in Figure 7.6. Because the sampling distribution with $n = 100$ has a smaller standard error, the values of $\bar{x}$ have less variation and tend to be closer to the population mean than the values of $\bar{x}$ with $n = 30$.

We can use the sampling distribution of $\bar{x}$ for the case with $n = 100$ to compute the probability that a simple random sample of 100 EAI managers will provide a sample mean that is within \$500 of the population mean. Because the sampling distribution is normal, with mean 71,800 and standard error of the mean 400, we can use the standard normal probability table to find the area or probability.

At $\bar{x} = 72,300$ (see Figure 7.7), we have

$$z = \frac{72,300 - 71,800}{400} = 1.25$$

Referring to the standard normal probability table, we find a cumulative probability corresponding to $z = 1.25$ of .8944.

FIGURE 7.6   A Comparison of the Sampling Distributions of $\bar{x}$ for Simple Random Samples of $n = 30$ and $n = 100$ EAI Managers

FIGURE 7.7   Probability of a Sample Mean being within $500 of the Population Mean for a Simple Random Sample of 100 EAI Managers

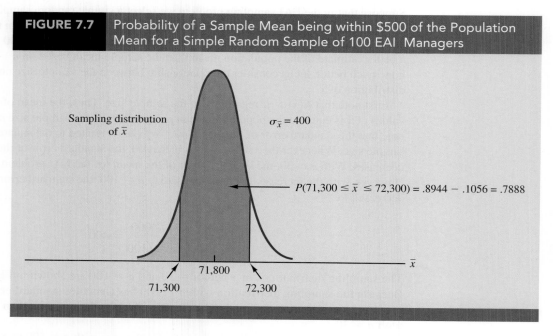

At $\bar{x} = 71{,}300$, we have

$$z = \frac{71{,}300 - 71{,}800}{400} = -1.25$$

The cumulative probability corresponding to $z = -1.25$ is .1056. Therefore, $P(71{,}300 \le \bar{x} \le 72{,}300) = P(z \le 1.25) - P(z \le -1.25) = .8944 - .1056 = .7888$. Thus, by increasing the sample size from 30 to 100 EAI managers, we increase the probability of obtaining a sample mean within $500 of the population mean from .5034 to .7888.

The important point in this discussion is that as the sample size is increased, the standard error of the mean decreases. As a result, the larger sample size provides a higher probability that the sample mean is within a specified distance of the population mean.

N O T E S   +   C O M M E N T S

1. In presenting the sampling distribution of $\bar{x}$ for the EAI problem, we took advantage of the fact that the population mean $\mu = 71{,}800$ and the population standard deviation $\sigma = 4000$ were known. However, usually the values of the population mean μ and the population standard deviation σ that are needed to determine the sampling distribution of $\bar{x}$ will be unknown. In Chapter 8 we will show how the sample mean $\bar{x}$ and the sample standard deviations are used when μ and σ are unknown.

2. The theoretical proof of the central limit theorem requires independent observations in the sample. This condition is met for infinite populations and for finite populations where sampling is done with replacement. Although the central limit theorem does not directly address sampling without replacement from finite populations, general statistical practice applies the findings of the central limit theorem when the population size is large.

E X E R C I S E S

Methods

18. A population has a mean of 200 and a standard deviation of 50. A sample of size 100 will be taken and the sample mean $\bar{x}$ will be used to estimate the population mean.
    a. What is the expected value of $\bar{x}$?
    b. What is the standard deviation of $\bar{x}$?
    c. Show the sampling distribution of $\bar{x}$.
    d. What does the sampling distribution of $\bar{x}$ show?

19. A population has a mean of 200 and a standard deviation of 50. Suppose a sample of size 100 is selected and $\bar{x}$ is used to estimate μ.
    a. What is the probability that the sample mean will be within ± 5 of the population mean?
    b. What is the probability that the sample mean will be within ± 10 of the population mean?

20. Assume the population standard deviation is $\sigma = 25$. Compute the standard error of the mean, $\sigma_{\bar{x}}$, for sample sizes of 50, 100, 150, and 200. What can you say about the size of the standard error of the mean as the sample size is increased?

21. Suppose a random sample of size 50 is selected from a population with $\sigma = 10$. Find the value of the standard error of the mean in each of the following cases (use the finite population correction factor if appropriate).
    a. The population size is infinite.
    b. The population size is $N = 50{,}000$.
    c. The population size is $N = 5000$.
    d. The population size is $N = 500$.

Applications

22. **Sampling Distribution for Electronic Associates, Inc., Managers.** Refer to the EAI sampling problem. Suppose a simple random sample of 60 managers is used.
    a. Sketch the sampling distribution of $\bar{x}$ when simple random samples of size 60 are used.
    b. What happens to the sampling distribution of $\bar{x}$ if simple random samples of size 120 are used?
    c. What general statement can you make about what happens to the sampling distribution of $\bar{x}$ as the sample size is increased? Does this generalization seem logical? Explain.

23. **Finding Probabilities for Electronic Associates, Inc., Managers.** In the EAI sampling problem (see Figure 7.5), we showed that for $n = 30$, there was .5034 probability of obtaining a sample mean within $\pm\$500$ of the population mean.

    a. What is the probability that $\bar{x}$ is within $500 of the population mean if a sample of size 60 is used?

    b. Answer part (a) for a sample of size 120.

24. **U.S. Unemployment.** *Barron's* reported that the average number of weeks an individual is unemployed is 17.5 weeks. Assume that for the population of all unemployed individuals the population mean length of unemployment is 17.5 weeks and that the population standard deviation is 4 weeks. Suppose you would like to select a sample of 50 unemployed individuals for a follow-up study.

    a. Show the sampling distribution of $\bar{x}$, the sample mean average for a sample of 50 unemployed individuals.

    b. What is the probability that a simple random sample of 50 unemployed individuals will provide a sample mean within 1 week of the population mean?

    c. What is the probability that a simple random sample of 50 unemployed individuals will provide a sample mean within 1/2 week of the population mean?

25. **SAT Scores.** In May 2018, The College Board reported the following mean scores for two parts of the Scholastic Aptitude Test (SAT):

Evidence-Based Reading and Writing	533
Mathematics	527

    Assume that the population standard deviation on each part of the test is $\sigma = 100$.

    a. What is the probability a sample of 90 test takers will provide a sample mean test score within 10 points of the population mean of 533 on the Evidence-Based Reading and Writing part of the test?

    b. What is the probability a sample of 90 test takers will provide a sample mean test score within 10 points of the population mean of 527 on the Mathematics part of the test?

    c. Comment on the differences between the values computed in parts (a) and (b).

26. **Federal Income Tax Returns.** *The Wall Street Journal* reports that 33% of taxpayers with adjusted gross incomes between $30,000 and $60,000 itemized deductions on their federal income tax return. The mean amount of deductions for this population of taxpayers was $16,642. Assume the standard deviation is $\sigma = \$2400$.

    a. What is the probability that a sample of taxpayers from this income group who have itemized deductions will show a sample mean within $200 of the population mean for each of the following sample sizes: 30, 50, 100, and 400?

    b. What is the advantage of a larger sample size when attempting to estimate the population mean?

27. **College Graduate-Level Wages.** The Economic Policy Institute periodically issues reports on worker's wages. The institute reported that mean wages for male college graduates were $37.39 per hour and for female college graduates were $27.83 per hour in 2017. Assume the standard deviation for male graduates is $4.60, and for female graduates it is $4.10.

    a. What is the probability that a sample of 50 male graduates will provide a sample mean within $1.00 of the population mean, $37.39?

    b. What is the probability that a sample of 50 female graduates will provide a sample mean within $1.00 of the population mean, $27.83?

    c. In which of the preceding two cases, part (a) or part (b), do we have a higher probability of obtaining a sample estimate within $1.00 of the population mean? Why?

d. What is the probability that a sample of 120 female graduates will provide a sample mean more than $.60 below the population mean, 27.83?

28. **State Rainfalls.** The state of California has a mean annual rainfall of 22 inches, whereas the state of New York has a mean annual rainfall of 42 inches. Assume that the standard deviation for both states is 4 inches. A sample of 30 years of rainfall for California and a sample of 45 years of rainfall for New York has been taken.
    a. Show the probability distribution of the sample mean annual rainfall for California.
    b. What is the probability that the sample mean is within 1 inch of the population mean for California?
    c. What is the probability that the sample mean is within 1 inch of the population mean for New York?
    d. In which case, part (b) or part (c), is the probability of obtaining a sample mean within 1 inch of the population mean greater? Why?

29. **Income Tax Return Preparation Fees.** The CPA Practice Advisor reports that the mean preparation fee for 2017 federal income tax returns was $273. Use this price as the population mean and assume the population standard deviation of preparation fees is $100.
    a. What is the probability that the mean price for a sample of 30 federal income tax returns is within $16 of the population mean?
    b. What is the probability that the mean price for a sample of 50 federal income tax returns is within $16 of the population mean?
    c. What is the probability that the mean price for a sample of 100 federal income tax returns is within $16 of the population mean?
    d. Which, if any, of the sample sizes in parts (a), (b), and (c) would you recommend to ensure at least a .95 probability that the sample mean is within $16 of the population mean?

30. **Employee Ages.** To estimate the mean age for a population of 4000 employees, a simple random sample of 40 employees is selected.
    a. Would you use the finite population correction factor in calculating the standard error of the mean? Explain.
    b. If the population standard deviation is $\sigma = 8.2$ years, compute the standard error both with and without the finite population correction factor. What is the rationale for ignoring the finite population correction factor whenever $n/N \leq .05$?
    c. What is the probability that the sample mean age of the employees will be within ± 2 years of the population mean age?

7.6 Sampling Distribution of $\bar{p}$

The sample proportion $\bar{p}$ is the point estimator of the population proportion p. The formula for computing the sample proportion is

$$\bar{p} = \frac{x}{n}$$

where

$x =$ the number of elements in the sample that possess the characteristic of interest

$n =$ sample size

As noted in Section 7.4, the sample proportion $\bar{p}$ is a random variable and its probability distribution is called the sampling distribution of $\bar{p}$.

SAMPLING DISTRIBUTION OF $\bar{p}$

The sampling distribution of $\bar{p}$ is the probability distribution of all possible values of the sample proportion $\bar{p}$.

To determine how close the sample proportion $\bar{p}$ is to the population proportion p, we need to understand the properties of the sampling distribution of $\bar{p}$: the expected value of $\bar{p}$, the standard deviation of $\bar{p}$, and the shape or form of the sampling distribution of $\bar{p}$.

Expected Value of $\bar{p}$

The expected value of $\bar{p}$, the mean of all possible values of $\bar{p}$, is equal to the population proportion p.

EXPECTED VALUE OF $\bar{p}$

$$E(\bar{p}) = p \tag{7.4}$$

where

$$E(\bar{p}) = \text{the expected value of } \bar{p}$$
$$p = \text{the population proportion}$$

Because $E(\bar{p}) = p$, $\bar{p}$ is an unbiased estimator of p. Recall from Section 7.1 we noted that $p = .60$ for the EAI population, where p is the proportion of the population of managers who participated in the company's management training program. Thus, the expected value of $\bar{p}$ for the EAI sampling problem is .60.

Standard Deviation of $\bar{p}$

Just as we found for the standard deviation of $\bar{x}$, the standard deviation of $\bar{p}$ depends on whether the population is finite or infinite. The two formulas for computing the standard deviation of $\bar{p}$ follow.

STANDARD DEVIATION OF $\bar{p}$

Finite Population	Infinite Population
$\sigma_{\bar{p}} = \sqrt{\dfrac{N-n}{N-1}}\sqrt{\dfrac{p(1-p)}{n}}$	$\sigma_{\bar{p}} = \sqrt{\dfrac{p(1-p)}{n}}$

$$\tag{7.5}$$

Comparing the two formulas in (7.5), we see that the only difference is the use of the finite population correction factor $\sqrt{(N-n)/(N-1)}$.

As was the case with the sample mean $\bar{x}$, the difference between the expressions for the finite population and the infinite population becomes negligible if the size of the finite population is large in comparison to the sample size. We follow the same rule of thumb that we recommended for the sample mean. That is, if the population is finite with $n/N \leq .05$, we will use $\sigma_{\bar{p}} = \sqrt{p(1-p)/n}$. However, if the population is finite with $n/N > .05$, the finite population correction factor should be used. Again, unless specifically noted, throughout the text we will assume that the population size is large in relation to the sample size and thus the finite population correction factor is unnecessary.

In Section 7.5 we used the term standard error of the mean to refer to the standard deviation of $\bar{x}$. We stated that in general the term standard error refers to the standard deviation of a point estimator. Thus, for proportions we use *standard error of the proportion* to refer to the standard deviation of $\bar{p}$. Let us now return to the EAI example and compute the standard error of the proportion associated with simple random samples of 30 EAI managers.

For the EAI study we know that the population proportion of managers who participated in the management training program is $p = .60$. With $n/N = 30/2500 = .012$, we can ignore the finite population correction factor when we compute the standard error of the proportion. For the simple random sample of 30 managers, $\sigma_{\bar{p}}$ is

$$\sigma_{\bar{p}} = \sqrt{\frac{p(1-p)}{n}} = \sqrt{\frac{.60(1-.60)}{30}} = .0894$$

Form of the Sampling Distribution of $\bar{p}$

Now that we know the mean and standard deviation of the sampling distribution of $\bar{p}$, the final step is to determine the form or shape of the sampling distribution. The sample proportion is $\bar{p} = x/n$. For a simple random sample from a large population, the value of x is a binomial random variable indicating the number of elements in the sample with the characteristic of interest. Because n is a constant, the probability of x/n is the same as the binomial probability of x, which means that the sampling distribution of $\bar{p}$ is also a discrete probability distribution and that the probability for each value of x/n is the same as the probability of x.

In Chapter 6 we also showed that a binomial distribution can be approximated by a normal distribution whenever the sample size is large enough to satisfy the following two conditions:

$$np \geq 5 \quad \text{and} \quad n(1-p) \geq 5$$

Assuming these two conditions are satisfied, the probability distribution of x in the sample proportion, $\bar{p} = x/n$, can be approximated by a normal distribution. And because n is a constant, the sampling distribution of $\bar{p}$ can also be approximated by a normal distribution. This approximation is stated as follows:

The sampling distribution of $\bar{p}$ can be approximated by a normal distribution whenever $np \geq 5$ and $n(1-p) \geq 5$.

In practical applications, when an estimate of a population proportion is desired, we find that sample sizes are almost always large enough to permit the use of a normal approximation for the sampling distribution of $\bar{p}$.

Recall that for the EAI sampling problem we know that the population proportion of managers who participated in the training program is $p = .60$. With a simple random sample of size 30, we have $np = 30(.60) = 18$ and $n(1-p) = 30(.40) = 12$. Thus, the sampling distribution of $\bar{p}$ can be approximated by a normal distribution shown in Figure 7.8.

Practical Value of the Sampling Distribution of $\bar{p}$

The practical value of the sampling distribution of $\bar{p}$ is that it can be used to provide probability information about the difference between the sample proportion and the population proportion. For instance, suppose that in the EAI problem the personnel

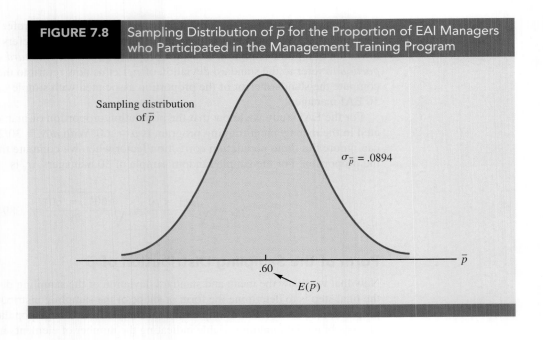

FIGURE 7.8   Sampling Distribution of $\bar{p}$ for the Proportion of EAI Managers who Participated in the Management Training Program

director wants to know the probability of obtaining a value of $\bar{p}$ that is within .05 of the population proportion of EAI managers who participated in the training program. That is, what is the probability of obtaining a sample with a sample proportion $\bar{p}$ between .55 and .65? The darkly shaded area in Figure 7.9 shows this probability. Using the fact that the sampling distribution of $\bar{p}$ can be approximated by a normal distribution with a mean of .60 and a standard error of the proportion of $\sigma_{\bar{p}} = .0894$, we find that the standard normal random variable corresponding to $\bar{p} = .65$ has a value of $z = (.65 - .60)/.0894 = .56$. Referring to the standard normal probability table, we see that the cumulative probability corresponding to $z = .56$ is .7123. Similarly, at $\bar{p} = .55$, we find $z = (.55 - .60)/.0894 = -.56$. From the standard normal probability table, we find the cumulative probability corresponding to $z = -.56$ is .2877. Thus, the probability of selecting a sample that provides a sample proportion $\bar{p}$ within .05 of the population proportion p is given by .7123 - .2877 = .4246.

FIGURE 7.9   Probability of Obtaining $\bar{p}$ Between .55 and .65

If we consider increasing the sample size to $n = 100$, the standard error of the proportion becomes

$$\sigma_{\bar{p}} = \sqrt{\frac{.60(1 - .60)}{100}} = .049$$

With a sample size of 100 EAI managers, the probability of the sample proportion having a value within .05 of the population proportion can now be computed. Because the sampling distribution is approximately normal, with mean .60 and standard deviation .049, we can use the standard normal probability table to find the area or probability. At $\bar{p} = .65$, we have $z = (.65 - .60)/.049 = 1.02$. Referring to the standard normal probability table, we see that the cumulative probability corresponding to $z = 1.02$ is .8461. Similarly, at $\bar{p} = .55$, we have $z = (.55 - .60)/.049 = -1.02$. We find the cumulative probability corresponding to $z = -1.02$ is .1539. Thus, if the sample size is increased from 30 to 100, the probability that the sample proportion $\bar{p}$ is within .05 of the population proportion p will increase to $.8461 - .1539 = .6922$.

EXERCISES

Methods

31. A sample of size 100 is selected from a population with $p = .40$.
    a. What is the expected value of $\bar{p}$?
    b. What is the standard error of $\bar{p}$?
    c. Show the sampling distribution of $\bar{p}$.
    d. What does the sampling distribution of $\bar{p}$ show?

32. A population proportion is .40. A sample of size 200 will be taken and the sample proportion $\bar{p}$ will be used to estimate the population proportion.
    a. What is the probability that the sample proportion will be within $\pm.03$ of the population proportion?
    b. What is the probability that the sample proportion will be within $\pm.05$ of the population proportion?

33. Assume that the population proportion is .55. Compute the standard error of the proportion, $\sigma_{\bar{p}}$, for sample sizes of 100, 200, 500, and 1000. What can you say about the size of the standard error of the proportion as the sample size is increased?

34. The population proportion is .30. What is the probability that a sample proportion will be within $\pm.04$ of the population proportion for each of the following sample sizes?
    a. $n = 100$
    b. $n = 200$
    c. $n = 500$
    d. $n = 1000$
    e. What is the advantage of a larger sample size?

Applications

35. **Orders from First-Time Customers.** The president of Doerman Distributors, Inc., believes that 30% of the firm's orders come from first-time customers. A random sample of 100 orders will be used to estimate the proportion of first-time customers.
    a. Assume that the president is correct and $p = .30$. What is the sampling distribution of $\bar{p}$ for this study?
    b. What is the probability that the sample proportion $\bar{p}$ will be between .20 and .40?
    c. What is the probability that the sample proportion will be between .25 and .35?

36. **Ages of Entrepreneurs.** *The Wall Street Journal* reported that the age at first startup for 55% of entrepreneurs was 29 years of age or less and the age at first startup for 45% of entrepreneurs was 30 years of age or more.
    a. Suppose a sample of 200 entrepreneurs will be taken to learn about the most important qualities of entrepreneurs. Show the sampling distribution of $\bar{p}$ where $\bar{p}$ is the sample proportion of entrepreneurs whose first startup was at 29 years of age or less.
    b. What is the probability that the sample proportion in part (a) will be within $\pm.05$ of its population proportion?
    c. Suppose a sample of 200 entrepreneurs will be taken to learn about the most important qualities of entrepreneurs. Show the sampling distribution of $\bar{p}$ where $\bar{p}$ is now the sample proportion of entrepreneurs whose first startup was at 30 years of age or more.
    d. What is the probability that the sample proportion in part (c) will be within $\pm.05$ of its population proportion?
    e. Is the probability different in parts (b) and (d)? Why?
    f. Answer part (b) for a sample of size 400. Is the probability smaller? Why?

37. **Food Waste.** In 2017, the Restaurant Hospitality website reported that only 10% of surplus food is being recovered in the food-service and restaurant sector, leaving approximately 1.5 billion meals per year uneaten. Assume this is the true population proportion and that you plan to take a sample survey of 525 companies in the in the food-service and restaurant sector to further investigate their behavior.
    a. Show the sampling distribution of $\bar{p}$, the proportion of food recovered by your sample respondents.
    b. What is the probability that your survey will provide a sample proportion within $\pm.03$ of the population proportion?
    c. What is the probability that your survey will provide a sample proportion within $\pm.015$ of the population proportion?

38. **Unnecessary Medical Care.** According to *Reader's Digest,* 42% of primary care doctors think their patients receive unnecessary medical care.
    a. Suppose a sample of 300 primary care doctors was taken. Show the sampling distribution of the proportion of the doctors who think their patients receive unnecessary medical care.
    b. What is the probability that the sample proportion will be within $\pm.03$ of the population proportion?
    c. What is the probability that the sample proportion will be within $\pm.05$ of the population proportion?
    d. What would be the effect of taking a larger sample on the probabilities in parts (b) and (c)? Why?

39. **Better Business Bureau Complaints.** In 2016 the Better Business Bureau settled 80% of complaints they received in the United States. Suppose you have been hired by the Better Business Bureau to investigate the complaints they received this year involving new car dealers. You plan to select a sample of new car dealer complaints to estimate the proportion of complaints the Better Business Bureau is able to settle. Assume the population proportion of complaints settled for new car dealers is .80, the same as the overall proportion of complaints settled in 2016.
    a. Suppose you select a sample of 200 complaints involving new car dealers. Show the sampling distribution of $\bar{p}$.
    b. Based upon a sample of 200 complaints, what is the probability that the sample proportion will be within .04 of the population proportion?
    c. Suppose you select a sample of 450 complaints involving new car dealers. Show the sampling distribution of $\bar{p}$.
    d. Based upon the smaller sample of only 450 complaints, what is the probability that the sample proportion will be within .04 of the population proportion?
    e. As measured by the increase in probability, how much do you gain in precision by taking the larger sample in part (d)?

40. **Product Labeling.** The Grocery Manufacturers of America reported that 76% of consumers read the ingredients listed on a product's label. Assume the population proportion is $p = .76$ and a sample of 400 consumers is selected from the population.
    a. Show the sampling distribution of the sample proportion $\bar{p}$ where $\bar{p}$ is the proportion of the sampled consumers who read the ingredients listed on a product's label.
    b. What is the probability that the sample proportion will be within $\pm.03$ of the population proportion?
    c. Answer part (b) for a sample of 750 consumers.
41. **Household Grocery Expenditures.** The Food Marketing Institute shows that 17% of households spend more than $100 per week on groceries. Assume the population proportion is $p = .17$ and a sample of 800 households will be selected from the population.
    a. Show the sampling distribution of $\bar{p}$, the sample proportion of households spending more than $100 per week on groceries.
    b. What is the probability that the sample proportion will be within $\pm.02$ of the population proportion?
    c. Answer part (b) for a sample of 1600 households.

7.7 Properties of Point Estimators

In this chapter we showed how sample statistics such as a sample mean $\bar{x}$, a sample standard deviation s, and a sample proportion $\bar{p}$ can be used as point estimators of their corresponding population parameters μ, σ, and p. It is intuitively appealing that each of these sample statistics is the point estimator of its corresponding population parameter. However, before using a sample statistic as a point estimator, statisticians check to see whether the sample statistic demonstrates certain properties associated with good point estimators. In this section we discuss three properties of good point estimators: unbiased, efficiency, and consistency.

Because several different sample statistics can be used as point estimators of different population parameters, we use the following general notation in this section.

$$\theta = \text{the population parameter of interest}$$
$$\hat{\theta} = \text{the sample statistic or point estimator of } \theta$$

The notation θ is the Greek letter theta, and the notation $\hat{\theta}$ is pronounced "theta-hat." In general, θ represents any population parameter such as a population mean, population standard deviation, population proportion, and so on; $\hat{\theta}$ represents the corresponding sample statistic such as the sample mean, sample standard deviation, and sample proportion.

Unbiased

If the expected value of the sample statistic is equal to the population parameter being estimated, the sample statistic is said to be an *unbiased estimator* of the population parameter.

UNBIASED

The sample statistic $\hat{\theta}$ is an unbiased estimator of the population parameter θ if

$$E(\hat{\theta}) = \theta$$

where

$$E(\hat{\theta}) = \text{the expected value of the sample statistic } \hat{\theta}$$

FIGURE 7.10   Examples of Unbiased and Biased Point Estimators

Sampling distribution of $\hat{\theta}$

Parameter θ is located at the mean of the sampling distribution;

$$E(\hat{\theta}) = \theta$$

Panel A: Unbiased Estimator

Sampling distribution of $\hat{\theta}$

Bias

θ $E(\hat{\theta})$

Parameter θ is not located at the mean of the sampling distribution;

$$E(\hat{\theta}) \neq \theta$$

Panel B: Biased Estimator

Hence, the expected value, or mean, of all possible values of an unbiased sample statistic is equal to the population parameter being estimated.

Figure 7.10 shows the cases of unbiased and biased point estimators. In the illustration showing the unbiased estimator, the mean of the sampling distribution is equal to the value of the population parameter. The estimation errors balance out in this case, because sometimes the value of the point estimator $\hat{\theta}$ may be less than θ and other times it may be greater than θ. In the case of a biased estimator, the mean of the sampling distribution is less than or greater than the value of the population parameter. In the illustration in Panel B of Figure 7.10, $E(\hat{\theta})$ is greater than θ; thus, the sample statistic has a high probability of overestimating the value of the population parameter. The amount of the bias is shown in the figure.

In discussing the sampling distributions of the sample mean and the sample proportion, we stated that $E(\bar{x}) = \mu$ and $E(\bar{p}) = p$. Thus, both $\bar{x}$ and $\bar{p}$ are unbiased estimators of their corresponding population parameters μ and p.

In the case of the sample standard deviation s and the sample variance s^2, it can be shown that $E(s^2) = \sigma^2$. Thus, we conclude that the sample variance s^2 is an unbiased estimator of the population variance σ^2. In fact, when we first presented the formulas for the sample variance and the sample standard deviation in Chapter 3, $n - 1$ rather than n was used in the denominator. The reason for using $n - 1$ rather than n is to make the sample variance an unbiased estimator of the population variance.

Efficiency

When sampling from a normal population, the standard error of the sample mean is less than the standard error of the sample median. Thus, the sample mean is more efficient than the sample median.

Assume that a simple random sample of n elements can be used to provide two unbiased point estimators of the same population parameter. In this situation, we would prefer to use the point estimator with the smaller standard error, because it tends to provide estimates closer to the population parameter. The point estimator with the smaller standard error is said to have greater **relative efficiency** than the other.

Figure 7.11 shows the sampling distributions of two unbiased point estimators, $\hat{\theta}_1$ and $\hat{\theta}_2$. Note that the standard error of $\hat{\theta}_1$ is less than the standard error of $\hat{\theta}_2$; thus, values of $\hat{\theta}_1$ have a greater chance of being close to the parameter θ than do values of $\hat{\theta}_2$. Because the standard error of point estimator $\hat{\theta}_1$ is less than the standard error of point estimator $\hat{\theta}_2$, $\hat{\theta}_1$ is relatively more efficient than $\hat{\theta}_2$ and is the preferred point estimator.

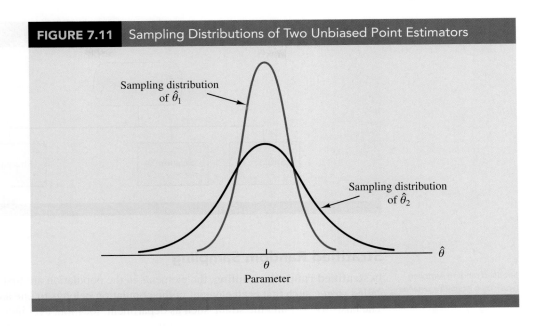

FIGURE 7.11 Sampling Distributions of Two Unbiased Point Estimators

Consistency

A third property associated with good point estimators is **consistency.** Loosely speaking, a point estimator is consistent if the values of the point estimator tend to become closer to the population parameter as the sample size becomes larger. In other words, a large sample size tends to provide a better point estimate than a small sample size. Note that for the sample mean $\bar{x}$, we showed that the standard error of $\bar{x}$ is given by $\sigma_{\bar{x}} = \sigma/\sqrt{n}$. Because $\sigma_{\bar{x}}$ is related to the sample size such that larger sample sizes provide smaller values for $\sigma_{\bar{x}}$, we conclude that a larger sample size tends to provide point estimates closer to the population mean μ. In this sense, we can say that the sample mean $\bar{x}$ is a consistent estimator of the population mean μ. Using a similar rationale, we can also conclude that the sample proportion $\bar{p}$ is a consistent estimator of the population proportion p.

N O T E S   +   C O M M E N T S

In Chapter 3 we stated that the mean and the median are two measures of central location. In this chapter we discussed only the mean. The reason is that in sampling from a normal population, where the population mean and population median are identical, the standard error of the median is approximately 25% larger than the standard error of the mean. Recall that in the EAI problem where n = 30, the standard error of the mean is $\sigma_{\bar{x}} = 730.3$. The standard error of the median for this problem would be 1.25 × (730.3) = 913. As a result, the sample mean is more efficient and will have a higher probability of being within a specified distance of the population mean.

7.8 Other Sampling Methods

This section provides a brief introduction to survey sampling methods other than simple random sampling.

We described simple random sampling as a procedure for sampling from a finite population and discussed the properties of the sampling distributions of $\bar{x}$ and $\bar{p}$ when simple random sampling is used. Other methods such as stratified random sampling, cluster sampling, and systematic sampling provide advantages over simple random sampling in some of these situations. In this section we briefly introduce these alternative sampling methods. A more in-depth treatment is provided in Chapter 22, which is located on the website that accompanies the text.

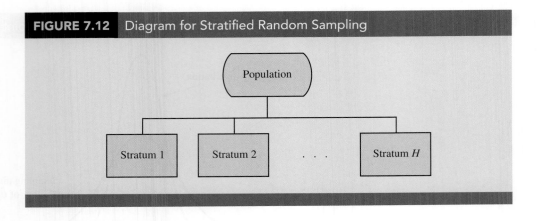

FIGURE 7.12 Diagram for Stratified Random Sampling

Stratified Random Sampling

Stratified random sampling works best when the variance among elements in each stratum is relatively small.

In **stratified random sampling**, the elements in the population are first divided into groups called *strata,* such that each element in the population belongs to one and only one stratum. The basis for forming the strata, such as department, location, age, industry type, and so on, is at the discretion of the designer of the sample. However, the best results are obtained when the elements within each stratum are as much alike as possible. Figure 7.12 is a diagram of a population divided into *H* strata.

After the strata are formed, a simple random sample is taken from each stratum. Formulas are available for combining the results for the individual stratum samples into one estimate of the population parameter of interest. The value of stratified random sampling depends on how homogeneous the elements are within the strata. If elements within strata are alike, the strata will have low variances. Thus relatively small sample sizes can be used to obtain good estimates of the strata characteristics. If strata are homogeneous, the stratified random sampling procedure provides results just as precise as those of simple random sampling by using a smaller total sample size.

Cluster Sampling

Cluster sampling works best when each cluster provides a small-scale representation of the population.

In **cluster sampling**, the elements in the population are first divided into separate groups called *clusters*. Each element of the population belongs to one and only one cluster (see Figure 7.13). A simple random sample of the clusters is then taken. All elements within each sampled cluster form the sample. Cluster sampling tends to provide the best results when the elements within the clusters are not alike. In the ideal case, each cluster is a representative small-scale version of the entire population. The value of cluster sampling depends on how representative each cluster is of the entire population. If all clusters are

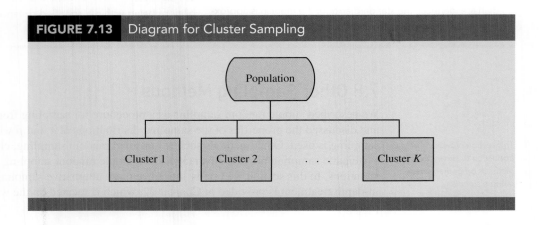

FIGURE 7.13 Diagram for Cluster Sampling

alike in this regard, sampling a small number of clusters will provide good estimates of the population parameters.

One of the primary applications of cluster sampling is area sampling, where clusters are city blocks or other well-defined areas. Cluster sampling generally requires a larger total sample size than either simple random sampling or stratified random sampling. However, it can result in cost savings because of the fact that when an interviewer is sent to a sampled cluster (e.g., a city-block location), many sample observations can be obtained in a relatively short time. Hence, a larger sample size may be obtainable with a significantly lower total cost.

Systematic Sampling

In some sampling situations, especially those with large populations, it is time-consuming to select a simple random sample by first finding a random number and then counting or searching through the list of the population until the corresponding element is found. An alternative to simple random sampling is **systematic sampling**. For example, if a sample size of 50 is desired from a population containing 5000 elements, we will sample one element for every 5000/50 = 100 elements in the population. A systematic sample for this case involves selecting randomly one of the first 100 elements from the population list. Other sample elements are identified by starting with the first sampled element and then selecting every 100th element that follows in the population list. In effect, the sample of 50 is identified by moving systematically through the population and identifying every 100th element after the first randomly selected element. The sample of 50 usually will be easier to identify in this way than it would be if simple random sampling were used. Because the first element selected is a random choice, a systematic sample is usually assumed to have the properties of a simple random sample. This assumption is especially applicable when the list of elements in the population is a random ordering of the elements.

Convenience Sampling

The sampling methods discussed thus far are referred to as *probability sampling* techniques. Elements selected from the population have a known probability of being included in the sample. The advantage of probability sampling is that the sampling distribution of the appropriate sample statistic generally can be identified. Formulas such as the ones for simple random sampling presented in this chapter can be used to determine the properties of the sampling distribution. Then the sampling distribution can be used to make probability statements about the error associated with using the sample results to make inferences about the population.

Convenience sampling is a *nonprobability sampling* technique. As the name implies, the sample is identified primarily by convenience. Elements are included in the sample without prespecified or known probabilities of being selected. For example, a professor conducting research at a university may use student volunteers to constitute a sample simply because they are readily available and will participate as subjects for little or no cost. Similarly, an inspector may sample a shipment of oranges by selecting oranges haphazardly from among several crates. Labeling each orange and using a probability method of sampling would be impractical. Samples such as wildlife captures and volunteer panels for consumer research are also convenience samples.

Convenience samples have the advantage of relatively easy sample selection and data collection; however, it is impossible to evaluate the "goodness" of the sample in terms of its representativeness of the population. A convenience sample may provide good results or it may not; no statistically justified procedure allows a probability analysis and inference about the quality of the sample results. Sometimes researchers apply statistical methods designed for probability samples to a convenience sample, arguing that the convenience sample can be treated as though it were a probability sample. However, this argument cannot be supported, and we should be cautious in interpreting the results of convenience samples that are used to make inferences about populations.

Judgment Sampling

One additional nonprobability sampling technique is **judgment sampling**. In this approach, the person most knowledgeable on the subject of the study selects elements of the population that he or she feels are most representative of the population. Often this method is a relatively easy way of selecting a sample. For example, a reporter may sample two or three senators, judging that those senators reflect the general opinion of all senators. However, the quality of the sample results depends on the judgment of the person selecting the sample. Again, great caution is warranted in drawing conclusions based on judgment samples used to make inferences about populations.

N O T E S + C O M M E N T S

We recommend using probability sampling methods when sampling from finite populations: simple random sampling, stratified random sampling, cluster sampling, or systematic sampling. For these methods, formulas are available for evaluating the "goodness" of the sample results in terms of the closeness of the results to the population parameters being estimated. An evaluation of the goodness cannot be made with convenience or judgment sampling. Thus, great care should be used in interpreting the results based on nonprobability sampling methods.

7.9 Big Data and Standard Errors of Sampling Distributions

The purpose of statistical inference is to use sample data to quickly and inexpensively gain insight into some characteristic of a population. Therefore, it is important that we can expect the sample to look like, or be representative of, the population that is being investigated. In practice, individual samples always, to varying degrees, fail to be perfectly representative of the populations from which they have been taken. There are two general reasons a sample may fail to be representative of the population of interest: sampling error and nonsampling error.

Sampling Error

One reason a sample may fail to represent the population from which it has been taken is **sampling error**, or deviation of the sample from the population that results from random sampling. If repeated independent random samples of the same size are collected from the population of interest using a probability sampling technique, on average the samples will be representative of the population. This is the justification for collecting sample data randomly. However, the random collection of sample data does not ensure that any single sample will be perfectly representative of the population of interest; when collecting a sample randomly, the data in the sample cannot be expected to be perfectly representative of the population from which it has been taken. Sampling error is unavoidable when collecting a random sample; this is a risk we must accept when we chose to collect a random sample rather than incur the costs associated with taking a census of the population.

As expressed by equations (6.2) and (6.5), the standard errors of the sampling distributions of the sample mean $\bar{x}$ and the sample proportion of $\bar{p}$ reflect the potential for sampling error when using sample data to estimate the population mean μ and the population proportion p, respectively. As the sample size n increases, the potential impact of extreme values on the statistic decreases, so there is less variation in the potential values of the statistic produced by the sample and the standard errors of these sampling distributions decrease. Because these standard errors reflect the potential for sampling error when using sample data to estimate the population mean μ and the population proportion p, we see that for an extremely large sample there may be little potential for sampling error.

Nonsampling Error

Although the standard error of a sampling distribution decreases as the sample size n increases, this does not mean that we can conclude that an extremely large sample will always provide reliable information about the population of interest; this is because sampling error is not the sole reason a sample may fail to represent the target population. Deviations of the sample from the population that occur for reasons other than random sampling are referred to as **nonsampling error**. Nonsampling error can occur for a variety of reasons.

Consider the online news service PenningtonDailyTimes.com (PDT). Because PDT's primary source of revenue is the sale of advertising, the news service is intent on collecting sample data on the behavior of visitors to its website in order to support its advertising sales. Prospective advertisers are willing to pay a premium to advertise on websites that have long visit times, so PDT's management is keenly interested in the amount of time customers spend during their visits to PDT's website. Advertisers are also concerned with how frequently visitors to a website click on any of the ads featured on the website, so PDT is also interested in whether visitors to its website clicked on any of the ads featured on PenningtonDailyTimes.com.

From whom should PDT collect its data? Should it collect data on current visits to PenningtonDailyTimes.com? Should it attempt to attract new visitors and collect data on these visits? If so, should it measure the time spent at its website by visitors it has attracted from competitors' websites or visitors who do not routinely visit online news sites? The answers to these questions depend on PDT's research objectives. Is the company attempting to evaluate its current market, assess the potential of customers it can attract from competitors, or explore the potential of an entirely new market such as individuals who do not routinely obtain their news from online news services? If the research objective and the population from which the sample is to be drawn are not aligned, the data that PDT collects will not help the company accomplish its research objective. This type of error is referred to as a **coverage error**.

Nonsampling error can occur in a sample or a census.

Even when the sample is taken from the appropriate population, nonsampling error can occur when segments of the target population are systematically underrepresented or overrepresented in the sample. This may occur because the study design is flawed or because some segments of the population are either more likely or less likely to respond. Suppose PDT implements a pop-up questionnaire that opens when a visitor leaves PenningtonDailyTimes.com. Visitors to PenningtonDailyTimes.com who have installed pop-up blockers will be likely underrepresented, and visitors to PenningtonDailyTimes. com who have not installed pop-up blockers will likely be overrepresented. If the behavior of PenningtonDailyTimes.com visitors who have installed pop-up blockers differs from the behaviors of PenningtonDailyTimes.com visitors who have not installed pop-up blockers, attempting to draw conclusions from this sample about how all visitors to the PDT website behave may be misleading. This type of error is referred to as a **nonresponse error**.

Another potential source of nonsampling error is incorrect measurement of the characteristic of interest. If PDT asks questions that are ambiguous or difficult for respondents to understand, the responses may not accurately reflect how the respondents intended to respond. For example, respondents may be unsure how to respond if PDT asks *"Are the news stories on PenningtonDailyTimes.com compelling and accurate?"*. How should a visitor respond if she or he feels the news stories on PenningtonDailyTimes.com are compelling but erroneous? What response is appropriate if the respondent feels the news stories on PenningtonDailyTimes.com are accurate but dull? A similar issue can arise if a question is asked in a biased or leading way. If PDT asks *"Many readers find the news stories on PenningtonDailyTimes.com to be compelling and accurate. Do you find the news stories on PenningtonDailyTimes.com to be compelling and accurate?"*, the qualifying statement PDT makes prior to the actual question will likely result in a bias toward positive responses. Incorrect measurement of the characteristic of interest can also occur when respondents provide incorrect answers; this may be due to a respondent's poor recall or unwillingness to respond honestly. This type of error is referred to as a **measurement error**.

Errors that are introduced by interviewers or during the recording and preparation of the data are other types of nonsampling error. These types of error are referred to as interviewer errors and processing errors, respectively.

Nonsampling error can introduce bias into the estimates produced using the sample, and this bias can mislead decision makers who use the sample data in their decision-making processes. No matter how small or large the sample, we must contend with this limitation of sampling whenever we use sample data to gain insight into a population of interest. Although sampling error decreases as the size of the sample increases, an extremely large sample can still suffer from nonsampling error and fail to be representative of the population of interest. When sampling, care must be taken to ensure that we minimize the introduction of nonsampling error into the data collection process. This can be done by carrying out the following steps:

- Carefully define the target population before collecting sample data, and subsequently design the data collection procedure so that a probability sample is drawn from this target population.
- Carefully design the data collection process and train the data collectors.
- Pretest the data collection procedure to identify and correct for potential sources of nonsampling error prior to final data collection.
- Use stratified random sampling when population-level information about an important qualitative variable is available to ensure that the sample is representative of the population with respect to that qualitative characteristic.
- Use cluster sampling when the population can be divided into heterogeneous subgroups or clusters.
- Use systematic sampling when population-level information about an important quantitative variable is available to ensure that the sample is representative of the population with respect to that quantitative characteristic.

Finally, recognize that every random sample (even an extremely large random sample) will suffer from some degree of sampling error, and eliminating all potential sources of nonsampling error may be impractical. Understanding these limitations of sampling will enable us to be more realistic and pragmatic when interpreting sample data and using sample data to draw conclusions about the target population.

Big Data

Recent estimates state that approximately 2.5 quintillion bytes of data are created worldwide each day. This represents a dramatic increase from the estimated 100 gigabytes (GB) of data generated worldwide per day in 1992, the 100 GB of data generated worldwide per hour in 1997, and the 100 GB of data generated worldwide per second in 2002. Every minute, there is an average of 216,000 Instagram posts, 204,000,000 emails sent, 12 hours of footage uploaded to YouTube, and 277,000 tweets posted on Twitter. Without question, the amount of data that is now generated is overwhelming, and this trend is certainly expected to continue.

In each of these cases the data sets that are generated are so large or complex that current data processing capacity and/or analytic methods are not adequate for analyzing the data. Thus, each is an example of **big data**. There are myriad other sources of big data. Sensors and mobile devices transmit enormous amounts of data. Internet activities, digital processes, and social media interactions also produce vast quantities of data.

The amount of data has increased so rapidly that our vocabulary for describing a data set by its size must expand. A few years ago, a petabyte of data seemed almost unimaginably large, but we now routinely describe data in terms of yottabytes. Table 7.6 summarizes terminology for describing the size of data sets.

Understanding What Big Data Is

The processes that generate big data can be described by four attributes or dimensions that are referred to as the four V's:

- **Volume**—the amount of data generated
- **Variety**—the diversity in types and structures of data generated
- **Veracity**—the reliability of the data generated
- **Velocity**—the speed at which the data are generated

TABLE 7.6	Terminology for Describing the Size of Data Sets	
Number of Bytes	**Metric**	**Name**
1000^1	kB	kilobyte
1000^2	MB	megabyte
1000^3	GB	gigabyte
1000^4	TB	terabyte
1000^5	PB	petabyte
1000^6	EB	exabyte
1000^7	ZB	zettabyte
1000^8	YB	yottabyte

A high degree of any of these attributes individually is sufficient to generate big data, and when they occur at high levels simultaneously the resulting amount of data can be overwhelmingly large. Technological advances and improvements in electronic (and often automated) data collection make it easy to collect millions, or even billions, of observations in a relatively short time. Businesses are collecting greater volumes of an increasing variety of data at a higher velocity than ever.

To understand the challenges presented by big data, we consider its structural dimensions. Big data can be **tall data**; a data set that has so many observations that traditional statistical inference has little meaning. For example, producers of consumer goods collect information on the sentiment expressed in millions of social media posts each day to better understand consumer perceptions of their products. Such data consist of the sentiment expressed (the variable) in millions (or over time, even billions) of social media posts (the observations). Big data can also be **wide data**; a data set that has so many variables that simultaneous consideration of all variables is infeasible. For example, a high-resolution image can comprise millions or billions of pixels. The data used by facial recognition algorithms consider each pixel in an image when comparing an image to other images in an attempt to find a match. Thus, these algorithms make use of the characteristics of millions or billions of pixels (the variables) for relatively few high-resolution images (the observations). Of course, big data can be both tall and wide, and the resulting data set can again be overwhelmingly large.

Statistics are useful tools for understanding the information embedded in a big data set, but we must be careful when using statistics to analyze big data. It is important that we understand the limitations of statistics when applied to big data and we temper our interpretations accordingly. Because tall data are the most common form of big data used in business, we focus on this structure in the discussions throughout the remainder of this section.

Implications of Big Data for Sampling Error

A sample of one million or more visitors might seem unrealistic, but keep in mind that Amazon.com had over 91 million visitors in March of 2016 (quantcast.com, May 13, 2016).

Let's revisit the data collection problem of online news service PenningtonDailyTimes.com (PDT). Because PDT's primary source of revenue is the sale of advertising, PDT's management is interested in the amount of time customers spend during their visits to PDT's website. From historical data, PDT has estimated that the standard deviation of the time spent by individual customers when they visit PDT's website is $s = 20$ seconds. Table 7.7 shows how the standard error of the sampling distribution of the sample mean time spent by individual customers when they visit PDT's website decreases as the sample size increases.

PDT also wants to collect information from its sample respondents on whether a visitor to its website clicked on any of the ads featured on the website. From its historical

TABLE 7.7	Standard Error of the Sample Mean $\bar{x}$ When $s = 20$ at Various Sample Sizes n
Sample Size n	**Standard Error $s_{\bar{x}} = s/\sqrt{n}$**
10	6.32456
100	2.00000
1,000	.63246
10,000	.20000
100,000	.06325
1,000,000	.02000
10,000,000	.00632
100,000,000	.00200
1,000,000,000	.00063

data, PDT knows that 51% of past visitors to its website clicked on an ad featured on the website, so it will use this value as $\bar{p}$ to estimate the standard error. Table 7.8 shows how the standard error of the sampling distribution of the proportion of the sample that clicked on any of the ads featured on PenningtonDailyTimes.com decreases as the sample size increases.

The PDT example illustrates the general relationship between standard errors and the sample size. We see in Table 7.7 that the standard error of the sample mean decreases as the sample size increases. For a sample of $n = 10$, the standard error of the sample mean is 6.32456; when we increase the sample size to $n = 100,000$, the standard error of the sample mean decreases to .06325; and at a sample size of $n = 1,000,000,000$, the standard error of the sample mean decreases to only .00063. In Table 7.8 we see that the standard error of the sample proportion also decreases as the sample size increases. For a sample of $n = 10$, the standard error of the sample proportion is .15808; when we increase the sample size to $n = 100,000$, the standard error of the sample proportion decreases to .00158; and at a sample size of $n = 1,000,000,000$, the standard error of the sample mean decreases to only .00002. In both Table 7.7 and Table 7.8, the standard error when $n = 1,000,000,000$ is *one ten-thousandth of the standard error when $n = 10$.*

TABLE 7.8	Standard Error of the Sample Proportion $\bar{p}$ When $p = .51$ at Various Sample Sizes n
Sample Size n	**Standard Error $\sigma_{\bar{p}} = \sqrt{p(1 - p)/n}$**
10	.15808
100	.04999
1,000	.01581
10,000	.00500
100,000	.00158
1,000,000	.00050
10,000,000	.00016
100,000,000	.00005
1,000,000,000	.00002

NOTES + COMMENTS

1. Nonsampling error can occur when either a probability sampling technique or a nonprobability sampling technique is used. However, nonprobability sampling techniques such as convenience sampling and judgment sampling often introduce nonsampling error into sample data because of the manner in which sample data are collected. Therefore, probability sampling techniques are preferred over nonprobability sampling techniques.

2. When taking an extremely large sample, it is conceivable that the sample size is at least 5% of the population size—that is, $n/N \geq .05$. Under these conditions, it is necessary to use the finite population correction factor when calculating the standard error of the sampling distribution to be used in confidence intervals and hypothesis testing.

EXERCISES

Methods

42. A population has a mean of 400 and a standard deviation of 100. A sample of size 100,000 will be taken, and the sample mean $\bar{x}$ will be used to estimate the population mean.
    a. What is the expected value of $\bar{x}$?
    b. What is the standard deviation of $\bar{x}$?
    c. Show the sampling distribution of $\bar{x}$.
    d. What does the sampling distribution of $\bar{x}$ show?

43. Assume the population standard deviation is $\sigma = 25$. Compute the standard error of the mean, $\sigma_{\bar{x}}$, for sample sizes of 500,000; 1,000,000; 5,000,000; 10,000,000; and 100,000,000. What can you say about the size of the standard error of the mean as the sample size is increased?

44. A sample of size 100,000 is selected from a population with $p = .75$.
    a. What is the expected value of $\bar{p}$?
    b. What is the standard error of $\bar{p}$?
    c. Show the sampling distribution of $\bar{p}$.
    d. What does the sampling distribution of $\bar{p}$ show?

45. Assume that the population proportion is .44. Compute the standard error of the proportion, $\sigma_{\bar{p}}$, for sample sizes of 500,000; 1,000,000; 5,000,000; 10,000,000; and 100,000,000. What can you say about the size of the standard error of the sample proportion as the sample size is increased?

Applications

46. **Vacation Hours Earned by Blue-Collar and Service Employees.** The U.S. Bureau of Labor Statistics (BLS) reported that the mean annual number of hours of vacation time earned by blue-collar and service employees who work for small private establishments and have at least 10 years of service is 100. Assume that for this population the standard deviation for the annual number of vacation hours earned is 48. Suppose the BLS would like to select a sample of 15,000 individuals from this population for a follow-up study.
    a. Show the sampling distribution of $\bar{x}$, the sample mean for a sample of 15,000 individuals from this population.
    b. What is the probability that a simple random sample of 15,000 individuals from this population will provide a sample mean that is within one hour of the population mean?
    c. Suppose the mean annual number of hours of vacation time earned for a sample of 15,000 blue-collar and service employees who work for small private establishments and have at least 10 years of service differs from the population mean μ by more than one hour. Considering your results for part (b), how would you interpret this result?

47. **MPG for New Cars.** *The New York Times* reported that 17.2 million new cars and light trucks were sold in the United States in 2017, and the U.S. Environmental Protection Agency projects the average efficiency for these vehicles to be 25.2 miles per gallon. Assume that that the population standard deviation in miles per gallon for these automobiles is $\sigma = 6$.

   a. What is the probability a sample of 70,000 new cars and light trucks sold in the United States in 2017 will provide a sample mean miles per gallon that is within .05 miles per gallon of the population mean of 25.2?

   b. What is the probability a sample of 70,000 new cars and light trucks sold in the United States in 2017 will provide a sample mean miles per gallon that is within .01 miles per gallon of the population mean of 25.2? Compare this probability to the value computed in part (a).

   c. What is the probability a sample of 90,000 new cars and light trucks sold in the United States in 2017 will provide a sample mean miles per gallon that is within .01 of the population mean of 25.2? Comment on the differences between this probability and the value computed in part (b).

   d. Suppose the mean miles per gallon for a sample of 70,000 new cars and light trucks sold in the United States in 2017 differs from the population mean μ by more than one gallon. How would you interpret this result?

48. **Repeat Purchases.** The president of Colossus.com, Inc., believes that 42% of the firm's orders come from customers who have purchased from Colossus.com in the past. A random sample of 108,700 orders from the past six months will be used to estimate the proportion of orders placed by repeat customers.

   a. Assume that Colossus.com's president is correct and the population proportion $p = .42$. What is the sampling distribution of $\bar{p}$ for this study?

   b. What is the probability that the sample proportion $\bar{p}$ will be within .1% of the population proportion?

   c. What is the probability that the sample proportion $\bar{p}$ will be within .25% of the population proportion? Comment on the difference between this probability and the value computed in part (b).

   d. Suppose the proportion of orders placed by repeat customers for a sample of 108,700 orders from the past six months differs from the population proportion p by more than 1%. How would you interpret this result?

49. **Landline Telephone Service.** According to the U.S. Department of Health and Human Services, only 49.2% of homes in the United States used landline telephone service in 2017.

   a. Suppose a sample of 207,000 U.S. homes will be taken to learn about home telephone usage. Show the sampling distribution of $\bar{p}$ where $\bar{p}$ is the sample proportion of homes that use landline phone service.

   b. What is the probability that the sample proportion in part (a) will be within $\pm .002$ of the population proportion?

   c. Suppose a sample of 86,800 entrepreneurs will be taken to learn about home telephone usage. Show the sampling distribution of $\bar{p}$ where $\bar{p}$ is the sample proportion of homes that use landline phone service.

   d. What is the probability that the sample proportion in part (c) will be within $\pm .002$ of the population proportion?

   e. Are the probabilities different in parts (b) and (d)? Why or why not?

SUMMARY

In this chapter we presented the concepts of sampling and sampling distributions. We demonstrated how a simple random sample can be selected from a finite population and how a random sample can be collected from an infinite population. The data collected from such samples can be used to develop point estimates of population parameters. Because different samples provide different values for the point estimators, point estimators such as $\bar{x}$ and $\bar{p}$ are random variables. The probability distribution of such a random variable is called a sampling distribution. In particular, we described the sampling distributions of the sample mean $\bar{x}$ and the sample proportion $\bar{p}$.

In considering the characteristics of the sampling distributions of $\bar{x}$ and $\bar{p}$, we stated that $E(\bar{x}) = \mu$ and $E(\bar{p}) = p$. Thus $\bar{x}$ and $\bar{p}$ are unbiased estimators. After developing the standard deviation or standard error formulas for these estimators, we described the conditions necessary for the sampling distributions of $\bar{x}$ and $\bar{p}$ to follow a normal distribution. Other sampling methods including stratified random sampling, cluster sampling, systematic sampling, convenience sampling, and judgment sampling were discussed. Finally, we discussed the concept of big data and the ramifications of extremely large samples on the sampling distributions of the sample mean and sample proportion.

GLOSSARY

Big data Any set of data that is too large or too complex to be handled by standard data-processing techniques and typical desktop software.

Central limit theorem A theorem that enables one to use the normal probability distribution to approximate the sampling distribution of $\bar{x}$ whenever the sample size is large.

Cluster sampling A probability sampling method in which the population is first divided into clusters and then a simple random sample of the clusters is taken.

Consistency A property of a point estimator that is present whenever larger sample sizes tend to provide point estimates closer to the population parameter.

Convenience sampling A nonprobability method of sampling whereby elements are selected for the sample on the basis of convenience.

Coverage error Nonsampling error that results when the research objective and the population from which the sample is to be drawn are not aligned.

Finite population correction factor The term $\sqrt{(N - n)/(N - 1)}$ that is used in the formulas for $\sigma_{\bar{x}}$ and $\sigma_{\bar{p}}$ whenever a finite population, rather than an infinite population, is being sampled. The generally accepted rule of thumb is to ignore the finite population correction factor whenever $n/N \leq .05$.

Frame A listing of the elements the sample will be selected from.

Judgment sampling A nonprobability method of sampling whereby elements are selected for the sample based on the judgment of the person doing the study.

Measurement error Nonsampling error that results from the incorrect measurement of the population characteristic of interest.

Nonresponse error Nonsampling error that results when some segments of the population are either more or less likely to respond to the survey mechanism.

Nonsampling error Any difference between the value of a sample statistic (such as the sample mean, sample standard deviation, or sample proportion) and the value of the corresponding population parameter (population mean, population standard deviation, or population proportion) that is not the result of sampling error. These include but are not limited to coverage error, nonresponse error, measurement error, interviewer error, and processing error.

Parameter A numerical characteristic of a population, such as a population mean μ, a population standard deviation σ, a population proportion p, and so on.

Point estimate The value of a point estimator used in a particular instance as an estimate of a population parameter.

Point estimator The sample statistic, such as $\bar{x}$, s, or $\bar{p}$, that provides the point estimate of the population parameter.

Random sample A random sample from an infinite population is a sample selected such that the following conditions are satisfied: (1) Each element selected comes from the same population; (2) each element is selected independently.

Relative efficiency Given two unbiased point estimators of the same population parameter, the point estimator with the smaller standard error is more efficient.

Sampling distribution A probability distribution consisting of all possible values of a sample statistic.

Sampled population The population from which the sample is taken.

Sample statistic A sample characteristic, such as a sample mean $\bar{x}$, a sample standard deviation s, a sample proportion $\bar{p}$, and so on. The value of the sample statistic is used to estimate the value of the corresponding population parameter.

Sampling error The difference between the value of a sample statistic (such as the sample mean, sample standard deviation, or sample proportion) and the value of the corresponding population parameter (population mean, population standard deviation, or population proportion) that occurs because a random sample is used to estimate the population parameter.

Sampling without replacement Once an element has been included in the sample, it is removed from the population and cannot be selected a second time.

Sampling with replacement Once an element has been included in the sample, it is returned to the population. A previously selected element can be selected again and therefore may appear in the sample more than once.

Simple random sample A simple random sample of size n from a finite population of size N is a sample selected such that each possible sample of size n has the same probability of being selected.

Standard error The standard deviation of a point estimator.

Stratified random sampling A probability sampling method in which the population is first divided into strata and a simple random sample is then taken from each stratum.

Systematic sampling A probability sampling method in which we randomly select one of the first k elements and then select every kth element thereafter.

Tall data A data set that has so many observations that traditional statistical inference has little meaning.

Target population The population for which statistical inferences such as point estimates are made. It is important for the target population to correspond as closely as possible to the sampled population.

Unbiased A property of a point estimator that is present when the expected value of the point estimator is equal to the population parameter it estimates.

Variety The diversity in types and structures of the data generated.

Velocity The speed at which the data are generated.

Veracity The reliability of the data generated.

Volume The amount of data generated.

Wide data A data set that has so many variables that simultaneous consideration of all variables is infeasible.

KEY FORMULAS

Expected Value of $\bar{x}$

$$E(\bar{x}) = \mu \tag{7.1}$$

Standard Deviation of $\bar{x}$ (Standard Error)

Finite Population	*Infinite Population*	
$\sigma_{\bar{x}} = \sqrt{\dfrac{N-n}{N-1}}\left(\dfrac{\sigma}{\sqrt{n}}\right)$	$\sigma_{\bar{x}} = \dfrac{\sigma}{\sqrt{n}}$	(7.2)

Expected Value of $\bar{p}$

$$E(\bar{p}) = p \tag{7.4}$$

Standard Deviation of $\bar{p}$ (Standard Error)

Finite Population	*Infinite Population*	
$\sigma_{\bar{p}} = \sqrt{\dfrac{N-n}{N-1}}\sqrt{\dfrac{p(1-p)}{n}}$	$\sigma_{\bar{p}} = \sqrt{\dfrac{p(1-p)}{n}}$	(7.5)

SUPPLEMENTARY EXERCISES

ShadowStocks

50. **Shadow Stocks.** Jack Lawler, a financial analyst, wants to prepare an article on the Shadow Stock portfolio developed by the American Association of Individual Investors (AAII). A list of the 30 companies in the Shadow Stock portfolio is contained in the file *ShadowStocks*. Jack would like to select a simple random sample of 5 of these companies for an interview concerning management practices.

  a. In the file *ShadowStock*, companies are listed in column A of an Excel worksheet. In column B we have generated a random number for each of the companies. Use these random numbers to select a simple random sample of 5 of these companies for Jack.

  b. Generate a new set of random numbers and use them to select a new simple random sample. Did you select the same companies?

51. **Personal Health Expenditures.** Data made available through the Petersen-Kaiser Health System Tracker in May 2018 showed health expenditures were $10,348 per person in the United States. Use $10,348 as the population mean and suppose a survey research firm will take a sample of 100 people to investigate the nature of their health expenditures. Assume the population standard deviation is $2500.

  a. Show the sampling distribution of the mean amount of health care expenditures for a sample of 100 people.

  b. What is the probability the sample mean will be within ±$200 of the population mean?

  c. What is the probability the sample mean will be greater than $12,000? If the survey research firm reports a sample mean greater than $12,000, would you question whether the firm followed correct sampling procedures? Why or why not?

52. **Foot Locker Store Productivity.** Foot Locker uses sales per square foot as a measure of store productivity. Sales are currently running at an annual rate of $406 per square foot. You have been asked by management to conduct a study of a sample of 64 Foot Locker stores. Assume the standard deviation in annual sales per square foot for the population of all 3400 Foot Locker stores is $80.

  a. Show the sampling distribution of $\bar{x}$, the sample mean annual sales per square foot for a sample of 64 Foot Locker stores.

  b. What is the probability that the sample mean will be within $15 of the population mean?

  c. Suppose you find a sample mean of $380. What is the probability of finding a sample mean of $380 or less? Would you consider such a sample to be an unusually low-performing group of stores?

53. **Airline Fares.** The mean airfare for flights departing from Buffalo Niagara International Airport during the first three months of 2017 was $320.51. Assume the standard deviation for this population of fares is known to be $80. Suppose a random sample of 60 flights departing from Buffalo Niagara International Airport during the first three months of 2018 is taken.

  a. If the mean and standard deviation of the population of airfares for flights departing from Buffalo Niagara International Airport didn't changed between the first three months of 2017 and the first three months of 2018, what is the probability the sample mean will be within $20 of the population mean cost per flight?

  b. What is the probability the sample mean will be within $10 of the population mean cost per flight?

54. **University Costs.** After deducting grants based on need, the average cost to attend the University of Southern California (USC) is $27,175. Assume the population standard deviation is $7400. Suppose that a random sample of 60 USC students will be taken from this population.

  a. What is the value of the standard error of the mean?

  b. What is the probability that the sample mean will be more than $27,175?

c. What is the probability that the sample mean will be within $1000 of the population mean?

d. How would the probability in part (c) change if the sample size were increased to 100?

55. **Inventory Costs.** Three firms carry inventories that differ in size. Firm A's inventory contains 2000 items, firm B's inventory contains 5000 items, and firm C's inventory contains 10,000 items. The population standard deviation for the cost of the items in each firm's inventory is $\sigma = 144$. A statistical consultant recommends that each firm take a sample of 50 items from its inventory to provide statistically valid estimates of the average cost per item. Managers of the small firm state that because it has the smallest population, it should be able to make the estimate from a much smaller sample than that required by the larger firms. However, the consultant states that to obtain the same standard error and thus the same precision in the sample results, all firms should use the same sample size regardless of population size.

a. Using the finite population correction factor, compute the standard error for each of the three firms given a sample of size 50.

b. What is the probability that for each firm the sample mean $\bar{x}$ will be within ± 25 of the population mean μ?

56. **Survey Research Results.** A researcher reports survey results by stating that the standard error of the mean is 20. The population standard deviation is 500.

a. How large was the sample used in this survey?

b. What is the probability that the point estimate was within ± 25 of the population mean?

57. **Production Quality Control.** A production process is checked periodically by a quality control inspector. The inspector selects simple random samples of 30 finished products and computes the sample mean product weights $\bar{x}$. If test results over a long period of time show that 5% of the $\bar{x}$ values are over 2.1 pounds and 5% are under 1.9 pounds, what are the mean and the standard deviation for the population of products produced with this process?

58. **Australians and Smoking.** Reuters reports that 15 percent of Australians smoke. By introducing tough laws banning brand labels on cigarette packages, Australia hopes to ultimately reduce the percentage of people smoking to 10%. Answer the following questions based on a sample of 240 Australians.

a. Show the sampling distribution of $\bar{p}$, the proportion of Australians who are smokers.

b. What is the probability the sample proportion will be within $\pm .04$ of the population proportion?

c. What is the probability the sample proportion will be within $\pm .02$ of the population proportion?

59. **Marketing Research Telephone Surveys.** A market research firm conducts telephone surveys with a 40% historical response rate. What is the probability that in a new sample of 400 telephone numbers, at least 150 individuals will cooperate and respond to the questions? In other words, what is the probability that the sample proportion will be at least $150/400 = .375$?

60. **Internet Advertising.** Advertisers contract with Internet service providers and search engines to place ads on websites. They pay a fee based on the number of potential customers who click on their ad. Unfortunately, click fraud—the practice of someone clicking on an ad solely for the purpose of driving up advertising revenue—has become a problem. *Businessweek* reports that 40 percent of advertisers claim they have been a victim of click fraud. Suppose a simple random sample of 380 advertisers will be taken to learn more about how they are affected by this practice.

a. What is the probability that the sample proportion will be within $\pm .04$ of the population proportion experiencing click fraud?

b. What is the probability that the sample proportion will be greater than .45?

61. **Traffic Tickets.** The proportion of individuals insured by the All-Driver Automobile Insurance Company who received at least one traffic ticket during a five-year period is .15.
   a. Show the sampling distribution of $\bar{p}$ if a random sample of 150 insured individuals is used to estimate the proportion having received at least one ticket.
   b. What is the probability that the sample proportion will be within ±.03 of the population proportion?

62. **Textbook Publishing.** Lori Jeffrey is a successful sales representative for a major publisher of college textbooks. Historically, Lori obtains a book adoption on 25% of her sales calls. Viewing her sales calls for one month as a sample of all possible sales calls, assume that a statistical analysis of the data yields a standard error of the proportion of .0625.
   a. How large was the sample used in this analysis? That is, how many sales calls did Lori make during the month?
   b. Let $\bar{p}$ indicate the sample proportion of book adoptions obtained during the month. Show the sampling distribution of $\bar{p}$.
   c. Using the sampling distribution of $\bar{p}$, compute the probability that Lori will obtain book adoptions on 30% or more of her sales calls during a one-month period.

63. **Life of Compact Fluorescent Lights.** In 2018, the Simple Dollar website reported that the mean life of 14-watt compact fluorescent lights (CFLs) is 8000 hours. Assume that for this population the standard deviation for CFL life is 480. Suppose the U.S. Department of Energy would like to select a random sample of 35,000 from the population of 14-watt CFLs for a follow-up study.
   a. Show the sampling distribution of $\bar{x}$, the sample mean for a sample of 35,000 individuals from this population.
   b. What is the probability that a simple random sample of 35,000 individuals from this population will provide a sample mean that is within four hours of the population mean?
   c. What is the probability that a simple random sample of 35,000 individuals from this population will provide a sample mean that is within one hour of the population mean?
   d. Suppose the mean life of a sample of 35,000 14-watt CFLs differs from the population mean life by more than four hours. How would you interpret this result?

64. **Typical Home Internet Usage.** According to USC Annenberg, the mean time spent by Americans on the Internet in their home per week is 17.6 hours. Assume that the standard deviation for the time spent by Americans on the Internet in their home per week is 5.1 hours. Suppose the Florida Department of State plans to select a random sample of 85,020 of the state's residents for a study of Floridians' Internet usage.
   a. Using the U.S. population figures provided in the problem (the population mean and standard deviation of time spent by Americans on the Internet in their home per week are 17.6 hours and 5.1 hours, respectively), what is the sampling distribution of the sample mean for the sample of 85,020 Floridians?
   b. Using the sampling distribution from part (a), what is the probability that a random sample of 85,020 Floridians will provide a sample mean that is within three minutes of the population mean?
   c. Suppose the mean time spent on the Internet in their home per week by the sample of 85,020 Floridians differs from the U.S population mean by more than three minutes? How would you interpret this result?

65. **Undeliverable Mail Pieces.** Of the 155 billion mailpieces the U.S. Postal Service (USPS) processed and delivered in 2017, 4.3% were undeliverable as addressed. Suppose that a brief questionnaire about USPS service is attached to each mailpiece in a random sample of 114,250 mailpieces.
   a. What is the sampling distribution of the sample proportion of undeliverable mailpieces $\bar{p}$ for this study?
   b. What is the probability that the sample proportion of undeliverable mailpieces $\bar{p}$ will be within .1% of the population proportion of undeliverable mailpieces?

c. What is the probability that the sample proportion of undeliverable mailpieces $\bar{p}$ will be within .05% of the population proportion of undeliverable mailpieces? Comment on the difference between this probability and the probability computed in part (b).

66. **U.S. Drivers and Speeding.** ABC News reports that 58% of U.S. drivers admit to speeding. Suppose that a new satellite technology can instantly measure the speed of any vehicle on a U.S. road and determine whether the vehicle is speeding, and this satellite technology was used to take a random sample of 20,000 vehicles at 6 P.M. EST on a recent Tuesday afternoon.

a. For this investigation, what is the sampling distribution for sample proportion of vehicles on U.S. roads that speed?

b. What is the probability that the sample proportion of speeders $\bar{p}$ will be within 1% of the population proportion of speeders?

c. Suppose the sample proportion of speeders $\bar{p}$ differs from the U.S population proportion of seeders by more than 1%? How would you interpret this result?

CASE PROBLEM: MARION DAIRIES

Last year Marion Dairies decided to enter the yogurt market, and it began cautiously by producing, distributing, and marketing a single flavor—a blueberry-flavored yogurt that it calls Blugurt. The company's initial venture into the yogurt market has been very successful; sales of Blugurt are higher than expected, and consumers' ratings of the product have a mean of 80 and a standard deviation of 25 on a 100-point scale for which 100 is the most favorable score and zero is the least favorable score. Past experience has also shown Marion Dairies that a consumer who rates one of its products with a score greater than 75 on this scale will consider purchasing the product, and a score of 75 or less indicates that the consumer will not consider purchasing the product.

Emboldened by the success and popularity of its blueberry-flavored yogurt, Marion Dairies management is now considering the introduction of a second flavor. Marion's marketing department is pressing to extend the product line through the introduction of a strawberry-flavored yogurt that would be called Strawgurt, but senior managers are concerned about whether or not Strawgurt will increase Marion's market share by appealing to potential customers who do not like Blugurt. That is, the goal in offering the new product is to increase Marion's market share rather than cannibalize existing sales of Blugurt. The marketing department has proposed giving tastes of both Blugurt and Strawgurt to a simple random sample of 50 customers and asking each of them to rate the two yogurts on the 100-point scale. If the mean score given to Blugurt by this sample of consumers is 75 or less, Marion's senior management believes the sample can be used to assess whether Strawgurt will appeal to potential customers who do not like Blugurt.

Managerial Report

Prepare a managerial report that addresses the following issues.

1. Calculate the probability that the mean score of Blugurt given by the simple random sample of Marion Dairies customers will be 75 or less.

2. If the Marketing Department increases the sample size to 150, what is the probability that the mean score of Blugurt given by the simple random sample of Marion Dairies customers will be 75 or less?

3. Explain to Marion Dairies senior management why the probability that the mean score of Blugurt given by the simple random sample of Marion Dairies customers will be 75 or less is different for these two sample sizes.

Chapter 7 Appendix

Appendix 7.1 The Expected Value and Standard Deviation of $\bar{x}$

In this appendix we present the mathematical basis for the expressions for $E(\bar{x})$, the expected value of $\bar{x}$ as given by equation (7.1), and $\sigma_{\bar{x}}$, the standard deviation of $\bar{x}$ as given by equation (7.2).

Expected Value of $\bar{x}$

Assume a population with mean μ and variance σ^2. A simple random sample of size n is selected with individual observations denoted $x_1, x_2, \ldots, x_n$. A sample mean $\bar{x}$ is computed as follows.

$$\bar{x} = \frac{\Sigma x_i}{n}$$

With repeated simple random samples of size n, $\bar{x}$ is a random variable that assumes different numerical values depending on the specific n items selected. The expected value of the random variable $\bar{x}$ is the mean of all possible $\bar{x}$ values.

$$\text{Mean of } \bar{x} = E(\bar{x}) = E\left(\frac{\Sigma x_i}{n}\right)$$

$$= \frac{1}{n}[E(x_1 + x_2 + \cdots + x_n)]$$

$$= \frac{1}{n}[E(x_1) + E(x_2) + \cdots + E(x_n)]$$

For any x_i we have $E(x_i) = \mu$; therefore we can write

$$E(\bar{x}) = \frac{1}{n}(\mu + \mu + \cdots + \mu)$$

$$= \frac{1}{n}(n\mu) = \mu$$

This result shows that the mean of all possible $\bar{x}$ values is the same as the population mean μ. That is, $E(\bar{x}) = \mu$.

Standard Deviation of $\bar{x}$

Again assume a population with mean μ, variance σ^2, and a sample mean given by

$$\bar{x} = \frac{\Sigma x_i}{n}$$

With repeated simple random samples of size n, we know that $\bar{x}$ is a random variable that takes different numerical values depending on the specific n items selected. What follows is the derivation of the expression for the standard deviation of the $\bar{x}$ values, $\sigma_{\bar{x}}$, for the case of an infinite population. The derivation of the expression for $\sigma_{\bar{x}}$ for a finite population when sampling is done without replacement is more difficult and is beyond the scope of this text.

Returning to the infinite population case, recall that a simple random sample from an infinite population consists of observations $x_1, x_2, \ldots, x_n$ that are independent. The following two expressions are general formulas for the variance of random variables.

$$Var(ax) = a^2 \, Var(x)$$

where a is a constant and x is a random variable, and

$$Var(x + y) = Var(x) + Var(y)$$

where x and y are *independent* random variables. Using the two preceding equations, we can develop the expression for the variance of the random variable $\bar{x}$ as follows.

$$Var(\bar{x}) = Var\left(\frac{\Sigma x_i}{n}\right) = Var\left(\frac{1}{n}\Sigma x_i\right)$$

Then, with $1/n$ a constant, we have

$$Var(\bar{x}) = \left(\frac{1}{n}\right)^2 Var(\Sigma x_i)$$

$$= \left(\frac{1}{n}\right)^2 Var(x_1 + x_2 + \cdots + x_n)$$

In the infinite population case, the random variables $x_1, x_2, \ldots, x_n$ are independent, which enables us to write

$$Var(\bar{x}) = \left(\frac{1}{n}\right)^2 [Var(x_1) + Var(x_2) + \cdots + Var(x_n)]$$

For any x_i, we have $Var(x_i) = \sigma^2$; therefore we have

$$Var(\bar{x}) = \left(\frac{1}{n}\right)^2 (\sigma^2 + \sigma^2 + \cdots + \sigma^2)$$

With n values of σ^2 in this expression, we have

$$Var(\bar{x}) = \left(\frac{1}{n}\right)^2 (n\sigma^2) = \frac{\sigma^2}{n}$$

Taking the square root provides the formula for the standard deviation of $\bar{x}$.

$$\sigma_{\bar{x}} = \sqrt{Var(\bar{x})} = \frac{\sigma}{\sqrt{n}}$$

Appendix 7.2 Random Sampling with JMP

Before using JMP to take a random sample from a set of data, you must first download and install the Random Seed Reset add-in from the JMP website (https://community.jmp.com/t5/JMP-Add-Ins/Random-Seed-Reset/ta-p/21973) as shown in Figure JMP 7.1). Once you have navigated to this site, click on the **JMPRandomSeed.jpg icon** button to download. After the download is complete, proceed with the installation by clicking on the downloaded

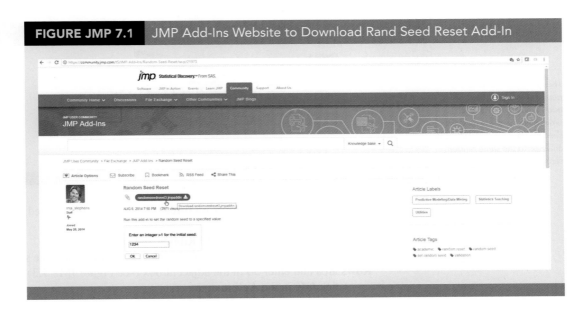

FIGURE JMP 7.1 JMP Add-Ins Website to Download Rand Seed Reset Add-In

file **randomseedreset3.jmpaddin** in its downloaded location. After installation, the Random Seed Reset option will appear under the Add-Ins tab in the JMP home window.

If a list of the elements in a population is available in a JMP file, JMP can be used to select a simple random sample. For example, a list of the 1000 most populous metropolitan areas in the United States as of 2018 is provided in column 1 of the file *USCitiesPop* (Biggest US Cities website). Column 2 contains the population of each metropolitan area. The first 10 metropolitan areas in the data set and their corresponding populations are shown in Table JMP 7.1.

Suppose that you would like to select a simple random sample of 30 metropolitan areas in order to do an in-depth study of the populations of metropolitan areas in the United States. The following steps can be used to select the sample using JMP.

Selecting a Random Sample in JMP

The following steps will generate a random sample of 30 cities from the data in the file *USCitiesPop*.

Step 1. Open the file *USCitiesPop.xlsx* with JMP using the steps provided in Appendix 1.1

Step 2. Click the **Add-Ins** tab on the JMP Ribbon

Select **Random Seed Reset** to open the **Set Random Seed** dialog box (see Figure JMP 7.2)

DATA *file*

USCitiesPop

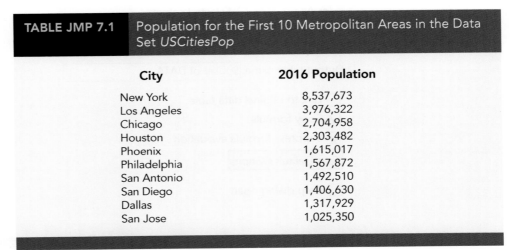

TABLE JMP 7.1 Population for the First 10 Metropolitan Areas in the Data Set *USCitiesPop*

City	2016 Population
New York	8,537,673
Los Angeles	3,976,322
Chicago	2,704,958
Houston	2,303,482
Phoenix	1,615,017
Philadelphia	1,567,872
San Antonio	1,492,510
San Diego	1,406,630
Dallas	1,317,929
San Jose	1,025,350

| FIGURE JMP 7.2 | Set Random Seed Dialog Box in JMP |

The random seed does not persist across analyses (the add-in must be rerun each time using the same random seed in order to apply different analyses to the same random sample).

Enter *12345* in the **Enter an integer** > 1 for the initial seed box
Click **OK**

Step 3. Click the **Tables** tab on the JMP Ribbon and select **Subset**
Step 4. When the **Subset** dialog box appears, select **Random—sample size:** in the **Rows** area and enter *30* in the adjacent box (see Figure JMP 7.3)
Click **OK** in the **Action** area

| FIGURE JMP 7.3 | JMP Subset Dialog Box |

FIGURE JMP 7.4   Random Sample from *USCitiesPop* file in JMP

These steps result in a new file containing 30 metropolitan areas that have been randomly selected from the original data as shown in Figure JMP 7.4. You can now analyze and save this data set just as you could any other JMP data set.

Appendix 7.3 Random Sampling with Excel

If a list of the elements in a population is available in an Excel file, Excel can be used to select a simple random sample. For example, a list of the top 100 metropolitan areas in the United States and Canada rated on livability scores according to the *Places Rated Almanac* is provided in the file *MetAreas*. Column A contains the metropolitan area name and column B contains the overall rating of each metropolitan area. The first 10 metropolitan areas in the data set and their corresponding ratings are shown in Table Excel 7.1. Assume that you would like to select a simple random sample of 30 metropolitan areas in order to do an in-depth study of the cost of living in the United States and Canada.

The rows of any Excel data set can be placed in a random order by adding an extra column to the data set and filling the column with random numbers using the =RAND() function. Then, using Excel's sort ascending capability on the random number column, the rows of the data set will be reordered randomly. The random sample of size *n* appears in the first *n* rows of the reordered data set.

In the metropolitan areas data set, labels are in row 1 and the 100 metropolitan areas are in rows 2 to 101. The following steps can be used to select a simple random sample of 30 metropolitan areas.

TABLE Excel 7.1	Overall Rating for the First 10 Metropolitan Areas in *MetAreas* File

MetAreas

Metropolitan Area	Rating
Albany, NY	64.18
Albuquerque, NM	66.16
Appleton, WI	60.56
Atlanta, GA	69.97
Austin, TX	71.48
Baltimore, MD	69.75
Birmingham, AL	69.59
Boise City, ID	68.36
Boston, MA	68.99
Buffalo, NY	66.10

Step 1. Enter =*RAND()* in cell C2
Step 2. Copy cell C2 to cells C3:C101
Step 3. Select any cell in column C
Step 4. Click the **Home** tab on the Ribbon
    In the **Editing** group, click **Sort & Filter**
    Select **Sort Smallest to Largest**

The random sample of 30 metropolitan areas appears in rows 2 to 31 of the reordered data set. The random numbers in column C are no longer necessary and can be deleted if desired.

Chapter 8

Interval Estimation

CONTENTS

STATISTICS IN PRACTICE: *FOOD LION*

STATISTICS IN PRACTICE

Food Lion*

SALISBURY, NORTH CAROLINA

Founded in 1957 as Food Town, Food Lion is one of the largest supermarket chains in the United States, with 1300 stores in 11 Southeastern and Mid-Atlantic states. The company sells more than 24,000 different products and offers nationally and regionally advertised brand-name merchandise, as well as a growing number of high-quality private label products manufactured especially for Food Lion. The company maintains its low price leadership and quality assurance through operating efficiencies such as standard store formats, innovative warehouse design, energy-efficient facilities, and data synchronization with suppliers. Food Lion looks to a future of continued innovation, growth, price leadership, and service to its customers.

Being in an inventory-intense business, Food Lion made the decision to adopt the LIFO (last-in, first-out) method of inventory valuation. This method matches current costs against current revenues, which minimizes the effect of radical price changes on profit and loss results. In addition, the LIFO method reduces net income thereby reducing income taxes during periods of inflation.

Food Lion establishes a LIFO index for each of seven inventory pools: Grocery, Paper/Household, Pet Supplies, Health & Beauty Aids, Dairy, Cigarette/Tobacco, and Beer/Wine. For example, a LIFO index of 1.008 for the Grocery pool would indicate that the company's grocery inventory value at current costs reflects a .8% increase due to inflation over the most recent one-year period.

A LIFO index for each inventory pool requires that the year-end inventory count for each product

As an inventory-intense business, Food Lion adopted the LIFO method of inventory valuation.
Source: Bloomberg/Getty Images

be valued at the current year-end cost and at the preceding year-end cost. To avoid excessive time and expense associated with counting the inventory in all 1200 store locations, Food Lion selects a random sample of 50 stores. Year-end physical inventories are taken in each of the sample stores. The current-year and preceding-year costs for each item are then used to construct the required LIFO indexes for each inventory pool.

For a recent year, the sample estimate of the LIFO index for the Health & Beauty Aids inventory pool was 1.015. Using a 95% confidence level, Food Lion computed a margin of error of .006 for the sample estimate. Thus, the interval from 1.009 to 1.021 provided a 95% confidence interval estimate of the population LIFO index. This level of precision was judged to be very good.

In this chapter you will learn how to compute the margin of error associated with sample estimates. You will also learn how to use this information to construct and interpret interval estimates of a population mean and a population proportion.

---

*The authors are indebted to Keith Cunningham, Tax Director, and Bobby Harkey, Staff Tax Accountant, at Food Lion for providing the context for this Statistics in Practice.

In Chapter 7, we stated that a point estimator is a sample statistic used to estimate a population parameter. For instance, the sample mean $\bar{x}$ is a point estimator of the population mean μ and the sample proportion $\bar{p}$ is a point estimator of the population proportion p. Because a point estimator cannot be expected to provide the exact value of the population parameter, an **interval estimate** is often computed by adding and subtracting a value, called the **margin of error**, to the point estimate. The general form of an interval estimate is as follows:

$$\text{Point estimate} \pm \text{Margin of error}$$

The purpose of an interval estimate is to provide information about how close the point estimate, provided by the sample, is to the value of the population parameter.

In this chapter we show how to compute interval estimates of a population mean μ and a population proportion p. The general form of an interval estimate of a population mean is

$$\bar{x} \pm \text{Margin of error}$$

Similarly, the general form of an interval estimate of a population proportion is

$$\bar{p} \pm \text{Margin of error}$$

The sampling distributions of $\bar{x}$ and $\bar{p}$ play key roles in computing these interval estimates.

8.1 Population Mean: σ Known

In order to develop an interval estimate of a population mean, either the population standard deviation σ or the sample standard deviation s must be used to compute the margin of error. In most applications σ is not known, and s is used to compute the margin of error. In some applications, large amounts of relevant historical data are available and can be used to estimate the population standard deviation prior to sampling. Also, in quality control applications where a process is assumed to be operating correctly, or "in control," it is appropriate to treat the population standard deviation as known. We refer to such cases as the σ **known** case. In this section we introduce an example in which it is reasonable to treat σ as known and show how to construct an interval estimate for this case.

Each week Lloyd's Department Store selects a simple random sample of 100 customers in order to learn about the amount spent per shopping trip. With x representing the amount spent per shopping trip, the sample mean $\bar{x}$ provides a point estimate of μ, the mean amount spent per shopping trip for the population of all Lloyd's customers. Lloyd's has been using the weekly survey for several years. Based on the historical data, Lloyd's now assumes a known value of $\sigma = \$20$ for the population standard deviation. The historical data also indicate that the population follows a normal distribution.

Lloyds

During the most recent week, Lloyd's surveyed 100 customers ($n = 100$) and obtained a sample mean of $\bar{x} = \$82$. The sample mean amount spent provides a point estimate of the population mean amount spent per shopping trip, μ. In the discussion that follows, we show how to compute the margin of error for this estimate and develop an interval estimate of the population mean.

Margin of Error and the Interval Estimate

In Chapter 7 we showed that the sampling distribution of $\bar{x}$ can be used to compute the probability that $\bar{x}$ will be within a given distance of μ. In the Lloyd's example, the historical data show that the population of amounts spent is normally distributed with a standard deviation of $\sigma = 20$. So, using what we learned in Chapter 7, we can conclude that the sampling distribution of $\bar{x}$ follows a normal distribution with a standard error of $\sigma_{\bar{x}} = \sigma/\sqrt{n} = 20/\sqrt{100} = 2$. This sampling distribution is shown in Figure 8.1.[1] Because the sampling distribution shows how values of $\bar{x}$ are distributed around the population mean μ, the sampling distribution of $\bar{x}$ provides information about the possible differences between $\bar{x}$ and μ.

Using the standard normal probability table, we find that 95% of the values of any normally distributed random variable are within ± 1.96 standard deviations of the mean. Thus, when the sampling distribution of $\bar{x}$ is normally distributed, 95% of the $\bar{x}$ values must be within $\pm 1.96\sigma_{\bar{x}}$ of the mean μ. In the Lloyd's example we know that the sampling distribution of $\bar{x}$ is normally distributed with a standard error of $\sigma_{\bar{x}} = 2$. Because $\pm 1.96\sigma_{\bar{x}} = 1.96(2) = 3.92$, we can conclude that 95% of all $\bar{x}$ values obtained using a sample size of $n = 100$ will be within ± 3.92 of the population mean μ. See Figure 8.2.

---

[1] We use the fact that the population of amounts spent has a normal distribution to conclude that the sampling distribution of $\bar{x}$ has a normal distribution. If the population did not have a normal distribution, we could rely on the central limit theorem and the sample size of $n = 100$ to conclude that the sampling distribution of $\bar{x}$ is approximately normal. In either case, the sampling distribution of $\bar{x}$ would appear as shown in Figure 8.1.

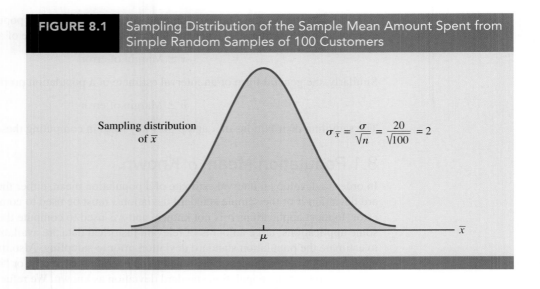

FIGURE 8.1 Sampling Distribution of the Sample Mean Amount Spent from Simple Random Samples of 100 Customers

Sampling distribution of $\bar{x}$

$$\sigma_{\bar{x}} = \frac{\sigma}{\sqrt{n}} = \frac{20}{\sqrt{100}} = 2$$

μ

$\bar{x}$

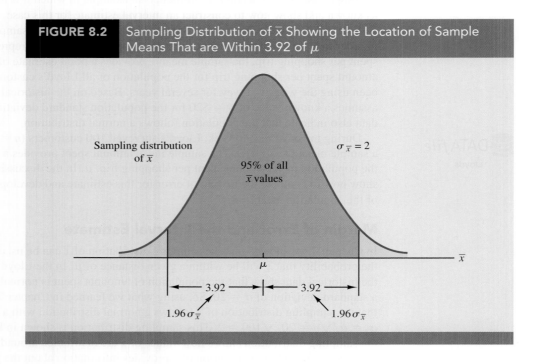

FIGURE 8.2 Sampling Distribution of $\bar{x}$ Showing the Location of Sample Means That are Within 3.92 of μ

Sampling distribution of $\bar{x}$

$\sigma_{\bar{x}} = 2$

95% of all $\bar{x}$ values

μ

$\bar{x}$

3.92

3.92

$1.96\,\sigma_{\bar{x}}$

$1.96\,\sigma_{\bar{x}}$

In the introduction to this chapter we said that the general form of an interval estimate of the population mean μ is $\bar{x} \pm$ margin of error. For the Lloyd's example, suppose we set the margin of error equal to 3.92 and compute the interval estimate of μ using $\bar{x} \pm 3.92$. To provide an interpretation for this interval estimate, let us consider the values of $\bar{x}$ that could be obtained if we took three *different* simple random samples, each consisting of 100 Lloyd's customers. The first sample mean might turn out to have the value shown as $\bar{x}_1$ in Figure 8.3. In this case, Figure 8.3 shows that the interval formed by subtracting 3.92 from $\bar{x}_1$ and adding 3.92 to $\bar{x}_1$ includes the population mean μ. Now consider what happens if the second sample mean turns out to have the value shown as $\bar{x}_2$ in Figure 8.3.

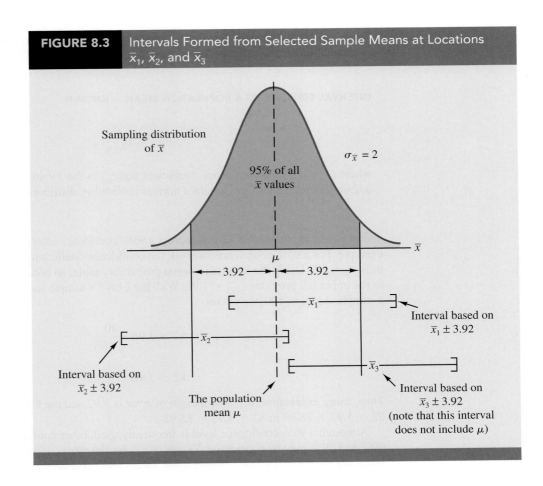

| **FIGURE 8.3** | Intervals Formed from Selected Sample Means at Locations $\bar{x}_1$, $\bar{x}_2$, and $\bar{x}_3$ |

Although this sample mean differs from the first sample mean, we see that the interval formed by subtracting 3.92 from $\bar{x}_2$ and adding 3.92 to $\bar{x}_2$ also includes the population mean μ. However, consider what happens if the third sample mean turns out to have the value shown as $\bar{x}_3$ in Figure 8.3. In this case, the interval formed by subtracting 3.92 from $\bar{x}_3$ and adding 3.92 to $\bar{x}_3$ does not include the population mean μ. Because $\bar{x}_3$ falls in the upper tail of the sampling distribution and is farther than 3.92 from μ, subtracting and adding 3.92 to $\bar{x}_3$ forms an interval that does not include μ.

Any sample mean $\bar{x}$ that is within the darkly shaded region of Figure 8.3 will provide an interval that contains the population mean μ. Because 95% of all possible sample means are in the darkly shaded region, 95% of all intervals formed by subtracting 3.92 from $\bar{x}$ and adding 3.92 to $\bar{x}$ will include the population mean μ.

Recall that during the most recent week, the quality assurance team at Lloyd's surveyed 100 customers and obtained a sample mean amount spent of $\bar{x} = 82$. Using $\bar{x} \pm 3.92$ to construct the interval estimate, we obtain 82 ± 3.92. Thus, the specific interval estimate of μ based on the data from the most recent week is $82 - 3.92 = 78.08$ to $82 + 3.92 = 85.92$. Because 95% of all the intervals constructed using $\bar{x} \pm 3.92$ will contain the population mean, we say that we are 95% confident that the interval 78.08 to 85.92 includes the population mean μ. We say that this interval has been established at the 95% **confidence level**. The value .95 is referred to as the **confidence coefficient**, and the interval 78.08 to 85.92 is called the 95% **confidence interval**.

This discussion provides insight as to why the interval is called a 95% confidence interval.

With the margin of error given by $z_{\alpha/2}(\sigma/\sqrt{n})$, the general form of an interval estimate of a population mean for the σ known case follows.

INTERVAL ESTIMATE OF A POPULATION MEAN: σ KNOWN

$$\bar{x} \pm z_{\alpha/2}\frac{\sigma}{\sqrt{n}} \tag{8.1}$$

where $(1 - \alpha)$ is the confidence coefficient and $z_{\alpha/2}$ is the z value providing an area of $\alpha/2$ in the upper tail of the standard normal probability distribution.

Let us use expression (8.1) to construct a 95% confidence interval for the Lloyd's example. For a 95% confidence interval, the confidence coefficient is $(1 - \alpha) = .95$ and thus, $\alpha = .05$. Using the standard normal probability table, an area of $\alpha/2 = .05/2 = .025$ in the upper tail provides $z_{.025} = 1.96$. With the Lloyd's sample mean $\bar{x} = 82$, $\sigma = 20$, and a sample size $n = 100$, we obtain

$$82 \pm 1.96\frac{20}{\sqrt{100}}$$

$$82 \pm 3.92$$

Thus, using expression (8.1), the margin of error is 3.92 and the 95% confidence interval is $82 - 3.92 = 78.08$ to $82 + 3.92 = 85.92$.

Although a 95% confidence level is frequently used, other confidence levels such as 90% and 99% may be considered. Values of $z_{\alpha/2}$ for the most commonly used confidence levels are shown in Table 8.1. Using these values and expression (8.1), the 90% confidence interval for the Lloyd's example is

$$82 \pm 1.645\frac{20}{\sqrt{100}}$$

$$82 \pm 3.29$$

Thus, at 90% confidence, the margin of error is 3.29 and the confidence interval is $82 - 3.29 = 78.71$ to $82 + 3.29 = 85.29$. Similarly, the 99% confidence interval is

$$82 \pm 2.576\frac{20}{\sqrt{100}}$$

$$82 \pm 5.15$$

Thus, at 99% confidence, the margin of error is 5.15 and the confidence interval is $82 - 5.15 = 76.85$ to $82 + 5.15 = 87.15$.

TABLE 8.1   Values of $z_{\alpha/2}$ for the Most Commonly Used Confidence Levels

Confidence Level	α	$\alpha/2$	$z_{\alpha/2}$
90%	.10	.05	1.645
95%	.05	.025	1.960
99%	.01	.005	2.576

Comparing the results for the 90%, 95%, and 99% confidence levels, we see that in order to have a higher degree of confidence, the margin of error and thus the width of the confidence interval must be larger.

Practical Advice

If the population follows a normal distribution, the confidence interval provided by expression (8.1) is exact. In other words, if expression (8.1) were used repeatedly to generate 95% confidence intervals, exactly 95% of the intervals generated would contain the population mean. If the population does not follow a normal distribution, the confidence interval provided by expression (8.1) will be approximate. In this case, the quality of the approximation depends on both the distribution of the population and the sample size.

In most applications, a sample size of $n \geq 30$ is adequate when using expression (8.1) to develop an interval estimate of a population mean. If the population is not normally distributed but is roughly symmetric, sample sizes as small as 15 can be expected to provide good approximate confidence intervals. With smaller sample sizes, expression (8.1) should only be used if the analyst believes, or is willing to assume, that the population distribution is at least approximately normal.

NOTES + COMMENTS

1. The interval estimation procedure discussed in this section is based on the assumption that the population standard deviation σ is known. We do not strictly mean that σ is known with certainty. We just mean that, in this case, we have obtained a good estimate of the population standard deviation prior to sampling and thus we won't be using the same sample to estimate both the population mean and the population standard deviation. This estimate of the population standard deviation may be based on historical data or other previously available information.

2. The sample size n appears in the denominator of the interval estimation expression (8.1). Thus, if a particular sample size provides too wide an interval to be of any practical use, we may want to consider increasing the sample size. With n in the denominator, a larger sample size will provide a smaller margin of error, a narrower interval, and greater precision. The procedure for determining the size of a simple random sample necessary to obtain a desired precision is discussed in Section 8.3.

EXERCISES

Methods

1. A simple random sample of 40 items resulted in a sample mean of 25. The population standard deviation is $\sigma = 5$.
   a. What is the standard error of the mean, $\sigma_{\bar{x}}$?
   b. At 95% confidence, what is the margin of error?

2. A simple random sample of 50 items from a population with $\sigma = 6$ resulted in a sample mean of 32.
   a. Provide a 90% confidence interval for the population mean.
   b. Provide a 95% confidence interval for the population mean.
   c. Provide a 99% confidence interval for the population mean.

3. A simple random sample of 60 items resulted in a sample mean of 80. The population standard deviation is $\sigma = 15$.
   a. Compute the 95% confidence interval for the population mean.
   b. Assume that the same sample mean was obtained from a sample of 120 items. Provide a 95% confidence interval for the population mean.
   c. What is the effect of a larger sample size on the interval estimate?

4. A 95% confidence interval for a population mean was reported to be 152 to 160. If $\sigma = 15$, what sample size was used in this study?

Applications

Houston

TravelTax

Setters

5. **Restaurant Bills.** Data were collected on the amount spent by 64 customers for lunch at a major Houston restaurant. These data are contained in the file *Houston*. Based upon past studies the population standard deviation is known with $\sigma = \$6$.
   a. At 99% confidence, what is the margin of error?
   b. Develop a 99% confidence interval estimate of the mean amount spent for lunch.

6. **Travel Taxes.** In an attempt to assess total daily travel taxes in various cities, the Global Business Travel Association conducted a study of daily travel taxes on lodging, rental car, and meals. The data contained in the file *TravelTax* are consistent with the findings of that study for business travel to Chicago. Assume the population standard deviation is known to be $8.50 and develop a 95% confidence interval of the population mean total daily travel taxes for Chicago.

7. **Cost of Dog Ownership.** *Money* reports that the average annual cost of the first year of owning and caring for a large dog in 2017 is $1448. The Irish Red and White Setter Association of America has requested a study to estimate the annual first-year cost for owners of this breed. A sample of 50 will be used. Based on past studies, the population standard deviation is assumed known with $\sigma = \$255$.
   a. What is the margin of error for a 95% confidence interval of the mean cost of the first year of owning and caring for this breed?
   b. The file *Setters* contains data collected from fifty owners of Irish Setters on the cost of the first year of owning and caring for their dogs. Use this data set to compute the sample mean. Using this sample, what is the 95% confidence interval for the mean cost of the first year of owning and caring for an Irish Red and White Setter?

8. **Cost of Message Therapy Sessions.** Studies show that massage therapy has a variety of health benefits and it is not too expensive. A sample of 10 typical one-hour massage therapy sessions showed an average charge of $59. The population standard deviation for a one-hour session is $\sigma = \$5.50$.
   a. What assumptions about the population should we be willing to make if a margin of error is desired?
   b. Using 95% confidence, what is the margin of error?
   c. Using 99% confidence, what is the margin of error?

TobaccoFires

9. **Cost to Repair Fire Damage.** The mean cost to repair the smoke and fire damage that results from home fires of all causes is $11,389 (HomeAdvisor). How does the damage that results from home fires caused by careless use of tobacco compare? The file *TobaccoFires* provides the cost to repair smoke and fire damage associated with a sample of 55 fires caused by careless use of tobacco products. Using past years' data, the population standard deviation can be assumed known with $\sigma = \$3027$. What is the 95% confidence interval estimate of the mean cost to repair smoke and fire damage that results from home fires caused by careless use of tobacco? How does this compare with the mean cost to repair the smoke and fire damage that results from home fires of all causes?

10. **Assisted-Living Facility Rent.** Costs are rising for all kinds of medical care. The mean monthly rent at assisted-living facilities was reported to have increased 17% over the last five years to $3486. Assume this cost estimate is based on a sample of 120 facilities and, from past studies, it can be assumed that the population standard deviation is $\sigma = \$650$.
    a. Develop a 90% confidence interval estimate of the population mean monthly rent.
    b. Develop a 95% confidence interval estimate of the population mean monthly rent.
    c. Develop a 99% confidence interval estimate of the population mean monthly rent.
    d. What happens to the width of the confidence interval as the confidence level is increased? Does this seem reasonable? Explain.

8.2 Population Mean: σ Unknown

When developing an interval estimate of a population mean we usually do not have a good estimate of the population standard deviation either. In these cases, we must use the same sample to estimate both μ and σ. This situation represents the σ **unknown** case. When s is used to estimate σ, the margin of error and the interval estimate for the population mean are based on a probability distribution known as the t **distribution**. Although the mathematical development of the t distribution is based on the assumption of a normal distribution for the population we are sampling from, research shows that the t distribution can be successfully applied in many situations where the population deviates significantly from normal. Later in this section we provide guidelines for using the t distribution if the population is not normally distributed.

The t distribution is a family of similar probability distributions, with a specific t distribution depending on a parameter known as the **degrees of freedom**. The t distribution with one degree of freedom is unique, as is the t distribution with two degrees of freedom, with three degrees of freedom, and so on. As the number of degrees of freedom increases, the difference between the t distribution and the standard normal distribution becomes smaller and smaller. Figure 8.4 shows t distributions with 10 and 20 degrees of freedom and their relationship to the standard normal probability distribution. Note that a t distribution with more degrees of freedom exhibits less variability and more closely resembles the standard normal distribution. Note also that the mean of the t distribution is zero.

We place a subscript on t to indicate the area in the upper tail of the t distribution. For example, just as we used $z_{.025}$ to indicate the z value providing a .025 area in the upper tail of a standard normal distribution, we will use $t_{.025}$ to indicate a .025 area in the upper tail of a t distribution. In general, we will use the notation $t_{\alpha/2}$ to represent a t value with an area of $\alpha/2$ in the upper tail of the t distribution. See Figure 8.5.

Table 2 in Appendix B contains a table for the t distribution. A portion of this table is shown in Table 8.2. Each row in the table corresponds to a separate t distribution with the degrees of freedom shown. For example, for a t distribution with 9 degrees of freedom, $t_{.025} = 2.262$. Similarly, for a t distribution with 60 degrees of freedom, $t_{.025} = 2.000$. As the degrees of freedom continue to increase, $t_{.025}$ approaches $z_{.025} = 1.96$. In fact, the standard normal distribution z values can be found in the infinite degrees of freedom row (labeled ∞) of the t distribution table. If the degrees of freedom exceed 100, the infinite

William Sealy Gosset, writing under the name "Student," is the founder of the t distribution. Gosset, an Oxford graduate in mathematics, worked for the Guinness Brewery in Dublin, Ireland. He developed the t distribution while working on small-scale materials and temperature experiments.

As the degrees of freedom increase, the t distribution approaches the standard normal distribution.

| **FIGURE 8.4** | Comparison of the Standard Normal Distribution with *t* Distributions Having 10 and 20 Degrees of Freedom |

Standard normal distribution

t distribution (20 degrees of freedom)

t distribution (10 degrees of freedom)

z, t

0

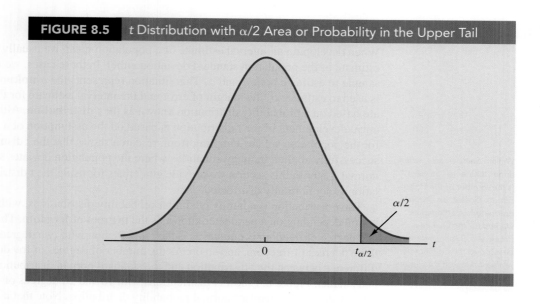

FIGURE 8.5 t Distribution with $\alpha/2$ Area or Probability in the Upper Tail

degrees of freedom row can be used to approximate the actual t value; in other words, for more than 100 degrees of freedom, the standard normal z value provides a good approximation to the t value.

Margin of Error and the Interval Estimate

In Section 8.1 we showed that an interval estimate of a population mean for the σ known case is

$$\bar{x} \pm z_{\alpha/2} \frac{\sigma}{\sqrt{n}}$$

To compute an interval estimate of μ for the σ unknown case, the sample standard deviation s is used to estimate σ, and $z_{\alpha/2}$ is replaced by the t distribution value $t_{\alpha/2}$. The margin of error is then given by $t_{\alpha/2} s/\sqrt{n}$. With this margin of error, the general expression for an interval estimate of a population mean when σ is unknown follows.

INTERVAL ESTIMATE OF A POPULATION MEAN: σ UNKNOWN

$$\bar{x} \pm t_{\alpha/2} \frac{s}{\sqrt{n}} \tag{8.2}$$

where s is the sample standard deviation, $(1 - \alpha)$ is the confidence coefficient, and $t_{\alpha/2}$ is the t value providing an area of $\alpha/2$ in the upper tail of the t distribution with $n - 1$ degrees of freedom.

The reason the number of degrees of freedom associated with the t value in expression (8.2) is $n - 1$ concerns the use of s as an estimate of the population standard deviation σ. The expression for the sample standard deviation is

$$s = \sqrt{\frac{\Sigma(x_i - \bar{x})^2}{n - 1}}$$

TABLE 8.2   Selected Values from the *t* Distribution Table*

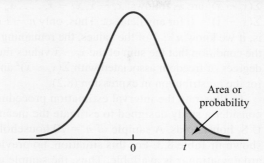

Area or probability

Degrees of Freedom	Area in Upper Tail					
	.20	**.10**	**.05**	**.025**	**.01**	**.005**
1	1.376	3.078	6.314	12.706	31.821	63.656
2	1.061	1.886	2.920	4.303	6.965	9.925
3	.978	1.638	2.353	3.182	4.541	5.841
4	.941	1.533	2.132	2.776	3.747	4.604
5	.920	1.476	2.015	2.571	3.365	4.032
6	.906	1.440	1.943	2.447	3.143	3.707
7	.896	1.415	1.895	2.365	2.998	3.499
8	.889	1.397	1.860	2.306	2.896	3.355
9	.883	1.383	1.833	2.262	2.821	3.250
⋮	⋮	⋮	⋮	⋮	⋮	⋮
60	.848	1.296	1.671	2.000	2.390	2.660
61	.848	1.296	1.670	2.000	2.389	2.659
62	.847	1.295	1.670	1.999	2.388	2.657
63	.847	1.295	1.669	1.998	2.387	2.656
64	.847	1.295	1.669	1.998	2.386	2.655
65	.847	1.295	1.669	1.997	2.385	2.654
66	.847	1.295	1.668	1.997	2.384	2.652
67	.847	1.294	1.668	1.996	2.383	2.651
68	.847	1.294	1.668	1.995	2.382	2.650
69	.847	1.294	1.667	1.995	2.382	2.649
⋮	⋮	⋮	⋮	⋮	⋮	⋮
90	.846	1.291	1.662	1.987	2.368	2.632
91	.846	1.291	1.662	1.986	2.368	2.631
92	.846	1.291	1.662	1.986	2.368	2.630
93	.846	1.291	1.661	1.986	2.367	2.630
94	.845	1.291	1.661	1.986	2.367	2.629
95	.845	1.291	1.661	1.985	2.366	2.629
96	.845	1.290	1.661	1.985	2.366	2.628
97	.845	1.290	1.661	1.985	2.365	2.627
98	.845	1.290	1.661	1.984	2.365	2.627
99	.845	1.290	1.660	1.984	2.364	2.626
100	.845	1.290	1.660	1.984	2.364	2.626
∞	.842	1.282	1.645	1.960	2.326	2.576

*Note: A more extensive table is provided as Table 2 of Appendix B.

Degrees of freedom refer to the number of independent pieces of information that go into the computation of $\Sigma(x_i - \bar{x})^2$. The n pieces of information involved in computing $\Sigma(x_i - \bar{x})^2$ are as follows: $x_1 - \bar{x}, x_2 - \bar{x}, \ldots, x_n - \bar{x}$. In Section 3.2 we indicated that $\Sigma(x_i - \bar{x}) = 0$ for any data set. Thus, only $n - 1$ of the $x_i - \bar{x}$ values are independent; that is, if we know $n - 1$ of the values, the remaining value can be determined exactly by using the condition that the sum of the $x_i - \bar{x}$ values must be 0. Thus, $n - 1$ is the number of degrees of freedom associated with $\Sigma(x_i - \bar{x})^2$ and hence the number of degrees of freedom for the t distribution in expression (8.2).

To illustrate the interval estimation procedure for the σ unknown case, we will consider a study designed to estimate the mean credit card debt for the population of U.S. households. A sample of $n = 70$ households provided the credit card balances shown in Table 8.3. For this situation, no previous estimate of the population standard deviation σ is available. Thus, the sample data must be used to estimate both the population mean and the population standard deviation. Using the data in Table 8.3, we compute the sample mean $\bar{x} = \$9312$ and the sample standard deviation $s = \$4007$. With 95% confidence and $n - 1 = 69$ degrees of freedom, Table 8.2 can be used to obtain the appropriate value for $t_{.025}$. We want the t value in the row with 69 degrees of freedom, and the column corresponding to .025 in the upper tail. The value shown is $t_{.025} = 1.995$.

We use expression (8.2) to compute an interval estimate of the population mean credit card balance.

$$9312 \pm 1.995 \frac{4007}{\sqrt{70}}$$

$$9312 \pm 955$$

The point estimate of the population mean is $9312, the margin of error is $955, and the 95% confidence interval is $9312 - 955 = \$8357$ to $9312 + 955 = \$10,267$. Thus, we are 95% confident that the mean credit card balance for the population of all households is between $8357 and $10,267.

The procedures used by JMP and Excel to develop confidence intervals for a population mean are described in Appendixes 8.1 and 8.2. For the household credit card balances study, the sample of 70 households provides a sample mean credit card balance of $9312, a sample standard deviation of $4007, a standard error of the mean of $479, and a 95% confidence interval of $8357 to $10,267.

TABLE 8.3 Credit Card Balances for a Sample of 70 Households

DATA*file*

NewBalance

9430	14661	7159	9071	9691	11032
7535	12195	8137	3603	11448	6525
4078	10544	9467	16804	8279	5239
5604	13659	12595	13479	5649	6195
5179	7061	7917	14044	11298	12584
4416	6245	11346	6817	4353	15415
10676	13021	12806	6845	3467	15917
1627	9719	4972	10493	6191	12591
10112	2200	11356	615	12851	9743
6567	10746	7117	13627	5337	10324
13627	12744	9465	12557	8372	
18719	5742	19263	6232	7445	

Practical Advice

If the population follows a normal distribution, the confidence interval provided by expression (8.2) is exact and can be used for any sample size. If the population does not follow a normal distribution, the confidence interval provided by expression (8.2) will be approximate. In this case, the quality of the approximation depends on both the distribution of the population and the sample size.

Larger sample sizes are needed if the distribution of the population is highly skewed or includes outliers.

In most applications, a sample size of $n \geq 30$ is adequate when using expression (8.2) to develop an interval estimate of a population mean. However, if the population distribution is highly skewed or contains outliers, most statisticians would recommend increasing the sample size to 50 or more. If the population is not normally distributed but is roughly symmetric, sample sizes as small as 15 can be expected to provide good approximate confidence intervals. With smaller sample sizes, expression (8.2) should only be used if the analyst believes, or is willing to assume, that the population distribution is at least approximately normal.

Using a Small Sample

In the following example we develop an interval estimate for a population mean when the sample size is small. As we already noted, an understanding of the distribution of the population becomes a factor in deciding whether the interval estimation procedure provides acceptable results.

Scheer Industries is considering a new computer-assisted program to train maintenance employees to do machine repairs. In order to fully evaluate the program, the director of manufacturing requested an estimate of the population mean time required for maintenance employees to complete the computer-assisted training.

A sample of 20 employees is selected, with each employee in the sample completing the training program. Data on the training time in days for the 20 employees are shown in Table 8.4. A histogram of the sample data appears in Figure 8.6. What can we say about the distribution of the population based on this histogram? First, the sample data do not support the conclusion that the distribution of the population is normal, yet we do not see any evidence of skewness or outliers. Therefore, using the guidelines in the previous subsection, we conclude that an interval estimate based on the t distribution appears acceptable for the sample of 20 employees.

We continue by computing the sample mean and sample standard deviation as follows.

$$\bar{x} = \frac{\Sigma x_i}{n} = \frac{1030}{20} = 51.5 \text{ days}$$

$$s = \sqrt{\frac{\Sigma(x_i - \bar{x})^2}{n - 1}} = \sqrt{\frac{889}{20 - 1}} = 6.84 \text{ days}$$

DATA *file*

Scheer

TABLE 8.4	Training Time In Days for a Sample of 20 Scheer Industries Employees			
	52	59	54	42
	44	50	42	48
	55	54	60	55
	44	62	62	57
	45	46	43	56

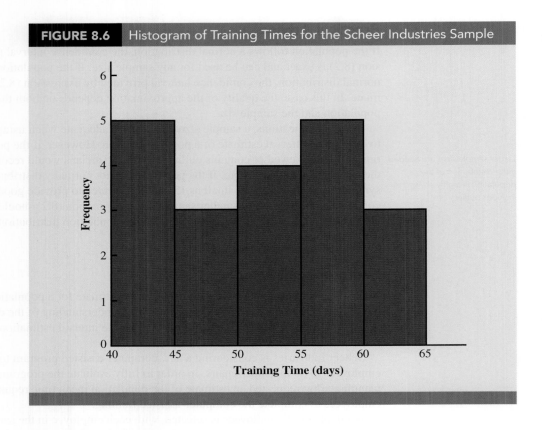

FIGURE 8.6   Histogram of Training Times for the Scheer Industries Sample

For a 95% confidence interval, we use Table 2 of Appendix B and $n - 1 = 19$ degrees of freedom to obtain $t_{.025} = 2.093$. Expression (8.2) provides the interval estimate of the population mean.

$$51.5 \pm 2.093\left(\frac{6.84}{\sqrt{20}}\right)$$

$$51.5 \pm 3.2$$

The point estimate of the population mean is 51.5 days. The margin of error is 3.2 days and the 95% confidence interval is $51.5 - 3.2 = 48.3$ days to $51.5 + 3.2 = 54.7$ days.

Using a histogram of the sample data to learn about the distribution of a population is not always conclusive, but in many cases it provides the only information available. The histogram, along with judgment on the part of the analyst, can often be used to decide whether expression (8.2) can be used to develop the interval estimate.

Summary of Interval Estimation Procedures

We provided two approaches to developing an interval estimate of a population mean. For the σ known case, σ and the standard normal distribution are used in expression (8.1) to compute the margin of error and to develop the interval estimate. For the σ unknown case, the sample standard deviation s and the t distribution are used in expression (8.2) to compute the margin of error and to develop the interval estimate.

A summary of the interval estimation procedures for the two cases is shown in Figure 8.7. In most applications, a sample size of $n \geq 30$ is adequate. If the population has a normal or approximately normal distribution, however, smaller sample sizes may be used. For the σ unknown case a sample size of $n \geq 50$ is recommended if the population distribution is believed to be highly skewed or has outliers.

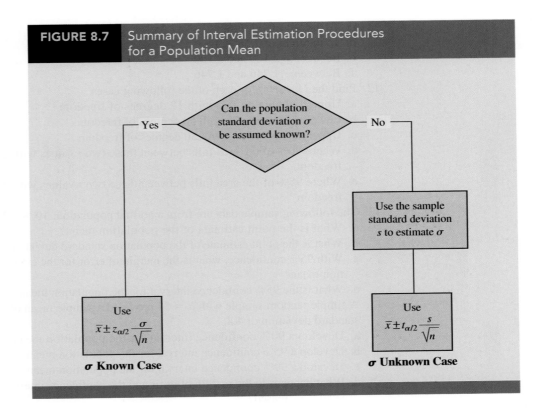

FIGURE 8.7   Summary of Interval Estimation Procedures for a Population Mean

Can the population standard deviation σ be assumed known?

Yes

No

Use the sample standard deviation s to estimate σ

Use

$$\bar{x} \pm z_{\alpha/2} \frac{\sigma}{\sqrt{n}}$$

σ Known Case

Use

$$\bar{x} \pm t_{\alpha/2} \frac{s}{\sqrt{n}}$$

σ Unknown Case

NOTES + COMMENTS

1. When σ is known, the margin of error, $z_{\alpha/2}(\sigma/\sqrt{n})$, is fixed and is the same for all samples of size n. When σ is unknown, the margin of error, $t_{\alpha/2}(s/\sqrt{n})$, varies from sample to sample. This variation occurs because the sample standard deviation s varies depending upon the sample selected. A large value for s provides a larger margin of error, while a small value for s provides a smaller margin of error.

2. What happens to confidence interval estimates when the population is skewed? Consider a population that is skewed to the right with large data values stretching the distribution to the right. When such skewness exists, the sample mean $\bar{x}$ and the sample standard deviation s are positively correlated. Larger values of s tend to be associated with larger values of $\bar{x}$. Thus, when $\bar{x}$ is larger than the population mean, s tends to be larger than σ. This skewness causes the margin of error, $t_{\alpha/2}(s/\sqrt{n})$, to be larger than it would be with σ known. The confidence interval with the larger margin of error tends to include the population mean μ more often than it would if the true value of σ were used. But when $\bar{x}$ is smaller than the population mean, the correlation between $\bar{x}$ and s causes the margin of error to be small. In this case, the confidence interval with the smaller margin of error tends to miss the population mean more than it would if we knew σ and used it. For this reason, we recommend using larger sample sizes with highly skewed population distributions.

EXERCISES

Methods

11. For a t distribution with 16 degrees of freedom, find the area, or probability, in each region.
    a. To the right of 2.120
    b. To the left of 1.337

c. To the left of -1.746
d. To the right of 2.583
e. Between -2.120 and 2.120
f. Between -1.746 and 1.746

12. Find the t value(s) for each of the following cases.
    a. Upper tail area of .025 with 12 degrees of freedom
    b. Lower tail area of .05 with 50 degrees of freedom
    c. Upper tail area of .01 with 30 degrees of freedom
    d. Where 90% of the area falls between these two t values with 25 degrees of freedom
    e. Where 95% of the area falls between these two t values with 45 degrees of freedom

13. The following sample data are from a normal population: 10, 8, 12, 15, 13, 11, 6, 5.
    a. What is the point estimate of the population mean?
    b. What is the point estimate of the population standard deviation?
    c. With 95% confidence, what is the margin of error for the estimation of the population mean?
    d. What is the 95% confidence interval for the population mean?

14. A simple random sample with $n = 54$ provided a sample mean of 22.5 and a sample standard deviation of 4.4.
    a. Develop a 90% confidence interval for the population mean.
    b. Develop a 95% confidence interval for the population mean.
    c. Develop a 99% confidence interval for the population mean.
    d. What happens to the margin of error and the confidence interval as the confidence level is increased?

Applications

15. **Weekly Sales Reports.** Sales personnel for Skillings Distributors submit weekly reports listing the customer contacts made during the week. A sample of 65 weekly reports showed a sample mean of 19.5 customer contacts per week. The sample standard deviation was 5.2. Provide 90% and 95% confidence intervals for the population mean number of weekly customer contacts for the sales personnel.

CorporateBonds

16. **Years to Bond Maturity.** A sample containing years to maturity and yield for 40 corporate bonds are contained in the file *CorporateBonds*.
    a. What is the sample mean years to maturity for corporate bonds and what is the sample standard deviation?
    b. Develop a 95% confidence interval for the population mean years to maturity.
    c. What is the sample mean yield on corporate bonds and what is the sample standard deviation?
    d. Develop a 95% confidence interval for the population mean yield on corporate bonds.

17. **Quality Ratings of Airports.** The International Air Transport Association surveys business travelers to develop quality ratings for transatlantic gateway airports. The maximum possible rating is 10. Suppose a simple random sample of 50 business travelers is selected and each traveler is asked to provide a rating for the Miami International Airport. The ratings obtained from the sample of 50 business travelers follow.

Miami

6	4	6	8	7	7	6	3	3	8	10	4	8
7	8	7	5	9	5	8	4	3	8	5	5	4
4	4	8	4	5	6	2	5	9	9	8	4	8
9	9	5	9	7	8	3	10	8	9	6		

Develop a 95% confidence interval estimate of the population mean rating for Miami.

JobSearch

18. **Unemployment in Older Workers.** Older people often have a hard time finding work. AARP reported on the number of weeks it takes a worker aged 55 plus to find a job. The data on number of weeks spent searching for a job contained in the file *JobSearch* are consistent with the AARP findings.

    a. Provide a point estimate of the population mean number of weeks it takes a worker aged 55 plus to find a job.
    b. At 95% confidence, what is the margin of error?
    c. What is the 95% confidence interval estimate of the mean?
    d. Discuss the degree of skewness found in the sample data. What suggestion would you make for a repeat of this study?

HongKongMeals

19. **Meal Cost in Hong Kong.** The mean cost of a meal for two in a mid-range restaurant in Tokyo is $40 (Numbeo.com website). How do prices for comparable meals in Hong Kong compare? The file *HongKongMeals* contains the costs for a sample of 42 recent meals for two in Hong Kong mid-range restaurants.

    a. With 95% confidence, what is the margin of error?
    b. What is the 95% confidence interval estimate of the population mean?
    c. How do prices for meals for two in mid-range restaurants in Hong Kong compare to prices for comparable meals in Tokyo restaurants?

AutoInsurance

20. **Automobile Insurance Premiums.** The average annual premium for automobile insurance in the United States is $1503. The following annual premiums ($) are representative of the website's findings for the state of Michigan.

1905	3112	2312
2725	2545	2981
2677	2525	2627
2600	2370	2857
2962	2545	2675
2184	2529	2115
2332	2442	

Assume the population is approximately normal.

    a. Provide a point estimate of the mean annual automobile insurance premium in Michigan.
    b. Develop a 95% confidence interval for the mean annual automobile insurance premium in Michigan.
    c. Does the 95% confidence interval for the annual automobile insurance premium in Michigan include the national average for the United States? What is your interpretation of the relationship between auto insurance premiums in Michigan and the national average?

TeleHealth

21. **Telemedicine.** Health insurers are beginning to offer telemedicine services online that replace the common office visit. Wellpoint provides a video service that allows subscribers to connect with a physician online and receive prescribed treatments (*Bloomberg Businessweek*, March 4–9, 2014). Wellpoint claims that users of its LiveHealth Online service saved a significant amount of money on a typical visit. The data shown below ($), for a sample of 20 online doctor visits, are consistent with the savings per visit reported by Wellpoint.

92	93	83	93	40
105	78	49	82	96
56	53	48	40	73
76	34	74	55	100

Assuming the population is roughly symmetric, construct a 95% confidence interval for the mean savings for a televisit to the doctor as opposed to an office visit.

Guardians

22. **Movie Ticket Sales.** Marvel Studio's motion picture *Guardians of the Galaxy* opened over the first two days of the 2014 Labor Day weekend to a then record-breaking $94.3 million in ticket sales revenue in North America. The ticket sales revenue in dollars for a sample of 30 theaters during the same dates is as follows.

a. What is the 95% confidence interval estimate for the mean ticket sales revenue per theater? Interpret this result.

b. Using the movie ticket price of $8.11 per ticket, what is the estimate of the mean number of customers per theater?

c. The movie was shown in 4080 theaters. Estimate the total number of customers who saw *Guardians of the Galaxy* and the total box office ticket sales for the weekend.

8.3 Determining the Sample Size

If a desired margin of error is selected prior to sampling, the procedures in this section can be used to determine the sample size necessary to satisfy the margin of error requirement.

In providing practical advice in the two preceding sections, we commented on the role of the sample size in providing good approximate confidence intervals when the population is not normally distributed. In this section, we focus on another aspect of the sample size issue. We describe how to choose a sample size large enough to provide a desired margin of error. To understand how this process works, we return to the σ known case presented in Section 8.1. Using expression (8.1), the interval estimate is

$$\bar{x} \pm z_{\alpha/2}\frac{\sigma}{\sqrt{n}}$$

The quantity $z_{\alpha/2}(\sigma/\sqrt{n})$ is the margin of error. Thus, we see that $z_{\alpha/2}$, the population standard deviation σ, and the sample size n combine to determine the margin of error. Once we select a confidence coefficient $1 - \alpha$, $z_{\alpha/2}$ can be determined. Then, if we have a value for σ, we can determine the sample size n needed to provide any desired margin of error. Development of the formula used to compute the required sample size n follows.

Let $E =$ the desired margin of error:

$$E = z_{\alpha/2}\frac{\sigma}{\sqrt{n}}$$

Solving for $\sqrt{n}$, we have

$$\sqrt{n} = \frac{z_{\alpha/2}\sigma}{E}$$

Squaring both sides of this equation, we obtain the following expression for the sample size.

SAMPLE SIZE FOR AN INTERVAL ESTIMATE OF A POPULATION MEAN

$$n = \frac{(z_{\alpha/2})^2\sigma^2}{E^2} \tag{8.3}$$

Equation (8.3) can be used to provide a good sample size recommendation. However, judgment on the part of the analyst should be used to determine whether the final sample size should be adjusted upward.

This sample size provides the desired margin of error at the chosen confidence level.

In equation (8.3), E is the margin of error that the user is willing to accept, and the value of $z_{\alpha/2}$ follows directly from the confidence level to be used in developing the interval estimate. Although user preference must be considered, 95% confidence is the most frequently chosen value ($z_{.025} = 1.96$).

Finally, use of equation (8.3) requires a value for the population standard deviation σ. However, even if σ is unknown, we can use equation (8.3) provided we have a preliminary or *planning value* for σ. In practice, one of the following procedures can be chosen.

A planning value for the population standard deviation s must be specified before the sample size can be determined. Three methods of obtaining a planning value for σ are discussed here.

1. Use the estimate of the population standard deviation computed from data of previous studies as the planning value for σ.
2. Use a pilot study to select a preliminary sample. The sample standard deviation from the preliminary sample can be used as the planning value for σ.
3. Use judgment or a "best guess" for the value of σ. For example, we might begin by estimating the largest and smallest data values in the population. The difference between the largest and smallest values provides an estimate of the range for the data. Finally, the range divided by 4 is often suggested as a rough approximation of the standard deviation and thus an acceptable planning value for σ.

Let us demonstrate the use of equation (8.3) to determine the sample size by considering the following example. A previous study that investigated the cost of renting automobiles in the United States found a mean cost of approximately $55 per day for renting a midsize automobile. Suppose that the organization that conducted this study would like to conduct a new study in order to estimate the population mean daily rental cost for a midsize automobile in the United States. In designing the new study, the project director specifies that the population mean daily rental cost be estimated with a margin of error of $2 and a 95% level of confidence.

The project director specified a desired margin of error of $E = 2$, and the 95% level of confidence indicates $z_{.025} = 1.96$. Thus, we only need a planning value for the population standard deviation σ in order to compute the required sample size. At this point, an analyst reviewed the sample data from the previous study and found that the sample standard deviation for the daily rental cost was $9.65. Using 9.65 as the planning value for σ, we obtain

Equation (8.3) provides the minimum sample size needed to satisfy the desired margin of error requirement. If the computed sample size is not an integer, rounding up to the next integer value will provide a margin of error slightly smaller than required.

$$n = \frac{(z_{\alpha/2})^2 \sigma^2}{E^2} = \frac{(1.96)^2(9.65)^2}{2^2} = 89.43$$

Thus, the sample size for the new study needs to be at least 89.43 midsize automobile rentals in order to satisfy the project director's $2 margin-of-error requirement. In cases where the computed n is not an integer, we round up to the next integer value; hence, the recommended sample size is 90 midsize automobile rentals.

EXERCISES

Methods

23. How large a sample should be selected to provide a 95% confidence interval with a margin of error of 10? Assume that the population standard deviation is 40.
24. The range for a set of data is estimated to be 36.
    a. What is the planning value for the population standard deviation?
    b. At 95% confidence, how large a sample would provide a margin of error of 3?
    c. At 95% confidence, how large a sample would provide a margin of error of 2?

Applications

25. **Computer-Assisted Training.** Refer to the Scheer Industries example in Section 8.2. Use 6.84 days as a planning value for the population standard deviation.
    a. Assuming 95% confidence, what sample size would be required to obtain a margin of error of 1.5 days?
    b. If the precision statement was made with 90% confidence, what sample size would be required to obtain a margin of error of 2 days?

26. **Gasoline Prices.** The U.S. Energy Information Administration (US EIA) reported that the average price for a gallon of regular gasoline is $2.94. The US EIA updates its estimates of average gas prices on a weekly basis. Assume the standard deviation is $.25 for the price of a gallon of regular gasoline and recommend the appropriate sample size for the US EIA to use if they wish to report each of the following margins of error at 95% confidence.

   a. The desired margin of error is $.10.

   b. The desired margin of error is $.07.

   c. The desired margin of error is $.05.

27. **Salaries of Business Graduates.** Annual starting salaries for college graduates with degrees in business administration are generally expected to be between $45,000 and $60,000. Assume that a 95% confidence interval estimate of the population mean annual starting salary is desired. What is the planning value for the population standard deviation? How large a sample should be taken if the desired margin of error is

   a. $500?

   b. $200?

   c. $100?

   d. Would you recommend trying to obtain the $100 margin of error? Explain.

28. **Beef Consumption.** Many medical professionals believe that eating too much red meat increases the risk of heart disease and cancer. Suppose you would like to conduct a survey to determine the yearly consumption of beef by a typical American and want to use 3 pounds as the desired margin of error for a confidence interval estimate of the population mean amount of beef consumed annually. Use 25 pounds as a planning value for the population standard deviation and recommend a sample size for each of the following situations.

   a. A 90% confidence interval is desired for the mean amount of beef consumed.

   b. A 95% confidence interval is desired for the mean amount of beef consumed.

   c. A 99% confidence interval is desired for the mean amount of beef consumed.

   d. When the desired margin of error is set, what happens to the sample size as the confidence level is increased? Would you recommend using a 99% confidence interval in this case? Discuss.

29. **Length of Theater Previews.** Customers arrive at a movie theater at the advertised movie time only to find that they have to sit through several previews and prepreview ads before the movie starts. Many complain that the time devoted to previews is too long. A preliminary sample conducted by *The Wall Street Journal* showed that the standard deviation of the amount of time devoted to previews was 4 minutes. Use that as a planning value for the standard deviation in answering the following questions.

   a. If we want to estimate the population mean time for previews at movie theaters with a margin of error of 75 seconds, what sample size should be used? Assume 95% confidence.

   b. If we want to estimate the population mean time for previews at movie theaters with a margin of error of 1 minute, what sample size should be used? Assume 95% confidence.

30. **Miles Driven by Young Drivers.** There has been a trend toward less driving in the last few years, especially by young people. Over the past eight years, the annual vehicle miles traveled by people from 16 to 34 years of age decreased from 10,300 to 7900 miles per person. Assume the standard deviation is now 2000 miles. Suppose you would like to conduct a survey to develop a 95% confidence interval estimate of the annual vehicle-miles per person for people 16 to 34 years of age at the current time. A margin of error of 100 miles is desired. How large a sample should be used for the current survey?

8.4 Population Proportion

In the introduction to this chapter we said that the general form of an interval estimate of a population proportion p is

$$\bar{p} \pm \text{Margin of error}$$

The sampling distribution of $\bar{p}$ plays a key role in computing the margin of error for this interval estimate.

In Chapter 7 we said that the sampling distribution of $\bar{p}$ can be approximated by a normal distribution whenever $np \geq 5$ and $n(1 - p) \geq 5$. Figure 8.8 shows the normal approximation of the sampling distribution of $\bar{p}$. The mean of the sampling distribution of $\bar{p}$ is the population proportion p, and the standard error of $\bar{p}$ is

$$\sigma_{\bar{p}} = \sqrt{\frac{p(1 - p)}{n}} \tag{8.4}$$

Because the sampling distribution of $\bar{p}$ is normally distributed, if we choose $z_{\alpha/2}\sigma_{\bar{p}}$ as the margin of error in an interval estimate of a population proportion, we know that $100(1 - \alpha)\%$ of the intervals generated will contain the true population proportion. But $\sigma_{\bar{p}}$ cannot be used directly in the computation of the margin of error because p will not be known; p is what we are trying to estimate. So $\bar{p}$ is substituted for p and the margin of error for an interval estimate of a population proportion is given by

$$\text{Margin of error} = z_{\alpha/2}\sqrt{\frac{\bar{p}(1 - \bar{p})}{n}} \tag{8.5}$$

With this margin of error, the general expression for an interval estimate of a population proportion is as follows.

When developing confidence intervals for proportions, the quantity $z_{\alpha/2}\sqrt{\bar{p}(1 - \bar{p})/n}$ provides the margin of error.

INTERVAL ESTIMATE OF A POPULATION PROPORTION

$$\bar{p} \pm z_{\alpha/2}\sqrt{\frac{\bar{p}(1 - \bar{p})}{n}} \tag{8.6}$$

where $1 - \alpha$ is the confidence coefficient and $z_{\alpha/2}$ is the z value providing an area of $\alpha/2$ in the upper tail of the standard normal distribution.

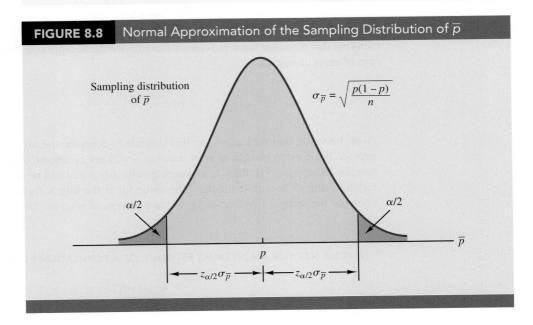

FIGURE 8.8   Normal Approximation of the Sampling Distribution of $\bar{p}$

The following example illustrates the computation of the margin of error and interval estimate for a population proportion. A national survey of 900 women golfers was conducted to learn how women golfers view their treatment at golf courses in the United States. The survey found that 396 of the women golfers were satisfied with the availability of tee times. Thus, the point estimate of the proportion of the population of women golfers who are satisfied with the availability of tee times is 396/900 = .44. Using expression (8.6) and a 95% confidence level,

$$\bar{p} \pm z_{\alpha/2} \sqrt{\frac{\bar{p}(1 - \bar{p})}{n}}$$

$$.44 \pm 1.96 \sqrt{\frac{.44(1 - .44)}{900}}$$

$$.44 \pm .0324$$

Thus, the margin of error is .0324 and the 95% confidence interval estimate of the population proportion is .4076 to .4724. Using percentages, the survey results enable us to state with 95% confidence that between 40.76% and 47.24% of all women golfers are satisfied with the availability of tee times.

Determining the Sample Size

Let us consider the question of how large the sample size should be to obtain an estimate of a population proportion at a specified level of precision. The rationale for the sample size determination in developing interval estimates of p is similar to the rationale used in Section 8.3 to determine the sample size for estimating a population mean.

Previously in this section we said that the margin of error associated with an interval estimate of a population proportion is $z_{\alpha/2} \sqrt{\bar{p}(1 - \bar{p})/n}$. The margin of error is based on the value of $z_{\alpha/2}$, the sample proportion $\bar{p}$, and the sample size n. Larger sample sizes provide a smaller margin of error and better precision.

Let E denote the desired margin of error.

$$E = z_{\alpha/2} \sqrt{\frac{\bar{p}(1 - \bar{p})}{n}}$$

Solving this equation for n provides a formula for the sample size that will provide a margin of error of size E.

$$n = \frac{(z_{\alpha/2})^2 \bar{p}(1 - \bar{p})}{E^2}$$

Note, however, that we cannot use this formula to compute the sample size that will provide the desired margin of error because $\bar{p}$ will not be known until after we select the sample. What we need, then, is a planning value for $\bar{p}$ that can be used to make the computation. Using p^* to denote the planning value for $\bar{p}$, the following formula can be used to compute the sample size that will provide a margin of error of size E.

SAMPLE SIZE FOR AN INTERVAL ESTIMATE OF A POPULATION PROPORTION

$$n = \frac{(z_{\alpha/2})^2 p^*(1 - p^*)}{E^2} \tag{8.7}$$

In practice, the planning value p^* can be chosen by one of the following procedures.

1. Use the sample proportion from a previous sample of the same or similar units.
2. Use a pilot study to select a preliminary sample. The sample proportion from this sample can be used as the planning value, p^*.
3. Use judgment or a "best guess" for the value of p^*.
4. If none of the preceding alternatives applies, use a planning value of $p^* = .50$.

Let us return to the survey of women golfers and assume that the company is interested in conducting a new survey to estimate the current proportion of the population of women golfers who are satisfied with the availability of tee times. How large should the sample be if the survey director wants to estimate the population proportion with a margin of error of .025 at 95% confidence? With $E = .025$ and $z_{\alpha/2} = 1.96$, we need a planning value p^* to answer the sample size question. Using the previous survey result of $\bar{p} = .44$ as the planning value p^*, equation (8.7) shows that

$$n = \frac{(z_{\alpha/2})^2 p^*(1 - p^*)}{E^2} = \frac{(1.96)^2(.44)(1 - .44)}{(.025)^2} = 1514.5$$

Thus, the sample size must be at least 1514.5 women golfers to satisfy the margin of error requirement. Rounding up to the next integer value indicates that a sample of 1515 women golfers is recommended to satisfy the margin of error requirement.

The fourth alternative suggested for selecting a planning value p^* is to use $p^* = .50$. This value of p^* is frequently used when no other information is available. To understand why, note that the numerator of equation (8.7) shows that the sample size is proportional to the quantity $p^*(1 - p^*)$. A larger value for the quantity $p^*(1 - p^*)$ will result in a larger sample size. Table 8.5 gives some possible values of $p^*(1 - p^*)$. Note that the largest value of $p^*(1 - p^*)$ occurs when $p^* = .50$. Thus, in case of any uncertainty about an appropriate planning value, we know that $p^* = .50$ will provide the largest sample size recommendation. In effect, we play it safe by recommending the largest necessary sample size. If the sample proportion turns out to be different from the .50 planning value, the margin of error will be smaller than anticipated. Thus, in using $p^* = .50$, we guarantee that the sample size will be sufficient to obtain the desired margin of error.

In the survey of women golfers example, a planning value of $p^* = .50$ would have provided the sample size

$$n = \frac{(z_{\alpha/2})^2 p^*(1 - p^*)}{E^2} = \frac{(1.96)^2(.50)(1 - .50)}{(.025)^2} = 1536.6$$

Thus, a slightly larger sample size of 1537 women golfers would be recommended.

TABLE 8.5	Some Possible Values for $p^*(1 - p^*)$	
p^*	$p^*(1 - p^*)$	
.10	$(.10)(.90) = .09$	
.30	$(.30)(.70) = .21$	
.40	$(.40)(.60) = .24$	
.50	$(.50)(.50) = .25$	← Largest value for $p^*(1 - p^*)$
.60	$(.60)(.40) = .24$	
.70	$(.70)(.30) = .21$	
.90	$(.90)(.10) = .09$	

NOTES + COMMENTS

1. The desired margin of error for estimating a population proportion is almost always .10 or less. In national public opinion polls conducted by organizations such as Gallup and Harris, a .03 or .04 margin of error is common. With such margins of error, equation (8.7) will almost always provide a sample size that is large enough to satisfy the requirements of $np \geq 5$ and $n(1 - p) \geq 5$ for using a normal distribution as an approximation for the sampling distribution of $\bar{x}$.

2. The binomial distribution can also be used to calculate an exact confidence interval for one proportion. This method is more accurate and more powerful than the normal approximation method. However, the calculations for the normal approximation method are simpler, and the accuracy and power of confidence intervals calculated using the normal approximation method improve as the sample size increases.

EXERCISES

Methods

31. A simple random sample of 400 individuals provides 100 Yes responses.
    a. What is the point estimate of the proportion of the population that would provide Yes responses?
    b. What is your estimate of the standard error of the proportion, $\sigma_{\bar{p}}$?
    c. Compute the 95% confidence interval for the population proportion.

32. A simple random sample of 800 elements generates a sample proportion $\bar{p} = .70$.
    a. Provide a 90% confidence interval for the population proportion.
    b. Provide a 95% confidence interval for the population proportion.

33. In a survey, the planning value for the population proportion is $p^* = .35$. How large a sample should be taken to provide a 95% confidence interval with a margin of error of .05?

34. At 95% confidence, how large a sample should be taken to obtain a margin of error of .03 for the estimation of a population proportion? Assume that past data are not available for developing a planning value for p^*.

Applications

35. **Health-Care Survey.** In the spring of 2017, the Consumer Reports National Research Center conducted a survey of 1007 adults to learn about their major health-care concerns. The survey results showed that 574 of the respondents lack confidence they will be able to afford health insurance in the future.
    a. What is the point estimate of the population proportion of adults who lack confidence they will be able to afford health insurance in the future.
    b. At 90% confidence, what is the margin of error?
    c. Develop a 90% confidence interval for the population proportion of adults who lack confidence they will be able to afford health insurance in the future.
    d. Develop a 95% confidence interval for this population proportion.

36. **Automobile Insurance Coverage.** According to statistics reported on CNBC, a surprising number of motor vehicles are not covered by insurance. Sample results, consistent with the CNBC report, showed 46 of 200 vehicles were not covered by insurance.
    a. What is the point estimate of the proportion of vehicles not covered by insurance?
    b. Develop a 95% confidence interval for the population proportion.

DATA *file*
RightDirection

37. **Voter Sentiment.** One of the questions Rasmussen Reports included on a 2018 survey of 2.500 likely voters asked if the country is headed in the right direction. Representative data are shown in the file *RightDirection*. A response of Yes indicates that the respondent does think the country is headed in the right direction. A response of No

indicates that the respondent does not think the country is headed in the right direction. Respondents may also give a response of Not Sure.

   a. What is the point estimate of the proportion of the population of likely voters who do think that the country is headed in the right direction?

   b. At 95% confidence, what is the margin of error?

   c. What is the 95% confidence interval for the proportion of likely voters who do think that the country is headed in the right direction?

   d. What is the 95% confidence interval for the proportion of likely voters who do not think that the country is headed in the right direction?

   e. Which of the confidence intervals in parts (c) and (d) has the smaller margin of error? Why?

CasualDining

38. **Franchise Profits.** According to *Franchise Business Review*, over 50% of all food franchises earn a profit of less than $50,000 a year. In a sample of 142 casual dining restaurants, 81 earned a profit of less than $50,000 last year.

   a. What is the point estimate of the proportion of casual dining restaurants that earned a profit of less than $50,000 last year?

   b. Determine the margin of error and provide a 95% confidence interval for the proportion of casual dining restaurants that earned a profit of less than $50,000 last year.

   c. How large a sample is needed if the desired margin of error is .03?

39. **Stay-at-Home Parenting.** In June 2014, Pew Research reported that in 16% of all homes with a stay-at-home parent, the father is the stay-at-home parent. An independent research firm has been charged with conducting a sample survey to obtain more current information.

   a. What sample size is needed if the research firm's goal is to estimate the current proportion of homes with a stay-at-home parent in which the father is the stay-at-home parent with a margin of error of .03? Use a 95% confidence level.

   b. Repeat part (a) using a 99% confidence level.

40. **Employee Contributions to Health-Care Coverage.** For many years businesses have struggled with the rising cost of health care. But recently, the increases have slowed due to less inflation in health care prices and employees paying for a larger portion of health care benefits. A recent survey showed that 52% of U.S. employers are likely to require higher employee contributions for health care coverage this year relative to last year. Suppose the survey was based on a sample of 800 companies. Compute the margin of error and a 95% confidence interval for the proportion of companies likely to require higher employee contributions for health care coverage this year relative to last year.

41. **Driver's License Rates.** Fewer young people are driving. In 1995, 63.9% of people under 20 years old who were eligible had a driver's license. Bloomberg reported that percentage had dropped to 41.7% in 2016. Suppose these results are based on a random sample of 1200 people under 20 years old who were eligible to have a driver's license in 1995 and again in 2016.

   a. At 95% confidence, what is the margin of error and the interval estimate of the number of eligible people under 20 years old who had a driver's license in 1995?

   b. At 95% confidence, what is the margin of error and the interval estimate of the number of eligible people under 20 years old who had a driver's license in 2016?

   c. Is the margin of error the same in parts (a) and (b)? Why or why not?

42. **Voter Intent.** A poll for the presidential campaign sampled 491 potential voters in June. A primary purpose of the poll was to obtain an estimate of the proportion of potential voters who favored each candidate. Assume a planning value of $p^* = .50$ and a 95% confidence level.

   a. For $p^* = .50$, what was the planned margin of error for the June poll?

   b. Closer to the November election, better precision and smaller margins of error are desired. Assume the following margins of error are requested for surveys to be conducted during the presidential campaign. Compute the recommended sample size for each survey.

Survey	Margin of Error
September	.04
October	.03
Early November	.02
Pre-Election Day	.01

43. **Internet Usage.** The Pew Research Center Internet Project, conducted in 2014 on the 25th anniversary of the Internet, involved a survey of 857 Internet users. It provided a variety of statistics on Internet users. For instance, in 2014, 87% of American adults were Internet users. In 1995 only 14% of American adults used the Internet.

   a. The sample survey showed that 90% of respondents said the Internet has been a good thing for them personally. Develop a 95% confidence interval for the proportion of respondents who say the Internet has been a good thing for them personally.

   b. The sample survey showed that 67% of Internet users said the Internet has generally strengthened their relationship with family and friends. Develop a 95% confidence interval for the proportion of respondents who say the Internet has strengthened their relationship with family and friends.

   c. Fifty-six percent of Internet users have seen an online group come together to help a person or community solve a problem, whereas only 25% have left an online group because of unpleasant interaction. Develop a 95% confidence interval for the proportion of Internet users who say online groups have helped solve a problem.

   d. Compare the margin of error for the interval estimates in parts (a), (b), and (c). How is the margin of error related to the sample proportion?

8.5 Big Data and Confidence Intervals

We have seen that confidence intervals are powerful tools for making inferences about population parameters. We now consider the ramifications of big data on confidences intervals for means and proportions, and we return to the data-collection problem of online news service PenningtonDailyTimes.com (PDT). Recall that PDT's primary source of revenue is the sale of advertising, so PDT's management is concerned about the time customers spend during their visits to PDT's website and whether visitors click on any of the ads featured on the website.

Big Data and the Precision of Confidence Intervals

A review of equations (8.2) and (8.6) shows that confidence intervals for the population mean μ and population proportion p become more narrow as the size of the sample increases. Therefore, the potential sampling error also decreases as the sample size increases. To illustrate the rate at which interval estimates narrow for a given confidence level, we consider the online news service PenningtonDailyTimes.com (PDT).

Prospective advertisers are willing to pay a premium to advertise on websites that have long visit times, so the time customers spend during their visits to PDT's website has a substantial impact on PDT's advertising revenues. Suppose PDT's management wants to develop a 95% confidence interval estimate of the mean amount of time customers spend during their visits to PDT's website. Table 8.6 shows how the margin of error at the 95% confidence level decreases as the sample size increases when $s = 20$.

Suppose that in addition to estimating the population mean amount of time customers spend during their visits to PDT's website, PDT would like to develop a 95% confidence interval estimate of the proportion of its website visitors that click on an ad. Table 8.7 shows how the margin of error for a 95% confidence interval estimate of the population proportion decreases as the sample size increases when the sample proportion is $\bar{p} = .51$

TABLE 8.6	Margin of Error for Interval Estimates of the Population Mean at the 95% Confidence Level for Various Sample Sizes *n*

Sample Size *n*	Margin of Error $t_{\alpha/2}s_{\bar{x}}$
10	14.30714
100	3.96843
1,000	1.24109
10,000	.39204
100,000	.12396
1,000,000	.03920
10,000,000	.01240
100,000,000	.00392
1,000,000,000	.00124

TABLE 8.7	Margin of Error for Interval Estimates of the Population Proportion at the 95% Confidence Level for Various Sample Sizes *n*

Sample Size *n*	Margin of Error $z_{\alpha/2}\sigma_{\bar{p}}$
10	.30984
100	.09798
1,000	.03098
10,000	.00980
100,000	.00310
1,000,000	.00098
10,000,000	.00031
100,000,000	.00010
1,000,000,000	.00003

The PDT example illustrates the relationship between the precision of interval estimates and the sample size. We see in Tables 8.6 and 8.7 that at a given confidence level, the margins of error decrease as the sample sizes increase. As a result, if the sample mean time spent by customers when they visit PDT's website is 84.1 seconds, the 95% confidence interval estimate of the population mean time spent by customers when they visit PDT's website decreases from (69.79286, 98.40714) for a sample of $n = 10$ to (83.97604, 84.22396) for a sample of $n = 100,000$ to (84.09876, 84.10124) for a sample of $n = 1,000,000,000$. Similarly, if the sample proportion of its website visitors who clicked on an ad is .51, the 95% confidence interval estimate of the population proportion of its website visitors who clicked on an ad decreases from (.20016, .81984) for a sample of $n = 10$ to (.50690, .51310) for a sample of $n = 100,000$ to (.50997, .51003) for a sample of $n = 1,000,000,000$. In both instances, as the sample size becomes extremely large, the margin of error becomes extremely small and the resulting confidence intervals become extremely narrow.

Implications of Big Data for Confidence Intervals

Last year the mean time spent by all visitors to PenningtonDailyTimes.com was 84 seconds. Suppose that PDT wants to assess whether the population mean time has changed since last year. PDT now collects a new sample of 1,000,000 visitors to its website and calculates the sample mean time spent by these visitors to the PDT website to be $\bar{x} = 84.1$

seconds. The estimated population standard deviation is $s = 20$ seconds, so the standard error is $s_{\bar{x}} = s/\sqrt{n} = .02000$. Furthermore, the sample is sufficiently large to ensure that the sampling distribution of the sample mean will be normally distributed. Thus, the 95% confidence interval estimate of the population mean is

$$\bar{x} \pm t_{\alpha/2} s_{\bar{x}} = 84.1 \pm .0392 = (84.06080, 84.13920)$$

What could PDT conclude from these results? There are three possible reasons that PDT's sample mean of 84.1 seconds differs from last year's population mean of 84 seconds: (1) sampling error, (2) nonsampling error, or (3) the population mean has changed since last year. The 95% confidence interval estimate of the population mean does not include the value for the mean time spent by all visitors to the PDT website for last year (84 seconds), suggesting that the difference between PDT's sample mean for the new sample (84.1 seconds) and the mean from last year (84 seconds) is not likely to be exclusively a consequence of sampling error. Nonsampling error is a possible explanation and should be investigated as the results of statistical inference become less reliable as nonsampling error is introduced into the sample data. If PDT determines that it introduced little or no nonsampling error into its sample data, the only remaining plausible explanation for a difference of this magnitude is that the population mean has changed since last year.

If PDT concludes that the sample has provided reliable evidence and the population mean has changed since last year, management must still consider the potential impact of the difference between the sample mean and the mean from last year. If a .1 second difference in the time spent by visitors to PenningtonDailyTimes.com has a consequential effect on what PDT can charge for advertising on its site, this result could have practical business implications for PDT. Otherwise, there may be no **practical significance** of the .1 second difference in the time spent by visitors to PenningtonDailyTimes.com.

Confidence intervals are extremely useful, but as with any other statistical tool, they are only effective when properly applied. Because interval estimates become increasingly precise as the sample size increases, extremely large samples will yield extremely precise estimates. However, no interval estimate, no matter how precise, will accurately reflect the parameter being estimated unless the sample is relatively free of nonsampling error. Therefore, when using interval estimation, it is always important to carefully consider whether a random sample of the population of interest has been taken.

EXERCISES

FedTaxErrors

44. **Federal Tax Return Errors.** Suppose a sample of 10,001 erroneous Federal income tax returns from last year has been taken and is provided in the file *FedTaxErrors*. A positive value indicates the taxpayer underpaid and a negative value indicates that the taxpayer overpaid.
    a. What is the sample mean error made on erroneous Federal income tax returns last year?
    b. Using 95% confidence, what is the margin of error?
    c. Using the results from parts (a) and (b), develop the 95% confidence interval estimate of the mean error made on erroneous Federal income tax returns last year.

FedSickHours

45. **Federal Government Employee Sick Hours.** According to the Census Bureau, 2,475,780 people are employed by the federal government in the United States as of 2018. Suppose that a random sample of 3,500 of these federal employees was selected and the number of sick hours each of these employees took last year was collected from an electronic personnel database. The data collected in this survey are provided in the file *FedSickHours*.
    a. What is the sample mean number of sick hours taken by federal employees last year?
    b. Using 99% confidence, what is the margin of error?
    c. Using the results from parts (a) and (b), develop the 99% confidence interval estimate of the mean number of sick hours taken by federal employees last year.

    d. If the mean sick hours federal employees took two years ago was 62.2, what would the confidence interval in part (c) lead you to conclude about last year?

46. **Web Browser Satisfaction.** Internet users were recently asked online to rate their satisfaction with the web browser they use most frequently. Of 102,519 respondents, 65,120 indicated they were very satisfied with the web browser they use most frequently.

    a. What is the sample proportion of Internet users who are very satisfied with the web browser they use most frequently?

    b. Using 95% confidence, what is the margin of error?

    c. Using the results from parts (a) and (b), develop the 95% confidence interval estimate of the proportion of Internet users who are very satisfied with the web browser they use most frequently.

47. **Speeding Drivers.** In 2017, ABC News reported that 58% of U.S. drivers admit to speeding. Suppose that a new satellite technology can instantly measure the speed of any vehicle on a U.S. road and determine whether the vehicle is speeding, and this satellite technology was used to take a sample of 20,000 vehicles at 6:00 p.m. EST on a recent Tuesday afternoon. Of these 20,000 vehicles, 9,252 were speeding.

    a. What is the sample proportion of vehicles on U.S. roads that speed?

    b. Using 99% confidence, what is the margin of error?

    c. Using the results from parts (a) and (b), develop the 99% confidence interval estimate of the proportion of vehicles on U.S. roads that speed.

    d. What does the confidence interval in part (c) lead you to conclude about the ABC News report?

SUMMARY

In this chapter we presented methods for developing interval estimates of a population mean and a population proportion. A point estimator may or may not provide a good estimate of a population parameter. The use of an interval estimate provides a measure of the precision of an estimate. Both the interval estimate of the population mean and the population proportion are of the form: point estimate $\pm$ margin of error.

We presented interval estimates for a population mean for two cases. In the σ known case, historical data or other information is used to develop an estimate of σ prior to taking a sample. Analysis of new sample data then proceeds based on the assumption that σ is known. In the σ unknown case, the sample data are used to estimate both the population mean and the population standard deviation. The final choice of which interval estimation procedure to use depends upon the analyst's understanding of which method provides the best estimate of σ.

In the σ known case, the interval estimation procedure is based on the assumed value of σ and the use of the standard normal distribution. In the σ unknown case, the interval estimation procedure uses the sample standard deviation s and the t distribution. In both cases the quality of the interval estimates obtained depends on the distribution of the population and the sample size. If the population is normally distributed the interval estimates will be exact in both cases, even for small sample sizes. If the population is not normally distributed, the interval estimates obtained will be approximate. Larger sample sizes will provide better approximations, but the more highly skewed the population is, the larger the sample size needs to be to obtain a good approximation. Practical advice about the sample size necessary to obtain good approximations was included in Sections 8.1 and 8.2. In most cases a sample of size 30 or more will provide good approximate confidence intervals.

The general form of the interval estimate for a population proportion is $\bar{p} \pm$ margin of error. In practice the sample sizes used for interval estimates of a population proportion are generally large. Thus, the interval estimation procedure is based on the standard normal distribution.

Often a desired margin of error is specified prior to developing a sampling plan. We showed how to choose a sample size large enough to provide the desired precision. Finally, we discussed the ramifications of extremely large samples on the precision of confidence interval estimates of the mean and proportion.

GLOSSARY

Confidence coefficient The confidence level expressed as a decimal value. For example, .95 is the confidence coefficient for a 95% confidence level.

Confidence interval Another name for an interval estimate.

Confidence level The confidence associated with an interval estimate. For example, if an interval estimation procedure provides intervals such that 95% of the intervals formed using the procedure will include the population parameter, the interval estimate is said to be constructed at the 95% confidence level.

Degrees of freedom A parameter of the t distribution. When the t distribution is used in the computation of an interval estimate of a population mean, the appropriate t distribution has $n - 1$ degrees of freedom, where n is the size of the sample.

Interval estimate An estimate of a population parameter that provides an interval believed to contain the value of the parameter. For the interval estimates in this chapter, it has the form: point estimate $\pm$ margin of error.

Margin of error The $\pm$ value added to and subtracted from a point estimate in order to develop an interval estimate of a population parameter.

Practical significance The real-world impact the result of statistical inference will have on business decisions.

t distribution A family of probability distributions that can be used to develop an interval estimate of a population mean whenever the population standard deviation σ is unknown and is estimated by the sample standard deviation s.

σ known The case when historical data or other information provides a good value for the population standard deviation prior to taking a sample. The interval estimation procedure uses this known value of σ in computing the margin of error.

σ unknown The more common case when no good basis exists for estimating the population standard deviation prior to taking the sample. The interval estimation procedure uses the sample standard deviation s in computing the margin of error.

KEY FORMULAS

Interval Estimate of a Population Mean: σ Known

$$\bar{x} \pm z_{\alpha/2} \frac{\sigma}{\sqrt{n}} \tag{8.1}$$

Interval Estimate of a Population Mean: σ Unknown

$$\bar{x} \pm t_{\alpha/2} \frac{s}{\sqrt{n}} \tag{8.2}$$

Sample Size for an Interval Estimate of a Population Mean

$$n = \frac{(z_{\alpha/2})^2 \sigma^2}{E^2} \tag{8.3}$$

Interval Estimate of a Population Proportion

$$\bar{p} \pm z_{\alpha/2} \sqrt{\frac{\bar{p}(1 - \bar{p})}{n}} \tag{8.6}$$

Sample Size for an Interval Estimate of a Population Proportion

$$n = \frac{(z_{\alpha/2})^2 p^*(1 - p^*)}{E^2} \tag{8.7}$$

SUPPLEMENTARY EXERCISES

48. **Discount Brokerage Trade Fees.** A sample survey of 54 discount brokers showed that the mean price charged for a trade of 100 shares at $50 per share was $33.77. The survey is conducted annually. With the historical data available, assume a known population standard deviation of $15.
    a. Using the sample data, what is the margin of error associated with a 95% confidence interval?
    b. Develop a 95% confidence interval for the mean price charged by discount brokers for a trade of 100 shares at $50 per share.

49. **Family Vacation Expenses.** A survey conducted by the American Automobile Association showed that a family of four spends an average of $215.60 per day while on vacation. Suppose a sample of 64 families of four vacationing at Niagara Falls resulted in a sample mean of $252.45 per day and a sample standard deviation of $74.50.
    a. Develop a 95% confidence interval estimate of the mean amount spent per day by a family of four visiting Niagara Falls.
    b. Based on the confidence interval from part (a), does it appear that the population mean amount spent per day by families visiting Niagara Falls differs from the mean reported by the American Automobile Association? Explain.

50. **Annual Restaurant Expenditures.** The 92 million Americans of age 50 and over control 50 percent of all discretionary income. AARP estimates that the average annual expenditure on restaurants and carryout food was $1873 for individuals in this age group. Suppose this estimate is based on a sample of 80 persons and that the sample standard deviation is $550.
    a. At 95% confidence, what is the margin of error?
    b. What is the 95% confidence interval for the population mean amount spent on restaurants and carryout food?
    c. What is your estimate of the total amount spent by Americans of age 50 and over on restaurants and carryout food?
    d. If the amount spent on restaurants and carryout food is skewed to the right, would you expect the median amount spent to be greater or less than $1873?

DATAfile
SleepHabits

51. **Healthy Sleep Duration.** The Centers for Disease Control and Prevention (CDC) define a healthy sleep duration to be at least seven hours per day. The CDC reports that the percentage of people who report a healthy sleep duration varies by marital status. The CDC also reports that in 2018, 67% of those who are married report a healthy sleep duration; 62% of those who have never been married report a healthy sleep duration; and 56% of those who are divorced, widowed, or separated report a healthy sleep duration. The file *SleepHabits* contains sample data on the sleeping habits of people who have never been married that are consistent with the CDC's findings. Use these data to answer the following questions.
    a. Develop a point estimate and a 95% confidence interval for the proportion of those who have never been married who report a healthy sleep duration.
    b. Develop a point estimate and a 95% confidence interval for the mean number of hours of sleep for those who have never been married.
    c. For those who have never been married, estimate the number of hours of sleep per day for those who report a healthy sleep duration.

DATAfile
DrugCost

52. **Health Care Expenditures.** The Health Care Cost Institute tracks health care expenditures for beneficiaries under the age of 65 who are covered by employer-sponsored private health insurance. The data contained in the file *DrugCost* are consistent with the institute's findings concerning annual prescription costs per employee. Analyze the data using Excel and answer the following questions.
    a. Develop a 90% confidence interval for the annual cost of prescription drugs.
    b. Develop a 90% confidence interval for the amount of out-of-pocket expense per employee.

    c. What is your point estimate of the proportion of employees who incurred no prescription drug costs?

    d. Which, if either, of the confidence intervals in parts (a) and (b) has a larger margin of error. Why?

Obesity

53. **Obesity.** Obesity is a risk factor for many health problems such as type 2 diabetes, high blood pressure, joint problems, and gallstones. Using data collected in 2018 through the National Health and Nutrition Examination Survey, the National Institute of Diabetes and Digestive and Kidney Diseases estimates that 37.7% of all adults in the United States have a body mass index (BMI) in excess of 30 and so are categorized as obese. The data in the file *Obesity* are consistent with these findings.

    a. Use the *Obesity* data set to develop a point estimate of the BMI for adults in the United States. Are adults in the United States obese on average?

    b. What is the sample standard deviation?

    c. Develop a 95% confidence interval for the BMI of adults in the United States.

54. **Automobile Mileage Tests.** Mileage tests are conducted for a particular model of automobile. If a 98% confidence interval with a margin of error of 1 mile per gallon is desired, how many automobiles should be used in the test? Assume that preliminary mileage tests indicate the standard deviation is 2.6 miles per gallon.

55. **Patient Treatment Time.** In developing patient appointment schedules, a medical center wants to estimate the mean time that a staff member spends with each patient. How large a sample should be taken if the desired margin of error is two minutes at a 95% level of confidence? How large a sample should be taken for a 99% level of confidence? Use a planning value for the population standard deviation of eight minutes.

56. **CEO Compensation.** Annual salary plus bonus data for chief executive officers are presented in the *BusinessWeek* Annual Pay Survey. A preliminary sample showed that the standard deviation is $675 with data provided in thousands of dollars. How many chief executive officers should be in a sample if we want to estimate the population mean annual salary plus bonus with a margin of error of $100,000? (*Note:* The desired margin of error would be $E = 100$ if the data are in thousands of dollars.) Use 95% confidence.

57. **Paying for College Tuition.** The National Center for Education Statistics reported that 47% of college students work to pay for tuition and living expenses. Assume that a sample of 450 college students was used in the study.

    a. Provide a 95% confidence interval for the population proportion of college students who work to pay for tuition and living expenses.

    b. Provide a 99% confidence interval for the population proportion of college students who work to pay for tuition and living expenses.

    c. What happens to the margin of error as the confidence is increased from 95% to 99%?

58. **Parenting Time.** A *USA Today*/CNN/Gallup survey of 369 working parents found 200 who said they spend too little time with their children because of work commitments.

    a. What is the point estimate of the proportion of the population of working parents who feel they spend too little time with their children because of work commitments?

    b. At 95% confidence, what is the margin of error?

    c. What is the 95% confidence interval estimate of the population proportion of working parents who feel they spend too little time with their children because of work commitments?

59. **Social Media Usage.** The Pew Research Center has conducted extensive research on social media usage. One finding, reported in June 2018, was that 78% of adults aged 18 to 24 use Snapchat. Another finding was that 45% of those aged 18 to 24 use Twitter. Assume the sample size associated with both findings is 500.

    a. Develop a 95% confidence interval for the proportion of adults aged 18 to 24 who use Snapchat.

    b. Develop a 99% confidence interval for the proportion of adults aged 18 to 24 who use Twitter.

    c. In which case, part (a) or part (b), is the margin of error larger? Explain why.

60. **Importance of Economy to Voters.** A survey of 750 likely voters in Ohio was conducted by the Rasmussen Poll just prior to the general election. The state of the economy was thought to be an important determinant of how people would vote. Among other things, the survey found that 165 of the respondents rated the economy as good or excellent and 315 rated the economy as poor.

    a. Develop a point estimate of the proportion of likely voters in Ohio who rated the economy as good or excellent.

    b. Construct a 95% confidence interval for the proportion of likely voters in Ohio who rated the economy as good or excellent.

    c. Construct a 95% confidence interval for the proportion of likely voters in Ohio who rated the economy as poor.

    d. Which of the confidence intervals in parts (b) and (c) is wider? Why?

61. **Smoking.** In 2014, the *Centers for Disease Control* reported the percentage of people 18 years of age and older who smoke. Suppose that a study designed to collect new data on smokers and nonsmokers uses a preliminary estimate of the proportion who smoke of .30.

    a. How large a sample should be taken to estimate the proportion of smokers in the population with a margin of error of .02? Use 95% confidence.

    b. Assume that the study uses your sample size recommendation in part (a) and finds 520 smokers. What is the point estimate of the proportion of smokers in the population?

    c. What is the 95% confidence interval for the proportion of smokers in the population?

62. **Credit Card Balances.** A well-known bank credit card firm wishes to estimate the proportion of credit card holders who carry a nonzero balance at the end of the month and incur an interest charge. Assume that the desired margin of error is .03 at 98% confidence.

    a. How large a sample should be selected if it is anticipated that roughly 70% of the firm's card holders carry a nonzero balance at the end of the month?

    b. How large a sample should be selected if no planning value for the proportion could be specified?

63. **Credit Card Ownership.** Credit card ownership varies across age groups. In 2018, CreditCards.com estimated that the percentage of people who own at least one credit card is 67% in the 18–24 age group, 83% in the 25–34 age group, 76% in the 35–49 age group, and 78% in the 50+ age group. Suppose these estimates are based on 455 randomly selected people from each age group.

    a. Construct a 95% confidence interval for the proportion of people in each of these age groups who owns at least one credit card.

    b. Assuming the same sample size will be used in each age group, how large would the sample need to be to ensure that the margin of error is .03 or less for each of the four confidence intervals?

64. **Factors in Choosing an Airline.** Although airline schedules and cost are important factors for business travelers when choosing an airline carrier, a *USA Today* survey found that business travelers list an airline's frequent flyer program as the most important factor. From a sample of $n = 1993$ business travelers who responded to the survey, 618 listed a frequent flyer program as the most important factor.

    a. What is the point estimate of the proportion of the population of business travelers who believe a frequent flyer program is the most important factor when choosing an airline carrier?

    b. Develop a 95% confidence interval estimate of the population proportion.

    c. How large a sample would be required to report the margin of error of .01 at 95% confidence? Would you recommend that *USA Today* attempt to provide this degree of precision? Why or why not?

DATA*file*

35MPH

65. **Driving Speeds.** Huston Systems Private Limited reports that smart traffic signals and signs can measure a passing vehicle's speed. Consider the speeds of 15,717 vehicles collected as they passed 35 MPH speed limit signs throughout the United States in 2018 that are provided in the file *35MPH*.

a. What is the sample mean speed of U.S. drivers in a 35-mph zone?

b. Using 95% confidence, what is the margin of error?

c. Using the results from parts (a) and (b), develop the 95% confidence interval estimate of the mean speed of U.S. drivers in a 35-mph zone.

UnderEmployed

66. **Underemployment.** A recent survey from PayScale found that 46% of U.S. workers—roughly 22 million—are underemployed, either working part-time or at jobs that don't allow them to use their education or skills. Suppose that the numbers of hours worked in the past week were collected from a random sample of 28,585 of these workers. The data collected in this survey are provided in the file *UnderEmployed*.

a. What is the sample mean number of hours worked by underemployed U.S. workers?

b. Using 99% confidence, what is the margin of error?

c. Using the results from parts (a) and (b), develop the 99% confidence interval estimate of the mean number of hours worked by underemployed U.S. workers.

d. If the mean hours worked by underemployed U.S. workers during the same week one year ago was 35.6, what would the confidence interval in part (c) lead you to conclude about last week?

FloridaFraud

67. **FTC Fraud Reports.** In 2017, 42.54% of the nearly 2.7 million reports taken nationwide by the Federal Trade Commission's Consumer Sentinel Network dealt with instances of fraud. Consider results of a random sample of 42,296 of the reports taken by the Consumer Sentinel Network from Florida that are provided the file *FloridaFraud*.

a. What is the sample proportion of reports filed from Florida that dealt with instances of fraud?

b. Using 95% confidence, what is the margin of error?

c. Using the results from parts (a) and (b), develop the 95% confidence interval estimate of the proportion reports filed from Florida that dealt with instances of fraud. What do you conclude about Florida from these results?

68. **Structurally Deficient Bridges.** The Infrastructure Report Card (IRC) reports that of 614,387 U.S. bridges, 9.1% were structurally deficient as of last year. The IRC also reports that more than 1300 California bridges fall under this category. How does California compare to the nation? Consider a random sample of 8749 bridges in California that includes 490 structurally deficient bridges.

a. What is the sample proportion of structurally deficient bridges in California?

b. Using 90% confidence, what is the margin of error?

c. Using the results from parts (a) and (b), develop the 90% confidence interval estimate of the proportion of structurally deficient bridges in California.

d. What does the confidence interval in part (c) lead you to conclude about California bridges?

CASE PROBLEM 1: *YOUNG PROFESSIONAL* MAGAZINE

Young Professional magazine was developed for a target audience of recent college graduates who are in their first 10 years in a business/professional career. In its two years of publication, the magazine has been fairly successful. Now the publisher is interested in expanding the magazine's advertising base. Potential advertisers continually ask about the demographics and interests of subscribers to *Young Professional*. To collect this information, the magazine commissioned a survey to develop a profile of its subscribers. The survey results will be used to help the magazine choose articles of interest and provide advertisers with a profile of subscribers. As a new employee of the magazine, you have been asked to help analyze the survey results.

Some of the survey questions follow:

Professional

1. What is your age? _____

2. Are you: Male _____   Female _____

TABLE 8.8		Partial Survey Results for *Young Professional* Magazine					
Age	Gender	Real Estate Purchases	Value of Investments($)	Number of Transactions	Broadband Access	Household Income($)	Children
38	Female	No	12200	4	Yes	75200	Yes
30	Male	No	12400	4	Yes	70300	Yes
41	Female	No	26800	5	Yes	48200	No
28	Female	Yes	19600	6	No	95300	No
31	Female	Yes	15100	5	No	73300	Yes
⋮	⋮	⋮	⋮	⋮	⋮	⋮	⋮

3. Do you plan to make any real estate purchases in the next two years?
   Yes _____ No _____
4. What is the approximate total value of financial investments, exclusive of your home, owned by you or members of your household?
5. How many stock/bond/mutual fund transactions have you made in the past year?
6. Do you have broadband access to the Internet at home? Yes _____ No _____
7. Please indicate your total household income last year. _____
8. Do you have children? Yes _____ No _____

The file *Professional* contains the responses to these questions. Table 8.8 shows the portion of the file pertaining to the first five survey respondents.

Managerial Report

Prepare a managerial report summarizing the results of the survey. In addition to statistical summaries, discuss how the magazine might use these results to attract advertisers. You might also comment on how the survey results could be used by the magazine's editors to identify topics that would be of interest to readers. Your report should address the following issues, but do not limit your analysis to just these areas.

1. Develop appropriate descriptive statistics to summarize the data.
2. Develop 95% confidence intervals for the mean age and household income of subscribers.
3. Develop 95% confidence intervals for the proportion of subscribers who have broadband access at home and the proportion of subscribers who have children.
4. Would *Young Professional* be a good advertising outlet for online brokers? Justify your conclusion with statistical data.
5. Would this magazine be a good place to advertise for companies selling educational software and computer games for young children?
6. Comment on the types of articles you believe would be of interest to readers of *Young Professional*.

CASE PROBLEM 2: GULF REAL ESTATE PROPERTIES

Gulf Real Estate Properties, Inc., is a real estate firm located in southwest Florida. The company, which advertises itself as "expert in the real estate market," monitors condominium sales by collecting data on location, list price, sale price, and number of days it takes to sell each unit. Each condominium is classified as *Gulf View* if it is located directly on the Gulf of Mexico or *No Gulf View* if it is located on the bay or a golf course, near but not on the Gulf. Sample data from the Multiple Listing Service in Naples, Florida, provided recent sales data for 40 Gulf View condominiums and 18 No Gulf View condominiums. Prices are in thousands of dollars. The data are shown in Table 8.9.

TABLE 8.9	Sales Data for Gulf Real Estate Properties				
Gulf View Condominiums			**No Gulf View Condominiums**		
List Price	**Sale Price**	**Days to Sell**	**List Price**	**Sale Price**	**Days to Sell**
495.0	475.0	130	217.0	217.0	182
379.0	350.0	71	148.0	135.5	338
529.0	519.0	85	186.5	179.0	122
552.5	534.5	95	239.0	230.0	150
334.9	334.9	119	279.0	267.5	169
550.0	505.0	92	215.0	214.0	58
169.9	165.0	197	279.0	259.0	110
210.0	210.0	56	179.9	176.5	130
975.0	945.0	73	149.9	144.9	149
314.0	314.0	126	235.0	230.0	114
315.0	305.0	88	199.8	192.0	120
885.0	800.0	282	210.0	195.0	61
975.0	975.0	100	226.0	212.0	146
469.0	445.0	56	149.9	146.5	137
329.0	305.0	49	160.0	160.0	281
365.0	330.0	48	322.0	292.5	63
332.0	312.0	88	187.5	179.0	48
520.0	495.0	161	247.0	227.0	52
425.0	405.0	149			
675.0	669.0	142			
409.0	400.0	28			
649.0	649.0	29			
319.0	305.0	140			
425.0	410.0	85			
359.0	340.0	107			
469.0	449.0	72			
895.0	875.0	129			
439.0	430.0	160			
435.0	400.0	206			
235.0	227.0	91			
638.0	618.0	100			
629.0	600.0	97			
329.0	309.0	114			
595.0	555.0	45			
339.0	315.0	150			
215.0	200.0	48			
395.0	375.0	135			
449.0	425.0	53			
499.0	465.0	86			
439.0	428.5	158			

DATA file

GulfProp

Managerial Report

1. Use appropriate descriptive statistics to summarize each of the three variables for the 40 Gulf View condominiums.
2. Use appropriate descriptive statistics to summarize each of the three variables for the 18 No Gulf View condominiums.
3. Compare your summary results. Discuss any specific statistical results that would help a real estate agent understand the condominium market.

4. Develop a 95% confidence interval estimate of the population mean sales price and population mean number of days to sell for Gulf View condominiums. Interpret your results.
5. Develop a 95% confidence interval estimate of the population mean sales price and population mean number of days to sell for No Gulf View condominiums. Interpret your results.
6. Assume the branch manager requested estimates of the mean selling price of Gulf View condominiums with a margin of error of $40,000 and the mean selling price of No Gulf View condominiums with a margin of error of $15,000. Using 95% confidence, how large should the sample sizes be?
7. Gulf Real Estate Properties just signed contracts for two new listings: a Gulf View condominium with a list price of $589,000 and a No Gulf View condominium with a list price of $285,000. What is your estimate of the final selling price and number of days required to sell each of these units?

CASE PROBLEM 3: METROPOLITAN RESEARCH, INC.

Metropolitan Research, Inc., a consumer research organization, conducts surveys designed to evaluate a wide variety of products and services available to consumers. In one particular study, Metropolitan looked at consumer satisfaction with the performance of automobiles produced by a major Detroit manufacturer. A questionnaire sent to owners of one of the manufacturer's full-sized cars revealed several complaints about early transmission problems. To learn more about the transmission failures, Metropolitan used a sample of actual transmission repairs provided by a transmission repair firm in the Detroit area. The following data show the actual number of miles driven for 50 vehicles at the time of transmission failure.

DATAfile
Auto

85,092	32,609	59,465	77,437	32,534	64,090	32,464	59,902
39,323	89,641	94,219	116,803	92,857	63,436	65,605	85,861
64,342	61,978	67,998	59,817	101,769	95,774	121,352	69,568
74,276	66,998	40,001	72,069	25,066	77,098	69,922	35,662
74,425	67,202	118,444	53,500	79,294	64,544	86,813	116,269
37,831	89,341	73,341	85,288	138,114	53,402	85,586	82,256
77,539	88,798						

Managerial Report

1. Use appropriate descriptive statistics to summarize the transmission failure data.
2. Develop a 95% confidence interval for the mean number of miles driven until transmission failure for the population of automobiles with transmission failure. Provide a managerial interpretation of the interval estimate.
3. Discuss the implication of your statistical findings in terms of the belief that some owners of the automobiles experienced early transmission failures.
4. How many repair records should be sampled if the research firm wants the population mean number of miles driven until transmission failure to be estimated with a margin of error of 5000 miles? Use 95% confidence.
5. What other information would you like to gather to evaluate the transmission failure problem more fully?

Chapter 8 Appendix

Appendix 8.1 Interval Estimation with JMP

In this chapter appendix, we describe the use of JMP in constructing confidence intervals for a population mean and a population proportion.

Population Mean: σ Known

We illustrate interval estimation of the population mean using the Lloyd's example in Section 8.1. The amounts spent per shopping trip for the sample of 100 customers are contained in the file *Lloyds*. The population standard deviation $\sigma = 20$ is assumed known. The following steps can be used to compute a 95% confidence interval estimate of the population mean.

DATA *file*

Lloyds

Step 1. Open the file *Lloyds* with JMP using the steps provided in Appendix 1.1
Step 2. Click the **Analyze** tab on the JMP Ribbon and select **Distribution**
Step 3. When the **Distribution** dialog box appears, drag **Amount Spent** from the **Select Columns** area to the **Y, Columns** box
    Click **OK** in the **Action** area

As Figure JMP 8.1 shows, these steps produce an output window with several results, including the upper limit and lower limit for the 95% confidence interval for Amount Spent, which are located in the **Summary Statistics** area of the output window and labeled **Upper 95% Mean** and **Lower 95% Mean.** However, this confidence interval is based on the sample standard deviation and so uses the Student's t distribution. Because we want to calculate a confidence interval for a known population standard deviation, we will need to execute the following additional steps to input the known population standard deviation for Amount Spent.

FIGURE JMP 8.1 Output Generated by the Distribution Dialog Box in JMP for the *Lloyds* data

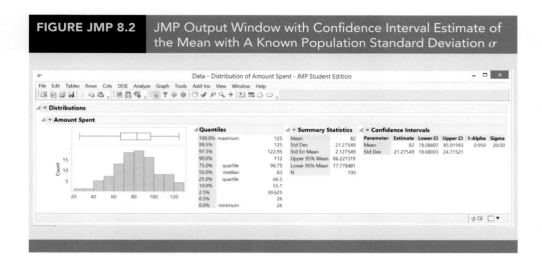

FIGURE JMP 8.2   JMP Output Window with Confidence Interval Estimate of the Mean with A Known Population Standard Deviation σ

Step 4. In the **Data - Distribution of Amount Spent** window, click on the red triangle next to **Amount Spent**

       Select **Confidence Interval** and click **Other . . .**

Step 5. When the **Confidence Intervals** dialog box appears

       Enter .*95* in the **Enter (1-alpha) for confidence interval** box

       Select **Two-sided**

       Select the check box for **Use known Sigma**

       Click **OK**

Step 6. When the **Please Enter a Number** dialog box appears

       Enter *20* in the **Enter known sigma** box

       Click **OK**

As Figure JMP 8.2 illustrates, the **Confidence Intervals** area contains several results, including the lower and upper limits for the 95% confidence interval for Amount Spent ([78.08, 85.92]), in the row labeled **Mean** and columns labeled **Lower CI** and **Upper CI.**

Population Mean: σ Unknown

We illustrate interval estimation of the population mean with an unknown population standard deviation using the credit card debt example in Section 8.2. The credit card balances for a sample of 70 households are provided in the file *NewBalance*. The population standard deviation σ will be estimated by the sample standard deviation s. The following steps can be used to compute a 95% confidence interval estimate of the population mean.

DATA*file*

NewBalance

Step 1. Open the file *NewBalance* with JMP using the steps provided in Appendix 1.1

Step 2. Click the **Analyze** tab on the JMP Ribbon and select **Distribution**

Step 3. When the **Distribution** dialog box appears

       Drag **NewBalance** from the **Select Columns** area to the **Y, Columns** box

       Click **OK** in the **Actions** area

As Figure JMP 8.3 shows, these steps produce an output window with several results, including the upper limit and lower limit for the 95% confidence interval for NewBalance ([8356.56, 10267.44]), which are located in the **Summary Statistics** area of the output window and labeled **Upper 95% Mean** and **Lower 95% Mean.**

To vary the confidence level for the confidence intervals of the population mean, click on the red triangle in the output window next to **NewBalance,** select **Confidence Interval,** and choose the desired confidence level.

| **FIGURE JMP 8.3** | Output Generated by the Distribution Dialog Box in JMP for the *NewBalance* data |

Population Proportion

We illustrate interval estimation of the population proportion using the survey data for women's golfers presented in Section 8.4. Individual responses are recorded as Yes if the golfer is satisfied with the availability of tee times and No otherwise. The following steps can be used to compute a 95% confidence interval estimate of the population proportion.

DATA*file*

TeeTimes

Step 1. Open the file *TeeTimes* with JMP using the steps provided in Appendix 1.1

Step 2. Click the **Analyze** tab on the JMP Ribbon and select **Distribution**

Step 3. When the **Distribution** dialog box appears

   Drag **Response** from the **Select Columns** area to the **Y, Columns** box

   Click **OK**

This produces an output window with several results as shown in Figure JMP 8.4.

| **FIGURE JMP 8.4** | Output Generated by the Distribution Dialog Box |

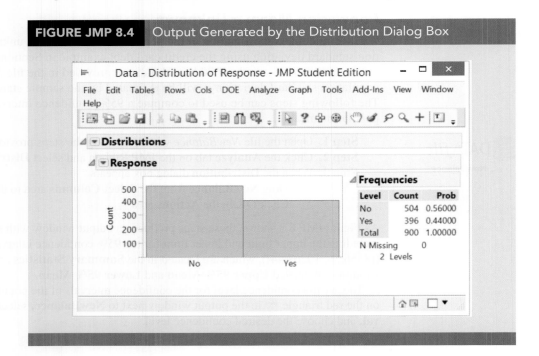

FIGURE JMP 8.5   JMP Output for Confidence Interval on the Population Proportion

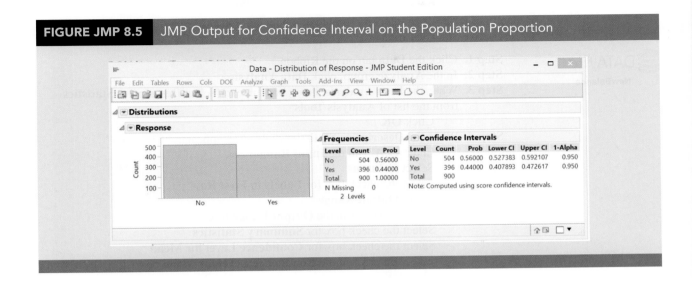

Step 4. In the **Data - Distribution of Response** window, click on the red triangle ⏷ next to **Response**
   Select Confidence Interval and select **0.95**

This produces a new output window that includes 95% confidence interval ([.5274, .5921] for No and [.4079, 4726] for Yes) for the proportion for each value of the variable Response as shown in Figure JMP 8.5 under **Confidence Intervals.**

   To vary the confidence level for the confidence intervals of the population proportion, click on the red triangle ⏷ in the output window next to **Response,** select **Confidence Interval,** and choose the desired confidence level.

Appendix 8.2 Interval Estimation Using Excel

In this chapter appendix, we describe the use of Excel in constructing confidence intervals for a population mean and a population proportion.

Population Mean: σ Known

We illustrate interval estimation using the Lloyd's example in Section 8.1. The population standard deviation $\sigma = 20$ is assumed known. The amounts spent for the sample of 100 customers are in column A in the Excel file *Lloyds*. Excel's AVERAGE and CONFIDENCE.NORM functions can be used to compute the point estimate and the margin of error for an estimate of the population mean.

DATA *file*

Lloyds

Step 1. Select cell C1 and enter the formula *=AVERAGE(A2:A101)*
Step 2. Select cell C2 and enter the formula *=CONFIDENCE.NORM(.05,20,100)*

The three inputs of the CONFIDENCE.NORM(alpha, σ, n) function are

   alpha = 1 − confidence coefficient = 1 − .95 = .05
   σ = population standard deviation = 20
   n = The sample size = 100

The point estimate of the population mean (82) in cell C1 and the margin of error (3.92) in cell C2 allow the confidence interval for the population mean to be easily computed.

Population Mean: σ Unknown

We illustrate interval estimation using the data in Table 8.3, which show the credit card balances for a sample of 70 households. The data are in column A of the Excel file *NewBalance*. The following steps can be used to compute the point estimate and the

Excel's Descriptive Statistics tool is introduced in Chapter 3.

margin of error for an interval estimate of a population mean. We will use Excel's Descriptive Statistics Tool.

DATA *file*

NewBalance

Step 1. Click the **Data** tab on the Ribbon
Step 2. In the **Analyze** group, click **Data Analysis**
Step 3. When the **Data Analysis** dialog box appears, select **Descriptive Statistics** from the list of **Analysis Tools**
   Click **OK**
Step 4. When the **Descriptive Statistics** dialog box appears:
   Enter *A1:A71* in the **Input Range:** box
   Select **Columns**
   Select the check box for **Labels in First Row**
   Select **Output Range**
      Enter *C1* in the **Output Range** box
   Select the check box for **Summary Statistics**
   Select the check box for **Confidence Level for Mean**
      Enter *95* in the **Confidence Level for Mean** box
   Click **OK**

The summary statistics will appear in columns C and D as shown in Figure Excel 8.1. The point estimate of the population mean appears in cell D3. The margin of error, labeled "Confidence Level(95.0%)," appears in cell D16. The point estimate (9312) in cell D3 and the margin of error (955) in cell D16 allow the confidence interval for the population mean to be easily computed.

FIGURE Excel 8.1   Interval Estimation of the Population Mean Credit Card Balance Using Excel

	A	B	C	D	E	F
1	**NewBalance**			*NewBalance*		
2	9430					
3	7535		Mean	9312	Point Estimate	
4	4078		Standard Error	478.9281		
5	5604		Median	9466		
6	5179		Mode	13627		
7	4416		Standard Deviation	4007		
8	10676		Sample Variance	16056048		
9	1627		Kurtosis	-0.2960		
10	10112		Skewness	0.1879		
11	6567		Range	18648		
12	13627		Minimum	615		
13	18719		Maximum	19263		
14	14661		Sum	651840		
15	12195		Count	70		
16	10544		Confidence Level(95.0%)	955	Margin of Error	
17	13659					
70	9743					
71	10324					
72						

Note: Rows 18 to 69 are hidden.

The file IntervalProp contains the same data as the file Tee-Times, but with the template for interval estimation added.

Population Proportion

We illustrate interval estimation using the survey data for women golfers presented in Section 8.4. The data are in column A in the file *IntervalProp*. Individual responses are recorded as Yes if the golfer is satisfied with the availability of tee times and No otherwise. Excel does not offer a built-in routine to handle the estimation of a population proportion; however, it is relatively easy to develop an Excel template that can be used for this purpose. The template shown in Figure Excel 8.2 provides the 95% confidence interval estimate of the proportion of women golfers who are satisfied with the availability of tee times. Note that the top worksheet in Figure Excel 8.2 shows the cell formulas that provide the interval

DATA *file*

IntervalProp

Note: Rows 19 to 900 are hidden.

FIGURE Excel 8.2	Excel Template for Interval Estimation of a Population Proportion

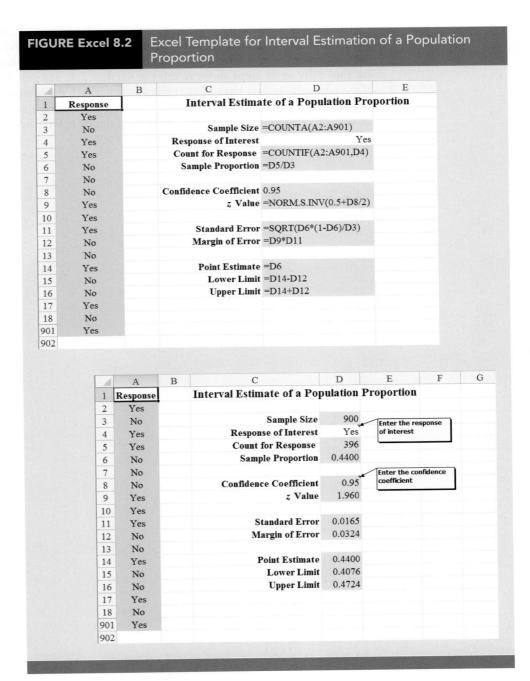

estimation results shown in the foreground worksheet. The following steps are necessary to use the template for this data set.

The Excel formula COUNTA counts the number of non-empty cells.

Step 1. Enter the data range A2:A901 into the =COUNTA cell formula in cell D3 to calculate **Sample Size**

Step 2. Enter *Yes* as the **Response of Interest** in cell D4

Step 3. Enter the formula *=COUNTIF(A2:A901,D4)* into cell D5 to count the number of Yes responses

Step 4. Enter *.95* as the **Confidence Coefficient** in cell D8

The template automatically provides the confidence interval in cells D15 and D16 as shown in Figure Excel 8.2.

This template can be used to compute the confidence interval for a population proportion for other applications. For instance, to compute the interval estimate for a new data set, enter the new sample data into column A of the worksheet and then change the four cells in the steps above to refer to the new data and new response of interest. If the new sample data have already been summarized, the sample data do not have to be entered into the worksheet. In this case, enter the sample size into cell D3 and the sample proportion into cell D6; the worksheet template will then provide the confidence interval for the population proportion.

Chapter 9

Hypothesis Tests

CONTENTS

STATISTICS IN PRACTICE

John Morrell & Company*

CINCINNATI, OHIO

John Morrell & Company, which began in England in 1827, is considered the oldest continuously operating meat manufacturer in the United States. It is a wholly owned and independently managed subsidiary of Smithfield Foods, Smithfield, Virginia. John Morrell & Company offers an extensive product line of processed meats and fresh pork to consumers under 13 regional brands including John Morrell, E-Z-Cut, Tobin's First Prize, Dinner Bell, Hunter, Kretschmar, Rath, Rodeo, Shenson, Farmers Hickory Brand, Iowa Quality, and Peyton's. Each regional brand enjoys high brand recognition and loyalty among consumers.

Market research at Morrell provides management with up-to-date information on the company's various products and how the products compare with competing brands of similar products. A recent study compared a Beef Pot Roast made by Morrell to similar beef products from two major competitors. In the three-product comparison test, a sample of consumers was used to indicate how the products rated in terms of taste, appearance, aroma, and overall preference.

One research question concerned whether the Beef Pot Roast made by Morrell was the preferred choice of more than 50% of the consumer population. Letting p indicate the population proportion preferring Morrell's product, the hypothesis test for the research question is as follows:

$$H_0: p \leq .50$$
$$H_a: p > .50$$

The null hypothesis H_0 indicates the preference for Morrell's product is less than or equal to 50%. If the sample data support rejecting H_0 in favor of the

Market research at Morrell provides up-to-date information on their various products and how they compare with competing brands.
Source: RosalreneBetancourt 12/Alamy Stock Photo

alternative hypothesis H_a, Morrell will draw the research conclusion that in a three-product comparison, their Beef Pot Roast is preferred by more than 50% of the consumer population.

In an independent taste test study using a sample of 224 consumers in Cincinnati, Milwaukee, and Los Angeles, 150 consumers selected the Beef Pot Roast made by Morrell as the preferred product. Using statistical hypothesis testing procedures, the null hypothesis H_0 was rejected. The study provided statistical evidence supporting H_a and the conclusion that the Morrell product is preferred by more than 50% of the consumer population.

The point estimate of the population proportion was $\bar{p} = 150/224 = .67$. Thus, the sample data provided support for a food magazine advertisement showing that in a three-product taste comparison, Beef Pot Roast made by Morrell was "preferred 2 to 1 over the competition."

In this chapter we will discuss how to formulate hypotheses and how to conduct tests like the one used by Morrell. Through the analysis of sample data, we will be able to determine whether a hypothesis should or should not be rejected.

---

*The authors are indebted to Marty Butler, Vice President of Marketing, John Morrell, for providing the context for this Statistics in Practice.

In Chapters 7 and 8 we showed how a sample could be used to develop point and interval estimates of population parameters. In this chapter we continue the discussion of statistical inference by showing how hypothesis testing can be used to determine whether a statement about the value of a population parameter should or should not be rejected.

In hypothesis testing we begin by making a tentative assumption about a population parameter. This tentative assumption is called the **null hypothesis** and is denoted by H_0. We then define another hypothesis, called the **alternative hypothesis**, which is the opposite of what is stated in the null hypothesis. The alternative hypothesis is denoted by H_a.

The hypothesis testing procedure uses data from a sample to test the two competing statements indicated by H_0 and H_a.

This chapter shows how hypothesis tests can be conducted about a population mean and a population proportion. We begin by providing examples that illustrate approaches to developing null and alternative hypotheses.

9.1 Developing Null and Alternative Hypotheses

It is not always obvious how the null and alternative hypotheses should be formulated. Care must be taken to structure the hypotheses appropriately so that the hypothesis testing conclusion provides the information the researcher or decision maker wants. The context of the situation is very important in determining how the hypotheses should be stated. All hypothesis testing applications involve collecting a sample and using the sample results to provide evidence for drawing a conclusion. Good questions to consider when formulating the null and alternative hypotheses are, What is the purpose of collecting the sample? What conclusions are we hoping to make?

Learning to correctly formulate hypotheses will take some practice. Expect some initial confusion over the proper choice of the null and alternative hypotheses. The examples in this section are intended to provide guidelines.

In the chapter introduction, we stated that the null hypothesis H_0 is a tentative assumption about a population parameter such as a population mean or a population proportion. The alternative hypothesis H_a is a statement that is the opposite of what is stated in the null hypothesis. In some situations it is easier to identify the alternative hypothesis first and then develop the null hypothesis. In other situations it is easier to identify the null hypothesis first and then develop the alternative hypothesis. We will illustrate these situations in the following examples.

The Alternative Hypothesis as a Research Hypothesis

Many applications of hypothesis testing involve an attempt to gather evidence in support of a research hypothesis. In these situations, it is often best to begin with the alternative hypothesis and make it the conclusion that the researcher hopes to support. Consider a particular automobile that currently attains a fuel efficiency of 24 miles per gallon in city driving. A product research group has developed a new fuel injection system designed to increase the miles-per-gallon rating. The group will run controlled tests with the new fuel injection system looking for statistical support for the conclusion that the new fuel injection system provides more miles per gallon than the current system.

Several new fuel injection units will be manufactured, installed in test automobiles, and subjected to research-controlled driving conditions. The sample mean miles per gallon for these automobiles will be computed and used in a hypothesis test to determine if it can be concluded that the new system provides more than 24 miles per gallon. In terms of the population mean miles per gallon μ, the research hypothesis $\mu > 24$ becomes the alternative hypothesis. Since the current system provides an average or mean of 24 miles per gallon, we will make the tentative assumption that the new system is not any better than the current system and choose $\mu \leq 24$ as the null hypothesis. The null and alternative hypotheses are:

$$H_0: \mu \leq 24$$
$$H_a: \mu > 24$$

The conclusion that the research hypothesis is true is made if the sample data provide sufficient evidence to show that the null hypothesis can be rejected.

If the sample results lead to the conclusion to reject H_0, the inference can be made that $H_a: \mu > 24$ is true. The researchers have the statistical support to state that the new fuel injection system increases the mean number of miles per gallon. The production of automobiles with the new fuel injection system should be considered. However, if the sample results lead to the conclusion that H_0 cannot be rejected, the researchers cannot conclude that the new fuel injection system is better than the current system. Production of automobiles with the new fuel injection system on the basis of better gas mileage cannot be justified. Perhaps more research and further testing can be conducted.

Successful companies stay competitive by developing new products, new methods, new systems, and the like, that are better than what is currently available. Before adopting something new, it is desirable to conduct research to determine if there is statistical support for the conclusion that the new approach is indeed better. In such cases, the research hypothesis is stated as the alternative hypothesis. For example, a new teaching method is developed that is believed to be better than the current method. The alternative hypothesis is that the new method is better. The null hypothesis is that the new method is no better than the old method. A new sales force bonus plan is developed in an attempt to increase sales. The alternative hypothesis is that the new bonus plan increases sales. The null hypothesis is that the new bonus plan does not increase sales. A new drug is developed with the goal of lowering blood pressure more than an existing drug. The alternative hypothesis is that the new drug lowers blood pressure more than the existing drug. The null hypothesis is that the new drug does not provide lower blood pressure than the existing drug. In each case, rejection of the null hypothesis H_0 provides statistical support for the research hypothesis. We will see many examples of hypothesis tests in research situations such as these throughout this chapter and in the remainder of the text.

The Null Hypothesis as an Assumption to Be Challenged

Of course, not all hypothesis tests involve research hypotheses. In the following discussion we consider applications of hypothesis testing where we begin with a belief or an assumption that a statement about the value of a population parameter is true. We will then use a hypothesis test to challenge the assumption and determine if there is statistical evidence to conclude that the assumption is incorrect. In these situations, it is helpful to develop the null hypothesis first. The null hypothesis H_0 expresses the belief or assumption about the value of the population parameter. The alternative hypothesis H_a is that the belief or assumption is incorrect.

As an example, consider the situation of a manufacturer of soft drink products. The label on a soft drink bottle states that it contains 67.6 fluid ounces. We consider the label correct provided the population mean filling weight for the bottles is *at least* 67.6 fluid ounces. Without any reason to believe otherwise, we would give the manufacturer the benefit of the doubt and assume that the statement provided on the label is correct. Thus, in a hypothesis test about the population mean fluid weight per bottle, we would begin with the assumption that the label is correct and state the null hypothesis as $\mu \geq 67.6$. The challenge to this assumption would imply that the label is incorrect and the bottles are being underfilled. This challenge would be stated as the alternative hypothesis $\mu < 67.6$. Thus, the null and alternative hypotheses are:

$$H_0: \mu \geq 67.6$$
$$H_a: \mu < 67.6$$

A manufacturer's product information is usually assumed to be true and stated as the null hypothesis. The conclusion that the information is incorrect can be made if the null hypothesis is rejected.

A government agency with the responsibility for validating manufacturing labels could select a sample of soft drinks bottles, compute the sample mean filling weight, and use the sample results to test the preceding hypotheses. If the sample results lead to the conclusion to reject H_0, the inference that $H_a: \mu < 67.6$ is true can be made. With this statistical support, the agency is justified in concluding that the label is incorrect and underfilling of the bottles is occurring. Appropriate action to force the manufacturer to comply with labeling standards would be considered. However, if the sample results indicate H_0 cannot be rejected, the assumption that the manufacturer's labeling is correct cannot be rejected. With this conclusion, no action would be taken.

Let us now consider a variation of the soft drink bottle filling example by viewing the same situation from the manufacturer's point of view. The bottle-filling operation has been designed to fill soft drink bottles with 67.6 fluid ounces as stated on the label. The company does not want to underfill the containers because that could result in an underfilling complaint from customers or, perhaps, a government agency. However, the company does not want to overfill containers either because putting more soft drink than necessary into the containers would be an unnecessary cost. The company's goal would be to adjust the bottle-filling operation so that the population mean filling weight per bottle is 67.6 fluid ounces as specified on the label.

Although this is the company's goal, from time to time any production process can get out of adjustment. If this occurs in our example, underfilling or overfilling of the soft drink bottles will occur. In either case, the company would like to know about it in order to correct the situation by readjusting the bottle-filling operation to the designed 67.6 fluid ounces. In a hypothesis testing application, we would again begin with the assumption that the production process is operating correctly and state the null hypothesis as $\mu = 67.6$ fluid ounces. The alternative hypothesis that challenges this assumption is that $\mu \neq 67.6$, which indicates either overfilling or underfilling is occurring. The null and alternative hypotheses for the manufacturer's hypothesis test are:

$$H_0: \mu = 67.6$$
$$H_a: \mu \neq 67.6$$

Suppose that the soft drink manufacturer uses a quality control procedure to periodically select a sample of bottles from the filling operation and computes the sample mean filling weight per bottle. If the sample results lead to the conclusion to reject H_0, the inference is made that H_a: $\mu \neq 67.6$ is true. We conclude that the bottles are not being filled properly and the production process should be adjusted to restore the population mean to 67.6 fluid ounces per bottle. However, if the sample results indicate H_0 cannot be rejected, the assumption that the manufacturer's bottle filling operation is functioning properly cannot be rejected. In this case, no further action would be taken and the production operation would continue to run.

The two preceding forms of the soft drink manufacturing hypothesis test show that the null and alternative hypotheses may vary depending upon the point of view of the researcher or decision maker. To correctly formulate hypotheses it is important to understand the context of the situation and structure the hypotheses to provide the information the researcher or decision maker wants.

Summary of Forms for Null and Alternative Hypotheses

The hypothesis tests in this chapter involve two population parameters: the population mean and the population proportion. Depending on the situation, hypothesis tests about a population parameter may take one of three forms: two use inequalities in the null hypothesis; the third uses an equality in the null hypothesis. For hypothesis tests involving a population mean, we let μ_0 denote the hypothesized value and we must choose one of the following three forms for the hypothesis test.

The three possible forms of hypotheses H_0 and H_a are shown here. Note that the equality always appears in the null hypothesis H_0.

$$H_0: \mu \geq \mu_0 \qquad H_0: \mu \leq \mu_0 \qquad H_0: \mu = \mu_0$$
$$H_a: \mu < \mu_0 \qquad H_a: \mu > \mu_0 \qquad H_a: \mu \neq \mu_0$$

For reasons that will be clear later, the first two forms are called one-tailed tests. The third form is called a two-tailed test.

In many situations, the choice of H_0 and H_a is not obvious and judgment is necessary to select the proper form. However, as the preceding forms show, the equality part of the expression (either $\geq$, $\leq$, or $=$) *always* appears in the null hypothesis. In selecting the proper form of H_0 and H_a, keep in mind that the alternative hypothesis is often what the test is attempting to establish. Hence, asking whether the user is looking for evidence to support $\mu < \mu_0$, $\mu > \mu_0$, or $\mu \neq \mu_0$ will help determine H_a. The following exercises are designed to provide practice in choosing the proper form for a hypothesis test involving a population mean.

EXERCISES

1. **Hotel Guest Bills.** The manager of the Danvers-Hilton Resort Hotel stated that the mean guest bill for a weekend is $600 or less. A member of the hotel's accounting staff noticed that the total charges for guest bills have been increasing in recent months. The accountant will use a sample of future weekend guest bills to test the manager's claim.
   a. Which form of the hypotheses should be used to test the manager's claim? Explain.

$$H_0: \mu \geq 600 \qquad H_0: \mu \leq 600 \qquad H_0: \mu = 600$$
$$H_a: \mu < 600 \qquad H_a: \mu > 600 \qquad H_a: \mu \neq 600$$

   b. What conclusion is appropriate when H_0 cannot be rejected?
   c. What conclusion is appropriate when H_0 can be rejected?

2. **Bonus Plan's Effect on Automobile Sales.** The manager of an automobile dealership is considering a new bonus plan designed to increase sales volume. Currently, the mean sales volume is 14 automobiles per month. The manager wants to conduct a research study to see whether the new bonus plan increases sales volume. To collect data on the plan, a sample of sales personnel will be allowed to sell under the new bonus plan for a one-month period.
   a. Develop the null and alternative hypotheses most appropriate for this situation.
   b. Comment on the conclusion when H_0 cannot be rejected.
   c. Comment on the conclusion when H_0 can be rejected.

3. **Filling Detergent Cartons.** A production line operation is designed to fill cartons with laundry detergent to a mean weight of 32 ounces. A sample of cartons is periodically selected and weighed to determine whether underfilling or overfilling is occurring. If the sample data lead to a conclusion of underfilling or overfilling, the production line will be shut down and adjusted to obtain proper filling.
   a. Formulate the null and alternative hypotheses that will help in deciding whether to shut down and adjust the production line.
   b. Comment on the conclusion and the decision when H_0 cannot be rejected.
   c. Comment on the conclusion and the decision when H_0 can be rejected.

4. **Process Improvement.** Because of high production-changeover time and costs, a director of manufacturing must convince management that a proposed manufacturing method reduces costs before the new method can be implemented. The current production method operates with a mean cost of $220 per hour. A research study will measure the cost of the new method over a sample production period.
   a. Develop the null and alternative hypotheses most appropriate for this study.
   b. Comment on the conclusion when H_0 cannot be rejected.
   c. Comment on the conclusion when H_0 can be rejected.

9.2 Type I and Type II Errors

The null and alternative hypotheses are competing statements about the population. Either the null hypothesis H_0 is true or the alternative hypothesis H_a is true, but not both. Ideally the hypothesis testing procedure should lead to the acceptance of H_0 when H_0 is true and the rejection of H_0 when H_a is true. Unfortunately, the correct conclusions are not always possible. Because hypothesis tests are based on sample information, we must allow for the possibility of errors. Table 9.1 illustrates the two kinds of errors that can be made in hypothesis testing.

The first row of Table 9.1 shows what can happen if the conclusion is to accept H_0. If H_0 is true, this conclusion is correct. However, if H_a is true, we make a **Type II error**; that is, we accept H_0 when it is false. The second row of Table 9.1 shows what can happen if the conclusion is to reject H_0. If H_0 is true, we make a **Type I error**; that is, we reject H_0 when it is true. However, if H_a is true, rejecting H_0 is correct.

Recall the hypothesis testing illustration discussed in Section 9.1 in which an automobile product research group developed a new fuel injection system designed to increase the

TABLE 9.1	Errors and Correct Conclusions in Hypothesis Testing	

| | | **Population Condition** | |
		H_0 True	H_a True
Conclusion	**Accept H_0**	Correct Conclusion	Type II Error
	Reject H_0	Type I Error	Correct Conclusion

miles-per-gallon rating of a particular automobile. With the current model obtaining an average of 24 miles per gallon, the hypothesis test was formulated as follows.

$$H_0: \mu \leq 24$$
$$H_a: \mu > 24$$

The alternative hypothesis, $H_a: \mu > 24$, indicates that the researchers are looking for sample evidence to support the conclusion that the population mean miles per gallon with the new fuel injection system is greater than 24.

In this application, the Type I error of rejecting H_0 when it is true corresponds to the researchers claiming that the new system improves the miles-per-gallon rating ($\mu > 24$) when in fact the new system is not any better than the current system. In contrast, the Type II error of accepting H_0 when it is false corresponds to the researchers concluding that the new system is not any better than the current system ($\mu \leq 24$) when in fact the new system improves miles-per-gallon performance.

For the miles-per-gallon rating hypothesis test, the null hypothesis is $H_0: \mu \leq 24$. Suppose the null hypothesis is true as an equality; that is, $\mu = 24$. The probability of making a Type I error when the null hypothesis is true as an equality is called the **level of significance**. Thus, for the miles-per-gallon rating hypothesis test, the level of significance is the probability of rejecting $H_0: \mu \leq 24$ when $\mu = 24$. Because of the importance of this concept, we now restate the definition of level of significance.

LEVEL OF SIGNIFICANCE

The level of significance is the probability of making a Type I error when the null hypothesis is true as an equality.

The Greek symbol α (alpha) is used to denote the level of significance, and common choices for α are .05 and .01.

In practice, the person responsible for the hypothesis test specifies the level of significance. By selecting α, that person is controlling the probability of making a Type I error. If the cost of making a Type I error is high, small values of α are preferred. If the cost of making a Type I error is not too high, larger values of α are typically used. Applications of hypothesis testing that only control for the Type I error are called *significance tests*. Many applications of hypothesis testing are of this type.

If the sample data are consistent with the null hypothesis H_0, we will follow the practice of concluding "do not reject H_0." This conclusion is preferred over "accept H_0," because the conclusion to accept H_0 puts us at risk of making a Type II error.

Although most applications of hypothesis testing control for the probability of making a Type I error, they do not always control for the probability of making a Type II error. Hence, if we decide to accept H_0, we cannot determine how confident we can be with that decision. Because of the uncertainty associated with making a Type II error when conducting significance tests, statisticians usually recommend that we use the statement "do not reject H_0" instead of "accept H_0." Using the statement "do not reject H_0" carries the recommendation to withhold both judgment and action. In effect, by not directly accepting H_0, the statistician avoids the risk of making a Type II error. Whenever the probability of making a Type II error has not been determined and controlled, we will not make the statement "accept H_0." In such cases, only two conclusions are possible: *do not reject H_0* or *reject H_0*.

Although controlling for a Type II error in hypothesis testing is not common, it can be done. In Sections 9.7 and 9.8 we will illustrate procedures for determining and controlling the probability of making a Type II error. If proper controls have been established for this error, action based on the "accept H_0" conclusion can be appropriate.

NOTES + COMMENTS

Walter Williams, syndicated columnist and professor of economics at George Mason University, points out that the possibility of making a Type I or a Type II error is always present in decision making (*The Cincinnati Enquirer*, August 14, 2005). He notes that the Food and Drug Administration (FDA) runs the risk of making these errors in its drug approval process.

The FDA must either approve a new drug or not approve it. Thus the FDA runs the risk of making a Type I error by approving a new drug that is not safe and effective, or making a Type II error by failing to approve a new drug that is safe and effective. Regardless of the decision made, the possibility of making a costly error cannot be eliminated.

EXERCISES

5. **Beer and Cider Consumption.** According to the National Beer Wholesalers Association, U.S. consumers 21 years and older consumed 26.9 gallons of beer and cider per person during 2017. A distributor in Milwaukee believes that beer and cider consumption are higher in that city. A sample of consumers 21 years and older in Milwaukee will be taken, and the sample mean 2017 beer and cider consumption will be used to test the following null and alternative hypotheses:

$$H_0: \mu \leq 26.9$$
$$H_a: \mu > 26.9$$

a. Assume the sample data led to rejection of the null hypothesis. What would be your conclusion about consumption of beer and cider in Milwaukee?
b. What is the Type I error in this situation? What are the consequences of making this error?
c. What is the Type II error in this situation? What are the consequences of making this error?

6. **Orange Juice Labels.** The label on a 3-quart container of orange juice states that the orange juice contains an average of 1 gram of fat or less. Answer the following questions for a hypothesis test that could be used to test the claim on the label.
a. Develop the appropriate null and alternative hypotheses.
b. What is the Type I error in this situation? What are the consequences of making this error?
c. What is the Type II error in this situation? What are the consequences of making this error?

7. **Carpet Salesperson Salaries.** Carpetland salespersons average $8000 per week in sales. Steve Contois, the firm's vice president, proposes a compensation plan with new selling incentives. Steve hopes that the results of a trial selling period will enable him to conclude that the compensation plan increases the average sales per salesperson.
a. Develop the appropriate null and alternative hypotheses.
b. What is the Type I error in this situation? What are the consequences of making this error?
c. What is the Type II error in this situation? What are the consequences of making this error?

8. **Production Operating Costs.** Suppose a new production method will be implemented if a hypothesis test supports the conclusion that the new method reduces the mean operating cost per hour.
   a. State the appropriate null and alternative hypotheses if the mean cost for the current production method is $220 per hour.
   b. What is the Type I error in this situation? What are the consequences of making this error?
   c. What is the Type II error in this situation? What are the consequences of making this error?

9.3 Population Mean: σ Known

In Chapter 8 we said that the σ known case corresponds to applications in which historical data and/or other information are available that enable us to obtain a good estimate of the population standard deviation prior to sampling. In such cases the population standard deviation can, for all practical purposes, be considered known. In this section we show how to conduct a hypothesis test about a population mean for the σ known case.

The methods presented in this section are exact if the sample is selected from a population that is normally distributed. In cases where it is not reasonable to assume the population is normally distributed, these methods are still applicable if the sample size is large enough. We provide some practical advice concerning the population distribution and the sample size at the end of this section.

One-Tailed Test

One-tailed tests about a population mean take one of the following two forms.

Lower Tail Test	Upper Tail Test
$H_0: \mu \geq \mu_0$	$H_0: \mu \leq \mu_0$
$H_a: \mu < \mu_0$	$H_a: \mu > \mu_0$

Let us consider an example involving a lower tail test.

The Federal Trade Commission (FTC) periodically conducts statistical studies designed to test the claims that manufacturers make about their products. For example, the label on a large can of Hilltop Coffee states that the can contains 3 pounds of coffee. The FTC knows that Hilltop's production process cannot place exactly 3 pounds of coffee in each can, even if the mean filling weight for the population of all cans filled is 3 pounds per can. However, as long as the population mean filling weight is at least 3 pounds per can, the rights of consumers will be protected. Thus, the FTC interprets the label information on a large can of coffee as a claim by Hilltop that the population mean filling weight is at least 3 pounds per can. We will show how the FTC can check Hilltop's claim by conducting a lower tail hypothesis test.

The first step is to develop the null and alternative hypotheses for the test. If the population mean filling weight is at least 3 pounds per can, Hilltop's claim is correct. This establishes the null hypothesis for the test. However, if the population mean weight is less than 3 pounds per can, Hilltop's claim is incorrect. This establishes the alternative hypothesis. With μ denoting the population mean filling weight, the null and alternative hypotheses are as follows:

$$H_0: \mu \geq 3$$
$$H_a: \mu < 3$$

Note that the hypothesized value of the population mean is $\mu_0 = 3$.

If the sample data indicate that H_0 cannot be rejected, the statistical evidence does not support the conclusion that a label violation has occurred. Hence, no action should be taken against Hilltop. However, if the sample data indicate H_0 can be rejected, we will conclude that the alternative hypothesis, $H_a: \mu < 3$, is true. In this case a conclusion of underfilling and a charge of a label violation against Hilltop would be justified.

Suppose a sample of 36 cans of coffee is selected and the sample mean $\bar{x}$ is computed as an estimate of the population mean μ. If the value of the sample mean $\bar{x}$ is less than 3 pounds, the sample results will cast doubt on the null hypothesis. What we want to know is how much less than 3 pounds must $\bar{x}$ be before we would be willing to declare the difference significant and risk making a Type I error by falsely accusing Hilltop of a label violation. A key factor in addressing this issue is the value the decision maker selects for the level of significance.

As noted in the preceding section, the level of significance, denoted by α, is the probability of making a Type I error by rejecting H_0 when the null hypothesis is true as an equality. The decision maker must specify the level of significance. If the cost of making a Type I error is high, a small value should be chosen for the level of significance. If the cost is not high, a larger value is more appropriate. In the Hilltop Coffee study, the director of the FTC's testing program made the following statement: "If the company is meeting its weight specifications at $\mu = 3$, I do not want to take action against them. But, I am willing to risk a 1% chance of making such an error." From the director's statement, we set the level of significance for the hypothesis test at $\alpha = .01$. Thus, we must design the hypothesis test so that the probability of making a Type I error when $\mu = 3$ is .01.

For the Hilltop Coffee study, by developing the null and alternative hypotheses and specifying the level of significance for the test, we carry out the first two steps required in conducting every hypothesis test. We are now ready to perform the third step of hypothesis testing: collect the sample data and compute the value of what is called a test statistic.

Test statistic For the Hilltop Coffee study, previous FTC tests show that the population standard deviation can be assumed known with a value of $\sigma = .18$. In addition, these tests also show that the population of filling weights can be assumed to have a normal distribution. From the study of sampling distributions in Chapter 7 we know that if the population from which we are sampling is normally distributed, the sampling distribution of $\bar{x}$ will also be normally distributed. Thus, for the Hilltop Coffee study, the sampling distribution of $\bar{x}$ is normally distributed. With a known value of $\sigma = .18$ and a sample size of *The standard error of $\bar{x}$ is the standard deviation of the sampling distribution of $\bar{x}$.* $n = 36$, Figure 9.1 shows the sampling distribution of $\bar{x}$ when the null hypothesis is true as an equality; that is, when $\mu = \mu_0 = 3$.[1] Note that the standard error of $\bar{x}$ is given by $\sigma_{\bar{x}} = \sigma/\sqrt{n} = .18/\sqrt{36} = .03$.

Because the sampling distribution of $\bar{x}$ is normally distributed, the sampling distribution of

$$z = \frac{\bar{x} - \mu_0}{\sigma_{\bar{x}}} = \frac{\bar{x} - 3}{.03}$$

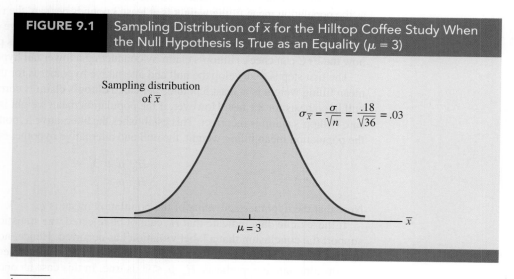

FIGURE 9.1   Sampling Distribution of $\bar{x}$ for the Hilltop Coffee Study When the Null Hypothesis Is True as an Equality ($\mu = 3$)

Sampling distribution of $\bar{x}$

$$\sigma_{\bar{x}} = \frac{\sigma}{\sqrt{n}} = \frac{.18}{\sqrt{36}} = .03$$

$\mu = 3$

[1]In constructing sampling distributions for hypothesis tests, it is assumed that H_0 is satisfied as an equality.

is a standard normal distribution. A value of $z = -1$ means that the value of $\bar{x}$ is one standard error below the hypothesized value of the mean, a value of $z = -2$ means that the value of $\bar{x}$ is two standard errors below the hypothesized value of the mean, and so on. We can use the standard normal probability table to find the lower tail probability corresponding to any z value. For instance, the lower tail area at $z = -3.00$ is .0013. Hence, the probability of obtaining a value of z that is three or more standard errors below the mean is .0013. As a result, the probability of obtaining a value of $\bar{x}$ that is 3 or more standard errors below the hypothesized population mean $\mu_0 = 3$ is also .0013. Such a result is unlikely if the null hypothesis is true.

For hypothesis tests about a population mean in the σ known case, we use the standard normal random variable z as a **test statistic** to determine whether $\bar{x}$ deviates from the hypothesized value of μ enough to justify rejecting the null hypothesis. With $\sigma_{\bar{x}} = \sigma/\sqrt{n}$, the test statistic is as follows.

TEST STATISTIC FOR HYPOTHESIS TESTS ABOUT A POPULATION MEAN: σ KNOWN

$$z = \frac{\bar{x} - \mu_0}{\sigma/\sqrt{n}} \tag{9.1}$$

The key question for a lower tail test is, How small must the test statistic z be before we choose to reject the null hypothesis? Two approaches can be used to answer this question: the p-value approach and the critical value approach.

p-value approach The p-value approach uses the value of the test statistic z to compute a probability called a **p-value**.

A small p-value indicates the value of the test statistic is unusual given the assumption that H_0 is true.

p-VALUE

A p-value is a probability that provides a measure of the evidence against the null hypothesis provided by the sample. Smaller p-values indicate more evidence against H_0.

The p-value is used to determine whether the null hypothesis should be rejected.

Let us see how the p-value is computed and used. The value of the test statistic is used to compute the p-value. The method used depends on whether the test is a lower tail, an upper tail, or a two-tailed test. For a lower tail test, the p-value is the probability of obtaining a value for the test statistic as small as or smaller than that provided by the sample. Thus, to compute the p-value for the lower tail test in the σ known case, we use the standard normal distribution to find the probability that z is less than or equal to the value of the test statistic. After computing the p-value, we must then decide whether it is small enough to reject the null hypothesis; as we will show, this decision involves comparing the p-value to the level of significance.

Let us now compute the p-value for the Hilltop Coffee lower tail test. Suppose the sample of 36 Hilltop coffee cans provides a sample mean of $\bar{x} = 2.92$ pounds. Is $\bar{x} = 2.92$ small enough to cause us to reject H_0? Because this is a lower tail test, the p-value is the area under the standard normal curve for values of $z \le$ the value of the test statistic. Using $\bar{x} = 2.92$, $\sigma = .18$, and $n = 36$, we compute the value of the test statistic z.

DATA *file*

Coffee

$$z = \frac{\bar{x} - \mu_0}{\sigma/\sqrt{n}} = \frac{2.92 - 3}{.18/\sqrt{36}} = -2.67$$

Thus, the p-value is the probability that z is less than or equal to -2.67 (the lower tail area corresponding to the value of the test statistic).

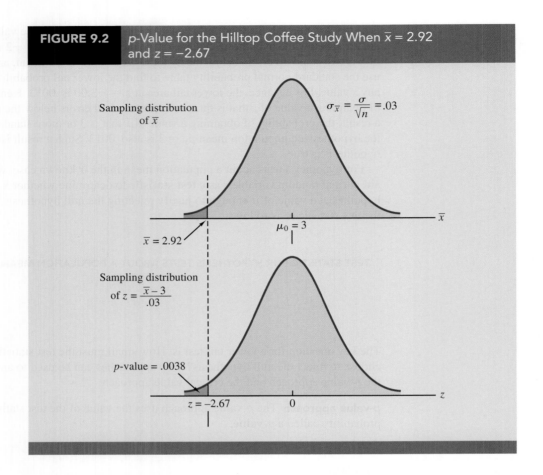

FIGURE 9.2   *p*-Value for the Hilltop Coffee Study When $\bar{x} = 2.92$ and $z = -2.67$

Using the standard normal probability table, we find that the lower tail area at $z = -2.67$ is .0038. Figure 9.2 shows that $\bar{x} = 2.92$ corresponds to $z = -2.67$ and a *p*-value $= .0038$. This *p*-value indicates a small probability of obtaining a sample mean of $\bar{x} = 2.92$ (and a test statistic of -2.67) or smaller when sampling from a population with $\mu = 3$. This *p*-value does not provide much support for the null hypothesis, but is it small enough to cause us to reject H_0? The answer depends upon the level of significance for the test.

As noted previously, the director of the FTC's testing program selected a value of .01 for the level of significance. The selection of $\alpha = .01$ means that the director is willing to tolerate a probability of .01 of rejecting the null hypothesis when it is true as an equality ($\mu_0 = 3$). The sample of 36 coffee cans in the Hilltop Coffee study resulted in a *p*-value $= .0038$, which means that the probability of obtaining a value of $\bar{x} = 2.92$ or less when the null hypothesis is true as an equality is .0038. Because .0038 is less than or equal to $\alpha = .01$, we reject H_0. Therefore, we find sufficient statistical evidence to reject the null hypothesis at the .01 level of significance.

We can now state the general rule for determining whether the null hypothesis can be rejected when using the *p*-value approach. For a level of significance α, the rejection rule using the *p*-value approach is as follows:

REJECTION RULE USING *p*-VALUE

$$\text{Reject } H_0 \text{ if } p\text{-value} \leq \alpha$$

In the Hilltop Coffee test, the *p*-value of .0038 resulted in the rejection of the null hypothesis. Although the basis for making the rejection decision involves a comparison of the *p*-value to the level of significance specified by the FTC director, the observed *p*-value of .0038 means that we would reject H_0 for any value of $\alpha \geq .0038$. For this reason, the *p*-value is also called the *observed level of significance.*

Different decision makers may express different opinions concerning the cost of making a Type I error and may choose a different level of significance. By providing the *p*-value as part of the hypothesis testing results, another decision maker can compare the reported *p*-value to his or her own level of significance and possibly make a different decision with respect to rejecting H_0.

Critical value approach The critical value approach requires that we first determine a value for the test statistic called the **critical value**. For a lower tail test, the critical value serves as a benchmark for determining whether the value of the test statistic is small enough to reject the null hypothesis. It is the value of the test statistic that corresponds to an area of α (the level of significance) in the lower tail of the sampling distribution of the test statistic. In other words, the critical value is the largest value of the test statistic that will result in the rejection of the null hypothesis. Let us return to the Hilltop Coffee example and see how this approach works.

In the σ known case, the sampling distribution for the test statistic z is a standard normal distribution. Therefore, the critical value is the value of the test statistic that corresponds to an area of $\alpha = .01$ in the lower tail of a standard normal distribution. Using the standard normal probability table, we find that $z = -2.33$ provides an area of .01 in the lower tail (see Figure 9.3). Thus, if the sample results in a value of the test statistic that is less than or equal to -2.33, the corresponding *p*-value will be less than or equal to .01; in this case, we should reject the null hypothesis. Hence, for the Hilltop Coffee study the critical value rejection rule for a level of significance of .01 is

$$\text{Reject } H_0 \text{ if } z \leq -2.33$$

In the Hilltop Coffee example, $\bar{x} = 2.92$ and the test statistic is $z = -2.67$. Because $z = -2.67 < -2.33$, we can reject H_0 and conclude that Hilltop Coffee is underfilling cans.

We can generalize the rejection rule for the critical value approach to handle any level of significance. The rejection rule for a lower tail test follows.

REJECTION RULE FOR A LOWER TAIL TEST: CRITICAL VALUE APPROACH

$$\text{Reject } H_0 \text{ if } z \leq -z_\alpha$$

where $-z_\alpha$ is the critical value; that is, the z value that provides an area of α in the lower tail of the standard normal distribution.

FIGURE 9.3 Critical Value = −2.33 for the Hilltop Coffee Hypothesis Test

Summary The *p*-value approach to hypothesis testing and the critical value approach will always lead to the same rejection decision; that is, whenever the *p*-value is less than or equal to α, the value of the test statistic will be less than or equal to the critical value. The advantage of the *p*-value approach is that the *p*-value tells us *how* significant the results are (the observed level of significance). If we use the critical value approach, we only know that the results are significant at the stated level of significance.

At the beginning of this section, we said that one-tailed tests about a population mean take one of the following two forms:

Lower Tail Test	Upper Tail Test
$H_0\colon \mu \geq \mu_0$	$H_0\colon \mu \leq \mu_0$
$H_a\colon \mu < \mu_0$	$H_a\colon \mu > \mu_0$

We used the Hilltop Coffee study to illustrate how to conduct a lower tail test. We can use the same general approach to conduct an upper tail test. The test statistic z is still computed using equation (9.1). But, for an upper tail test, the *p*-value is the probability of obtaining a value for the test statistic as large as or larger than that provided by the sample. Thus, to compute the *p*-value for the upper tail test in the σ known case, we must use the standard normal distribution to find the probability that z is greater than or equal to the value of the test statistic. Using the critical value approach causes us to reject the null hypothesis if the value of the test statistic is greater than or equal to the critical value z_α; in other words, we reject H_0 if $z \geq z_\alpha$.

Let us summarize the steps involved in computing *p*-values for one-tailed hypothesis tests.

COMPUTATION OF *p*-VALUES FOR ONE-TAILED TESTS

1. Compute the value of the test statistic using equation (9.1).
2. **Lower tail test:** Using the standard normal distribution, compute the probability that z is less than or equal to the value of the test statistic (area in the lower tail).
3. **Upper tail test:** Using the standard normal distribution, compute the probability that z is greater than or equal to the value of the test statistic (area in the upper tail).

Two-Tailed Test

In hypothesis testing, the general form for a **two-tailed test** about a population mean is as follows:

$$H_0\colon \mu = \mu_0$$
$$H_a\colon \mu \neq \mu_0$$

In this subsection we show how to conduct a two-tailed test about a population mean for the σ known case. As an illustration, we consider the hypothesis testing situation facing MaxFlight, Inc.

The U.S. Golf Association (USGA) establishes rules that manufacturers of golf equipment must meet if their products are to be acceptable for use in USGA events. MaxFlight uses a high-technology manufacturing process to produce golf balls with a mean driving distance of 295 yards. Sometimes, however, the process gets out of adjustment and produces golf balls with a mean driving distance different from 295 yards. When the mean distance falls below 295 yards, the company worries about losing sales because the golf balls do not provide as much distance as advertised. When the mean distance passes 295 yards, MaxFlight's golf balls may be rejected by the USGA for exceeding the overall distance standard concerning carry and roll.

MaxFlight's quality control program involves taking periodic samples of 50 golf balls to monitor the manufacturing process. For each sample, a hypothesis test is conducted to determine whether the process has fallen out of adjustment. Let us develop the null and alternative hypotheses. We begin by assuming that the process is functioning correctly; that is, the golf balls being produced have a mean distance of 295 yards. This assumption establishes the null hypothesis. The alternative hypothesis is that the mean distance is not equal to 295 yards. With a hypothesized value of $\mu_0 = 295$, the null and alternative hypotheses for the MaxFlight hypothesis test are as follows:

$$H_0: \mu = 295$$
$$H_a: \mu \neq 295$$

If the sample mean $\bar{x}$ is significantly less than 295 yards or significantly greater than 295 yards, we will reject H_0. In this case, corrective action will be taken to adjust the manufacturing process. On the other hand, if $\bar{x}$ does not deviate from the hypothesized mean $\mu_0 = 295$ by a significant amount, H_0 will not be rejected and no action will be taken to adjust the manufacturing process.

The quality control team selected $\alpha = .05$ as the level of significance for the test. Data from previous tests conducted when the process was known to be in adjustment show that the population standard deviation can be assumed known with a value of $\sigma = 12$. Thus, with a sample size of $n = 50$, the standard error of $\bar{x}$ is

$$\sigma_{\bar{x}} = \frac{\sigma}{\sqrt{n}} = \frac{12}{\sqrt{50}} = 1.7$$

Because the sample size is large, the central limit theorem (see Chapter 7) allows us to conclude that the sampling distribution of $\bar{x}$ can be approximated by a normal distribution. Figure 9.4 shows the sampling distribution of $\bar{x}$ for the MaxFlight hypothesis test with a hypothesized population mean of $\mu_0 = 295$.

Suppose that a sample of 50 golf balls is selected and that the sample mean is $\bar{x} = 297.6$ yards. This sample mean provides support for the conclusion that the population mean is larger than 295 yards. Is this value of $\bar{x}$ enough larger than 295 to cause us to reject H_0 at the .05 level of significance? In the previous section we described two approaches that can be used to answer this question: the p-value approach and the critical value approach.

DATAfile

GolfTest

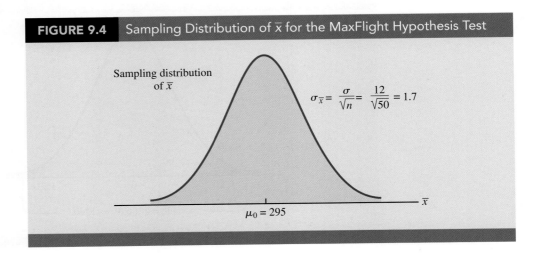

FIGURE 9.4   Sampling Distribution of $\bar{x}$ for the MaxFlight Hypothesis Test

p-value approach Recall that the *p*-value is a probability used to determine whether the null hypothesis should be rejected. For a two-tailed test, values of the test statistic in *either* tail provide evidence against the null hypothesis. For a two-tailed test, the *p*-value is the probability of obtaining a value for the test statistic *as unlikely as or more unlikely than* that provided by the sample. Let us see how the *p*-value is computed for the MaxFlight hypothesis test.

First we compute the value of the test statistic. For the σ known case, the test statistic z is a standard normal random variable. Using equation (9.1) with $\bar{x} = 297.6$, the value of the test statistic is

$$ z = \frac{\bar{x} - \mu_0}{\sigma/\sqrt{n}} = \frac{297.6 - 295}{12/\sqrt{50}} = 1.53 $$

Now to compute the *p*-value we must find the probability of obtaining a value for the test statistic *at least as unlikely as* $z = 1.53$. Clearly values of $z \geq 1.53$ are *at least as unlikely*. But, because this is a two-tailed test, values of $z \leq -1.53$ are also *at least as unlikely as* the value of the test statistic provided by the sample. In Figure 9.5, we see that the two-tailed *p*-value in this case is given by $P(z \leq -1.53) + P(z \geq 1.53)$. Because the normal curve is symmetric, we can compute this probability by finding the upper tail area at $z = 1.53$ and doubling it. The table for the standard normal distribution shows that $P(z < 1.53) = .9370$. Thus, the upper tail area is $P(z \geq 1.53) = 1.0000 - .9370 = .0630$. Doubling this, we find the *p*-value for the MaxFlight two-tailed hypothesis test is *p*-value = 2(.0630) = .1260.

Next we compare the *p*-value to the level of significance to see whether the null hypothesis should be rejected. With a level of significance of $\alpha = .05$, we do not reject H_0 because the *p*-value = .1260 > .05. Because the null hypothesis is not rejected, no action will be taken to adjust the MaxFlight manufacturing process.

The computation of the *p*-value for a two-tailed test may seem a bit confusing as compared to the computation of the *p*-value for a one-tailed test. But it can be simplified by following three steps.

COMPUTATION OF p-VALUES FOR TWO-TAILED TESTS

1. Compute the value of the test statistic using equation (9.1).
2. If the value of the test statistic is in the upper tail, compute the probability that z is greater than or equal to the value of the test statistic (the upper tail area). If the value of the test statistic is in the lower tail, compute the probability that z is less than or equal to the value of the test statistic (the lower tail area).
3. Double the probability (or tail area) from step 2 to obtain the *p*-value.

FIGURE 9.5 *p*-Value for the MaxFlight Hypothesis Test

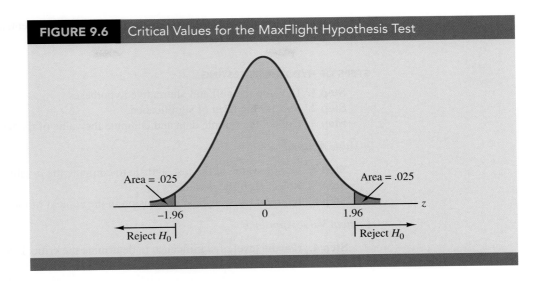

FIGURE 9.6   Critical Values for the MaxFlight Hypothesis Test

Critical value approach Before leaving this section, let us see how the test statistic z can be compared to a critical value to make the hypothesis testing decision for a two-tailed test. Figure 9.6 shows that the critical values for the test will occur in both the lower and upper tails of the standard normal distribution. With a level of significance of $\alpha = .05$, the area in each tail corresponding to the critical values is $\alpha/2 = .05/2 = .025$. Using the standard normal probability table, we find the critical values for the test statistic are $-z_{.025} = -1.96$ and $z_{.025} = 1.96$. Thus, using the critical value approach, the two-tailed rejection rule is

$$\text{Reject } H_0 \text{ if } z \leq -1.96 \text{ or if } z \geq 1.96$$

Because the value of the test statistic for the MaxFlight study is $z = 1.53$, the statistical evidence will not permit us to reject the null hypothesis at the .05 level of significance.

Summary and Practical Advice

We presented examples of a lower tail test and a two-tailed test about a population mean. Based upon these examples, we can now summarize the hypothesis testing procedures about a population mean for the σ known case as shown in Table 9.2. Note that μ_0 is the hypothesized value of the population mean.

TABLE 9.2   Summary of Hypothesis Tests About a Population Mean: σ Known Case

	Lower Tail Test	Upper Tail Test	Two-Tailed Test
Hypotheses	$H_0: \mu \geq \mu_0$ $H_a: \mu < \mu_0$	$H_0: \mu \leq \mu_0$ $H_a: \mu > \mu_0$	$H_0: \mu = \mu_0$ $H_a: \mu \neq \mu_0$
Test Statistic	$z = \dfrac{\bar{x} - \mu_0}{\sigma/\sqrt{n}}$	$z = \dfrac{\bar{x} - \mu_0}{\sigma/\sqrt{n}}$	$z = \dfrac{\bar{x} - \mu_0}{\sigma/\sqrt{n}}$
Rejection Rule: p-Value Approach	Reject H_0 if $p\text{-value} \leq \alpha$	Reject H_0 if $p\text{-value} \leq \alpha$	Reject H_0 if $p\text{-value} \leq \alpha$

Rejection Rule:
    Critical Value
    Approach
	Reject H_0 if
	 $z \leq -z_\alpha$
		Reject H_0 if
		 $z \geq z_\alpha$
			Reject H_0 if
			 $z \leq -z_{\alpha/2}$
			 or if $z \geq z_{\alpha/2}$

The hypothesis testing steps followed in the two examples presented in this section are common to every hypothesis test.

STEPS OF HYPOTHESIS TESTING

Step 1. Develop the null and alternative hypotheses.
Step 2. Specify the level of significance.
Step 3. Collect the sample data and compute the value of the test statistic.

p-Value Approach

Step 4. Use the value of the test statistic to compute the *p*-value.
Step 5. Reject H_0 if the *p*-value $\leq \alpha$.
Step 6. Interpret the statistical conclusion in the context of the application.

Critical Value Approach

Step 4. Use the level of significance to determine the critical value and the rejection rule.
Step 5. Use the value of the test statistic and the rejection rule to determine whether to reject H_0.
Step 6. Interpret the statistical conclusion in the context of the application.

Practical advice about the sample size for hypothesis tests is similar to the advice we provided about the sample size for interval estimation in Chapter 8. In most applications, a sample size of $n \geq 30$ is adequate when using the hypothesis testing procedure described in this section. In cases where the sample size is less than 30, the distribution of the population from which we are sampling becomes an important consideration. If the population is normally distributed, the hypothesis testing procedure that we described is exact and can be used for any sample size. If the population is not normally distributed but is at least roughly symmetric, sample sizes as small as 15 can be expected to provide acceptable results.

Relationship Between Interval Estimation and Hypothesis Testing

In Chapter 8 we showed how to develop a confidence interval estimate of a population mean. For the σ known case, the $(1 - \alpha)\%$ confidence interval estimate of a population mean is given by

$$\bar{x} \pm z_{\alpha/2} \frac{\sigma}{\sqrt{n}}$$

In this chapter, we showed that a two-tailed hypothesis test about a population mean takes the following form:

$$H_0: \mu = \mu_0$$
$$H_a: \mu \neq \mu_0$$

where μ_0 is the hypothesized value for the population mean.

Suppose that we follow the procedure described in Chapter 8 for constructing a $100(1 - \alpha)\%$ confidence interval for the population mean. We know that $100(1 - \alpha)\%$ of the confidence intervals generated will contain the population mean and $100\alpha\%$ of the confidence intervals generated will not contain the population mean. Thus, if we reject H_0 whenever the confidence interval does not contain μ_0, we will be rejecting the null hypothesis when it is true ($\mu = \mu_0$) with probability α. Recall that the level of significance is the probability of rejecting the null hypothesis when it is true. So constructing a $100(1 - \alpha)\%$ confidence interval and rejecting H_0 whenever the interval does not contain μ_0 is equivalent to conducting a two-tailed hypothesis test with α as the level of significance. The procedure for using a confidence interval to conduct a two-tailed hypothesis test can now be summarized.

> **A CONFIDENCE INTERVAL APPROACH TO TESTING A HYPOTHESIS OF THE FORM**
>
> $$H_0: \mu = \mu_0$$
> $$H_a: \mu \neq \mu_0$$
>
> 1. Select a simple random sample from the population and use the value of the sample mean $\bar{x}$ to develop the confidence interval for the population mean μ.
>
> $$\bar{x} \pm z_{\alpha/2} \frac{\sigma}{\sqrt{n}}$$
>
> 2. If the confidence interval contains the hypothesized value μ_0, do not reject H_0. Otherwise, reject[2] H_0.

For a two-tailed hypothesis test, the null hypothesis can be rejected if the confidence interval does not include μ_0.

Let us illustrate by conducting the MaxFlight hypothesis test using the confidence interval approach. The MaxFlight hypothesis test takes the following form:

$$H_0: \mu = 295$$
$$H_a: \mu \neq 295$$

To test these hypotheses with a level of significance of $\alpha = .05$, we sampled 50 golf balls and found a sample mean distance of $\bar{x} = 297.6$ yards. Recall that the population standard deviation is $\sigma = 12$. Using these results with $z_{.025} = 1.96$, we find that the 95% confidence interval estimate of the population mean is

$$\bar{x} \pm z_{.025} \frac{\sigma}{\sqrt{n}}$$
$$297.6 \pm 1.96 \frac{12}{\sqrt{50}}$$
$$297.6 \pm 3.3$$

or

$$294.3 \text{ to } 300.9$$

This finding enables the quality control manager to conclude with 95% confidence that the mean distance for the population of golf balls is between 294.3 and 300.9 yards. Because the hypothesized value for the population mean, $\mu_0 = 295$, is in this interval, the hypothesis testing conclusion is that the null hypothesis, $H_0: \mu = 295$, cannot be rejected.

Note that this discussion and example pertain to two-tailed hypothesis tests about a population mean. However, the same confidence interval and two-tailed hypothesis testing relationship exists for other population parameters. The relationship can also be extended to one-tailed tests about population parameters. Doing so, however, requires the development of one-sided confidence intervals, which are rarely used in practice.

NOTES + COMMENTS

We have shown how to use p-values. The smaller the p-value the greater the evidence against H_0 and the more the evidence in favor of H_a. Here are some guidelines statisticians suggest for interpreting small p-values.

- Less than .01—Overwhelming evidence to conclude H_a is true.

- Between .01 and .05—Strong evidence to conclude H_a is true.
- Between .05 and .10—Weak evidence to conclude H_a is true.
- Greater than .10—Insufficient evidence to conclude H_a is true.

---

[2]To be consistent with the rule for rejecting H_0 when the p-value $\leq \alpha$, we would also reject H_0 using the confidence interval approach if μ_0 happens to be equal to one of the end points of the $100(1 - \alpha)$% confidence interval.

EXERCISES

Note to Student: Some of the exercises that follow ask you to use the *p*-value approach and others ask you to use the critical value approach. Both methods will provide the same hypothesis testing conclusion. We provide exercises with both methods to give you practice using both. In later sections and in following chapters, we will generally emphasize the *p*-value approach as the preferred method, but you may select either based on personal preference.

Methods

9. Consider the following hypothesis test:

$$H_0: \mu \geq 20$$
$$H_a: \mu < 20$$

A sample of 50 provided a sample mean of 19.4. The population standard deviation is 2.
   a. Compute the value of the test statistic.
   b. What is the *p*-value?
   c. Using $\alpha = .05$, what is your conclusion?
   d. What is the rejection rule using the critical value? What is your conclusion?

10. Consider the following hypothesis test:

$$H_0: \mu \leq 25$$
$$H_a: \mu > 25$$

A sample of 40 provided a sample mean of 26.4. The population standard deviation is 6.
   a. Compute the value of the test statistic.
   b. What is the *p*-value?
   c. At $\alpha = .01$, what is your conclusion?
   d. What is the rejection rule using the critical value? What is your conclusion?

11. Consider the following hypothesis test:

$$H_0: \mu = 15$$
$$H_a: \mu \neq 15$$

A sample of 50 provided a sample mean of 14.15. The population standard deviation is 3.
   a. Compute the value of the test statistic.
   b. What is the *p*-value?
   c. At $\alpha = .05$, what is your conclusion?
   d. What is the rejection rule using the critical value? What is your conclusion?

12. Consider the following hypothesis test:

$$H_0: \mu \geq 80$$
$$H_a: \mu < 80$$

A sample of 100 is used and the population standard deviation is 12. Compute the *p*-value and state your conclusion for each of the following sample results. Use $\alpha = .01$.
   a. $\bar{x} = 78.5$
   b. $\bar{x} = 77$
   c. $\bar{x} = 75.5$
   d. $\bar{x} = 81$

13. Consider the following hypothesis test:

$$H_0: \mu \leq 50$$
$$H_a: \mu > 50$$

A sample of 60 is used and the population standard deviation is 8. Use the critical value approach to state your conclusion for each of the following sample results. Use $\alpha = .05$.

a. $\bar{x} = 52.5$

b. $\bar{x} = 51$

c. $\bar{x} = 51.8$

14. Consider the following hypothesis test:

$$H_0: \mu = 22$$
$$H_a: \mu \neq 22$$

A sample of 75 is used and the population standard deviation is 10. Compute the p-value and state your conclusion for each of the following sample results. Use $\alpha = .01$.

a. $\bar{x} = 23$

b. $\bar{x} = 25.1$

c. $\bar{x} = 20$

Applications

15. **Federal Tax Returns.** According to the IRS, individuals filing federal income tax returns prior to March 31 received an average refund of $1056 in 2018. Consider the population of "last-minute" filers who mail their tax return during the last five days of the income tax period (typically April 10 to April 15).

a. A researcher suggests that a reason individuals wait until the last five days is that on average these individuals receive lower refunds than do early filers. Develop appropriate hypotheses such that rejection of H_0 will support the researcher's contention.

b. For a sample of 400 individuals who filed a tax return between April 10 and 15, the sample mean refund was $910. Based on prior experience a population standard deviation of $\sigma = \$1600$ may be assumed. What is the p-value?

c. At $\alpha = .05$, what is your conclusion?

d. Repeat the preceding hypothesis test using the critical value approach.

16. **Credit Card Use by Undergraduates.** In a study entitled How Undergraduate Students Use Credit Cards, it was reported that undergraduate students have a mean credit card balance of $3173. This figure was an all-time high and had increased 44% over the previous five years. Assume that a current study is being conducted to determine if it can be concluded that the mean credit card balance for undergraduate students has continued to increase compared to the original report. Based on previous studies, use a population standard deviation $\sigma = \$1000$.

a. State the null and alternative hypotheses.

b. What is the p-value for a sample of 180 undergraduate students with a sample mean credit card balance of $3325?

c. Using a .05 level of significance, what is your conclusion?

17. **Use of Texting.** TextRequest reports that adults 18–24 years old send and receive 128 texts every day. Suppose we take a sample of 25–34 year olds to see if their mean number of daily texts differs from the mean for 18–24 year olds reported by TextRequest.

a. State the null and alternative hypotheses we should use to test whether the population mean daily number of texts for 25–34 year olds differs from the population daily mean number of texts for 18–24 year olds.

b. Suppose a sample of thirty 25–34 year olds showed a sample mean of 118.6 texts per day. Assume a population standard deviation of 33.17 texts per day and compute the p-value.

c. With $\alpha = .05$ as the level of significance, what is your conclusion?

d. Repeat the preceding hypothesis test using the critical value approach.

18. **CPA Work Hours.** The American Institute of Certified Tax Planners reports that the average U.S. CPA works 60 hours per week during tax season. Do CPAs in states that

have flat state income tax rates work fewer hours per week during tax season? Conduct a hypothesis test to determine if this is so.

a. Formulate hypotheses that can be used to determine whether the mean hours worked per week during tax season by CPAs in states that have flat state income tax rates is less than the mean hours worked per week by all U.S. CPAs during tax season?

b. Based on a sample, the mean number of hours worked per week during tax season by CPAs in states with flat tax rates was 55. Assume the sample size was 150 and that, based on past studies, the population standard deviation can be assumed to be $\sigma = 27.4$. Use the sample results to compute the test statistic and p-value for your hypothesis test.

c. At $\alpha = .05$, what is your conclusion?

19. **Length of Calls to the IRS.** According to the IRS, taxpayers calling the IRS in 2017 waited 13 minutes on average for an IRS telephone assister to answer. Do callers who use the IRS help line early in the day have a shorter wait? Suppose a sample of 50 callers who placed their calls to the IRS in the first 30 minutes that the line is open during the day have a mean waiting time of 11 minutes before an IRS telephone assister answers. Based on data from past years, you decide that it is reasonable to assume that the standard deviation of waiting times is 8 minutes. Using these sample results, can you conclude that the waiting time for calls placed during the first 30 minutes the IRS help line is open each day is significantly less that the overall mean waiting time of 13 minutes? Use $\alpha = .05$.

20. **Prescription Drug Costs.** Annual expenditure for prescription drugs was $838 per person in the Northeast of the country. A sample of 60 individuals in the Midwest showed a per person annual expenditure for prescription drugs of $745. Use a population standard deviation of $300 to answer the following questions.

a. Formulate hypotheses for a test to determine whether the sample data support the conclusion that the population annual expenditure for prescription drugs per person is lower in the Midwest than in the Northeast.

b. What is the value of the test statistic?

c. What is the p-value?

d. At $\alpha = .01$, what is your conclusion?

Fowle

21. **Cost of Telephone Surveys.** Fowle Marketing Research, Inc., bases charges to a client on the assumption that telephone surveys can be completed in a mean time of 15 minutes or less. If a longer mean survey time is necessary, a premium rate is charged. A sample of 35 surveys provided the survey times shown in the file *Fowle*. Based upon past studies, the population standard deviation is assumed known with $\sigma = 4$ minutes. Is the premium rate justified?

a. Formulate the null and alternative hypotheses for this application.

b. Compute the value of the test statistic.

c. What is the p-value?

d. At $\alpha = .01$, what is your conclusion?

22. **Time in Supermarket Checkout Lines.** CCN and ActMedia provided a television channel targeted to individuals waiting in supermarket checkout lines. The channel showed news, short features, and advertisements. The length of the program was based on the assumption that the population mean time a shopper stands in a supermarket checkout line is 8 minutes. A sample of actual waiting times will be used to test this assumption and determine whether actual mean waiting time differs from this standard.

a. Formulate the hypotheses for this application.

b. A sample of 120 shoppers showed a sample mean waiting time of 8.4 minutes. Assume a population standard deviation of $\sigma = 3.2$ minutes. What is the p-value?

c. At $\alpha = .05$, what is your conclusion?

d. Compute a 95% confidence interval for the population mean. Does it support your conclusion?

9.4 Population Mean: σ Unknown

In this section we describe how to conduct hypothesis tests about a population mean for the σ unknown case. Because the σ unknown case corresponds to situations in which an estimate of the population standard deviation cannot be developed prior to sampling, the sample must be used to develop an estimate of both μ and σ. Thus, to conduct a hypothesis test about a population mean for the σ unknown case, the sample mean $\bar{x}$ is used as an estimate of μ and the sample standard deviation s is used as an estimate of σ.

The steps of the hypothesis testing procedure for the σ unknown case are the same as those for the σ known case described in Section 9.3. But, with σ unknown, the computation of the test statistic and p-value is a bit different. Recall that for the σ known case, the sampling distribution of the test statistic has a standard normal distribution. For the σ unknown case, however, the sampling distribution of the test statistic follows the t distribution; it has slightly more variability because the sample is used to develop estimates of both μ and σ.

In Section 8.2 we showed that an interval estimate of a population mean for the σ unknown case is based on a probability distribution known as the t distribution. Hypothesis tests about a population mean for the σ unknown case are also based on the t distribution. For the σ unknown case, the test statistic has a t distribution with $n - 1$ degrees of freedom.

TEST STATISTIC FOR HYPOTHESIS TESTS ABOUT A POPULATION MEAN: σ UNKNOWN

$$t = \frac{\bar{x} - \mu_0}{s/\sqrt{n}} \tag{9.2}$$

In Chapter 8 we said that the t distribution is based on an assumption that the population from which we are sampling has a normal distribution. However, research shows that this assumption can be relaxed considerably when the sample size is large enough. We provide some practical advice concerning the population distribution and sample size at the end of the section.

One-Tailed Test

DATAfile

AirRating

Let us consider an example of a one-tailed test about a population mean for the σ unknown case. A business travel magazine wants to classify transatlantic gateway airports according to the mean rating for the population of business travelers. A rating scale with a low score of 0 and a high score of 10 will be used, and airports with a population mean rating greater than 7 will be designated as superior service airports. The magazine staff surveyed a sample of 60 business travelers at each airport to obtain the ratings data. The sample for London's Heathrow Airport provided a sample mean rating of $\bar{x} = 7.25$ and a sample standard deviation of $s = 1.052$. Do the data indicate that Heathrow should be designated as a superior service airport?

We want to develop a hypothesis test for which the decision to reject H_0 will lead to the conclusion that the population mean rating for the Heathrow Airport is *greater* than 7. Thus, an upper tail test with H_a: $\mu > 7$ is required. The null and alternative hypotheses for this upper tail test are as follows:

$$H_0: \mu \leq 7$$
$$H_a: \mu > 7$$

We will use $\alpha = .05$ as the level of significance for the test.

Using equation (9.2) with $\bar{x} = 7.25$, $\mu_0 = 7$, $s = 1.052$, and $n = 60$, the value of the test statistic is

$$t = \frac{\bar{x} - \mu_0}{s/\sqrt{n}} = \frac{7.25 - 7}{1.052/\sqrt{60}} = 1.84$$

The sampling distribution of t has $n - 1 = 60 - 1 = 59$ degrees of freedom. Because the test is an upper tail test, the p-value is $P(t \geq 1.84)$, that is, the upper tail area corresponding to the value of the test statistic.

The t distribution table provided in most textbooks will not contain sufficient detail to determine the exact p-value, such as the p-value corresponding to $t = 1.84$. For instance, using Table 2 in Appendix B, the t distribution with 59 degrees of freedom provides the following information.

Area in Upper Tail	.20	.10	.05	.025	.01	.005
t Value (59 *df*)	.848	1.296	1.671	2.001	2.391	2.662

$t = 1.84$

We see that $t = 1.84$ is between 1.671 and 2.001. Although the table does not provide the exact p-value, the values in the "Area in Upper Tail" row show that the p-value must be less than .05 and greater than .025. With a level of significance of $\alpha = .05$, this placement is all we need to know to make the decision to reject the null hypothesis and conclude that Heathrow should be classified as a superior service airport.

Appendix F shows how to compute p-values using Excel or JMP.

Because it is cumbersome to use a t table to compute p-values, and only approximate values are obtained, we show how to compute the exact p-value using Excel or JMP. Using Excel or JMP with $t = 1.84$ provides the upper tail p-value of .0354 for the Heathrow Airport hypothesis test. With $.0354 < .05$, we reject the null hypothesis and conclude that Heathrow should be classified as a superior service airport.

The decision whether to reject the null hypothesis in the σ unknown case can also be made using the critical value approach. The critical value corresponding to an area of $\alpha = .05$ in the upper tail of a t distribution with 59 degrees of freedom is $t_{.05} = 1.671$. Thus the rejection rule using the critical value approach is to reject H_0 if $t \geq 1.671$. Because $t = 1.84 > 1.671$, H_0 is rejected. Heathrow should be classified as a superior service airport.

Two-Tailed Test

To illustrate how to conduct a two-tailed test about a population mean for the σ unknown case, let us consider the hypothesis testing situation facing Holiday Toys. The company manufactures and distributes its products through more than 1000 retail outlets. In planning production levels for the coming winter season, Holiday must decide how many units of each product to produce prior to knowing the actual demand at the retail level. For this year's most important new toy, Holiday's marketing director is expecting demand to average 40 units per retail outlet. Prior to making the final production decision based upon this estimate, Holiday decided to survey a sample of 25 retailers in order to develop more information about the demand for the new product. Each retailer was provided with information about the features of the new toy along with the cost and the suggested selling price. Then each retailer was asked to specify an anticipated order quantity.

With μ denoting the population mean order quantity per retail outlet, the sample data will be used to conduct the following two-tailed hypothesis test:

$$H_0: \mu = 40$$
$$H_a: \mu \neq 40$$

If H_0 cannot be rejected, Holiday will continue its production planning based on the marketing director's estimate that the population mean order quantity per retail outlet will be $\mu = 40$ units. However, if H_0 is rejected, Holiday will immediately reevaluate its production plan for the product. A two-tailed hypothesis test is used because Holiday wants to reevaluate the production plan if the population mean quantity per retail outlet is less than anticipated or greater than anticipated. Because no historical data are available (it's a new product), the population mean μ and the population standard deviation must both be estimated using $\bar{x}$ and s from the sample data.

DATA *file*

Orders

The sample of 25 retailers provided a mean of $\bar{x} = 37.4$ and a standard deviation of $s = 11.79$ units. Before going ahead with the use of the t distribution, the analyst constructed a histogram of the sample data in order to check on the form of the population distribution. The histogram of the sample data showed no evidence of skewness or any extreme outliers, so the analyst concluded that the use of the t distribution with $n - 1 = 24$ degrees of freedom was appropriate. Using equation (9.2) with $\bar{x} = 37.4$, $\mu_0 = 40$, $s = 11.79$, and $n = 25$, the value of the test statistic is

$$t = \frac{\bar{x} - \mu_0}{s/\sqrt{n}} = \frac{37.4 - 40}{11.79/\sqrt{25}} = -1.10$$

Because we have a two-tailed test, the p-value is two times the area under the curve of the t distribution for $t \leq -1.10$. Using Table 2 in Appendix B, the t distribution table for 24 degrees of freedom provides the following information.

Area in Upper Tail	.20	.10	.05	.025	.01	.005
t-Value (24 *df*)	.857	1.318	1.711	2.064	2.492	2.797

$t = 1.10$

The t distribution table only contains positive t values. Because the t distribution is symmetric, however, the upper tail area at $t = 1.10$ is the same as the lower tail area at $t = -1.10$. We see that $t = 1.10$ is between .857 and 1.318. From the "Area in Upper Tail" row, we see that the area in the upper tail at $t = 1.10$ is between .20 and .10. When we double these amounts, we see that the p-value must be between .40 and .20. With a level of significance of $\alpha = .05$, we now know that the p-value is greater than α. Therefore, H_0 cannot be rejected. Sufficient evidence is not available to conclude that Holiday should change its production plan for the coming season.

Appendix F shows how the p-value for this test can be computed using Excel or JMP. The p-value obtained is .2822. With a level of significance of $\alpha = .05$, we cannot reject H_0 because $.2822 > .05$.

The test statistic can also be compared to the critical value to make the two-tailed hypothesis testing decision. With $\alpha = .05$ and the t distribution with 24 degrees of freedom, $-t_{.025} = -2.064$ and $t_{.025} = 2.064$ are the critical values for the two-tailed test. The rejection rule using the test statistic is

$$\text{Reject } H_0 \text{ if } t \leq -2.064 \text{ or if } t \geq 2.064$$

Based on the test statistic $t = -1.10$, H_0 cannot be rejected. This result indicates that Holiday should continue its production planning for the coming season based on the expectation that $\mu = 40$.

Summary and Practical Advice

Table 9.3 provides a summary of the hypothesis testing procedures about a population mean for the σ unknown case. The key difference between these procedures and the ones for the σ known case is that s is used, instead of σ, in the computation of the test statistic. For this reason, the test statistic follows the t distribution.

TABLE 9.3	Summary of Hypothesis Tests About a Population Mean: σ Unknown Case		
	Lower Tail Test	**Upper Tail Test**	**Two-Tailed Test**
Hypotheses	$H_0: \mu \geq \mu_0$ $H_a: \mu < \mu_0$	$H_0: \mu \leq \mu_0$ $H_a: \mu > \mu_0$	$H_0: \mu = \mu_0$ $H_a: \mu \neq \mu_0$
Test Statistic	$t = \dfrac{\bar{x} - \mu_0}{s/\sqrt{n}}$	$t = \dfrac{\bar{x} - \mu_0}{s/\sqrt{n}}$	$t = \dfrac{\bar{x} - \mu_0}{s/\sqrt{n}}$
Rejection Rule: **p-Value Approach**	Reject H_0 if p-value $\leq \alpha$	Reject H_0 if p-value $\leq \alpha$	Reject H_0 if p-value $\leq \alpha$
Rejection Rule: **Critical Value** **Approach**	Reject H_0 if $t \leq -t_\alpha$	Reject H_0 if $t \geq t_\alpha$	Reject H_0 if $t \leq -t_{\alpha/2}$ or if $t \geq t_{\alpha/2}$

The applicability of the hypothesis testing procedures of this section is dependent on the distribution of the population being sampled from and the sample size. When the population is normally distributed, the hypothesis tests described in this section provide exact results for any sample size. When the population is not normally distributed, the procedures are approximations. Nonetheless, we find that sample sizes of 30 or greater will provide good results in most cases. If the population is approximately normal, small sample sizes (e.g., $n < 15$) can provide acceptable results. If the population is highly skewed or contains outliers, sample sizes approaching 50 are recommended.

EXERCISES

Methods

23. Consider the following hypothesis test:

$$H_0: \mu \leq 12$$
$$H_a: \mu > 12$$

A sample of 25 provided a sample mean $\bar{x} = 14$ and a sample standard deviation $s = 4.32$.
a. Compute the value of the test statistic.
b. Use the t distribution table (Table 2 in Appendix B) to compute a range for the p-value.
c. At $\alpha = .05$, what is your conclusion?
d. What is the rejection rule using the critical value? What is your conclusion?

24. Consider the following hypothesis test:

$$H_0: \mu = 18$$
$$H_a: \mu \neq 18$$

A sample of 48 provided a sample mean $\bar{x} = 17$ and a sample standard deviation $s = 4.5$.
a. Compute the value of the test statistic.
b. Use the t distribution table (Table 2 in Appendix B) to compute a range for the p-value.
c. At $\alpha = .05$, what is your conclusion?
d. What is the rejection rule using the critical value? What is your conclusion?

25. Consider the following hypothesis test:

$$H_0: \mu \geq 45$$
$$H_a: \mu < 45$$

A sample of 36 is used. Identify the p-value and state your conclusion for each of the following sample results. Use $\alpha = .01$.
   a. $\bar{x} = 44$ and $s = 5.2$
   b. $\bar{x} = 43$ and $s = 4.6$
   c. $\bar{x} = 46$ and $s = 5.0$

26. Consider the following hypothesis test:

$$H_0: \mu = 100$$
$$H_a: \mu \neq 100$$

A sample of 65 is used. Identify the p-value and state your conclusion for each of the following sample results. Use $\alpha = .05$.
   a. $\bar{x} = 103$ and $s = 11.5$
   b. $\bar{x} = 96.5$ and $s = 11.0$
   c. $\bar{x} = 102$ and $s = 10.5$

Applications

27. **Price of Good Red Wine.** According to the Vivino website, the mean price for a bottle of red wine that scores 4.0 or higher on the Vivino Rating System is $32.48. A New England–based lifestyle magazine wants to determine if red wines of the same quality are less expensive in Providence, and it has collected prices for 56 randomly selected red wines of similar quality from wine stores throughout Providence. The mean and standard deviation for this sample are $30.15 and $12, respectively.
   a. Develop appropriate hypotheses for a test to determine whether the sample data support the conclusion that the mean price in Providence for a bottle of red wine that scores 4.0 or higher on the Vivino Rating System is less than the population mean of $32.48.
   b. Using the sample from the 56 bottles, what is the p-value?
   c. At $\alpha = .05$, what is your conclusion?
   d. Repeat the preceding hypothesis test using the critical value approach.

28. **CEO Tenure.** A shareholders' group, in lodging a protest, claimed that the mean tenure for a chief executive office (CEO) was at least nine years. A survey of companies reported in *The Wall Street Journal* found a sample mean tenure of $\bar{x} = 7.27$ years for CEOs with a standard deviation of $s = 6.38$ years.
   a. Formulate hypotheses that can be used to challenge the validity of the claim made by the shareholders' group.
   b. Assume 85 companies were included in the sample. What is the p-value for your hypothesis test?
   c. At $\alpha = .01$, what is your conclusion?

DATA *file*
ResidentialWater

29. **Cost of Residential Water.** On its municipal website, the city of Tulsa states that the rate it charges per 5 CCF of residential water is $21.62. How do the residential water rates of other U.S. public utilities compare to Tulsa's rate? The file *ResidentialWater* contains the rate per 5 CCF of residential water for 42 randomly selected U.S. cities.
   a. Formulate hypotheses that can be used to determine whether the population mean rate per 5 CCF of residential water charged by U.S. public utilities differs from the $21.62 rate charged by Tulsa.
   b. What is the p-value for your hypothesis test in part (a)?
   c. At $\alpha = .05$, can your null hypothesis be rejected? What is your conclusion?
   d. Repeat the preceding hypothesis test using the critical value approach.

DATA *file*
ChildCare

30. **Time in Child Care.** The time married men with children spend on child care averages 6.4 hours per week. You belong to a professional group on family practices

that would like to do its own study to determine if the time married men in your area spend on child care per week differs from the reported mean of 6.4 hours per week. A sample of 40 married couples will be used with the data collected showing the hours per week the husband spends on child care. The sample data are contained in the file *ChildCare*.

a. What are the hypotheses if your group would like to determine if the population mean number of hours married men are spending in child care differs from the mean reported by *Time* in your area?

b. What is the sample mean and the *p*-value?

c. Select your own level of significance. What is your conclusion?

31. **Chocolate Consumption.** The United States ranks ninth in the world in per capita chocolate consumption; *Forbes* reports that the average American eats 9.5 pounds of chocolate annually. Suppose you are curious whether chocolate consumption is higher in Hershey, Pennsylvania, the location of the Hershey Company's corporate headquarters. A sample of 36 individuals from the Hershey area showed a sample mean annual consumption of 10.05 pounds and a standard deviation of $s = 1.5$ pounds. Using $\alpha = .05$, do the sample results support the conclusion that mean annual consumption of chocolate is higher in Hershey than it is throughout the United States?

DATA *file*

UsedCars

32. **Used Car Prices.** According to the National Automobile Dealers Association, the mean price for used cars is \$10,192. A manager of a Kansas City used car dealership reviewed a sample of 50 recent used car sales at the dealership in an attempt to determine whether the population mean price for used cars at this particular dealership differed from the national mean. The prices for the sample of 50 cars are shown in the file *UsedCars*.

a. Formulate the hypotheses that can be used to determine whether a difference exists in the mean price for used cars at the dealership.

b. What is the *p*-value?

c. At $\alpha = .05$, what is your conclusion?

33. **Automobile Insurance Premiums.** The Onsure.com website reports that the mean annual premium for automobile insurance in the United States was \$1503 in March 2014. Being from Pennsylvania at that time, you believed automobile insurance was cheaper there and decided to develop statistical support for your opinion. A sample of 25 automobile insurance policies from the state of Pennsylvania showed a mean annual premium of \$1440 with a standard deviation of $s = \$165$.

a. Develop a hypothesis test that can be used to determine whether the mean annual premium in Pennsylvania was lower than the national mean annual premium.

b. What is a point estimate of the difference between the mean annual premium in Pennsylvania and the national mean?

c. At $\alpha = .05$, test for a significant difference. What is your conclusion?

34. **Landscaping Labor Costs.** Joan's Nursery specializes in custom-designed landscaping for residential areas. The estimated labor cost associated with a particular landscaping proposal is based on the number of plantings of trees, shrubs, and so on to be used for the project. For cost-estimating purposes, managers use two hours of labor time for the planting of a medium-sized tree. Actual times from a sample of 10 plantings during the past month follow (times in hours).

1.7	1.5	2.6	2.2	2.4	2.3	2.6	3.0	1.4	2.3

With a .05 level of significance, test to see whether the mean tree-planting time differs from two hours.

a. State the null and alternative hypotheses.

b. Compute the sample mean.

c. Compute the sample standard deviation.

d. What is the *p*-value?

e. What is your conclusion?

9.5 **Population Proportion**

In this section we show how to conduct a hypothesis test about a population proportion p. Using p_0 to denote the hypothesized value for the population proportion, the three forms for a hypothesis test about a population proportion are as follows.

$$H_0: p \geq p_0 \qquad H_0: p \leq p_0 \qquad H_0: p = p_0$$
$$H_a: p < p_0 \qquad H_a: p > p_0 \qquad H_a: p \neq p_0$$

The first form is called a lower tail test, the second form is called an upper tail test, and the third form is called a two-tailed test.

Hypothesis tests about a population proportion are based on the difference between the sample proportion $\bar{p}$ and the hypothesized population proportion p_0. The methods used to conduct the hypothesis test are similar to those used for hypothesis tests about a population mean. The only difference is that we use the sample proportion and its standard error to compute the test statistic. The p-value approach or the critical value approach is then used to determine whether the null hypothesis should be rejected.

Let us consider an example involving a situation faced by Pine Creek golf course. Over the past year, 20% of the players at Pine Creek were women. In an effort to increase the proportion of women players, Pine Creek implemented a special promotion designed to attract women golfers. One month after the promotion was implemented, the course manager requested a statistical study to determine whether the proportion of women players at Pine Creek had increased. Because the objective of the study is to determine whether the proportion of women golfers increased, an upper tail test with $H_a: p > .20$ is appropriate. The null and alternative hypotheses for the Pine Creek hypothesis test are as follows:

$$H_0: p \leq .20$$
$$H_a: p > .20$$

If H_0 can be rejected, the test results will give statistical support for the conclusion that the proportion of women golfers increased and the promotion was beneficial. The course manager specified that a level of significance of $\alpha = .05$ be used in carrying out this hypothesis test.

The next step of the hypothesis testing procedure is to select a sample and compute the value of an appropriate test statistic. To show how this step is done for the Pine Creek upper tail test, we begin with a general discussion of how to compute the value of the test statistic for any form of a hypothesis test about a population proportion. The sampling distribution of $\bar{p}$, the point estimator of the population parameter p, is the basis for developing the test statistic.

When the null hypothesis is true as an equality, the expected value of $\bar{p}$ equals the hypothesized value p_0; that is, $E(\bar{p}) = p_0$. The standard error of $\bar{p}$ is given by

$$\sigma_{\bar{p}} = \sqrt{\frac{p_0(1 - p_0)}{n}}$$

In Chapter 7 we said that if $np \geq 5$ and $n(1 - p) \geq 5$, the sampling distribution of $\bar{p}$ can be approximated by a normal distribution.[3] Under these conditions, which usually apply in practice, the quantity

$$z = \frac{\bar{p} - p_0}{\sigma_{\bar{p}}} \qquad \qquad \textbf{(9.3)}$$

has a standard normal probability distribution. With $\sigma_{\bar{p}} = \sqrt{p_0(1 - p_0)/n}$, the standard normal random variable z is the test statistic used to conduct hypothesis tests about a population proportion.

---

[3]In most applications involving hypothesis tests of a population proportion, sample sizes are large enough to use the normal approximation. The exact sampling distribution of $\bar{p}$ is discrete with the probability for each value of $\bar{p}$ given by the binomial distribution. So hypothesis testing is a bit more complicated for small samples when the normal approximation cannot be used.

TEST STATISTIC FOR HYPOTHESIS TESTS ABOUT A POPULATION PROPORTION

$$z = \frac{\bar{p} - p_0}{\sqrt{\dfrac{p_0(1 - p_0)}{n}}} \qquad (9.4)$$

DATA *file*

WomenGolf

We can now compute the test statistic for the Pine Creek hypothesis test. Suppose a random sample of 400 players was selected, and that 100 of the players were women. The proportion of women golfers in the sample is

$$\bar{p} = \frac{100}{400} = .25$$

Using equation (9.4), the value of the test statistic is

$$z = \frac{\bar{p} - p_0}{\sqrt{\dfrac{p_0(1 - p_0)}{n}}} = \frac{.25 - .20}{\sqrt{\dfrac{.20(1 - .20)}{400}}} = \frac{.05}{.02} = 2.50$$

Because the Pine Creek hypothesis test is an upper tail test, the *p*-value is the probability that *z* is greater than or equal to *z* = 2.50; that is, it is the upper tail area corresponding to *z* ≥ 2.50. Using the standard normal probability table, we find that the area to the left of *z* = 2.50 is .9938. Thus, the *p*-value for the Pine Creek test is 1.0000 − .9938 = .0062. Figure 9.7 shows this *p*-value calculation.

Recall that the course manager specified a level of significance of *α* = .05. A *p*-value = .0062 < .05 gives sufficient statistical evidence to reject H_0 at the .05 level of significance. Thus, the test provides statistical support for the conclusion that the special promotion increased the proportion of women players at the Pine Creek golf course.

The decision whether to reject the null hypothesis can also be made using the critical value approach. The critical value corresponding to an area of .05 in the upper tail of a normal probability distribution is $z_{.05} = 1.645$. Thus, the rejection rule using the critical value approach is to reject H_0 if *z* ≥ 1.645. Because *z* = 2.50 > 1.645, H_0 is rejected.

Again, we see that the *p*-value approach and the critical value approach lead to the same hypothesis testing conclusion, but the *p*-value approach provides more information. With a *p*-value = .0062, the null hypothesis would be rejected for any level of significance greater than or equal to .0062.

FIGURE 9.7   Calculation of the *p*-Value for the Pine Creek Hypothesis Test

	Lower Tail Test	Upper Tail Test	Two-Tailed Test
TABLE 9.4	**Summary of Hypothesis Tests About a Population Proportion**		
Hypotheses	$H_0: p \geq p_0$ $H_a: p < p_0$	$H_0: p \leq p_0$ $H_a: p > p_0$	$H_0: p = p_0$ $H_a: p \neq p_0$
Test Statistic	$z = \dfrac{\bar{p} - p_0}{\sqrt{\dfrac{p_0(1 - p_0)}{n}}}$	$z = \dfrac{\bar{p} - p_0}{\sqrt{\dfrac{p_0(1 - p_0)}{n}}}$	$z = \dfrac{\bar{p} - p_0}{\sqrt{\dfrac{p_0(1 - p_0)}{n}}}$
Rejection Rule: **p-Value Approach**	Reject H_0 if p-value $\leq \alpha$	Reject H_0 if p-value $\leq \alpha$	Reject H_0 if p-value $\leq \alpha$
Rejection Rule: **Critical Value** **Approach**	Reject H_0 if $z \leq -z_\alpha$	Reject H_0 if $z \geq z_\alpha$	Reject H_0 if $z \leq -z_{\alpha/2}$ or if $z \geq z_{\alpha/2}$

Summary

The procedure used to conduct a hypothesis test about a population proportion is similar to the procedure used to conduct a hypothesis test about a population mean. Although we only illustrated how to conduct a hypothesis test about a population proportion for an upper tail test, similar procedures can be used for lower tail and two-tailed tests. Table 9.4 provides a summary of the hypothesis tests about a population proportion. We assume that $np \geq 5$ and $n(1 - p) \geq 5$; thus the normal probability distribution can be used to approximate the sampling distribution of $\bar{p}$.

NOTES + COMMENTS

The binomial distribution can also be used to perform an exact hypothesis test for one proportion. This method is more accurate and more powerful than the normal approximation method. However, the calculations for the normal approximation method are simpler, and the accuracy and power of hypothesis tests performed using the normal approximation method improves as the sample size increases.

EXERCISES

Methods

35. Consider the following hypothesis test:

$$H_0: p = .20$$
$$H_a: p \neq .20$$

   A sample of 400 provided a sample proportion $\bar{p} = .175$.
   a. Compute the value of the test statistic.
   b. What is the *p*-value?
   c. At $\alpha = .05$, what is your conclusion?
   d. What is the rejection rule using the critical value? What is your conclusion?

36. Consider the following hypothesis test:

$$H_0: p \geq .75$$
$$H_a: p < .75$$

A sample of 300 items was selected. Compute the *p*-value and state your conclusion for each of the following sample results. Use $\alpha = .05$.

a. $\bar{p} = .68$ c. $\bar{p} = .70$

b. $\bar{p} = .72$ d. $\bar{p} = .77$

Applications

37. **Union Membership.** The U.S. Bureau of Labor Statistics reports that 11.3% of U.S. workers belonged to unions in 2013. Suppose a sample of 400 U.S. workers is collected in 2018 to determine whether union efforts to organize have increased union membership.

    a. Formulate the hypotheses that can be used to determine whether union membership increased in 2018.
    b. If the sample results show that 52 of the workers belonged to unions, what is the *p*-value for your hypothesis test?
    c. At $\alpha = .05$, what is your conclusion?

38. **Attitudes toward Supermarket Brands.** A study by *Consumer Reports* showed that 64% of supermarket shoppers believe supermarket brands to be as good as national name brands. To investigate whether this result applies to its own product, the manufacturer of a national name-brand ketchup asked a sample of shoppers whether they believed that supermarket ketchup was as good as the national brand ketchup.

    a. Formulate the hypotheses that could be used to determine whether the percentage of supermarket shoppers who believe that the supermarket ketchup was as good as the national brand ketchup differed from 64%.
    b. If a sample of 100 shoppers showed 52 stating that the supermarket brand was as good as the national brand, what is the *p*-value?
    c. At $\alpha = .05$, what is your conclusion?
    d. Should the national brand ketchup manufacturer be pleased with this conclusion? Explain.

39. **Population Mobility.** What percentage of the population live in their state of birth? According to the U.S. Census Bureau's 2014 American Community Survey, the figure ranges from 25% in Nevada to 78.7% in Louisiana. The average percentage across all states and the District of Columbia is 57.7%. The data in the file *HomeState* are consistent with the findings in this American Community Survey. The data are for a random sample of 120 Arkansas residents and for a random sample of 180 Virginia residents.

    a. Formulate hypotheses that can be used to determine whether the percentage of stay-at-home residents in the two states differs from the overall average of 57.7%.
    b. Estimate the proportion of stay-at-home residents in Arkansas. Does this proportion differ significantly from the mean proportion for all states? Use $\alpha = .05$.
    c. Estimate the proportion of stay-at-home residents in Virginia. Does this proportion differ significantly from the mean proportion for all states? Use $\alpha = .05$.
    d. Would you expect the proportion of stay-at-home residents to be higher in Virginia than in Arkansas? Support your conclusion with the results obtained in parts (b) and (c).

40. **Holiday Gifts from Employers.** Last year, 46% of business owners gave a holiday gift to their employees. A survey of business owners conducted this year indicates that 35% plan to provide a holiday gift to their employees. Suppose the survey results are based on a sample of 60 business owners.

    a. How many business owners in the survey plan to provide a holiday gift to their employees this year?
    b. Suppose the business owners in the sample did as they plan. Compute the *p*-value for a hypothesis test that can be used to determine if the proportion of business owners providing holiday gifts had decreased from last year.
    c. Using a .05 level of significance, would you conclude that the proportion of business owners providing gifts decreased? What is the smallest level of significance for which you could draw such a conclusion?

41. **Adequate Preparation for Retirement.** In 2018, RAND Corporation researchers found that 71% of all individuals ages 66 to 69 are adequately prepared financially for retirement. Many financial planners have expressed concern that a smaller percentage of those in this age group who did not complete high school are adequately prepared financially for retirement.

    a. Develop appropriate hypotheses such that rejection of H_0 will support the conclusion that the proportion of those who are adequately prepared financially for retirement is smaller for people in the 66–69 age group who did not complete high school than it is for the population of the 66–69 year old.

    b. In a random sample of 300 people from the 66–69 age group who did not complete high school, 165 were not prepared financially for retirement. What is the p-value for your hypothesis test?

    c. At $\alpha = .01$, what is your conclusion?

42. **Returned Merchandise.** According to the University of Nevada Center for Logistics Management, 6% of all merchandise sold in the United States gets returned. A Houston department store sampled 80 items sold in January and found that 12 of the items were returned.

    a. Construct a point estimate of the proportion of items returned for the population of sales transactions at the Houston store.

    b. Construct a 95% confidence interval for the proportion of returns at the Houston store.

    c. Is the proportion of returns at the Houston store significantly different from the returns for the nation as a whole? Provide statistical support for your answer.

DATA_file_

Eagle

43. **Coupon Usage.** Eagle Outfitters is a chain of stores specializing in outdoor apparel and camping gear. They are considering a promotion that involves mailing discount coupons to all their credit card customers. This promotion will be considered a success if more than 10% of those receiving the coupons use them. Before going national with the promotion, coupons were sent to a sample of 100 credit card customers.

    a. Develop hypotheses that can be used to test whether the population proportion of those who will use the coupons is sufficient to go national.

    b. The file *Eagle* contains the sample data. Develop a point estimate of the population proportion.

    c. Use $\alpha = .05$ to conduct your hypothesis test. Should Eagle go national with the promotion?

DATA_file_

LawSuit

44. **Malpractice Suits.** One of the reasons health care costs have been rising rapidly in recent years is the increasing cost of malpractice insurance for physicians. Also, fear of being sued causes doctors to run more precautionary tests (possibly unnecessary) just to make sure they are not guilty of missing something. These precautionary tests also add to health care costs. Data in the file *LawSuit* are consistent with findings in a *Reader's Digest* article and can be used to estimate the proportion of physicians over the age of 55 who have been sued at least once.

    a. Formulate hypotheses that can be used to see if these data can support a finding that more than half of physicians over the age of 55 have been sued at least once.

    b. Use Excel and the file *LawSuit* to compute the sample proportion of physicians over the age of 55 who have been sued at least once. What is the p-value for your hypothesis test?

    c. At $\alpha = .01$, what is your conclusion?

45. **Bullish, Neutral, or Bearish.** The American Association of Individual Investors conducts a weekly survey of its members to measure the percent who are bullish, bearish, and neutral on the stock market for the next six months. For the week ending November 7, 2012, the survey results showed 35.0% bullish, 38.6% neutral, and 26.4% bearish. Assume these results are based on a sample of 300 AAII members.

    a. Over the long term, the proportion of bullish AAII members is .39. Conduct a hypothesis test at the 5% level of significance to see if the current sample results show that bullish sentiment differs from its long-term average of .39. What are your findings?

b. Over the long term, the proportion of bearish AAII members is .30. Conduct a hypothesis test at the 1% level of significance to see if the current sample results show that bearish sentiment is below its long term average of .30. What are your findings?

c. Would you feel comfortable extending these results to all investors? Why or why not?

9.6 Hypothesis Testing and Decision Making

In the previous sections of this chapter we have illustrated hypothesis testing applications that are considered significance tests. After formulating the null and alternative hypotheses, we selected a sample and computed the value of a test statistic and the associated p-value. We then compared the p-value to a controlled probability of a Type I error, α, which is called the level of significance for the test. If p-value $\leq \alpha$, we made the conclusion "reject H_0," and declared the results significant; otherwise, we made the conclusion "do not reject H_0." With a significance test, we control the probability of making the Type I error, but not the Type II error. Thus, we recommended the conclusion "do not reject H_0" rather than "accept H_0" because the latter puts us at risk of making the Type II error of accepting H_0 when it is false. With the conclusion "do not reject H_0," the statistical evidence is considered inconclusive and is usually an indication to postpone a decision or action until further research and testing can be undertaken.

However, if the purpose of a hypothesis test is to make a decision when H_0 is true and a different decision when H_a is true, the decision maker may want to, and in some cases be forced to, take action with both the conclusion *do not reject H_0* and the conclusion *reject H_0*. If this situation occurs, statisticians generally recommend controlling the probability of making a Type II error. With the probabilities of both the Type I and Type II error controlled, the conclusion from the hypothesis test is either to *accept H_0* or *reject H_0*. In the first case, H_0 is concluded to be true, while in the second case, H_a is concluded true. Thus, a decision and appropriate action can be taken when either conclusion is reached.

A good illustration of hypothesis testing for decision making is lot-acceptance sampling, a topic we will discuss in more depth in Chapter 20. For example, a quality control manager must decide to accept a shipment of batteries from a supplier or to return the shipment because of poor quality. Assume that design specifications require batteries from the supplier to have a mean useful life of at least 120 hours. To evaluate the quality of an incoming shipment, a sample of 36 batteries will be selected and tested. On the basis of the sample, a decision must be made to accept the shipment of batteries or to return it to the supplier because of poor quality. Let μ denote the mean number of hours of useful life for batteries in the shipment. The null and alternative hypotheses about the population mean follow.

$$H_0: \mu \geq 120$$
$$H_a: \mu < 120$$

If H_0 is rejected, the alternative hypothesis is concluded to be true. This conclusion indicates that the appropriate action is to return the shipment to the supplier. However, if H_0 is not rejected, the decision maker must still determine what action should be taken. Thus, without directly concluding that H_0 is true, but merely by not rejecting it, the decision maker will have made the decision to accept the shipment as being of satisfactory quality.

In such decision-making situations, it is recommended that the hypothesis testing procedure be extended to control the probability of making a Type II error. Because a decision will be made and action taken when we do not reject H_0, knowledge of the probability of making a Type II error will be helpful. In Sections 9.7 and 9.8 we explain how to compute the probability of making a Type II error and how the sample size can be adjusted to help control the probability of making a Type II error.

9.7 Calculating the Probability of Type II Errors

In this section we show how to calculate the probability of making a Type II error for a hypothesis test about a population mean. We illustrate the procedure by using the lot-acceptance example described in Section 9.6. The null and alternative hypotheses about the mean number of hours of useful life for a shipment of batteries are H_0: $\mu \geq 120$ and H_a: $\mu < 120$. If H_0 is rejected, the decision will be to return the shipment to the supplier because the mean hours of useful life are less than the specified 120 hours. If H_0 is not rejected, the decision will be to accept the shipment.

Suppose a level of significance of $\alpha = .05$ is used to conduct the hypothesis test. The test statistic in the σ known case is

$$z = \frac{\bar{x} - \mu_0}{\sigma/\sqrt{n}} = \frac{\bar{x} - 120}{\sigma/\sqrt{n}}$$

Based on the critical value approach and $z_{.05} = 1.645$, the rejection rule for the lower tail test is

$$\text{Reject } H_0 \text{ if } z \leq -1.645$$

Suppose a sample of 36 batteries will be selected and based upon previous testing the population standard deviation can be assumed known with a value of $\sigma = 12$ hours. The rejection rule indicates that we will reject H_0 if

$$z = \frac{\bar{x} - 120}{12/\sqrt{36}} \leq -1.645$$

Solving for $\bar{x}$ in the preceding expression indicates that we will reject H_0 if

$$\bar{x} \leq 120 - 1.645\left(\frac{12}{\sqrt{36}}\right) = 116.71$$

Rejecting H_0 when $\bar{x} \leq 116.71$ means that we will make the decision to accept the shipment whenever

$$\bar{x} > 116.71$$

With this information, we are ready to compute probabilities associated with making a Type II error. First, recall that we make a Type II error whenever the true shipment mean is less than 120 hours and we make the decision to accept H_0: $\mu \geq 120$. Hence, to compute the probability of making a Type II error, we must select a value of μ less than 120 hours. For example, suppose the shipment is considered to be of poor quality if the batteries have a mean life of $\mu = 112$ hours. If $\mu = 112$ is really true, what is the probability of accepting H_0: $\mu \geq 120$ and hence committing a Type II error? Note that this probability is the probability that the sample mean $\bar{x}$ is greater than 116.71 when $\mu = 112$.

Figure 9.8 shows the sampling distribution of $\bar{x}$ when the mean is $\mu = 112$. The shaded area in the upper tail gives the probability of obtaining $\bar{x} > 116.71$. Using the standard normal distribution, we see that at $\bar{x} = 116.71$

$$z = \frac{\bar{x} - \mu}{\sigma/\sqrt{n}} = \frac{116.71 - 112}{12/\sqrt{36}} = 2.36$$

The standard normal probability table shows that with $z = 2.36$, the area in the upper tail is $1.0000 - .9909 = .0091$. Thus, $.0091$ is the probability of making a Type II error when $\mu = 112$. Denoting the probability of making a Type II error as β, we see that when $\mu = 112$, $\beta = .0091$. Therefore, we can conclude that if the mean of the population is 112 hours, the probability of making a Type II error is only $.0091$.

We can repeat these calculations for other values of μ less than 120. Doing so will show a different probability of making a Type II error for each value of μ. For example, suppose the shipment of batteries has a mean useful life of $\mu = 115$ hours. Because we will accept H_0 whenever $\bar{x} > 116.71$, the z value for $\mu = 115$ is given by

$$z = \frac{\bar{x} - \mu}{\sigma/\sqrt{n}} = \frac{116.71 - 115}{12/\sqrt{36}} = .86$$

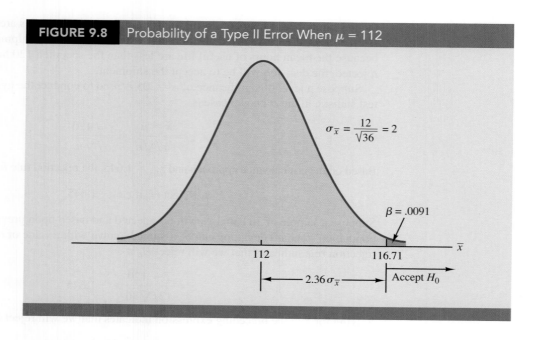

FIGURE 9.8   Probability of a Type II Error When $\mu = 112$

From the standard normal probability table, we find that the area in the upper tail of the standard normal distribution for $z = .86$ is $1.0000 - .8051 = .1949$. Thus, the probability of making a Type II error is $\beta = .1949$ when the true mean is $\mu = 115$.

In Table 9.5 we show the probability of making a Type II error for a variety of values of μ less than 120. Note that as μ increases toward 120, the probability of making a Type II error increases toward an upper bound of .95. However, as μ decreases to values farther below 120, the probability of making a Type II error diminishes. This pattern is what we should expect. When the true population mean μ is close to the null hypothesis value of $\mu = 120$, the probability is high that we will make a Type II error. However, when the true population mean μ is far below the null hypothesis value of $\mu = 120$, the probability is low that we will make a Type II error.

The probability of correctly rejecting H_0 when it is false is called the **power** of the test. For any particular value of μ, the power is $1 - \beta$; that is, the probability of correctly rejecting the null hypothesis is 1 minus the probability of making a Type II error. Values of power are also listed in Table 9.5. On the basis of these values, the power associated with

As Table 9.5 shows, the probability of a Type II error depends on the value of the population mean μ. For values of μ near μ_0, the probability of making the Type II error can be high.

TABLE 9.5   Probability of Making a Type II Error for the Lot-Acceptance Hypothesis Test

Value of μ	$z = \dfrac{116.71 - \mu}{12/\sqrt{36}}$	Probability of a Type II Error (β)	Power $(1 - \beta)$
112	2.36	.0091	.9909
114	1.36	.0869	.9131
115	.86	.1949	.8051
116.71	.00	.5000	.5000
117	−.15	.5596	.4404
118	−.65	.7422	.2578
119.999	−1.645	.9500	.0500

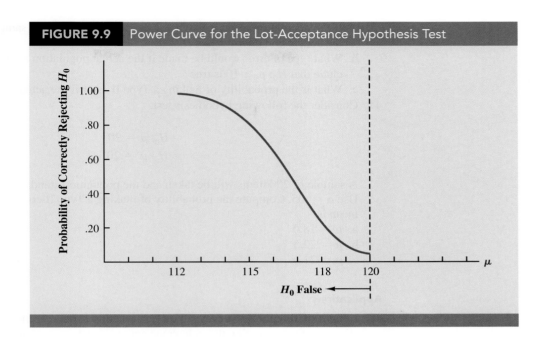

FIGURE 9.9   Power Curve for the Lot-Acceptance Hypothesis Test

each value of μ is shown graphically in Figure 9.9. Such a graph is called a **power curve**. Note that the power curve extends over the values of μ for which the null hypothesis is false. The height of the power curve at any value of μ indicates the probability of correctly rejecting H_0 when H_0 is false.[4]

In summary, the following step-by-step procedure can be used to compute the probability of making a Type II error in hypothesis tests about a population mean.

1. Formulate the null and alternative hypotheses.
2. Use the level of significance α and the critical value approach to determine the critical value and the rejection rule for the test.
3. Use the rejection rule to solve for the value of the sample mean corresponding to the critical value of the test statistic.
4. Use the results from step 3 to state the values of the sample mean that lead to the acceptance of H_0. These values define the acceptance region for the test.
5. Use the sampling distribution of $\bar{x}$ for a value of μ satisfying the alternative hypothesis, and the acceptance region from step 4, to compute the probability that the sample mean will be in the acceptance region. This probability is the probability of making a Type II error at the chosen value of μ.

EXERCISES

Methods

46. Consider the follow ing hypothesis test.

$$H_0\!: \mu \geq 10$$
$$H_a\!: \mu < 10$$

The sample size is 120 and the population standard deviation is assumed known with $\sigma = 5$. Use $\alpha = .05$.

---

[4]Another graph, called the operating characteristic curve, is sometimes used to provide information about the probability of making a Type II error. The operating characteristic curve shows the probability of accepting H_0 and thus provides β for the values of μ where the null hypothesis is false. The probability of making a Type II error can be read directly from this graph.

   a. If the population mean is 9, what is the probability that the sample mean leads to the conclusion *do not reject* H_0?
   b. What type of error would be made if the actual population mean is 9 and we conclude that H_0: $\mu \geq 10$ is true?
   c. What is the probability of making a Type II error if the actual population mean is 8?
47. Consider the following hypothesis test.

$$H_0: \mu = 20$$
$$H_a: \mu \neq 20$$

A sample of 200 items will be taken and the population standard deviation is $\sigma = 10$. Use $\alpha = .05$. Compute the probability of making a Type II error if the population mean is:
   a. $\mu = 18.0$
   b. $\mu = 22.5$
   c. $\mu = 21.0$

Applications

48. **Length of Telephone Surveys.** Fowle Marketing Research, Inc., bases charges to a client on the assumption that telephone surveys can be completed within 15 minutes or less. If more time is required, a premium rate is charged. With a sample of 35 surveys, a population standard deviation of 4 minutes, and a level of significance of .01, the sample mean will be used to test the null hypothesis H_0: $\mu \leq 15$.
   a. What is your interpretation of the Type II error for this problem? What is its impact on the firm?
   b. What is the probability of making a Type II error when the actual mean time is $\mu = 17$ minutes?
   c. What is the probability of making a Type II error when the actual mean time is $\mu = 18$ minutes?
   d. Sketch the general shape of the power curve for this test.
49. **Miles per Gallon.** A consumer research group is interested in testing an automobile manufacturer's claim that a new economy model will travel at least 25 miles per gallon of gasoline (H_0: $\mu \geq 25$).
   a. With a .02 level of significance and a sample of 30 cars, what is the rejection rule based on the value of $\bar{x}$ for the test to determine whether the manufacturer's claim should be rejected? Assume that σ is 3 miles per gallon.
   b. What is the probability of committing a Type II error if the actual mileage is 23 miles per gallon?
   c. What is the probability of committing a Type II error if the actual mileage is 24 miles per gallon?
   d. What is the probability of committing a Type II error if the actual mileage is 25.5 miles per gallon?
50. **Age of Magazine Subscribers.** *Young Adult* magazine states the following hypotheses about the mean age of its subscribers.

$$H_0: \mu = 28$$
$$H_a: \mu \neq 28$$

   a. What would it mean to make a Type II error in this situation?
   b. The population standard deviation is assumed known at $\sigma = 6$ years and the sample size is 100. With $\alpha = .05$, what is the probability of accepting H_0 for μ equal to 26, 27, 29, and 30?
   c. What is the power at $\mu = 26$? What does this result tell you?

51. **Production Line Accuracy.** A production line operation is tested for filling weight accuracy using the following hypotheses.

Hypothesis	Conclusion and Action
$H_0: \mu = 16$	Filling okay; keep running
$H_a: \mu \neq 16$	Filling off standard; stop and adjust machine

The sample size is 30 and the population standard deviation is $\sigma = .8$. Use $\alpha = .05$.
   a. What would a Type II error mean in this situation?
   b. What is the probability of making a Type II error when the machine is overfilling by .5 ounces?
   c. What is the power of the statistical test when the machine is overfilling by .5 ounces?
   d. Show the power curve for this hypothesis test. What information does it contain for the production manager?

52. **Length of Telephone Surveys.** Refer to exercise 48. Assume the firm selects a sample of 50 surveys and repeat parts (b) and (c). What observation can you make about how increasing the sample size affects the probability of making a Type II error?

53. **Employee Participation in Investment Plans.** Sparr Investments, Inc., specializes in tax-deferred investment opportunities for its clients. Recently Sparr offered a payroll deduction investment program for the employees of a particular company. Sparr estimates that the employees are currently averaging $100 or less per month in tax-deferred investments. A sample of 40 employees will be used to test Sparr's hypothesis about the current level of investment activity among the population of employees. Assume the employee monthly tax-deferred investment amounts have a standard deviation of $75 and that a .05 level of significance will be used in the hypothesis test.
   a. What is the Type II error in this situation?
   b. What is the probability of the Type II error if the actual mean employee monthly investment is $120?
   c. What is the probability of the Type II error if the actual mean employee monthly investment is $130?
   d. Assume a sample size of 80 employees is used and repeat parts (b) and (c).

9.8 Determining the Sample Size for a Hypothesis Test About a Population Mean

Assume that a hypothesis test is to be conducted about the value of a population mean. The level of significance specified by the user determines the probability of making a Type I error for the test. By controlling the sample size, the user can also control the probability of making a Type II error. Let us show how a sample size can be determined for the following lower tail test about a population mean.

$$H_0: \mu \geq \mu_0$$
$$H_a: \mu < \mu_0$$

The upper panel of Figure 9.10 is the sampling distribution of $\bar{x}$ when H_0 is true with $\mu = \mu_0$. For a lower tail test, the critical value of the test statistic is denoted $-z_\alpha$. In the upper panel of the figure the vertical line, labeled c, is the corresponding value of $\bar{x}$. Note that, if we reject H_0 when $\bar{x} \leq c$, the probability of a Type I error will be α. With z_α representing the z value corresponding to an area of α in the upper tail of the standard normal distribution, we compute c using the following formula:

$$c = \mu_0 - z_\alpha \frac{\sigma}{\sqrt{n}} \tag{9.5}$$

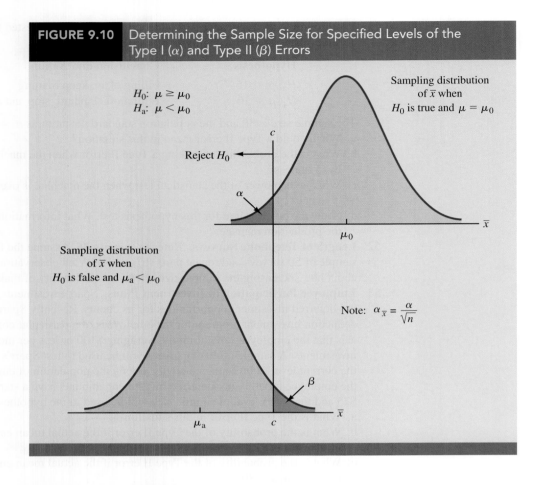

FIGURE 9.10   Determining the Sample Size for Specified Levels of the Type I (α) and Type II (β) Errors

The lower panel of Figure 9.10 is the sampling distribution of $\bar{x}$ when the alternative hypothesis is true with $\mu = \mu_a < \mu_0$. The shaded region shows β, the probability of a Type II error that the decision maker will be exposed to if the null hypothesis is accepted when $\bar{x} > c$. With z_β representing the z value corresponding to an area of β in the upper tail of the standard normal distribution, we compute c using the following formula:

$$c = \mu_a + z_\beta \frac{\sigma}{\sqrt{n}} \tag{9.6}$$

Now what we want to do is to select a value for c so that when we reject H_0 and accept H_a, the probability of a Type I error is equal to the chosen value of α and the probability of a Type II error is equal to the chosen value of β. Therefore, both equations (9.5) and (9.6) must provide the same value for c, and the following equation must be true.

$$\mu_0 - z_\alpha \frac{\sigma}{\sqrt{n}} = \mu_a + z_\beta \frac{\sigma}{\sqrt{n}}$$

To determine the required sample size, we first solve for the $\sqrt{n}$ as follows.

$$\mu_0 - \mu_a = z_\alpha \frac{\sigma}{\sqrt{n}} + z_\beta \frac{\sigma}{\sqrt{n}}$$

$$\mu_0 - \mu_a = \frac{(z_\alpha + z_\beta)\sigma}{\sqrt{n}}$$

and

$$\sqrt{n} = \frac{(z_\alpha + z_\beta)\sigma}{(\mu_0 - \mu_a)}$$

Squaring both sides of the expression provides the following sample size formula for a one-tailed hypothesis test about a population mean.

SAMPLE SIZE FOR A ONE-TAILED HYPOTHESIS TEST ABOUT A POPULATION MEAN

$$n = \frac{(z_\alpha + z_\beta)^2 \sigma^2}{(\mu_0 - \mu_a)^2} \tag{9.7}$$

where

z_α = z value providing an area of α in the upper tail of a standard normal distribution
z_β = z value providing an area of β in the upper tail of a standard normal distribution
σ = the population standard deviation
μ_0 = the value of the population mean in the null hypothesis
μ_a = the value of the population mean used for the Type II error

Note: In a two-tailed hypothesis test, use (9.7) with $z_{\alpha/2}$ replacing z_α.

Although the logic of equation (9.7) was developed for the hypothesis test shown in Figure 9.10, it holds for any one-tailed test about a population mean. In a two-tailed hypothesis test about a population mean, $z_{\alpha/2}$ is used instead of z_α in equation (9.7).

Let us return to the lot-acceptance example from Sections 9.6 and 9.7. The design specification for the shipment of batteries indicated a mean useful life of at least 120 hours for the batteries. Shipments were rejected if H_0: $\mu \geq 120$ was rejected. Let us assume that the quality control manager makes the following statements about the allowable probabilities for the Type I and Type II errors.

Type I error statement: If the mean life of the batteries in the shipment is $\mu = 120$, I am willing to risk an $\alpha = .05$ probability of rejecting the shipment.

Type II error statement: If the mean life of the batteries in the shipment is 5 hours under the specification (i.e., $\mu = 115$), I am willing to risk a $\beta = .10$ probability of accepting the shipment.

These statements are based on the judgment of the manager. Someone else might specify different restrictions on the probabilities. However, statements about the allowable probabilities of both errors must be made before the sample size can be determined.

In the example, $\alpha = .05$ and $\beta = .10$. Using the standard normal probability distribution, we have $z_{.05} = 1.645$ and $z_{.10} = 1.28$. From the statements about the error probabilities, we note that $\mu_0 = 120$ and $\mu_a = 115$. Finally, the population standard deviation was assumed known at $\sigma = 12$. By using equation (9.7), we find that the recommended sample size for the lot-acceptance example is

$$n = \frac{(1.645 + 1.28)^2 (12)^2}{(120 - 115)^2} = 49.3$$

Rounding up, we recommend a sample size of 50.

Because both the Type I and Type II error probabilities have been controlled at allowable levels with $n = 50$, the quality control manager is now justified in using the *accept* H_0 and *reject* H_0 statements for the hypothesis test. The accompanying inferences are made with allowable probabilities of making Type I and Type II errors.

We can make three observations about the relationship among α, β, and the sample size n.

1. Once two of the three values are known, the other can be computed.
2. For a given level of significance α, increasing the sample size will reduce β.
3. For a given sample size, decreasing α will increase β, whereas increasing α will decrease β.

The third observation should be kept in mind when the probability of a Type II error is not being controlled. It suggests that one should not choose unnecessarily small values for the level of significance α. For a given sample size, choosing a smaller level of significance means more exposure to a Type II error. Inexperienced users of hypothesis testing often think that smaller values of α are always better. They are better if we are concerned only about making a Type I error. However, smaller values of α have the disadvantage of increasing the probability of making a Type II error.

EXERCISES

Methods

54. Consider the following hypothesis test.

$$H_0: \mu \geq 10$$
$$H_a: \mu < 10$$

The sample size is 120 and the population standard deviation is 5. Use $\alpha = .05$. If the actual population mean is 9, the probability of a Type II error is .2912. Suppose the researcher wants to reduce the probability of a Type II error to .10 when the actual population mean is 9. What sample size is recommended?

55. Consider the following hypothesis test.

$$H_0: \mu = 20$$
$$H_a: \mu \neq 20$$

The population standard deviation is 10. Use $\alpha = .05$. How large a sample should be taken if the researcher is willing to accept a .05 probability of making a Type II error when the actual population mean is 22?

Applications

56. **Underfilling Packages of Coffee.** Suppose the project director for the Hilltop Coffee study (see Section 9.3) asked for a .10 probability of claiming that Hilltop was not in violation when it really was underfilling by 1 ounce ($\mu_a = 2.9375$ pounds). What sample size would have been recommended?

57. **Battery Life.** A special industrial battery must have a life of at least 400 hours. A hypothesis test is to be conducted with a .02 level of significance. If the batteries from a particular production run have an actual mean use life of 385 hours, the production manager wants a sampling procedure that only 10% of the time would show erroneously that the batch is acceptable. What sample size is recommended for the hypothesis test? Use 30 hours as an estimate of the population standard deviation.

58. **Mean Age of Magazine Subscribers.** *Young Adult* magazine states the following hypotheses about the mean age of its subscribers.

$$H_0: \mu = 28$$
$$H_a: \mu \neq 28$$

If the manager conducting the test will permit a .15 probability of making a Type II error when the true mean age is 29, what sample size should be selected? Assume $\sigma = 6$ and a .05 level of significance.

59. **Automobile Mileage.** An automobile mileage study tested the following hypotheses.

Hypothesis	Conclusion
$H_0: \mu \geq 25$ mpg	Manufacturer's claim supported
$H_a: \mu < 25$ mpg	Manufacturer's claim rejected; average mileage per gallon less than stated

For $\sigma = 3$ and a .02 level of significance, what sample size would be recommended if the researcher wants an 80% chance of detecting that μ is less than 25 miles per gallon when it is actually 24?

9.9 BIG DATA AND HYPOTHESIS TESTING

We have seen that interval estimates of the population mean μ and the population proportion p narrow as the sample size increases. This occurs because the standard error of the associated sampling distributions decrease as the sample size increases. Now consider the relationship between interval estimation and hypothesis testing that we discussed earlier in this chapter. If we construct a $100(1 - \alpha)\%$ interval estimate for the population mean, we reject $H_0: \mu = \mu_0$ if the $100(1 - \alpha)\%$ interval estimate does not contain μ_0. Thus, for a given level of confidence, as the sample size increases we will reject $H_0: \mu = \mu_0$ for increasingly smaller differences between the sample mean $\bar{x}$ and the hypothesized population mean μ_0. We can see that when the sample size n is very large, almost any difference between the sample mean $\bar{x}$ and the hypothesized population mean μ_0 results in rejection of the null hypothesis.

Big Data, Hypothesis Testing, and p Values

In this section, we will elaborate how big data affects hypothesis testing and the magnitude of p values. Specifically, we will examine how rapidly the p value associated with a given difference between a point estimate and a hypothesized value of a parameter decreases as the sample size increases.

Let us consider the online news service PenningtonDailyTimes.com (PDT). PDT's primary source of revenue is the sale of advertising, and prospective advertisers are willing to pay a premium to advertise on websites that have long visit times. To promote its news service, PDT's management wants to promise potential advertisers that the mean time spent by customers when they visit PenningtonDailyTimes.com is greater than last year, that is, more than 84 seconds. PDT therefore decides to collect a sample tracking the amount of time spent by individual customers when they visit PDT's website in order to test its null hypothesis $H_0: \mu \leq 84$.

For a sample mean of 84.1 seconds and a sample standard deviation of $s = 20$ seconds, Table 9.6 provides the values of the test statistic t and the p values for the test of the null hypothesis $H_0: \mu \leq 84$. The p value for this hypothesis test is essentially 0 for all samples in Table 9.6 with at least $n = 1{,}000{,}000$.

PDT's management also wants to promise potential advertisers that the proportion of its website visitors who click on an ad this year exceeds the proportion of its website visitors who clicked on an ad last year, which was .50. PDT collects information from its sample on whether the visitor to its website clicked on any of the ads featured on the website, and it wants to use these data to test its null hypothesis $H_0: p \leq .50$.

For a sample proportion of .51, Table 9.7 provides the values of the test statistic z and the p values for the test of the null hypothesis $H_0: p \leq .5$ p value for this hypothesis test is essentially 0 for all samples in Table 9.7 with at least $n = 100{,}000$.

We see in Tables 9.6 and 9.7 that the p value associated with a given difference between a point estimate and a hypothesized value of a parameter decreases as the sample size increases. As a result, if the sample mean time spent by customers when they visit PDT's website is 84.1 seconds, PDT's null hypothesis $H_o: \mu \leq 84$ is not rejected at $\alpha = .01$ for samples with $n \leq 100{,}000$, and is rejected at $\alpha = .01$ for samples with $n \geq 1{,}000{,}000$.

TABLE 9.6	Values of the Test Statistic t and the p Values for the Test of the Null Hypothesis H_0: $\mu \le 84$ and Sample Mean $\bar{x} = 84.1$ Seconds for Various Sample Sizes n	

Sample Size n	t	p Value
10	.01581	.49386
100	.05000	.48011
1,000	.15811	.43720
10,000	.50000	.30854
100,000	1.58114	.05692
1,000,000	5.00000	2.87E-07
10,000,000	15.81139	1.30E-56
100,000,000	50.00000	.00E+00
1,000,000,000	158.11388	.00E+00

TABLE 9.7	Values of the Test Statistic z and the p Values for the Test of the Null Hypothesis H_0: $p \le .50$ and Sample Proporton $\bar{p} = .51$ for Various Sample Sizes n	

Sample Size n	z	p Value
10	.06325	.47479
100	.20000	.42074
1,000	.63246	.26354
10,000	2.00000	.02275
100,000	6.32456	1.27E-10
1,000,000	20.00000	.00E+00
10,000,000	63.24555	.00E+00
100,000,000	200.00000	.00E+00
1,000,000,000	632.45553	.00E+00

Similarly, if the sample proportion of visitors to its website clicked on an ad featured on the website is .51, PDT's null hypothesis H_0: $p \le .50$ is not rejected at $\alpha = .01$ for samples with $n \le 10,000$, and is rejected at $\alpha = .01$ for samples with $n \ge 100,000$. In both instances, as the sample size becomes extremely large the p value associated with the given difference between a point estimate and the hypothesized value of the parameter becomes extremely small.

Implications of Big Data in Hypothesis Testing

Suppose PDT collects a sample of 1,000,000 visitors to its website and uses these data to test its null hypotheses H_0: $\mu \le 84$ and H_0: $p \le .50$ at the .05 level of significance. The sample mean is 84.1 and the sample proportion is .51, so the null hypothesis is rejected in both tests as Tables 9.6 and 9.7 show. As a result, PDT can promise potential advertisers that the mean time spent by individual customers who visit PDT's website exceeds 84 seconds and the proportion individual visitors to of its website who click on an ad exceeds .50. These results suggest that for each of these hypothesis tests, the difference between the point estimate and the hypothesized value of the parameter being tested is not likely solely a consequence of sampling error. However, the results of any hypothesis test, no matter the sample size, are only reliable if the sample is relatively free of nonsampling error. If nonsampling error is introduced in the data collection process, the likelihood of making a Type I or Type II error may be higher than if the sample data are free of nonsampling error. Therefore, when testing a hypothesis, it is always important to think carefully about whether a random sample of the population of interest has been taken.

If PDT determines that it has introduced little or no nonsampling error into its sample data, the only remaining plausible explanation for these results is that these null hypotheses are false. At this point, PDT and the companies that advertise on PenningtonDailyTimes.com should also consider whether these statistically significant differences between the point estimates and the hypothesized values of the parameters being tested are of **practical significance**. Although a .1 second increase in the mean time spent by customers when they visit PDT's website is statistically significant, it may not be meaningful to companies that might advertise on PenningtonDailyTimes.com. Similarly, although an increase of .01 in the proportion of visitors to its website that click on an ad is statistically significant, it may not be meaningful to companies that might advertise on PenningtonDailyTimes.com. Determining whether these statistically significant differences have meaningful implications for ensuing business decisions of PDT and its advertisers.

Ultimately, no business decision should be based solely on statistical inference. Practical significance should always be considered in conjunction with statistical significance. This is particularly important when the hypothesis test is based on an extremely large sample because even an extremely small difference between the point estimate and the hypothesized value of the parameter being tested will be statistically significant. When done properly, statistical inference provides evidence that should be considered in combination with information collected from other sources to make the most informed decision possible.

NOTES + COMMENTS

1. Nonsampling error can occur when either a probability sampling technique or a nonprobability sampling technique is used. However, nonprobability sampling techniques such as convenience sampling and judgment sampling often introduce nonsampling error into sample data because of the manner in which sample data are collected. Therefore, probability sampling techniques are preferred over nonprobability sampling techniques.

2. When taking an extremely large sample, it is conceivable that the sample size is at least 5% of the population size; that is, $n/N \geq .05$. Under these conditions, it is necessary to use the finite population correction factor when calculating the standard error of the sampling distribution to be used in confidence intervals and hypothesis testing.

DATA *file*

FedEmail

60. **Governmental Use of email.** The Federal Government wants to determine if the mean number of business emails sent and received per business day by its employees differs from the mean number of emails sent and received per day by corporate employees, which is 101.5. Suppose the department electronically collects information on the number of business emails sent and received on a randomly selected business day over the past year from each of 10,163 randomly selected Federal employees. The results are provided in the file *FedEmail*. Test the Federal Government's hypothesis at $\alpha = .01$. Discuss the practical significance of the results.

DATA *file*

SocialNetwork

61. **CEOs and Social Networks.** CEOs who belong to a popular business-oriented social networking service have an average of 930 connections. Do other members have fewer connections than CEOs? The number of connections for a random sample of 7,515 members who are not CEOs is provided in the file *SocialNetwork*. Using this sample, test the hypothesis that other members have fewer connections than CEOs at $\alpha = .01$. Discuss the practical significance of the results.

62. **French Fry Purchases.** The American Potato Growers Association (APGA) would like to test the claim that the proportion of fast-food orders this year that include French fries exceeds the proportion of fast-food orders that included French fries last year. Suppose that a random sample of 49,581 electronic receipts for fast-food

orders placed this year shows that 31,038 included French fries. Assuming that the proportion of fast-food orders that included French fries last year is .62, use this information to test APGA's claim at $\alpha = .05$. Discuss the practical significance of the results.

63. **GPS Usage in Canada.** According to CNN, 55% of all U.S. smartphone users have used their GPS capability to get directions. Suppose a major provider of wireless telephone service in Canada wants to know how GPS usage by its customers compares with U.S. smartphone users. The company collects usage records for this year for a random sample of 547,192 of its Canadian customers and determines that 302,050 of these customers have used their telephone's GPS capability this year. Use this data to test whether Canadian smartphone users' GPS usage differs from U.S. smartphone users' GPS usage at $\alpha = .01$. Discuss the practical significance of the results.

SUMMARY

Hypothesis testing is a statistical procedure that uses sample data to determine whether a statement about the value of a population parameter should or should not be rejected. The hypotheses are two competing statements about a population parameter. One statement is called the null hypothesis (H_0), and the other statement is called the alternative hypothesis (H_a). In Section 9.1 we provided guidelines for developing hypotheses for situations frequently encountered in practice.

Whenever historical data or other information provides a basis for assuming that the population standard deviation is known, the hypothesis testing procedure for the population mean is based on the standard normal distribution. Whenever σ is unknown, the sample standard deviation s is used to estimate σ and the hypothesis testing procedure is based on the t distribution. In both cases, the quality of results depends on both the form of the population distribution and the sample size. If the population has a normal distribution, both hypothesis testing procedures are applicable, even with small sample sizes. If the population is not normally distributed, larger sample sizes are needed. General guidelines about the sample size were provided in Sections 9.3 and 9.4. In the case of hypothesis tests about a population proportion, the hypothesis testing procedure uses a test statistic based on the standard normal distribution.

In all cases, the value of the test statistic can be used to compute a p-value for the test. A p-value is a probability used to determine whether the null hypothesis should be rejected. If the p-value is less than or equal to the level of significance α, the null hypothesis can be rejected.

Hypothesis testing conclusions can also be made by comparing the value of the test statistic to a critical value. For lower tail tests, the null hypothesis is rejected if the value of the test statistic is less than or equal to the critical value. For upper tail tests, the null hypothesis is rejected if the value of the test statistic is greater than or equal to the critical value. Two-tailed tests consist of two critical values: one in the lower tail of the sampling distribution and one in the upper tail. In this case, the null hypothesis is rejected if the value of the test statistic is less than or equal to the critical value in the lower tail or greater than or equal to the critical value in the upper tail.

Extensions of hypothesis testing procedures to include an analysis of the Type II error were also presented. In Section 9.7 we showed how to compute the probability of making a Type II error. In Section 9.8 we showed how to determine a sample size that will control for the probability of making both a Type I error and a Type II error. Finally, we discussed the ramifications of extremely large samples on hypothesis tests of the mean and proportion.

GLOSSARY

Alternative hypothesis The hypothesis concluded to be true if the null hypothesis is rejected.

Critical value A value that is compared with the test statistic to determine whether H_0 should be rejected.

Level of significance The probability of making a Type I error when the null hypothesis is true as an equality.

Null hypothesis The hypothesis tentatively assumed true in the hypothesis testing procedure.

One-tailed test A hypothesis test in which rejection of the null hypothesis occurs for values of the test statistic in one tail of its sampling distribution.

p-value A probability that provides a measure of the evidence against the null hypothesis given by the sample. Smaller *p*-values indicate more evidence against H_0. For a lower tail test, the *p*-value is the probability of obtaining a value for the test statistic as small as or smaller than that provided by the sample. For an upper tail test, the *p*-value is the probability of obtaining a value for the test statistic as large as or larger than that provided by the sample. For a two-tailed test, the *p*-value is the probability of obtaining a value for the test statistic at least as unlikely as or more unlikely than that provided by the sample.

Power The probability of correctly rejecting H_0 when it is false.

Power curve A graph of the probability of rejecting H_0 for all possible values of the population parameter not satisfying the null hypothesis. The power curve provides the probability of correctly rejecting the null hypothesis.

Practical significance The real-world impact that statistical inference will have on business decisions.

Test statistic A statistic whose value helps determine whether a null hypothesis should be rejected.

Two-tailed test A hypothesis test in which rejection of the null hypothesis occurs for values of the test statistic in either tail of its sampling distribution.

Type I error The error of rejecting H_0 when it is true.

Type II error The error of accepting H_0 when it is false.

KEY FORMULAS

Test Statistic for Hypothesis Tests About a Population Mean: σ Known

$$z = \frac{\bar{x} - \mu_0}{\sigma/\sqrt{n}} \tag{9.1}$$

Test Statistic for Hypothesis Tests About a Population Mean: σ Unknown

$$t = \frac{\bar{x} - \mu_0}{s/\sqrt{n}} \tag{9.2}$$

Test Statistic for Hypothesis Tests About a Population Proportion

$$z = \frac{\bar{p} - p_0}{\sqrt{\dfrac{p_0(1 - p_0)}{n}}} \tag{9.4}$$

Sample Size for a One-Tailed Hypothesis Test About a Population Mean

$$n = \frac{(z_\alpha + z_\beta)^2 \sigma^2}{(\mu_0 - \mu_a)^2} \tag{9.7}$$

In a two-tailed test, replace z_α with $z_{\alpha/2}$.

SUPPLEMENTARY EXERCISES

64. **Production Line Fill Weights.** A production line operates with a mean filling weight of 16 ounces per container. Overfilling or underfilling presents a serious problem and when detected requires the operator to shut down the production line to readjust the

filling mechanism. From past data, a population standard deviation $\sigma = .8$ ounces is assumed. A quality control inspector selects a sample of 30 items every hour and at that time makes the decision of whether to shut down the line for readjustment. The level of significance is $\alpha = .05$.

a. State the hypothesis test for this quality control application.

b. If a sample mean of $\bar{x} = 16.32$ ounces were found, what is the p-value? What action would you recommend?

c. If a sample mean of $\bar{x} = 15.82$ ounces were found, what is the p-value? What action would you recommend?

d. Use the critical value approach. What is the rejection rule for the preceding hypothesis testing procedure? Repeat parts (b) and (c). Do you reach the same conclusion?

65. **Scholarship Examination Scores.** At Western University the historical mean of scholarship examination scores for freshman applications is 900. A historical population standard deviation $\sigma = 180$ is assumed known. Each year, the assistant dean uses a sample of applications to determine whether the mean examination score for the new freshman applications has changed.

a. State the hypotheses.

b. What is the 95% confidence interval estimate of the population mean examination score if a sample of 200 applications provided a sample mean $\bar{x} = 935$?

c. Use the confidence interval to conduct a hypothesis test. Using $\alpha = .05$, what is your conclusion?

d. What is the p-value?

66. **Exposure to Background Television.** CNN reports that young children in the United States are exposed to an average of 4 hours of background television per day. Having the television on in the background while children are doing other activities may have adverse consequences on a child's well-being. You have a research hypothesis that children from low-income families are exposed to more than 4 hours of daily background television. In order to test this hypothesis, you have collected a random sample of 60 children from low-income families and found that these children were exposed to a sample mean of 4.5 hours of daily background television.

a. Develop hypotheses that can be used to test your research hypothesis.

b. Based on a previous study, you are willing to assume that the population standard deviation is $\sigma = 1.5$ hours. What is the p-value based on your sample of 60 children from low-income families?

c. Use $\alpha = .01$ as the level of significance. What is your conclusion?

67. **Starting Salaries for Business Graduates.** Michigan State University's Collegiate Employment Research Institute found that starting salary for recipients of bachelor's degrees in business was $50,032 in 2017. The results for a sample of 100 business majors receiving a bachelor's degree in 2018 showed a mean starting salary of $51,276 with a sample standard deviation of $5200. Conduct a hypothesis test to determine whether the mean starting salary for business majors in 2018 is greater than the mean starting salary in 2017. Use $\alpha = .01$ as the level of significance.

BritainMarriages

68. **British Men's Age at Marriage.** Data from the Office for National Statistics show that the mean age at which men in Great Britain married in 2013 is 30.8 years. A news reporter noted that this represents a continuation of the trend of waiting until a later age to wed. A new sample of 47 recently wed British men provided their age at the time of marriage. These data are contained in the file *BritainMarriages*. Do these data indicate that the mean age of British men at the time of marriage exceeds the mean age in 2013? Test this hypothesis at $\alpha = .05$. What is your conclusion?.

WeeklyHSGradPay

69. **Wages of Workers Without High School Diploma.** SmartAsset reports that the average weekly earnings for workers who have not received a high school diploma is $493 in 2018. Suppose you would like to determine if the average weekly earnings for workers who have received a high school diploma is significantly greater than average

weekly earnings for workers who have not received a high school diploma. Data providing the weekly pay for a sample of 50 workers who have received a high school diploma are available in the file *WeeklyHSGradPay*. These data are consistent with the findings reported by SmartAsset.

   a. State the hypotheses that should be used to test whether the mean weekly pay for workers who have received a high school diploma is significantly greater than the mean weekly pay for workers who have not received a high school diploma.

   b. Use the data in the file *WeeklyHSGradPay* to compute the sample mean, the test statistic, and the p-value.

   c. Use $\alpha = .05$. What is your conclusion? Is this result surprising? Why did these data likely lead to this conclusion?

   d. Repeat the hypothesis test using the critical value approach.

70. **Residential Property Values.** The chamber of commerce of a Florida Gulf Coast community advertises that area residential property is available at a mean cost of $125,000 or less per lot. Suppose a sample of 32 properties provided a sample mean of $130,000 per lot and a sample standard deviation of $12,500. Use a .05 level of significance to test the validity of the advertising claim.

71. **Length of Time to Sell a Home.** According to the the National Association of Realtors, it took an average of three weeks to sell a home in 2017. Data for the sale of 40 randomly selected homes sold in Greene County, Ohio, in 2017 showed a sample mean of 3.6 weeks with a sample standard deviation of 2 weeks. Conduct a hypothesis test to determine whether the number of weeks until a house sold in Greene County differed from the national average in 2017. Use $\alpha = .05$ for the level of significance, and state your conclusion.

72. **Sleeping on Flights.** According to Expedia, 52% of Americans report that they generally can sleep during flights. Are people who fly frequently more likely to be able to sleep during flights? Suppose we have a random sample of 510 individuals who flew at least 25,000 miles last year and 285 indicated that they were able to sleep during flights.

   a. Conduct a hypothesis test to determine if the results justify concluding that people who fly frequently are more likely to be able to sleep during flights. Use $\alpha = .05$.

   b. Conduct the same hypothesis test you performed in (a) at $\alpha = .01$. What is your conclusion?

73. **Using Laptops on Flights.** An airline promotion to business travelers is based on the assumption that two-thirds of business travelers use a laptop computer on overnight business trips.

   a. State the hypotheses that can be used to test the assumption.

   b. What is the sample proportion from an American Express sponsored survey that found 355 of 546 business travelers use a laptop computer on overnight business trips?

   c. What is the p-value?

   d. Use $\alpha = .05$. What is your conclusion?

74. **Millennial Dependency on Parents.** Members of the millennial generation are continuing to be dependent on their parents (either living with or otherwise receiving support from parents) into early adulthood. A family research organization has claimed that, in past generations, no more than 30% of individuals aged 18 to 32 continued to be dependent on their parents. Suppose that a sample of 400 individuals aged 18 to 32 showed that 136 of them continue to be dependent on their parents.

   a. Develop hypotheses for a test to determine whether the proportion of millennials continuing to be dependent on their parents is higher than for past generations.

   b. What is your point estimate of the proportion of millennials that are continuing to be dependent on their parents?

   c. What is the p-value provided by the sample data?

   d. What is your hypothesis testing conclusion? Use $\alpha = .05$ as the level of significance.

75. **Using Social Media in a Job Search.** According to Inc.com, 79% of job seekers used social media in their job search in 2018. Many believe this number is inflated by the proportion of 22- to 30-year-old job seekers who use social media in their job search. A survey of 22- to 30-year-old job seekers showed that 310 of the 370 respondents use social media in their job search. In addition, 275 of the 370 respondents indicated they have electronically submitted a resume to an employer.
    a. Conduct a hypothesis test to determine if the results of the survey justify concluding the proportion of 22- to 30-year-old job seekers who use social media in their job search exceeds the proportion of the population that use social media in their job search. Use $\alpha = .05$.
    b. Conduct a hypothesis test to determine if the results of the survey justify concluding that more than 70% of 22- to 30-year-old job seekers have electronically submitted a resume to an employer. Using $\alpha = .05$, what is your conclusion?

76. **Hotel Availability Over Holiday Weekend.** A radio station in Myrtle Beach announced that at least 90% of the hotels and motels would be full for the Memorial Day weekend. The station advised listeners to make reservations in advance if they planned to be in the resort over the weekend. On Saturday night a sample of 58 hotels and motels showed 49 with a no-vacancy sign and 9 with vacancies. What is your reaction to the radio station's claim after seeing the sample evidence? Use $\alpha = .05$ in making the statistical test. What is the p-value?

77. **Vegetarianism in the United States.** Vegetarians are much less common in the United States than in the rest of the world. In a 2018 survey of 11,000 people in the United States, VeganBits found 55 who are vegetarians.
    a. Develop a point estimate of the proportion of people in the United States who are vegetarians.
    b. Set up a hypothesis test so that the rejection of H_0 will allow you to conclude that the proportion of people in the United States who are vegetarians exceeds .004.
    c. Conduct your hypothesis test using $\alpha = .05$. What is your conclusion?

78. **Construction Worker Idle Time.** Shorney Construction Company bids on projects assuming that the mean idle time per worker is 72 or fewer minutes per day. A sample of 30 construction workers will be used to test this assumption. Assume that the population standard deviation is 20 minutes.
    a. State the hypotheses to be tested.
    b. What is the probability of making a Type II error when the population mean idle time is 80 minutes?
    c. What is the probability of making a Type II error when the population mean idle time is 75 minutes?
    d. What is the probability of making a Type II error when the population mean idle time is 70 minutes?
    e. Sketch the power curve for this problem.

79. **Federal Funding for Neighborhood Projects.** A federal funding program is available to low-income neighborhoods. To qualify for the funding, a neighborhood must have a mean household income of less than $15,000 per year. Neighborhoods with mean annual household income of $15,000 or more do not qualify. Funding decisions are based on a sample of residents in the neighborhood. A hypothesis test with a .02 level of significance is conducted. If the funding guidelines call for a maximum probability of .05 of not funding a neighborhood with a mean annual household income of $14,000, what sample size should be used in the funding decision study? Use $\sigma = \$4000$ as a planning value.

80. **Soap Production Process.** $H_0: \mu = 120$ and $H_a: \mu \neq 120$ are used to test whether a bath soap production process is meeting the standard output of 120 bars per batch. Use a .05 level of significance for the test and a planning value of 5 for the standard deviation.

a. If the mean output drops to 117 bars per batch, the firm wants to have a 98% chance of concluding that the standard production output is not being met. How large a sample should be selected?

b. With your sample size from part (a), what is the probability of concluding that the process is operating satisfactorily for each of the following actual mean outputs: 117, 118, 119, 121, 122, and 123 bars per batch? That is, what is the probability of a Type II error in each case?

ChannelSurfing

81. **Time Spent Channel Surfing.** According to Ericsson's 2016 ConsumerLab TV & Media report, the average person in the United States spends 23 minutes per day channel surfing. The file *ChannelSurfing* provides the number of minutes per day looking for something to watch on television for a random sample 8783 people in December. Do these data support the conclusion that people spend less time channel surfing during December than they do throughout the year? Test this hypothesis at $\alpha = .01$. Discuss the practical significance of the results.

82. **Potato Chip Quality Control.** NDC Technology's MM710e On-Line Snacks Gauge rapidly measures surface brownness of potato chips just before packaging. This allows for a high degree of control over this important characteristic of a potato chip; chips that are too brown are overfried, and chips that are not sufficiently brown are underfried. A potato chip manufacturer is now using the MM710e to assess the quality of the chips it produces; one of this manufacturer's goals is to produce less than 1 overfried chip in every 1000 chips. In a recent random sample of 111,667 chips taken from the production lines of the manufacturer's production facilities nationwide, the MM710e found 98 overfried chips. Conduct a hypothesis test to determine if the sample data indicates the manufacturer is meeting its goal for overfried chips at $\alpha = .05$.

TSAWaitTimes

83. **TSA Security Line Wait Times.** According to the U.S. Transportation Security Administration (TSA), 2% of the 771,556,886 travelers who utilized 440 federalized airports in 2017 waited more than 20 minutes in the TSA security line. The file *TSAWaitTimes* contains waiting times in TSA security lines at a major U.S. airport for a recent random sample 10,531 travelers. Use these data to test the hypothesis that the proportion of travelers waiting more than 20 minutes in TSA security lines at this airport is the same as the national proportion at $\alpha = .05$.

CASE PROBLEM 1: QUALITY ASSOCIATES, INC.

Quality Associates, Inc., a consulting firm, advises its clients about sampling and statistical procedures that can be used to control their manufacturing processes. In one particular application, a client gave Quality Associates a sample of 800 observations taken during a time in which that client's process was operating satisfactorily. The sample standard deviation for these data was .21; hence, with so much data, the population standard deviation was assumed to be .21. Quality Associates then suggested that random samples of size 30 be taken periodically to monitor the process on an ongoing basis. By analyzing the new samples, the client could quickly learn whether the process was operating satisfactorily. When the process was not operating satisfactorily, corrective action could be taken to eliminate the problem. The design specification indicated the mean for the process should be 12. The hypothesis test suggested by Quality Associates follows.

$$H_0: \mu = 12$$
$$H_a: \mu \neq 12$$

Corrective action will be taken any time H_0 is rejected.

The following samples were collected at hourly intervals during the first day of operation of the new statistical process control procedure. These data are available in the data set Quality.

Quality

Sample 1	Sample 2	Sample 3	Sample 4
11.55	11.62	11.91	12.02
11.62	11.69	11.36	12.02
11.52	11.59	11.75	12.05
11.75	11.82	11.95	12.18
11.90	11.97	12.14	12.11
11.64	11.71	11.72	12.07
11.80	11.87	11.61	12.05
12.03	12.10	11.85	11.64
11.94	12.01	12.16	12.39
11.92	11.99	11.91	11.65
12.13	12.20	12.12	12.11
12.09	12.16	11.61	11.90
11.93	12.00	12.21	12.22
12.21	12.28	11.56	11.88
12.32	12.39	11.95	12.03
11.93	12.00	12.01	12.35
11.85	11.92	12.06	12.09
11.76	11.83	11.76	11.77
12.16	12.23	11.82	12.20
11.77	11.84	12.12	11.79
12.00	12.07	11.60	12.30
12.04	12.11	11.95	12.27
11.98	12.05	11.96	12.29
12.30	12.37	12.22	12.47
12.18	12.25	11.75	12.03
11.97	12.04	11.96	12.17
12.17	12.24	11.95	11.94
11.85	11.92	11.89	11.97
12.30	12.37	11.88	12.23
12.15	12.22	11.93	12.25

Managerial Report

1. Conduct a hypothesis test for each sample at the .01 level of significance and determine what action, if any, should be taken. Provide the test statistic and p-value for each test.
2. Compute the standard deviation for each of the four samples. Does the assumption of .21 for the population standard deviation appear reasonable?
3. Compute limits for the sample mean $\bar{x}$ around $\mu = 12$ such that, as long as a new sample mean is within those limits, the process will be considered to be operating satisfactorily. If $\bar{x}$ exceeds the upper limit or if $\bar{x}$ is below the lower limit, corrective action will be taken. These limits are referred to as upper and lower control limits for quality control purposes.
4. Discuss the implications of changing the level of significance to a larger value. What mistake or error could increase if the level of significance is increased?

CASE PROBLEM 2: ETHICAL BEHAVIOR OF BUSINESS STUDENTS AT BAYVIEW UNIVERSITY

During the global recession of 2008 and 2009, there were many accusations of unethical behavior by Wall Street executives, financial managers, and other corporate officers. At that time, an article appeared that suggested that part of the reason for such unethical business behavior may stem from the fact that cheating has become more prevalent among business students (*Chronicle of Higher Education,* February 10, 2009). The article reported that 56% of business students admitted to cheating at some time during their academic career as compared to 47% of nonbusiness students.

Cheating has been a concern of the dean of the College of Business at Bayview University for several years. Some faculty members in the college believe that cheating is more widespread at Bayview than at other universities, while other faculty members think that cheating is not a major problem in the college. To resolve some of these issues, the dean commissioned a study to assess the current ethical behavior of business students at Bayview. As part of this study, an anonymous exit survey was administered to a sample of 90 business students from this year's graduating class. Responses to the following questions were used to obtain data regarding three types of cheating.

During your time at Bayview, did you ever present work copied off the Internet as your own?

Yes _____   No _____

During your time at Bayview, did you ever copy answers off another student's exam?

Yes _____   No _____

During your time at Bayview, did you ever collaborate with other students on projects that were supposed to be completed individually?

Yes _____   No _____

Any student who answered Yes to one or more of these questions was considered to have been involved in some type of cheating. A portion of the data collected follows. The complete data set is in the file *Bayview*.

DATA*file*

Bayview

Student	Copied from Internet	Copied on Exam	Collaborated on Individual Project	Gender
1	No	No	No	Female
2	No	No	No	Male
3	Yes	No	Yes	Male
4	Yes	Yes	No	Male
5	No	No	Yes	Male
6	Yes	No	No	Female
.	.	.	.	.
.	.	.	.	.
.	.	.	.	.
88	No	No	No	Male
89	No	Yes	Yes	Male
90	No	No	No	Female

Managerial Report

Prepare a report for the dean of the college that summarizes your assessment of the nature of cheating by business students at Bayview University. Be sure to include the following items in your report.

1. Use descriptive statistics to summarize the data and comment on your findings.
2. Develop 95% confidence intervals for the proportion of all students, the proportion of male students, and the proportion of female students who were involved in some type of cheating.
3. Conduct a hypothesis test to determine if the proportion of business students at Bayview University who were involved in some type of cheating is less than that of business students at other institutions as reported by the *Chronicle of Higher Education*.
4. Conduct a hypothesis test to determine if the proportion of business students at Bayview University who were involved in some form of cheating is less than that of nonbusiness students at other institutions as reported by the *Chronicle of Higher Education*.
5. What advice would you give to the dean based upon your analysis of the data?

Chapter 9 Appendix

Appendix 9.1 Hypothesis Testing with JMP

We describe the use of JMP in constructing hypothesis tests about a population mean and a population proportion.

Population Mean: σ Known

We illustrate conducting a hypothesis test about a population mean with a known population standard deviation σ using the Maxflight golf ball distance example in Section 9.3. The distances for 50 drives are provided in the file *GolfTest*. The population standard deviation $\sigma = 12$ is assumed known, and the level of significance for the test is $\alpha = .05$. The following steps can be used to test the hypothesis H_0: $\mu = 295$ against H_a: $\mu \neq 295$.

DATA*file*

GolfTest

Step 1. Open the file *GolfTest* with JMP using the steps provided in Appendix 1.1

Step 2. Click the **Analyze** tab on the JMP Ribbon and select **Distribution**

Step 3. In the **Distribution** dialog box, drag **Yards** to the **Y, Columns** box
Click **OK** in the **Action** area

This produces an output window with several results that are located in the **Summary Statistics** area of the output window as shown in Figure JMP 9.1.

Step 4. In the **Data - Distribution of Yards** window, click on the red triangle next to **Yards** and select **Test Mean**
Enter *295* into the **Specify Hypothesized Mean** box and enter *12* into the **Enter True Standard Deviation to do z-test rather than t test** box
Click **OK**

FIGURE JMP 9.1	Output Generated by the Distribution Dialog Box for Maxflight Golf Ball Distance Data in JMP

FIGURE JMP 9.2   JMP Output Window with Test Mean Output for Maxflight Golf Ball Distance Data

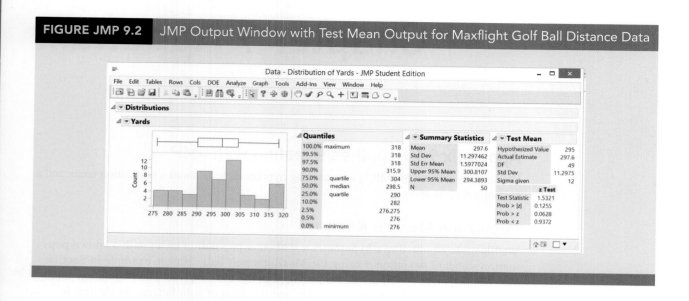

As Figure JMP 9.2 shows, the **Test Mean** area provides the results of our hypothesis test. In addition to providing the hypothesized mean ("Hypothesized Value"), sample mean ("Actual Estimate"), degrees of freedom ("DF"), and sample standard deviation ("Std Dev"), these results show that the calculated value of the test statistic is 1.5321. JMP also provides the *p*-values for two-tailed, lower tail, and upper tail tests.

- Prob |z| = .1255 is the *p*-value for H_0: $\mu = 295$ and H_a: $\mu \neq 295$
- Prob > z = .0628 is the *p*-value for H_0: $\mu \leq 295$ and H_a: $\mu > 295$
- Prob < z = .9372 is the *p*-value for H_0: $\mu \geq 295$ and H_a: $\mu < 295$

With these results, you can use either the *p*-value approach or the critical value approach to test the hypothesis H_0: $\mu = 295$ against H_a: $\mu \neq 295$.

Population Mean: σ Unknown

We illustrate interval estimation of the population mean with an unknown population standard deviation σ using the international airport ratings example in Section 9.4. The ratings that 60 travelers gave for Heathrow Airport are provided in the file *AirRating*. The level of significance for the test is $\alpha = .05$, and the population standard deviation σ will be estimated by the sample standard deviation *s*. The following steps can be used to test the hypothesis H_0: $\mu \leq 7$ against H_a: $\mu > 7$.

AirRating

Step 1. Open the file *AirRating* with JMP using the steps provided in Appendix 1.1

Step 2. Click the **Analyze** tab on the JMP Ribbon and select **Distribution**

Step 3. In the **Distribution** dialog box, drag **Rating** to the **Y, Columns** box
Click **OK** in the **Action** area

This produces an output window with several results that are located in the **Summary Statistics** area of the output window as shown in Figure JMP 9.3.

Step 4. Click on the red triangle ⬇ next to **Rating** and select **Test Mean**
Enter 7 into the **Specify Hypothesized Mean** box of the **Test Mean** dialog box
Click **OK**

As Figure JMP 9.4 displays, **Test Mean** mean contains the results of our hypothesis test. In addition to providing the hypothesized mean ("Hypothesized Value"), sample mean ("Actual Estimate"), degrees of freedom ("DF"), and sample standard deviation

FIGURE JMP 9.3 Output Generated by the Distribution Dialog Box for Airport Ratings Data in JMP

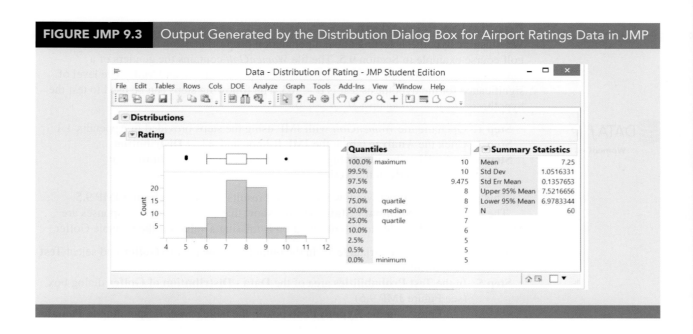

FIGURE JMP 9.4 JMP Output Window with Test Mean Output for Airport Ratings Data

("Std Dev"), these results show that the calculated value of the test statistic is 1.8414. JMP also provides the p-values for two-tailed, lower tail, and upper tail tests.

- Prob $> |t| = .0706$ is the p-value for $H_0: \mu = 7$ and $H_a: \mu \neq 7$
- Prob $> t = .0353$ is the p-value for $H_0: \mu \leq 7$ and $H_a: \mu > 7$
- Prob $< t = .9647$ is the p-value for $H_0: \mu \geq 7$ and $H_a: \mu < 7$

With these results, you can use either the p-value approach or the critical value approach to test the hypothesis $H_0: \mu \leq 7$ against $H_a: \mu > 7$.

Population Proportion

We illustrate hypothesis testing about a population proportion using the Pine Creek golf course example in Section 9.5. The file *WomenGolf* contains the genders of a random sample of 400 golfers at Pine Creek recorded as Female and Male. The level of significance for the hypothesis test is $\alpha = .05$. The following steps can be used to test the hypothesis $H_0: p \le .20$ against $H_a: p > .20$.

DATA *file*

WomenGolf

Step 1. Open the file *WomenGolf* with JMP using the steps provided in Appendix 1.1
Step 2. Click the **Analyze** tab on the JMP Ribbon and select **Distribution**
Step 3. In the **Distribution** dialog box, drag **Golfer** to the **Y, Columns** box
Click **OK** in the **Action** area

This produces an output window with several results as shown in Figure JMP 9.5.

The results in the **Summary Statistics** area show that 75% of the 400 responses are Male and 25% are Female, and no observation is missing a value for the variable Golfer.

Step 4. Click on the red triangle ▼ in the output window next to **Golfer** and select **Test Probabilities**
Step 5. In the **Test Probabilities** area of the **Data - Distribution of Golfer** dialog box (see Figure JMP 9.6)
Enter *.2* in the **Hypoth Prob** box in the table row corresponding to **Female**
Click on **probability greater than hypothesized value (exact one-sided binomial test)** to indicate this is an upper-tailed hypothesis test
Click **Done**

This produces a new JMP output window that includes the results of test of the hypothesis $H_0: p \le .20$ against $H_a: p > .20$ (Figure JMP 9.7).

The *p*-value for this test is .0086, which differs slightly from the *p*-value of .0062 we found in section 9.5. This is because the test we used in section 9.5 is based on a normal approximation (which is much easier to calculate), and the test used by JMP is the exact binomial test (which is best performed by a computer). As the sample size increases, the results of the normal approximation test used in section 9.5 will better approximate the exact binomial test used by JMP.

FIGURE JMP 9.5	Output Generated by the Distribution Dialog Box for Gender of Golfers Data in JMP

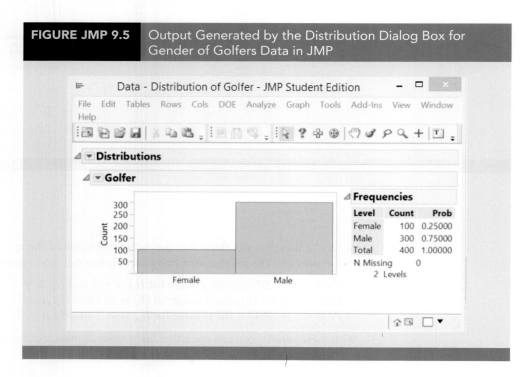

FIGURE JMP 9.6   JMP Data Dialog Box with Test Probabilities Area Open for Gender of Golfers Data

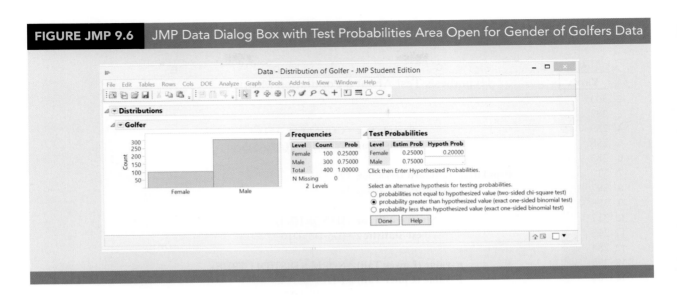

FIGURE JMP 9.7   JMP Data Dialog Box with Hypothesis Test Results for Gender of Golfers Data

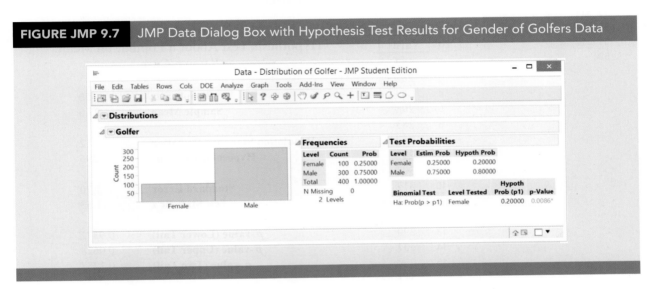

Appendix 9.2 Hypothesis Testing with Excel

Excel does not provide built-in routines for the hypothesis tests presented in this chapter. To handle these situations, we present Excel worksheets that we designed to use as templates for testing hypotheses about a population mean and a population proportion. The worksheets are easy to use and can be modified to handle any sample data. The worksheets are available on the website that accompanies this book.

Population Mean: σ Known

We illustrate using the MaxFlight golf ball distance example in Section 9.3. The data are in column A of an Excel worksheet in the file *HypSigmaKnown*. The population standard deviation $\sigma = 12$ is assumed known and the level of significance is $\alpha = .05$. The following steps can be used to test the hypothesis $H_0: \mu = 295$ versus $H_a: \mu \neq 295$.

Refer to Figure Excel 9.1 as we describe the procedure. The worksheet in the background shows the cell formulas used to compute the results shown in the foreground worksheet. The data are entered into cells A2:A51. The following steps are necessary to use the template for this data set.

FIGURE Excel 9.1   Excel Worksheet for Hypothesis Tests About a Population Mean with σ Known

	A	B	C	D	E
1	**Yards**		Hypothesis Test About a Population Mean:		
2	303		σ Known Case		
3	282				
4	289		Sample Size	=COUNT(A2:A51)	
5	298		Sample Mean	=AVERAGE(A2:A51)	
6	283				
7	317		Population Standard Deviation	12	
8	297		Hypothesized Value	295	
9	308				
10	317		Standard Error	=D7/SQRT(D4)	
11	293		Test Statistic z	=(D5-D8)/D10	
12	284				
13	290		p-value (Lower Tail)	=NORM.S.DIST(D11,TRUE)	
14	304		p-value (Upper Tail)	=1-D13	
15	290		p-value (Two Tail)	=2*(MIN(D13,D14))	
16	311				
50	301				
51	292				
52					

	A	B	C	D	E
1	**Yards**		Hypothesis Test About a Population Mean:		
2	303		σ Known Case		
3	282				
4	289		Sample Size	50	
5	298		Sample Mean	297.6	
6	283				
7	317		Population Standard Deviation	12	
8	297		Hypothesized Value	295	
9	308				
10	317		Standard Error	1.70	
11	293		Test Statistic z	1.53	
12	284				
13	290		p-value (Lower Tail)	0.9372	
14	304		p-value (Upper Tail)	0.0628	
15	290		p-value (Two Tail)	0.1255	
16	311				
50	301				
51	292				
52					

Note: Rows 17 to 49 are hidden.

DATA *file*

HypSigmaKnown

Step 1. Enter the formula $=COUNT(A2:A51)$ in cell D4 to calculate the Sample Size
Step 2. Enter the formula $=AVERAGE(A2:A51)$ in cell D5 to calculate the Sample Mean
Step 3. Enter the population standard deviation $\sigma = 12$ in cell D7
Step 4. Enter the hypothesized value for the population mean *295* in cell D8

The remaining cell formulas automatically provide the standard error (cell D10), the value of the test statistic z (cell D11), and three p-values (cells D13 through D15). Because the alternative hypothesis ($\mu_0 \neq 295$) indicates a two-tailed test, the p-value (Two Tail) in cell D15 is used to make the rejection decision. With p-value $= .1255 > \alpha = .05$, the null hypothesis cannot be rejected. The p-values in cells D13 or D14 would be used if the hypotheses involved a one-tailed test.

This template can be used to make hypothesis testing computations for other applications. For instance, to conduct a hypothesis test for a new data set, enter the new sample data into column A of the worksheet. Modify the formulas in cells D4 and D5 to correspond to the new data range. Enter the population standard deviation in cell D7 and the hypothesized value for the population mean in cell D8 to obtain the results. If the new sample data have already been summarized, the new sample data do not have to be entered into the worksheet. In this case, enter the sample size in cell D4, the sample mean in cell D5, the population standard deviation in cell D7, and the hypothesized value for the population mean in cell D8 to obtain the results.

Population Mean: σ Unknown

We illustrate using the Heathrow Airport rating example in Section 9.4. The data are in column A of an Excel worksheet in the file *HypSigmaUnknown*. The population standard deviation σ is unknown and will be estimated by the sample standard deviation s. The level of significance is $\alpha = .05$. The following steps can be used to test the hypothesis $H_0: \mu \leq 7$ versus $H_a: \mu > 7$.

Refer to Figure Excel 9.2 as we describe the procedure. The background worksheet shows the cell formulas used to compute the results shown in the foreground version of the worksheet. The data are entered into cells A2:A61. The following steps are necessary to use the template for this data set.

HypSigmaUnknown

Step 1. Enter the formula =*COUNT(A2:A61)* in cell D4 to calculate the Sample Size
Step 2. Enter the formula =*AVERAGE(A2:A61)* in cell D5 to calculate the Sample Mean
Step 3. Enter the formula =*STDEV.S(A2:A61)* in cell D6 to calculate the Sample Standard Deviation
Step 4. Enter the hypothesized value for the population mean *7* into cell D8

The remaining cell formulas automatically provide the standard error (cell D10), the value of the test statistic t (cell D11), the number of degrees of freedom (cell D12), and three *p*-values (cells D14 through D16). Because the alternative hypothesis ($\mu > 7$) indicates an upper tail test, the *p*-value (Upper Tail) in cell D15 is used to make the decision. With *p*-value $= .0353 < \alpha = .05$, the null hypothesis is rejected. The *p*-values in cells D14 or D16 would be used if the hypotheses involved a lower tail test or a two-tailed test.

This template can be used to make hypothesis testing computations for other applications. For instance, to conduct a hypothesis test for a new data set, enter the new sample data into column A of the worksheet and modify the formulas in cells D4, D5, and D6 to correspond to the new data range. Enter the hypothesized value for the population mean in cell D8 to obtain the results. If the new sample data have already been summarized, the new sample data do not have to be entered into the worksheet. In this case, enter the sample size in cell D4, the sample mean in cell D5, the sample standard deviation in cell D6, and the hypothesized value for the population mean in cell D8 to obtain the results.

Population Proportion

We illustrate using the Pine Creek golf course survey data presented in Section 9.5. The data of Male or Female golfer are in column A of an Excel worksheet in the file *HypothsisProp*. Refer to Figure Excel 9.3 as we describe the procedure. The background worksheet shows the cell formulas used to compute the results shown in the foreground worksheet. The data are entered into cells A2:A401. The following steps can be used to test the hypothesis $H_0: p \leq .20$ versus $H_a: p > .20$.

HypothesisProp

Step 1. Enter the formula =*COUNTA(A2:A401)* in cell D3 to calculate the Sample Size
Step 2. Enter *Female* as the response of interest in cell D4
Step 3. Enter the formula =COUNTIF(A2:A401) in cell D5 to count the number of positive responses
Step 4. Enter the hypothesized value for the population proportion *.20* in cell D8

FIGURE Excel 9.2 Excel Worksheet for Hypothesis Tests About a Population Mean with σ Unknown

	A	B	C	D	E
1	**Rating**		**Hypothesis Test About a Population Mean**		
2	5		**With σ Unknown**		
3	7				
4	8		Sample Size	=COUNT(A2:A61)	
5	7		Sample Mean	=AVERAGE(A2:A61)	
6	8		Sample Std. Deviation	=STDEV.S(A2:A61)	
7	8				
8	8		Hypothesized Value	7	
9	7				
10	8		Standard Error	=D6/SQRT(D4)	
11	10		Test Statistic *t*	=(D5-D8)/D10	
12	6		Degrees of Freedom	=D4-1	
13	7				
14	8		*p*-value (Lower Tail)	=T.DIST(D11,D12,TRUE)	
15	8		*p*-value (Upper Tail)	=1-D14	
16	9		*p*-value (Two Tail)	=2*(MIN(D14,D15))	
17	7				
59	7				
60	7				
61	8				
62					

Note: Rows 18 to 58 are hidden.

	A	B	C	D	E	F
1	**Rating**		**Hypothesis Test About a Population Mean**			
2	5		**With σ Unknown**			
3	7					
4	8		Sample Size	60		
5	7		Sample Mean	7.25		
6	8		Sample Std. Deviation	1.05		
7	8					
8	8		Hypothesized Value	7		
9	7					
10	8		Standard Error	0.136		
11	10		Test Statistic *t*	1.841		
12	6		Degrees of Freedom	59		
13	7					
14	8		*p*-value (Lower Tail)	0.9647		
15	8		*p*-value (Upper Tail)	0.0353		
16	9		*p*-value (Two Tail)	0.0706		
17	7					
59	7					
60	7					
61	8					
62						

The remaining cell formulas automatically provide the standard error (cell D10), the value of the test statistic z (cell D11), and three p-values (cells D13 through D15). Because the alternative hypothesis ($p > .20$) indicates an upper tail test, the p-value (Upper Tail) in cell D14 is used to make the decision. With p-value $= .0062 < \alpha = .05$, the null hypothesis is rejected. The p-values in cells D13 or D15 would be used if the hypothesis involved a lower tail test or a two-tailed test.

This template can be used to make hypothesis testing computations for other applications. For instance, to conduct a hypothesis test for a new data set, enter the new

FIGURE Excel 9.3   Excel Worksheet for Hypothesis Tests About a Population Proportion

	A	B	C	D	E
1	**Golfer**		\multicolumn{2}{c}{Hypothesis Test About a Population Proportion}	
2	Female				
3	Male		**Sample Size**	=COUNTA(A2:A401)	
4	Female		**Response of Interest**	Female	
5	Male		**Count for Response**	=COUNTIF(A2:A903,D4)	
6	Male		**Sample Proportion**	=D5/D3	
7	Female				
8	Male		**Hypothesized Value**	0.2	
9	Male				
10	Female		**Standard Error**	=SQRT(D8*(1-D8)/D3)	
11	Male		**Test Statistic z**	=(D6-D8)/D10	
12	Male				
13	Male		p-**value (Lower Tail)**	=NORM.S.DIST(D11,TRUE)	
14	Male		p-**value (Upper Tail)**	=1-D13	
15	Male		p-**value (TwoTail)**	=2*MIN(D13,D14)	
16	Female				
400	Male				
401	Male				
402					

	A	B	C	D	E	F
1	**Golfer**		\multicolumn{3}{c}{Hypothesis Test About a Population Proportion}	
2	Female					
3	Male		**Sample Size**	400		
4	Female		**Response of Interest**	Female		
5	Male		**Count for Response**	100		
6	Male		**Sample Proportion**	0.25		
7	Female					
8	Male		**Hypothesized Value**	0.20		
9	Male					
10	Female		**Standard Error**	0.02		
11	Male		**Test Statistic z**	2.5000		
12	Male					
13	Male		p-**value (Lower Tail)**	0.9938		
14	Male		p-**value (Upper Tail)**	0.0062		
15	Male		p-**value (TwoTail)**	0.0124		
16	Female					
400	Male					
401	Male					
402						

Note: Rows 17 to 399 are hidden.

sample data into column A of the worksheet. Modify the formulas in cells D3 and D5 to correspond to the new data range. Enter the response of interest in cell D4 and the hypothesized value for the population proportion in cell D8 to obtain the results. If the new sample data have already been summarized, the new sample data do not have to be entered into the worksheet. In this case, enter the sample size in cell D3, the sample proportion in cell D6, and the hypothesized value for the population proportion in cell D8 to obtain the results.

Chapter 10

Inference About Means and Proportions with Two Populations

STATISTICS IN PRACTICE

U.S. Food and Drug Administration

WASHINGTON, D.C.

It is the responsibility of the U.S. Food and Drug Administration (FDA), through its Center for Drug Evaluation and Research (CDER), to ensure that drugs are safe and effective. But CDER does not do the actual testing of new drugs itself. It is the responsibility of the company seeking to market a new drug to test it and submit evidence that it is safe and effective. CDER statisticians and scientists then review the evidence submitted.

Companies seeking approval of a new drug conduct extensive statistical studies to support their application. The testing process in the pharmaceutical industry usually consists of three stages: (1) preclinical testing, (2) testing for long-term usage and safety, and (3) clinical efficacy testing. At each successive stage, the chance that a drug will pass the rigorous tests decreases; however, the cost of further testing increases dramatically. Industry surveys indicate that on average the research and development for one new drug costs $250 million and takes 12 years. Hence, it is important to eliminate unsuccessful new drugs in the early stages of the testing process, as well as to identify promising ones for further testing.

Statistics plays a major role in pharmaceutical research, where government regulations are stringent and rigorously enforced. In preclinical testing, a two- or three-population statistical study typically is used to determine whether a new drug should continue to be studied in the long-term usage and safety program. The populations may consist of the new drug, a control, and a standard drug. The preclinical testing process begins when a new drug is sent to the pharmacology group for evaluation of efficacy—the capacity of the drug to produce the desired effects. As part of the process, a statistician is asked to design an experiment that can be used to test the new drug. The design must specify the sample size and the statistical methods of analysis. In a two-population study, one sample is used to obtain data on the efficacy of the new drug (population 1) and a second sample is used to obtain data on the efficacy of a standard drug (population 2). Depending on the

Statistical methods are used to test and develop new drugs. Source: Lisa S./Shutterstock.com

intended use, the new and standard drugs are tested in such disciplines as neurology, cardiology, and immunology. In most studies, the statistical method involves hypothesis testing for the difference between the means of the new drug population and the standard drug population. If a new drug lacks efficacy or produces undesirable effects in comparison with the standard drug, the new drug is rejected and withdrawn from further testing. Only new drugs that show promising comparisons with the standard drugs are forwarded to the long-term usage and safety testing program.

Further data collection and multipopulation studies are conducted in the long-term usage and safety testing program and in the clinical testing programs. The FDA requires that statistical methods be defined prior to such testing to avoid data-related biases. In addition, to avoid human biases, some of the clinical trials are double or triple blind. That is, neither the subject nor the investigator knows what drug is administered to whom. If the new drug meets all requirements in relation to the standard drug, a new drug application (NDA) is filed with the FDA. The application is rigorously scrutinized by statisticians and scientists at the agency.

In this chapter you will learn how to construct interval estimates and make hypothesis tests about means and proportions with two populations. Techniques will be presented for analyzing independent random samples as well as matched samples.

In Chapters 8 and 9 we showed how to develop interval estimates and conduct hypothesis tests for situations involving a single population mean and a single population proportion.

In this chapter, we extend the discussion of statistical inference beyond single sample analyses of a population mean or population proportion by showing how interval estimates and hypothesis tests can be developed for situations involving two populations when the difference between the two population means or the two population proportions is of prime importance. For example, we may want to develop an interval estimate of the difference between the mean starting salary for a population of men and the mean starting salary for a population of women or conduct a hypothesis test to determine whether any difference is present between the proportion of defective parts in a population of parts produced by supplier A and the proportion of defective parts in a population of parts produced by supplier B. We begin our discussion of statistical inference about two populations by showing how to develop interval estimates and conduct hypothesis tests about the difference between the means of two populations when the standard deviations of the two populations are assumed known.

10.1 Inferences About the Difference Between Two Population Means: σ_1 and σ_2 Known

Letting μ_1 denote the mean of population 1 and μ_2 denote the mean of population 2, we will focus on inferences about the difference between the means: $\mu_1 - \mu_2$. To make an inference about this difference, we select a simple random sample of n_1 units from population 1 and a second simple random sample of n_2 units from population 2. The two samples, taken separately and independently, are referred to as **independent simple random samples**. In this section, we assume that information is available such that the two population standard deviations, σ_1 and σ_2, can be assumed known prior to collecting the samples. We refer to this situation as the σ_1 and σ_2 known case. In the following example we show how to compute a margin of error and develop an interval estimate of the difference between the two population means when σ_1 and σ_2 are known.

Interval Estimation of $\mu_1 - \mu_2$

Greystone Department Stores, Inc., operates two stores in Buffalo, New York: One is in the inner city and the other is in a suburban shopping center. The regional manager noticed that products that sell well in one store do not always sell well in the other. The manager believes this situation may be attributable to differences in customer demographics at the two locations. Customers may differ in age, education, income, and so on. Suppose the manager asks us to investigate the difference between the mean ages of the customers who shop at the two stores.

Let us define population 1 as all customers who shop at the inner-city store and population 2 as all customers who shop at the suburban store.

μ_1 = mean of population 1 (i.e., the mean age of all customers who shop at the inner-city store)

μ_2 = mean of population 2 (i.e., the mean age of all customers who shop at the suburban store)

The difference between the two population means is $\mu_1 - \mu_2$.

To estimate $\mu_1 - \mu_2$, we will select a simple random sample of n_1 customers from population 1 and a simple random sample of n_2 customers from population 2. We then compute the two sample means.

$\bar{x}_1$ = sample mean age for the simple random sample of n_1 inner-city customers

$\bar{x}_2$ = sample mean age for the simple random sample of n_2 suburban customers

The point estimator of the difference between the two population means is the difference between the two sample means.

POINT ESTIMATOR OF THE DIFFERENCE BETWEEN TWO POPULATION MEANS

$$\bar{x}_1 - \bar{x}_2 \tag{10.1}$$

Figure 10.1 provides an overview of the process used to estimate the difference between two population means based on two independent simple random samples.

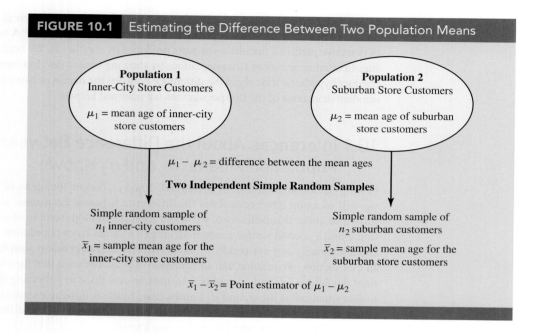

FIGURE 10.1 Estimating the Difference Between Two Population Means

The standard error of $\bar{x}_1 - \bar{x}_2$ is the standard deviation of the sampling distribution of $\bar{x}_1 - \bar{x}_2$.

As with other point estimators, the point estimator $\bar{x}_1 - \bar{x}_2$ has a standard error that describes the variation in the sampling distribution of the estimator. With two independent simple random samples, the standard error of $\bar{x}_1 - \bar{x}_2$ is as follows:

STANDARD ERROR OF $\bar{x}_1 - \bar{x}_2$

$$\sigma_{\bar{x}_1 - \bar{x}_2} = \sqrt{\frac{\sigma_1^2}{n_1} + \frac{\sigma_2^2}{n_2}} \qquad (10.2)$$

If both populations have a normal distribution, or if the sample sizes are large enough that the central limit theorem enables us to conclude that the sampling distributions of $\bar{x}_1$ and $\bar{x}_2$ can be approximated by a normal distribution, the sampling distribution of $\bar{x}_1 - \bar{x}_2$ will have a normal distribution with mean given by $\mu_1 - \mu_2$.

In general, an interval estimate is given by a point estimate ± a margin of error. In the case of estimation of the difference between two population means, an interval estimate will take the following form:

$$\bar{x}_1 - \bar{x}_2 \pm \text{Margin of error}$$

With the sampling distribution of $\bar{x}_1 - \bar{x}_2$ having a normal distribution, we can write the margin of error as follows:

The margin of error is given by multiplying the standard error by $z_{\alpha/2}$.

$$\text{Margin of error} = z_{\alpha/2}\,\sigma_{\bar{x}_1 - \bar{x}_2} = z_{\alpha/2}\sqrt{\frac{\sigma_1^2}{n_1} + \frac{\sigma_2^2}{n_2}} \qquad (10.3)$$

Thus the interval estimate of the difference between two population means is as follows:

INTERVAL ESTIMATE OF THE DIFFERENCE BETWEEN TWO POPULATION MEANS: σ_1 AND σ_2 KNOWN

$$\bar{x}_1 - \bar{x}_2 \pm z_{\alpha/2}\sqrt{\frac{\sigma_1^2}{n_1} + \frac{\sigma_2^2}{n_2}} \qquad (10.4)$$

where $1 - \alpha$ is the confidence coefficient.

Let us return to the Greystone example. Based on data from previous customer demographic studies, the two population standard deviations are known with $\sigma_1 = 9$ years and $\sigma_2 = 10$ years. The data collected from the two independent simple random samples of Greystone customers provided the following results.

	Inner City Store	Suburban Store
Sample Size	$n_1 = 36$	$n_2 = 49$
Sample Mean	$\bar{x}_1 = 40$ years	$\bar{x}_2 = 35$ years

Using expression (10.1), we find that the point estimate of the difference between the mean ages of the two populations is $\bar{x}_1 - \bar{x}_2 = 40 - 35 = 5$ years. Thus, we estimate that the customers at the inner-city store have a mean age five years greater than the mean age of the suburban store customers. We can now use expression (10.4) to compute the margin of error and provide the interval estimate of $\mu_1 - \mu_2$. Using 95% confidence and $z_{\alpha/2} = z_{.025} = 1.96$, we have

$$\bar{x}_1 - \bar{x}_2 \pm z_{\alpha/2} \sqrt{\frac{\sigma_1^2}{n_1} + \frac{\sigma_2^2}{n_2}}$$

$$40 - 35 \pm 1.96 \sqrt{\frac{9^2}{36} + \frac{10^2}{49}}$$

$$5 \pm 4.06$$

Thus, the margin of error is 4.06 years and the 95% confidence interval estimate of the difference between the two population means is $5 - 4.06 = .94$ years to $5 + 4.06 = 9.06$ years.

Hypothesis Tests About $\mu_1 - \mu_2$

Let us consider hypothesis tests about the difference between two population means. Using D_0 to denote the hypothesized difference between μ_1 and μ_2, the three forms for a hypothesis test are as follows:

$$H_0: \mu_1 - \mu_2 \geq D_0 \qquad H_0: \mu_1 - \mu_2 \leq D_0 \qquad H_0: \mu_1 - \mu_2 = D_0$$
$$H_a: \mu_1 - \mu_2 < D_0 \qquad H_a: \mu_1 - \mu_2 > D_0 \qquad H_a: \mu_1 - \mu_2 \neq D_0$$

In many applications, $D_0 = 0$. Using the two-tailed test as an example, when $D_0 = 0$ the null hypothesis is $H_0: \mu_1 - \mu_2 = 0$. In this case, the null hypothesis is that μ_1 and μ_2 are equal. Rejection of H_0 leads to the conclusion that $H_a: \mu_1 - \mu_2 \neq 0$ is true; that is, μ_1 and μ_2 are not equal.

Chapter 9 introduces the general steps for hypothesis testing for a single population mean and single population proportion.

The general steps for conducting hypothesis tests are still applicable here. We must choose a level of significance, compute the value of the test statistic, and find the p-value to determine whether the null hypothesis should be rejected. With two independent simple random samples, we showed that the point estimator $\bar{x}_1 - \bar{x}_2$ has a standard error $\sigma_{\bar{x}_1 - \bar{x}_2}$ given by expression (10.2) and, when the sample sizes are large enough, the distribution of $\bar{x}_1 - \bar{x}_2$ can be described by a normal distribution. In this case, the test statistic for the difference between two population means when σ_1 and σ_2 are known is as follows.

TEST STATISTIC FOR HYPOTHESIS TESTS ABOUT $\mu_1 - \mu_2$: σ_1 AND σ_2 KNOWN

$$z = \frac{(\bar{x}_1 - \bar{x}_2) - D_0}{\sqrt{\dfrac{\sigma_1^2}{n_1} + \dfrac{\sigma_2^2}{n_2}}} \tag{10.5}$$

Let us demonstrate the use of this test statistic in the following hypothesis testing example.

As part of a study to evaluate differences in education quality between two training centers, a standardized examination is given to individuals who are trained at the centers. The difference between the mean examination scores is used to assess quality differences between the centers. The population means for the two centers are as follows.

$$\mu_1 = \text{the mean examination score for the population}$$
$$\text{of individuals trained at center A}$$

$$\mu_2 = \text{the mean examination score for the population}$$
$$\text{of individuals trained at center B}$$

We begin with the tentative assumption that no difference exists between the training quality provided at the two centers. Hence, in terms of the mean examination scores, the null hypothesis is that $\mu_1 - \mu_2 = 0$. If sample evidence leads to the rejection of this hypothesis, we will conclude that the mean examination scores differ for the two populations. This conclusion indicates a quality differential between the two centers and suggests that a follow-up study investigating the reason for the differential may be warranted. The null and alternative hypotheses for this two-tailed test are written as follows.

$$H_0: \mu_1 - \mu_2 = 0$$
$$H_a: \mu_1 - \mu_2 \neq 0$$

The standardized examination given previously in a variety of settings always resulted in an examination score standard deviation near 10 points. Thus, we will use this information to assume that the population standard deviations are known with $\sigma_1 = 10$ and $\sigma_2 = 10$. An $\alpha = .05$ level of significance is specified for the study.

DATA *file*

ExamScores

Independent simple random samples of $n_1 = 30$ individuals from training center A and $n_2 = 40$ individuals from training center B are taken. The respective sample means are $\bar{x}_1 = 82$ and $\bar{x}_2 = 78$. Do these data suggest a significant difference between the population means at the two training centers? To help answer this question, we compute the test statistic using equation (10.5).

$$z = \frac{(\bar{x}_1 - \bar{x}_2) - D_0}{\sqrt{\dfrac{\sigma_1^2}{n_1} + \dfrac{\sigma_2^2}{n_2}}} = \frac{(82 - 78) - 0}{\sqrt{\dfrac{10^2}{30} + \dfrac{10^2}{40}}} = 1.66$$

Next let us compute the *p*-value for this two-tailed test. Because the test statistic z is in the upper tail, we first compute the area under the curve to the right of $z = 1.66$. Using the standard normal distribution table, the area to the left of $z = 1.66$ is .9515. Thus, the area in the upper tail of the distribution is $1.0000 - .9515 = .0485$. Because this test is a two-tailed test, we must double the tail area: *p*-value $= 2(.0485) = .0970$. Following the usual rule to reject H_0 if *p*-value $\leq \alpha$, we see that the *p*-value of .0970 does not allow us to reject H_0 at the .05 level of significance. The sample results do not provide sufficient evidence to conclude the training centers differ in quality.

In this chapter we will use the *p*-value approach to hypothesis testing. However, if you prefer, the test statistic and the critical value rejection rule may be used. With $\alpha = .05$ and $z_{\alpha/2} = z_{.025} = 1.96$, the rejection rule employing the critical value approach would be reject H_0 if $z \leq -1.96$ or if $z \geq 1.96$. With $z = 1.66$, we reach the same do not reject H_0 conclusion.

In the preceding example, we demonstrated a two-tailed hypothesis test about the difference between two population means. Lower tail and upper tail tests can also be considered. These tests use the same test statistic as given in equation (10.5). The procedure for computing the *p*-value and the rejection rules for these one-tailed tests are the same as those for hypothesis tests involving a single population mean and single population proportion.

Practical Advice

In most applications of the interval estimation and hypothesis testing procedures presented in this section, random samples with $n_1 \geq 30$ and $n_2 \geq 30$ are adequate. In cases where either or both sample sizes are less than 30, the distributions of the populations become important considerations. In general, with smaller sample sizes, it is more important for the analyst to be satisfied that it is reasonable to assume that the distributions of the two populations are at least approximately normal.

EXERCISES

Methods

1. The following results come from two independent random samples taken of two populations.

Sample 1	Sample 2
$n_1 = 50$	$n_2 = 35$
$\bar{x}_1 = 13.6$	$\bar{x}_2 = 11.6$
$\sigma_1 = 2.2$	$\sigma_2 = 3.0$

   a. What is the point estimate of the difference between the two population means?
   b. Provide a 90% confidence interval for the difference between the two population means.
   c. Provide a 95% confidence interval for the difference between the two population means.

2. Consider the following hypothesis test.

$$H_0: \mu_1 - \mu_2 \leq 0$$
$$H_a: \mu_1 - \mu_2 > 0$$

   The following results are for two independent samples taken from the two populations.

Sample 1	Sample 2
$n_1 = 40$	$n_2 = 50$
$\bar{x}_1 = 25.2$	$\bar{x}_2 = 22.8$
$\sigma_1 = 5.2$	$\sigma_2 = 6.0$

   a. What is the value of the test statistic?
   b. What is the p-value?
   c. With $\alpha = .05$, what is your hypothesis testing conclusion?

3. Consider the following hypothesis test.

$$H_0: \mu_1 - \mu_2 = 0$$
$$H_a: \mu_1 - \mu_2 \neq 0$$

   The following results are for two independent samples taken from the two populations.

Sample 1	Sample 2
$n_1 = 80$	$n_2 = 70$
$\bar{x}_1 = 104$	$\bar{x}_2 = 106$
$\sigma_1 = 8.4$	$\sigma_2 = 7.6$

a. What is the value of the test statistic?

b. What is the p-value?

c. With $\alpha = .05$, what is your hypothesis testing conclusion?

Applications

4. **Cruise Ship Ratings.** *Condé Nast Traveler* conducts an annual survey in which readers rate their favorite cruise ship. All ships are rated on a 100-point scale, with higher values indicating better service. A sample of 37 ships that carry fewer than 500 passengers resulted in an average rating of 85.36, and a sample of 44 ships that carry 500 or more passengers provided an average rating of 81.40. Assume that the population standard deviation is 4.55 for ships that carry fewer than 500 passengers and 3.97 for ships that carry 500 or more passengers.

   a. What is the point estimate of the difference between the population mean rating for ships that carry fewer than 500 passengers and the population mean rating for ships that carry 500 or more passengers?

   b. At 95% confidence, what is the margin of error?

   c. What is a 95% confidence interval estimate of the difference between the population mean ratings for the two sizes of ships?

5. **Valentine's Day Expenditures.** *USA Today* reports that the average expenditure on Valentine's Day is $100.89. Do male and female consumers differ in the amounts they spend? The average expenditure in a sample survey of 40 male consumers was $135.67, and the average expenditure in a sample survey of 30 female consumers was $68.64. Based on past surveys, the standard deviation for male consumers is assumed to be $35, and the standard deviation for female consumers is assumed to be $20.

   a. What is the point estimate of the difference between the population mean expenditure for males and the population mean expenditure for females?

   b. At 99% confidence, what is the margin of error?

   c. Develop a 99% confidence interval for the difference between the two population means.

6. **Hotel Price Comparison.** Suppose that you are responsible for making arrangements for a business convention and that you have been charged with choosing a city for the convention that has the least expensive hotel rooms. You have narrowed your choices to Atlanta and Houston. The file named *Hotel* contains samples of prices for rooms in Atlanta and Houston that are consistent with a *SmartMoney* survey conducted by Smith Travel Research. Because considerable historical data on the prices of rooms in both cities are available, the population standard deviations for the prices can be assumed to be $20 in Atlanta and $25 in Houston. Based on the sample data, can you conclude that the mean price of a hotel room in Atlanta is lower than one in Houston?

DATA *file*

Hotel

7. **Supermarket Customer Satisfaction.** *Consumer Reports* uses a survey of readers to obtain customer satisfaction ratings for the nation's largest supermarkets (*Consumer Reports*, https://www.consumerreports.org/products/grocery-stores-supermarkets/ratings-overview/). Each survey respondent is asked to rate a specified supermarket based on a variety of factors such as: quality of products, selection, value, checkout efficiency, service, and store layout. An overall satisfaction score summarizes the rating for each respondent with 100 meaning the respondent is completely satisfied in terms of all factors. Sample data representative of independent samples of Publix and Trader Joe's customers are shown below.

Publix	Trader Joe's
$n_1 = 250$	$n_2 = 300$
$\bar{x}_1 = 86$	$\bar{x}_2 = 85$

   a. Formulate the null and alternative hypotheses to test whether there is a difference between the population mean customer satisfaction scores for the two retailers.

b. Assume that experience with the *Consumer Reports* satisfaction rating scale indicates that a population standard deviation of 12 is a reasonable assumption for both retailers. Conduct the hypothesis test and report the *p*-value. At a .05 level of significance what is your conclusion?

c. Which retailer, if either, appears to have the greater customer satisfaction? Provide a 95% confidence interval for the difference between the population mean customer satisfaction scores for the two retailers.

8. **Increases in Customer Satisfaction.** Will improving customer service result in higher stock prices for the companies providing the better service? "When a company's satisfaction score has improved over the prior year's results and is above the national average (75.7), studies show its shares have a good chance of outperforming the broad stock market in the long run." The following satisfaction scores of three companies for the 4th quarters of two previous years were obtained from the American Customer Satisfaction Index. Assume that the scores are based on a poll of 60 customers from each company. Because the polling has been done for several years, the standard deviation can be assumed to equal 6 points in each case.

Company	Year 1	Year 2
Rite Aid	73	76
Expedia	75	77
J.C. Penney	77	78

a. For Rite Aid, is the increase in the satisfaction score from year 1 to year 2 statistically significant? Use $\alpha = .05$. What can you conclude?

b. Can you conclude that the year 2 score for Rite Aid is above the national average of 75.7? Use $\alpha = .05$.

c. For Expedia, is the increase from year 1 to year 2 statistically significant? Use $\alpha = .05$.

d. When conducting a hypothesis test with the values given for the standard deviation, sample size, and α, how large must the increase from year 1 to year 2 be for it to be statistically significant?

e. Use the result of part (d) to state whether the increase for J.C. Penney from year 1 to year 2 is statistically significant.

10.2 Inferences About the Difference Between Two Population Means: σ_1 and σ_2 Unknown

In this section we extend the discussion of inferences about the difference between two population means to the case when the two population standard deviations, σ_1 and σ_2, are unknown. In this case, we will use the sample standard deviations, s_1 and s_2, to estimate the unknown population standard deviations. When we use the sample standard deviations, the interval estimation and hypothesis testing procedures will be based on the *t* distribution rather than the standard normal distribution.

Interval Estimation of $\mu_1 - \mu_2$

In the following example we show how to compute a margin of error and develop an interval estimate of the difference between two population means when σ_1 and σ_2 are unknown. Clearwater National Bank is conducting a study designed to identify differences between checking account practices by customers at two of its branch banks. A simple random sample of 28 checking accounts is selected from the Cherry Grove Branch and an independent simple random sample of 22 checking accounts is selected from the Beechmont Branch. The current checking account balance is recorded for each of the checking accounts. A summary of the account balances follows:

DATA *file*

CheckAcct

	Cherry Grove	Beechmont
Sample Size	$n_1 = 28$	$n_2 = 22$
Sample Mean	$\bar{x}_1 = \$1025$	$\bar{x}_2 = \$910$
Sample Standard Deviation	$s_1 = \$150$	$s_2 = \$125$

Clearwater National Bank would like to estimate the difference between the mean checking account balance maintained by the population of Cherry Grove customers and the population of Beechmont customers. Let us develop the margin of error and an interval estimate of the difference between these two population means.

In Section 10.1, we provided the following interval estimate for the case when the population standard deviations, σ_1 and σ_2, are known.

$$\bar{x}_1 - \bar{x}_2 \pm z_{\alpha/2}\sqrt{\frac{\sigma_1^2}{n_1} + \frac{\sigma_2^2}{n_2}}$$

When σ_1 and σ_2 are estimated by s_1 and s_2, the t distribution is used to make inferences about the difference between two population means.

With σ_1 and σ_2 unknown, we will use the sample standard deviations s_1 and s_2 to estimate σ_1 and σ_2 and replace $z_{\alpha/2}$ with $t_{\alpha/2}$. As a result, the interval estimate of the difference between two population means is given by the following expression:

INTERVAL ESTIMATE OF THE DIFFERENCE BETWEEN TWO POPULATION MEANS: σ_1 AND σ_2 UNKNOWN

$$\bar{x}_1 - \bar{x}_2 \pm t_{\alpha/2}\sqrt{\frac{s_1^2}{n_1} + \frac{s_2^2}{n_2}} \tag{10.6}$$

where $1 - \alpha$ is the confidence coefficient.

In this expression, the use of the t distribution is an approximation, but it provides excellent results and is relatively easy to use. The only difficulty that we encounter in using expression (10.6) is determining the appropriate degrees of freedom for $t_{\alpha/2}$. Statistical software packages compute the appropriate degrees of freedom automatically. The formula used is as follows:

DEGREES OF FREEDOM: t DISTRIBUTION WITH TWO INDEPENDENT RANDOM SAMPLES

$$df = \frac{\left(\dfrac{s_1^2}{n_1} + \dfrac{s_2^2}{n_2}\right)^2}{\dfrac{1}{n_1 - 1}\left(\dfrac{s_1^2}{n_1}\right)^2 + \dfrac{1}{n_2 - 1}\left(\dfrac{s_2^2}{n_2}\right)^2} \tag{10.7}$$

Let us return to the Clearwater National Bank example and show how to use expression (10.6) to provide a 95% confidence interval estimate of the difference between the population mean checking account balances at the two branch banks. The sample data show $n_1 = 28$, $\bar{x}_1 = \$1025$, and $s_1 = \$150$ for the Cherry Grove branch, and $n_2 = 22$, $\bar{x}_2 = \$910$, and $s_2 = \$125$ for the Beechmont branch. The calculation for degrees of freedom for $t_{\alpha/2}$ is as follows:

$$df = \frac{\left(\dfrac{s_1^2}{n_1} + \dfrac{s_2^2}{n_2}\right)^2}{\dfrac{1}{n_1 - 1}\left(\dfrac{s_1^2}{n_1}\right)^2 + \dfrac{1}{n_2 - 1}\left(\dfrac{s_2^2}{n_2}\right)^2} = \frac{\left(\dfrac{150^2}{28} + \dfrac{125^2}{22}\right)^2}{\dfrac{1}{28 - 1}\left(\dfrac{150^2}{28}\right)^2 + \dfrac{1}{22 - 1}\left(\dfrac{125^2}{22}\right)^2} = 47.8$$

We round the noninteger degrees of freedom *down* to 47 to provide a larger *t*-value and a more conservative interval estimate. Using the *t* distribution table with 47 degrees of freedom, we find $t_{.025} = 2.012$. Using expression (10.6), we develop the 95% confidence interval estimate of the difference between the two population means as follows.

$$\bar{x}_1 - \bar{x}_2 \pm t_{.025} \sqrt{\frac{s_1^2}{n_1} + \frac{s_2^2}{n_2}}$$

$$1025 - 910 \pm 2.012 \sqrt{\frac{150^2}{28} + \frac{125^2}{22}}$$

$$115 \pm 78$$

The point estimate of the difference between the population mean checking account balances at the two branches is $115. The margin of error is $78, and the 95% confidence interval estimate of the difference between the two population means is $115 - 78 = \$37$ to $115 + 78 = \$193$.

Hypothesis Tests About $\mu_1 - \mu_2$

Let us now consider hypothesis tests about the difference between the means of two populations when the population standard deviations σ_1 and σ_2 are unknown. Letting D_0 denote the hypothesized difference between μ_1 and μ_2, Section 10.1 showed that the test statistic used for the case where σ_1 and σ_2 are known is as follows.

$$z = \frac{(\bar{x}_1 - \bar{x}_2) - D_0}{\sqrt{\frac{\sigma_1^2}{n_1} + \frac{\sigma_2^2}{n_2}}}$$

The test statistic, z, follows the standard normal distribution.

When σ_1 and σ_2 are unknown, we use s_1 as an estimator of σ_1 and s_2 as an estimator of σ_2. Substituting these sample standard deviations for σ_1 and σ_2 provides the following test statistic when σ_1 and σ_2 are unknown.

TEST STATISTIC FOR HYPOTHESIS TESTS ABOUT $\mu_1 - \mu_2$: σ_1 AND σ_2 UNKNOWN

$$t = \frac{(\bar{x}_1 - \bar{x}_2) - D_0}{\sqrt{\frac{s_1^2}{n_1} + \frac{s_2^2}{n_2}}} \tag{10.8}$$

The degrees of freedom for *t* are given by equation (10.7).

Let us demonstrate the use of this test statistic in the following hypothesis testing example.

Consider a new computer software package developed to help systems analysts reduce the time required to design, develop, and implement an information system. To evaluate the benefits of the new software package, a random sample of 24 systems analysts is selected. Each analyst is given specifications for a hypothetical information system. Then 12 of the analysts are instructed to produce the information system by using current technology. The other 12 analysts are trained in the use of the new software package and then instructed to use it to produce the information system.

This study involves two populations: a population of systems analysts using the current technology and a population of systems analysts using the new software package. In terms of the time required to complete the information system design project, the population means are as follows.

μ_1 = the mean project completion time for systems analysts using the current technology

μ_2 = the mean project completion time for systems analysts using the new software package

The researcher in charge of the new software evaluation project hopes to show that the new software package will provide a shorter mean project completion time. Thus, the researcher is looking for evidence to conclude that μ_2 is less than μ_1; in this case, the difference between the two population means, $\mu_1 - \mu_2$, will be greater than zero. The research hypothesis $\mu_1 - \mu_2 > 0$ is stated as the alternative hypothesis. Thus, the hypothesis test becomes

$$H_0: \mu_1 - \mu_2 \leq 0$$
$$H_a: \mu_1 - \mu_2 > 0$$

We will use α = .05 as the level of significance.

Suppose that the 24 analysts complete the study with the results shown in Table 10.1. Using the test statistic in equation (10.8), we have

$$t = \frac{(\bar{x}_1 - \bar{x}_2) - D_0}{\sqrt{\dfrac{s_1^2}{n_1} + \dfrac{s_2^2}{n_2}}} = \frac{(325 - 286) - 0}{\sqrt{\dfrac{40^2}{12} + \dfrac{44^2}{12}}} = 2.27$$

DATA *file*

SoftwareTest

TABLE 10.1	Completion Time Data and Summary Statistics for the Software Testing Study	
	Current Technology	**New Software**
	300	274
	280	220
	344	308
	385	336
	372	198
	360	300
	288	315
	321	258
	376	318
	290	310
	301	332
	283	263
Summary Statistics		
Sample size	$n_1 = 12$	$n_2 = 12$
Sample mean	$\bar{x}_1 = 325$ hours	$\bar{x}_2 = 286$ hours
Sample standard deviation	$s_1 = 40$	$s_2 = 44$

Computing the degrees of freedom using equation (10.7), we have

$$df = \frac{\left(\dfrac{s_1^2}{n_1} + \dfrac{s_2^2}{n_2}\right)^2}{\dfrac{1}{n_1-1}\left(\dfrac{s_1^2}{n_1}\right)^2 + \dfrac{1}{n_2-1}\left(\dfrac{s_2^2}{n_2}\right)^2} = \frac{\left(\dfrac{40^2}{12} + \dfrac{44^2}{12}\right)^2}{\dfrac{1}{12-1}\left(\dfrac{40^2}{12}\right)^2 + \dfrac{1}{12-1}\left(\dfrac{44^2}{12}\right)^2} = 21.8$$

Rounding down, we will use a t distribution with 21 degrees of freedom. This row of the t distribution table is as follows:

Area in Upper Tail	.20	.10	.05	.025	.01	.005
t-Value (21 df)	0.859	1.323	1.721	2.080	2.518	2.831

$$t = 2.27$$

Using the t distribution table, we can only determine a range for the p-value. Software computes the exact p-value = .017.

With an upper tail test, the p-value is the area in the upper tail to the right of $t = 2.27$. From the above results, we see that the p-value is between .025 and .01. Thus, the p-value is less than $\alpha = .05$ and H_0 is rejected. The sample results enable the researcher to conclude that $\mu_1 - \mu_2 > 0$, or $\mu_1 > \mu_2$. Thus, the research study supports the conclusion that the new software package provides a smaller population mean completion time.

Statistical software can be used to facilitate the testing hypotheses about the difference between two population means. Sample output comparing the current and new software technology is shown in Table 10.2. Table 10.2 displays the test statistic $t = 2.27$ and its one-tail p-value $= .017$. Note that statistical software uses equation (10.7) to compute 21 degrees of freedom for this analysis.

Practical Advice

Whenever possible, equal sample sizes, $n_1 = n_2$, are recommended.

The interval estimation and hypothesis testing procedures presented in this section are robust and can be used with relatively small sample sizes. In most applications, equal or nearly equal sample sizes such that the total sample size $n_1 + n_2$ is at least 20 can be expected to provide very good results even if the populations are not normal. Larger sample sizes are recommended if the distributions of the populations are highly skewed or contain outliers. Smaller sample sizes should only be used if the analyst is satisfied that the distributions of the populations are at least approximately normal.

TABLE 10.2 Output for the Hypothesis Test on the Difference Between the Current and New Software Technology

	Current	New
Mean	325	286
Variance	1600	1936
Observations	12	12
Hypothesized Mean Difference	0	
Degrees of Freedom	21	
Test Statistic	2.272	
One-Tail p-value	0.017	
One-Tail Critical Value	1.717	

NOTES + COMMENTS

Another approach used to make inferences about the difference between two population means when σ_1 and σ_2 are unknown is based on the assumption that the two population standard deviations are equal ($\sigma_1 = \sigma_2 = \sigma$). Under this assumption, the two sample standard deviations are combined to provide the following *pooled sample variance*:

$$s_p^2 = \frac{(n_1 - 1)s_1^2 + (n_2 - 1)s_2^2}{n_1 + n_2 - 2}$$

The *t* test statistic becomes

$$t = \frac{(\bar{x}_1 - \bar{x}_2) - D_0}{s_p\sqrt{\dfrac{1}{n_1} + \dfrac{1}{n_2}}}$$

and has $n_1 + n_2 - 2$ degrees of freedom. At this point, the computation of the *p*-value and the interpretation of the sample results are identical to the procedures discussed earlier in this section.

A difficulty with this procedure is that the assumption that the two population standard deviations are equal is usually difficult to verify. Unequal population standard deviations are frequently encountered. Using the pooled procedure may not provide satisfactory results, especially if the sample sizes n_1 and n_2 are quite different.

The *t* procedure that we presented in this section does not require the assumption of equal population standard deviations and can be applied whether the population standard deviations are equal or not. It is a more general procedure and is recommended for most applications.

EXERCISES

Methods

9. The following results are for independent random samples taken from two populations.

	Sample 1	Sample 2
	$n_1 = 20$	$n_2 = 30$
	$\bar{x}_1 = 22.5$	$\bar{x}_2 = 20.1$
	$s_1 = 2.5$	$s_2 = 4.8$

  a. What is the point estimate of the difference between the two population means?
  b. What is the degrees of freedom for the *t* distribution?
  c. At 95% confidence, what is the margin of error?
  d. What is the 95% confidence interval for the difference between the two population means?

10. Consider the following hypothesis test.

$$H_0: \mu_1 - \mu_2 = 0$$
$$H_a: \mu_1 - \mu_2 \neq 0$$

The following results are from independent samples taken from two populations.

	Sample 1	Sample 2
	$n_1 = 35$	$n_2 = 40$
	$\bar{x}_1 = 13.6$	$\bar{x}_2 = 10.1$
	$s_1 = 5.2$	$s_2 = 8.5$

  a. What is the value of the test statistic?
  b. What is the degrees of freedom for the *t* distribution?
  c. What is the *p*-value?
  d. At $\alpha = .05$, what is your conclusion?

11. Consider the following data for two independent random samples taken from two normal populations.

Sample 1	10	7	13	7	9	8
Sample 2	8	7	8	4	6	9

   a. Compute the two sample means.
   b. Compute the two sample standard deviations.
   c. What is the point estimate of the difference between the two population means?
   d. What is the 90% confidence interval estimate of the difference between the two population means?

Applications

12. **Miles Driven Per Day.** The U.S. Department of Transportation provides the number of miles that residents of the 75 largest metropolitan areas travel per day in a car. Suppose that for a simple random sample of 50 Buffalo residents the mean is 22.5 miles a day and the standard deviation is 8.4 miles a day, and for an independent simple random sample of 40 Boston residents the mean is 18.6 miles a day and the standard deviation is 7.4 miles a day.

   a. What is the point estimate of the difference between the mean number of miles that Buffalo residents travel per day and the mean number of miles that Boston residents travel per day?
   b. What is the 95% confidence interval for the difference between the two population means?

DATA *file*
CollegeCosts

13. **Annual Cost of College.** The increasing annual cost (including tuition, room, board, books, and fees) to attend college has been widely discussed (http://time.com/money /4543839/college-costs-record-2016/). The following random samples show the annual cost of attending private and public colleges. Data are in thousands of dollars.

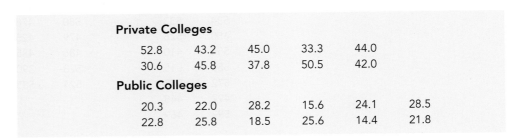

Private Colleges

52.8	43.2	45.0	33.3	44.0
30.6	45.8	37.8	50.5	42.0

Public Colleges

20.3	22.0	28.2	15.6	24.1	28.5
22.8	25.8	18.5	25.6	14.4	21.8

   a. Compute the sample mean and sample standard deviation for private and public colleges.
   b. What is the point estimate of the difference between the two population means? Interpret this value in terms of the annual cost of attending private and public colleges.
   c. Develop a 95% confidence interval of the difference between the mean annual cost of attending private and public colleges.

14. **Salaries of Recent College Graduates.** The Tippie College of Business obtained the following results on the salaries of a recent graduating class:

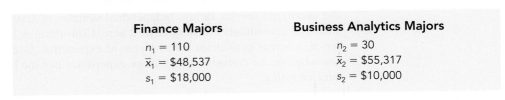

Finance Majors	Business Analytics Majors
$n_1 = 110$	$n_2 = 30$
$\bar{x}_1 = \$48,537$	$\bar{x}_2 = \$55,317$
$s_1 = \$18,000$	$s_2 = \$10,000$

a. Formulate hypothesis so that, if the null hypothesis is rejected, we can conclude that salaries for Finance majors are significantly lower than the salaries of Business Analytics majors. Use $\alpha = .05$.
b. What is the value of the test statistic?
c. What is the p-value?
d. What is your conclusion?

DATAfile

IntHotels

15. **Hotel Prices.** Hotel room pricing changes over time (*Lodging Magazine*), but is there a difference between Europe hotel prices and U.S. hotel prices? The file *IntHotels* contains changes in the hotel prices for 47 major European cities and 53 major U.S. cities.

a. On the basis of the sample results, can we conclude that the mean change in hotel rates in Europe and the United States are different? Develop appropriate null and alternative hypotheses.
b. Use $\alpha = .01$. What is your conclusion?

DATAfile

SATMath

16. **Effect of Parents' Education on Student SAT Scores.** The College Board provided comparisons of Scholastic Aptitude Test (SAT) scores based on the highest level of education attained by the test taker's parents. A research hypothesis was that students whose parents had attained a higher level of education would on average score higher on the SAT. The overall mean SAT math score was 514. SAT math scores for independent samples of students follow. The first sample shows the SAT math test scores for students whose parents are college graduates with a bachelor's degree. The second sample shows the SAT math test scores for students whose parents are high school graduates but do not have a college degree.

Student's Parents			
College Grads		**High School Grads**	
485	487	442	492
534	533	580	478
650	526	479	425
554	410	486	485
550	515	528	390
572	578	524	535
497	448		
592	469		

a. Formulate the hypotheses that can be used to determine whether the sample data support the hypothesis that students show a higher population mean math score on the SAT if their parents attained a higher level of education.
b. What is the point estimate of the difference between the means for the two populations?
c. Compute the p-value for the hypothesis test.
d. At $\alpha = .05$, what is your conclusion?

17. **Comparing Financial Consultant Ratings.** Periodically, Merrill Lynch customers are asked to evaluate Merrill Lynch financial consultants and services. Higher ratings on the client satisfaction survey indicate better service, with 7 the maximum service rating. Independent samples of service ratings for two financial consultants are summarized here. Consultant A has 10 years of experience, whereas consultant B has 1 year of experience. Use $\alpha = .05$ and test to see whether the consultant with more experience has the higher population mean service rating.

	Consultant A	Consultant B
	$n_1 = 16$	$n_2 = 10$
	$\bar{x}_1 = 6.82$	$\bar{x}_2 = 6.25$
	$s_1 = .64$	$s_2 = .75$

    a. State the null and alternative hypotheses.
    b. Compute the value of the test statistic.
    c. What is the p-value?
    d. What is your conclusion?

LateFlights

18. **Comparing Length of Flight Delays.** The success of an airline depends heavily on its ability to provide a pleasant customer experience. One dimension of customer service on which airlines compete is on-time arrival. The file *LateFlights* contains a sample of data from delayed flights showing the number of minutes each delayed flight was late for two different airlines, Delta and Southwest.
    a. Formulate the hypotheses that can be used to test for a difference between the population mean minutes late for delayed flights by these two airlines.
    b. What is the sample mean number of minutes late for delayed flights for each of these two airlines?
    c. Using a .05 level of significance, what is the p-value and what is your conclusion?

10.3 Inferences About the Difference Between Two Population Means: Matched Samples

Suppose employees at a manufacturing company can use two different methods to perform a production task. To maximize production output, the company wants to identify the method with the smaller population mean completion time. Let μ_1 denote the population mean completion time for production method 1 and μ_2 denote the population mean completion time for production method 2. With no preliminary indication of the preferred production method, we begin by tentatively assuming that the two production methods have the same population mean completion time. Thus, the null hypothesis is H_0: $\mu_1 - \mu_2 = 0$. If this hypothesis is rejected, we can conclude that the population mean completion times differ. In this case, the method providing the smaller mean completion time would be recommended. The null and alternative hypotheses are written as follows.

$$H_0\text{: } \mu_1 - \mu_2 = 0$$
$$H_a\text{: } \mu_1 - \mu_2 \neq 0$$

In choosing the sampling procedure that will be used to collect production time data and test the hypotheses, we consider two alternative designs. One is based on independent samples and the other is based on **matched samples**.

    1. *Independent sample design:* A simple random sample of workers is selected and each worker in the sample uses method 1. A second independent simple random sample of workers is selected and each worker in this sample uses method 2. The test of the difference between population means is based on the procedures in Section 10.2.
    2. *Matched sample design:* One simple random sample of workers is selected. Each worker first uses one method and then uses the other method. The order of the two methods is assigned randomly to the workers, with some workers performing method 1 first and others performing method 2 first. Each worker provides a pair of data values, one value for method 1 and another value for method 2.

	TABLE 10.3	Task Completion Times for a Matched Sample Design	
Worker	**Completion Time for Method 1 (minutes)**	**Completion Time for Method 2 (minutes)**	**Difference in Completion Times (d_i)**
1	6.0	5.4	.6
2	5.0	5.2	−.2
3	7.0	6.5	.5
4	6.2	5.9	.3
5	6.0	6.0	.0
6	6.4	5.8	.6

DATA*file*

Matched

In the matched sample design the two production methods are tested under similar conditions (i.e., with the same workers); hence this design often leads to a smaller sampling error than the independent sample design. The primary reason is that in a matched sample design, variation between workers is eliminated because the same workers are used for both production methods.

Let us demonstrate the analysis of a matched sample design by assuming it is the method used to test the difference between population means for the two production methods. A random sample of six workers is used. The data on completion times for the six workers are given in Table 10.3. Note that each worker provides a pair of data values, one for each production method. Also note that the last column contains the difference in completion times d_i for each worker in the sample.

The key to the analysis of the matched sample design is to realize that we consider only the column of differences. Therefore, we have six data values (.6, −.2, .5, .3, .0, and .6) that will be used to analyze the difference between population means of the two production methods.

Let μ_d = the mean of the *difference* in values for the population of workers. With this notation, the null and alternative hypotheses are rewritten as follows.

$$H_0: \mu_d = 0$$
$$H_a: \mu_d \neq 0$$

If H_0 is rejected, we can conclude that the population mean completion times differ.

Other than the use of the d notation, the formulas for the sample mean and sample standard deviation are the same ones used previously in the text.

The d notation is a reminder that the matched sample provides *difference* data. The sample mean and sample standard deviation for the six difference values in Table 10.3 follow.

$$\bar{d} = \frac{\sum d_i}{n} = \frac{1.8}{6} = .30$$

$$s_d = \sqrt{\frac{\sum(d_i - \bar{d})^2}{n - 1}} = \sqrt{\frac{.56}{5}} = .335$$

It is not necessary to make the assumption that the population has a normal distribution if the sample size is large. Sample size guidelines for using the t distribution were presented in Chapters 8 and 9.

With the small sample of $n = 6$ workers, we need to make the assumption that the population of differences has a normal distribution. This assumption is necessary so that we may use the t distribution for hypothesis testing and interval estimation procedures. Based on this assumption, the following test statistic has a t distribution with $n - 1$ degrees of freedom.

TEST STATISTIC FOR HYPOTHESIS TESTS INVOLVING MATCHED SAMPLES

$$t = \frac{\bar{d} - \mu_d}{s_d/\sqrt{n}} \tag{10.9}$$

Once the difference data are computed, the t distribution procedure for matched samples is the same as the one-population estimation and hypothesis testing procedures described in Chapters 8 and 9.

Let us use equation (10.9) to test the hypotheses H_0: $\mu_d = 0$ and H_a: $\mu_d \neq 0$, using $\alpha = .05$. Substituting the sample results $\bar{d} = .30$, $s_d = .335$, and $n = 6$ into equation (10.9), we compute the value of the test statistic.

$$t = \frac{\bar{d} - \mu_d}{s_d/\sqrt{n}} = \frac{.30 - 0}{.335/\sqrt{6}} = 2.20$$

Now let us compute the p-value for this two-tailed test. Because $t = 2.20 > 0$, the test statistic is in the upper tail of the t distribution. With $t = 2.20$, the area in the upper tail to the right of the test statistic can be found by using the t distribution table with degrees of freedom $= n - 1 = 6 - 1 = 5$. Information from the 5 degrees of freedom row of the t distribution table is as follows:

Area in Upper Tail	.20	.10	.05	.025	.01	.005
t-Value (5 df)	0.920	1.476	2.015	2.571	3.365	4.032

$t = 2.20$

Thus, we see that the area in the upper tail is between .05 and .025. Because this test is a two-tailed test, we double these values to conclude that the p-value is between .10 and .05. This p-value is greater than $\alpha = .05$. Thus, the null hypothesis H_0: $\mu_d = 0$ is not rejected. Applying statistical software to the data in Table 10.3, we find the exact p-value $= .080$.

Chapter 8 discusses the construction of an interval estimate for a single population mean.

In addition, we can obtain an interval estimate of the difference between the two population means by using the single population methodology. At 95% confidence, the calculation follows.

$$\bar{d} \pm t_{.025}\frac{s_d}{\sqrt{n}}$$

$$.3 \pm 2.571\left(\frac{.335}{\sqrt{6}}\right)$$

$$.3 \pm .35$$

Thus, the margin of error is .35 and the 95% confidence interval for the difference between the population means of the two production methods is $-.05$ minutes to .65 minutes.

NOTES + COMMENTS

1. In the example presented in this section, workers performed the production task with first one method and then the other method. This example illustrates a matched sample design in which each sampled element (worker) provides a pair of data values. It is also possible to use different but "similar" elements to provide the pair of data values. For example, a worker at one location could be matched with a similar worker at another location (similarity based on age, education, gender, experience, etc.). The pairs of workers would provide the difference data that could be used in the matched sample analysis.

2. A matched sample procedure for inferences about two population means generally provides better precision than the independent sample approach; therefore it is the recommended design. However, in some applications the matching cannot be achieved, or perhaps the time and cost associated with matching are excessive. In such cases, the independent sample design should be used.

EXERCISES

Methods

19. Consider the following hypothesis test.

$$H_0: \mu_d \leq 0$$
$$H_a: \mu_d > 0$$

The following data are from matched samples taken from two populations.

	Population	
Element	1	2
1	21	20
2	28	26
3	18	18
4	20	20
5	26	24

a. Compute the difference value for each element.
b. Compute $\bar{d}$.
c. Compute the standard deviation s_d.
d. Conduct a hypothesis test using $\alpha = .05$. What is your conclusion?

20. The following data are from matched samples taken from two populations.

	Population	
Element	1	2
1	11	8
2	7	8
3	9	6
4	12	7
5	13	10
6	15	15
7	15	14

a. Compute the difference value for each element.
b. Compute $\bar{d}$.
c. Compute the standard deviation s_d.
d. What is the point estimate of the difference between the two population means?
e. Provide a 95% confidence interval for the difference between the two population means.

Applications

21. **Television Commercials and Product Purchase Potential.** A market research firm used a sample of individuals to rate the purchase potential of a particular product before and after the individuals saw a new television commercial about the product. The purchase potential ratings were based on a 0 to 10 scale, with higher values indicating a higher purchase potential. The null hypothesis stated that the mean rating "after" would be less than or equal to the mean rating "before." Rejection of this hypothesis would show that the commercial improved the mean purchase potential rating. Use $\alpha = .05$ and the following data to test the hypothesis and comment on the value of the commercial.

Individual	Purchase Rating After	Before	Individual	Purchase Rating After	Before
1	6	5	5	3	5
2	6	4	6	9	8
3	7	7	7	7	5
4	4	3	8	6	6

DATA *file*

StockQuarter

22. **First-Quarter Stock Market Performance.** The price per share of stock for a sample of 25 companies was recorded at the beginning of the first financial quarter and then again at the end of the first financial quarter. How stocks perform during the first financial quarter is an indicator of what is ahead for the stock market and the economy. Use the sample data in the file *StockQuarter* to answer the following.
   a. Let d_i denote the percentage change in price per share for company i where

   $$d_i = \frac{\text{end of 1}^{st} \text{ quarter price per share} - \text{beginning of 1}^{st} \text{ quarter price per share}}{\text{beginning of 1}^{st} \text{ quarter price per share}}$$

   Use the sample mean of these values to estimate the percentage change in the stock price over the first quarter.
   b. What is the 95% confidence interval estimate of the population mean percentage change in the price per share of stock during the first quarter? Interpret this result.

23. **Credit Card Expenditures.** Bank of America's Consumer Spending Survey collected data on annual credit card charges in seven different categories of expenditures: transportation, groceries, dining out, household expenses, home furnishings, apparel, and entertainment. Using data from a sample of 42 credit card accounts, assume that each account was used to identify the annual credit card charges for groceries (population 1) and the annual credit card charges for dining out (population 2). Using the difference data, the sample mean difference was $\bar{d} = \$850$, and the sample standard deviation was $s_d = \$1123$.
   a. Formulate the null and alternative hypotheses to test for no difference between the population mean credit card charges for groceries and the population mean credit card charges for dining out.
   b. Use a .05 level of significance. Can you conclude that the population means differ? What is the p-value?
   c. Which category, groceries or dining out, has a higher population mean annual credit card charge? What is the point estimate of the difference between the population means? What is the 95% confidence interval estimate of the difference between the population means?

24. **Domestic Airfare.** The Global Business Travel Association reported the domestic airfare for business travel for the current year and the previous year. Below is a sample of 12 flights with their domestic airfares shown for both years.

DATA *file*

BusinessTravel

Current Year	Previous Year	Current Year	Previous Year
345	315	635	585
526	463	710	650
420	462	605	545
216	206	517	547
285	275	570	508
405	432	610	580

   a. Formulate the hypotheses and test for a significant increase in the mean domestic airfare for business travel for the one-year period. What is the p-value? Using a .05 level of significance, what is your conclusion?
   b. What is the sample mean domestic airfare for business travel for each year?
   c. What is the percentage change in the airfare for the one-year period?

25. **SAT Scores.** The College Board SAT college entrance exam consists of three parts: math, writing, and critical reading. Sample data showing the math and writing scores for a sample of 12 students who took the SAT follow.

DATA *file*

TestScores

Student	Math	Writing	Student	Math	Writing
1	540	474	7	480	430
2	432	380	8	499	459
3	528	463	9	610	615
4	574	612	10	572	541
5	448	420	11	390	335
6	502	526	12	593	613

a. Use a .05 level of significance and test for a difference between the population mean for the math scores and the population mean for the writing scores. What is the *p*-value and what is your conclusion?

b. What is the point estimate of the difference between the mean scores for the two tests? What are the estimates of the population mean scores for the two tests? Which test reports the higher mean score?

26. **PGA Tour Scores.** Scores in the first and fourth (final) rounds for a sample of 20 golfers who competed in PGA tournaments are shown in the following table. Suppose you would like to determine if the mean score for the first round of a PGA Tour event is significantly different than the mean score for the fourth and final round. Does the pressure of playing in the final round cause scores to go up? Or does the increased player concentration cause scores to come down?

DATA *file*

GolfScores

Player	First Round	Final Round	Player	First Round	Final Round
Michael Letzig	70	72	Aron Price	72	72
Scott Verplank	71	72	Charles Howell	72	70
D. A. Points	70	75	Jason Dufner	70	73
Jerry Kelly	72	71	Mike Weir	70	77
Soren Hansen	70	69	Carl Pettersson	68	70
D. J. Trahan	67	67	Bo Van Pelt	68	65
Bubba Watson	71	67	Ernie Els	71	70
Reteif Goosen	68	75	Cameron Beckman	70	68
Jeff Klauk	67	73	Nick Watney	69	68
Kenny Perry	70	69	Tommy Armour III	67	71

a. Use $\alpha = .10$ to test for a statistically significantly difference between the population means for first- and fourth-round scores. What is the *p*-value? What is your conclusion?

b. What is the point estimate of the difference between the two population means? For which round is the population mean score lower?

c. What is the margin of error for a 90% confidence interval estimate for the difference between the population means? Could this confidence interval have been used to test the hypothesis in part (a)? Explain.

27. **Price Comparison of Smoothie Blenders.** A personal fitness company produces both a deluxe and a standard model of a smoothie blender for home use. Selling prices obtained from a sample of retail outlets follow.

Retail Outlet	Model Price ($) Deluxe	Model Price ($) Standard	Retail Outlet	Model Price ($) Deluxe	Model Price ($) Standard
1	39	27	5	40	30
2	39	28	6	39	34
3	45	35	7	35	29
4	38	30			

a. The manufacturer's suggested retail prices for the two models show a $10 price differential. Use a .05 level of significance and test that the mean difference between the prices of the two models is $10.
b. What is the 95% confidence interval for the difference between the mean prices of the two models?

10.4 Inferences About the Difference Between Two Population Proportions

Letting p_1 denote the proportion for population 1 and p_2 denote the proportion for population 2, we next consider inferences about the difference between the two population proportions: $p_1 - p_2$. To make an inference about this difference, we will select two independent random samples consisting of n_1 units from population 1 and n_2 units from population 2.

Interval Estimation of $p_1 - p_2$

In the following example, we show how to compute a margin of error and develop an interval estimate of the difference between two population proportions.

A tax preparation firm is interested in comparing the quality of work at two of its regional offices. By randomly selecting samples of tax returns prepared at each office and verifying the sample returns' accuracy, the firm will be able to estimate the proportion of erroneous returns prepared at each office. Of particular interest is the difference between these proportions.

$p_1 =$ proportion of erroneous returns for population 1 (office 1)
$p_2 =$ proportion of erroneous returns for population 2 (office 2)
$\bar{p}_1 =$ sample proportion for a simple random sample from population 1
$\bar{p}_2 =$ sample proportion for a simple random sample from population 2

The difference between the two population proportions is given by $p_1 - p_2$. The point estimator of $p_1 - p_2$ is as follows.

POINT ESTIMATOR OF THE DIFFERENCE BETWEEN TWO POPULATION PROPORTIONS

$$\bar{p}_1 - \bar{p}_2 \qquad\qquad \textbf{(10.10)}$$

Thus, the point estimator of the difference between two population proportions is the difference between the sample proportions of two independent simple random samples.

As with other point estimators, the point estimator $\bar{p}_1 - \bar{p}_2$ has a sampling distribution that reflects the possible values of $\bar{p}_1 - \bar{p}_2$ if we repeatedly took two independent random samples. The mean of this sampling distribution is $p_1 - p_2$ and the standard error of $\bar{p}_1 - \bar{p}_2$ is as follows:

STANDARD ERROR OF $\bar{p}_1 - \bar{p}_2$

$$\sigma_{\bar{p}_1 - \bar{p}_1} = \sqrt{\frac{p_1(1 - p_1)}{n_1} + \frac{p_2(1 - p_2)}{n_2}} \qquad\qquad \textbf{(10.11)}$$

If the sample sizes are large enough that $n_1 p_1$, $n_1(1 - p_1)$, $n_2 p_2$, and $n_2(1 - p_2)$ are all greater than or equal to 5, the sampling distribution of $\bar{p}_1 - \bar{p}_2$ can be approximated by a normal distribution.

As we showed previously, an interval estimate is given by a point estimate $\pm$ a margin of error. In the estimation of the difference between two population proportions, an interval estimate will take the following form:

$$\bar{p}_1 - \bar{p}_2 \pm \text{Margin of error}$$

With the sampling distribution of $\bar{p}_1 - \bar{p}_2$ approximated by a normal distribution, we would like to use $z_{\alpha/2}\sigma_{\bar{p}_1-\bar{p}_2}$ as the margin of error. However, $\sigma_{\bar{p}_1-\bar{p}_2}$ given by equation (10.11) cannot be used directly because the two population proportions, p_1 and p_2, are unknown. Using the sample proportion $\bar{p}_1$ to estimate p_1 and the sample proportion $\bar{p}_2$ to estimate p_2, the margin of error is as follows.

$$\text{Margin of error} = z_{\alpha/2}\sqrt{\frac{\bar{p}_1(1-\bar{p}_1)}{n_1} + \frac{\bar{p}_2(1-\bar{p}_2)}{n_2}} \qquad (10.12)$$

The general form of an interval estimate of the difference between two population proportions is as follows.

INTERVAL ESTIMATE OF THE DIFFERENCE BETWEEN TWO POPULATION PROPORTIONS

$$\bar{p}_1 - \bar{p}_2 \pm z_{\alpha/2}\sqrt{\frac{\bar{p}_1(1-\bar{p}_1)}{n_1} + \frac{\bar{p}_2(1-\bar{p}_2)}{n_2}} \qquad (10.13)$$

where $1 - \alpha$ is the confidence coefficient.

Returning to the tax preparation example, we find that independent simple random samples from the two offices provide the following information.

Office 1	**Office 2**
$n_1 = 250$	$n_2 = 300$
Number of returns with errors = 35	Number of returns with errors = 27

DATA*file*

TaxPrep

The sample proportions for the two offices follow.

$$\bar{p}_1 = \frac{35}{250} = .14$$

$$\bar{p}_2 = \frac{27}{300} = .09$$

The point estimate of the difference between the proportions of erroneous tax returns for the two populations is $\bar{p}_1 - \bar{p}_2 = .14 - .09 = .05$. Thus, we estimate that office 1 has a .05, or 5%, greater error rate than office 2.

Expression (10.13) can now be used to provide a margin of error and interval estimate of the difference between the two population proportions. Using a 90% confidence interval with $z_{\alpha/2} = z_{.05} = 1.645$, we have

$$\bar{p}_1 - \bar{p}_2 \pm z_{\alpha/2}\sqrt{\frac{\bar{p}_1(1-\bar{p}_1)}{n_1} + \frac{\bar{p}_2(1-\bar{p}_2)}{n_2}}$$

$$.14 - .09 \pm 1.645\sqrt{\frac{.14(1-.14)}{250} + \frac{.09(1-.09)}{300}}$$

$$.05 \pm .045$$

Thus, the margin of error is .045, and the 90% confidence interval is .005 to .095.

Hypothesis Tests About $p_1 - p_2$

Let us now consider hypothesis tests about the difference between the proportions of two populations. We focus on tests involving no difference between the two population proportions. In this case, the three forms for a hypothesis test are as follows:

All hypotheses considered use 0 as the difference of interest.

$$H_0: p_1 - p_2 \geq 0 \qquad H_0: p_1 - p_2 \leq 0 \qquad H_0: p_1 - p_2 = 0$$
$$H_a: p_1 - p_2 < 0 \qquad H_a: p_1 - p_2 > 0 \qquad H_a: p_1 - p_2 \neq 0$$

When we assume H_0 is true as an equality, we have $p_1 - p_2 = 0$, which is the same as saying that the population proportions are equal, $p_1 = p_2$.

We will base the test statistic on the sampling distribution of the point estimator $\bar{p}_1 - \bar{p}_2$. In equation (10.11), we showed that the standard error of $\bar{p}_1 - \bar{p}_2$ is given by

$$\sigma_{\bar{p}_1 - \bar{p}_2} = \sqrt{\frac{p_1(1 - p_1)}{n_1} + \frac{p_2(1 - p_2)}{n_2}}$$

Under the assumption H_0 is true as an equality, the population proportions are equal and $p_1 = p_2 = p$. In this case, $\sigma_{\bar{p}_1 - \bar{p}_2}$ becomes

STANDARD ERROR OF $\bar{p}_1 - \bar{p}_2$ WHEN $p_1 = p_2 = p$

$$\sigma_{\bar{p}_1 - \bar{p}_2} = \sqrt{\frac{p(1 - p)}{n_1} + \frac{p(1 - p)}{n_2}} = \sqrt{p(1 - p)\left(\frac{1}{n_1} + \frac{1}{n_2}\right)} \qquad \text{(10.14)}$$

With p unknown, we pool, or combine, the point estimators from the two samples ($\bar{p}_1$ and $\bar{p}_2$) to obtain a single point estimator of p as follows:

POOLED ESTIMATOR OF p WHEN $p_1 = p_2 = p$

$$\bar{p} = \frac{n_1 \bar{p}_1 + n_2 \bar{p}_2}{n_1 + n_2} \qquad \text{(10.15)}$$

This **pooled estimator of p** is a weighted average of $\bar{p}_1$ and $\bar{p}_2$.

Substituting $\bar{p}$ for p in equation (10.14), we obtain an estimate of the standard error of $\bar{p}_1 - \bar{p}_2$. This estimate of the standard error is used in the test statistic. The general form of the test statistic for hypothesis tests about the difference between two population proportions is the point estimator divided by the estimate of $\sigma_{\bar{p}_1 - \bar{p}_2}$.

TEST STATISTIC FOR HYPOTHESIS TESTS ABOUT $p_1 - p_2$

$$z = \frac{\bar{p}_1 - \bar{p}_2}{\sqrt{\bar{p}(1 - \bar{p})\left(\frac{1}{n_1} + \frac{1}{n_2}\right)}} \qquad \text{(10.16)}$$

This test statistic applies to large sample situations where $n_1 p_1$, $n_1(1 - p_1)$, $n_2 p_2$, and $n_2(1 - p_2)$ are all greater than or equal to 5.

Let us return to the tax preparation firm example and assume that the firm wants to use a hypothesis test to determine whether the error proportions differ between the two offices. A two-tailed test is required. The null and alternative hypotheses are as follows:

$$H_0: p_1 - p_2 = 0$$
$$H_a: p_1 - p_2 \neq 0$$

If H_0 is rejected, the firm can conclude that the error rates at the two offices differ. We will use $\alpha = .10$ as the level of significance.

The sample data previously collected showed $\bar{p}_1 = .14$ for the $n_1 = 250$ returns sampled at office 1 and $\bar{p}_2 = .09$ for the $n_2 = 300$ returns sampled at office 2. We continue by computing the pooled estimate of p.

$$\bar{p} = \frac{n_1\bar{p}_1 + n_2\bar{p}_2}{n_1 + n_2} = \frac{250(.14) + 300(.09)}{250 + 300} = .1127$$

Using this pooled estimate and the difference between the sample proportions, the value of the test statistic is as follows.

$$z = \frac{\bar{p}_1 - \bar{p}_2}{\sqrt{\bar{p}(1 - \bar{p})\left(\dfrac{1}{n_1} + \dfrac{1}{n_2}\right)}} = \frac{.14 - .09}{\sqrt{.1127(1 - .1127)\left(\dfrac{1}{250} + \dfrac{1}{300}\right)}} = 1.85$$

In computing the p-value for this two-tailed test, we first note that $z = 1.85$ is in the upper tail of the standard normal distribution. Using $z = 1.85$ and the standard normal distribution table, we find the area in the upper tail is $1.0000 - .9678 = .0322$. Doubling this area for a two-tailed test, we find the p-value $= 2(.0322) = .0644$. With the p-value less than $\alpha = .10$, H_0 is rejected at the .10 level of significance. The firm can conclude that the error rates differ between the two offices. This hypothesis testing conclusion is consistent with the earlier interval estimation results that showed the interval estimate of the difference between the population error rates at the two offices to be .005 to .095, with Office 1 having the higher error rate.

EXERCISES

Methods

28. Consider the following results for independent samples taken from two populations.

Sample 1	Sample 2
$n_1 = 400$	$n_2 = 300$
$\bar{p}_1 = .48$	$\bar{p}_2 = .36$

   a. What is the point estimate of the difference between the two population proportions?
   b. Develop a 90% confidence interval for the difference between the two population proportions.
   c. Develop a 95% confidence interval for the difference between the two population proportions.

29. Consider the hypothesis test

$$H_0: p_1 - p_2 \leq 0$$
$$H_a: p_1 - p_2 > 0$$

The following results are for independent samples taken from the two populations.

Sample 1	Sample 2
$n_1 = 200$	$n_2 = 300$
$\bar{p}_1 = .22$	$\bar{p}_2 = .16$

   a. What is the p-value?
   b. With $\alpha = .05$, what is your hypothesis testing conclusion?

Applications

30. **Corporate Hiring Outlook.** A *Businessweek/Harris* poll asked senior executives at large corporations their opinions about the economic outlook for the future. One question was, "Do you think that there will be an increase in the number of full-time employees at your company over the next 12 months?" In the current survey, 220 of 400 executives answered Yes, while in a previous year survey, 192 of 400 executives had answered Yes. Provide a 95% confidence interval estimate for the difference between the proportions at the two points in time. What is your interpretation of the interval estimate?

31. **Impact of Pinterest on Purchase Decisions.** *Forbes* reports that women trust recommendations from Pinterest more than recommendations from any other social network platform *(https://www.forbes.com/sites/marketshare/2012/03/20/why-brand-managers -need-to-take-an-interest-in-pinterest/#5e3b22fb6375)*. But does trust in Pinterest differ by gender? The following sample data show the number of women and men who stated in a recent sample that they trust recommendations made on Pinterest.

	Women	Men
Sample	150	170
Trust Recommendations Made on Pinterest	117	102

    a. What is the point estimate of the proportion of women who trust recommendations made on Pinterest?
    b. What is the point estimate of the proportion of men who trust recommendations made on Pinterest?
    c. Provide a 95% confidence interval estimate of the difference between the proportion of women and men who trust recommendations made on Pinterest.

32. **Mislabeled Fish.** Researchers with Oceana, a group dedicated to preserving the ocean ecosystem, reported finding that 33% of fish sold in retail outlets, grocery stores, and sushi bars throughout the United States had been mislabeled (*San Francisco Chronicle*, https://www.sfgate.com/science/article/Mislabeled-fish-a-widespread-problem-4295946 .php). Does this mislabeling differ for different species of fish? The following data show the number labeled incorrectly for samples of tuna and mahi mahi.

	Tuna	Mahi Mahi
Sample	220	160
Mislabeled	99	56

    a. What is the point estimate of the proportion of tuna that is mislabeled?
    b. What is the point estimate of the proportion of mahi mahi that is mislabeled?
    c. Provide a 95% confidence interval estimate of the difference between the proportion of tuna and mahi mahi that is mislabeled.

33. **Voter Turnout.** Minnesota had the highest turnout rate of any state for the 2016 presidential election (*United States Election Project* website). Political analysts wonder if turnout in rural Minnesota was higher than turnout in the urban areas of the state. A sample shows that 663 of 884 registered voters from rural Minnesota voted in the 2016 presidential election, while 414 out of 575 registered voters from urban Minnesota voted.
    a. Formulate the null and alternative hypotheses that can be used to test whether registered voters in rural Minnesota were more likely than registered voters in urban Minnesota to vote in the 2016 presidential election.
    b. What is the proportion of sampled registered voters in rural Minnesota that voted in the 2016 presidential election?
    c. What is the proportion of sampled registered voters in urban Minnesota that voted in the 2016 presidential election?
    d. At $\alpha = .05$, test the political analysts' hypothesis. What is the *p*-value, and what conclusion do you draw from your results?

34. **Oil Well Drilling.** Oil wells are expensive to drill, and dry wells are a great concern to oil exploration companies. The domestic oil and natural gas producer Aegis Oil, LLC describes on its website how improvements in technologies such as three-dimensional seismic imaging have dramatically reduced the number of dry (nonproducing) wells it and other oil exploration companies drill. The following sample data for wells drilled in 2012 and 2018 show the number of dry wells that were drilled in each year.

	2012	2018
Wells Drilled	119	162
Dry Wells	24	18

a. Formulate the null and alternative hypotheses that can be used to test whether the wells drilled in 2012 were more likely to be dry than wells drilled in 2018.
b. What is the point estimate of the proportion of wells drilled in 2012 that were dry?
c. What is the point estimate of the proportion of wells drilled in 2018 that were dry?
d. What is the p-value of your hypothesis test? At $\alpha = .05$, what conclusion do you draw from your results?

35. **Hotel Occupancy Rates.** Tourism is extremely important to the economy of Florida. Hotel occupancy is an often-reported measure of visitor volume and visitor activity (*Orlando Sentinel*, https://www.orlandosentinel.com/business/tourism/os-bz-hotel -occupancy-dip-20180522-story.html). Hotel occupancy data for February in two consecutive years are as follows.

	Current Year	Previous Year
Occupied Rooms	1470	1458
Total Rooms	1750	1800

a. Formulate the hypothesis test that can be used to determine if there has been an increase in the proportion of rooms occupied over the one-year period.
b. What is the estimated proportion of hotel rooms occupied each year?
c. Using a .05 level of significance, what is your hypothesis test conclusion? What is the p-value?
d. What is the 95% confidence interval estimate of the change in occupancy for the one-year period? Do you think area officials would be pleased with the results?

36. **Gender Differences in Raise or Promotion Expectations.** The Adecco Workplace Insights Survey sampled men and women workers and asked if they expected to get a raise or promotion this year. Suppose the survey sampled 200 men and 200 women. If 104 of the men replied Yes and 74 of the women replied Yes, are the results statistically significant in that you can conclude a greater proportion of men are expecting to get a raise or a promotion this year?
a. State the hypothesis test in terms of the population proportion of men and the population proportion of women.
b. What is the sample proportion for men? For women?
c. Use a .01 level of significance. What is the p-value and what is your conclusion?

37. **Default Rates on Bank Loans.** Carl Allen and Norm Nixon are two loan officers at Brea Federal Savings and Loan Bank. The bank manager is interested in comparing the default rate on the loans approved by Carl to the default rate on the loans approved by Norm. In the sample of loans collected, there are 60 loans approved by Carl (9 of which defaulted) and 80 loans approved by Norm (7 of which defaulted).

a. State the hypothesis test that the default rates are the same for the two loan officers.
b. What is the sample default proportion for Carl? For Norm?
c. Use a .05 level of significance. What is the *p*-value and what is your conclusion?

SUMMARY

In this chapter we discussed procedures for developing interval estimates and conducting hypothesis tests involving two populations. First, we showed how to make inferences about the difference between two population means when independent simple random samples are selected. We first considered the case where the population standard deviations, σ_1 and σ_2, could be assumed known. The standard normal distribution z was used to develop the interval estimate and served as the test statistic for hypothesis tests. We then considered the case where the population standard deviations were unknown and estimated by the sample standard deviations s_1 and s_2. In this case, the t distribution was used to develop the interval estimate and served as the test statistic for hypothesis tests.

Inferences about the difference between two population means were then discussed for the matched sample design. In the matched sample design each element provides a pair of data values, one from each population. The difference between the paired data values is then used in the statistical analysis. The matched sample design is generally preferred to the independent sample design because the matched-sample procedure often improves the precision of the estimate.

Finally, interval estimation and hypothesis testing about the difference between two population proportions were discussed. Statistical procedures for analyzing the difference between two population proportions are similar to the procedures for analyzing the difference between two population means.

GLOSSARY

Independent simple random samples Samples selected from two populations in such a way that the elements making up one sample are chosen independently of the elements making up the other sample.
Matched samples Samples in which each data value of one sample is matched with a corresponding data value of the other sample.
Pooled estimator of p An estimator of a population proportion obtained by computing a weighted average of the point estimators obtained from two independent samples.

KEY FORMULAS

Point Estimator of the Difference Between Two Population Means

$$\bar{x}_1 - \bar{x}_2 \tag{10.1}$$

Standard Error of $\bar{x}_1 - \bar{x}_2$

$$\sigma_{\bar{x}_1 - \bar{x}_2} = \sqrt{\frac{\sigma_1^2}{n_1} + \frac{\sigma_2^2}{n_2}} \tag{10.2}$$

Interval Estimate of the Difference Between Two Population Means: σ_1 and σ_2 Known

$$\bar{x}_1 - \bar{x}_2 \pm z_{\alpha/2} \sqrt{\frac{\sigma_1^2}{n_1} + \frac{\sigma_2^2}{n_2}} \tag{10.4}$$

Test Statistic for Hypothesis Tests About $\mu_1 - \mu_2$: σ_1 and σ_2 Known

$$z = \frac{(\bar{x}_1 - \bar{x}_2) - D_0}{\sqrt{\dfrac{\sigma_1^2}{n_1} + \dfrac{\sigma_2^2}{n_2}}}$$

(10.5)

Interval Estimate of the Difference Between Two Population Means: σ_1 and σ_2 Unknown

$$\bar{x}_1 - \bar{x}_2 \pm t_{\alpha/2} \sqrt{\frac{s_1^2}{n_1} + \frac{s_2^2}{n_2}}$$

(10.6)

Degrees of Freedom: t Distribution with Two Independent Random Samples

$$df = \frac{\left(\dfrac{s_1^2}{n_1} + \dfrac{s_2^2}{n_2}\right)^2}{\dfrac{1}{n_1 - 1}\left(\dfrac{s_1^2}{n_1}\right)^2 + \dfrac{1}{n_2 - 1}\left(\dfrac{s_2^2}{n_2}\right)^2}$$

(10.7)

Test Statistic for Hypothesis Tests About $\mu_1 - \mu_2$: σ_1 and σ_2 Unknown

$$t = \frac{(\bar{x}_1 - \bar{x}_2) - D_0}{\sqrt{\dfrac{s_1^2}{n_1} + \dfrac{s_2^2}{n_2}}}$$

(10.8)

Test Statistic for Hypothesis Tests Involving Matched Samples

$$t = \frac{\bar{d} - \mu_d}{s_d/\sqrt{n}}$$

(10.9)

Point Estimator of the Difference Between Two Population Proportions

$$\bar{p}_1 - \bar{p}_2$$

(10.10)

Standard Error of $\bar{p}_1 - \bar{p}_2$

$$\sigma_{\bar{p}_1 - \bar{p}_2} = \sqrt{\frac{p_1(1 - p_1)}{n_1} + \frac{p_2(1 - p_2)}{n_2}}$$

(10.11)

Interval Estimate of the Difference Between Two Population Proportions

$$\bar{p}_1 - \bar{p}_2 \pm z_{\alpha/2} \sqrt{\frac{\bar{p}_1(1 - \bar{p}_1)}{n_1} + \frac{\bar{p}_2(1 - \bar{p}_2)}{n_2}}$$

(10.13)

Standard Error of $\bar{p}_1 - \bar{p}_2$ when $p_1 = p_2 = p$

$$\sigma_{\bar{p}_1 - \bar{p}_2} = \sqrt{p(1 - p)\left(\frac{1}{n_1} + \frac{1}{n_2}\right)}$$

(10.14)

Pooled Estimator of p when $p_1 = p_2 = p$

$$\bar{p} = \frac{n_1\bar{p}_1 + n_2\bar{p}_2}{n_1 + n_2}$$

(10.15)

Test Statistic for Hypothesis Tests About $p_1 - p_2$

$$z = \frac{\bar{p}_1 - \bar{p}_2}{\sqrt{\bar{p}(1 - \bar{p})\left(\dfrac{1}{n_1} + \dfrac{1}{n_2}\right)}}$$

(10.16)

SUPPLEMENTARY EXERCISES

38. **Supermarket Checkout Lane Design.** Safegate Foods, Inc., is redesigning the checkout lanes in its supermarkets throughout the country and is considering two designs. Tests on customer checkout times conducted at two stores where the two new systems have been installed result in the following summary of the data.

System A	System B
$n_1 = 120$	$n_2 = 100$
$\bar{x}_1 = 4.1$ minutes	$\bar{x}_2 = 3.4$ minutes
$\sigma_1 = 2.2$ minutes	$\sigma_2 = 1.5$ minutes

Test at the .05 level of significance to determine whether the population mean checkout times of the two systems differ. Which system is preferred?

SUVLease

39. **SUV Lease Payments.** Statista reports that the average monthly lease payment for an automobile is falling in the United States (*Statista.com*), but does this apply to all classes of automobiles? Suppose you are interested in whether this trend is true for sport utility vehicles (SUVs). The file *SUVLease* contains monthly lease payment data for 33 randomly selected SUVs in 2015 and 46 randomly selected SUVs in 2016.
    a. Provide and interpret a point estimate of the difference between the population mean monthly lease payments for the two years.
    b. Develop a 99% confidence interval estimate of the difference between the mean monthly lease payments in 2015 and 2016.
    c. Would you feel justified in concluding that monthly lease payments have declined from 2015 to 2016? Why or why not?

40. **Load Versus No-Load Mutal Funds.** Mutual funds are classified as *load* or *no-load* funds. Load funds require an investor to pay an initial fee based on a percentage of the amount invested in the fund. The no-load funds do not require this initial fee. Some financial advisors argue that the load mutual funds may be worth the extra fee because these funds provide a higher mean rate of return than the no-load mutual funds. A sample of 30 load mutual funds and a sample of 30 no-load mutual funds were selected. Data in the file *Mutual* were collected on the annual return for the funds over a five-year period.

Mutual

    a. Formulate H_0 and H_a such that rejection of H_0 leads to the conclusion that the load mutual funds have a higher mean annual return over the five-year period.
    b. Conduct the hypothesis test. What is the *p*-value? At $\alpha = .05$, what is your conclusion?

41. **Kitchen Versus Bedroom Remodeling Costs.** The National Association of Home Builders provided data on the cost of the most popular home remodeling projects. Sample data on cost in thousands of dollars for two types of remodeling projects are as follows.

Kitchen	Master Bedroom	Kitchen	Master Bedroom
25.2	18.0	23.0	17.8
17.4	22.9	19.7	24.6
22.8	26.4	16.9	21.0
21.9	24.8	21.8	
19.7	26.9	23.6	

a. Develop a point estimate of the difference between the population mean remodeling costs for the two types of projects.
b. Develop a 90% confidence interval for the difference between the two population means.

42. **Effect of Siblings on SAT Scores.** In *Born Together—Reared Apart: The Landmark Minnesota Twin Study* (http://www.hup.harvard.edu/catalog.php?isbn=9780674055469), Nancy Segal discusses the efforts of research psychologists at the University of Minnesota to understand similarities and differences between twins by studying sets of twins who were raised separately. Below are critical reading SAT scores for several pairs of identical twins (twins who share all of their genes), one of whom was raised in a family with no other children (no siblings) and one of whom was raised in a family with other children (with siblings).

DATA *file*

Twins

No Siblings		With Siblings	
Name	**SAT Score**	**Name**	**SAT Score**
Bob	440	Donald	420
Matthew	610	Ronald	540
Shannon	590	Kedriana	630
Tyler	390	Kevin	430
Michelle	410	Erin	460
Darius	430	Michael	490
Wilhelmina	510	Josephine	460
Donna	620	Jasmine	540
Drew	510	Kraig	460
Lucinda	680	Bernadette	650
Barry	580	Larry	450
Julie	610	Jennifer	640
Hannah	510	Diedra	460
Roger	630	Latishia	580
Garrett	570	Bart	490
Roger	630	Kara	640
Nancy	530	Rachel	560
Sam	590	Joey	610
Simon	500	Drew	520
Megan	610	Annie	640

a. What is the mean difference between the critical reading SAT scores for the twins raised with no siblings and the twins raised with siblings?

b. Provide a 90% confidence interval estimate of the mean difference between the critical reading SAT scores for the twins raised with no siblings and the twins raised with siblings.

c. Conduct a hypothesis test of equality of the critical reading SAT scores for the twins raised with no siblings and the twins raised with siblings at $\alpha = .01$. What is your conclusion?

43. **Change in Financial Security.** Country Financial, a financial services company, uses surveys of adults age 18 and older to determine if personal financial fitness is changing over time. A recent sample of 1000 adults showed 410 indicating that their financial security was more than fair. Just a year before, a sample of 900 adults showed 315 indicating that their financial security was more than fair.

a. State the hypotheses that can be used to test for a significant difference between the population proportions for the two years.

b. Conduct the hypothesis test and compute the p-value. At a .05 level of significance, what is your conclusion?

c. What is the 95% confidence interval estimate of the difference between the two population proportions? What is your conclusion?

44. **Differences in Insurance Claims Based on Marital Status.** A large automobile insurance company selected samples of single and married male policyholders and recorded the number who made an insurance claim over the preceding three-year period.

Single Policyholders	Married Policyholders
$n_1 = 400$	$n_2 = 900$
Number making claims $= 76$	Number making claims $= 90$

a. Use $\alpha = .05$. Test to determine whether the claim rates differ between single and married male policyholders.

b. Provide a 95% confidence interval for the difference between the proportions for the two populations.

45. **Drug-Resistant Gonorrhea.** Each year, more than 2 million people in the United States become infected with bacteria that are resistant to antibiotics. In particular, the Centers of Disease Control and Prevention have launched studies of drug-resistant gonorrhea (*CDC.gov*). Of 142 cases tested in Alabama, 9 were found to be drug-resistant. Of 268 cases tested in Texas, 5 were found to be drug-resistant. Do these data suggest a statistically significant difference between the proportions of drug-resistant cases in the two states? Use a .02 level of significance. What is the p-value, and what is your conclusion?

46. **News Access Via Computer.** The American Press Institute reports that almost 70% of all American adults use a computer to gain access to news. Based on generational differences, you suspect that the proportion of American adults under 30 years old who use a computer to gain access to news exceeds the proportion of Americans 30 years and older who use a computer to gain access to news. Data in the file *ComputerNews* represent responses to the question, "Do you use a computer to gain access to news?" given by random samples of American adults under 30 years old and Americans over 30 years old.

DATA *file*

ComputerNews

a. Estimate the proportion of American adults under 30 years old who use a computer to gain access to news and the proportion of Americans over 30 years old who use a computer to gain access to news.

b. Provide a 95% confidence interval for the difference in proportions.

c. On the basis of your findings, does it appear the proportion of American adults under 30 years old who use a computer to gain access to news exceeds the proportion of Americans over 30 years old who use a computer to gain access to news?

CASE PROBLEM: PAR, INC.

Par, Inc., is a major manufacturer of golf equipment. Management believes that Par's market share could be increased with the introduction of a cut-resistant, longer-lasting golf ball. Therefore, the research group at Par has been investigating a new golf ball coating designed to resist cuts and provide a more durable ball. The tests with the coating have been promising.

One of the researchers voiced concern about the effect of the new coating on driving distances. Par would like the new cut-resistant ball to offer driving distances comparable to those of the current-model golf ball. To compare the driving distances for the two balls, 40 balls of both the new and current models were subjected to distance tests. The testing was performed with a mechanical hitting machine so that any difference between the mean distances for the two models could be attributed to a difference in the two models. The results of the tests, with distances measured to the nearest yard, follow. These data are available on the website that accompanies the text.

DATA *file*

Golf

Model		Model		Model		Model	
Current	New	Current	New	Current	New	Current	New
264	277	270	272	263	274	281	283
261	269	287	259	264	266	274	250
267	263	289	264	284	262	273	253
272	266	280	280	263	271	263	260
258	262	272	274	260	260	275	270
283	251	275	281	283	281	267	263
258	262	265	276	255	250	279	261
266	289	260	269	272	263	274	255
259	286	278	268	266	278	276	263
270	264	275	262	268	264	262	279

Managerial Report

1. Formulate and present the rationale for a hypothesis test that Par could use to compare the driving distances of the current and new golf balls.
2. Analyze the data to provide the hypothesis testing conclusion. What is the *p*-value for your test? What is your recommendation for Par, Inc.?
3. Provide descriptive statistical summaries of the data for each model.
4. What is the 95% confidence interval for the population mean driving distance of each model, and what is the 95% confidence interval for the difference between the means of the two populations?
5. Do you see a need for larger sample sizes and more testing with the golf balls? Discuss.

Chapter 10 Appendix

Appendix 10.1 Inferences About Two Populations with JMP

We describe the use of JMP to develop interval estimates and conduct hypothesis tests about the difference between two population means and the difference between two population proportions. We note that JMP does not provide a separate procedure for inferences about the difference between two population means when the population standard deviations σ_1 and σ_2 are known.

Difference Between Two Population Means: σ_1 and σ_2 Unknown

We will use the data for the checking account balances example presented in Section 10.2.

CheckAcct

Step 1. Open the file *CheckAcct* following the steps in Appendix 1.1

Step 2. Convert the file to stacked format following the steps in Appendix 1.1, entering *Balance* as the new **Stacked Data Column** name and *Branch* as the new **Source Label Column** name

Step 3. Click **Analyze** and select **Fit Y by X**

Step 4. When the **Fit Y by X – Contextual** dialog box appears:

Drag **Balance** from the **Select Columns** area to the **Y, Response** box in the **Cast Selected Columns into Roles** area

Drag **Branch** from the **Select Columns** area to the **X, Factor** box in the **Cast Selected Columns into Roles** area

Click **OK** in the **Action** area

Step 5. When the **Fit Y by X of Balance by Branch** window appears:

Click the red triangle ⊟ next to **Oneway Analysis of Balance By Branch** and select **t Test**

These steps will produce the chart displayed in Figure JMP 10.1. As Figure JMP 10.1 shows, the 95% confidence interval is \$36.755 (**Lower CL Dif**) to \$193.252 (**Upper CL Dif**), which agrees with Section 10.2. The *p*-value = 0.048 (**Prob > |t|** in Figure JMP 10.1) shows that the null hypothesis of equal population means can be rejected at the $\alpha = .01$ level of significance.

Difference Between Two Population Means with Matched Samples

We will use the data on production times in Table 10.3 to illustrate the matched-sample procedure. After opening the file *Matched* in JMP (these data are already stacked), we first create a new column that computes the difference between the production times of method 1 and method 2.

Matched

Step 1. Open the file *Matched* following the steps in Appendix 1.1

Step 2. In the **Data** window, click **Cols** and select **New Columns …**

Step 3. When the **New Column** dialog box appears:

Enter *Difference* in the **Column Name** box

Click **Column Properties** and select **Formula**

When the **Difference** window appears:

Click **Method 1** in the **4 Columns** area, then the minus button ⊟, and finally **Method 2** from the **4 Columns** area (see Figure JMP 10.2)

Click **OK** to close the **Difference** window

Click **OK** to close the **New Column** window

FIGURE JMP 10.1   JMP One-Way Analysis Chart for *Checking Account* Data

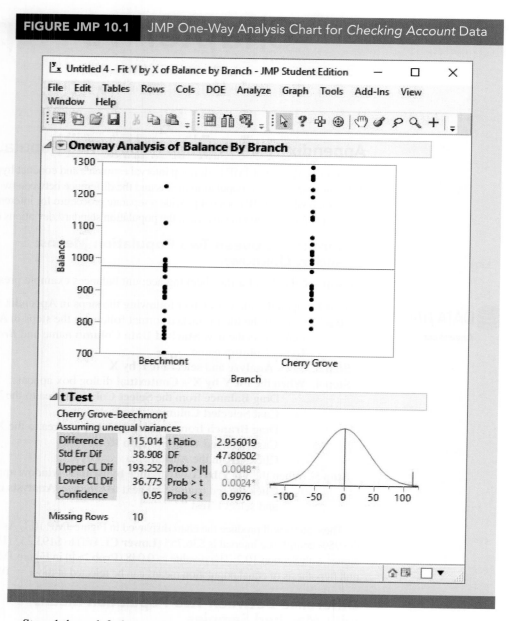

Steps 1 through 3 above create a new column titled "Difference" in the Data window that calculates the difference between Method 1 and Method 2. We now can compute a hypothesis test and confidence interval on the Difference column:

Step 1. In the **Data** window, click **Analyze** and select **Distribution**

Step 2. When the **Distribution** dialog box appears:

> Drag **Difference** from the **Select Columns** area to the **Y, Columns** box in the **Cast Selected Columns into Roles** area
>
> Click **OK** in the **Action** area

Step 3. When the **Distribution of Difference** window appears:

> Click the red triangle ▾ next to **Difference** and select **Test Mean**

Step 4. When the **Test Mean** dialog box appears:

> Enter *0* in the **Specify Hypothesized Mean** text box
>
> Click **OK**

Step 5. In the **Distribution of Difference** window

> Click the red triangle ▾ next to **Difference,** select **Confidence Interval** and then select **0.95**

FIGURE JMP 10.2 Creating Column to Compute the Difference Between Method 1 and Method 2 in JMP

FIGURE JMP 10.3 Inference on the Matched Difference using Production Time Data in JMP

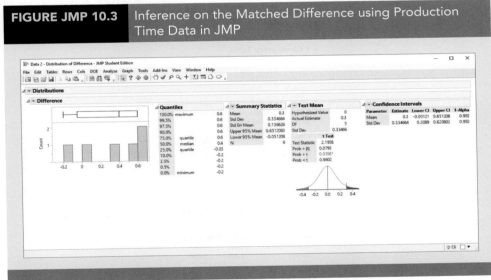

These steps will generate the output in Figure JMP 10.3, which matches the results of Section 10.3. The *p*-value (**Prob > |t|**) of .0795 shows that the null hypothesis of no difference in production times cannot be rejected at the $\alpha = .05$ level of significance. Correspondingly, the 95% confidence interval estimate is -0.05121 (**Lower 95% Mean**) to 0.651208 (**Upper 95% Mean**).

Difference Between Two Population Proportions

DATA *file*

TaxPrep

We will use the data on tax preparation errors presented in Section 10.4 found in the file *TaxPrep*.

Step 1. Open the file *TaxPrep* following the steps in Appendix 1.1
Step 2. Convert the file to stacked format following the steps in Appendix 1.1, entering *Error* as the new **Stacked Data Column** name and *Office* as the new **Source Label Column** name

Step 3. Click **Analyze** and select **Fit Y by X**

Step 4. When the **Fit Y by X—Contextual** dialog box appears:

Drag **Error** from the **Select Columns** area to the **Y, Response** box in the **Cast Selected Columns into Roles** area

Drag **Office** from the **Select Columns** area to the **X, Factor** box in the **Cast Selected Columns into Roles** area

Click **OK** in the **Action** area

Step 5. When the **Fit Y by X of Error by Office** window appears:

Click the red triangle ▼ next to **Contingency Analysis of Error By Office**, select **Set α Level** and select **0.10**

Click the red triangle ▼ next to **Contingency Analysis of Error By Office**, select **Two Sample Test for Proportions**

In the **Two Sample Test for Proportions** area, select **Yes** in the **Response Error category of interest** box

Figure JMP 10.4 displays the resulting JMP output. Observe that the 90% confidence interval estimate on the difference in the proportions is .004664 (**Lower 90%** in the **Two**

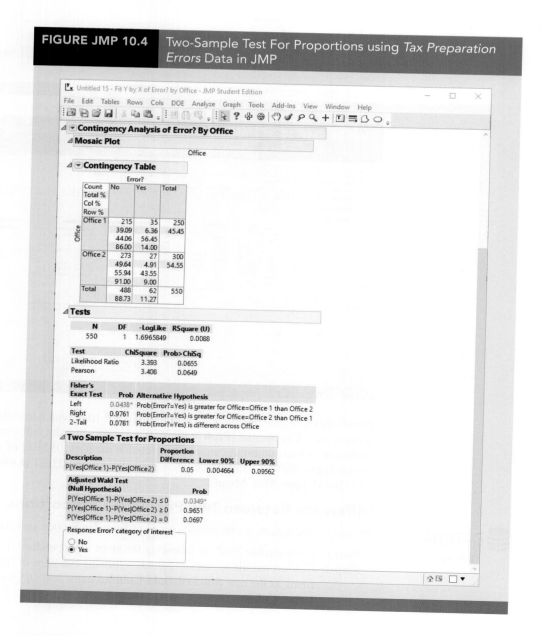

FIGURE JMP 10.4 — Two-Sample Test For Proportions using *Tax Preparation Errors* Data in JMP

Sample Test for Proportions area) to .09562 (**Upper 90%** in the **Two Sample Test for Proportions** area) as described in Section 10.4. The *p*-value = 0.0697 (**P(Yes|Office 1) − P(Yes|Office 2) = 0** in the **Two Sample Test for Proportions** area) shows the null hypothesis of no difference in error rates can be rejected at the $\alpha = .10$ level of significance. We note that JMP employs a slightly different calculation for the inference on the difference between two proportions than the one described in Section 10.4. Thus, the interval estimates and *p*-values may differ slightly but should provide the same interpretation and qualitative conclusion.

Appendix 10.2 Inferences About Two Populations with Excel

We describe the use of Excel to conduct hypothesis tests about the difference between two population means.[1] We begin with inferences about the difference between the means of two populations when the population standard deviations σ_1 and σ_2 are known.

Difference Between Two Population Means: σ_1 and σ_2 Known

We will use the examination scores for the two training centers discussed in Section 10.1 and contained in the file *ExamScores*. The label "Center A" is in cell A1 and the label "Center B" is in cell B1. The examination scores for Center A are in cells A2:A31 and examination scores for Center B are in cells B2:B41. The population standard deviations are assumed known with $\sigma_1 = 10$ and $\sigma_2 = 10$. The Excel routine will request the input of variances which are $\sigma_1^2 = 100$ and $\sigma_2^2 = 100$. The following steps can be used to conduct a hypothesis test about the difference between the two population means.

DATA *file*

ExamScores

Step 1. Click the **Data** tab on the Ribbon
Step 2. In the **Analyze** group, click **Data Analysis**
Step 3. When the **Data Analysis** dialog box appears (see Figure Excel 10.1):
          Select **z-Test: Two Sample for Means**
          Click **OK**
Step 4. When the **z-Test: Two Sample for Means** dialog box appears (see Figure Excel 10.2):
          Enter *A1:A31* in the **Variable 1 Range:** box
          Enter *B1:B41* in the **Variable 2 Range:** box
          Enter *0* in the **Hypothesized Mean Difference:** box
          Enter *100* in the **Variable 1 Variance (known):** box

| **FIGURE Excel 10.1** | Selecting z-Test: Two Sample for Means from the Data Analysis Dialog Box in Excel |

---

[1]Excel's data analysis tools provide hypothesis testing procedures for the difference between two population means. No routines are available for interval estimation of the difference between two population means nor for inferences about the difference between two population proportions.

FIGURE Excel 10.2 z-Test: Two Sample for Means Dialog Box using Examination Scores Data in Excel

FIGURE Excel 10.3 Output of Difference Between Two Population Means with Known Standard Deviations using Examination Scores Data in Excel

	A	B	C	D	E	F
1	**Center A**	**Center B**		z-Test: Two Sample for Means		
2	97	64				
3	95	85			*Center A*	*Center B*
4	89	72		Mean	82	78
5	79	64		Known Variance	100	100
6	78	74		Observations	30	40
7	87	93		Hypothesized Mean Difference	0	
8	83	70		z	1.65616	
9	94	79		P(Z<=z) one-tail	0.04884	
10	76	79		z Critical one-tail	1.64485	
11	79	75		P(Z<=z) two-tail	0.09769	
12	83	66		z Critical two-tail	1.95996	

Enter *100* in the **Variable 2 Variance (known):** box
Select the check box for **Labels**
Enter *.05* in the **Alpha:** box
Select **Output Range** and enter *D1* in the **Output Range:** box
Click **OK**

As Figure Excel 10.3 illustrates, the two-tailed *p*-value is denoted **P(Z<=z) two-tail.** Its value of .09769 in cell E11 does not allow us to reject the null hypothesis at $\alpha = .05$.

Difference Between Two Population Means: σ_1 and σ_2 Unknown

We use the data for the software testing study in Table 10.1. The data are already entered into an Excel worksheet with the label "Current" in cell A1 and the label "New" in cell B1 of file *SoftwareTest*. The completion times for the current technology are in cells A2:A13, and the completion times for the new software are in cells B2:B13. The following steps can be used to conduct a hypothesis test about the difference between two population means with σ_1 and σ_2 unknown.

DATA *file*

SoftwareTest

Step 1. Click the **Data** tab on the Ribbon
Step 2. In the **Analyze** group, click **Data Analysis**
Step 3. When the **Data Analysis** dialog box appears (see Figure Excel 10.4):
Select **t-Test: Two Sample Assuming Unequal Variances**
Click **OK**
Step 4. When the **t-Test: Two Sample Assuming Unequal Variances** dialog box appears (see Figure Excel 10.5):
Enter *A1:A13* in the **Variable 1 Range:** box
Enter *B1:B13* in the **Variable 2 Range:** box

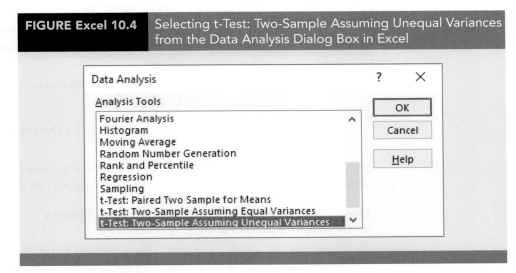

FIGURE Excel 10.4	Selecting t-Test: Two-Sample Assuming Unequal Variances from the Data Analysis Dialog Box in Excel

FIGURE Excel 10.5	t-Test: Two-Sample Assuming Unequal Variances Dialog Box using Software Testing Data in Excel

FIGURE Excel 10.6   Output of Difference Between Two Population Means with Unknown Standard Deviations using Software Testing Data in Excel

	A	B	C	D	E	F
1	**Current**	**New**		t-Test: Two-Sample Assuming Unequal Variances		
2	300	274				
3	280	220			*Current*	*New*
4	344	308		Mean	325	286
5	385	336		Variance	1599.64	1935.82
6	372	198		Observations	12	12
7	360	300		Hypothesized Mean Difference	0	
8	288	315		df	22	
9	321	258		t Stat	2.27213	
10	376	318		P(T<=t) one-tail	0.0166	
11	290	310		t Critical one-tail	1.71714	
12	301	332		P(T<=t) two-tail	0.0332	
13	283	263		t Critical two-tail	2.07387	

Enter *0* in the **Hypothesized Mean Difference:** box
Select the check box for **Labels**
Enter *.05* in the **Alpha:** box
Select **Output Range** and enter *D1* in the **Output Range:** box
Click **OK**

As Figure Excel 10.6 illustrates, the appropriate *p*-value is denoted **P(T<=t) one-tail.** Its value of .0166 in cell E10 allows us to reject the null hypothesis at $\alpha = .05$.

Difference Between Two Population Means with Matched Samples

We use the matched-sample completion times in Table 10.3 to illustrate. The data are entered into a worksheet with the label "Method 1" in cell B1 and the label "Method 2" in cell C1 of the file *Matched*. The completion times for method 1 are in cells B2:B7 and the completion times for method 2 are in cells C2:C7. The following steps can be used to conduct a hypothesis test about the difference between two population means with matched samples.

Step 1. Click the **Data** tab on the Ribbon
Step 2. In the **Analyze** group, click **Data Analysis**
Step 3. When the **Data Analysis** dialog box appears (see Figure Excel 10.7):
      Select **t-Test: Paired Two Sample for Means**
      Click **OK**
Step 4. When the **t-Test: Paired Two Sample for Means** dialog box appears (see Figure Excel 10.8):
      Enter *B1:B7* in the **Variable 1 Range:** box
      Enter *C1:C7* in the **Variable 2 Range:** box
      Enter *0* in the **Hypothesized Mean Difference:** box
      Select the check box for **Labels**
      Enter *.05* in the **Alpha:** box
      Select **Output Range** and enter *E1* in the **Output Range:** box
      Click **OK**

DATA*file*

Matched

As Figure Excel 10.9 illustrates, appropriate *p*-value is denoted **P(T<=t) one-tail.** Its value of .079516 in cell F13 does not allow us to reject the null hypothesis at $\alpha = .05$.

FIGURE Excel 10.7 Selecting t-Test: Paired Two Sample for Means from the Data Analysis Dialog Box in Excel

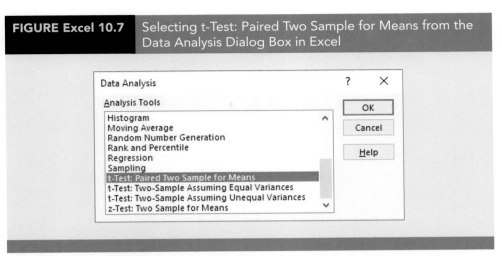

FIGURE Excel 10.8 t-Test: Paired Two Sample for Means Dialog Box using Completion Times Data in Excel

FIGURE Excel 10.9 Output of Difference Between Two Population Means with Matched Samples using Completion Times Data in Excel

	A	B	C	D	E	F	G
1	Worker	Method 1	Method 2		t-Test: Paired Two Sample for Means		
2	1	6.0	5.4				
3	2	5.0	5.2			Method 1	Method 2
4	3	7.0	6.5		Mean	6.1	5.8
5	4	6.2	5.9		Variance	0.428	0.212
6	5	6.0	6.0		Observations	6	6
7	6	6.4	5.8		Pearson Correlation	0.876424	
8					Hypothesized Mean Difference	0	
9					df	5	
10					t Stat	2.195775	
11					P(T<=t) one-tail	0.039758	
12					t Critical one-tail	2.015048	
13					P(T<=t) two-tail	0.079516	
14					t Critical two-tail	2.570582	

Chapter 11

Inferences About Population Variances

CONTENTS

STATISTICS IN PRACTICE

U.S. Government Accountability Office*

WASHINGTON, D.C.

The U.S. Government Accountability Office (GAO) is an independent, nonpolitical audit organization in the legislative branch of the federal government. GAO evaluators determine the effectiveness of current and proposed federal programs. To carry out their duties, evaluators must be proficient in records review, legislative research, and statistical analysis techniques.

In one case, GAO evaluators studied a Department of Interior program established to help clean up the nation's rivers and lakes. As part of this program, federal grants were made to small cities throughout the United States. Congress asked the GAO to determine how effectively the program was operating. To do so, the GAO examined records and visited the sites of several waste treatment plants.

One objective of the GAO audit was to ensure that the effluent (treated sewage) at the plants met certain standards. Among other things, the audits reviewed sample data on the oxygen content, the pH level, and the amount of suspended solids in the effluent. A requirement of the program was that a variety of tests be taken daily at each plant and that the collected data be sent periodically to the state engineering department. The GAO's investigation of the data showed whether various characteristics of the effluent were within acceptable limits.

For example, the mean or average pH level of the effluent was examined carefully. In addition, the variance in the reported pH levels was reviewed. The following hypothesis test was conducted about the variance in pH level for the population of effluent.

$$H_0: \sigma^2 = \sigma_0^2$$
$$H_a: \sigma^2 \neq \sigma_0^2$$

Effluent at this facility must fall within a statistically determined pH range.
Source: Kekyalyaynen/Shutterstock.com

In this test, σ_0^2 is the population variance in pH level expected at a properly functioning plant. In one particular plant, the null hypothesis was rejected. Further analysis showed that this plant had a variance in pH level that was significantly less than normal.

The auditors visited the plant to examine the measuring equipment and to discuss their statistical findings with the plant manager. The auditors found that the measuring equipment was not being used because the operator did not know how to work it. Instead, the operator had been told by an engineer what level of pH was acceptable and had simply recorded similar values without actually conducting the test. The unusually low variance in this plant's data resulted in rejection of H_0. The GAO suspected that other plants might have similar problems and recommended an operator training program to improve the data collection aspect of the pollution control program.

In this chapter you will learn how to conduct statistical inferences about the variances of one and two populations. Two new distributions, the chi-square distribution and the F distribution, will be introduced and used to make interval estimates and hypothesis tests about population variances.

*The authors thank Mr. Art Foreman and Mr. Dale Ledman of the U.S. Government Accountability Office for providing the context for this Statistics in Practice.

In this chapter we examine methods of statistical inference involving population variances. As an example of a case in which a variance can provide important decision-making information, consider the production process of filling containers with a liquid detergent product. The filling mechanism for the process is adjusted so that the mean filling weight is 16 ounces per container. Although a mean of 16 ounces is desired, the variance of the filling weights is also critical. That is, even with the filling mechanism properly adjusted for the mean of 16 ounces, we cannot expect every container to have exactly 16 ounces. By selecting a sample of containers, we can compute a sample variance for the number of ounces placed in a container. This value will serve as an estimate of the variance for the population of containers being filled by the production process. If the sample variance is modest, the production process will be continued. However, if the sample variance is excessive, overfilling and underfilling may be occurring even though the mean is correct at 16 ounces. In this case, the filling mechanism will be readjusted in an attempt to reduce the filling variance for the containers.

In many manufacturing applications, controlling the process variance is extremely important in maintaining quality.

In the first section we consider inferences about the variance of a single population. Subsequently, we will discuss procedures that can be used to make inferences about the variances of two populations.

11.1 Inferences About a Population Variance

The sample variance

$$s^2 = \frac{\Sigma(x_i - \bar{x})^2}{n - 1} \tag{11.1}$$

is the point estimator of the population variance σ^2. In using the sample variance as a basis for making inferences about a population variance, the sampling distribution of the quantity $(n - 1)s^2/\sigma^2$ is helpful. This sampling distribution is described as follows.

SAMPLING DISTRIBUTION OF $(n - 1)s^2/\sigma^2$

The chi-square distribution is based on sampling from a normal population.

Whenever a simple random sample of size n is selected from a normal population, the sampling distribution of

$$\frac{(n - 1)s^2}{\sigma^2} \tag{11.2}$$

is a chi-square distribution with $n - 1$ degrees of freedom.

Figure 11.1 shows some possible forms of the sampling distribution of $(n - 1)s^2/\sigma^2$.

Because the sampling distribution of $(n - 1)s^2/\sigma^2$ is known to have a chi-square distribution whenever a simple random sample of size n is selected from a normal population, we can use the chi-square distribution to develop interval estimates and conduct hypothesis tests about a population variance.

Interval Estimation

To show how the chi-square distribution can be used to develop a confidence interval estimate of a population variance σ^2, suppose that we are interested in estimating the population variance for the production filling process mentioned at the beginning of this chapter. A sample of 20 containers is taken, and the sample variance for the filling quantities is found to be $s^2 = .0025$. However, we know we cannot expect the variance of a sample of 20 containers to provide the exact value of the variance for the population of containers filled by the production process. Hence, our interest will be in developing an interval estimate for the population variance.

We will use the notation χ^2_α to denote the value for the chi-square distribution that provides an area or probability of α to the *right* of the χ^2_α value. For example, in Figure 11.2

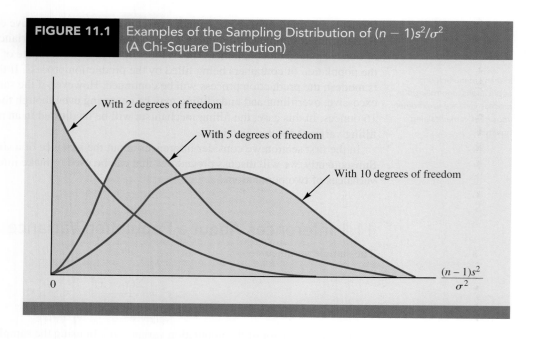

FIGURE 11.1   Examples of the Sampling Distribution of $(n-1)s^2/\sigma^2$ (A Chi-Square Distribution)

the chi-square distribution with 19 degrees of freedom is shown with $\chi^2_{.025} = 32.852$ indicating that 2.5% of the chi-square values are to the right of 32.852, and $\chi^2_{.975} = 8.907$ indicating that 97.5% of the chi-square values are to the right of 8.907. Tables of areas or probabilities are readily available for the chi-square distribution. Refer to Table 11.1 and verify that these chi-square values with 19 degrees of freedom (19th row of the table) are correct. Table 3 of Appendix B provides a more extensive table of chi-square values.

From the graph in Figure 11.2 we see that .95, or 95%, of the chi-square values are between $\chi^2_{.975}$ and $\chi^2_{.025}$. That is, there is a .95 probability of obtaining a χ^2 value such that

$$\chi^2_{.975} \leq \chi^2 \leq \chi^2_{.025}$$

FIGURE 11.2   A Chi-Square Distribution with 19 Degrees of Freedom

TABLE 11.1	Selected Values from the Chi-Square Distribution Table*

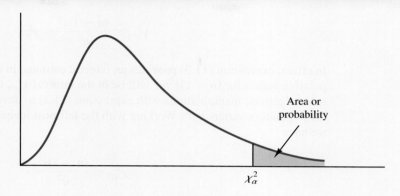

Area or probability

χ_α^2

Degrees of Freedom	.99	.975	.95	.90	.10	.05	.025	.01
				Area in Upper Tail				
1	.000	.001	.004	.016	2.706	3.841	5.024	6.635
2	.020	.051	.103	.211	4.605	5.991	7.378	9.210
3	.115	.216	.352	.584	6.251	7.815	9.348	11.345
4	.297	.484	.711	1.064	7.779	9.488	11.143	13.277
5	.554	.831	1.145	1.610	9.236	11.070	12.832	15.086
6	.872	1.237	1.635	2.204	10.645	12.592	14.449	16.812
7	1.239	1.690	2.167	2.833	12.017	14.067	16.013	18.475
8	1.647	2.180	2.733	3.490	13.362	15.507	17.535	20.090
9	2.088	2.700	3.325	4.168	14.684	16.919	19.023	21.666
10	2.558	3.247	3.940	4.865	15.987	18.307	20.483	23.209
11	3.053	3.816	4.575	5.578	17.275	19.675	21.920	24.725
12	3.571	4.404	5.226	6.304	18.549	21.026	23.337	26.217
13	4.107	5.009	5.892	7.041	19.812	22.362	24.736	27.688
14	4.660	5.629	6.571	7.790	21.064	23.685	26.119	29.141
15	5.229	6.262	7.261	8.547	22.307	24.996	27.488	30.578
16	5.812	6.908	7.962	9.312	23.542	26.296	28.845	32.000
17	6.408	7.564	8.672	10.085	24.769	27.587	30.191	33.409
18	7.015	8.231	9.390	10.865	25.989	28.869	31.526	34.805
19	7.633	8.907	10.117	11.651	27.204	30.144	32.852	36.191
20	8.260	9.591	10.851	12.443	28.412	31.410	34.170	37.566
21	8.897	10.283	11.591	13.240	29.615	32.671	35.479	38.932
22	9.542	10.982	12.338	14.041	30.813	33.924	36.781	40.289
23	10.196	11.689	13.091	14.848	32.007	35.172	38.076	41.638
24	10.856	12.401	13.848	15.659	33.196	36.415	39.364	42.980
25	11.524	13.120	14.611	16.473	34.382	37.652	40.646	44.314
26	12.198	13.844	15.379	17.292	35.563	38.885	41.923	45.642
27	12.878	14.573	16.151	18.114	36.741	40.113	43.195	46.963
28	13.565	15.308	16.928	18.939	37.916	41.337	44.461	48.278
29	14.256	16.047	17.708	19.768	39.087	42.557	45.722	49.588
30	14.953	16.791	18.493	20.599	40.256	43.773	46.979	50.892
40	22.164	24.433	26.509	29.051	51.805	55.758	59.342	63.691
60	37.485	40.482	43.188	46.459	74.397	79.082	83.298	88.379
80	53.540	57.153	60.391	64.278	96.578	101.879	106.629	112.329
100	70.065	74.222	77.929	82.358	118.498	124.342	129.561	135.807

*Note: A more extensive table is provided as Table 3 of Appendix B.

We stated in expression (11.2) that $(n - 1)s^2/\sigma^2$ follows a chi-square distribution; therefore we can substitute $(n - 1)s^2/\sigma^2$ for χ^2 and write

$$\chi^2_{.975} \leq \frac{(n - 1)s^2}{\sigma^2} \leq \chi^2_{.025} \tag{11.3}$$

In effect, expression (11.3) provides an interval estimate in that .95, or 95%, of all possible values for $(n - 1)s^2/\sigma^2$ will be in the interval $\chi^2_{.975}$ to $\chi^2_{.025}$. We now need to do some algebraic manipulations with expression (11.3) to develop an interval estimate for the population variance σ^2. Working with the leftmost inequality in expression (11.3), we have

$$\chi^2_{.975} \leq \frac{(n - 1)s^2}{\sigma^2}$$

Thus

$$\sigma^2 \chi^2_{.975} \leq (n - 1)s^2$$

or

$$\sigma^2 \leq \frac{(n - 1)s^2}{\chi^2_{.975}} \tag{11.4}$$

Performing similar algebraic manipulations with the rightmost inequality in expression (11.3) gives

$$\frac{(n - 1)s^2}{\chi^2_{.025}} \leq \sigma^2 \tag{11.5}$$

The results of expressions (11.4) and (11.5) can be combined to provide

$$\frac{(n - 1)s^2}{\chi^2_{.025}} \leq \sigma^2 \leq \frac{(n - 1)s^2}{\chi^2_{.975}} \tag{11.6}$$

Because expression (11.3) is true for 95% of the $(n - 1)s^2/\sigma^2$ values, expression (11.6) provides a 95% confidence interval estimate for the population variance σ^2.

Let us return to the problem of providing an interval estimate for the population variance of filling quantities. Recall that the sample of 20 containers provided a sample variance of $s^2 = .0025$. With a sample size of 20, we have 19 degrees of freedom. As shown in Figure 11.2, we have already determined that $\chi^2_{.975} = 8.907$ and $\chi^2_{.025} = 32.852$. Using these values in expression (11.6) provides the following interval estimate for the population variance.

$$\frac{(19)(.0025)}{32.852} \leq \sigma^2 \leq \frac{(19)(.0025)}{8.907}$$

or

A confidence interval for a population standard deviation can be found by computing the square roots of the lower limit and upper limit of the confidence interval for the population variance.

$$.0014 \leq \sigma^2 \leq .0053$$

Taking the square root of these values provides the following 95% confidence interval for the population standard deviation.

$$.0380 \leq \sigma \leq .0730$$

Thus, we illustrated the process of using the chi-square distribution to establish interval estimates of a population variance and a population standard deviation. Note specifically that because $\chi^2_{.975}$ and $\chi^2_{.025}$ were used, the interval estimate has a .95 confidence coefficient. Extending expression (11.6) to the general case of any confidence coefficient, we have the following interval estimate of a population variance.

INTERVAL ESTIMATE OF A POPULATION VARIANCE

$$\frac{(n-1)s^2}{\chi^2_{\alpha/2}} \leq \sigma^2 \leq \frac{(n-1)s^2}{\chi^2_{(1-\alpha/2)}} \qquad (11.7)$$

where the χ^2 values are based on a chi-square distribution with $n-1$ degrees of freedom and where $1-\alpha$ is the confidence coefficient.

Hypothesis Testing

Using σ_0^2 to denote the hypothesized value for the population variance, the three forms for a hypothesis test about a population variance are as follows:

$$H_0: \sigma^2 \geq \sigma_0^2 \qquad H_0: \sigma^2 \leq \sigma_0^2 \qquad H_0: \sigma^2 = \sigma_0^2$$
$$H_a: \sigma^2 < \sigma_0^2 \qquad H_a: \sigma^2 > \sigma_0^2 \qquad H_a: \sigma^2 \neq \sigma_0^2$$

We discuss hypothesis tests about population means and proportions in Chapters 9 and 10.

These three forms are similar to the three forms used to conduct one-tailed and two-tailed hypothesis tests about population means and proportions.

The procedure for conducting a hypothesis test about a population variance uses the hypothesized value for the population variance σ_0^2 and the sample variance s^2 to compute the value of a χ^2 test statistic. Assuming that the population has a normal distribution, the test statistic is as follows:

TEST STATISTIC FOR HYPOTHESIS TESTS ABOUT A POPULATION VARIANCE

$$\chi^2 = \frac{(n-1)s^2}{\sigma_0^2} \qquad (11.8)$$

where χ^2 has a chi-square distribution with $n-1$ degrees of freedom.

After computing the value of the χ^2 test statistic, either the p-value approach or the critical value approach, may be used to determine whether the null hypothesis can be rejected.

Let us consider the following example. The St. Louis Metro Bus Company wants to promote an image of reliability by encouraging its drivers to maintain consistent schedules. As a standard policy, the company would like arrival times at bus stops to have low variability. In terms of the variance of arrival times, the company standard specifies an arrival time variance of 4 or less when arrival times are measured in minutes. The following hypothesis test is formulated to help the company determine whether the arrival time population variance is excessive.

$$H_0: \sigma^2 \leq 4$$
$$H_a: \sigma^2 > 4$$

In tentatively assuming H_0 is true, we are assuming that the population variance of arrival times is within the company guideline. We reject H_0 if the sample evidence indicates that the population variance exceeds the guideline. In this case, follow-up steps should be taken to reduce the population variance. We conduct the hypothesis test using a level of significance of $\alpha = .05$.

BusTimes

Suppose that a random sample of 24 bus arrivals taken at a downtown intersection provides a sample variance of $s^2 = 4.9$. Assuming that the population distribution of arrival times is approximately normal, the value of the test statistic is as follows.

$$\chi^2 = \frac{(n-1)s^2}{\sigma_0^2} = \frac{(24-1)(4.9)}{4} = 28.18$$

The chi-square distribution with $n - 1 = 24 - 1 = 23$ degrees of freedom is shown in Figure 11.3. Because this is an upper tail test, the area under the curve to the right of the test statistic $\chi^2 = 28.18$ is the p-value for the test.

Like the t distribution table, the chi-square distribution table does not contain sufficient detail to enable us to determine the p-value exactly. However, we can use the chi-square distribution table to obtain a range for the p-value. For example, using Table 11.1, we find the following information for a chi-square distribution with 23 degrees of freedom.

Area in Upper Tail	.10	.05	.025	.01
χ^2 Value (23 *df*)	32.007	35.172	38.076	41.638

$\chi^2 = 28.18$

Because $\chi^2 = 28.18$ is less than 32.007, the area in upper tail (the p-value) is greater than .10. With the p-value $> \alpha = .05$, we cannot reject the null hypothesis. The sample does not support the conclusion that the population variance of the arrival times is excessive.

Because of the difficulty of determining the exact p-value directly from the chi-square distribution table, statistical software is helpful. Appendix F, at the back of the book, describes how to compute p-values using JMP or Excel. In the appendix, we show that the exact p-value corresponding to $\chi^2 = 28.18$ is .2091.

As with other hypothesis testing procedures, the critical value approach can also be used to draw the hypothesis testing conclusion. With $\alpha = .05$, $\chi^2_{.05}$ provides the critical value for

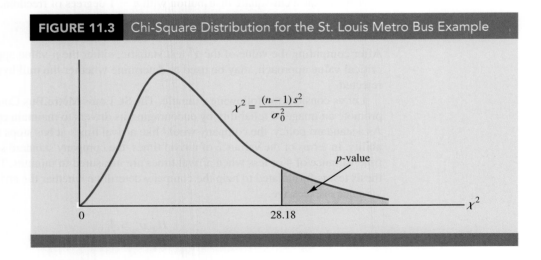

FIGURE 11.3   Chi-Square Distribution for the St. Louis Metro Bus Example

the upper tail hypothesis test. Using Table 11.1 and 23 degrees of freedom, $\chi^2_{.05} = 35.172$. Thus, the rejection rule for the bus arrival time example is as follows:

$$\text{Reject } H_0 \text{ if } \chi^2 \geq 35.172$$

Because the value of the test statistic is $\chi^2 = 28.18$, we cannot reject the null hypothesis.

In practice, upper tail tests as presented here are the most frequently encountered tests about a population variance. In situations involving arrival times, production times, filling weights, part dimensions, and so on, low variances are desirable, whereas large variances are unacceptable. With a statement about the maximum allowable population variance, we can test the null hypothesis that the population variance is less than or equal to the maximum allowable value against the alternative hypothesis that the population variance is greater than the maximum allowable value. With this test structure, corrective action will be taken whenever rejection of the null hypothesis indicates the presence of an excessive population variance.

As we saw with population means and proportions, other forms of hypothesis tests can be developed. Let us demonstrate a two-tailed test about a population variance by considering a situation faced by a bureau of motor vehicles. Historically, the variance in test scores for individuals applying for driver's licenses has been $\sigma^2 = 100$. A new examination with new test questions has been developed. Administrators of the bureau of motor vehicles would like the variance in the test scores for the new examination to remain at the historical level. To evaluate the variance in the new examination test scores, the following two-tailed hypothesis test has been proposed.

$$H_0\colon \sigma^2 = 100$$
$$H_a\colon \sigma^2 \neq 100$$

Rejection of H_0 will indicate that a change in the variance has occurred and suggest that some questions in the new examination may need revision to make the variance of the new test scores similar to the variance of the old test scores. A sample of 30 applicants for driver's licenses will be given the new version of the examination. We will use a level of significance $\alpha = .05$ to conduct the hypothesis test.

The sample of 30 examination scores provided a sample variance $s^2 = 162$. The value of the chi-square test statistic is as follows:

$$\chi^2 = \frac{(n-1)s^2}{\sigma_0^2} = \frac{(30-1)(162)}{100} = 46.98$$

Now, let us compute the p-value. Using Table 11.1 and $n - 1 = 30 - 1 = 29$ degrees of freedom, we find the following.

Area in Upper Tail	.10	.05	.025	.01
χ^2 Value (29 df)	39.087	42.557	45.722	49.588

$$\chi^2 = 46.98$$

Thus, the value of the test statistic $\chi^2 = 46.98$ provides an area between .025 and .01 in the upper tail of the chi-square distribution. Doubling these values shows that the two-tailed p-value is between .05 and .02. Statistical software can be used to show the exact p-value = .0374. With p-value $\leq \alpha = .05$, we reject H_0 and conclude that the new examination test

TABLE 11.2	Summary of Hypothesis Tests About a Population Variance		
	Lower Tail Test	**Upper Tail Test**	**Two-Tailed Test**
Hypotheses	$H_0: \sigma^2 \geq \sigma_0^2$ $H_a: \sigma^2 < \sigma_0^2$	$H_0: \sigma^2 \leq \sigma_0^2$ $H_a: \sigma^2 > \sigma_0^2$	$H_0: \sigma^2 = \sigma_0^2$ $H_a: \sigma^2 \neq \sigma_0^2$
Test Statistic	$\chi^2 = \dfrac{(n-1)s^2}{\sigma_0^2}$	$\chi^2 = \dfrac{(n-1)s^2}{\sigma_0^2}$	$\chi^2 = \dfrac{(n-1)s^2}{\sigma_0^2}$
Rejection Rule: **p-value Approach**	Reject H_0 if p-value $\leq \alpha$	Reject H_0 if p-value $\leq \alpha$	Reject H_0 if p-value $\leq \alpha$
Rejection Rule: **Critical Value** **Approach**	Reject H_0 if $\chi^2 \leq \chi^2_{(1-\alpha)}$	Reject H_0 if $\chi^2 \geq \chi^2_{\alpha}$	Reject H_0 if $\chi^2 \leq \chi^2_{(1-\alpha/2)}$ or if $\chi^2 \geq \chi^2_{\alpha/2}$

scores have a population variance different from the historical variance of $\sigma^2 = 100$. A summary of the hypothesis testing procedures for a population variance is shown in Table 11.2.

EXERCISES

Methods

1. Find the following chi-square distribution values from Table 11.1 or Table 3 of Appendix B.
   a. $\chi^2_{.05}$ with $df = 5$
   b. $\chi^2_{.025}$ with $df = 15$
   c. $\chi^2_{.975}$ with $df = 20$
   d. $\chi^2_{.01}$ with $df = 10$
   e. $\chi^2_{.95}$ with $df = 18$

2. A sample of 20 items provides a sample standard deviation of 5.
   a. Compute the 90% confidence interval estimate of the population variance.
   b. Compute the 95% confidence interval estimate of the population variance.
   c. Compute the 95% confidence interval estimate of the population standard deviation.

3. A sample of 16 items provides a sample standard deviation of 9.5. Test the following hypotheses using $\alpha = .05$. What is your conclusion? Use both the p-value approach and the critical value approach.

$$H_0: \sigma^2 \leq 50$$
$$H_a: \sigma^2 > 50$$

Applications

4. **Package Delivery by Drones.** Amazon.com is testing the use of drones to deliver packages for same-day delivery. In order to quote narrow time windows, the variability in delivery times must be sufficiently small. Consider a sample of 24 drone deliveries with a sample variance of $s^2 = .81$.
   a. Construct a 90% confidence interval estimate of the population variance for the drone delivery time.
   b. Construct a 90% confidence interval estimate of the population standard deviation.

CoachSalary

5. **College Basketball Coaches' Salaries.** In 2018, Mike Krzyewski and John Calipari topped the list of highest-paid college basketball coaches (*Sports Illustrated* website, https://www.si.com/college-basketball/2018/03/01/highest-paid-college-basketball -coaches-salaries-mike-krzyewski-john-calipari). The sample below shows the head basketball coach's salary for a sample of 10 schools playing NCAA Division I basketball. Salary data are in millions of dollars.

University	Coach's Salary	University	Coach's Salary
North Carolina State	2.2	Miami (FL)	1.5
Iona	.5	Creighton	1.3
Texas A&M	2.4	Texas Tech	1.5
Oregon	2.7	South Dakota State	.3
Iowa State	2.0	New Mexico State	.3

   a. Use the sample mean for the 10 schools to estimate the population mean annual salary for head basketball coaches at colleges and universities playing NCAA Division I basketball.
   b. Use the data to estimate the population standard deviation for the annual salary for head basketball coaches.
   c. What is the 95% confidence interval for the population variance?
   d. What is the 95% confidence interval for the population standard deviation?

6. **Volatility of General Electric Stock.** To analyze the risk, or volatility, associated with investing in General Electric common stock, consider a sample of the eight quarterly percent total returns. The percent total return includes the stock price change plus the dividend payment for the quarter.

$$20.0 \quad -20.5 \quad 12.2 \quad 12.6 \quad 10.5 \quad -5.8 \quad -18.7 \quad 15.3$$

   a. What is the value of the sample mean? What is its interpretation?
   b. Compute the sample variance and sample standard deviation as measures of volatility for the quarterly return for General Electric.
   c. Construct a 95% confidence interval for the population variance.
   d. Construct a 95% confidence interval for the population standard deviation.

Halloween

7. **Halloween Spending.** In 2017, Americans spent a record-high $9.1 billion on Halloween-related purchases (*the balance* website, https://www.thebalance.com /halloween-spending-statistics-facts-and-trends-3305716). Sample data showing the amount, in dollars, 16 adults spent on a Halloween costume are as follows.

12	69	22	64
33	36	31	44
52	16	13	98
45	32	63	26

   a. What is the estimate of the population mean amount adults spend on a Halloween costume?
   b. What is the sample standard deviation?
   c. Provide a 95% confidence interval estimate of the population standard deviation for the amount adults spend on a Halloween costume.

8. **Variability in Daily Change in Stock Price.** Consider a day when the Dow Jones Industrial Average went up 149.82 points. The following table shows the stock price changes for a sample of 12 companies on that day.
   a. Compute the sample variance for the daily price change.
   b. Compute the sample standard deviation for the price change.

Price Change		Price Change	
Company	**($)**	**Company**	**($)**
Aflac	.81	Johnson & Johnson	1.46
Altice USA	.41	Loews Corporation	.92
Bank of America	−.05	Nokia Corporation	.21
Diageo plc	1.32	Sempra Energy	.97
Fluor Corporation	2.37	Sunoco LP	.52
Goodrich Petroleum	.3	Tyson Foods, Inc.	.12

   c. Provide 95% confidence interval estimates of the population variance and the population standard deviation.

9. **Aerospace Part Manufacturing.** The competitive advantage of small American factories such as Tolerance Contract Manufacturing lies in their ability to produce parts with highly narrow requirements, or tolerances, that are typical in the aerospace industry. Consider a product with specifications that call for a maximum variance in the lengths of the parts of .0004. Suppose the sample variance for 30 parts turns out to be $s^2 = .0005$. Use $\alpha = .05$ to test whether the population variance specification is being violated.

10. **Costco Customer Satisfaction.** *Consumer Reports* uses a 100-point customer satisfaction score to rate the nation's major chain stores. Assume that from past experience with the satisfaction rating score, a population standard deviation of $\sigma = 12$ is expected. In 2012, Costco, with its 432 warehouses in 40 states, was the only chain store to earn an outstanding rating for overall quality. A sample of 15 Costco customer satisfaction scores follows.

95	90	83	75	95
98	80	83	82	93
86	80	94	64	62

   a. What is the sample mean customer satisfaction score for Costco?

   b. What is the sample variance?

   c. What is the sample standard deviation?

   d. Construct a hypothesis test to determine whether the population standard deviation of $\sigma = 12$ should be rejected for Costco. With a .05 level of significance, what is your conclusion?

11. **Variability in GMAT Scores.** In 2016, the Graduate Management Admission Council reported that the variance in GMAT scores was 14,660. At a recent summit, a group of economics professors met to discuss the GMAT performance of undergraduate students majoring in economics. Some expected the variability in GMAT scores achieved by undergraduate economics students to be greater than the variability in GMAT scores of the general population of GMAT takers. However, others took the opposite view. The file *EconGMAT* contains GMAT scores for 51 randomly selected undergraduate students majoring in economics.

   a. Compute the mean, variance, and standard deviation of the GMAT scores for the 51 observations.

   b. Develop hypotheses to test whether the sample data indicate that the variance in GMAT scores for undergraduate students majoring in economics differs from the general population of GMAT takers.

   c. Use $\alpha = .05$ to conduct the hypothesis test formulated in part (b). What is your conclusion?

12. **Vehicle Ownership by Fortune Magazine Subscribers.** A *Fortune* study found that the variance in the number of vehicles owned or leased by subscribers to *Fortune* magazine is .94. Assume a sample of 12 subscribers to another magazine provided the

following data on the number of vehicles owned or leased: 2, 1, 2, 0, 3, 2, 2, 1, 2, 1, 0, and 1.

a. Compute the sample variance in the number of vehicles owned or leased by the 12 subscribers.

b. Test the hypothesis H_0: $\sigma^2 = .94$ to determine whether the variance in the number of vehicles owned or leased by subscribers of the other magazine differs from $\sigma^2 = .94$ for *Fortune*. At a .05 level of significance, what is your conclusion?

11.2 Inferences About Two Population Variances

In some statistical applications we may want to compare the variances in product quality resulting from two different production processes, the variances in assembly times for two assembly methods, or the variances in temperatures for two heating devices. In making comparisons about the two population variances, we will be using data collected from two independent random samples, one from population 1 and another from population 2. The two sample variances s_1^2 and s_2^2 will be the basis for making inferences about the two population variances σ_1^2 and σ_2^2. Whenever the variances of two normal populations are equal ($\sigma_1^2 = \sigma_2^2$), the sampling distribution of the ratio of the two sample variances s_1^2/s_2^2 is as follows.

SAMPLING DISTRIBUTION OF s_1^2/s_2^2 WHEN $\sigma_1^2 = \sigma_2^2$

Whenever independent simple random samples of sizes n_1 and n_2 are selected from two normal populations with equal variances, the sampling distribution of

$$\frac{s_1^2}{s_2^2} \qquad\qquad\textbf{(11.9)}$$

The F distribution is based on sampling from two normal populations.

is an *F* distribution with $n_1 - 1$ degrees of freedom for the numerator and $n_2 - 1$ degrees of freedom for the denominator; s_1^2 is the sample variance for the random sample of n_1 items from population 1, and s_2^2 is the sample variance for the random sample of n_2 items from population 2.

Figure 11.4 is a graph of the *F* distribution with 20 degrees of freedom for both the numerator and denominator. As indicated by this graph, the *F* distribution is not symmetric,

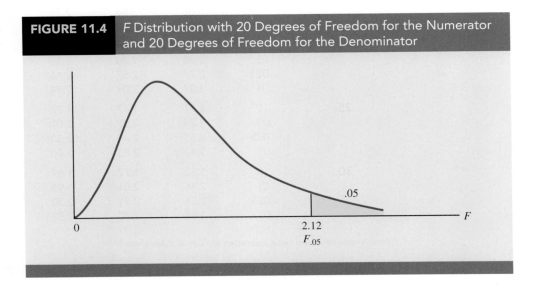

| **FIGURE 11.4** | *F* Distribution with 20 Degrees of Freedom for the Numerator and 20 Degrees of Freedom for the Denominator |

and the F values can never be negative. The shape of any particular F distribution depends on its numerator and denominator degrees of freedom.

We will use F_α to denote the value of F that provides an area or probability of α in the upper tail of the distribution. For example, as noted in Figure 11.4, $F_{.05}$ denotes the upper tail area of .05 for an F distribution with 20 degrees of freedom for the numerator and 20 degrees of freedom for the denominator. The specific value of $F_{.05}$ can be found by referring to the F distribution table, a portion of which is shown in Table 11.3. Using 20 degrees of freedom for the numerator, 20 degrees of freedom for the denominator, and the row corresponding to an area of .05 in the upper tail, we find $F_{.05} = 2.12$. Note that the

TABLE 11.3 Selected Values from the F Distribution Table*

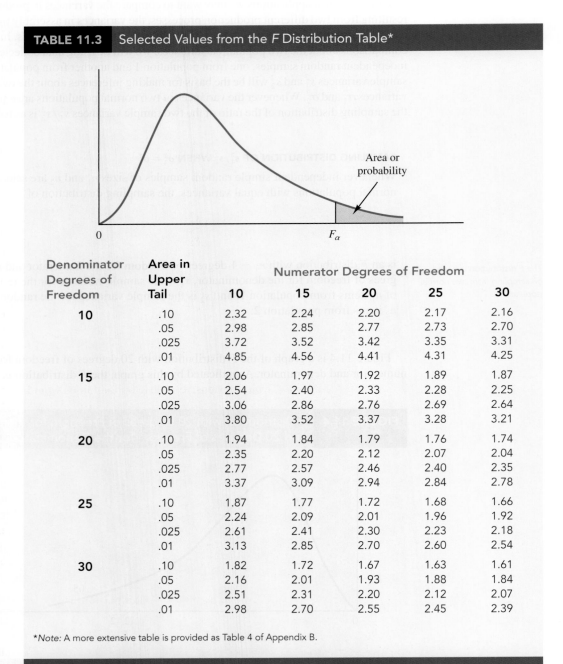

Denominator Degrees of Freedom	Area in Upper Tail	Numerator Degrees of Freedom				
		10	15	20	25	30
10	.10	2.32	2.24	2.20	2.17	2.16
	.05	2.98	2.85	2.77	2.73	2.70
	.025	3.72	3.52	3.42	3.35	3.31
	.01	4.85	4.56	4.41	4.31	4.25
15	.10	2.06	1.97	1.92	1.89	1.87
	.05	2.54	2.40	2.33	2.28	2.25
	.025	3.06	2.86	2.76	2.69	2.64
	.01	3.80	3.52	3.37	3.28	3.21
20	.10	1.94	1.84	1.79	1.76	1.74
	.05	2.35	2.20	2.12	2.07	2.04
	.025	2.77	2.57	2.46	2.40	2.35
	.01	3.37	3.09	2.94	2.84	2.78
25	.10	1.87	1.77	1.72	1.68	1.66
	.05	2.24	2.09	2.01	1.96	1.92
	.025	2.61	2.41	2.30	2.23	2.18
	.01	3.13	2.85	2.70	2.60	2.54
30	.10	1.82	1.72	1.67	1.63	1.61
	.05	2.16	2.01	1.93	1.88	1.84
	.025	2.51	2.31	2.20	2.12	2.07
	.01	2.98	2.70	2.55	2.45	2.39

*Note: A more extensive table is provided as Table 4 of Appendix B.

table can be used to find F values for upper tail areas of .10, .05, .025, and .01. See Table 4 of Appendix B for a more extensive table for the F distribution.

Let us show how the F distribution can be used to conduct a hypothesis test about the variances of two populations. We begin with a test of the equality of two population variances. The hypotheses are stated as follows.

$$H_0: \sigma_1^2 = \sigma_2^2$$
$$H_a: \sigma_1^2 \neq \sigma_2^2$$

We make the tentative assumption that the population variances are equal. If H_0 is rejected, we will draw the conclusion that the population variances are not equal.

The procedure used to conduct the hypothesis test requires two independent random samples, one from each population. The two sample variances are then computed. We refer to the population providing the *larger* sample variance as population 1. Thus, a sample size of n_1 and a sample variance of s_1^2 correspond to population 1, and a sample size of n_2 and a sample variance of s_2^2 correspond to population 2. Based on the assumption that both populations have a normal distribution, the ratio of sample variances provides the following F test statistic.

TEST STATISTIC FOR HYPOTHESIS TESTS ABOUT POPULATION VARIANCES WITH $\sigma_1^2 = \sigma_2^2$

$$F = \frac{s_1^2}{s_2^2} \tag{11.10}$$

Denoting the population with the larger sample variance as population 1, the test statistic has an F distribution with $n_1 - 1$ degrees of freedom for the numerator and $n_2 - 1$ degrees of freedom for the denominator.

Because the F test statistic is constructed with the larger sample variance s_1^2 in the numerator, the value of the test statistic will be in the upper tail of the F distribution. Therefore, the F distribution table as shown in Table 11.3 and in Table 4 of Appendix B need only provide upper tail areas or probabilities. If we did not construct the test statistic in this manner, lower tail areas or probabilities would be needed. In this case, additional calculations or more extensive F distribution tables would be required. Let us now consider an example of a hypothesis test about the equality of two population variances.

Dullus County Schools is renewing its school bus service contract for the coming year and must select one of two bus companies, the Milbank Company or the Gulf Park Company. We will use the variance of the arrival or pickup/delivery times as a primary measure of the quality of the bus service. Low variance values indicate the more consistent and higher-quality service. If the variances of arrival times associated with the two services are equal, Dullus School administrators will select the company offering the better financial terms. However, if the sample data on bus arrival times for the two companies indicate a significant difference between the variances, the administrators may want to give special consideration to the company with the better or lower variance service. The appropriate hypotheses follow.

$$H_0: \sigma_1^2 = \sigma_2^2$$
$$H_a: \sigma_1^2 \neq \sigma_2^2$$

If H_0 can be rejected, the conclusion of unequal service quality is appropriate. We will use a level of significance of $\alpha = .10$ to conduct the hypothesis test.

SchoolBus

A sample of 26 arrival times for the Milbank service provides a sample variance of 48 and a sample of 16 arrival times for the Gulf Park service provides a sample variance of 20. Because the Milbank sample provided the larger sample variance, we will denote Milbank as population 1. Using equation (11.10), we find the value of the test statistic:

$$F = \frac{s_1^2}{s_2^2} = \frac{48}{20} = 2.40$$

The corresponding F distribution has $n_1 - 1 = 26 - 1 = 25$ numerator degrees of freedom and $n_2 - 1 = 16 - 1 = 15$ denominator degrees of freedom.

As with other hypothesis testing procedures, we can use the p-value approach or the critical value approach to obtain the hypothesis testing conclusion. Table 11.3 shows the following areas in the upper tail and corresponding F values for an F distribution with 25 numerator degrees of freedom and 15 denominator degrees of freedom.

Area in Upper Tail	.10	.05	.025	.01
F Value ($df_1 = 25, df_2 = 15$)	1.89	2.28	2.69	3.28

$$F = 2.40$$

Because $F = 2.40$ is between 2.28 and 2.69, the area in the upper tail of the distribution is between .05 and .025. For this two-tailed test, we double the upper tail area, which results in a p-value between .10 and .05. Because we selected $\alpha = .10$ as the level of significance, the p-value $< \alpha = .10$. Thus, the null hypothesis is rejected. This finding leads to the conclusion that the two bus services differ in terms of pickup/delivery time variances. The recommendation is that the Dullus County School administrators give special consideration to the better or lower variance service offered by the Gulf Park Company.

We can use statistical software to show that the test statistic $F = 2.40$ provides a two-tailed p-value $= .0811$. With $.0811 < \alpha = .10$, the null hypothesis of equal population variances is rejected.

To use the critical value approach to conduct the two-tailed hypothesis test at the $\alpha = .10$ level of significance, we would select critical values with an area of $\alpha/2 = .10/2 = .05$ in each tail of the distribution. Because the value of the test statistic computed using equation (11.10) will always be in the upper tail, we only need to determine the upper tail critical value. From Table 11.3, we see that $F_{.05} = 2.28$. Thus, even though we use a two-tailed test, the rejection rule is stated as follows.

$$\text{Reject } H_0 \text{ if } F \geq 2.28$$

Because the test statistic $F = 2.40$ is greater than 2.28, we reject H_0 and conclude that the two bus services differ in terms of pickup/delivery time variances.

One-tailed tests involving two population variances are also possible. In this case, we use the F distribution to determine whether one population variance is significantly greater than the other. A one-tailed hypothesis test about two population variances will always be formulated as an *upper tail* test:

$$H_0: \sigma_1^2 \leq \sigma_2^2$$
$$H_a: \sigma_1^2 > \sigma_2^2$$

A one-tailed hypothesis test about two population variances can always be formulated as an upper tail test. This approach eliminates the need for lower tail F values.

This form of the hypothesis test always places the p-value and the critical value in the upper tail of the F distribution. As a result, only upper tail F values will be needed, simplifying both the computations and the table for the F distribution.

Let us demonstrate the use of the F distribution to conduct a one-tailed test about the variances of two populations by considering a public opinion survey. Samples of 31 men and 41 women will be used to study attitudes about current political issues. The researcher conducting the study wants to test to see whether the sample data indicate that women show a greater variation in attitude on political issues than men. In the form of the one-tailed hypothesis test given previously, women will be denoted as population 1 and men will be denoted as population 2. The hypothesis test will be stated as follows.

$$H_0: \sigma^2_{\text{women}} \leq \sigma^2_{\text{men}}$$
$$H_a: \sigma^2_{\text{women}} > \sigma^2_{\text{men}}$$

A rejection of H_0 gives the researcher the statistical support necessary to conclude that women show a greater variation in attitude on political issues.

With the sample variance for women in the numerator and the sample variance for men in the denominator, the F distribution will have $n_1 - 1 = 41 - 1 = 40$ numerator degrees of freedom and $n_2 - 1 = 31 - 1 = 30$ denominator degrees of freedom. We will use a level of significance $\alpha = .05$ to conduct the hypothesis test. The survey results provide a sample variance of $s^2_1 = 120$ for women and a sample variance of $s^2_2 = 80$ for men. The test statistic is as follows.

$$F = \frac{s^2_1}{s^2_2} = \frac{120}{80} = 1.50$$

Referring to Table 4 in Appendix B, we find that an F distribution with 40 numerator degrees of freedom and 30 denominator degrees of freedom has $F_{.10} = 1.57$. Because the test statistic $F = 1.50$ is less than 1.57, the area in the upper tail must be greater than .10. Thus, we can conclude that the p-value is greater than .10. Using statistical software provides a p-value = .1256. Because the p-value > $\alpha = .05$, H_0 cannot be rejected. Hence, the sample results do not support the conclusion that women show greater variation in attitude on political issues than men. Table 11.4 provides a summary of hypothesis tests about two population variances.

TABLE 11.4   Summary of Hypothesis Tests About Two Population Variances

	Upper Tail Test	Two-Tailed Test
Hypotheses	$H_0: \sigma^2_1 \leq \sigma^2_2$ $H_a: \sigma^2_1 > \sigma^2_2$	$H_0: \sigma^2_1 = \sigma^2_2$ $H_a: \sigma^2_1 \neq \sigma^2_2$
		Note: Population 1 has the larger sample variance
Test Statistic	$F = \dfrac{s^2_1}{s^2_2}$	$F = \dfrac{s^2_1}{s^2_2}$
Rejection Rule: *p*-value	Reject H_0 if p-value $\leq \alpha$	Reject H_0 if p-value $\leq \alpha$
Rejection Rule: **Critical Value** **Approach**	Reject H_0 if $F \geq F_\alpha$	Reject H_0 if $F \geq F_{\alpha/2}$

NOTES + COMMENTS

Research confirms the fact that the F distribution is sensitive to the assumption of normal populations. The F distribution should not be used unless it is reasonable to assume that both populations are at least approximately normally distributed.

EXERCISES

Methods

13. Find the following F distribution values from Table 4 of Appendix B.
    a. $F_{.05}$ with degrees of freedom 5 and 10
    b. $F_{.025}$ with degrees of freedom 20 and 15
    c. $F_{.01}$ with degrees of freedom 8 and 12
    d. $F_{.10}$ with degrees of freedom 10 and 20

14. A sample of 16 items from population 1 has a sample variance $s_1^2 = 5.8$ and a sample of 21 items from population 2 has a sample variance $s_2^2 = 2.4$. Test the following hypotheses at the .05 level of significance.

$$H_0: \sigma_1^2 \leq \sigma_2^2$$
$$H_a: \sigma_1^2 > \sigma_2^2$$

a. What is your conclusion using the p-value approach?
b. Repeat the test using the critical value approach.

15. Consider the following hypothesis test.

$$H_0: \sigma_1^2 = \sigma_2^2$$
$$H_a: \sigma_1^2 \neq \sigma_2^2$$

a. What is your conclusion if $n_1 = 21$, $s_1^2 = 8.2$, $n_2 = 26$, and $s_2^2 = 4.0$? Use $\alpha = .05$ and the p-value approach.
b. Repeat the test using the critical value approach.

Applications

16. **Comparing Risk of Mutual Funds.** Investors commonly use the standard deviation of the monthly percentage return for a mutual fund as a measure of the risk for the fund; in such cases, a fund that has a larger standard deviation is considered more risky than a fund with a lower standard deviation. The standard deviation for the American Century Equity Growth fund and the standard deviation for the Fidelity Growth Discovery fund were recently reported to be 15.0% and 18.9%, respectively. Assume that each of these standard deviations is based on a sample of 60 months of returns. Do the sample results support the conclusion that the Fidelity fund has a larger population variance than the American Century fund? Which fund is more risky?

17. **Repair Costs as Automobiles Age.** In its 2016 Auto Reliability Survey, *Consumer Reports* asked subscribers to report their maintenance and repair costs. Most individuals are aware of the fact that the average annual repair cost for an automobile depends on the age of the automobile. A researcher is interested in finding out whether the variance of the annual repair costs also increases with the age of the automobile. A sample of 26 automobiles 4 years old showed a sample standard deviation for annual repair costs of $170 and a sample of 25 automobiles 2 years old showed a sample standard deviation for annual repair costs of $100.
    a. State the null and alternative versions of the research hypothesis that the variance in annual repair costs is larger for the older automobiles.
    b. At a .01 level of significance, what is your conclusion? What is the p-value? Discuss the reasonableness of your findings.

18. **Variance in Fund Amounts: Merrill Lynch versus Morgan Stanley.** Barron's has collected data on the top 1000 financial advisers. Merrill Lynch and Morgan Stanley have many of their advisers on this list. A sample of 16 of the Merrill Lynch advisers and 10 of the Morgan Stanley advisers showed that the advisers managed many very large accounts with a large variance in the total amount of funds managed. The standard deviation of the amount managed by the Merrill Lynch advisers was $s_1 =$ \$587 million. The standard deviation of the amount managed by the Morgan Stanley advisers was $s_2 =$ \$489 million. Conduct a hypothesis test at $\alpha = .10$ to determine if there is a significant difference in the population variances for the amounts managed by the two companies. What is your conclusion about the variability in the amount of funds managed by advisers from the two firms?

DATA *file*

Bags

19. **Bag-Filling Machines at Jelly Belly.** The variance in a production process is an important measure of the quality of the process. A large variance often signals an opportunity for improvement in the process by finding ways to reduce the process variance. Jelly Belly Candy Company is testing two machines that use different technologies to fill three pound bags of jelly beans. The file *Bags* contains a sample of data on the weights of bags (in pounds) filled by each machine. Conduct a statistical test to determine whether there is a significant difference between the variances in the bag weights for two machines. Use a .05 level of significance. What is your conclusion? Which machine, if either, provides the greater opportunity for quality improvements?

20. **Salaries at Public Accounting Firms.** On the basis of data provided by a Romac salary survey, the variance in annual salaries for senior partners in public accounting firms is approximately 2.1 and the variance in annual salaries for managers in public accounting firms is approximately 11.1. The salary data were provided in thousands of dollars. Assuming that the salary data were based on samples of 25 senior partners and 26 managers, test the hypothesis that the population variances in the salaries are equal. At a .05 level of significance, what is your conclusion?

DATA *file*

BatteryLife

21. **Smartphone Battery Life.** Battery life is an important issue for many smartphone owners. Public health studies have examined "low-battery anxiety" and acute anxiety called *nomophobia* that results when a smartphone user's phone battery charge runs low and then dies (*Wall Street Journal*, https://www.wsj.com/articles/your-phone-is-almost -out-of-battery-remain-calm-call-a-doctor-1525449283). Battery life between charges for the Samsung Galaxy S9 averages 31 hours when the primary use is talk time and 10 hours when the primary use is Internet applications. Because the mean hours for talk time usage is greater than the mean hours for Internet usage, the question was raised as to whether the variance in hours of usage is also greater when the primary use is talk time. Sample data showing battery life between charges for the two applications follows.

Primary Use: Talking

35.8	22.2	24.0	32.6	18.5	42.5
28.0	23.8	30.0	22.8	20.3	35.5

Primary Use: Internet

14.0	12.5	16.4	11.9	9.9	3.1
5.4	11.0	15.2	4.0	4.7	

a. Formulate hypotheses about the two population variances that can be used to determine if the population variance in battery life is greater for the talk time application.

b. What are the standard deviations of battery life for the two samples?

c. Conduct the hypothesis test and compute the *p*-value. Using a .05 level of significance, what is your conclusion?

22. **Stopping Distances of Automobiles.** A research hypothesis is that the variance of stopping distances of automobiles on wet pavement is substantially greater than the variance of stopping distances of automobiles on dry pavement. In the research study, 16 automobiles traveling at the same speeds are tested for stopping distances on wet pavement and then tested for stopping distances on dry pavement. On wet pavement, the standard deviation of stopping distances is 32 feet. On dry pavement, the standard deviation is 16 feet.

a. At a .05 level of significance, do the sample data justify the conclusion that the variance in stopping distances on wet pavement is greater than the variance in stopping distances on dry pavement? What is the *p*-value?

b. What are the implications of your statistical conclusions in terms of driving safety recommendations?

SUMMARY

In this chapter we presented statistical procedures that can be used to make inferences about population variances. In the process we introduced two new probability distributions: the chi-square distribution and the *F* distribution. The chi-square distribution can be used as the basis for interval estimation and hypothesis tests about the variance of a normal population.

We illustrated the use of the *F* distribution in hypothesis tests about the variances of two normal populations. In particular, we showed that with independent simple random samples of sizes n_1 and n_2 selected from two normal populations with equal variances $\sigma_1^2 = \sigma_2^2$, the sampling distribution of the ratio of the two sample variances s_1^2/s_2^2 has an *F* distribution with $n_1 - 1$ degrees of freedom for the numerator and $n_2 - 1$ degrees of freedom for the denominator.

KEY FORMULAS

Interval Estimate of a Population Variance

$$\frac{(n-1)s^2}{\chi_{\alpha/2}^2} \le \sigma^2 \le \frac{(n-1)s^2}{\chi_{(1-\alpha/2)}^2} \qquad (11.7)$$

Test Statistic for Hypothesis Tests About a Population Variance

$$\chi^2 = \frac{(n-1)s^2}{\sigma_0^2} \qquad (11.8)$$

Test Statistic for Hypothesis Tests About Population Variances with $\sigma_1^2 = \sigma_2^2$

$$F = \frac{s_1^2}{s_2^2} \qquad (11.10)$$

SUPPLEMENTARY EXERCISES

23. **Daily Hotel Room Occupancy.** Because of staffing decisions, managers of the Gibson-Marimont Hotel are interested in the variability in the number of rooms occupied per day during a particular season of the year. A sample of 20 days of operation shows a sample mean of 290 rooms occupied per day and a sample standard deviation of 30 rooms.

a. What is the point estimate of the population variance?

b. Provide a 90% confidence interval estimate of the population variance.

c. Provide a 90% confidence interval estimate of the population standard deviation.

24. **Pricing of Initial Public Offerings.** Initial public offerings (IPOs) of stocks are on average underpriced. The standard deviation measures the dispersion, or variation, in the underpricing-overpricing indicator. A sample of 13 Canadian IPOs that were subsequently traded on the Toronto Stock Exchange had a standard deviation of 14.95. Develop a 95% confidence interval estimate of the population standard deviation for the underpricing-overpricing indicator.

25. **Business Travel Costs.** According to the 2017 Corporate Travel Index compiled by *Business Travel News*, the average daily cost for business travel in the United States rose to $321 per day (*Executive Travel* website, https://executivetravel.com/new -business-travel-study-says-average-per-diem-is-now-321day/). The file *Travel* contains sample data for an analogous study on the estimated daily living costs for an executive traveling to various international cities. The estimates include a single room at a four-star hotel, beverages, breakfast, taxi fares, and incidental costs.

Travel

City	Daily Living Cost ($)	City	Daily Living Cost ($)
Bangkok	242.87	Mexico City	212.00
Bogotá	260.93	Milan	284.08
Cairo	194.19	Mumbai	139.16
Dublin	260.76	Paris	436.72
Frankfurt	355.36	Rio de Janeiro	240.87
Hong Kong	346.32	Seoul	310.41
Johannesburg	165.37	Tel Aviv	223.73
Lima	250.08	Toronto	181.25
London	326.76	Warsaw	238.20
Madrid	283.56	Washington, D.C.	250.61

a. Compute the sample mean.

b. Compute the sample standard deviation.

c. Compute a 95% confidence interval for the population standard deviation.

26. **Manufacture of Ball Bearings.** Ball bearing manufacturing is a highly precise business in which minimal part variability is critical. Large variances in the size of the ball bearings cause bearing failure and rapid wearout. Production standards call for a maximum variance of .0001 inches^2. Gerry Liddy has gathered a sample of 15 bearings that shows a sample standard deviation of .014 inches.

a. Use $\alpha = .10$ to determine whether the sample indicates that the maximum acceptable variance is being exceeded.

b. Compute the 90% confidence interval estimate of the variance of the ball bearings in the population.

27. **Count Chocula Cereal.** Filling boxes with consistent amounts of its cereals is critical to General Mills's success. The filling variance for boxes of Count Chocula cereal is designed to be .02 ounces^2 or less. A sample of 41 boxes of Count Chocula shows a sample standard deviation of .16 ounces. Use $\alpha = .05$ to determine whether the variance in the cereal box fillings is exceeding the design specification.

28. **OrderUp Food Delivery.** OrderUp is a service that delivers food that its customers order online from participating restaurants. OrderUp claims consistent delivery times for its deliveries. A sample of 22 meal deliveries shows a sample variance of 1.5. Test to determine whether $H_0: \sigma^2 \leq 1$ can be rejected. Use $\alpha = .10$.

29. **Daily Patient Volume at Dental Clinic.** A sample of 9 days over the past six months showed that Philip Sherman, DDS, treated the following numbers of patients at his dental clinic: 22, 25, 20, 18, 15, 22, 24, 19, and 26. If the number of patients seen per day is normally distributed, would an analysis of these sample data reject the hypothesis that the variance in the number of patients seen per day is equal to 10? Use a .10 level of significance. What is your conclusion?

30. **Passenger Volume on Allegiant Airlines.** A sample standard deviation for the number of passengers taking a particular Allegiant Airlines flight is 8. A 95% confidence interval estimate of the population standard deviation is 5.86 passengers to 12.62 passengers.

    a. Was a sample size of 10 or 15 used in the statistical analysis?
    b. Suppose the sample standard deviation of $s = 8$ was based on a sample of 25 flights. What change would you expect in the confidence interval for the population standard deviation? Compute a 95% confidence interval estimate of σ with a sample size of 25.

31. **Golf Scores.** Is there any difference in the variability in golf scores for players on the LPGA Tour (the women's professional golf tour) and players on the PGA Tour (the men's professional golf tour)? A sample of 20 tournament scores from LPGA events showed a standard deviation of 2.4623 strokes, and a sample of 30 tournament scores from PGA events showed a standard deviation of 2.2118. Conduct a hypothesis test for equal population variances to determine if there is any statistically significant difference in the variability of golf scores for male and female professional golfers. Use $\alpha = .10$. What is your conclusion?

32. **Grade Point Average Comparison.** The grade point averages of 352 students who completed a college course in financial accounting have a standard deviation of .940. The grade point averages of 73 students who dropped out of the same course have a standard deviation of .797. Do the data indicate a difference between the variances of grade point averages for students who completed a financial accounting course and students who dropped out? Use a .05 level of significance. *Note:* $F_{.025}$ with 351 and 72 degrees of freedom is 1.466.

33. **Weekly Cost Reporting.** Stable cost reporting in a manufacturing setting is typically a sign that operations are running smoothly. The accounting department at Rockwell Collins, an avionics manufacturer, analyzes the variance of the weekly costs reported by two of its production departments. A sample of 16 cost reports for each of the two departments shows cost variances of 2.3 and 5.4, respectively. Is this sample sufficient to conclude that the two production departments differ in terms of weekly cost variance? Use $\alpha = .10$.

34. **Lean Process Improvement at the New York City Food Bank.** In an effort to make better use of its resources, the New York City Food Bank engaged in lean process improvement. This employee-driven kaizen effort resulted in a new method for packing meals for distribution to needy families. One goal of the process improvement effort was to reduce the variability in the meal-packing time. The following table summarizes information from a sample of data using the current method and the new method. Did the kaizen event successfully reduce the population variation? Use $\alpha = .10$ and formulate the appropriate hypothesis test.

	Current Method	New Method
Sample Size	$n_1 = 31$	$n_2 = 25$
Sample Variance	$s_1^2 = 25$	$s_2^2 = 12$

CASE PROBLEM 1: AIR FORCE TRAINING PROGRAM

An Air Force introductory course in electronics uses a personalized system of instruction whereby each student views a videotaped lecture and then is given a programmed instruction text. The students work independently with the text until they have completed the training and passed a test. Of concern is the varying pace at which the students complete this portion of their training program. Some students are able to cover the programmed instruction text relatively quickly, whereas other students work much longer with the text and require additional time to complete the course. The fast students wait until the slow students complete the introductory course before the entire group proceeds together with other aspects of their training.

A proposed alternative system involves use of computer-assisted instruction. In this method, all students view the same videotaped lecture and then each is assigned to a computer terminal for further instruction. The computer guides the student, working independently, through the self-training portion of the course.

To compare the proposed and current methods of instruction, an entering class of 122 students was assigned randomly to one of the two methods. One group of 61 students used the current programmed-text method and the other group of 61 students used the proposed computer-assisted method. The time in hours was recorded for each student in the study. The following data are provided in the data set Training.

Course Completion Times (hours) for Current Training Method

76	76	77	74	76	74	74	77	72	78	73
78	75	80	79	72	69	79	72	70	70	81
76	78	72	82	72	73	71	70	77	78	73
79	82	65	77	79	73	76	81	69	75	75
77	79	76	78	76	76	73	77	84	74	74
69	79	66	70	74	72					

DATA*file*

Training

Course Completion Times (hours) for Proposed Computer-Assisted Method

74	75	77	78	74	80	73	73	78	76	76
74	77	69	76	75	72	75	72	76	72	77
73	77	69	77	75	76	74	77	75	78	72
77	78	78	76	75	76	76	75	76	80	77
76	75	73	77	77	77	79	75	75	72	82
76	76	74	72	78	71					

Managerial Report

We discuss interval estimation and hypothesis testing on the difference between population means in Chapter 10.

1. Use appropriate descriptive statistics to summarize the training time data for each method. What similarities or differences do you observe from the sample data?
2. Conduct a hypothesis test on the difference between the population means for the two methods. Discuss your findings.
3. Compute the standard deviation and variance for each training method. Conduct a hypothesis test about the equality of population variances for the two training methods. Discuss your findings.
4. What conclusion can you reach about any differences between the two methods? What is your recommendation? Explain.
5. Can you suggest other data or testing that might be desirable before making a final decision on the training program to be used in the future?

CASE PROBLEM 2: METICULOUS DRILL & REAMER

Meticulous Drill & Reamer (MD&R) specializes in drilling and boring precise holes in hard metals (e.g., steel alloys, tungsten carbide, and titanium). The company recently contracted to drill holes with 3-centimeter diameters in large carbon-steel alloy disks, and it will have to purchase a special drill to complete this job. MD&R has eliminated all but two of the drills it has been considering: Davis Drills' T2005 and Worth Industrial Tools' AZ100. These producers have each agreed to allow MD&R to use a T2005 and an AZ100 for one week to determine which drill it will purchase. During the one-week trial, MD&R uses each of these drills to drill 31 holes with a target diameter of 3 centimeters in one large carbon-steel alloy disk, then measures the diameter of each hole and records the results. MD&R's results are provided in the table that follows and are available in the DATAfile named *MeticulousDrills*.

Hole Diameter

T2005	AZ100	T2005	AZ100	T2005	AZ100
3.06	2.91	3.05	2.97	3.04	3.06
3.04	3.31	3.01	3.05	3.01	3.25
3.13	2.82	2.73	2.95	2.95	2.82
3.01	3.01	3.12	2.92	3.14	3.22
2.95	2.94	3.04	2.71	3.31	2.93
3.02	3.17	3.10	2.77	3.01	3.24
3.02	3.25	3.02	2.73	2.93	2.77
3.12	3.39	2.92	3.18	3.00	2.94
3.00	3.22	3.01	2.95	3.04	3.31
3.04	2.97	3.15	2.86		
3.03	2.93	2.69	3.16		

MeticulousDrills

MD&R wants to consider both the accuracy (closeness of the diameter to 3 centimeters) and the precision (the variance of the diameter) of the holes drilled by the T2005 and the AZ100 when deciding which model to purchase.

Managerial Report

In making this assessment for MD&R, consider the following four questions:

1. Are the holes drilled by the T2005 or the AZ100 more accurate? That is, which model of drill produces holes with a mean diameter closer to 3 centimeters?
2. Are the holes drilled by the T2005 or the AZ100 more precise? That is, which model of drill produces holes with a smaller variance?
3. Conduct a test of the hypothesis that the T2005 and the AZ100 are equally precise (that is, have equal variances) at $a = .05$. Discuss your findings.
4. Which drill do you recommend to MD&R? Why?

Chapter 11 Appendix

Appendix 11.1 Population Variances with JMP

We describe the use of JMP to conduct a hypothesis test involving two population variances. We will use the data for the Dullus County School bus study in Section 11.2. The arrival times for Milbank appear in column A, and the arrival times for Gulf Park appear in column B. The following procedure can be used to conduct the hypothesis test $H_0: \sigma_1^2 = \sigma_2^2$ and $H_1: \sigma_1^2 \neq \sigma_2^2$.

DATA *file*

SchoolBus

Step 1. Open the file *SchoolBus* following the steps in Appendix 1.1

Step 2. Convert the file to stacked format following the steps in Appendix 1.1, entering *Time* as the new **Stacked Data Column** name and *Company* as the new **Source Label Column** name

Step 3. Click **Analyze** and select **Fit Y by X**

Step 4. When the **Fit Y by X—Contextual** dialog box appears:

Drag **Time** from the **Select Columns** area to the **Y, Response** box in the **Cast Selected Columns into Roles** area

Drag **Company** from the **Select Columns** area to the **X, Factor** box in the **Cast Selected Columns into Roles** area

Click **OK** in the **Action** area

Step 5. When the **Fit Y by X of Time by Company** window appears:

Click the red triangle next to **Oneway Analysis of Time By Company** and select **Unequal Variances**

These steps will produce the chart displayed in Figure JMP 11.1. The two-tailed *F* test generates the test statistic $F = 2.401$ and the corresponding *p*-value of .0811.

FIGURE JMP 11.1	JMP Output of Hypothesis Test of Equal Variances for School Bus Study Data

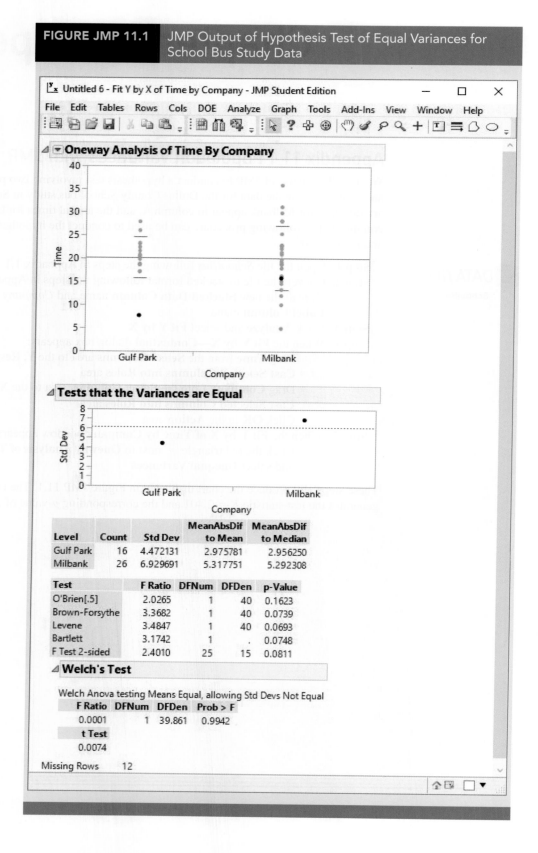

Appendix 11.2 Population Variances with Excel

Here we describe how to use Excel to conduct a hypothesis test involving two population variances.

DATA *file*

SchoolBus

We will use the data for the Dullus County School bus study in Section 11.2. The Excel worksheet has the label "Milbank" in cell A1 and the label "Gulf Park" in cell B1. The times for the Milbank sample are in cells A2:A27 and the times for the Gulf Park sample are in cells B2:B17. The steps to conduct the hypothesis test H_0: $\sigma_1^2 = \sigma_2^2$ and H_a: $\sigma_1^2 \neq \sigma_2^2$ are as follows:

Step 1. Click the **Data** tab on the Ribbon
Step 2. In the **Analyze** group, click **Data Analysis**
Step 3. When the **Data Analysis** dialog box appears:
　　　　　Choose **F-Test Two-Sample for Variances**
　　　　　Click **OK**
Step 4. When the **F-Test Two Sample for Variances** dialog box appears
　　　　　(see Figure Excel 11.1):
　　　　　Enter *A1:A27* in the **Variable 1 Range** box
　　　　　Enter *B1:B17* in the **Variable 2 Range** box
　　　　　Select **Labels**
　　　　　Enter *.05* in the **Alpha** box
　　　　　Select **Output Range** and enter *D1* in the box
　　　　　Click **OK**

This Excel procedure uses alpha as the area in the upper tail.

FIGURE EXCEL 11.1　Conducting Hypothesis Test Involving Two Population Variances for School Bus Study Data in Excel

As Figure Excel 11.2 illustrates, **P(F<=f) one-tail** $= .0405$ in cell E9 is the one-tailed area associated with the test statistic $F = 2.40$. Thus, the two-tailed p-value is $2(.0405) = .081$. If the hypothesis test had been a one-tailed test, the one-tailed area in the cell **P(F<=f) one-tail** provides the information necessary to determine the p-value for the test.

| FIGURE EXCEL 11.2 | Excel Output for Hypothesis Test Involving Two Population Variances for School Bus Study Data |

◢	A	B	C	D	E	F
1	**Milbank**	**Gulf Park**		F-Test Two-Sample for Variances		
2	35.9	21.6				
3	29.9	20.5			*Milbank*	*Gulf Park*
4	31.2	23.3		Mean	20.23077	20.24375
5	16.2	18.8		Variance	48.02062	19.99996
6	19.0	17.2		Observations	26	16
7	15.9	7.7		df	25	15
8	18.8	18.6		F	2.401036	
9	22.2	18.7		P(F<=f) one-tail	0.040527	
10	19.9	20.4		F Critical one-tail	2.279729	

Chapter 12

Comparing Multiple Proportions, Test of Independence and Goodness of Fit

CONTENTS

STATISTICS IN PRACTICE

United Way*

ROCHESTER, NEW YORK

United Way of Greater Rochester is a nonprofit organization dedicated to improving the quality of life for all people in the seven counties it serves by meeting the community's most important human care needs.

The annual United Way/Red Cross fund-raising campaign funds hundreds of programs offered by more than 200 service providers. These providers meet a wide variety of human needs—physical, mental, and social—and serve people of all ages, backgrounds, and economic means.

The United Way of Greater Rochester decided to conduct a survey to learn more about community perceptions of charities. Focus-group interviews were held with professional, service, and general worker groups to obtain preliminary information on perceptions. The information obtained was then used to help develop the questionnaire for the survey. The questionnaire was pretested, modified, and distributed to 440 individuals.

A variety of descriptive statistics, including frequency distributions and crosstabulations, were provided from the data collected. An important part of the analysis involved the use of chi-square tests of independence. One use of such statistical tests was to determine whether perceptions of administrative expenses were independent of the occupation of the respondent.

The hypotheses for the test of independence were:

H_0: Perception of United Way administrative expenses is independent of the occupation of the respondent.

H_a: Perception of United Way administrative expenses is not independent of the occupation of the respondent.

United Way programs meet the needs of children as well as adults.
Source: Hero Images/Getty Images

Two questions in the survey provided categorical data for the statistical test. One question obtained data on perceptions of the percentage of funds going to administrative expenses (up to 10%, 11–20%, and 21% or more). The other question asked for the occupation of the respondent.

The test of independence led to rejection of the null hypothesis and to the conclusion that perception of United Way administrative expenses is not independent of the occupation of the respondent. Actual administrative expenses were less than 9%, but 35% of the respondents perceived that administrative expenses were 21% or more. Hence, many respondents had inaccurate perceptions of administrative expenses. In this group, production-line, clerical, sales, and professional-technical employees had the more inaccurate perceptions.

The community perceptions study helped United Way of Rochester develop adjustments to its programs and fund-raising activities. In this chapter, you will learn how tests, such as described here, are conducted.

---

*The authors are indebted to Dr. Philip R. Tyler, marketing consultant to the United Way, for providing the context for this Statistics in Practice.

We introduce hypothesis tests about the means, proportions, and variances of one and two populations in Chapters 9, 10, and 11.

In this chapter, we introduce three hypothesis testing procedures that extend our ability to make statistical inferences about populations. Specifically, we consider cases in which the data are categorical by using a test statistic based on the chi-square (χ^2) distribution. In cases in which data are not naturally categorical, we define categories and consider the observation count in each category. These chi-square tests are versatile and expand hypothesis testing with the following applications.

1. Testing the equality of population proportions for three or more populations
2. Testing the independence of two categorical variables

3. Testing whether a probability distribution for a population follows a specific histor- ical or theoretical probability distribution

We begin by considering hypothesis tests for the equality of population proportions for three or more populations.

12.1 Testing the Equality of Population Proportions for Three or More Populations

We use the chi-square test statistic in a similar manner to how we have used the normal (z) test statistic, t test statistic, and the F test statistic for hypothesis testing in Chapters 9, 10, and 11.

In this section, we show how the chi-square (χ^2) test statistic can be used to make statist- ical inferences about the equality of population proportions for three or more populations. Using the notation

$$p_1 = \text{population proportion for population 1}$$
$$p_2 = \text{population proportion for population 2}$$

and

$$p_k = \text{population proportion for population } k$$

the hypotheses for the equality of population proportions for $k \geq 3$ populations are as follows:

$$H_0: p_1 = p_2 = \cdots = p_k$$
$$H_a: \text{Not all population proportions are equal}$$

If the sample data and the chi-square test computations indicate H_0 cannot be rejected, we cannot detect a difference among the k population proportions. However, if the sample data and the chi-square test computations indicate H_0 can be rejected, we have the stat- istical evidence to conclude that not all k population proportions are equal; that is, one or more population proportions differ from the other population proportions. Further analyses can be done to conclude which population proportion or proportions are signi- ficantly different from others. Let us demonstrate this chi-square test by considering an application.

Organizations such as J.D. Power and Associates use the proportion of owners likely to repurchase a particular automobile as an indication of customer loyalty for the automobile. An automobile with a greater proportion of owners likely to repur- chase is concluded to have greater customer loyalty. Suppose that in a particular study we want to compare the customer loyalty for three automobiles: Chevrolet Impala, Ford Fusion, and Honda Accord. The current owners of each of the three automobiles form the three populations for the study. The three population proportions of interest are as follows:

p_1 = proportion likely to repurchase an Impala for the population of Chevrolet Impala owners

p_2 = proportion likely to repurchase a Fusion for the population of Ford Fusion owners

p_3 = proportion likely to repurchase an Accord for the population of Honda Accord owners

The hypotheses are stated as follows:

$$H_0: p_1 = p_2 = p_3$$
$$H_a: \text{Not all population proportions are equal}$$

To conduct this hypothesis test we begin by taking a sample of owners from each of the three populations. Thus we will have a sample of Chevrolet Impala owners, a sample of Ford Fusion owners, and a sample of Honda Accord owners. Each sample provides categorical

| TABLE 12.1 | Sample Results of Likely to Repurchase for Three Populations of Automobile Owners (Observed Frequencies) |

		Automobile Owners			
		Chevrolet Impala	Ford Fusion	Honda Accord	Total
Likely to	Yes	69	120	123	312
Repurchase	No	56	80	52	188
	Total	125	200	175	500

DATA *file*

AutoLoyalty

In studies such as these, we often use the same sample size for each population. We have chosen different sample sizes in this example to show that the chi-square test is not restricted to equal sample sizes for each of the k populations.

data indicating whether the respondents are likely or not likely to repurchase the automobile. The data for samples of 125 Chevrolet Impala owners, 200 Ford Fusion owners, and 175 Honda Accord owners are summarized in the tabular format shown in Table 12.1. This table has two rows for the responses Yes and No and three columns, one corresponding to each of the populations. The observed frequencies are summarized in the six cells of the table corresponding to each combination of the likely to repurchase responses and the three populations.

Using Table 12.1, we see that 69 of the 125 Chevrolet Impala owners indicated that they were likely to repurchase a Chevrolet Impala. One hundred and twenty of the 200 Ford Fusion owners and 123 of the 175 Honda Accord owners indicated that they were likely to repurchase their current automobile. Also, across all three samples, 312 of the 500 owners in the study indicated that they were likely to repurchase their current automobile. The question now is how do we analyze the data in Table 12.1 to determine if the hypothesis $H_0: p_1 = p_2 = p_3$ should be rejected?

The data in Table 12.1 are the *observed frequencies* for each of the six cells that represent the six combinations of the likely to repurchase response and the owner population. If we can determine the *expected frequencies under the assumption H_0 is true*, we can use the chi-square test statistic to determine whether there is a significant difference between the observed and expected frequencies. If a significant difference exists between the observed and expected frequencies, the hypothesis H_0 can be rejected and there is evidence that not all the population proportions are equal.

Expected frequencies for the six cells of the table are based on the following rationale. First, we assume that the null hypothesis of equal population proportions is true. Then we note that in the entire sample of 500 owners, a total of 312 owners indicated that they were likely to repurchase their current automobile. Thus, 312/500 = .624 is the overall sample proportion of owners indicating they are likely to repurchase their current automobile. If $H_0: p_1 = p_2 = p_3$ is true, .624 would be the best estimate of the proportion responding likely to repurchase for each of the automobile owner populations. So if the assumption of H_0 is true, we would expect .624 of the 125 Chevrolet Impala owners, or .624(125) = 78 owners to indicate they are likely to repurchase the Impala. Using the .624 overall sample proportion, we would expect .624(200) = 124.8 of the 200 Ford Fusion owners and .624(175) = 109.2 of the Honda Accord owners to respond that they are likely to repurchase their respective model of automobile.

Let us generalize the approach to computing expected frequencies by letting e_{ij} denote the expected frequency for the cell in row i and column j of the table. With this notation, now reconsider the expected frequency calculation for the response of likely to repurchase Yes (row 1) for Chevrolet Impala owners (column 1), that is, the expected frequency e_{11}.

Note that 312 is the total number of Yes responses (row 1 total), 175 is the total sample size for Chevrolet Impala owners (column 1 total), and 500 is the total sample size. Following the logic in the preceding paragraph, we can show

$$e_{11} = \left(\frac{\text{Row 1 Total}}{\text{Total Sample Size}} \right)(\text{Column 1 Total}) = \left(\frac{312}{500} \right)125 = (.624)125 = 78$$

Starting with the first part of the above expression, we can write

$$e_{11} = \frac{(\text{Row 1 Total})(\text{Column 1 Total})}{\text{Total Sample Size}}$$

Generalizing this expression shows that the following formula can be used to provide the expected frequencies under the assumption H_0 is true.

> **EXPECTED FREQUENCIES UNDER THE ASSUMPTION H_0 IS TRUE**
>
> $$e_{ij} = \frac{(\text{Row } i \text{ Total})(\text{Column } j \text{ Total})}{\text{Total Sample Size}} \tag{12.1}$$

Using equation (12.1), we see that the expected frequency of Yes responses (row 1) for Honda Accord owners (column 3) would be e_{13} = (Row 1 Total)(Column 3 Total)/(Total Sample Size) = (312)(175)/500 = 109.2. Use equation (12.1) to verify the other expected frequencies are as shown in Table 12.2.

The test procedure for comparing the observed frequencies of Table 12.1 with the expected frequencies of Table 12.2 involves the computation of the following chi-square statistic:

> **CHI-SQUARE TEST STATISTIC**
>
> $$\chi^2 = \sum_i \sum_j \frac{(f_{ij} - e_{ij})^2}{e_{ij}} \tag{12.2}$$
>
> where
>
> f_{ij} = observed frequency for the cell in row i and column j
> e_{ij} = expected frequency for the cell in row i and column j under the assumption H_0 is true
>
> *Note:* In a chi-square test involving the equality of k population proportions, the above test statistic has a chi-square distribution with $k - 1$ degrees of freedom provided the expected frequency is 5 *or more* for each cell.

Reviewing the expected frequencies in Table 12.2, we see that the expected frequency is at least five for each cell in the table. We therefore proceed with the computation of the chi-square test statistic. The calculations necessary to compute the value of the test statistic are shown in Table 12.3. In this case, we see that the value of the test statistic is $\chi^2 = 7.89$.

TABLE 12.2	Expected Frequencies for Likely to Repurchase for Three Populations of Automobile Owners if H_0 is True			
		Automobile Owners		
		Chevrolet Impala	Ford Fusion	Honda Accord	Total
Likely to	Yes	78	124.8	109.2	312
Repurchase	No	47	75.2	65.8	188
	Total	125	200	175	500

TABLE 12.3	Computation of the Chi-Square Test Statistic for the Test of Equal Population Proportions

Likely to Repurchase?	Automobile Owner	Observed Frequency f_{ij}	Expected Frequency e_{ij}	Difference $f_{ij} - e_{ij}$	Squared Difference $(f_{ij} - e_{ij})^2$	Squared Difference Divided by Expected Frequency $(f_{ij} - e_{ij})^2/e_{ij}$
Yes	Impala	69	78.0	−9.0	81.00	1.04
Yes	Fusion	120	124.8	−4.8	23.04	.18
Yes	Accord	123	109.2	13.8	190.44	1.74
No	Impala	56	47.0	9.0	81.00	1.72
No	Fusion	80	75.2	4.8	23.04	.31
No	Accord	52	65.8	−13.8	190.44	2.89
	Total	500	500			$\chi^2 = 7.89$

In order to understand whether or not $\chi^2 = 7.89$ leads us to reject H_0: $p_1 = p_2 = p_3$, you will need to understand and refer to values of the chi-square distribution. Table 12.4 shows the general shape of the chi-square distribution, but note that the shape of a specific chi-square distribution depends upon the number of degrees of freedom. The table shows the upper tail areas of .10, .05, .025, .01, and .005 for chi-square distributions with up to 15 degrees of freedom. This version of the chi-square table will enable you to conduct the hypothesis tests presented in this chapter.

Since the expected frequencies shown in Table 12.2 are based on the assumption that H_0: $p_1 = p_2 = p_3$ is true, observed frequencies, f_{ij}, that are in agreement with expected frequencies, e_{ij}, provide small values of $(f_{ij} - e_{ij})^2$ in equation (12.2). If this is the case, the value of the chi-square test statistic will be relatively small and H_0 cannot be rejected. On the other hand, if the differences between the observed and expected frequencies are *large*, values of $(f_{ij} - e_{ij})^2$ and the computed value of the test statistic will be large. In this case, the null hypothesis of equal population proportions can be rejected. Thus a chi-square test for equal population proportions will always be an upper tail test with rejection of H_0 occurring when the test statistic is in the upper tail of the chi-square distribution.

The chi-square test presented in this section is always a one-tailed test with the rejection of H_0 occurring in the upper tail of the chi-square distribution.

We can use the upper tail area of the appropriate chi-square distribution and the p-value approach to determine whether the null hypothesis can be rejected. In the automobile brand loyalty study, the three owner populations indicate that the appropriate chi-square distribution has $k - 1 = 3 - 1 = 2$ degrees of freedom. Using row two of the chi-square distribution table, we have the following:

Area in Upper Tail	.10	.05	.025	.01	.005
χ^2 Value (2 df)	4.605	5.991	7.378	9.210	10.597

$$\chi^2 = 7.89$$

We see the upper tail area at $\chi^2 = 7.89$ is between .025 and .01. Thus, the corresponding upper tail area or p-value must be between .025 and .01. With p-value $\leq$ .05, we reject H_0 and conclude that the three population proportions are not all equal and thus there is a difference in brand loyalties among the Chevrolet Impala, Ford Fusion, and Honda Accord owners. JMP or Excel procedures provided in Appendix F can be used to show $\chi^2 = 7.89$ with 2 degrees of freedom yields a p-value = .0193.

TABLE 12.4	Selected Values of the Chi-Square Distribution

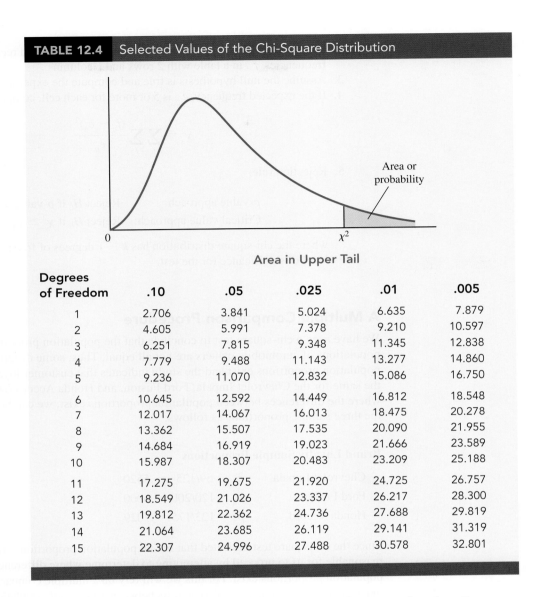

Area or probability

$$\chi^2$$

0

Area in Upper Tail

Degrees of Freedom	.10	.05	.025	.01	.005
1	2.706	3.841	5.024	6.635	7.879
2	4.605	5.991	7.378	9.210	10.597
3	6.251	7.815	9.348	11.345	12.838
4	7.779	9.488	11.143	13.277	14.860
5	9.236	11.070	12.832	15.086	16.750
6	10.645	12.592	14.449	16.812	18.548
7	12.017	14.067	16.013	18.475	20.278
8	13.362	15.507	17.535	20.090	21.955
9	14.684	16.919	19.023	21.666	23.589
10	15.987	18.307	20.483	23.209	25.188
11	17.275	19.675	21.920	24.725	26.757
12	18.549	21.026	23.337	26.217	28.300
13	19.812	22.362	24.736	27.688	29.819
14	21.064	23.685	26.119	29.141	31.319
15	22.307	24.996	27.488	30.578	32.801

Instead of using the p-value, we could use the critical value approach to draw the same conclusion. With $\alpha = .05$ and 2 degrees of freedom, the critical value for the chi-square test statistic is $\chi^2 = 5.991$. The upper tail rejection region becomes

$$\text{Reject } H_0 \text{ if } \chi^2 \geq 5.991$$

With $7.89 \geq 5.991$, we reject H_0. Thus, the p-value approach and the critical value approach provide the same hypothesis-testing conclusion.

Let us summarize the general steps that can be used to conduct a chi-square test for the equality of the population proportions for three or more populations.

A CHI-SQUARE TEST FOR THE EQUALITY OF POPULATION PROPORTIONS FOR $k \geq 3$ POPULATIONS

1. State the null and alternative hypotheses

$$H_0: p_1 = p_2 = \cdots = p_k$$
$$H_a: \text{Not all population proportions are equal}$$

2. Select a random sample from each of the populations and record the observed frequencies, f_{ij}, in a table with 2 rows and k columns
3. Assume the null hypothesis is true and compute the expected frequencies, e_{ij}
4. If the expected frequency, e_{ij}, is 5 or more for each cell, compute the test statistic:

$$\chi^2 = \sum_i \sum_j \frac{(f_{ij} - e_{ij})^2}{e_{ij}}$$

5. Rejection rule:

p-value approach: Reject H_0 if p-value $\leq \alpha$

Critical value approach: Reject H_0 if $\chi^2 \geq \chi_\alpha^2$

where the chi-square distribution has $k - 1$ degrees of freedom and α is the level of significance for the test.

A Multiple Comparison Procedure

We have used a chi-square test to conclude that the population proportions for the three populations of automobile owners are not all equal. Thus, some differences among the population proportions exist and the study indicates that customer loyalties are not all the same for the Chevrolet Impala, Ford Fusion, and Honda Accord owners. To identify where the differences between population proportions exist, we can begin by computing the three sample proportions as follows:

Brand Loyalty Sample Proportions

Chevrolet Impala $\bar{p}_1 = 69/125 = .5520$

Ford Fusion $\bar{p}_2 = 120/200 = .6000$

Honda Accord $\bar{p}_3 = 123/175 = .7029$

Since the chi-square test indicated that not all population proportions are equal, it is reasonable for us to proceed by attempting to determine where differences among the population proportions exist. For this we will rely on a multiple comparison procedure that can be used to conduct statistical tests between all pairs of population proportions. In the following, we discuss a multiple comparison procedure known as the **Marascuilo procedure**. This is a relatively straightforward procedure for making pairwise comparisons of all pairs of population proportions. We will demonstrate the computations required by this multiple comparison test procedure for the automobile customer loyalty study.

We begin by computing the absolute value of the pairwise difference between sample proportions for each pair of populations in the study. In the three-population automobile brand loyalty study we compare populations 1 and 2, populations 1 and 3, and then populations 2 and 3 using the sample proportions as follows:

Chevrolet Impala and Ford Fusion

$$|\bar{p}_1 - \bar{p}_2| = |.5520 - .6000| = .0480$$

Chevrolet Impala and Honda Accord

$$|\bar{p}_1 - \bar{p}_3| = |.5520 - .7029| = .1509$$

Ford Fusion and Honda Accord

$$|\bar{p}_2 - \bar{p}_3| = |.6000 - .7029| = .1029$$

In a second step, we select a level of significance and compute the corresponding critical value for each pairwise comparison using the following expression.

CRITICAL VALUES FOR THE MARASCUILO PAIRWISE COMPARISON PROCEDURE FOR k POPULATION PROPORTIONS

For each pairwise comparison compute a critical value as follows:

$$CV_{ij} = \sqrt{\chi_\alpha^2} \sqrt{\frac{\bar{p}_i(1 - \bar{p}_i)}{n_i} + \frac{\bar{p}_j(1 - \bar{p}_j)}{n_j}} \tag{12.3}$$

where

χ_α^2 = chi-square with a level of significance α and $k - 1$ degrees of freedom
$\bar{p}_i$ and $\bar{p}_j$ = sample proportions for populations i and j
n_i and n_j = sample sizes for populations i and j

Using the chi-square distribution in Table 12.4, $k - 1 = 3 - 1 = 2$ degrees of freedom, and a .05 level of significance, we have $\chi_{.05}^2 = 5.991$. Now using the sample proportions $\bar{p}_1 = .5520$, $\bar{p}_2 = .6000$, and $\bar{p}_3 = .7029$, the critical values for the three pairwise comparison tests are as follows:

Chevrolet Impala and Ford Fusion

$$CV_{12} = \sqrt{5.991} \sqrt{\frac{.5520(1 - .5520)}{125} + \frac{.6000(1 - .6000)}{200}} = .1380$$

Chevrolet Impala and Honda Accord

$$CV_{13} = \sqrt{5.991} \sqrt{\frac{.5520(1 - .5520)}{125} + \frac{.7029(1 - .7029)}{175}} = .1379$$

Ford Fusion and Honda Accord

$$CV_{23} = \sqrt{5.991} \sqrt{\frac{.6000(1 - .6000)}{200} + \frac{.7029(1 - .7029)}{175}} = .1198$$

If the absolute value of any pairwise sample proportion difference $|\bar{p}_i - \bar{p}_j|$ exceeds its corresponding critical value, CV_{ij}, the pairwise difference is significant at the .05 level of significance and we can conclude that the two corresponding population proportions are different. The final step of the pairwise comparison procedure is summarized in Table 12.5.

The conclusion from the pairwise comparison procedure is that the only significant difference in customer loyalty occurs between the Chevrolet Impala and the Honda Accord. Our

TABLE 12.5   Pairwise Comparison Tests for the Automobile Brand Loyalty Study

Pairwise Comparison	$\|\bar{p}_i - \bar{p}_j\|$	CV_{ij}	Significant if $\|\bar{p}_i - \bar{p}_j\| > CV_{ij}$
Chevrolet Impala vs. Ford Fusion	.0480	.1380	Not significant
Chevrolet Impala vs. Honda Accord	.1509	.1379	Significant
Ford Fusion vs. Honda Accord	.1029	.1198	Not significant

sample results indicate that the Honda Accord had a greater population proportion of owners who say they are likely to repurchase the Honda Accord. Thus, we can conclude that the Honda Accord ($\bar{p}_3 = .7029$) has a greater customer loyalty than the Chevrolet Impala ($\bar{p}_1 = .5520$).

The results of the study are inconclusive as to the comparative loyalty of the Ford Fusion. While the Ford Fusion did not show significantly different results when compared to the Chevrolet Impala or Honda Accord, a larger sample may have revealed a significant difference between Ford Fusion and the other two automobiles in terms of customer loyalty. It is not uncommon for a multiple comparison procedure to show significance for some pairwise comparisons and yet not show significance for other pairwise comparisons in the study.

NOTES + COMMENTS

1. In Chapter 10, we used the standard normal distribution and the z test statistic to conduct hypothesis tests about the proportions of two populations. However, the chi-square test introduced in this section can also be used to conduct the hypothesis test that the proportions of two populations are equal. The results will be the same under both test procedures and the value of the test statistic χ^2 will be equal to the square of the value of the test statistic z. An advantage of the methodology in Chapter 10 is that it can be used for either a one-tailed or a two-tailed hypothesis about the proportions of two populations, whereas the chi-square test in this section can be used only for two-tailed tests. Exercise 12.6 will give you a chance to use the chi-square test for the hypothesis that the proportions of two populations are equal.

2. Each of the k populations in this section had two response outcomes, Yes or No. In effect, each population had a binomial distribution with parameter p the population proportion of Yes responses. An extension of the chi-square procedure in this section applies when each of the k populations has three or more possible responses. In this case, each population is said to have a multinomial distribution. The chi-square calculations for the expected frequencies, e_{ij}, and the test statistic, χ^2, are the same as shown in expressions (12.1) and (12.2). The only difference is that the null hypothesis assumes that the multinomial distribution for the response variable is the same for all populations. With r responses for each of the k populations, the chi-square test statistic has $(r - 1)(k - 1)$ degrees of freedom. Exercise 12.8 will give you a chance to use the chi-square test to compare three populations with multinomial distributions.

EXERCISES

Methods

1. Use the sample data below to test the hypotheses

$$H_0: p_1 = p_2 = p_3$$
$$H_a: \text{Not all population proportions are equal}$$

where p_i is the population proportion of Yes responses for population i. Using a .05 level of significance, what is the p-value and what is your conclusion?

	Populations		
Response	1	2	3
Yes	150	150	96
No	100	150	104

2. Reconsider the observed frequencies in exercise 1
   a. Compute the sample proportion for each population.
   b. Use the multiple comparison procedure to determine which population proportions differ significantly. Use a .05 level of significance.

Applications

3. **Late Flight Comparison Across Airlines.** The sample data below represent the number of late and on time flights for Delta, United, and US Airways.

Flight	Airline		
	Delta	**United**	**US Airways**
Late	39	51	56
On Time	261	249	344

a. Formulate the hypotheses for a test that will determine if the population proportion of late flights is the same for all three airlines.
b. Conduct the hypothesis test with a .05 level of significance. What is the p-value and what is your conclusion?
c. Compute the sample proportion of late flights for each airline. What is the overall proportion of late flights for the three airlines?

4. **Electronic Component Supplier Quality Comparison.** Benson Manufacturing is considering ordering electronic components from three different suppliers. The suppliers may differ in terms of quality in that the proportion or percentage of defective components may differ among the suppliers. To evaluate the proportion of defective components for the suppliers, Benson has requested a sample shipment of 500 components from each supplier. The number of defective components and the number of good components found in each shipment are as follows.

Component	Supplier		
	A	**B**	**C**
Defective	15	20	40
Good	485	480	460

a. Formulate the hypotheses that can be used to test for equal proportions of defective components provided by the three suppliers.
b. Using a .05 level of significance, conduct the hypothesis test. What is the p-value and what is your conclusion?
c. Conduct a multiple comparison test to determine if there is an overall best supplier or if one supplier can be eliminated because of poor quality.

5. **Research Classification of Higher Education.** The Carnegie Classification of Institutes of Higher Education categorizes colleges and universities on the basis of their research and degree-granting activities. Universities that grant doctoral degrees are placed into one of three classifications: moderate research activity, higher research activity, or highest research activity. The Carnegie classifications for public and not-for-profit private doctoral degree-granting universities are summarized in the following table.

Type of University	Carnegie Classification		
	Moderate Research Activity	**Higher Research Activity**	**Highest Research Activity**
Public	38	76	81
Private	58	31	34

Test the hypothesis that the population proportions of public universities are equal in each Carnegie classification category. Use a .05 level of significance. What is the *p*-value and what is your conclusion?

Exercise 6 shows a chi-square test can be used when the hypothesis is about the equality of two population proportions.

6. **Error Rates in Tax Preparation.** A tax preparation firm is interested in comparing the quality of work at two of its regional offices. The observed frequencies showing the number of sampled returns with errors and the number of sampled returns that were correct are as follows.

	Regional Office	
Return	Office 1	Office 2
Error	35	27
Correct	215	273

a. What are the sample proportions of returns with errors at the two offices?

b. Use the chi-square test procedure to see if there is a significant difference between the population proportion of error rates for the two offices. Test the null hypothesis $H_0: p_1 = p_2$ with a .10 level of significance. What is the *p*-value and what is your conclusion? *Note*: We generally use the chi-square test of equal proportions when there are three or more populations, but this example shows that the same chi-square test can be used for testing equal proportions with two populations.

c. In the Section 10.2, a *z* test was used to conduct the above test. Either a χ^2 test statistic or a *z* test statistic may be used to test the hypothesis. However, when we want to make inferences about the proportions for two populations, we generally prefer the *z* test statistic procedure. Refer to the Notes and Comments at the end of this section and comment on why the *z* test statistic provides the user with more options for inferences about the proportions of two populations.

7. **Use of Social Media.** Social media is becoming more and more popular around the world. *Statista.com* provides estimates of the number of social media users in various countries in 2017 as well as the projections for 2022. Assume that the results for surveys in the United Kingdom, China, Russia, and the United States are as follows.

DATA *file*

SocialMedia

	Country			
Use Social Media	United Kingdom	China	Russia	United States
Yes	480	215	343	640
No	320	285	357	360

a. Conduct a hypothesis test to determine whether the proportion of adults using social media is equal for all four countries. What is the *p*-value? Using a .05 level of significance, what is your conclusion?

b. What are the sample proportions for each of the four countries? Which country has the largest proportion of adults using social media?

c. Using a .05 level of significance, conduct multiple pairwise comparison tests among the four countries. What is your conclusion?

Exercise 8 shows a chi-square test can also be used for multiple population tests when the categorical response variable has three or more outcomes.

8. **Supplier Quality: Three Inspection Outcomes.** The Ertl Company is well known for its high-quality die-cast metal alloy toy replicas of tractors and other farm equipment. As part of a periodic procurement evaluation, Ertl is considering purchasing parts for a toy tractor line from three different suppliers. The parts received from the suppliers are classified as having a minor defect, having a major defect, or being good. Test results from samples of parts received from each of the three suppliers are shown below. Note that any test with these data is no longer a test of proportions for the three

supplier populations because the categorical response variable has three outcomes: minor defect, major defect, and good.

Part Tested	Supplier		
	A	B	C
Minor Defect	15	13	21
Major Defect	5	11	5
Good	130	126	124

Using the data above, conduct a hypothesis test to determine if the distribution of defects is the same for the three suppliers. Use the chi-square test calculations as presented in this section with the exception that a table with r rows and c columns results in a chi-square test statistic with $(r-1)(c-1)$ degrees of freedom. Using a .05 level of significance, what is the p-value and what is your conclusion?

12.2 Test of Independence

An important application of a chi-square test involves using sample data to test for the independence of two categorical variables. For this test we take one sample from a population and record the observations for two categorical variables. We will summarize the data by counting the number of responses for each combination of a category for variable 1 and a category for variable 2. The null hypothesis for this test is that the two categorical variables are independent. Thus, the test is referred to as a **test of independence**. We will illustrate this test with the following example.

A beer industry association conducts a survey to determine the preferences of beer drinkers for light, regular, and dark beers. A sample of 200 beer drinkers is taken with each person in the sample asked to indicate a preference for one of the three types of beers: light, regular, or dark. At the end of the survey questionnaire, the respondent is asked to provide information on a variety of demographics including gender: male or female. A research question of interest to the association is whether preference for the three types of beer is independent of the gender of the beer drinker. If the two categorical variables, beer preference and gender, are independent, beer preference does not depend on gender and the preference for light, regular, and dark beer can be expected to be the same for male and female beer drinkers. However, if the test conclusion is that the two categorical variables are not independent, we have evidence that beer preference is associated or dependent upon the gender of the beer drinker. As a result, we can expect beer preferences to differ for male and female beer drinkers. In this case, a beer manufacturer could use this information to customize its promotions and advertising for the different target markets of male and female beer drinkers.

The hypotheses for this test of independence are as follows:

H_0: Beer preference is independent of gender

H_a: Beer preference is not independent of gender

The sample data will be summarized in a two-way table with beer preferences of light, regular, and dark as one of the variables and gender of male and female as the other variable. Since an objective of the study is to determine if there is difference between the beer preferences for male and female beer drinkers, we consider gender an explanatory variable and follow the usual practice of making the explanatory variable the column variable in the data tabulation table. The beer preference is the categorical response variable and is shown as the row variable. The sample results of the 200 beer drinkers in the study are summarized in Table 12.6.

The sample data are summarized based on the combination of beer preference and gender for the individual respondents. For example, 51 individuals in the study were males who preferred light beer, 56 individuals in the study were males who preferred regular beer, and so on. Let us now analyze the data in the table and test for independence of beer preference and gender.

DATA *file*

BeerPreference

TABLE 12.6	Sample Results for Beer Preferences of Male and Female Beer Drinkers (Observed Frequencies)		
		Gender		
		Male	Female	Total
Beer Preference	Light	51	39	90
	Regular	56	21	77
	Dark	25	8	33
	Total	132	68	200

First of all, since we selected a sample of beer drinkers, summarizing the data for each variable separately will provide some insights into the characteristics of the beer drinker population. For the categorical variable gender, we see 132 of the 200 in the sample were male. This gives us the estimate that $132/200 = .66$, or 66%, of the beer drinker population is male. Similarly we estimate that $68/200 = .34$, or 34%, of the beer drinker population is female. Thus male beer drinkers appear to outnumber female beer drinkers approximately 2 to 1. Sample proportions or percentages for the three types of beer are

Prefer Light Beer	$90/200 = .450$, or 45.0%
Prefer Regular Beer	$77/200 = .385$, or 38.5%
Prefer Dark Beer	$33/200 = .165$, or 16.5%

Across all beer drinkers in the sample, light beer is preferred most often and dark beer is preferred least often.

Let us now conduct the chi-square test to determine if beer preference and gender are independent. The computations and formulas used are the same as those used for the chi-square test in Section 12.1. Utilizing the observed frequencies in Table 12.6 for row i and column j, f_{ij}, we compute the expected frequencies, e_{ij}, under the assumption that the beer preferences and gender are independent. The computation of the expected frequencies follows the same logic and formula used in Section 12.1. Thus the expected frequency for row i and column j is given by

$$e_{ij} = \frac{(\text{Row } i \text{ Total})(\text{Column } j \text{ Total})}{\text{Sample Size}} \qquad (12.4)$$

For example, $e_{11} = (90)(132)/200 = 59.40$ is the expected frequency for male beer drinkers who would prefer light beer if beer preference is independent of gender. Show that equation (12.4) can be used to find the other expected frequencies shown in Table 12.7.

TABLE 12.7	Expected Frequencies If Beer Preference Is Independent of the Gender of the Beer Drinker		
		Gender		
		Male	Female	Total
Beer Preference	Light	59.40	30.60	90
	Regular	50.82	26.18	77
	Dark	21.78	11.22	33
	Total	132	68	200

| **TABLE 12.8** | Computation of the Chi-Square Test Statistic for the Test of Independence Between Beer Preference and Gender | | | | |

Beer Preference	Gender	Observed Frequency f_{ij}	Expected Frequency e_{ij}	Difference $f_{ij} - e_{ij}$	Squared Difference $(f_{ij} - e_{ij})^2$	Squared Difference Divided by Expected Frequency $(f_{ij} - e_{ij})^2/e_{ij}$
Light	Male	51	59.40	−8.40	70.56	1.19
Light	Female	39	30.60	8.40	70.56	2.31
Regular	Male	56	50.82	5.18	26.83	.53
Regular	Female	21	26.18	−5.18	26.83	1.02
Dark	Male	25	21.78	3.22	10.37	.48
Dark	Female	8	11.22	−3.22	10.37	.92
	Total	200	200			$\chi^2 = 6.45$

Following the chi-square test procedure discussed in Section 12.1, we use the following expression to compute the value of the chi-square test statistic.

$$\chi^2 = \sum_i \sum_j \frac{(f_{ij} - e_{ij})^2}{e_{ij}} \tag{12.5}$$

With r rows and c columns in the table, the chi-square distribution will have $(r-1)(c-1)$ degrees of freedom provided the expected frequency is at least 5 for each cell. Thus, in this application we will use a chi-square distribution with $(3-1)(2-1) = 2$ degrees of freedom. The complete steps to compute the chi-square test statistic are summarized in Table 12.8.

We can use the upper tail area of the chi-square distribution with 2 degrees of freedom and the p-value approach to determine whether the null hypothesis that beer preference is independent of gender can be rejected. Using row two of the chi-square distribution table shown in Table 12.4, we have the following:

Area in Upper Tail	**.10**	**.05**	**.025**	**.01**	**.005**
χ^2 **Value (2 df)**	4.605	5.991	7.378	9.210	10.597

$$\chi^2 = 6.45$$

Thus, we see the upper tail area at $\chi^2 = 6.45$ is between .05 and .025, and so the corresponding upper tail area or p-value must be between .05 and .025. With p-value $\leq .05$, we reject H_0 and conclude that beer preference is not independent of the gender of the beer drinker. Stated another way, the study shows that beer preference can be expected to differ for male and female beer drinkers. JMP or Excel procedures provided in Appendix F can be used to show $\chi^2 = 6.45$ with two degrees of freedom yields a p-value $= .0398$.

Instead of using the p-value, we could use the critical value approach to draw the same conclusion. With $\alpha = .05$ and 2 degrees of freedom, the critical value for the chi-square test statistic is $\chi^2_{.05} = 5.991$. The upper tail rejection region becomes

$$\text{Reject } H_0 \text{ if} \geq 5.991$$

With $6.45 \geq 5.991$, we reject H_0. Again we see that the p-value approach and the critical value approach provide the same conclusion.

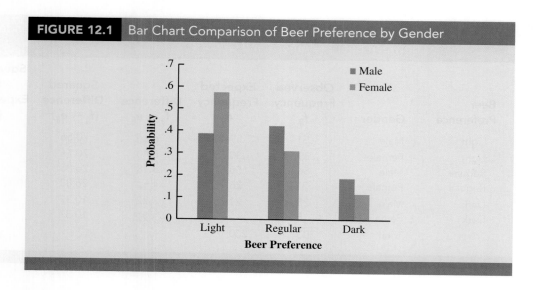

FIGURE 12.1   Bar Chart Comparison of Beer Preference by Gender

While we now have evidence that beer preference and gender are not independent, we will need to gain additional insight from the data to assess the nature of the association between these two variables. One way to do this is to compute the probability of the beer preference responses for males and females separately. These calculations are as follows:

Beer Preference	Male	Female
Light	51/132 = .3864, or 38.64%	39/68 = .5735, or 57.35%
Regular	56/132 = .4242, or 42.42%	21/68 = .3088, or 30.88%
Dark	25/132 = .1894, or 18.94%	8/68 = .1176, or 11.76%

The bar chart for male and female beer drinkers of the three kinds of beer is shown in Figure 12.1.

What observations can you make about the association between beer preference and gender? For female beer drinkers in the sample, the highest preference is for light beer at 57.35%. For male beer drinkers in the sample, regular beer is most frequently preferred at 42.42%. While female beer drinkers have a higher preference for light beer than males, male beer drinkers have a higher preference for both regular beer and dark beer. Data visualization through bar charts such as shown in Figure 12.1 is helpful in gaining insight as to how two categorical variables are associated.

Before we leave this discussion, we summarize the steps for a test of independence.

CHI-SQUARE TEST FOR INDEPENDENCE OF TWO CATEGORICAL VARIABLES

1. State the null and alternative hypotheses.

H_0: The two categorical variables are independent
H_a: The two categorical variables are not independent

The expected frequencies must all be 5 or more for the chi-square test to be valid.

2. Select a random sample from the population and collect data for both variables for every element in the sample. Record the observed frequencies, f_{ij}, in a table with r rows and c columns.

3. Assume the null hypothesis is true and compute the expected frequencies, e_{ij}
4. If the expected frequency, e_{ij}, is 5 or more for each cell, compute the test statistic:

$$\chi^2 = \sum_i \sum_j \frac{(f_{ij} - e_{ij})^2}{e_{ij}}$$

5. Rejection rule:

> *p*-value approach: Reject H_0 if *p*-value $\leq \alpha$
> Critical value approach: Reject H_0 if $\chi^2 \geq \chi_\alpha^2$

where the chi-square distribution has $(r-1)(c-1)$ degrees of freedom and α is the level of significance for the test.

This chi-square test is also a one-tailed test with rejection of H_0 occurring in the upper tail of a chi-square distribution with $(r-1)(c-1)$ degrees of freedom.

Finally, if the null hypothesis of independence is rejected, summarizing the probabilities as shown in the above example will help the analyst determine where the association or dependence exists for the two categorical variables.

EXERCISES

Methods

9. The following table contains observed frequencies for a sample of 200. Test for independence of the row and column variables using $\alpha = .05$.

	Column Variable		
Row Variable	A	B	C
P	20	44	50
Q	30	26	30

10. The following table contains observed frequencies for a sample of 240. Test for independence of the row and column variables using $\alpha = .05$.

	Column Variable		
Row Variable	A	B	C
P	20	30	20
Q	30	60	25
R	10	15	30

Applications

11. **Airline Ticket Purchases for Domestic and International Flights.** A *Bloomberg Businessweek* subscriber study asked, "In the past 12 months, when traveling for

business, what type of airline ticket did you purchase most often?" A second question asked if the type of airline ticket purchased most often was for domestic or international travel. Sample data obtained are shown in the following table.

Type of Ticket	Type of Flight	
	Domestic	**International**
First class	29	22
Business class	95	121
Economy class	518	135

a. Using a .05 level of significance, is the type of ticket purchased independent of the type of flight? What is your conclusion?
b. Discuss any dependence that exists between the type of ticket and type of flight.

WorkforcePlan

12. **Hiring and Firing Plans at Private and Public Companies.** A Deloitte employment survey asked a sample of human resource executives how their company planned to change its workforce over the next 12 months. A categorical response variable showed three options: The company plans to hire and add to the number of employees, the company plans no change in the number of employees, or the company plans to lay off and reduce the number of employees. Another categorical variable indicated if the company was private or public. Sample data for 180 companies are summarized as follows.

Employment Plan	Company	
	Private	**Public**
Add Employees	37	32
No Change	19	34
Lay-Off Employees	16	42

a. Conduct a test of independence to determine if the employment plan for the next 12 months is independent of the type of company. At a .05 level of significance, what is your conclusion?
b. Discuss any differences in the employment plans for private and public companies over the next 12 months.

Millenials

13. **Generational Differences in Workplace Attitudes.** In 2015, Addison Group (a provider of professional staffing services) and Kelton (a global insights firm) surveyed the work preferences and attitudes of 1,006 working adults spread over three generations: baby boomers, Generation X, and millennials (*Society for Human Resource Management* website, https://www.shrm.org/resourcesandtools/hr-topics/talent-acquisition/pages/millennials-raises-promotions-generations.aspx). In one question, individuals were asked if they would leave their current job to make more money at another job. The file *Millenials* contains the sample data, which are also summarized in the following table.

Leave Job for More Money?	Generation		
	Baby Boomer	**Generation X**	**Millennial**
Yes	129	152	164
No	207	183	171

Conduct a test of independence to determine whether interest in leaving a current job for more money is independent of employee generation. What is the *p*-value? Using a .05 level of significance, what is your conclusion?

AutoQuality

14. **Vehicle Quality Ratings.** A J. D. Power and Associates vehicle quality survey asked new owners a variety of questions about their recently purchased automobile. One question asked for the owner's rating of the vehicle using categorical responses of average, outstanding, and exceptional. Another question asked for the owner's education level with the categorical responses some high school, high school graduate, some college, and college graduate. Assume the sample data below are for 500 owners who had recently purchased an automobile.

	Education			
Quality Rating	Some HS	HS Grad	Some College	College Grad
Average	35	30	20	60
Outstanding	45	45	50	90
Exceptional	20	25	30	50

a. Use a .05 level of significance and a test of independence to determine if a new owner's vehicle quality rating is independent of the owner's education. What is the *p*-value and what is your conclusion?

b. Use the overall percentage of average, outstanding, and exceptional ratings to comment upon how new owners rate the quality of their recently purchased automobiles.

15. **Company Reputation and Management Quality Survey.** *The Wall Street Journal* Annual Corporate Perceptions Study surveyed readers and asked how they rated the quality of management and the reputation of the company for more than 250 worldwide corporations. Both the quality of management and the reputation of the company were rated on a categorical scale of excellent, good, and fair categorical. Assume the sample data for 200 respondents below applies to this study.

	Reputation of Company		
Quality of Management	Excellent	Good	Fair
Excellent	40	25	5
Good	35	35	10
Fair	25	10	15

a. Use a .05 level of significance and test for independence of the quality of management and the reputation of the company. What is the *p*-value and what is your conclusion?

b. If there is a dependence or association between the two ratings, discuss and use probabilities to justify your answer.

16. **Academy Awards and Movie Fan Sentiment.** The race for the 2013 Academy Award for Actress in a Leading Role was extremely tight, featuring several worthy performances. The nominees were Jessica Chastain for *Zero Dark Thirty*, Jennifer Lawrence for *Silver Linings Playbook*, Emmanuelle Riva for *Amour*, Quvenzhané Wallis for *Beasts of the Southern Wild*, and Naomi Watts for *The Impossible*. In a survey, movie fans who had seen each of the movies for which these five actresses had been nominated were asked to select the actress who was most deserving of the 2013 Academy Award for Actress in a Leading Role. The responses follow.

	18–30	31–44	45–58	Over 58
Jessica Chastain	51	50	41	42
Jennifer Lawrence	63	55	37	50
Emmanuelle Riva	15	44	56	74
Quvenzhané Wallis	48	25	22	31
Naomi Watts	36	65	62	33

a. How large was the sample in this survey?
b. Jennifer Lawrence received the 2013 Academy Award for Actress in a Leading Role for her performance in *Silver Linings Playbook*. Did the respondents favor Ms. Lawrence?
c. At $\alpha = .05$, conduct a hypothesis test to determine whether people's attitude toward the actress who was most deserving of the 2013 Academy Award for Actress in a Leading Role is independent of respondent age. What is your conclusion?

17. **Amount of Sleep by Age Group.** The National Sleep Foundation used a survey to determine whether hours of sleep per night are independent of age. A sample of individuals was asked to indicate the number of hours of sleep per night with categorical options: fewer than 6 hours, 6 to 6.9 hours, 7 to 7.9 hours, and 8 hours or more. Later in the survey, the individuals were asked to indicate their age with categorical options: age 39 or younger and age 40 or older. Sample data follow.

	Age Group	
Hours of Sleep	39 or younger	40 or older
Fewer than 6	38	36
6 to 6.9	60	57
7 to 7.9	77	75
8 or more	65	92

a. Conduct a test of independence to determine whether hours of sleep are independent of age. Using a .05 level of significance, what is the p-value and what is your conclusion?
b. What is your estimate of the percentages of individuals who sleep fewer than 6 hours, 6 to 6.9 hours, 7 to 7.9 hours, and 8 hours or more per night?

18. **Movie Critic Opinions.** On a television program, two movie critics provide their reviews of recent movies and discuss. It is suspected that these hosts deliberately disagree in order to make the program more interesting for viewers. Each movie review is categorized as Pro ("thumbs up"), Con ("thumbs down"), or Mixed. The results of 160 movie ratings by the two hosts are shown here.

	Host B		
Host A	Con	Mixed	Pro
Con	24	8	13
Mixed	8	13	11
Pro	10	9	64

Use a test of independence with a .01 level of significance to analyze the data. What is your conclusion?

12.3 Goodness of Fit Test

In this section we use a chi-square test to determine whether a population being sampled has a specific probability distribution. We first consider a population with a historical multinomial probability distribution and use a goodness of fit test to determine if new sample data indicate there has been a change in the population distribution compared to the historical distribution. We then consider a situation where an assumption is made that a population has a normal probability distribution. In this case, we use a goodness of fit test to determine if sample data indicate that the assumption of a normal probability distribution is or is not appropriate. Both tests are referred to as **goodness of fit tests**.

Multinomial Probability Distribution

The multinomial probability distribution is an extension of the binomial probability distribution to the case where there are three or more outcomes per trial.

With a **multinomial probability distribution**, each element of a population is assigned to one and only one of three or more categories. As an example, consider the market share study being conducted by Scott Marketing Research. Over the past year, market shares for a certain product have stabilized at 30% for company A, 50% for company B, and 20% for company C. Since each customer is classified as buying from one of these companies, we have a multinomial probability distribution with three possible outcomes. The probability for each of the three outcomes is as follows.

$$p_A = \text{probability a customer purchases the company A product}$$
$$p_B = \text{probability a customer purchases the company B product}$$
$$p_C = \text{probability a customer purchases the company C product}$$

The sum of the probabilities for a multinomial probability distribution equals 1.

Using the historical market shares, we have multinomial probability distribution with $p_A = .30$, $p_B = .50$, and $p_C = .20$.

Company C plans to introduce a "new and improved" product to replace its current entry in the market. Company C has retained Scott Marketing Research to determine whether the new product will alter or change the market shares for the three companies. Specifically, the Scott Marketing Research study will introduce a sample of customers to the new company C product and then ask the customers to indicate a preference for the company A product, the company B product, or the new company C product. Based on the sample data, the following hypothesis test can be used to determine if the new company C product is likely to change the historical market shares for the three companies.

$$H_0: p_A = .30, p_B = .50, \text{ and } p_C = .20$$
$$H_a: \text{The population proportions are not } p_A = .30, p_B = .50, \text{ and } p_C = .20$$

The null hypothesis is based on the historical multinomial probability distribution for the market shares. If sample results lead to the rejection of H_0, Scott Marketing Research will have evidence to conclude that the introduction of the new company C product will change the market shares.

Let us assume that the market research firm has used a consumer panel of 200 customers. Each customer was asked to specify a purchase preference among the three alternatives: company A's product, company B's product, and company C's new product. The 200 responses are summarized here.

Observed Frequency		
Company A's Product	Company B's Product	Company C's New Product
48	98	54

We now can perform a goodness of fit test that will determine whether the sample of 200 customer purchase preferences is consistent with the null hypothesis. Like other chi-square tests, the goodness of fit test is based on a comparison of observed frequencies with the expected frequencies under the assumption that the null hypothesis is true. Hence, the next step is to compute expected purchase preferences for the 200 customers under the assumption that $H_0: p_A = .30$, $p_B = .50$, and $p_C = .20$ is true. Doing so provides the expected frequencies as follows.

	Expected Frequency	
Company A's Product	Company B's Product	Company C's New Product
200(.30) = 60	200(.50) = 100	200(.20) = 40

Note that the expected frequency for each category is found by multiplying the sample size of 200 by the hypothesized proportion for the category.

The goodness of fit test now focuses on the differences between the observed frequencies and the expected frequencies. Whether the differences between the observed and expected frequencies are "large" or "small" is a question answered with the aid of the following chi-square test statistic.

TEST STATISTIC FOR GOODNESS OF FIT

$$\chi^2 = \sum_{i=1}^{k} \frac{(f_i - e_i)^2}{e_i} \tag{12.6}$$

where

$$f_i = \text{observed frequency for category } i$$
$$e_i = \text{expected frequency for category } i$$
$$k = \text{the number of categories}$$

Note: The test statistic has a chi-square distribution with $k - 1$ degrees of freedom provided that the expected frequencies are 5 *or more* for all categories.

Let us continue with the Scott Marketing Research example and use the sample data to test the hypothesis that the multinomial population has the market share proportions $p_A = .30$, $p_B = .50$, and $p_C = .20$. We will use an $\alpha = .05$ level of significance. We proceed by using the observed and expected frequencies to compute the value of the test statistic. With the expected frequencies all 5 or more, the computation of the chi-square test statistic is shown in Table 12.9. Thus, we have $\chi^2 = 7.34$.

The test for goodness of fit is always a one-tailed test with the rejection occurring in the upper tail of the chi-square distribution.

We will reject the null hypothesis if the differences between the observed and expected frequencies are large. Thus the test of goodness of fit will always be an upper tail test. We can use the upper tail area for the test statistic and the p-value approach to determine whether the null hypothesis can be rejected. With $k - 1 = 3 - 1 = 2$ degrees

TABLE 12.9	Computation of the Chi-Square Test Statistic for the Scott Marketing Research Market Share Study

Category	Hypothesized Proportion	Observed Frequency f_i	Expected Frequency e_i	Difference $f_i - e_i$	Squared Difference $(f_i - e_i)^2$	Squared Difference Divided by Expected Frequency $(f_i - e_i)^2/e_i$
Company A	.30	48	60	−12	144	2.40
Company B	.50	98	100	−2	4	.04
Company C	.20	54	40	14	196	4.90
Total		200				$\chi^2 = 7.34$

of freedom, row two of the chi-square distribution table in Table 12.4 provides the following:

Area in Upper Tail	.10	.05	.025	.01	.005
χ^2 Value (2 df)	4.605	5.991	7.378	9.210	10.597

$$\chi^2 = 7.34$$

The test statistic $\chi^2 = 7.34$ is between 5.991 and 7.378. Thus, the corresponding upper tail area or p-value must be between .05 and .025. With p-value $\leq$ .05, we reject H_0 and conclude that the introduction of the new product by company C will alter the historical market shares. JMP or Excel procedures provided in Appendix F can be used to show $\chi^2 = 7.34$ provides a p-value $= .0255$.

Instead of using the p-value, we could use the critical value approach to draw the same conclusion. With $\alpha = .05$ and 2 degrees of freedom, the critical value for the test statistic is $\chi^2_{.05} = 5.991$. The upper tail rejection rule becomes

$$\text{Reject } H_0 \text{ if } \chi^2 \geq 5.991$$

With $7.34 > 5.991$, we reject H_0. The p-value approach and critical value approach provide the same hypothesis testing conclusion.

Now that we have concluded the introduction of a new company C product will alter the market shares for the three companies, we are interested in knowing more about how the market shares are likely to change. Using the historical market shares and the sample data, we summarize the data as follows:

Company	Historical Market Share (%)	Sample Data Market Share (%)
A	30	48/200 = .24, or 24
B	50	98/200 = .49, or 49
C	20	54/200 = .27, or 27

The historical market shares and the sample market shares are compared in the bar chart shown in Figure 12.2. This data visualization process shows that the new product will likely increase the market share for company C. Comparisons for the other two companies indicate that company C's gain in market share will hurt company A more than company B.

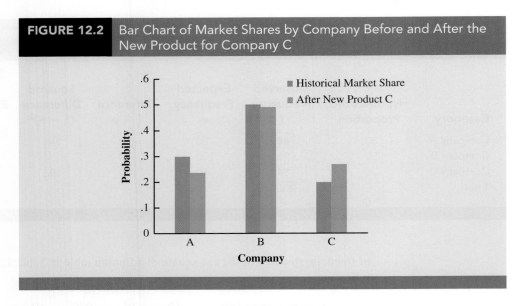

FIGURE 12.2   Bar Chart of Market Shares by Company Before and After the New Product for Company C

Let us summarize the steps that can be used to conduct a goodness of fit test for a hypothesized multinomial population distribution.

MULTINOMIAL PROBABILITY DISTRIBUTION GOODNESS OF FIT TEST

1. State the null and alternative hypotheses.

   H_0: The population follows a multinomial probability distribution with specified probabilities for each of the k categories

   H_a: The population does not follow a multinomial distribution with the specified probabilities for each of the k categories

2. Select a random sample and record the observed frequencies f_i for each category.
3. Assume the null hypothesis is true and determine the expected frequency e_i in each category by multiplying the category probability by the sample size.
4. If the expected frequency e_i is at least 5 for each category, compute the value of the test statistic.

$$\chi^2 = \sum_{i=1}^{k} \frac{(f_i - e_i)^2}{e_i}$$

5. Rejection rule:

   p-value approach: Reject H_0 if p-value $\leq \alpha$
   Critical value approach: Reject H_0 if $\chi^2 \geq \chi^2_\alpha$

   where α is the level of significance for the test and there are $k - 1$ degrees of freedom.

Normal Probability Distribution

The goodness of fit test for a normal probability distribution is also based on the use of the chi-square distribution. In particular, observed frequencies for several categories of sample data are compared to expected frequencies under the assumption that the population has a normal probability distribution. Because the normal probability distribution is continuous, we must modify the way the categories are defined and how the expected frequencies are computed. Let us demonstrate the goodness of fit test for a normal distribution by considering the job applicant test data for Chemline, Inc., shown in Table 12.10.

TABLE 12.10	Chemline Employee Aptitude Test Scores for 50 Randomly Chosen Job Applicants				
71	66	61	65	54	93
60	86	70	70	73	73
55	63	56	62	76	54
82	79	76	68	53	58
85	80	56	61	61	64
65	62	90	69	76	79
77	54	64	74	65	65
61	56	63	80	56	71
79	84				

Chemline hires approximately 400 new employees annually for its four plants located throughout the United States. The personnel director asks whether a normal distribution applies for the population of test scores. If such a distribution can be used, the distribution would be helpful in evaluating specific test scores; that is, scores in the upper 20%, lower 40%, and so on, could be identified quickly. Hence, we want to test the null hypothesis that the population of test scores has a normal distribution.

Let us first use the data in Table 12.10 to develop estimates of the mean and standard deviation of the normal distribution that will be considered in the null hypothesis. We use the sample mean $\bar{x}$ and the sample standard deviation s as point estimators of the mean and standard deviation of the normal distribution. The calculations follow.

$$\bar{x} = \frac{\sum x_i}{n} = \frac{3421}{50} = 68.42$$

$$s = \sqrt{\frac{\sum (x_i - \bar{x})^2}{n-1}} = \sqrt{\frac{5310.0369}{49}} = 10.41$$

DATA *file*

Chemline

Using these values, we state the following hypotheses about the distribution of the job applicant test scores.

H_0: The population of test scores has a normal distribution with mean 68.42 and standard deviation 10.41

H_a: The population of test scores does not have a normal distribution with mean 68.42 and standard deviation 10.41

The hypothesized normal distribution is shown in Figure 12.3.

With the continuous normal probability distribution, we must use a different procedure for defining the categories. We need to define the categories in terms of *intervals* of test scores.

With a continuous probability distribution, establish intervals such that each interval has an expected frequency of five or more.

Recall the rule of thumb for an expected frequency of at least five in each interval or category. We define the categories of test scores such that the expected frequencies will be at least five for each category. With a sample size of 50, one way of establishing categories is to divide the normal probability distribution into 10 equal-probability intervals (see Figure 12.4). With a sample size of 50, we would expect five outcomes in each interval or category, and the rule of thumb for expected frequencies would be satisfied.

Let us look more closely at the procedure for calculating the category boundaries. When the normal probability distribution is assumed, the standard normal probability tables can be used to determine these boundaries. First consider the test score cutting off the lowest 10% of the test scores. From the table for the standard normal distribution we find that the z value for this test score is -1.28. Therefore, the test score of $x = 68.42 - 1.28(10.41) = 55.10$ provides this cutoff value for the lowest 10% of the scores. For the lowest 20%, we find

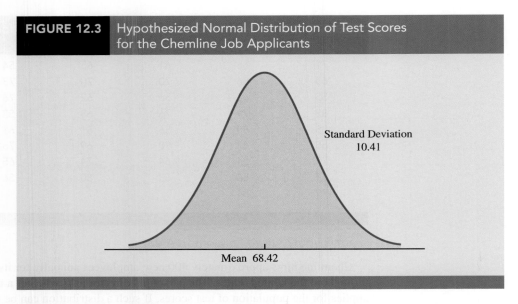

FIGURE 12.3   Hypothesized Normal Distribution of Test Scores for the Chemline Job Applicants

FIGURE 12.4   Normal Distribution for the Chemline Example with 10 Equal-Probability Intervals

$z = -.84$, and thus $x = 68.42 - .84(10.41) = 59.68$. Working through the normal distribution in that way provides the following test score values.

Percentage	z	Test Score
10%	−1.28	$68.42 - 1.28(10.41) = 55.10$
20%	−.84	$68.42 - .84(10.41) = 59.68$
30%	−.52	$68.42 - .52(10.41) = 63.01$
40%	−.25	$68.42 - .25(10.41) = 65.82$
50%	.00	$68.42 + 0(10.41) = 68.42$
60%	+.25	$68.42 + .25(10.41) = 71.02$
70%	+.52	$68.42 + .52(10.41) = 73.83$
80%	+.84	$68.42 + .84(10.41) = 77.16$
90%	+1.28	$68.42 + 1.28(10.41) = 81.74$

These cutoff or interval boundary points are identified on the graph in Figure 12.4.

TABLE 12.11	Observed and Expected Frequencies for Chemline Job Applicant Test Scores	
Test Score Interval	**Observed Frequency f_i**	**Expected Frequency e_i**
Less than 55.10	5	5
55.10 to 59.68	5	5
59.68 to 63.01	9	5
63.01 to 65.82	6	5
65.82 to 68.42	2	5
68.42 to 71.02	5	5
71.02 to 73.83	2	5
73.83 to 77.16	5	5
77.16 to 81.74	5	5
81.74 and over	6	5
Total	50	50

TABLE 12.12	Computation of the Chi-Square Test Statistic for the Chemline Job Applicant Example				
Test Score Interval	**Observed Frequency f_i**	**Expected Frequency e_i**	**Difference $f_i - e_i$**	**Squared Difference $(f_i - e_i)^2$**	**Squared Difference Divided by Expected Frequency $(f_i - e_i)^2/e_i$**
Less than 55.10	5	5	0	0	.0
55.10 to 59.68	5	5	0	0	.0
59.68 to 63.01	9	5	4	16	3.2
63.01 to 65.82	6	5	1	1	.2
65.82 to 68.42	2	5	−3	9	1.8
68.42 to 71.02	5	5	0	0	.0
71.02 to 73.83	2	5	−3	9	1.8
73.83 to 77.16	5	5	0	0	.0
77.16 to 81.74	5	5	0	0	.0
81.74 and over	6	5	1	1	.2
Total	50	50			$\chi^2 = 7.2$

With the categories or intervals of test scores now defined and with the known expected frequency of five per category, we can return to the sample data of Table 12.10 and determine the observed frequencies for the categories. Doing so provides the results in Table 12.11.

With the results in Table 12.11, the goodness of fit calculations proceed exactly as before. Namely, we compare the observed and expected results by computing a χ^2 value. The calculations necessary to compute the chi-square test statistic are shown in Table 12.12. We see that the value of the test statistic is $\chi^2 = 7.2$.

To determine whether the computed χ^2 value of 7.2 is large enough to reject H_0, we need to refer to the appropriate chi-square distribution table. Using the rule for computing the number of degrees of freedom for the goodness of fit test, we have $k - p - 1 = 10 - 2 - 1 = 7$ degrees of freedom based on $k = 10$ categories and $p = 2$ parameters (mean and standard deviation) estimated from the sample data.

Estimating the two parameters of the normal distribution will cause a loss of two degrees of freedom in the χ^2 test.

Suppose that we test the null hypothesis that the distribution for the test scores is a normal distribution with a .10 level of significance. To test this hypothesis, we need to determine the p-value for the test statistic $\chi^2 = 7.2$ by finding the area in the upper tail of a chi-square distribution with 7 degrees of freedom. Using row seven of Table 12.4, we find that $\chi^2 = 7.2$ provides an area in the upper tail greater than .10. Thus, we know that the p-value is greater than .10. JMP or Excel procedures in Appendix F can be used to show $\chi^2 = 7.2$ provides a p-value = .4084. With p-value $>.10$, the hypothesis that the probability distribution for the Chemline job applicant test scores is a normal probability distribution cannot be rejected. The normal probability distribution may be applied to assist in the interpretation of test scores. A summary of the goodness fit test for a normal probability distribution follows.

NORMAL PROBABILITY DISTRIBUTION GOODNESS OF FIT TEST

1. State the null and alternative hypotheses.

   H_0: The population has a normal probability distribution.
   H_a: The population does not have a normal probability distribution.

2. Select a random sample and
   a. Compute the sample mean and sample standard deviation.
   b. Define k intervals of values so that the expected frequency is at least five for each interval. Using equal probability intervals is a good approach.
   c. Record the observed frequency of data values f_i in each interval defined.
3. Compute the expected number of occurrences e_i for each interval of values defined in step 2(b). Multiply the sample size by the probability of a normal random variable being in the interval.
4. Compute the value of the test statistic.

$$\chi^2 = \sum_{i=1}^{k} \frac{(f_i - e_i)^2}{e_i}$$

5. Rejection rule:

   p-value approach: Reject H_0 if p-value $\leq \alpha$
   Critical value approach: Reject H_0 if $\chi^2 \geq \chi^2_\alpha$

   where α is the level of significance. The degrees of freedom $= k - p - 1$, where p is the number of parameters of the distribution estimated by the sample. In step 2a, the sample is used to estimate the mean and standard deviation. Thus, $p = 2$ and the degrees of freedom $= k - 2 - 1 = k - 3$.

EXERCISES

Methods

19. Test the following hypotheses by using the χ^2 goodness of fit test.

$$H_0: p_A = .40, p_B = .40, \text{ and } p_C = .20$$
$$H_a: \text{The population proportions are not}$$
$$p_A = .40, p_B = .40, \text{ and } p_C = .20$$

A sample of size 200 yielded 60 in category A, 120 in category B, and 20 in category C. Use $\alpha = .01$ and test to see whether the proportions are as stated in H_0.
a. Use the p-value approach.
b. Repeat the test using the critical value approach.

20. The following data are believed to have come from a normal distribution. Use the goodness of fit test and $\alpha = .05$ to test this claim.

17	23	22	24	19	23	18	22	20	13	11	21	18	20	21
21	18	15	24	23	23	43	29	27	26	30	28	33	23	29

Applications

21. **Television Audiences Across Networks.** During the first 13 weeks of the television season, the Saturday evening 8 P.M. to 9 P.M. audience proportions were recorded as ABC 29%, CBS 28%, NBC 25%, and independents 18%. A sample of 300 homes two weeks after a Saturday night schedule revision yielded the following viewing audience data: ABC 95 homes, CBS 70 homes, NBC 89 homes, and independents 46 homes. Test with $\alpha = .05$ to determine whether the viewing audience proportions changed.

M&M

22. **M&M Candy Colors.** Mars, Inc. manufactures M&M's, one of the most popular candy treats in the world. The milk chocolate candies come in a variety of colors including blue, brown, green, orange, red, and yellow. The overall proportions for the colors are .24 blue, .13 brown, .20 green, .16 orange, .13 red, and .14 yellow. In a sampling study, several bags of M&M milk chocolates were opened and the following color counts were obtained.

Blue	Brown	Green	Orange	Red	Yellow
105	72	89	84	70	80

Use a .05 level of significance and the sample data to test the hypothesis that the overall proportions for the colors are as stated above. What is your conclusion?

23. **Shareholder Scoreboard Ratings.** *The Wall Street Journal's* Shareholder Scoreboard tracks the performance of 1000 major U.S. companies. The performance of each company is rated based on the annual total return, including stock price changes and the reinvestment of dividends. Ratings are assigned by dividing all 1000 companies into five groups from A (top 20%), B (next 20%), to E (bottom 20%). Shown here are the one-year ratings for a sample of 60 of the largest companies. Do the largest companies differ in performance from the performance of the 1000 companies in the Shareholder Scoreboard? Use $\alpha = .05$.

A	B	C	D	E
5	8	15	20	12

24. **Traffic Accidents by Day of Week.** The National Highway Traffic Safety Administration reported the percentage of traffic accidents occurring each day of the week. Assume that a sample of 420 accidents provided the following data.

Sunday	Monday	Tuesday	Wednesday	Thursday	Friday	Saturday
66	50	53	47	55	69	80

a. Conduct a hypothesis test to determine if the proportion of traffic accidents is the same for each day of the week. What is the p-value? Using a .05 level of significance, what is your conclusion?

b. Compute the percentage of traffic accidents occurring on each day of the week. What day has the highest percentage of traffic accidents? Does this seem reasonable? Discuss.

Temperatures

25. **Daily High Temperatures.** Bob Feller, an Iowa farmer, has recorded the daily high temperatures during the same five-day stretch in May over the past five years. Bob is interested in whether this data suggests that the daily high temperature obeys a normal

distribution. Use $\alpha = .01$ and conduct a goodness of fit test to see whether the follow-ing sample appears to have been selected from a normal probability distribution.

55	86	94	58	55	95	55	52	69	95	90	65	87	50	56
55	57	98	58	79	92	62	59	88	65					

After you complete the goodness of fit calculations, construct a histogram of the data. Does the histogram representation support the conclusion reached with the goodness of fit test? (*Note:* $\bar{x} = 71$ and $s = 17$.)

26. **Weekly Demand at Whole Foods Market.** The manager at a Whole Foods Market is responsible for managing store inventory. The mathematical models that she uses to determine how much inventory to stock rely on product demand being normally dis-tributed. In particular, the weekly demand of sriracha chili kale chips at a Whole Foods Market store is believed to be normally distributed. Use a goodness of fit test and the following data to test this assumption. Use $\alpha = .10$.

DATA *file*
Demand

18	20	22	27	22
25	22	27	25	24
26	23	20	24	26
27	25	19	21	25
26	25	31	29	25
25	28	26	28	24

SUMMARY

In this chapter we have introduced hypothesis tests for the following applications.

1. Testing the equality of population proportions for three or more populations.
2. Testing the independence of two categorical variables.
3. Testing whether a probability distribution for a population follows a specific historical or theoretical probability distribution.

All tests apply to categorical variables and all tests use a chi-square (χ^2) test statistic that is based on the differences between observed frequencies and expected frequencies. In each case, expected frequencies are computed under the assumption that the null hypothesis is true. These chi-square tests are upper tailed tests. Large differences between observed and expected frequencies provide a large value for the chi-square test statistic and indicate that the null hypothesis should be rejected.

The test for the equality of population proportions for three or more populations is based on independent random samples selected from each of the populations. The sample data show the counts for each of two categorical responses for each population. The null hypothesis is that the population proportions are equal. Rejection of the null hypothesis supports the conclusion that the population proportions are not all equal.

The test of independence between two categorical variables uses one sample from a population with the data showing the counts for each combination of two categorical vari-ables. The null hypothesis is that the two variables are independent and the test is referred to as a test of independence. If the null hypothesis is rejected, there is statistical evidence of an association or dependency between the two variables.

The goodness of fit test is used to test the hypothesis that a population has a specific historical or theoretical probability distribution. We showed applications for populations with a multinomial probability distribution and with a normal probability distribution. Since the normal probability distribution applies to continuous data, intervals of data values were estab-lished to create the categories for the categorical variable required for the goodness of fit test.

GLOSSARY

Goodness of fit test A chi-square test that can be used to test that a population probability distribution has a specific historical or theoretical probability distribution. This test was demon-strated for both a multinomial probability distribution and a normal probability distribution.

Marascuilo procedure A multiple comparison procedure that can be used to test for a significant difference between pairs of population proportions. This test can be helpful in identifying differences between pairs of population proportions whenever the hypothesis of equal population proportions has been rejected.

Multinomial probability distribution A probability distribution where each outcome belongs to one of three or more categories. The multinomial probability distribution extends the binomial probability from two to three or more outcomes per trial.

Test of independence A chi-square test that can be used to test for the independence between two categorical variables. If the hypothesis of independence is rejected, it can be concluded that the categorical variables are associated or dependent.

KEY FORMULAS

Expected Frequencies Under the Assumption H_0 Is True

$$e_{ij} = \frac{(\text{Row } i \text{ Total})(\text{Column } j \text{ Total})}{\text{Sample Size}} \tag{12.1}$$

Chi-Square Test Statistic

$$\chi^2 = \sum_i \sum_j \frac{(f_{ij} - e_{ij})^2}{e_{ij}} \tag{12.2}$$

Critical Values for the Marascuilo Pairwise Comparison Procedure

$$CV_{ij} = \sqrt{\chi_\alpha^2} \sqrt{\frac{\bar{p}_i(1 - \bar{p}_i)}{n_i} + \frac{\bar{p}_j(1 - \bar{p}_j)}{n_j}} \tag{12.3}$$

Chi-Square Test Statistic for the Goodness of Fit Test

$$\chi^2 = \sum_i \frac{(f_i - e_i)^2}{e_i} \tag{12.6}$$

SUPPLEMENTARY EXERCISES

27. **Where Millionaires Live in America.** In a 2018 study, Phoenix Marketing International identified Bridgeport, Connecticut; San Jose, California; Washington, D.C.; and Lexington Park, Maryland as the four U.S. cities with the highest percentage of millionaires (*Kiplinger* website, https://www.kiplinger.com/slideshow/investing/T064-S001-where-millionaires -live-in-america-2018/index.html). The following data show the following number of millionaires for samples of individuals from each of the four cities.

	City			
Millionaire	Bridgeport, CT	San Jose, CA	Washington, D.C.	Lexington Park, MD
Yes	44	35	35	34
No	356	350	364	366

a. What is the estimate of the percentage of millionaires in each of these cities?

b. Using a .05 level of significance, test for the equality of the population proportion of millionaires for these four cities. What is the *p*-value and what is your conclusion?

28. **Quality Comparison Across Production Shifts.** Arconic Inc. is a producer of aluminum components for the avionics and automotive industries. At its Davenport Works plant, an engineer has conducted a quality-control test in which aluminum coils produced in all three shifts were inspected. The study was designed to determine if the population proportion of good parts was the same for all three shifts. Sample data follow.

	Production Shift		
Quality	**First**	**Second**	**Third**
Good	285	368	176
Defective	15	32	24

a. Using a .05 level of significance, conduct a hypothesis test to determine if the population proportion of good parts is the same for all three shifts. What is the *p*-value and what is your conclusion?

b. If the conclusion is that the population proportions are not all equal, use a multiple comparison procedure to determine how the shifts differ in terms of quality. What shift or shifts need to improve the quality of parts produced?

29. **Ratings of Most-Visited Art Museums.** As listed by *The Art Newspaper* Visitor Figures Survey (https://www.theartnewspaper.com/visitor-figures-2017), the five most-visited art museums in the world are the Louvre Museum, the National Museum in China, the Metropolitan Museum of Art, the Vatican Museums, and the British Museum. Which of these five museums would visitors most frequently rate as spectacular? Samples of recent visitors of each of these museums were taken, and the results of these samples follow.

	Louvre Museum	National Museum in China	Metropolitan Museum of Art	Vatican Museums	British Museum
Spectacular	113	88	94	98	96
Not Spectacular	37	44	46	72	64

a. Use the sample data to calculate the point estimate of the population proportion of visitors who rated each of these museums as spectacular.

b. Conduct a hypothesis test to determine if the population proportion of visitors who rated the museum as spectacular is equal for these five museums. Using a .05 level of significance, what is the *p*-value and what is your conclusion?

30. **Pace-of-Life Preference By Gender.** A Pew Research Center survey asked respondents if they would rather live in a place with a slower pace of life or a place with a faster pace of life. The survey also asked the respondent's gender. Consider the following sample data.

	Gender	
Preferred Pace of Life	**Male**	**Female**
Slower	230	218
No Preference	20	24
Faster	90	48

a. Is the preferred pace of life independent of gender? Using a .05 level of significance, what is the *p*-value and what is your conclusion?

b. Discuss any differences between the preferences of men and women.

31. **Church Attendance by Age Group.** The Barna Group conducted a survey about church attendance. The survey respondents were asked about their church attendance and asked to indicate their age. Use the sample data to determine

whether church attendance is independent of age. Using a .05 level of significance, what is the *p*-value and what is your conclusion? What conclusion can you draw about church attendance as individuals grow older?

	Age			
Church Attendance	20 to 29	30 to 39	40 to 49	50 to 59
Yes	31	63	94	72
No	69	87	106	78

Ambulance

32. **Ambulance Calls by Day of Week.** An ambulance service responds to emergency calls for two counties in Virginia. One county is an urban county and the other is a rural county. A sample of 471 ambulance calls over the past two years showed the county and the day of the week for each emergency call. Data are as follows.

	Day of Week						
County	Sun	Mon	Tue	Wed	Thu	Fri	Sat
Urban	61	48	50	55	63	73	43
Rural	7	9	16	13	9	14	10

Test for independence of the county and the day of the week. Using a .05 level of significance, what is the *p*-value and what is your conclusion?

33. **Attitudes Toward New Nuclear Power Plants.** A *Financial Times/Harris Poll* surveyed people in six countries to assess attitudes toward a variety of alternate forms of energy. The data in the following table are a portion of the poll's findings concerning whether people favor or oppose the building of new nuclear power plants.

	Country					
Response	Great Britain	France	Italy	Spain	Germany	United States
Strongly favor	141	161	298	133	128	204
Favor more than oppose	348	366	309	222	272	326
Oppose more than favor	381	334	219	311	322	316
Strongly oppose	217	215	219	443	389	174

a. How large was the sample in this poll?
b. Conduct a hypothesis test to determine whether people's attitude toward building new nuclear power plants is independent of country. What is your conclusion?
c. Using the percentage of respondents who "strongly favor" and "favor more than oppose," which country has the most favorable attitude toward building new nuclear power plants? Which country has the least favorable attitude?

34. **America's Favorite Sports.** *The Harris Poll* tracks the favorite sport of Americans who follow at least one sport. Results of the poll show that professional football is the favorite sport of 33% of Americans who follow at least one sport, followed by baseball at 15%, men's college football at 10%, auto racing at 6%, men's professional basketball at 5%, and ice hockey at 5%, with other sport at 26%. Consider a survey in which 344 college

undergraduates who follow at least one sport were asked to identify their favorite sport produced the following results:

Professional Football	Baseball	Men's College Football	Auto Racing	Men's Professional Basketball	Ice Hockey	Other Sports
111	39	46	14	6	20	108

Do college undergraduate students differ from the general public with regard to their favorite sports? Use $\alpha = .05$.

35. **Best-Selling Small Cars in America.** Based on 2017 sales, the six top-selling compact cars are the Honda Civic, Toyota Corolla, Nissan Sentra, Hyundai Elantra, Chevrolet Cruze, and Ford Focus (*New York Daily News*, http://www.nydailynews.com/autos/street-smarts/best-selling-small-cars-2016-list-article-1.2945432). The 2017 market shares are: Honda Civic 20%, Toyota Corolla 17%, Nissan Sentra 12%, Hyundai Elantra 10%, Chevrolet Cruze 10%, and Ford Focus 8%, with other small car models making up the remaining 23%. A sample of 400 compact car sales in Chicago showed the following number of vehicles sold.

Honda Civic	98
Toyota Corolla	72
Nissan Sentra	54
Hyundai Elantra	44
Chevrolet Cruze	42
Ford Focus	25
Others	65

Use a goodness of fit test to determine if the sample data indicate that the market shares for compact cars in Chicago are different than the market shares suggested by nationwide 2017 sales. Using a .05 level of significance, what is the *p*-value and what is your conclusion? If the Chicago market appears to differ significantly from the nationwide sales, which categories contribute most to this difference?

Grades

36. **Testing Normality of Final Exam Grades.** A random sample of final examination grades for a college course follows.

55	85	72	99	48	71	88	70	59	98	80	74	93	85	74
82	90	71	83	60	95	77	84	73	63	72	95	79	51	85
76	81	78	65	75	87	86	70	80	64					

Use $\alpha = .05$ and test to determine whether a normal probability distribution should be rejected as being representative of the population distribution of grades.

37. **Testing If Daily Sales Obey a Binomial Probability Distribution.** A salesperson makes four calls per day. A sample of 100 days gives the following frequencies of sales volumes.

Number of Sales	Observed Frequency (days)
0	30
1	32
2	25
3	10
4	3
Total	100

Records show sales result from 30% of all sales calls. Assuming independent sales calls, the number of sales per day should follow a binomial probability distribution. The binomial probability function is

Chapter 5 contains further discussion of the binomial probability distribution.

$$f(x) = \frac{n!}{x!(n-x)!} p^x (1-p)^{n-x}$$

For this exercise, assume that the population has a binomial probability distribution with $n = 4$, $p = .30$, and $x = 0, 1, 2, 3$, and 4.

a. Compute the expected frequencies for $x = 0, 1, 2, 3$, and 4 by using the binomial probability function. Combine categories if necessary to satisfy the requirement that the expected frequency is five or more for all categories.

b. Use the goodness of fit test to determine whether the assumption of a binomial probability distribution should be rejected. Use $\alpha = .05$. Because no parameters of the binomial probability distribution were estimated from the sample data, set the degrees of freedom to $k - 1$ when k is the number of categories.

CASE PROBLEM 1: A BIPARTISAN AGENDA FOR CHANGE

In a study conducted by Zogby International for the *Democrat and Chronicle,* more than 700 New Yorkers were polled to determine whether the New York state government works. Respondents surveyed were asked questions involving pay cuts for state legislators, restrictions on lobbyists, term limits for legislators, and whether state citizens should be able to put matters directly on the state ballot for a vote. The results regarding several proposed reforms had broad support, crossing all demographic and political lines.

Suppose that a follow-up survey of 100 individuals who live in the western region of New York was conducted. The party affiliation (Democrat, Independent, Republican) of each individual surveyed was recorded, as well as their responses to the following three questions.

1. Should legislative pay be cut for every day the state budget is late?

   Yes _____   No _____

2. Should there be more restrictions on lobbyists?

   Yes _____   No _____

3. Should there be term limits requiring that legislators serve a fixed number of years?

   Yes _____   No _____

NYReform

The responses were coded using 1 for a Yes response and 2 for a No response. The complete data set is available in the file *NYReform*.

Managerial Report

1. Use descriptive statistics to summarize the data from this study. What are your preliminary conclusions about the independence of the response (Yes or No) and party affiliation for each of the three questions in the survey?

2. With regard to question 1, test for the independence of the response (Yes and No) and party affiliation. Use $\alpha = .05$.

3. With regard to question 2, test for the independence of the response (Yes and No) and party affiliation. Use $\alpha = .05$.

4. With regard to question 3, test for the independence of the response (Yes and No) and party affiliation. Use $\alpha = .05$.

5. Does it appear that there is broad support for change across all political lines? Explain.

CASE PROBLEM 2: FUENTES SALTY SNACKS, INC.

Six months ago, Fuentes Salty Snacks, Inc., added a new flavor to its line of potato chips. The new flavor, candied bacon, was introduced through a nationwide rollout supported by an extensive promotional campaign. Fuentes' management is convinced that quick penetration into grocery stores is a key to the successful introduction of a new salty snack product, and management now wants determine whether availability of Fuentes' Candied Bacon Potato Chips is consistent in grocery stores across regions of the United States. The marketing department has selected random samples of 40 grocery stores in each of its eight U.S. sales regions:

- New England (Connecticut, Maine, Massachusetts, New Hampshire, Rhode Island, and Vermont)
- Mid-Atlantic (New Jersey, New York, and Pennsylvania)
- Midwest (Illinois, Indiana, Michigan, Ohio, and Wisconsin)
- Great Plains (Iowa, Kansas, Minnesota, Missouri, Nebraska, North Dakota Oklahoma, and South Dakota)
- South Atlantic (Delaware, Florida, Georgia, Maryland, North Carolina, South Carolina, Virginia, West Virginia, and Washington, D.C.)
- Deep South (Alabama, Arkansas, Kentucky, Louisiana, Mississippi, Tennessee, and Texas)
- Mountain (Arizona, Colorado Idaho, Montana, Nevada, New Mexico, Utah, and Wyoming)
- Pacific (Alaska, California, Hawaii, Oregon, and Washington)

DATAfile

FuentesChips

The stores in each sample were then contacted, and the manager of each store was asked whether the store currently carries Fuentes' Candied Bacon Potato Chips. The complete data set is available in the file *FuentesChips*.

Fuentes' senior management now wants to use these data to assess whether penetration of Fuentes' Candied Bacon Potato Chips in grocery stores is consistent across its eight U.S. sales regions. If penetration of Fuentes' Candied Bacon Potato Chips in grocery stores differs across its eight U.S. sales regions, Fuentes' management would also like to identify sales regions in which penetration of Fuentes' Candied Bacon Potato Chips is lower or higher than expected.

Managerial Report

Prepare a managerial report that addresses the following issues.

1. Use descriptive statistics to summarize the data from Fuentes' study. Based on your descriptive statistics, what are your preliminary conclusions about the penetration of Fuentes' Candied Bacon Potato Chips in grocery stores across its eight U.S. sales regions?
2. Use the data from Fuentes' study to test the hypothesis that the proportion of grocery stores that currently carries Fuentes' Candied Bacon Potato Chips is equal across its eight U.S. sales regions. Use $\alpha = .05$.
3. Do the results of your hypothesis test provide evidence that Fuentes' Candied Bacon Potato Chips have penetrated grocery stores across its eight U.S. sales regions? In which sales region(s) is penetration of Fuentes' Candied Bacon Potato Chips lower or higher than expected? Use the Marascuilo pairwise comparison procedure at $\alpha = .05$ to test for differences between regions.

CASE PROBLEM 3: FRESNO BOARD GAMES

Fresno Board Games manufactures and sells several different board games online and through department stores nationwide. Fresno's most popular game, ¡Cabestrillo Cinco!, is played with 5 six-sided dice. Fresno has purchased dice for this game from

Box Cars, Ltd., for twenty-five years, but the company is now considering a move to Big Boss Gaming, Inc. (BBG), a new supplier that has offered to sell dice to Fresno at a substantially lower price. Fresno management is intrigued by the potential savings offered by BBG, but is also concerned about the quality of the dice produced by the new supplier. Fresno has a reputation for high integrity, and its management feels that it is imperative that the dice included with ¡Cabestrillo Cinco! are fair.

BBG

To alleviate concerns about the quality of the dice it produces, BBG allows Fresno's manager of product quality to randomly sample five dice from its most recent production run. While being observed by several members of the BBG management team, Fresno's manager of product quality rolls each of these five randomly selected dice 500 times and records each outcome. The results for each of these five randomly selected dice are available in the file *BBG*.

Fresno management now wants to use these data to assess whether any of these five six-sided dice is not fair; that is, does one outcome occur more frequently or less frequently than the other outcomes?

Managerial Report

Prepare a managerial report that addresses the following issues.

1. Use descriptive statistics to summarize the data collected by Fresno's manager of product quality for each of the five randomly selected dice. Based on these descriptive statistics, what are your preliminary conclusions about the fairness of the five selected dice?

2. Use the data collected by Fresno's manager of product quality to test the hypothesis that the first of the five randomly selected dice is fair, i.e., the distribution of outcomes for the first of the five randomly selected dice is multinomial with $p_1 = p_2 = p_3 = p_4 = p_5 = p_6 = 1/6$. Repeat this process for each of the other four randomly selected dice. Use $\alpha = .01$. Do the results of your hypothesis tests provide evidence that BBG is producing unfair dice?

Chapter 12 Appendix

Appendix 12.1 Chi-Square Tests with JMP

We describe the use of JMP to execute hypothesis tests based on the chi-square distribution.

Test the Equality of Population Proportions and Test of Independence from Source Data

The JMP procedure is identical for the chi-square test of the equality of population proportions and the chi-square test of independence. In this section, we describe the procedure for the case when a data set is available that shows the responses for each element in the sample.

We begin with the automobile loyalty example presented in Section 12.1. Responses for a sample of 500 automobile owners are contained in the file *AutoLoyalty*. Column A shows the population the owner belongs to (Chevrolet Impala, Ford Fusion, or Honda Accord), and column B contains the likely-to-purchase response (Yes or No). The JMP steps to conduct a chi-square test using this data set follow.

DATA*file*

AutoLoyalty

Step 1. Open the file *AutoLoyalty* following the steps in Appendix 1.1
Step 2. Click **Analyze** and select **Fit Y by X**
Step 3. When the **Fit Y by X – Contextual** dialog box appears
    Drag **Likely Repurchase** from the **Select Columns** area to the
    Y, Response box in the **Cast Selected Columns into Roles** area
    Drag **Automobile** from the **Select Columns** area to the **X, Factor** box
    in the **Cast Selected Columns into Roles** area
    Click **OK** in the **Action** area
Step 4. When the **Fit Y by X of Likely Repurchase by Automobile** window appears
    Click the red triangle 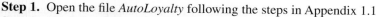 next to **Contingency Table**, select **Expected** and
    deselect **Total %, Col %,** and **Row %**

These steps will produce the chart displayed in Figure JMP 12.1. In the **Tests** area, the row corresponding to Pearson provides the test statistic $\chi^2 = 7.891$, and the corresponding p-value = .0193. Because the p-value $\le$ .05, we reject the null hypothesis that the three population proportions are equal at the $\alpha = .05$ level of significance. Thus, we conclude that the three population proportions are not all equal and there is a difference in brand loyalties among the three cars.

Test the Equality of Population Proportions and Test of Independence from a Summary Table

The JMP procedure is identical for the chi-square test of the equality of population proportions and the chi-square test of independence. In this section, we describe the procedure for the case a tabular summary is provided (rather than the source data set) that shows the observed frequencies for the response categories.

Again, we will use the automobile loyalty example presented in Section 12.1. The file *AutoLoyaltySummary* contains a table resembling Table 12.2 that summarizes the responses for a sample of 500 automobile owners. The following steps demonstrate how to use this summary table as input for a chi-square test about the equality of population proportions.

DATA*file*

AutoLoyaltySummary

Step 1. Open the file *AutoLoyaltySummary* following the steps in Appendix 1.1
Step 2. Convert the file to stacked format following the steps in Appendix 1.1, by
    dragging **Chevrolet Impala, Ford Fusion** and **Honda Accord** to the **Stack**

FIGURE JMP 12.1   JMP Output of Chi-Square Test of Population Proportions for Automobile Loyalty Data

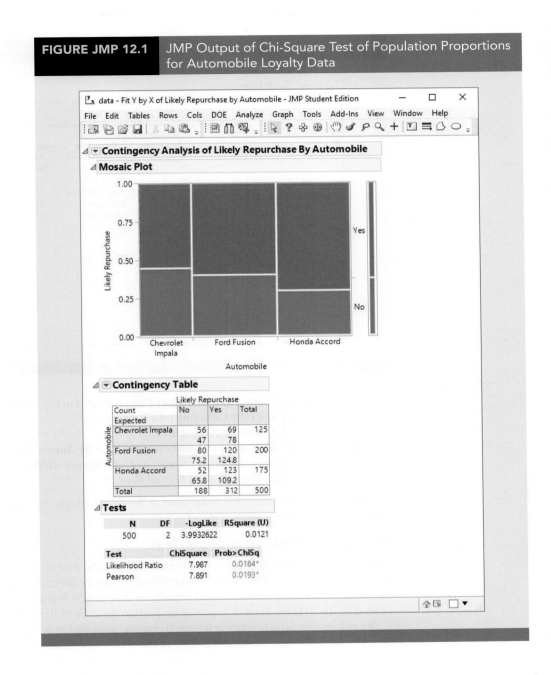

Columns box, entering *Count* as the new **Stacked Data Column** name, and entering *Automobile* as the new **Source Label Column** name

These steps will produce the data table displayed in Figure JMP 12.2.

Using the stacked data table in Figure JMP 12.2, we can proceed with the chi-square test of population proportions.

Step 3.   When the JMP stacked data table appears, click **Analyze** and select **Fit Y by X**

Step 4.   When the **Fit Y by X – Contextual** dialog box appears

Drag **Likely Repurchase** from the **Select Columns** area to the **Y, Response** box in the **Cast Selected Columns into Roles** area

Drag **Automobile** from the **Select Columns** area to the **X, Factor** box in the **Cast Selected Columns into Roles** area

FIGURE JMP 12.2   Stacked Data from *AutoLoyaltySummary* File

	Likely Repurchase	Automobile	Count
1	Yes	Chevrolet Impala	69
2	Yes	Ford Fusion	120
3	Yes	Honda Accord	123
4	No	Chevrolet Impala	56
5	No	Ford Fusion	80
6	No	Honda Accord	52

Columns (3/0)
Likely Repurchase
Automobile
Count

Rows
All rows   6
Selected   0
Excluded   0
Hidden   0
Labelled   0

Drag **Count** from the **Select Columns** area to the **Freq** box in the **Cast Selected Columns into Roles** area

Click **OK** in the **Action** area

Step 5. When the **Fit Y by X of Likely Repurchase by Automobile** window appears

Click the red triangle ▼ next to **Contingency Table**, select **Expected** and deselect **Total %**, **Col %**, and **Row %**

These steps will produce the same chart as the one displayed in Figure JMP 12.1 constructed from the source data.

Chi-Square Goodness-of-Fit Test

To execute a chi-square goodness-of-fit test with JMP, the user must first obtain a sample from the population and determine the observed frequency for each of k categories. Under the assumption that the hypothesized population distribution is true, the user must also determine the hypothesized or expected proportion for each of the k categories.

We will use the Scott Marketing Research example presented in Section 12.3. The file *ScottMarketingSummary* contains a table of the observed frequencies of customer's preferred product. The following steps demonstrate how to use this summary table as input for a chi-square goodness-of-fit test to the multinomial probability distribution with hypothesized proportions of .3, .5, and .2 for Company A's product, Company B's product, and Company C's product, respectively.

DATA*file*

ScottMarketingSummary

Step 1. Open the file *ScottMarketingSummary* following the steps in Appendix 1.1

Step 2. Click **Analyze** and select **Distribution**

Step 3. When the **Distribution** dialog box appears

Drag **Company** from the **Select Columns** area to the **Y, Columns** box in the **Cast Selected Columns into Roles** area

Drag **Count** from the **Select Columns** area to the **Freq** box in the **Cast Selected Columns into Roles** area

Click **OK** in the **Action** area

Step 4. When the **Distribution of Company** window appears

Click the red triangle ▼ next to **Company** and select **Test Probabilities**

FIGURE JMP 12.3 Entering Probabilities for Chi-Square Goodness-of-Fit Test in JMP

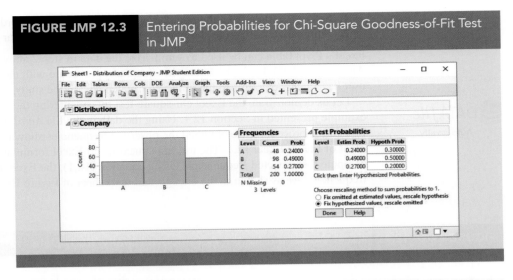

FIGURE JMP 12.4 JMP Output for Chi-Square Goodness-of-Fit Test for Scott Marketing Research Data

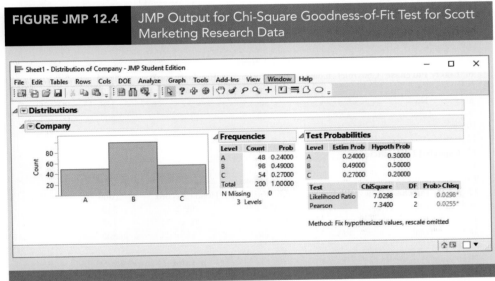

> **Step 5.** In the **Test Probabilities** area (see Figure JMP 12.3),
> > Enter *.3* in the **Hypoth Prob** box for **Level A**
> > Enter *.5* in the **Hypoth Prob** box for **Level B**
> > Enter *.2* in the **Hypoth Prob** box for **Level C**
> > Select **Fix hypothesized values, rescale omitted**
> > Click **Done**

These steps will produce the display in Figure JMP 12.4. In the **Test Probabilities** area, the row corresponding to Pearson provides the test statistic $\chi^2 = 7.34$ and the corresponding *p*-value $= .0255$. Because the *p*-value $\leq .05$, we reject the null hypothesis that customer preferences obey a multinomial probability distribution with the hypothesized probabilities of .3, .5, and .2 for Company A's product, Company B's product, and Company C's product, respectively.

Appendix 12.2 Chi-Square Tests with Excel

The Excel procedure for tests for the equality of population proportions, tests of independence, and goodness of fit tests are essentially the same as all make use of the Excel chi-square function CHISQ.TEST. Regardless of the application, the user must do the following before creating an Excel worksheet that will perform the test.

1. Select a sample from the population or populations and record the data
2. Summarize the data to show observed frequencies in a tabular format

Excel's PivotTable can be used to summarize the data in step 2 above, as we describe in Appendix 2.2. We begin the Excel chi-square test procedure with the understanding that the user has already determined the observed frequencies for the study.

DATA *file*
AutoLoyalty

Let us demonstrate the Excel chi-square test by considering the automobile loyalty example presented in Section 12.1. Using the data in the file *AutoLoyalty* and the Excel PivotTable procedure, we obtained the observed frequencies shown in the Excel worksheet of Figure Excel 12.1. The user must next insert Excel formulas in the worksheet to compute the expected frequencies. Using equation (12.1), the Excel formulas for expected frequencies are as shown in the background worksheet of Figure Excel 12.1.

FIGURE Excel 12.1   Excel Worksheet for the Automobile Loyalty Study Data

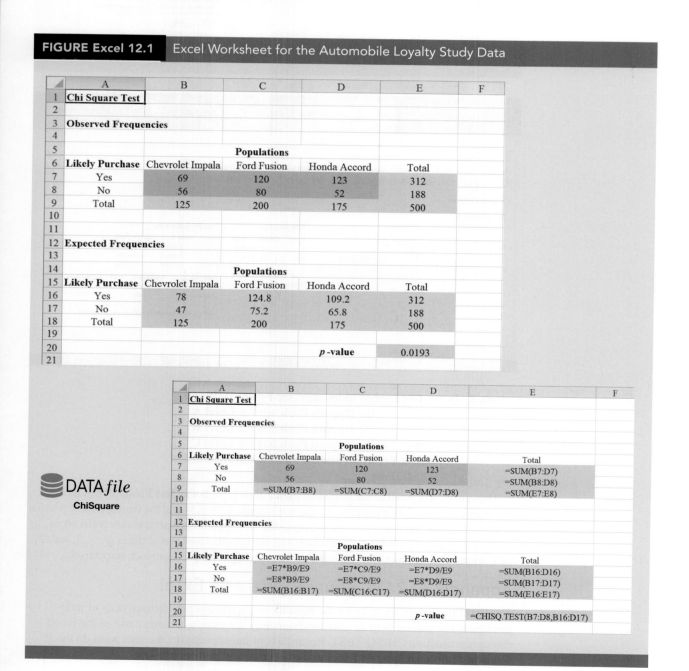

The last step is to insert the Excel function CHISQ.TEST. The format of this function is as follows:

=CHISQ.TEST(*Observed Frequency Cells, Expected Frequency Cells*)

In Figure Excel 12.1, the *Observed Frequency Cells* are B7:D8 and the *Expected Frequency Cells* are B16:D17. The function =CHISQ.TEST(B7:D8,B16:D17) is shown in cell E20 of the background worksheet. This function does all the chi-square test computations and returns the *p*-value for the test.

The test of independence summarizes the observed frequencies in a tabular format very similar to the one shown in Figure Excel 12.1. The formulas to compute expected frequencies are also very similar to the formulas shown in the background worksheet. For the goodness of fit test, the user provides the observed frequencies in a column rather than a table. The user must also provide the associated expected frequencies in another column. Lastly, the CHISQ.TEST function is used to obtain the *p*-value as described above.

Chapter 13

Experimental Design and Analysis of Variance

CONTENTS

STATISTICS IN PRACTICE: *BURKE MARKETING SERVICES, INC.*

STATISTICS IN PRACTICE

Burke Marketing Services, Inc.*

CINCINNATI, OHIO

Burke Marketing Services, Inc., is one of the most experienced market research firms in the industry. Burke writes more proposals, on more projects, every day than any other market research company in the world. Supported by state-of-the-art technology, Burke offers a wide variety of research capabilities, providing answers to nearly any marketing question.

In one study, a firm retained Burke to evaluate potential new versions of a children's dry cereal. To maintain confidentiality, we refer to the cereal manufacturer as the Anon Company. The four key factors that Anon's product developers thought would enhance the taste of the cereal were the following:

1. Ratio of wheat to corn in the cereal flake
2. Type of sweetener: sugar, honey, or artificial
3. Presence or absence of flavor bits with a fruit taste
4. Short or long cooking time

Burke designed an experiment to determine what effects these four factors had on cereal taste. For example, one test cereal was made with a specified ratio of wheat to corn, sugar as the sweetener, flavor bits, and a short cooking time; another test cereal was made with a different ratio of wheat to corn and the other three factors the same, and so on. Groups of children then taste-tested the cereals and stated what they thought about the taste of each.

---

*The authors are indebted to Dr. Ronald Tatham of Burke Marketing Services for providing the context for this Statistics in Practice.

Burke uses taste tests to provide valuable statistical information on what customers want from a product.
Source: Skydive Erick/Shutterstock.com

Analysis of variance was the statistical method used to study the data obtained from the taste tests. The results of the analysis showed the following:

- The flake composition and sweetener type were highly influential in taste evaluation.
- The flavor bits actually detracted from the taste of the cereal.
- The cooking time had no effect on the taste.

This information helped Anon identify the factors that would lead to the best-tasting cereal.

The experimental design employed by Burke and the subsequent analysis of variance were helpful in making a product design recommendation. In this chapter, we will see how such procedures are carried out.

In Chapter 1 we stated that statistical studies can be classified as either experimental or observational. In an experimental statistical study, an experiment is conducted to generate the data. An experiment begins with identifying a variable of interest. Then one or more other variables, thought to be related, are identified and controlled, and data are collected about how those variables influence the variable of interest.

In an observational study, data are usually obtained through sample surveys and not a controlled experiment. Good design principles are still employed, but the rigorous controls associated with an experimental statistical study are often not possible. For instance, in a study of the relationship between smoking and lung cancer the researcher cannot assign a smoking habit to subjects. The researcher is restricted to simply observing the effects of smoking on people who already smoke and the effects of not smoking on people who do not already smoke.

In this chapter we introduce three types of experimental designs: a completely randomized design, a randomized block design, and a factorial experiment. For each

Sir Ronald Aylmer Fisher (1890–1962) invented the branch of statistics known as experimental design. In addition to being accomplished in statistics, he was a noted scientist in the field of genetics.

design we show how a statistical procedure called analysis of variance (ANOVA) can be used to analyze the data available. ANOVA can also be used to analyze the data obtained through an observational study. For instance, we will see that the ANOVA procedure used for a completely randomized experimental design also works for testing the equality of three or more population means when data are obtained through an observational study. In the following chapters we will see that ANOVA plays a key role in analyzing the results of regression studies involving both experimental and observational data.

In the first section, we introduce the basic principles of an experimental study and show how they are employed in a completely randomized design. In the second section, we then show how ANOVA can be used to analyze the data from a completely randomized experimental design. In later sections we discuss multiple comparison procedures and two other widely used experimental designs, the randomized block design and the factorial experiment.

13.1 An Introduction to Experimental Design and Analysis of Variance

Cause-and-effect relationships can be difficult to establish in observational studies; such relationships are easier to establish in experimental studies.

As an example of an experimental statistical study, let us consider the problem facing Chemitech, Inc. Chemitech developed a new filtration system for municipal water supplies. The components for the new filtration system will be purchased from several suppliers, and Chemitech will assemble the components at its plant in Columbia, South Carolina. The industrial engineering group is responsible for determining the best assembly method for the new filtration system. After considering a variety of possible approaches, the group narrows the alternatives to three: method A, method B, and method C. These methods differ in the sequence of steps used to assemble the system. Managers at Chemitech want to determine which assembly method can produce the greatest number of filtration systems per week.

In the Chemitech experiment, assembly method is the independent variable or **factor**. Because three assembly methods correspond to this factor, we say that three treatments are associated with this experiment; each **treatment** corresponds to one of the three assembly methods. The Chemitech problem is an example of a **single-factor experiment**; it involves one categorical factor (method of assembly). More complex experiments may consist of multiple factors; some factors may be categorical and others may be quantitative.

The three assembly methods or treatments define the three populations of interest for the Chemitech experiment. One population is all Chemitech employees who use assembly method A, another is those who use method B, and the third is those who use method C. Note that for each population the dependent or **response variable** is the number of filtration systems assembled per week, and the primary statistical objective of the experiment is to determine whether the mean number of units produced per week is the same for all three populations (methods).

Randomization is the process of assigning the treatments to the experimental units at random. Prior to the work of Sir R. A. Fisher, treatments were assigned on a systematic or subjective basis.

Suppose a random sample of three employees is selected from all assembly workers at the Chemitech production facility. In experimental design terminology, the three randomly selected workers are the **experimental units**. The experimental design that we will use for the Chemitech problem is called a **completely randomized design**. This type of design requires that each of the three assembly methods or treatments be assigned randomly to one of the experimental units or workers. For example, method A might be randomly assigned to the second worker, method B to the first worker, and method C to the third worker. The concept of *randomization*, as illustrated in this example, is an important principle of all experimental designs.

Note that this experiment would result in only one measurement or number of units assembled for each treatment. To obtain additional data for each assembly method, we must repeat or replicate the basic experimental process. Suppose, for example, that instead

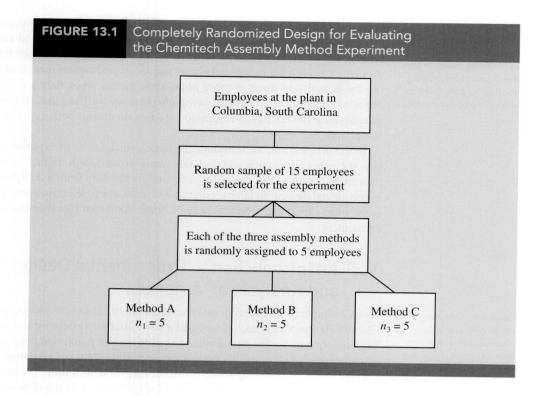

FIGURE 13.1   Completely Randomized Design for Evaluating the Chemitech Assembly Method Experiment

of selecting just three workers at random we selected 15 workers and then randomly assigned each of the three treatments to 5 of the workers. Because each method of assembly is assigned to 5 workers, we say that five replicates have been obtained. The process of *replication* is another important principle of experimental design. Figure 13.1 shows the completely randomized design for the Chemitech experiment.

Data Collection

Once we are satisfied with the experimental design, we proceed by collecting and analyzing the data. In the Chemitech case, the employees would be instructed in how to perform the assembly method assigned to them and then would begin assembling the new filtration systems using that method. After this assignment and training, the number of units assembled by each employee during one week is as shown in Table 13.1. The sample

DATA *file*

Chemitech

TABLE 13.1   Number of Units Produced by 15 Workers

	Method		
	A	B	C
	58	58	48
	64	69	57
	55	71	59
	66	64	47
	67	68	49
Sample mean	62	66	52
Sample variance	27.5	26.5	31.0
Sample standard deviation	5.244	5.148	5.568

means, sample variances, and sample standard deviations for each assembly method are also provided. Thus, the sample mean number of units produced using method A is 62; the sample mean using method B is 66; and the sample mean using method C is 52. From these data, method B appears to result in higher production rates than either of the other methods.

The real issue is whether the three sample means observed are different enough for us to conclude that the means of the populations corresponding to the three methods of assembly are different. To write this question in statistical terms, we introduce the following notation.

$$\mu_1 = \text{mean number of units produced per week using method A}$$
$$\mu_2 = \text{mean number of units produced per week using method B}$$
$$\mu_3 = \text{mean number of units produced per week using method C}$$

Although we will never know the actual values of μ_1, μ_2, and μ_3, we want to use the sample means to test the following hypotheses.

$$H_0: \mu_1 = \mu_2 = \mu_3$$
$$H_a: \text{Not all population means are equal}$$

> *If H_0 is rejected, we cannot conclude that all population means are different. Rejecting H_0 means that at least two population means have different values.*

As we will demonstrate shortly, analysis of variance (ANOVA) is the statistical procedure used to determine whether the observed differences in the three sample means are large enough to reject H_0.

Assumptions for Analysis of Variance

Three assumptions are required to use analysis of variance.

> *If the sample sizes are equal, analysis of variance is not sensitive to departures from the assumption of normally distributed populations.*

1. **For each population, the response variable is normally distributed.** Implication: In the Chemitech experiment, the number of units produced per week (response variable) must be normally distributed for each assembly method.
2. **The variance of the response variable, denoted σ^2, is the same for all of the populations.** Implication: In the Chemitech experiment, the variance of the number of units produced per week must be the same for each assembly method.
3. **The observations must be independent.** Implication: In the Chemitech experiment, the number of units produced per week for each employee must be independent of the number of units produced per week for any other employee.

Analysis of Variance: A Conceptual Overview

If the means for the three populations are equal, we would expect the three sample means to be close together. In fact, the closer the three sample means are to one another, the weaker the evidence we have for the conclusion that the population means differ. Alternatively, the more the sample means differ, the stronger the evidence we have for the conclusion that the population means differ. In other words, if the variability among the sample means is "small," it supports H_0; if the variability among the sample means is "large," it supports H_a.

If the null hypothesis, $H_0: \mu_1 = \mu_2 = \mu_3$, is true, we can use the variability among the sample means to develop an estimate of σ^2. First, note that if the assumptions for analysis of variance are satisfied and the null hypothesis is true, each sample will have come from the same normal distribution with mean μ and variance σ^2. Recall from Chapter 7 that the sampling distribution of the sample mean $\bar{x}$ for a simple random sample of size n from a normal population will be normally distributed with mean μ and variance σ^2/n. Figure 13.2 illustrates such a sampling distribution.

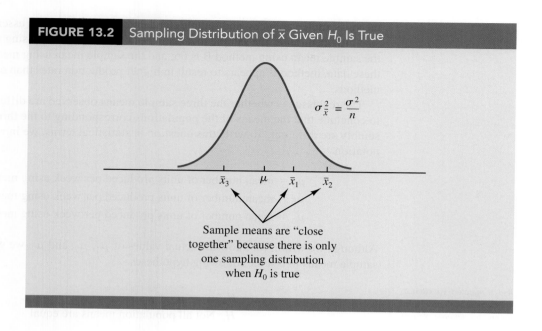

FIGURE 13.2   Sampling Distribution of $\bar{x}$ Given H_0 Is True

$$\sigma_{\bar{x}}^2 = \frac{\sigma^2}{n}$$

$\bar{x}_3$ μ $\bar{x}_1$ $\bar{x}_2$

Sample means are "close together" because there is only one sampling distribution when H_0 is true

Thus, if the null hypothesis is true, we can think of each of the three sample means, $\bar{x}_1 = 62$, $\bar{x}_2 = 66$, and $\bar{x}_3 = 52$ from Table 13.1, as values drawn at random from the sampling distribution shown in Figure 13.2. In this case, the mean and variance of the three $\bar{x}$ values can be used to estimate the mean and variance of the sampling distribution. When the sample sizes are equal, as in the Chemitech experiment, the best estimate of the mean of the sampling distribution of $\bar{x}$ is the mean or average of the sample means. In the Chemitech experiment, an estimate of the mean of the sampling distribution of $\bar{x}$ is $(62 + 66 + 52)/3 = 60$. We refer to this estimate as the *overall sample mean*. An estimate of the variance of the sampling distribution of $\bar{x}$, $\sigma_{\bar{x}}^2$, is provided by the variance of the three sample means.

$$s_{\bar{x}}^2 = \frac{(62 - 60)^2 + (66 - 60)^2 + (52 - 60)^2}{3 - 1} = \frac{104}{2} = 52$$

Because $\sigma_{\bar{x}}^2 = \sigma^2/n$, solving for σ^2 gives

$$\sigma^2 = n\sigma_{\bar{x}}^2$$

Hence,

$$\text{Estimate of } \sigma^2 = n \text{ (Estimate of } \sigma_{\bar{x}}^2) = ns_{\bar{x}}^2 = 5(52) = 260$$

The result, $ns_{\bar{x}}^2 = 260$, is referred to as the *between-treatments* estimate of σ^2.

The between-treatments estimate of σ^2 is based on the assumption that the null hypothesis is true. In this case, each sample comes from the same population, and there is only one sampling distribution of $\bar{x}$. To illustrate what happens when H_0 is false, suppose the population means all differ. Note that because the three samples are from normal populations with different means, they will result in three different sampling distributions. Figure 13.3 shows that in this case, the sample means are not as close together as they were when H_0 was true. Thus, $s_{\bar{x}}^2$ will be larger, causing the between-treatments estimate of σ^2

FIGURE 13.3   Sampling Distributions of $\bar{x}$ Given H_0 Is False

Sample means come from
different sampling distributions
and are not as close together when
H_0 is false

to be larger. In general, when the population means are not equal, the between-treatments estimate will overestimate the population variance σ^2.

The variation within each of the samples also has an effect on the conclusion we reach in analysis of variance. When a simple random sample is selected from each population, each of the sample variances provides an unbiased estimate of σ^2. Hence, we can combine or pool the individual estimates of σ^2 into one overall estimate. The estimate of σ^2 obtained in this way is called the *pooled* or *within-treatments* estimate of σ^2. Because each sample variance provides an estimate of σ^2 based only on the variation within each sample, the within-treatments estimate of σ^2 is not affected by whether the population means are equal. When the sample sizes are equal, the within-treatments estimate of σ^2 can be obtained by computing the average of the individual sample variances. For the Chemitech experiment we obtain

$$\text{Within-treatments estimate of } \sigma^2 = \frac{27.5 + 26.5 + 31.0}{3} = \frac{85}{3} = 28.33$$

In the Chemitech experiment, the between-treatments estimate of σ^2 (260) is much larger than the within-treatments estimate of σ^2 (28.33). In fact, the ratio of these two estimates is $260/28.33 = 9.18$. Recall, however, that the between-treatments approach provides a good estimate of σ^2 only if the null hypothesis is true; if the null hypothesis is false, the between-treatments approach overestimates σ^2. The within-treatments approach provides a good estimate of σ^2 in either case. Thus, if the null hypothesis is true, the two estimates will be similar and their ratio will be close to 1. If the null hypothesis is false, the between-treatments estimate will be larger than the within-treatments estimate, and their ratio will be large. In the next section we will show how large this ratio must be to reject H_0.

In summary, the logic behind ANOVA is based on the development of two independent estimates of the common population variance σ^2. One estimate of σ^2 is based on the variability among the sample means themselves, and the other estimate of σ^2 is based on the variability of the data within each sample. By comparing these two estimates of σ^2, we will be able to determine whether the population means are equal.

1. Randomization in experimental design is the analog of probability sampling in an observational study.

2. In many medical experiments, potential bias is eliminated by using a double-blind experimental design. With this design, neither the physician applying the treatment nor the subject knows which treatment is being applied. Many other types of experiments could benefit from this type of design.

3. In this section we provided a conceptual overview of how analysis of variance can be used to test for the equality of k population means for a completely randomized experimental design. We will see that the same procedure can also be used to test for the equality of k population means for an observational or nonexperimental study.

4. In Sections 10.1 and 10.2 we presented statistical methods for testing the hypothesis that the means of two populations are equal. ANOVA can also be used to test the hypothesis that the means of two populations are equal. In practice, however, analysis of variance is usually not used except when dealing with three or more population means.

13.2 Analysis of Variance and the Completely Randomized Design

In this section we show how analysis of variance can be used to test for the equality of k population means for a completely randomized design. The general form of the hypotheses tested is

$$H_0: \mu_1 = \mu_2 = \cdots = \mu_k$$
$$H_a: \text{Not all population means are equal}$$

where

$$\mu_j = \text{mean of the } j\text{th population}$$

We assume that a simple random sample of size n_j has been selected from each of the k populations or treatments. For the resulting sample data, let

$$x_{ij} = \text{value of observation } i \text{ for treatment } j$$
$$n_j = \text{number of observations for treatment } j$$
$$\bar{x}_j = \text{sample mean for treatment } j$$
$$s_j^2 = \text{sample variance for treatment } j$$
$$s_j = \text{sample standard deviation for treatment } j$$

The formulas for the sample mean and sample variance for treatment j are as follows:

$$\bar{x}_j = \frac{\sum_{i=1}^{n_j} x_{ij}}{n_j} \tag{13.1}$$

$$s_j^2 = \frac{\sum_{i=1}^{n_j} (x_{ij} - \bar{x}_j)^2}{n_j - 1} \tag{13.2}$$

The overall sample mean, denoted $\bar{\bar{x}}$, is the sum of all the observations divided by the total number of observations. That is,

$$\bar{\bar{x}} = \frac{\sum\limits_{j=1}^{k}\sum\limits_{i=1}^{n_j} x_{ij}}{n_T} \qquad (13.3)$$

where

$$n_T = n_1 + n_2 + \cdots + n_k \qquad (13.4)$$

If the size of each sample is n, $n_T = kn$; in this case equation (13.3) reduces to

$$\bar{\bar{x}} = \frac{\sum\limits_{j=1}^{k}\sum\limits_{i=1}^{n_j} x_{ij}}{kn} = \frac{\sum\limits_{j=1}^{k}\sum\limits_{i=1}^{n_j} x_{ij}/n}{k} = \frac{\sum\limits_{j=1}^{k} \bar{x}_j}{k} \qquad (13.5)$$

In other words, whenever the sample sizes are the same, the overall sample mean is just the average of the k sample means.

Because each sample in the Chemitech experiment consists of $n = 5$ observations, the overall sample mean can be computed by using equation (13.5). For the data in Table 13.1 we obtained the following result:

$$\bar{\bar{x}} = \frac{62 + 66 + 52}{3} = 60$$

If the null hypothesis is true ($\mu_1 = \mu_2 = \mu_3 = \mu$), the overall sample mean of 60 is the best estimate of the population mean μ.

Between-Treatments Estimate of Population Variance

In the preceding section, we introduced the concept of a between-treatments estimate of σ^2 and showed how to compute it when the sample sizes were equal. This estimate of σ^2 is called the *mean square due to treatments* and is denoted MSTR. The general formula for computing MSTR is

$$\text{MSTR} = \frac{\sum\limits_{j=1}^{k} n_j(\bar{x}_j - \bar{\bar{x}})^2}{k-1} \qquad (13.6)$$

The numerator in equation (13.6) is called the *sum of squares due to treatments* and is denoted SSTR. The denominator, $k - 1$, represents the degrees of freedom associated with SSTR. Hence, the mean square due to treatments can be computed using the following formula.

MEAN SQUARE DUE TO TREATMENTS

$$\text{MSTR} = \frac{\text{SSTR}}{k-1} \qquad (13.7)$$

where

$$\text{SSTR} = \sum\limits_{j=1}^{k} n_j(\bar{x}_j - \bar{\bar{x}})^2 \qquad (13.8)$$

If H_0 is true, MSTR provides an unbiased estimate of σ^2. However, if the means of the k populations are not equal, MSTR is not an unbiased estimate of σ^2; in fact, in that case, MSTR should overestimate σ^2.

For the Chemitech data in Table 13.1, we obtain the following results:

$$\text{SSTR} = \sum_{j=1}^{k} n_j(\bar{x}_j - \bar{\bar{x}})^2 = 5(62 - 60)^2 + 5(66 - 60)^2 + 5(52 - 60)^2 = 520$$

$$\text{MSTR} = \frac{\text{SSTR}}{k - 1} = \frac{520}{2} = 260$$

Within-Treatments Estimate of Population Variance

Earlier, we introduced the concept of a within-treatments estimate of σ^2 and showed how to compute it when the sample sizes were equal. This estimate of σ^2 is called the *mean square due to error* and is denoted MSE. The general formula for computing MSE is

$$\text{MSE} = \frac{\sum_{j=1}^{k}(n_j - 1)s_j^2}{n_T - k} \tag{13.9}$$

The numerator in equation (13.9) is called the *sum of squares due to error* and is denoted SSE. The denominator of MSE is referred to as the degrees of freedom associated with SSE. Hence, the formula for MSE can also be stated as follows:

MEAN SQUARE DUE TO ERROR

$$\text{MSE} = \frac{\text{SSE}}{n_T - k} \tag{13.10}$$

where

$$\text{SSE} = \sum_{j=1}^{k}(n_j - 1)s_j^2 \tag{13.11}$$

Note that MSE is based on the variation within each of the treatments; it is not influenced by whether the null hypothesis is true. Thus, MSE always provides an unbiased estimate of σ^2.

For the Chemitech data in Table 13.1 we obtain the following results.

$$\text{SSE} = \sum_{j=1}^{k}(n_j - 1)s_j^2 = (5 - 1)27.5 + (5 - 1)26.5 + (5 - 1)31 = 340$$

$$\text{MSE} = \frac{\text{SSE}}{n_T - k} = \frac{340}{15 - 3} = \frac{340}{12} = 28.33$$

Comparing the Variance Estimates: The F Test

An introduction to the F distribution and the use of the F distribution table were presented in Section 11.2.

If the null hypothesis is true, MSTR and MSE provide two independent, unbiased estimates of σ^2. Based on the material covered in Chapter 11 we know that for normal populations, the sampling distribution of the ratio of two independent estimates of σ^2 follows an F distribution. Hence, if the null hypothesis is true and the ANOVA assumptions are valid, the sampling distribution of MSTR/MSE is an F distribution with numerator degrees of freedom equal to $k - 1$ and denominator degrees of freedom equal to $n_T - k$. In other words, if the null hypothesis is true, the value of MSTR/MSE should appear to have been selected from this F distribution.

However, if the null hypothesis is false, the value of MSTR/MSE will be inflated because MSTR overestimates σ^2. Hence, we will reject H_0 if the resulting value of MSTR/MSE appears to be too large to have been selected from an F distribution with $k - 1$ numerator degrees of freedom and $n_T - k$ denominator degrees of freedom. Because the decision to reject H_0 is based on the value of MSTR/MSE, the test statistic used to test for the equality of k population means is as follows:

TEST STATISTIC FOR THE EQUALITY OF k POPULATION MEANS

$$F = \frac{\text{MSTR}}{\text{MSE}}$$

(13.12)

The test statistic follows an F distribution with $k - 1$ degrees of freedom in the numerator and $n_T - k$ degrees of freedom in the denominator.

Let us return to the Chemitech experiment and use a level of significance $\alpha = .05$ to conduct the hypothesis test. The value of the test statistic is

$$F = \frac{\text{MSTR}}{\text{MSE}} = \frac{260}{28.33} = 9.18$$

The numerator degrees of freedom is $k - 1 = 3 - 1 = 2$ and the denominator degrees of freedom is $n_T - k = 15 - 3 = 12$. Because we will only reject the null hypothesis for large values of the test statistic, the p-value is the upper tail area of the F distribution to the right of the test statistic $F = 9.18$. Figure 13.4 shows the sampling distribution of $F = \text{MSTR/MSE}$, the value of the test statistic, and the upper tail area that is the p-value for the hypothesis test.

From Table 4 of Appendix B we find the following areas in the upper tail of an F distribution with 2 numerator degrees of freedom and 12 denominator degrees of freedom.

Area in Upper Tail	.10	.05	.025	.01
F Value ($df_1 = 2$, $df_2 = 12$)	2.81	3.89	5.10	6.93

$F = 9.18$

FIGURE 13.4 Computation of p-Value Using the Sampling Distribution of MSTR/MSE

Sampling distribution of MSTR/MSE

p-value

MSTR/MSE

$F = 9.18$

Appendix F shows how to compute p-values using JMP or Excel.

Because $F = 9.18$ is greater than 6.93, the area in the upper tail at $F = 9.18$ is less than .01. Thus, the p-value is less than .01. Statistical software can be used to show that the exact p-value is .004. With p-value $\leq \alpha = .05$, H_0 is rejected. The test provides sufficient evidence to conclude that the means of the three populations are not equal. In other words, analysis of variance supports the conclusion that the population mean number of units produced per week for the three assembly methods are not equal.

As with other hypothesis testing procedures, the critical value approach may also be used. With $\alpha = .05$, the critical F value occurs with an area of .05 in the upper tail of an F distribution with 2 and 12 degrees of freedom. From the F distribution table, we find $F_{.05} = 3.89$. Hence, the appropriate upper tail rejection rule for the Chemitech experiment is

$$\text{Reject } H_0 \text{ if } F \geq 3.89$$

With $F = 9.18$, we reject H_0 and conclude that the means of the three populations are not equal. A summary of the overall procedure for testing for the equality of k population means follows.

TEST FOR THE EQUALITY OF *k* POPULATION MEANS

$$H_0: \mu_1 = \mu_2 = \cdots = \mu_k$$
$$H_a: \text{Not all population means are equal}$$

TEST STATISTIC

$$F = \frac{\text{MSTR}}{\text{MSE}}$$

REJECTION RULE

p-value approach: Reject H_0 if p-value $\leq \alpha$

Critical value approach: Reject H_0 if $F \geq F_\alpha$

where the value of F_α is based on an F distribution with $k - 1$ numerator degrees of freedom and $n_T - k$ denominator degrees of freedom.

ANOVA Table

The results of the preceding calculations can be displayed conveniently in a table referred to as the analysis of variance or **ANOVA table**. The general form of the ANOVA table for a completely randomized design is shown in Table 13.2; Table 13.3 is the corresponding

TABLE 13.2   ANOVA Table for a Completely Randomized Design

Source of Variation	Sum of Squares	Degrees of Freedom	Mean Square	F	p-value
Treatments	SSTR	$k - 1$	$\text{MSTR} = \dfrac{\text{SSTR}}{k - 1}$	$\dfrac{\text{MSTR}}{\text{MSE}}$	
Error	SSE	$n_T - k$	$\text{MSE} = \dfrac{\text{SSE}}{n_T - k}$		
Total	SST	$n_T - 1$			

TABLE 13.3	Analysis of Variance Table for the Chemitech Experiment

Source of Variation	Sum of Squares	Degrees of Freedom	Mean Square	F	p-value
Treatments	520	2	260.00	9.18	.004
Error	340	12	28.33		
Total	860	14			

ANOVA table for the Chemitech experiment. The sum of squares associated with the source of variation referred to as "Total" is called the total sum of squares (SST). Note that the results for the Chemitech experiment suggest that SST = SSTR + SSE, and that the degrees of freedom associated with this total sum of squares is the sum of the degrees of freedom associated with the sum of squares due to treatments and the sum of squares due to error.

We point out that SST divided by its degrees of freedom $n_T - 1$ is nothing more than the overall sample variance that would be obtained if we treated the entire set of 15 observations as one data set. With the entire data set as one sample, the formula for computing the total sum of squares, SST, is

$$\text{SST} = \sum_{j=1}^{k} \sum_{i=1}^{n_j} (x_{ij} - \bar{\bar{x}})^2 \tag{13.13}$$

It can be shown that the results we observed for the analysis of variance table for the Chemitech experiment also apply to other problems. That is,

$$\text{SST} = \text{SSTR} + \text{SSE} \tag{13.14}$$

Analysis of variance can be thought of as a statistical procedure for partitioning the total sum of squares into separate components.

In other words, SST can be partitioned into two sums of squares: the sum of squares due to treatments and the sum of squares due to error. Note also that the degrees of freedom corresponding to SST, $n_T - 1$, can be partitioned into the degrees of freedom corresponding to SSTR, $k - 1$, and the degrees of freedom corresponding to SSE, $n_T - k$. The analysis of variance can be viewed as the process of **partitioning** the total sum of squares and the degrees of freedom into their corresponding sources: treatments and error. Dividing the sum of squares by the appropriate degrees of freedom provides the variance estimates, the F value, and the p-value used to test the hypothesis of equal population means.

Computer Results for Analysis of Variance

Using statistical software, analysis of variance computations with large sample sizes or a large number of populations can be performed easily. Appendixes 13.1 and 13.2 show the steps required to use JMP and Excel to perform the analysis of variance computations. In Figure 13.5 we show statistical software output for the Chemitech experiment. The first part of the output contains the familiar ANOVA table format. Comparing Figure 13.5 with Table 13.3, we see that the same information is available, although some of the headings are slightly different. The heading Source is used for the source of variation column, Factor identifies the treatments row, and the sum of squares and degrees of freedom columns are interchanged.

Following the ANOVA table in Figure 13.5, the output contains the respective sample sizes, the sample means, and the standard deviations. In addition, 95% confidence interval estimates of each population mean are given. In developing these confidence

FIGURE 13.5 Output for the Chemitech Experiment Analysis of Variance

For completely randomized designs, Adj SS and Adj MS output are the same as the SS and MS values as described in this chapter.

Source	DF	Adj SS	Adj MS	F-Value	P-Value
Factor	2	520.0	260.00	9.18	.004
Error	12	340.0	28.33		
Total	14	860.0			

Model Summary

S	R-sq	R-sq (adj)
5.32291	60.47%	53.88%

Means

Factor	N	Mean	StDev	95% CI
Method A	5	62.00	5.24	(56.81, 67.19)
Method B	5	66.00	5.15	(60.81, 71.19)
Method C	5	52.00	5.57	(46.81, 57.19)

Pooled StDev = 5.32291

interval estimates, MSE is used as the estimate of σ^2. Thus, the square root of MSE provides the best estimate of the population standard deviation σ. This estimate of σ in Figure 13.5 is Pooled StDev; it is equal to 5.323. To provide an illustration of how these interval estimates are developed, we will compute a 95% confidence interval estimate of the population mean for Method A.

From our study of interval estimation in Chapter 8, we know that the general form of an interval estimate of a population mean is

$$\bar{x} \pm t_{\alpha/2} \frac{s}{\sqrt{n}} \tag{13.15}$$

where s is the estimate of the population standard deviation σ. Because the best estimate of σ is provided by the Pooled StDev, we use a value of 5.323 for s in expression (13.15). The degrees of freedom for the t value is 12, the degrees of freedom associated with the error sum of squares. Hence, with $t_{.025} = 2.179$ we obtain

$$62 \pm 2.179 \frac{5.323}{\sqrt{5}} = 62 \pm 5.19$$

Thus, the individual 95% confidence interval for Method A goes from $62 - 5.19 = 56.81$ to $62 + 5.19 = 67.19$. Because the sample sizes are equal for the Chemitech experiment, the individual confidence intervals for Method B and Method C are also constructed by adding and subtracting 5.19 from each sample mean.

Testing for the Equality of k Population Means: An Observational Study

We have shown how analysis of variance can be used to test for the equality of k population means for a completely randomized experimental design. It is important to understand that

TABLE 13.4	Examination Scores for 18 Employees		
	Plant 1 **Atlanta**	**Plant 2** **Dallas**	**Plant 3** **Seattle**
	85	71	59
	75	75	64
	82	73	62
	76	74	69
	71	69	75
	85	82	67
Sample mean	79	74	66
Sample variance	34	20	32
Sample standard deviation	5.83	4.47	5.66

DATA *file*

NCP

ANOVA can also be used to test for the equality of three or more population means using data obtained from an observational study. As an example, let us consider the situation at National Computer Products, Inc. (NCP).

NCP manufactures printers and fax machines at plants located in Atlanta, Dallas, and Seattle. To measure how much employees at these plants know about quality management, a random sample of 6 employees was selected from each plant and the employees selected were given a quality awareness examination. The examination scores for these 18 employees are shown in Table 13.4. The sample means, sample variances, and sample standard deviations for each group are also provided. Managers want to use these data to test the hypothesis that the mean examination score is the same for all three plants.

We define population 1 as all employees at the Atlanta plant, population 2 as all employees at the Dallas plant, and population 3 as all employees at the Seattle plant. Let

$$\mu_1 = \text{mean examination score for population 1}$$
$$\mu_2 = \text{mean examination score for population 2}$$
$$\mu_3 = \text{mean examination score for population 3}$$

Although we will never know the actual values of μ_1, μ_2, and μ_3, we want to use the sample results to test the following hypotheses:

$$H_0: \mu_1 = \mu_2 = \mu_3$$
$$H_a: \text{Not all population means are equal}$$

Exercise 8 will ask you to analyze the NCP data using the analysis of variance procedure.

Note that the hypothesis test for the NCP observational study is exactly the same as the hypothesis test for the Chemitech experiment. Indeed, the same analysis of variance methodology we used to analyze the Chemitech experiment can also be used to analyze the data from the NCP observational study.

Even though the same ANOVA methodology is used for the analysis, it is worth noting how the NCP observational statistical study differs from the Chemitech experimental statistical study. The individuals who conducted the NCP study had no control over how the plants were assigned to individual employees. That is, the plants were already in operation and a particular employee worked at one of the three plants. All that NCP could do was to select a random sample of 6 employees from each plant and administer the quality awareness examination. To be classified as an experimental study, NCP would have had to be able to randomly select 18 employees and then assign the plants to each employee in a random fashion.

1. The overall sample mean can also be computed as a weighted average of the k sample means.

$$\bar{\bar{x}} = \frac{n_1\bar{x}_1 + n_2\bar{x}_2 + \cdots + n_k\bar{x}_k}{n_T}$$

In problems where the sample means are provided, this formula is simpler than equation (13.3) for computing the overall mean.

2. If each sample consists of n observations, equation (13.6) can be written as

$$MSTR = \frac{n\sum_{j=1}^{k}(\bar{x}_j - \bar{\bar{x}})^2}{k-1} = n\left[\frac{\sum_{j=1}^{k}(\bar{x}_j - \bar{\bar{x}})^2}{k-1}\right]$$

$$= ns_{\bar{x}}^2$$

Note that this result is the same as presented in Section 13.1 when we introduced the concept of the between-treatments estimate of σ^2. Equation (13.6) is simply a generalization of this result to the unequal sample-size case.

3. If each sample has n observations, $n_T = kn$; thus, $n_T - k = k(n-1)$, and equation (13.9) can be rewritten as

$$MSE = \frac{\sum_{j=1}^{k}(n-1)s_j^2}{k(n-1)} = \frac{(n-1)\sum_{j=1}^{k}s_j^2}{k(n-1)} = \frac{\sum_{j=1}^{k}s_j^2}{k}$$

In other words, if the sample sizes are the same, MSE is the average of the k sample variances. Note that it is the same result we used in Section 13.1 when we introduced the concept of the within-treatments estimate of σ^2.

EXERCISES

Methods

1. The following data are from a completely randomized design.

	Treatment		
	A	B	C
	162	142	126
	142	156	122
	165	124	138
	145	142	140
	148	136	150
	174	152	128
Sample mean	156	142	134
Sample variance	164.4	131.2	110.4

a. Compute the sum of squares between treatments.
b. Compute the mean square between treatments.
c. Compute the sum of squares due to error.
d. Compute the mean square due to error.
e. Set up the ANOVA table for this problem.
f. At the $\alpha = .05$ level of significance, test whether the means for the three treatments are equal.

2. In a completely randomized design, seven experimental units were used for each of the five levels of the factor. Complete the following ANOVA table.

Source of Variation	Sum of Squares	Degrees of Freedom	Mean Square	F	p-value
Treatments	300				
Error					
Total	460				

3. Refer to exercise 2.
    a. What hypotheses are implied in this problem?
    b. At the $\alpha = .05$ level of significance, can we reject the null hypothesis in part (a)? Explain.
4. In an experiment designed to test the output levels of three different treatments, the following results were obtained: SST = 400, SSTR = 150, $n_T = 19$. Set up the ANOVA table and test for any significant difference between the mean output levels of the three treatments. Use $\alpha = .05$.
5. In a completely randomized design, 12 experimental units were used for the first treatment, 15 for the second treatment, and 20 for the third treatment. Complete the following analysis of variance. At a .05 level of significance, is there a significant difference between the treatments?

Source of Variation	Sum of Squares	Degrees of Freedom	Mean Square	F	p-value
Treatments	1200				
Error					
Total	1800				

6. Develop the analysis of variance computations for the following completely randomized design. At $\alpha = .05$, is there a significant difference between the treatment means?

DATA *file*

Exer6

	Treatment		
	A	**B**	**C**
	136	107	92
	120	114	82
	113	125	85
	107	104	101
	131	107	89
	114	109	117
	129	97	110
	102	114	120
		104	98
		89	106
$\bar{x}_j$	119	107	100
s_j^2	146.86	96.44	173.78

Applications

7. **Product Assembly.** Three different methods for assembling a product were proposed by an industrial engineer. To investigate the number of units assembled correctly with each method, 30 employees were randomly selected and randomly assigned to the three proposed methods in such a way that each method was used by 10 workers. The number of units assembled correctly was recorded, and the analysis of variance procedure was applied to the resulting data set. The following results were obtained: SST = 10,800; SSTR = 4560.
    a. Set up the ANOVA table for this problem.
    b. Use $\alpha = .05$ to test for any significant difference in the means for the three assembly methods.
8. **Testing Quality Awareness.** Refer to the NCP data in Table 13.4. Set up the ANOVA table and test for any significant difference in the mean examination score for the three plants. Use $\alpha = .05$.

9. **Temperature's Effect on a Chemical Process.** To study the effect of temperature on yield in a chemical process, five batches were produced at each of three temperature levels. The results follow. Construct an analysis of variance table. Use a .05 level of significance to test whether the temperature level has an effect on the mean yield of the process.

	Temperature	
50°C	**60°C**	**70°C**
34	30	23
24	31	28
36	34	28
39	23	30
32	27	31

10. **Auditing Errors.** Auditors must make judgments about various aspects of an audit on the basis of their own direct experience, indirect experience, or a combination of the two. In a study, auditors were asked to make judgments about the frequency of errors to be found in an audit. The judgments by the auditors were then compared to the actual results. Suppose the following data were obtained from a similar study; lower scores indicate better judgments.

DATA *file*
AudJudg

Direct	**Indirect**	**Combination**
17.0	16.6	25.2
18.5	22.2	24.0
15.8	20.5	21.5
18.2	18.3	26.8
20.2	24.2	27.5
16.0	19.8	25.8
13.3	21.2	24.2

Use $\alpha = .05$ to test to see whether the basis for the judgment affects the quality of the judgment. What is your conclusion?

11. **Paint-Drying Robots.** How long it takes paint to dry can have an impact on the production capacity of a business. In May 2018, Deal's Auto Body & Paint in Prescott, Arizona, invested in a paint-drying robot to speed up its process (The Daily Courier website, https://www.dcourier.com/photos/2018/may/26/984960336/). An interesting question is, "Do all paint-drying robots have the same drying time?" To test this, suppose we sample five drying times for each of different brands of paint-drying robots. The time in minutes until the paint was dry enough for a second coat to be applied was recorded. The following data were obtained.

DATA *file*
Paint

Robot 1	**Robot 2**	**Robot 3**	**Robot 4**
128	144	133	150
137	133	143	142
135	142	137	135
124	146	136	140
141	130	131	153

At the $\alpha = .05$ level of significance, test to see whether the mean drying time is the same for each brand of robot.

12. **Restaurant Satisfaction.** The *Consumer Reports* Restaurant Customer Satisfaction Survey is based upon 148,599 visits to full-service restaurant chains (*Consumer Reports* website, https://www.consumerreports.org/cro/restaurants/buying-guide/index .htm). One of the variables in the study is meal price, the average amount paid per

person for dinner and drinks, minus the tip. Suppose a reporter for the *Sun Coast Times* thought that it would be of interest to her readers to conduct a similar study for restaurants located on the Grand Strand section in Myrtle Beach, South Carolina. The reporter selected a sample of 8 seafood restaurants, 8 Italian restaurants, and 8 steakhouses. The following data show the meal prices ($) obtained for the 24 restaurants sampled. Use $\alpha = .05$ to test whether there is a significant difference among the mean meal price for the three types of restaurants.

DATA *file*

GrandStrand

Italian	Seafood	Steakhouse
$12	$16	$24
13	18	19
15	17	23
17	26	25
18	23	21
20	15	22
17	19	27
24	18	31

13.3 Multiple Comparison Procedures

When we use analysis of variance to test whether the means of *k* populations are equal, rejection of the null hypothesis allows us to conclude only that the population means are *not all equal*. In some cases we will want to go a step further and determine where the differences among means occur. The purpose of this section is to show how **multiple comparison procedures** can be used to conduct statistical comparisons between pairs of population means.

Fisher's LSD

Suppose that analysis of variance provides statistical evidence to reject the null hypothesis of equal population means. In this case, Fisher's least significant difference (LSD) procedure can be used to determine where the differences occur. To illustrate the use of Fisher's LSD procedure in making pairwise comparisons of population means, recall the Chemitech experiment introduced in Section 13.1. Using analysis of variance, we concluded that the mean number of units produced per week are not the same for the three assembly methods. In this case, the follow-up question is: We believe the assembly methods differ, but where do the differences occur? That is, do the means of populations 1 and 2 differ? Or those of populations 1 and 3? Or those of populations 2 and 3? The following summarizes Fisher's LSD procedure for comparing pairs of population means.

FISHER'S LSD PROCEDURE

$$H_0: \mu_i = \mu_j$$
$$H_a: \mu_i \neq \mu_j$$

TEST STATISTIC

$$t = \frac{\bar{x}_i - \bar{x}_j}{\sqrt{MSE\left(\frac{1}{n_i} + \frac{1}{n_j}\right)}} \qquad (13.16)$$

REJECTION RULE

p-value approach: Reject H_0 if *p*-value $\leq \alpha$

Critical value approach: Reject H_0 if $t \leq -t_{\alpha/2}$ or $t \geq t_{\alpha/2}$

where the value of $t_{\alpha/2}$ is based on a *t* distribution with $n_T - k$ degrees of freedom.

Let us now apply this procedure to determine whether there is a significant difference between the means of population 1 (Method A) and population 2 (Method B) at the $\alpha = .05$ level of significance. Table 13.1 showed that the sample mean is 62 for Method A and 66 for Method B. Table 13.3 showed that the value of MSE is 28.33; it is the estimate of σ^2 and is based on 12 degrees of freedom. For the Chemitech data the value of the test statistic is

$$t = \frac{62 - 66}{\sqrt{28.33\left(\dfrac{1}{5} + \dfrac{1}{5}\right)}} = -1.19$$

Because we have a two-tailed test, the p-value is two times the area under the curve for the t distribution to the left of $t = -1.19$. Using Table 2 in Appendix B, the t distribution table for 12 degrees of freedom provides the following information.

Area in Upper Tail	.20	.10	.05	.025	.01	.005
t Value (12 df)	.873	1.356	1.782	2.179	2.681	3.055

$t = 1.19$

Appendix F shows how to compute p-values using Excel or JMP.

The t distribution table only contains positive t values. Because the t distribution is symmetric, however, we can find the area under the curve to the right of $t = 1.19$ and double it to find the p-value corresponding to $t = -1.19$. We see that $t = 1.19$ is between .20 and .10. Doubling these amounts, we see that the p-value must be between .40 and .20. Statistical software can be used to show that the exact p-value is .2571. Because the p-value is greater than $\alpha = .05$, we cannot reject the null hypothesis. Hence, we cannot conclude that the population mean number of units produced per week for Method A is different from the population mean for Method B.

Many practitioners find it easier to determine how large the difference between the sample means must be to reject H_0. In this case the test statistic is $\bar{x}_i - \bar{x}_j$, and the test is conducted by the following procedure.

FISHER'S LSD PROCEDURE BASED ON THE TEST STATISTIC $\bar{x}_i - \bar{x}_j$

$$H_0: \mu_i = \mu_j$$
$$H_a: \mu_i \neq \mu_j$$

TEST STATISTIC

$$\bar{x}_i - \bar{x}_j$$

REJECTION RULE AT A LEVEL OF SIGNIFICANCE α

$$\text{Reject } H_0 \text{ if } |\bar{x}_i - \bar{x}_j| \geq \text{LSD}$$

where

$$\text{LSD} = t_{\alpha/2}\sqrt{\text{MSE}\left(\frac{1}{n_i} + \frac{1}{n_j}\right)} \tag{13.17}$$

For the Chemitech experiment the value of LSD is

$$\text{LSD} = 2.179\sqrt{28.33\left(\frac{1}{5} + \frac{1}{5}\right)} = 7.34$$

Note that when the sample sizes are equal, only one value for LSD is computed. In such cases we can simply compare the magnitude of the difference between any two sample means with the value of LSD. For example, the difference between the sample means for population 1 (Method A) and population 3 (Method C) is $62 - 52 = 10$. This difference is greater than LSD $= 7.34$, which means we can reject the null hypothesis that the population mean number of units produced per week for Method A is equal to the population mean for Method C. Similarly, with the difference between the sample means for populations 2 and 3 of $66 - 52 = 14 > 7.34$, we can also reject the hypothesis that the population mean for Method B is equal to the population mean for Method C. In effect, our conclusion is that the population means for Method A and Method B both differ from the population mean for Method C.

Fisher's LSD can also be used to develop a confidence interval estimate of the difference between the means of two populations. The general procedure follows.

CONFIDENCE INTERVAL ESTIMATE OF THE DIFFERENCE BETWEEN TWO POPULATION MEANS USING FISHER'S LSD PROCEDURE

$$\bar{x}_i - \bar{x}_j \pm \text{LSD} \tag{13.18}$$

where

$$\text{LSD} = t_{\alpha/2} \sqrt{\text{MSE}\left(\frac{1}{n_i} + \frac{1}{n_j}\right)} \tag{13.19}$$

and $t_{\alpha/2}$ is based on a t distribution with $n_T - k$ degrees of freedom.

If the confidence interval in expression (13.18) includes the value zero, we cannot reject the hypothesis that the two population means are equal. However, if the confidence interval does not include the value zero, we conclude that there is a difference between the population means. For the Chemitech experiment, recall that LSD $= 7.34$ (corresponding to $t_{.025} = 2.179$). Thus, a 95% confidence interval estimate of the difference between the means of populations 1 and 2 is $62 - 66 \pm 7.34 = -4 \pm 7.34 = -11.34$ to 3.34; because this interval includes zero, we cannot reject the hypothesis that the two population means are equal.

Type I Error Rates

We began the discussion of Fisher's LSD procedure with the premise that analysis of variance gave us statistical evidence to reject the null hypothesis of equal population means. We showed how Fisher's LSD procedure can be used in such cases to determine where the differences occur. Technically, it is referred to as a *protected* or *restricted* LSD test because it is employed only if we first find a significant F value by using analysis of variance. To see why this distinction is important in multiple comparison tests, we need to explain the difference between a *comparisonwise* Type I error rate and an *experimentwise* Type I error rate.

In the Chemitech experiment we used Fisher's LSD procedure to make three pairwise comparisons.

Test 1	Test 2	Test 3
$H_0: \mu_1 = \mu_2$	$H_0: \mu_1 = \mu_3$	$H_0: \mu_2 = \mu_3$
$H_a: \mu_1 \neq \mu_2$	$H_a: \mu_1 \neq \mu_3$	$H_a: \mu_2 \neq \mu_3$

In each case, we used a level of significance of $\alpha = .05$. Therefore, for each test, if the null hypothesis is true, the probability that we will make a Type I error is $\alpha = .05$; hence, the probability that we will not make a Type I error on each test is $1 - .05 = .95$. In discussing multiple comparison procedures we refer to this probability of a Type I error ($\alpha = .05$) as the **comparisonwise Type I error rate**; comparisonwise Type I error rates indicate the level of significance associated with a single pairwise comparison.

Let us now consider a slightly different question. What is the probability that in making three pairwise comparisons, we will commit a Type I error on at least one of the three tests? To answer this question, note that the probability that we will not make a Type I error on any of the three tests is $(.95)(.95)(.95) = .8574$.[1] Therefore, the probability of making at least one Type I error is $1 - .8574 = .1426$. Thus, when we use Fisher's LSD procedure to make all three pairwise comparisons, the Type I error rate associated with this approach is not .05, but actually .1426; we refer to this error rate as the *overall* or **experimentwise Type I error rate**. To avoid confusion, we denote the experimentwise Type I error rate as α_{EW}.

The experimentwise Type I error rate gets larger for problems with more populations. For example, a problem with five populations has 10 possible pairwise comparisons. If we tested all possible pairwise comparisons by using Fisher's LSD with a comparisonwise error rate of $\alpha = .05$, the experimentwise Type I error rate would be $1 - (1 - .05)^{10} = .40$. In such cases, practitioners look to alternatives that provide better control over the experimentwise error rate.

One alternative for controlling the overall experimentwise error rate, referred to as the Bonferroni adjustment, involves using a smaller comparisonwise error rate for each test. For example, if we want to test C pairwise comparisons and want the maximum probability of making a Type I error for the overall experiment to be α_{EW}, we simply use a comparison-wise error rate equal to α_{EW}/C. In the Chemitech experiment, if we want to use Fisher's LSD procedure to test all three pairwise comparisons with a maximum experimentwise error rate of $\alpha_{EW} = .05$, we set the comparisonwise error rate to be $\alpha = .05/3 = .017$. For a problem with five populations and 10 possible pairwise comparisons, the Bonferroni adjustment would suggest a comparisonwise error rate of $.05/10 = .005$. Recall from our discussion of hypothesis testing in Chapter 9 that for a fixed sample size, any decrease in the probability of making a Type I error will result in an increase in the probability of making a Type II error, which corresponds to accepting the hypothesis that the two population means are equal when in fact they are not equal. As a result, many practitioners are reluctant to perform individual tests with a low comparisonwise Type I error rate because of the increased risk of making a Type II error.

Several other procedures, such as Tukey's procedure and Duncan's multiple range test, have been developed to help in such situations. However, there is considerable controversy in the statistical community as to which procedure is "best." The truth is that no one procedure is best for all types of problems.

EXERCISES

Methods

13. The following data are from a completely randomized design.

	Treatment A	Treatment B	Treatment C
	32	44	33
	30	43	36
	30	44	35
	26	46	36
	32	48	40
Sample mean	30	45	36
Sample variance	6.00	4.00	6.50

---

[1]The assumption is that the three tests are independent, and hence the joint probability of the three events can be obtained by simply multiplying the individual probabilities. In fact, the three tests are not independent because MSE is used in each test; therefore, the error involved is even greater than that shown.

   a. At the $\alpha = .05$ level of significance, can we reject the null hypothesis that the means of the three treatments are equal?
   b. Use Fisher's LSD procedure to test whether there is a significant difference between the means for treatments A and B, treatments A and C, and treatments B and C. Use $\alpha = .05$.
   c. Use Fisher's LSD procedure to develop a 95% confidence interval estimate of the difference between the means of treatments A and B.

14. The following data are from a completely randomized design. In the following calculations, use $\alpha = .05$.

	Treatment 1	Treatment 2	Treatment 3
	63	82	69
	47	72	54
	54	88	61
	40	66	48
$\bar{x}_j$	51	77	58
s_j^2	96.67	97.34	81.99

   a. Use analysis of variance to test for a significant difference among the means of the three treatments.
   b. Use Fisher's LSD procedure to determine which means are different.

Applications

15. **Testing Chemical Processes.** To test whether the mean time needed to mix a batch of material is the same for machines produced by three manufacturers, the Jacobs Chemical Company obtained the following data on the time (in minutes) needed to mix the material.

Manufacturer 1	Manufacturer 2	Manufacturer 3
20	28	20
26	26	19
24	31	23
22	27	22

   a. Use these data to test whether the population mean times for mixing a batch of material differ for the three manufacturers. Use $\alpha = .05$.
   b. At the $\alpha = .05$ level of significance, use Fisher's LSD procedure to test for the equality of the means for manufacturers 1 and 3. What conclusion can you draw after carrying out this test?

16. **Confidence Intervals for Different Processes.** Refer to exercise 15. Use Fisher's LSD procedure to develop a 95% confidence interval estimate of the difference between the means for manufacturer 1 and manufacturer 2.

17. **Marketing Ethics.** In the digital age of marketing, special care must be taken to make sure that programmatic ads appearing on websites align with a company's strategy, culture and ethics. For example, in 2017, Nordstrom, Amazon and Whole Foods each faced boycotts form social media users when automated ads for these companies showed up on the Breitbart website (*ChiefMarketer.com*). It is important for marketing professionals to understand a company's values and culture. The following data are from an experiment designed to investigate the perception of corporate ethical values among individuals specializing in marketing (higher scores indicate higher ethical values).

Marketing Managers	Marketing Research	Advertising
6	5	6
5	5	7
4	4	6
5	4	5
6	5	6
4	4	6

a. Use $\alpha = .05$ to test for significant differences in perception among the three groups.

b. At the $\alpha = .05$ level of significance, we can conclude that there are differences in the perceptions for marketing managers, marketing research specialists, and advertising specialists. Use the procedures in this section to determine where the differences occur. Use $\alpha = .05$.

18. **Machine Breakdowns.** To test for any significant difference in the number of hours between breakdowns for four machines, the following data were obtained.

Machine 1	Machine 2	Machine 3	Machine 4
6.4	8.7	11.1	9.9
7.8	7.4	10.3	12.8
5.3	9.4	9.7	12.1
7.4	10.1	10.3	10.8
8.4	9.2	9.2	11.3
7.3	9.8	8.8	11.5

a. At the $\alpha = .05$ level of significance, what is the difference, if any, in the population mean times among the four machines?

b. Use Fisher's LSD procedure to test for the equality of the means for machines 2 and 4. Use a .05 level of significance.

19. **Testing Time to Breakdown Between All Pairs of Machines.** Refer to exercise 18. Use the Bonferroni adjustment to test for a significant difference between all pairs of means. Assume that a maximum overall experimentwise error rate of .05 is desired.

20. **Minor League Baseball Attendance.** The International League of Triple-A minor league baseball consists of 14 teams organized into three divisions: North, South, and West. The following data show the average attendance for the 14 teams in the International League. Also shown are the teams' records; W denotes the number of games won, L denotes the number of games lost, and PCT is the proportion of games played that were won.

DATA*file*

Triple-A

Team Name	Division	W	L	PCT	Attendance
Buffalo Bisons	North	66	77	.462	8812
Lehigh Valley IronPigs	North	55	89	.382	8479
Pawtucket Red Sox	North	85	58	.594	9097
Rochester Red Wings	North	74	70	.514	6913
Scranton-Wilkes Barre Yankees	North	88	56	.611	7147
Syracuse Chiefs	North	69	73	.486	5765
Charlotte Knights	South	63	78	.447	4526
Durham Bulls	South	74	70	.514	6995
Norfolk Tides	South	64	78	.451	6286
Richmond Braves	South	63	78	.447	4455
Columbus Clippers	West	69	73	.486	7795
Indianapolis Indians	West	68	76	.472	8538
Louisville Bats	West	88	56	.611	9152
Toledo Mud Hens	West	75	69	.521	8234

a. Use $\alpha = .05$ to test for any difference in the mean attendance for the three divisions.
b. Use Fisher's LSD procedure to determine where the differences occur. Use $\alpha = .05$.

13.4 Randomized Block Design

Thus far we have considered the completely randomized experimental design. Recall that to test for a difference among treatment means, we computed an F value by using the ratio

$$F = \frac{\text{MSTR}}{\text{MSE}} \tag{13.20}$$

*A completely randomized design is useful when the experimental units are homogeneous. If the experimental units are heterogeneous, **blocking** is often used to form homogeneous groups.*

A problem can arise whenever differences due to extraneous factors (ones not considered in the experiment) cause the MSE term in this ratio to become large. In such cases, the F value in equation (13.20) can become small, signaling no difference among treatment means when in fact such a difference exists.

In this section we present an experimental design known as a **randomized block design**. Its purpose is to control some of the extraneous sources of variation by removing such variation from the MSE term. This design tends to provide a better estimate of the true error variance and leads to a more powerful hypothesis test in terms of the ability to detect differences among treatment means. To illustrate, let us consider a stress study for air traffic controllers.

Air Traffic Controller Stress Test

A study measuring the fatigue and stress of air traffic controllers resulted in proposals for modification and redesign of the controller's workstation. After consideration of several designs for the workstation, three specific alternatives are selected as having the best potential for reducing controller stress. The key question is: To what extent do the three alternatives differ in terms of their effect on controller stress? To answer this question, we need to design an experiment that will provide measurements of air traffic controller stress under each alternative.

Experimental studies in business often involve experimental units that are highly heterogeneous; as a result, randomized block designs are often employed.

In a completely randomized design, a random sample of controllers would be assigned to each workstation alternative. However, controllers are believed to differ substantially in their ability to handle stressful situations. What is high stress to one controller might be only moderate or even low stress to another. Hence, when considering the within-group source of variation (MSE), we must realize that this variation includes both random error and error due to individual controller differences. In fact, managers expected controller variability to be a major contributor to the MSE term.

Blocking in experimental design is similar to stratification in sampling.

One way to separate the effect of the individual differences is to use a randomized block design. Such a design will identify the variability stemming from individual controller differences and remove it from the MSE term. The randomized block design calls for a single sample of controllers. Each controller in the sample is tested with each of the three workstation alternatives. In experimental design terminology, the workstation is the *factor of interest* and the controllers are the *blocks*. The three treatments or populations associated with the workstation factor correspond to the three workstation alternatives. For simplicity, we refer to the workstation alternatives as system A, system B, and system C.

The *randomized* aspect of the randomized block design is the random order in which the treatments (systems) are assigned to the controllers. If every controller were to test the three systems in the same order, any observed difference in systems might be due to the order of the test rather than to true differences in the systems.

DATA *file*

AirTraffic

TABLE 13.5	A Randomized Block Design for the Air Traffic Controller Stress Test		
		Treatments	
	System A	System B	System C
Blocks	Controller 1	15	15	18
	Controller 2	14	14	14
	Controller 3	10	11	15
	Controller 4	13	12	17
	Controller 5	16	13	16
	Controller 6	13	13	13

To provide the necessary data, the three workstation alternatives were installed at the Cleveland Control Center in Oberlin, Ohio. Six controllers were selected at random and assigned to operate each of the systems. A follow-up interview and a medical examination of each controller participating in the study provided a measure of the stress for each controller on each system. The data are reported in Table 13.5.

Table 13.6 is a summary of the stress data collected. In this table we include column totals (treatments) and row totals (blocks) as well as some sample means that will be helpful in making the sum of squares computations for the ANOVA procedure. Because lower stress values are viewed as better, the sample data seem to favor system B with its mean stress rating of 13. However, the usual question remains: Do the sample results justify the conclusion that the population mean stress levels for the three systems differ? That is, are the differences statistically significant? An analysis of variance computation similar to the one performed for the completely randomized design can be used to answer this statistical question.

TABLE 13.6	Summary of Stress Data for the Air Traffic Controller Stress Test				
		Treatments			Row or Block Totals	Block Means
		System A	System B	System C		
Blocks	Controller 1	15	15	18	48	$\bar{x}_{1.} = 48/3 = 16.0$
	Controller 2	14	14	14	42	$\bar{x}_{2.} = 42/3 = 14.0$
	Controller 3	10	11	15	36	$\bar{x}_{3.} = 36/3 = 12.0$
	Controller 4	13	12	17	42	$\bar{x}_{4.} = 42/3 = 14.0$
	Controller 5	16	13	16	45	$\bar{x}_{5.} = 45/3 = 15.0$
	Controller 6	13	13	13	39	$\bar{x}_{6.} = 39/3 = 13.0$
Column or Treatment Totals		81	78	93	252	$\bar{\bar{x}} = \dfrac{252}{18} = 14.0$
Treatment Means		$\bar{x}_{.1} = \dfrac{81}{6}$ $= 13.5$	$\bar{x}_{.2} = \dfrac{78}{6}$ $= 13.0$	$\bar{x}_{.3} = \dfrac{93}{6}$ $= 15.5$		

ANOVA Procedure

The ANOVA procedure for the randomized block design requires us to partition the sum of squares total (SST) into three groups: sum of squares due to treatments (SSTR), sum of squares due to blocks (SSBL), and sum of squares due to error (SSE). The formula for this partitioning follows.

$$SST = SSTR + SSBL + SSE \qquad (13.21)$$

This sum of squares partition is summarized in the ANOVA table for the randomized block design as shown in Table 13.7. The notation used in the table is

$$k = \text{the number of treatments}$$
$$b = \text{the number of blocks}$$
$$n_T = \text{the total sample size } (n_T = kb)$$

Note that the ANOVA table also shows how the $n_T - 1$ total degrees of freedom are partitioned such that $k - 1$ degrees of freedom go to treatments, $b - 1$ go to blocks, and $(k - 1)(b - 1)$ go to the error term. The mean square column shows the sum of squares divided by the degrees of freedom, and $F = MSTR/MSE$ is the F ratio used to test for a significant difference among the treatment means. The primary contribution of the randomized block design is that by including blocks, we remove the individual controller differences from the MSE term and obtain a more powerful test for the stress differences in the three workstation alternatives.

Computations and Conclusions

To compute the F statistic needed to test for a difference among treatment means with a randomized block design, we need to compute MSTR and MSE. To calculate these two mean squares, we must first compute SSTR and SSE; in doing so, we will also compute SSBL and SST. To simplify the presentation, we perform the calculations in four steps. In addition to k, b, and n_T as previously defined, the following notation is used.

$$x_{ij} = \text{value of the observation corresponding to treatment } j \text{ in block } i$$
$$\bar{x}_{.j} = \text{sample mean of the } j\text{th treatment}$$
$$\bar{x}_{i.} = \text{sample mean for the } i\text{th block}$$
$$\bar{\bar{x}} = \text{overall sample mean}$$

TABLE 13.7 ANOVA Table for the Randomized Block Design with k Treatments and b Blocks

Source of Variation	Sum of Squares	Degrees of Freedom	Mean Square	F	p-value
Treatments	SSTR	$k - 1$	$MSTR = \dfrac{SSTR}{k - 1}$	$\dfrac{MSTR}{MSE}$	
Blocks	SSBL	$b - 1$	$MSBL = \dfrac{SSBL}{b - 1}$		
Error	SSE	$(k - 1)(b - 1)$	$MSE = \dfrac{SSE}{(k - 1)(b - 1)}$		
Total	SST	$n_T - 1$			

Step 1. Compute the total sum of squares (SST).

$$\text{SST} = \sum_{i=1}^{b} \sum_{j=1}^{k} (x_{ij} - \bar{\bar{x}})^2 \tag{13.22}$$

Step 2. Compute the sum of squares due to treatments (SSTR).

$$\text{SSTR} = b \sum_{j=1}^{k} (\bar{x}_{.j} - \bar{\bar{x}})^2 \tag{13.23}$$

Step 3. Compute the sum of squares due to blocks (SSBL).

$$\text{SSBL} = k \sum_{i=1}^{b} (\bar{x}_{i.} - \bar{\bar{x}})^2 \tag{13.24}$$

Step 4. Compute the sum of squares due to error (SSE).

$$\text{SSE} = \text{SST} - \text{SSTR} - \text{SSBL} \tag{13.25}$$

For the air traffic controller data in Table 13.6, these steps lead to the following sums of squares.

Step 1. $\text{SST} = (15 - 14)^2 + (15 - 14)^2 + (18 - 14)^2 + \cdots + (13 - 14)^2 = 70$
Step 2. $\text{SSTR} = 6[(13.5 - 14)^2 + (13.0 - 14)^2 + (15.5 - 14)^2] = 21$
Step 3. $\text{SSBL} = 3[(16 - 14)^2 + (14 - 14)^2 + (12 - 14)^2 + (14 - 14)^2 +$
  $(15 - 14)^2 + (13 - 14)^2] = 30$
Step 4. $\text{SSE} = 70 - 21 - 30 = 19$

These sums of squares divided by their degrees of freedom provide the corresponding mean square values shown in Table 13.8.

Let us use a level of significance $\alpha = .05$ to conduct the hypothesis test. The value of the test statistic is

$$F = \frac{\text{MSTR}}{\text{MSE}} = \frac{10.5}{1.9} = 5.53$$

The numerator degrees of freedom is $k - 1 = 3 - 1 = 2$ and the denominator degrees of freedom is $(k - 1)(b - 1) = (3 - 1)(6 - 1) = 10$. Because we will only reject the null hypothesis for large values of the test statistic, the p-value is the area under the F distribution to the right of $F = 5.53$. From Table 4 of Appendix B we find that with the degrees of freedom 2 and 10, $F = 5.53$ is between $F_{.025} = 5.46$ and $F_{.01} = 7.56$. As a result, the area in the upper tail, or the p-value, is between .01 and .025. Alternatively, we can use statistical software to show that the exact p-value for $F = 5.53$ is .024. With p-value $\leq \alpha = .05$, we reject the null hypothesis H_0: $\mu_1 = \mu_2 = \mu_3$ and conclude that the population mean stress levels differ for the three workstation alternatives.

TABLE 13.8   ANOVA Table for the Air Traffic Controller Stress Test

Source of Variation	Sum of Squares	Degrees of Freedom	Mean Square	F	p-value
Treatments	21	2	10.5	10.5/1.9 = 5.53	.024
Blocks	30	5	6.0		
Error	19	10	1.9		
Total	70	17			

Some general comments can be made about the randomized block design. The experimental design described in this section is a *complete* block design; the word "complete" indicates that each block is subjected to all k treatments. That is, all controllers (blocks) were tested with all three systems (treatments). Experimental designs in which some but not all treatments are applied to each block are referred to as *incomplete* block designs. A discussion of incomplete block designs is beyond the scope of this text.

Because each controller in the air traffic controller stress test was required to use all three systems, this approach guarantees a complete block design. In some cases, however, blocking is carried out with "similar" experimental units in each block. For example, assume that in a pretest of air traffic controllers, the population of controllers was divided into groups ranging from extremely high-stress individuals to extremely low-stress individuals. The blocking could still be accomplished by having three controllers from each of the stress classifications participate in the study. Each block would then consist of three controllers in the same stress group. The randomized aspect of the block design would be the random assignment of the three controllers in each block to the three systems.

Finally, note that the ANOVA table shown in Table 13.7 provides an F value to test for treatment effects but *not* for blocks. The reason is that the experiment was designed to test a single factor—workstation design. The blocking based on individual stress differences was conducted to remove such variation from the MSE term. However, the study was not designed to test specifically for individual differences in stress.

Some analysts compute $F = \text{MSB}/\text{MSE}$ and use that statistic to test for significance of the blocks. Then they use the result as a guide to whether the same type of blocking would be desired in future experiments. However, if individual stress difference is to be a factor in the study, a different experimental design should be used. A test of significance on blocks should not be performed as a basis for a conclusion about a second factor.

NOTES + COMMENTS

The error degrees of freedom are less for a randomized block design than for a completely randomized design because $b - 1$ degrees of freedom are lost for the b blocks. If n is small, the potential effects due to blocks can be masked because of the loss of error degrees of freedom; for large n, the effects are minimized.

EXERCISES

Methods

21. Consider the experimental results for the following randomized block design. Make the calculations necessary to set up the analysis of variance table.

		Treatments		
		A	B	C
	1	10	9	8
	2	12	6	5
Blocks	3	18	15	14
	4	20	18	18
	5	8	7	8

Use $\alpha = .05$ to test for any significant differences.

22. The following data were obtained for a randomized block design involving five treatments and three blocks: SST = 430, SSTR = 310, SSBL = 85. Set up the ANOVA table and test for any significant differences. Use $\alpha = .05$.

23. An experiment has been conducted for four treatments with eight blocks. Complete the following analysis of variance table.

Source of Variation	Sum of Squares	Degrees of Freedom	Mean Square	F
Treatments	900			
Blocks	400			
Error				
Total	1800			

Use $\alpha = .05$ to test for any significant differences.

Applications

24. **Auto Tune-Ups.** An automobile dealer conducted a test to determine if the time in minutes needed to complete a minor engine tune-up depends on whether a computerized engine analyzer or an electronic analyzer is used. Because tune-up time varies among compact, intermediate, and full-sized cars, the three types of cars were used as blocks in the experiment. The data obtained follow.

		Analyzer	
		Computerized	Electronic
Car	Compact	50	42
	Intermediate	55	44
	Full-sized	63	46

Use $\alpha = .05$ to test for any significant differences.

25. **Airfares on Travel Websites.** Are there differences in airfare depending on which travel agency website you utilize? The following data were collected on travel agency websites on July 9, 2018. The following table contains the prices in U.S. dollars for a one-way ticket between the cities listed on the left for each of the three travel agency websites. Here the pairs of cities are the blocks and the treatments are the different websites. Use $\alpha = .05$ to test for any significant differences in the mean price of a one-way airline ticket for the three travel agency websites.

Airfares

	Website		
Flight From–To	Expedia ($)	TripAdvisor ($)	Priceline ($)
Atlanta to Seattle	176.00	166.00	175.80
New York to Los Angeles	195.00	195.00	206.20
Cleveland to Orlando	77.00	72.00	76.21
Dallas to Indianapolis	149.00	149.00	148.20

26. **SAT Performance.** The Scholastic Aptitude Test (SAT) contains three areas: critical reading, mathematics, and writing. Each area is scored on an 800-point scale. A sample of SAT scores for six students follows.

DATA *file*

SATScores

Student	Critical Reading	Mathematics	Writing
1	526	534	530
2	594	590	586
3	465	464	445
4	561	566	553
5	436	478	430
6	430	458	420

   a. Using a .05 level of significance, do students perform differently on the three areas of the SAT?

   b. Which area of the test seems to give the students the most trouble? Explain.

27. **Consumer Preferences.** In 2018, consumer goods giant Procter and Gamble (P&G) had more than 20 brands with more than $1 billion in annual sales (P&G website, https://us.pg.com/). How does a company like P&G create so many successful consumer products? P&G effectively invests in research and development to understand what consumers want. One method used to determine consumer preferences is called *conjoint analysis*. Conjoint analysis allows a company to ascertain the utility that a respondent in the conjoint study places on a design of a given product. The higher the utility, the more valuable a respondent finds the design. Suppose we have conducted a conjoint study and have the following estimated utilities (higher is preferred) for each of three different designs for a new whitening toothpaste.

DATA *file*

Toothpaste

Respondent	Utilities		
	Design A	Design B	Design C
1	24.6	34.6	28.6
2	31.4	31.6	33.7
3	31.8	20.4	27.6
4	15.4	26.6	24.9
5	20.7	18.5	18.0
6	41.0	34.2	44.6
7	27.1	22.7	27.1
8	20.2	22.0	27.7
9	31.6	29.6	31.1
10	24.4	29.2	29.1

At the .05 level of significance, test for any significant differences.

13.5 Factorial Experiment

The experimental designs we have considered thus far enable us to draw statistical conclusions about one factor. However, in some experiments we want to draw conclusions about more than one variable or factor. A **factorial experiment** is an experimental design that allows simultaneous conclusions about two or more factors. The term *factorial* is used because the experimental conditions include all possible combinations of the factors. For example, for *a* levels of factor A and *b* levels of factor B, the experiment will involve collecting data on *ab* treatment combinations. In this section we will show the analysis for a two-factor factorial experiment. The basic approach can be extended to experiments involving more than two factors.

As an illustration of a two-factor factorial experiment, we will consider a study involving the Graduate Management Admissions Test (GMAT), a standardized test used by graduate schools of business to evaluate an applicant's ability to pursue a graduate program in that field. Scores on the GMAT range from 200 to 800, with higher scores implying higher aptitude.

In an attempt to improve students' performance on the GMAT, a major Texas university is considering offering the following three GMAT preparation programs.

1. A three-hour review session covering the types of questions generally asked on the GMAT.
2. A one-day program covering relevant exam material, along with the taking and grading of a sample exam.
3. An intensive 10-week course involving the identification of each student's weaknesses and the setting up of individualized programs for improvement.

Hence, one factor in this study is the GMAT preparation program, which has three treatments: three-hour review, one-day program, and 10-week course. Before selecting the preparation program to adopt, further study will be conducted to determine how the proposed programs affect GMAT scores.

The GMAT is usually taken by students from three colleges: the College of Business, the College of Engineering, and the College of Arts and Sciences. Therefore, a second factor of interest in the experiment is whether a student's undergraduate college affects the GMAT score. This second factor, undergraduate college, also has three treatments: business, engineering, and arts and sciences. The factorial design for this experiment with three treatments corresponding to factor A, the preparation program, and three treatments corresponding to factor B, the undergraduate college, will have a total of $3 \times 3 = 9$ treatment combinations. These treatment combinations or experimental conditions are summarized in Table 13.9.

Assume that a sample of two students will be selected corresponding to each of the nine treatment combinations shown in Table 13.9: Two business students will take the three-hour review, two will take the one-day program, and two will take the 10-week course. In addition, two engineering students and two arts and sciences students will take each of the three preparation programs. In experimental design terminology, the sample size of two for each treatment combination indicates that we have two **replications**. Additional replications and a larger sample size could easily be used, but we elect to minimize the computational aspects for this illustration.

This experimental design requires that 6 students who plan to attend graduate school be randomly selected from *each* of the three undergraduate colleges. Then 2 students from each college should be assigned randomly to each preparation program, resulting in a total of 18 students being used in the study.

Let us assume that the randomly selected students participated in the preparation programs and then took the GMAT. The scores obtained are reported in Table 13.10.

TABLE 13.9   Nine Treatment Combinations for the Two-Factor GMAT Experiment

		Factor B: College		
		Business	Engineering	Arts and Sciences
Factor A:	Three-hour review	1	2	3
Preparation	One-day program	4	5	6
Program	10-week course	7	8	9

GMATStudy

TABLE 13.10	GMAT Scores for the Two-Factor Experiment		
		Factor B: College	
		Business	**Engineering**	**Arts and Sciences**

		Business	Engineering	Arts and Sciences
Factor A: Preparation Program	**Three-hour review**	500	540	480
		580	460	400
	One-day program	460	560	420
		540	620	480
	10-week course	560	600	480
		600	580	410

The analysis of variance computations with the data in Table 13.10 will provide answers to the following questions.

- **Main effect (factor A):** Do the preparation programs differ in terms of effect on GMAT scores?
- **Main effect (factor B):** Do the undergraduate colleges differ in terms of effect on GMAT scores?
- **Interaction effect (factors A and B):** Do students in some colleges do better on one type of preparation program whereas others do better on a different type of preparation program?

The term **interaction** refers to a new effect that we can now study because we used a factorial experiment. If the interaction effect has a significant impact on the GMAT scores, we can conclude that the effect of the type of preparation program depends on the undergraduate college.

ANOVA Procedure

The ANOVA procedure for the two-factor factorial experiment requires us to partition the sum of squares total (SST) into four groups: sum of squares for factor A (SSA), sum of squares for factor B (SSB), sum of squares for interaction (SSAB), and sum of squares due to error (SSE). The formula for this partitioning follows.

$$SST = SSA + SSB + SSAB + SSE \tag{13.26}$$

The partitioning of the sum of squares and degrees of freedom is summarized in Table 13.11. The following notation is used.

a = number of levels of factor A

b = number of levels of factor B

r = number of replications

n_T = total number of observations taken in the experiment; $n_T = abr$

Computations and Conclusions

To compute the F statistics needed to test for the significance of factor A, factor B, and interaction, we need to compute MSA, MSB, MSAB, and MSE. To calculate these four mean squares, we must first compute SSA, SSB, SSAB, and SSE; in doing so we will also

TABLE 13.11   ANOVA Table for the Two-Factor Factorial Experiment With r Replications

Source of Variation	Sum of Squares	Degrees of Freedom	Mean Square	F	p-value
Factor A	SSA	$a - 1$	$MSA = \dfrac{SSA}{a - 1}$	$\dfrac{MSA}{MSE}$	
Factor B	SSB	$b - 1$	$MSB = \dfrac{SSB}{b - 1}$	$\dfrac{MSB}{MSE}$	
Interaction	SSAB	$(a - 1)(b - 1)$	$MSAB = \dfrac{SSAB}{(a - 1)(b - 1)}$	$\dfrac{MSAB}{MSE}$	
Error	SSE	$ab(r - 1)$	$MSE = \dfrac{SSE}{ab(r - 1)}$		
Total	SST	$n_T - 1$			

compute SST. To simplify the presentation, we perform the calculations in five steps. In addition to a, b, r, and n_T as previously defined, the following notation is used.

x_{ijk} = observation corresponding to the kth replicate taken from treatment i of factor A and treatment j of factor B

$\bar{x}_{i\cdot}$ = sample mean for the observations in treatment i (factor A)

$\bar{x}_{\cdot j}$ = sample mean for the observations in treatment j (factor B)

$\bar{x}_{ij}$ = sample mean for the observations corresponding to the combination of treatment i (factor A) and treatment j (factor B)

$\bar{\bar{x}}$ = overall sample mean of all n_T observations

Step 1.   Compute the total sum of squares.

$$SST = \sum_{i=1}^{a} \sum_{j=1}^{b} \sum_{k=1}^{r} (x_{ijk} - \bar{\bar{x}})^2 \tag{13.27}$$

Step 2.   Compute the sum of squares for factor A.

$$SSA = br \sum_{i=1}^{a} (\bar{x}_{i\cdot} - \bar{\bar{x}})^2 \tag{13.28}$$

Step 3.   Compute the sum of squares for factor B.

$$SSB = ar \sum_{j=1}^{b} (\bar{x}_{\cdot j} - \bar{\bar{x}})^2 \tag{13.29}$$

Step 4.   Compute the sum of squares for interaction.

$$SSAB = r \sum_{i=1}^{a} \sum_{j=1}^{b} (\bar{x}_{ij} - \bar{x}_{i\cdot} - \bar{x}_{\cdot j} + \bar{\bar{x}})^2 \tag{13.30}$$

Step 5.   Compute the sum of squares due to error.

$$SSE = SST - SSA - SSB - SSAB \tag{13.31}$$

Table 13.12 reports the data collected in the experiment and the various sums that will help us with the sum of squares computations. Using equations (13.27) through

TABLE 13.12 GMAT Summary Data for the Two-Factor Experiment

		Factor B: College			Row Totals	Factor A Means
		Business	Engineering	Arts and Sciences		
Factor A: Preparation Program	**Three-hour review**	$\begin{array}{c}500\\580\\\hline 1080\end{array}$ $\bar{x}_{11}=\dfrac{1080}{2}=540$	$\begin{array}{c}540\\460\\\hline 1000\end{array}$ $\bar{x}_{12}=\dfrac{1000}{2}=500$	$\begin{array}{c}480\\400\\\hline 880\end{array}$ $\bar{x}_{13}=\dfrac{880}{2}=440$	2960	$\bar{x}_{1\cdot}=\dfrac{2960}{6}=493.33$
	One-day program	$\begin{array}{c}460\\540\\\hline 1000\end{array}$ $\bar{x}_{21}=\dfrac{1000}{2}=500$	$\begin{array}{c}560\\620\\\hline 1180\end{array}$ $\bar{x}_{22}=\dfrac{1180}{2}=590$	$\begin{array}{c}420\\480\\\hline 900\end{array}$ $\bar{x}_{23}=\dfrac{900}{2}=450$	3080	$\bar{x}_{2\cdot}=\dfrac{3080}{6}=513.33$
	10-week course	$\begin{array}{c}560\\600\\\hline 1160\end{array}$ $\bar{x}_{31}=\dfrac{1160}{2}=580$	$\begin{array}{c}600\\580\\\hline 1180\end{array}$ $\bar{x}_{32}=\dfrac{1180}{2}=590$	$\begin{array}{c}480\\410\\\hline 890\end{array}$ $\bar{x}_{33}=\dfrac{890}{2}=445$	3230	$\bar{x}_{3\cdot}=\dfrac{3230}{6}=538.33$
	Column Totals	3240	3360	2670	9270 ← Overall total	
	Factor B Means	$\bar{x}_{\cdot 1}=\dfrac{3240}{6}=540$	$\bar{x}_{\cdot 2}=\dfrac{3360}{6}=560$	$\bar{x}_{\cdot 3}=\dfrac{2670}{6}=445$		$\bar{\bar{x}}=\dfrac{9270}{18}=515$

Treatment combination totals

(13.31), we calculate the following sums of squares for the GMAT two-factor factorial experiment.

Step 1. $\text{SST} = (500 - 515)^2 + (580 - 515)^2 + (540 - 515)^2 + \cdots +$
$(410 - 515)^2 = 82{,}450$

Step 2. $\text{SSA} = (3)(2)[(493.33 - 515)^2 + (513.33 - 515)^2 +$
$(538.33 - 515)^2] = 6100$

Step 3. $\text{SSB} = (3)(2)[(540 - 515)^2 + (560 - 515)^2 + (445 - 515)^2] = 45{,}300$

Step 4. $\text{SSAB} = 2[(540 - 493.33 - 540 + 515)^2 + (500 - 493.33 -$
$560 + 515)^2 + \cdots + (445 - 538.33 - 445 + 515)^2] = 11{,}200$

Step 5. $\text{SSE} = 82{,}450 - 6100 - 45{,}300 - 11{,}200 = 19{,}850$

These sums of squares divided by their corresponding degrees of freedom provide the appropriate mean square values for testing the two main effects (preparation program and undergraduate college) and the interaction effect.

Because of the computational effort involved in any modest- to large-size factorial experiment, the computer usually plays an important role in performing the analysis of variance computations shown above and in the calculation of the p-values used to make the hypothesis testing decisions. Table 13.13 shows the output for the analysis of variance for the GMAT two-factor factorial experiment. Let us use the output and a level of significance $\alpha = .05$ to conduct the hypothesis tests for the two-factor GMAT study. The p-value used to test for significant differences among the three preparation programs (Factor A) is .299. Because the p-value $= .299$ is greater than $\alpha = .05$, there is no significant difference in the mean GMAT test scores for the three preparation programs. However, for the undergraduate college effect (Factor B), the p-value $= .005$ is less than $\alpha = .05$; thus, there is a significant difference in the mean GMAT test scores among the three undergraduate colleges. Finally, because the p-value of .350 for the interaction effect is greater than $\alpha = .05$, there is no significant interaction effect. Therefore, the study provides no reason to believe that the three preparation programs differ in their ability to prepare students from the different colleges for the GMAT.

Undergraduate college was found to be a significant factor. Checking the calculations in Table 13.12, we see that the sample means are: business students $\bar{x}_{.1} = 540$, engineering students $\bar{x}_{.2} = 560$, and arts and sciences students $\bar{x}_{.3} = 445$. Tests on individual treatment means can be conducted, yet after reviewing the three sample means, we would anticipate no difference in preparation for business and engineering graduates. However, the arts and sciences students appear to be significantly less prepared for the GMAT than students in the other colleges. Perhaps this observation will lead the university to consider other options for assisting these students in preparing for the Graduate Management Admission Test.

TABLE 13.13 Output for the GMAT Two-Factor Design

SOURCE	DF	SS	MS	F	P
Factor A	2	6100	3050	1.38	.299
Factor B	2	45300	22650	10.27	.005
Interaction	4	11200	2800	1.27	.350
Error	9	19850	2206		
Total	17	82450			

EXERCISES

Methods

28. A factorial experiment involving two levels of factor A and three levels of factor B resulted in the following data.

		Factor B		
		Level 1	Level 2	Level 3
	Level 1	135	90	75
		165	66	93
Factor A				
	Level 2	125	127	120
		95	105	136

Test for any significant main effects and any interaction. Use $\alpha = .05$.

29. The calculations for a factorial experiment involving four levels of factor A, three levels of factor B, and three replications resulted in the following data: SST = 280, SSA = 26, SSB = 23, SSAB = 175. Set up the ANOVA table and test for any significant main effects and any interaction effect. Use $\alpha = .05$.

Applications

30. **Mobile App Website Design.** Based on a 2018 study, the average elapsed time between when a user navigates to a website on a mobile device until its main content is available was 14.6 seconds. This is more than a 20% increase from 2017 (searchenginejournal.com, https://www.searchenginejournal.com/). Responsiveness is certainly an important feature of any website and is perhaps even more important on a mobile device. What other web design factors need to be considered for a mobile device to make it more user friendly? Among other things, navigation menu placement and amount of text entry required are important on a mobile device. The following data provide the time it took (in seconds) randomly selected students (two for each factor combination) to perform a prespecified task with the different combinations of navigation menu placement and amount of text entry required.

DATA*file*

MobileApps

		Amount of Text Entry Required	
		Low	High
	Right	8	12
		12	8
Navigation Menu Position	Middle	22	36
		14	20
	Left	10	18
		18	14

Use the ANOVA procedure for factorial designs to test for any significant effects resulting from navigation menu position and amount of text entry required. Use $\alpha = .05$.

31. **Amusement Park Queues.** An amusement park studied methods for decreasing the waiting time (minutes) for rides by loading and unloading riders more efficiently. Two alternative loading/unloading methods have been proposed. To account for potential differences due to the type of ride and the possible interaction between the method of loading and unloading and the type of ride, a factorial experiment was designed. Use the following data to test for any significant effect due to the loading and unloading method, the type of ride, and interaction. Use $\alpha = .05$.

	Type of Ride		
	Roller Coaster	**Screaming Demon**	**Log Flume**
Method 1	41	52	50
	43	44	46
Method 2	49	50	48
	51	46	44

32. **Auto Fuel Efficiency.** As part of a study designed to compare hybrid and similarly equipped conventional vehicles, *Consumer Reports* tested a variety of classes of hybrid and all-gas model cars and sport utility vehicles (SUVs). The following data show the miles-per-gallon rating *Consumer Reports* obtained for two hybrid small cars, two hybrid midsize cars, two hybrid small SUVs, and two hybrid midsize SUVs; also shown are the miles per gallon obtained for eight similarly equipped conventional models.

DATA*file*

HybridTest

Make/Model	Class	Type	MPG
Honda Civic	Small Car	Hybrid	37
Honda Civic	Small Car	Conventional	28
Toyota Prius	Small Car	Hybrid	44
Toyota Corolla	Small Car	Conventional	32
Chevrolet Malibu	Midsize Car	Hybrid	27
Chevrolet Malibu	Midsize Car	Conventional	23
Nissan Altima	Midsize Car	Hybrid	32
Nissan Altima	Midsize Car	Conventional	25
Ford Escape	Small SUV	Hybrid	27
Ford Escape	Small SUV	Conventional	21
Saturn Vue	Small SUV	Hybrid	28
Saturn Vue	Small SUV	Conventional	22
Lexus RX	Midsize SUV	Hybrid	23
Lexus RX	Midsize SUV	Conventional	19
Toyota Highlander	Midsize SUV	Hybrid	24
Toyota Highlander	Midsize SUV	Conventional	18

At the $\alpha = .05$ level of significance, test for significant effects due to class, type, and interaction.

33. **Tax Research.** A study reported in *The Accounting Review* examined the separate and joint effects of two levels of time pressure (low and moderate) and three levels of knowledge (naive, declarative, and procedural) on key word selection behavior in tax research. Subjects were given a tax case containing a set of facts, a tax issue, and a key word index consisting of 1336 key words. They were asked to select the key words they believed would refer them to a tax authority relevant to resolving the tax case. Prior to the experiment, a group of tax experts determined that the text contained 19 relevant key words. Subjects in the naive group had little or no declarative or procedural knowledge, subjects in the declarative group had significant declarative knowledge but little or no procedural knowledge, and subjects in the procedural group had significant declarative knowledge and procedural knowledge. Declarative knowledge consists of knowledge of both the applicable tax rules and the technical terms used to describe such rules. Procedural knowledge is knowledge of the rules that guide the tax researcher's search for relevant key words. Subjects in the low time pressure situation were told they had 25 minutes to complete the problem, an amount of time which should be "more than adequate" to complete the case; subjects in the moderate time pressure situation were told they would have "only" 11 minutes to complete the case. Suppose 25 subjects were selected for each of the six treatment combinations and the sample means for each treatment combination are as follows (standard deviations are in parentheses).

| | Knowledge | | |
	Naive	Declarative	Procedural
Low	1.13 (1.12)	1.56 (1.33)	2.00 (1.54)
Time Pressure			
Moderate	.48 (.80)	1.68 (1.36)	2.86 (1.80)

Use the ANOVA procedure to test for any significant differences due to time pressure, knowledge, and interaction. Use a .05 level of significance. Assume that the total sum of squares for this experiment is 327.50.

SUMMARY

In this chapter we showed how analysis of variance can be used to test for differences among means of several populations or treatments. We introduced the completely randomized design, the randomized block design, and the two-factor factorial experiment. The completely randomized design and the randomized block design are used to draw conclusions about differences in the means of a single factor. The primary purpose of blocking in the randomized block design is to remove extraneous sources of variation from the error term. Such blocking provides a better estimate of the true error variance and a better test to determine whether the population or treatment means of the factor differ significantly.

We showed that the basis for the statistical tests used in analysis of variance and experimental design is the development of two independent estimates of the population variance σ^2. In the single-factor case, one estimator is based on the variation between the treatments; this estimator provides an unbiased estimate of σ^2 only if the means $\mu_1, \mu_2, \ldots, \mu_k$ are all equal. A second estimator of σ^2 is based on the variation of the observations within each sample; this estimator will always provide an unbiased estimate of σ^2. By computing the ratio of these two estimators (the F statistic) we developed a rejection rule for determining whether to reject the null hypothesis that the population or treatment means are equal. In all the experimental designs considered, the partitioning of the sum of squares and degrees of freedom into their various sources enabled us to compute the appropriate values for the analysis of variance calculations and tests. We also showed how Fisher's LSD procedure and the Bonferroni adjustment can be used to perform pairwise comparisons to determine which means are different.

GLOSSARY

ANOVA table A table used to summarize the analysis of variance computations and results. It contains columns showing the source of variation, the sum of squares, the degrees of freedom, the mean square, and the F value(s).

Blocking The process of using the same or similar experimental units for all treatments. The purpose of blocking is to remove a source of variation from the error term and hence provide a more powerful test for a difference in population or treatment means.

Comparisonwise Type I error rate The probability of a Type I error associated with a single pairwise comparison.

Completely randomized design An experimental design in which the treatments are randomly assigned to the experimental units.

Experimental units The objects of interest in the experiment.

Experimentwise Type I error rate The probability of making a Type I error on at least one of several pairwise comparisons.

Factor Another word for the independent variable of interest.

Factorial experiment An experimental design that allows simultaneous conclusions about two or more factors.

Interaction The effect produced when the levels of one factor interact with the levels of another factor in influencing the response variable.

Multiple comparison procedures Statistical procedures that can be used to conduct statistical comparisons between pairs of population means.

Partitioning The process of allocating the total sum of squares and degrees of freedom to the various components.

Randomized block design An experimental design employing blocking.

Replications The number of times each experimental condition is repeated in an experiment.

Response variable Another word for the dependent variable of interest.

Single-factor experiment An experiment involving only one factor with k populations or treatments.

Treatments Different levels of a factor.

KEY FORMULAS

Completely Randomized Design

Sample Mean for Treatment j

$$\bar{x}_j = \frac{\sum_{i=1}^{n_j} x_{ij}}{n_j} \tag{13.1}$$

Sample Variance for Treatment j

$$s_j^2 = \frac{\sum_{i=1}^{n_j} (x_{ij} - \bar{x}_j)^2}{n_j - 1} \tag{13.2}$$

Overall Sample Mean

$$\bar{\bar{x}} = \frac{\sum_{j=1}^{k} \sum_{i=1}^{n_j} x_{ij}}{n_T} \tag{13.3}$$

$$n_T = n_1 + n_2 + \cdots + n_k \tag{13.4}$$

Mean Square Due to Treatments

$$\text{MSTR} = \frac{\text{SSTR}}{k - 1} \tag{13.7}$$

Sum of Squares Due to Treatments

$$\text{SSTR} = \sum_{j=1}^{k} n_j (\bar{x}_j - \bar{\bar{x}})^2 \tag{13.8}$$

Mean Square Due to Error

$$\text{MSE} = \frac{\text{SSE}}{n_T - k} \tag{13.10}$$

Sum of Squares Due to Error

$$SSE = \sum_{j=1}^{k} (n_j - 1)s_j^2 \tag{13.11}$$

Test Statistic for the Equality of k Population Means

$$F = \frac{MSTR}{MSE} \tag{13.12}$$

Total Sum of Squares

$$SST = \sum_{j=1}^{k} \sum_{i=1}^{n_j} (x_{ij} - \bar{\bar{x}})^2 \tag{13.13}$$

Partitioning of Sum of Squares

$$SST = SSTR + SSE \tag{13.14}$$

Multiple Comparison Procedures

Test Statistic for Fisher's LSD Procedure

$$t = \frac{\bar{x}_i - \bar{x}_j}{\sqrt{MSE\left(\dfrac{1}{n_i} + \dfrac{1}{n_j}\right)}} \tag{13.16}$$

Fisher's LSD

$$LSD = t_{\alpha/2} \sqrt{MSE\left(\frac{1}{n_i} + \frac{1}{n_j}\right)} \tag{13.17}$$

Randomized Block Design

Total Sum of Squares

$$SST = \sum_{i=1}^{b} \sum_{j=1}^{k} (x_{ij} - \bar{\bar{x}})^2 \tag{13.22}$$

Sum of Squares Due to Treatments

$$SSTR = b \sum_{j=1}^{k} (\bar{x}_{\cdot j} - \bar{\bar{x}})^2 \tag{13.23}$$

Sum of Squares Due to Blocks

$$SSBL = k \sum_{i=1}^{b} (\bar{x}_{i\cdot} - \bar{\bar{x}})^2 \tag{13.24}$$

Sum of Squares Due to Error

$$SSE = SST - SSTR - SSBL \tag{13.25}$$

Factorial Experiment

Total Sum of Squares

$$SST = \sum_{i=1}^{a} \sum_{j=1}^{b} \sum_{k=1}^{r} (x_{ijk} - \bar{\bar{x}})^2 \tag{13.27}$$

Sum of Squares for Factor A

$$SSA = br \sum_{i=1}^{a} (\bar{x}_{i.} - \bar{\bar{x}})^2 \tag{13.28}$$

Sum of Squares for Factor B

$$SSB = ar \sum_{j=1}^{b} (\bar{x}_{.j} - \bar{\bar{x}})^2 \tag{13.29}$$

Sum of Squares for Interaction

$$SSAB = r \sum_{i=1}^{a} \sum_{j=1}^{b} (\bar{x}_{ij} - \bar{x}_{i.} - \bar{x}_{.j} + \bar{\bar{x}})^2 \tag{13.30}$$

Sum of Squares for Error

$$SSE = SST - SSA - SSB - SSAB \tag{13.31}$$

SUPPLEMENTARY EXERCISES

34. **Paper Towel Absorption.** In a completely randomized experimental design, three brands of paper towels were tested for their ability to absorb water. Equal-size towels were used, with four sections of towels tested per brand. The absorbency rating data follow. At a .05 level of significance, does there appear to be a difference in the ability of the brands to absorb water?

	Brand	
x	**y**	**z**
91	99	83
100	96	88
88	94	89
89	99	76

35. **Job Satisfaction.** A study reported in the *Journal of Small Business Management* concluded that self-employed individuals do not experience higher job satisfaction than individuals who are not self-employed. In this study, job satisfaction is measured using 18 items, each of which is rated using a Likert-type scale with 1–5 response options ranging from strong agreement to strong disagreement. A higher score on this scale indicates a higher degree of job satisfaction. The sum of the ratings for the 18 items, ranging from 18 to 90, is used as the measure of job satisfaction. Suppose that this approach was used to measure the job satisfaction for lawyers, physical therapists, cabinetmakers, and systems analysts. The results obtained for a sample of 10 individuals from each profession follow.

SatisJob

Lawyer	Physical Therapist	Cabinetmaker	Systems Analyst
44	55	54	44
42	78	65	73
74	80	79	71
42	86	69	60
53	60	79	64
50	59	64	66
45	62	59	41
48	52	78	55
64	55	84	76
38	50	60	62

At the $\alpha = .05$ level of significance, test for any difference in the job satisfaction among the four professions.

36. **Monitoring Air Pollution.** The U.S. Environmental Protection Agency (EPA) monitors levels of pollutants in the air for cities across the country. Ozone pollution levels are measured using a 500-point scale; lower scores indicate little health risk, and higher scores indicate greater health risk. The following data show the peak levels of ozone pollution in four cities (Birmingham, Alabama; Memphis, Tennessee; Little Rock, Arkansas; and Jackson, Mississippi) for 10 dates from last year.

DATA*file*

OzoneLevels

	City			
Date	Birmingham AL	Memphis TN	Little Rock AR	Jackson MS
Jan 9	18	20	18	14
Jan 17	23	31	22	30
Jan 18	19	25	22	21
Jan 31	29	36	28	35
Feb 1	27	31	28	24
Feb 6	26	31	31	25
Feb 14	31	24	19	25
Feb 17	31	31	28	28
Feb 20	33	35	35	34
Feb 29	20	42	42	21

Use $\alpha = .05$ to test for any significant difference in the mean peak ozone levels among the four cities.

37. **College Attendance Rates.** The following data show the percentage of 17- to 24-year-olds who are attending college in several metropolitan statistical areas in four geographic regions of the United States (U.S. Census Bureau website, https://www.census.gov/data.html).

DATA*file*

CollegeRates

Northeast	Midwest	South	West
28.6	36.7	59.9	16.4
39.9	33.4	37.2	33.5
31.9	22.8	28.0	22.3
46.3	43.8	41.1	12.4
32.5	32.1	33.9	43.7
14.9	58.3	18.8	26.8
36.8	31.1	30.3	57.3
36.3	64.0	67.4	14.3
37.7	27.6	32.6	37.0
58.4	55.5	30.0	28.1
60.6	78.8	39.1	17.5
	42.2	29.7	32.3
	74.7	29.8	52.4
	36.5	23.7	51.5
	28.7	34.0	25.4
	60.4	24.5	29.6
	58.2	54.2	27.6
	21.0	31.0	31.5
	28.8	41.9	22.8
	25.5	70.2	34.6
	73.9	22.7	33.0

(continued)

Northeast	Midwest	South	West
	36.8	30.7	37.0
	28.4	30.8	33.8
	27.2	21.6	28.7
	31.8	31.5	21.8
	56.8	38.2	
	28.3	40.2	
	33.3	35.4	
	39.4	21.6	
	39.2	35.5	
		26.1	
		32.7	

Use $\alpha = .05$ to test whether the mean percentage of 17- to 24-year-olds who are attending college is the same for the four geographic regions.

38. **Assembly Methods.** Three different assembly methods have been proposed for a new product. A completely randomized experimental design was chosen to determine which assembly method results in the greatest number of parts produced per hour, and 30 workers were randomly selected and assigned to use one of the proposed methods. The number of units produced by each worker follows.

DATA *file*

Assembly

	Method	
A	**B**	**C**
97	93	99
73	100	94
93	93	87
100	55	66
73	77	59
91	91	75
100	85	84
86	73	72
92	90	88
95	83	86

Use these data and test to see whether the mean number of parts produced is the same with each method. Use $\alpha = .05$.

39. **Job Automation.** A Pew Research study conducted in 2017 found that approximately 75% of Americans believe that robots and computers might one day do many of the jobs currently done by people (Pew Research website, http://www.pewinternet .org/2017/10/04/americans-attitudes-toward-a-future-in-which-robots-and-computers -can-do-many-human-jobs/). Suppose we have the following data collected from nurses, tax auditors, and fast-food workers in which a higher score means the person feels his or her job is more likely to be automated.

DATA *file*

JobAutomation

Nurse	Tax Auditor	Fast-Food Worker
4	5	5
5	6	7
6	5	5
3	4	7
3	7	4
4	4	6
5	6	5
4	5	7

a. Use $\alpha = .05$ to test for differences in the belief that a person's job is likely to be automated for the three professions.

b. Use Fisher's LSD procedure to compare the belief that a person's job will be automated for nurses and tax auditors.

40. **Fuel Efficiency of Gasoline Brands.** A research firm tests the miles-per-gallon characteristics of three brands of gasoline. Because of different gasoline performance characteristics in different brands of automobiles, five brands of automobiles are selected and treated as blocks in the experiment; that is, each brand of automobile is tested with each type of gasoline. The results of the experiment (in miles per gallon) follow.

		Gasoline Brands		
		I	II	III
Automobiles	A	18	21	20
	B	24	26	27
	C	30	29	34
	D	22	25	24
	E	20	23	24

a. At $\alpha = .05$, is there a significant difference in the mean miles-per-gallon characteristics of the three brands of gasoline?

b. Analyze the experimental data using the ANOVA procedure for completely randomized designs. Compare your findings with those obtained in part (a). What is the advantage of attempting to remove the block effect?

41. **Late-Night Talk Show Viewership.** *Jimmy Kimmel Live!* on ABC, *The Tonight Show Starring Jimmy Fallon* on NBC, and *The Late Show with Stephen Colbert* on CBS are three popular late-night talk shows. The following table shows the number of viewers in millions for a 10-week period during the spring for each of these shows (TV by the Numbers website, https://tvbythenumbers.zap2it.com/).

DATA*file*

TalkShows

Week	Jimmy Kimmel Live (ABC)	The Tonight Show Starring Jimmy Fallon (NBC)	The Late Show with Stephen Colbert (CBS)
June 13–June 17	2.67	3.24	2.27
June 6–June 10	2.58	3.32	2.05
May 30–June 3	2.64	2.66	2.08
May 23–May 27	2.47	3.30	2.07
May 16–May 20	1.97	3.10	2.31
May 9–May 16	2.21	3.31	2.45
May 2–May 6	2.12	3.20	2.57
April 25–April 29	2.24	3.15	2.45
April 18–April 22	2.10	2.77	2.56
April 11–April 15	2.21	3.24	2.16

At the .05 level of significance, test for a difference in the mean number of viewers per week for the three late-night talk shows.

42. **Golf Club Design.** A major manufacturer of golf equipment is considering three designs for a new driver: Design A, Design B, and Design C. Each design differs slightly in terms of the material used to construct the driver's head and shaft. The company would like to know if there is any difference in the overall driving distance

for the three designs. Twelve PGA Tour players who represent the company were asked to test each model. After a warm-up period, each player hit each a drive with one of the new designs in a randomly selected order, and the overall distance (in yards) was recorded. The results follow.

DATA *file*

ClubHead

Design A	Design B	Design C
306	323	320
279	313	289
293	318	314
277	288	282
281	286	287
272	312	283
297	326	332
271	306	284
279	325	294
323	319	289
301	307	293

At the .05 level of significance, test whether the mean driving distance is the same for the three designs.

43. **Language Translation.** A factorial experiment was designed to test for any significant differences in the time needed to translate other languages into English with two computerized language translators. Because the type of language translated was also considered a significant factor, translations were made with both systems for three different languages: Spanish, French, and German. Use the following data for translation time in hours.

	Language		
	Spanish	French	German
System 1	8	10	12
	12	14	16
System 2	6	14	16
	10	16	22

Test for any significant differences due to language translator, type of language, and interaction. Use $\alpha = .05$.

44. **Defective Parts.** A manufacturing company designed a factorial experiment to determine whether the number of defective parts produced by two machines differed and if the number of defective parts produced also depended on whether the raw material needed by each machine was loaded manually or by an automatic feed system. The following data give the numbers of defective parts produced. Use $\alpha = .05$ to test for any significant effect due to machine, loading system, and interaction.

	Loading System	
	Manual	Automatic
Machine 1	30	30
	34	26
Machine 2	20	24
	22	28

CASE PROBLEM 1: WENTWORTH MEDICAL CENTER

As part of a long-term study of individuals 65 years of age or older, sociologists and physicians at the Wentworth Medical Center in upstate New York investigated the relationship between geographic location and depression. A sample of 60 individuals, all in reasonably good health, was selected; 20 individuals were residents of Florida, 20 were residents of New York, and 20 were residents of North Carolina. Each of the individuals sampled was given a standardized test to measure depression. The data collected follow; higher test scores indicate higher levels of depression. These data are contained in the file Medical1.

A second part of the study considered the relationship between geographic location and depression for individuals 65 years of age or older who had a chronic health condition such as arthritis, hypertension, and/or heart ailment. A sample of 60 individuals with such conditions was identified. Again, 20 were residents of Florida, 20 were residents of New York, and 20 were residents of North Carolina. The levels of depression recorded for this study follow. These data are contained in the file named Medical2.

DATA *file*

Medical1

DATA *file*

Medical2

Data from Medical1			Data from Medical2		
Florida	New York	North Carolina	Florida	New York	North Carolina
3	8	10	13	14	10
7	11	7	12	9	12
7	9	3	17	15	15
3	7	5	17	12	18
8	8	11	20	16	12
8	7	8	21	24	14
8	8	4	16	18	17
5	4	3	14	14	8
5	13	7	13	15	14
2	10	8	17	17	16
6	6	8	12	20	18
2	8	7	9	11	17
6	12	3	12	23	19
6	8	9	15	19	15
9	6	8	16	17	13
7	8	12	15	14	14
5	5	6	13	9	11
4	7	3	10	14	12
7	7	8	11	13	13
3	8	11	17	11	11

Managerial Report

1. Use descriptive statistics to summarize the data from the two studies. What are your preliminary observations about the depression scores?
2. Use analysis of variance on both data sets. State the hypotheses being tested in each case. What are your conclusions?
3. Use inferences about individual treatment means where appropriate. What are your conclusions?

CASE PROBLEM 2: COMPENSATION FOR SALES PROFESSIONALS

Suppose that a local chapter of sales professionals in the greater San Francisco area conducted a survey of its membership to study the relationship, if any, between the years of experience and salary for individuals employed in inside and outside sales positions. On the survey, respondents were asked to specify one of three levels of years of experience: low (1–10 years), medium (11–20 years), and high (21 or more years). A portion of the data obtained follow. The complete data set, consisting of 120 observations, is contained in the file named SalesSalary.

DATA *file*

SalesSalary

Observation	Salary $	Position	Experience
1	53,938	Inside	Medium
2	52,694	Inside	Medium
3	70,515	Outside	Low
4	52,031	Inside	Medium
5	62,283	Outside	Low
6	57,718	Inside	Low
7	79,081	Outside	High
8	48,621	Inside	Low
9	72,835	Outside	High
10	54,768	Inside	Medium
⋮	⋮	⋮	⋮
115	58,080	Inside	High
116	78,702	Outside	Medium
117	83,131	Outside	Medium
118	57,788	Inside	High
119	53,070	Inside	Medium
120	60,259	Outside	Low

Managerial Report

1. Use descriptive statistics to summarize the data.
2. Develop a 95% confidence interval estimate of the mean annual salary for all salespersons, regardless of years of experience and type of position.
3. Develop a 95% confidence interval estimate of the mean salary for inside salespersons.
4. Develop a 95% confidence interval estimate of the mean salary for outside salespersons.
5. Use analysis of variance to test for any significant differences due to position. Use a .05 level of significance, and for now, ignore the effect of years of experience.
6. Use analysis of variance to test for any significant differences due to years of experience. Use a .05 level of significance, and for now, ignore the effect of position.
7. At the .05 level of significance test for any significant differences due to position, years of experience, and interaction.

CASE PROBLEM 3: TOURISTOPIA TRAVEL

DATA *file*

TourisTopia

TourisTopia Travel (Triple T) is an online travel agency that specializes in trips to exotic locations around the world for groups of ten or more travelers. Triple T's marketing manager has been working on a major revision of the homepage of Triple T's website. The content for the homepage has been selected and the only remaining decisions involve the selection of the background color (white, green, or pink) and the type of font (Arial, Calibri, or Tahoma).

Triple T's IT group has designed prototype homepages featuring every combination of these background colors and fonts, and it has implemented computer code that will randomly direct each Triple T website visitor to one of these prototype homepages. For three weeks, the prototype homepage to which each visitor was directed and the amount of time in seconds spent at Triple T's website during each visit were recorded. Ten visitors to each of the prototype homepages were then selected randomly; the complete data set for these visitors is available in the DATAfile named *TourisTopia*.

Triple T wants to use these data to determine if the time spent by visitors to Triple T's website differs by background color or font. It would also like to know if the time spent by visitors to the Triple T website differs by different combinations of background color and font.

Managerial Report

Prepare a managerial report that addresses the following issues.

1. Use descriptive statistics to summarize the data from Triple T's study. Based on descriptive statistics, what are your preliminary conclusions about whether the time spent by visitors to the Triple T website differs by background color or font? What are your preliminary conclusions about whether time spent by visitors to the Triple T website differs by different combinations of background color and font?
2. Has Triple T used an observational study or a controlled experiment? Explain.
3. Use the data from Triple T's study to test the hypothesis that the time spent by visitors to the Triple T website is equal for the three background colors. Include both factors and their interaction in the ANOVA model, and use $\alpha = .05$.
4. Use the data from Triple T's study to test the hypothesis that the time spent by visitors to the Triple T website is equal for the three fonts. Include both factors and their interaction in the ANOVA model, and use $\alpha = .05$.
5. Use the data from Triple T's study to test the hypothesis that time spent by visitors to the Triple T website is equal for the nine combinations of background color and font. Include both factors and their interaction in the ANOVA model, and use $\alpha = .05$.
6. Do the results of your analysis of the data provide evidence that the time spent by visitors to the Triple T website differs by background color, font, or combination of background color and font? What is your recommendation?

Chapter 13 Appendix

Appendix 13.1 Analysis of Variance with JMP

In this appendix we describe how to use JMP to perform an analysis of variance.

Completely Randomized Design

In Section 13.2 we showed how analysis of variance could be used to test for the equality of k population means using data from a completely randomized design. To illustrate how JMP can be used for this type of experimental design, we show how to test whether the mean number of units produced per week is the same for each assembly method in the Chemitech experiment introduced in Section 13.1.

DATA *file*

Chemitech

Step 1. Open the file *Chemitech* using JMP with the steps provided in Appendix 1.1
Step 2. Convert the file to stacked format following the steps in Appendix 1.1, entering *Units Assembled* as the new **Stacked Data Column** name and *Method* as the new **Source Label Column** name
Step 3. When the JMP stacked data table appears, click **Analyze** and select **Fit Y by X**
Step 4. When the **Fit Y by X—Contextual** window appears:
Drag **Units Assembled** in the **Select Columns** area to the **Y, Response** box in the Cast **Selected Columns into Roles** area
Drag **Method** in the **Select Columns** to the **X, Factor** box in the **Cast Selected Columns into Roles** area
Click **OK** in the **Action** area
Step 5. When the **Fit Y by X of Units Assembled by Method** window appears:
Click on the red triangle next to **Oneway Analysis of Units Assembled by Method** and select **Means/Anova**

The output appears in Figure JMP 13.1. The **Analysis of Variance** section shows that the p-value is .0038 < .05, which indicates a significant difference in the means of the methods. The results match those in Figure 13.5.

Randomized Block Design

In Section 13.4 we showed how analysis of variance could be used to test for the equality of k population means using the data from a randomized block design. To illustrate how JMP can be used for this type of experimental design, we show how to test whether the mean stress levels for air traffic controllers are the same for three workstations using the data in Table 13.5. The blocks (controllers), treatments (system), and stress-level scores shown in Table 13.5 are in the file *AirTraffic*. The following steps produce the JMP output shown in Figure JMP 13.2.

DATA *file*

AirTraffic

Step 1. Open the file *AirTraffic* using JMP with the steps provided in Appendix 1.1
Step 2. Convert the file to stacked format following the steps in Appendix 1.1, by dragging **System A, System B,** and **System C** to the **Stack Columns** box and entering *Stress Value* as the new **Stacked Data Column** name and *Workstation* as the new **Source Label Column** name
Step 3. When the JMP stacked data table appears, click **Analyze** and select **Fit Y by X**
Step 4. When the **Fit Y by X—Contextual** window appears:
Drag **Stress Value** in the **Select Columns** area to the **Y, Response** box in the **Cast Selected Columns into Roles** area
Drag **Workstation** in the **Select Columns** area to the **X, Factor** box in the **Cast Selected Columns into Roles** area

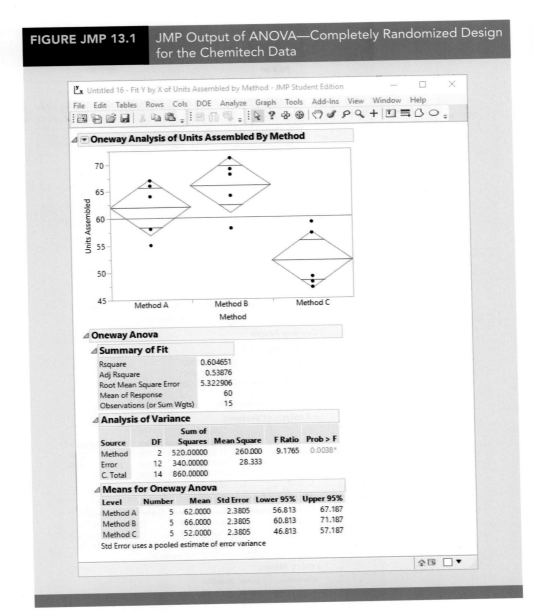

FIGURE JMP 13.1 JMP Output of ANOVA—Completely Randomized Design for the Chemitech Data

Click **Controller** in the **Select Columns** area and click **Block** in the **Cast Selected Columns into Roles** area

Click **OK** in the **Action** area

Step 5. When the **Fit Y by X of Data of Stress Value by Workstation** window appears:

Click on the red triangle ▼ next to **Oneway Analysis of Data by Label** and select **Means/Anova**

The **Analysis of Variance** section gives output corresponding to the ANOVA table shown in Table 13.8.

Factorial Experiment

In Section 13.5 we showed how analysis of variance could be used to test for the equality of k population means using data from a factorial experiment. To illustrate how JMP can be used for this type of experimental design, we show how to analyze the data for the two-factor GMAT experiment introduced in Section 13.5. The GMAT scores shown in Table 13.10 are in the file *GMATStudy*. The following steps produce the JMP output corresponding to the ANOVA table shown in Table 13.13.

FIGURE JMP 13.2   JMP Output of ANOVA—Randomized Block Design for the GMAT Experiment Data

DATA *file*
GMATStudy

Step 1. Open the file *GMATStudy* using JMP with the steps provided in Appendix 1.1

Step 2. Convert the file to stacked format following the steps in Appendix 1.1, selecting **Business, Engineering,** and **Arts and Sciences** for the **Stack Columns** area and entering *GMAT Score* as the new **Stacked Data Column** name and *College* as the new **Source Label Column** name

Step 3. When the JMP stacked data table opens, click **Analyze** and select **Fit Model**

Step 4. When the **Fit Model** window appears (see Figure JMP 13.3):

Drag **GMAT Score** in the **Select Columns** area to the **Y** box in the **Pick Role Variables** area

FIGURE JMP 13.3   The Fit Model Dialog Box in JMP for the GMAT Experiment Data

FIGURE JMP 13.4   Partial JMP ANOVA Output for the GMAT Experiment Data

Click **Preparation** in the **Select Columns** area and click **Add** in the **Construct Model Effects** area

Click **College** in the **Select Columns** area and click **Add** in the **Construct Model Effects** area

Click **Preparation** and **College** in the **Select Columns** area and click **Cross** in the **Construct Model Effects** area

Click **Run**

The **Fit Model** dialog box appears in Figure JMP 13.3.

A portion of the output appears in Figure JMP 13.4 and matches the output shown in Table 13.13.

Appendix 13.2 Analysis of Variance with Excel

Completely Randomized Design

In Section 13.2 we showed how analysis of variance could be used to test for the equality of k population means using data from a completely randomized design. To illustrate how Excel can be used to test for the equality of *k* population means for this type of experimental design, we show how to test whether the mean number of units produced per week is the same for each assembly method in the Chemitech experiment introduced in Section 13.1. The sample data are entered into cells A2:C6 as shown in Figure Excel 13.1. The following steps are used to obtain the output shown in cells A8:G22; the ANOVA portion of this output corresponds to the ANOVA table shown in Table 13.3.

DATA *file*

Chemitech

Step 1. Click the **Data** tab on the Ribbon
Step 2. In the **Analyze** group, click **Data Analysis**
Step 3. Choose **Anova: Single Factor** from the list of Analysis Tools
Click **OK**
Step 4. When the **Anova: Single Factor** dialog box appears:
Enter *A1:C6* in **Input Range:** box
Select **Columns**
Select the check box for **Labels in First Row**
Enter *.05* in the **Alpha:** box
Select **Output Range:** and enter *A8* in the box
Click **OK**

Randomized Block Design

In Section 13.4 we showed how analysis of variance could be used to test for the equality of *k* population means using data from a randomized block design. To illustrate how Excel can be used for this type of experimental design, we show how to test whether the mean stress levels for air traffic controllers are the same for three workstations. The stress level scores shown in Table 13.5 are entered into cells B2:D7 as shown in Figure Excel 13.2. Cells A2:A7 contain the number of each controller (1, 2, 3, 4, 5, 6). The following steps produce the Excel output

---

FIGURE Excel 13.1   Excel Solution for the Chemitech Experiment

	A1	▾	*fx*	Method A			
	A	B	C	D	E	F	G	H
1	**Method A**	**Method B**	**Method C**					
2	58	58	48					
3	64	69	57					
4	55	71	59					
5	66	64	47					
6	67	68	49					
7								
8	Anova: Single Factor							
9								
10	SUMMARY							
11	*Groups*	*Count*	*Sum*	*Average*	*Variance*			
12	Method A	5	310	62	27.5			
13	Method B	5	330	66	26.5			
14	Method C	5	260	52	31			
15								
16								
17	ANOVA							
18	*Source of Variation*	*SS*	*df*	*MS*	*F*	*P-value*	*F crit*	
19	Between Groups	520	2	260	9.1765	0.0038	3.8853	
20	Within Groups	340	12	28.3333				
21								
22	Total	860	14					
23								

shown in cells A9:G30. The ANOVA portion of this output corresponds to the ANOVA table shown in Table 13.8.

AirTraffic

Step 1. Click the **Data** tab on the Ribbon
Step 2. In the **Analyze** group, click **Data Analysis**
Step 3. Choose **Anova: Two-Factor Without Replication** from the list of Analysis Tools
Click **OK**
Step 4. When the **Anova: Two-Factor Without Replication** dialog box appears:
Enter *A1:D7* in **Input Range:** box
Select the check box for **Labels**
Enter *.05* in the **Alpha:** box
Select **Output Range:** and enter *A9* in the box
Click **OK**

Factorial Experiment

In Section 13.5 we showed how analysis of variance could be used to test for the equality of *k* population means using data from a factorial experiment. To illustrate how Excel can be used for this type of experimental design, we show how to analyze the data for the two-factor

---

FIGURE Excel 13.2   Excel Solution for the Air Traffic Controller Stress Test

	A	B	C	D	E	F	G	H
	A1			f_x	Controller			
1	**Controller**	**System A**	**System B**	**System C**				
2	1	15	15	18				
3	2	14	14	14				
4	3	10	11	15				
5	4	13	12	17				
6	5	16	13	16				
7	6	13	13	13				
8								
9	Anova: Two-Factor Without Replication							
10								
11	*SUMMARY*	*Count*	*Sum*	*Average*	*Variance*			
12	1	3	48	16	3			
13	2	3	42	14	0			
14	3	3	36	12	7			
15	4	3	42	14	7			
16	5	3	45	15	3			
17	6	3	39	13	0			
18								
19	System A	6	81	13.5	4.3			
20	System B	6	78	13	2			
21	System C	6	93	15.5	3.5			
22								
23								
24	ANOVA							
25	*Source of Variation*	*SS*	*df*	*MS*	*F*	*P-value*	*F crit*	
26	Rows	30	5	6	3.1579	0.0574	3.3258	
27	Columns	21	2	10.5	5.5263	0.0242	4.1028	
28	Error	19	10	1.9				
29								
30	Total	70	17					
31								

GMAT experiment introduced in that section. The GMAT scores shown in Table 13.10 are entered into cells B2:D7 as shown in Figure Excel 13.3. The following steps are used to obtain the output shown in cells A9:G44.

DATA *file*

GMATStudy

Step 1. Click the **Data** tab on the Ribbon
Step 2. In the **Analyze** group, click **Data Analysis**
Step 3. Choose **Anova: Two-Factor With Replication** from the list of Analysis Tools Click **OK**
Step 4. When the **Anova: Two-Factor With Replication** dialog box appears:
Enter *A1:D7* in **Input Range:** box
Enter *2* in **Rows per sample:** box
Enter *.05* in the **Alpha:** box
Select **Output Range:** and enter *A9* in the box
Click **OK**

FIGURE Excel 13.3   Excel Solution for the Two-Factor GMAT Experiment

A1 f_x

	A	B	C	D	E	F	G	H
1		Business	Engineering	Arts and Sciences				
2	3-hour review	500	540	480				
3		580	460	400				
4	1-day program	460	560	420				
5		540	620	480				
6	10-week course	560	600	480				
7		600	580	410				
8								
9	Anova: Two-Factor With Replication							
10								
11	SUMMARY	Business	Engineering	Arts and Sciences	Total			
12	*3-hour review*							
13	Count	2	2	2	6			
14	Sum	1080	1000	880	2960			
15	Average	540	500	440	493.3333			
16	Variance	3200	3200	3200	3946.667			
17								
18	*1-day program*							
19	Count	2	2	2	6			
20	Sum	1000	1180	900	3080			
21	Average	500	590	450	513.3333			
22	Variance	3200	1800	1800	5386.667			
23								
24	*10-week course*							
25	Count	2	2	2	6			
26	Sum	1160	1180	890	3230			
27	Average	580	590	445	538.3333			
28	Variance	800	200	2450	5936.667			
29								
30	*Total*							
31	Count	6	6	6				
32	Sum	3240	3360	2670				
33	Average	540	560	445				
34	Variance	2720	3200	1510				
35								
36								
37	ANOVA							
38	*Source of Variation*	*SS*	*df*	*MS*	*F*	*P-value*	*F crit*	
39	Sample	6100	2	3050	1.3829	0.2994	4.2565	
40	Columns	45300	2	22650	10.2695	0.0048	4.2565	
41	Interaction	11200	4	2800	1.2695	0.3503	3.6331	
42	Within	19850	9	2205.5556				
43								
44	Total	82450	17					
45								

Chapter 14

Simple Linear Regression

CONTENTS

STATISTICS IN PRACTICE

Alliance Data Systems*

DALLAS, TEXAS

Alliance Data Systems (ADS) provides transaction processing, credit services, and marketing services for clients in the rapidly growing customer relationship management (CRM) industry. ADS operates through three businesses: LoyaltyOne, Epsilon, and Private Label Services and Credit. The LoyaltyOne business provides customer loyalty services, such as customer analytics, creative services, and mobile solutions. The Epsilon business is focused on marketing programs that utilize transactional data and includes customer database technologies and predictive modeling. The Private Label Services and Credit business provides, among other services, credit card processing, billing/payment processing, and collections services for private label retailers. Formed in 1996 with its headquarters in Plano, Texas, ADS today has 20,000 full-time employees.

As one of its marketing services, ADS designs direct mail campaigns and promotions. With its database containing information on the spending habits of more than 100 million consumers, ADS can target those consumers most likely to benefit from a direct mail promotion. The Analytical Development Group uses regression analysis to build models that measure and predict the responsiveness of consumers to direct market campaigns. Some regression models predict the probability of purchase for individuals receiving a promotion, and others predict the amount spent by those consumers making a purchase.

For one particular campaign, a retail store chain wanted to attract new customers. To predict the effect of the campaign, ADS analysts selected a sample from the consumer database, sent the sampled individuals

Alliance Data Systems analysts discuss use of a regression model to predict sales for a direct marketing campaign.
Source: Courtesy of Alliance Data Systems

promotional materials, and then collected transaction data on the consumers' response. Sample data were collected on the amount of purchase made by the consumers responding to the campaign, as well as a variety of consumer-specific variables thought to be useful in predicting sales. The consumer-specific variable that contributed most to predicting the amount purchased was the total amount of credit purchases at related stores over the past 39 months. ADS analysts developed an estimated regression equation relating the amount of purchase to the amount spent at related stores:

$$\hat{y} = 26.7 + .00205x$$

where

$\hat{y}$ = amount of purchase

x = amount spent at related stores

---

*The authors are indebted to Philip Clemance, Director of Analytical Development at Alliance Data Systems, for providing the context for this Statistics in Practice

Using this equation, we could predict that someone spending $10,000 over the past 39 months at related stores would spend $47.20 when responding to the direct mail promotion. In this chapter, you will learn how to develop this type of estimated regression equation.

The final model developed by ADS analysts also included several other variables that increased the predictive power of the preceding equation. Some of these variables included the absence/presence of a bank credit card, estimated income, and the average amount spent per trip at a selected store. In the following chapter, we will learn how such additional variables can be incorporated into a multiple regression model.

Managerial decisions often are based on the relationship between two or more variables. For example, after considering the relationship between advertising expenditures and sales, a marketing manager might attempt to predict sales for a given level of advertising expenditures. In another case, a public utility might use the relationship between the daily high temperature and the demand for electricity to predict electricity usage on the basis of next month's anticipated daily high temperatures. Sometimes a manager will rely on intuition to judge how two variables are related. However, if data can be obtained, a statistical procedure called *regression analysis* can be used to develop an equation showing how the variables are related.

The statistical methods used in studying the relationship between two variables were first employed by Sir Francis Galton (1822–1911). Galton was interested in studying the relationship between a father's height and the son's height. Galton's disciple, Karl Pearson (1857–1936), analyzed the relationship between the father's height and the son's height for 1078 pairs of subjects.

In regression terminology, the variable being predicted is called the **dependent variable**. The variable or variables being used to predict the value of the dependent variable are called the **independent variables**. For example, in analyzing the effect of advertising expenditures on sales, a marketing manager's desire to predict sales would suggest making sales the dependent variable. Advertising expenditure would be the independent variable used to help predict sales. In statistical notation, y denotes the dependent variable and x denotes the independent variable.

In this chapter we consider the simplest type of regression analysis involving one independent variable and one dependent variable in which the relationship between the variables is approximated by a straight line. It is called **simple linear regression**. Regression analysis involving two or more independent variables is called multiple regression analysis; multiple regression and cases involving curvilinear relationships are covered in Chapters 15 and 16.

14.1 Simple Linear Regression Model

Armand's Pizza Parlors is a chain of Italian-food restaurants located in a five-state area. Armand's most successful locations are near college campuses. The managers believe that quarterly sales for these restaurants (denoted by y) are related positively to the size of the student population (denoted by x); that is, restaurants near campuses with a large student population tend to generate more sales than those located near campuses with a small student population. Using regression analysis, we can develop an equation showing how the dependent variable y is related to the independent variable x.

Regression Model and Regression Equation

In the Armand's Pizza Parlors example, the population consists of all the Armand's restaurants. For every restaurant in the population, there is a value of x (student population) and a corresponding value of y (quarterly sales). The equation that describes how y is related to x and an error term is called the **regression model**. The regression model used in simple linear regression follows.

SIMPLE LINEAR REGRESSION MODEL

$$y = \beta_0 + \beta_1 x + \epsilon \tag{14.1}$$

β_0 and β_1 are referred to as the parameters of the model, and ϵ (the Greek letter epsilon) is a random variable referred to as the error term. The error term accounts for the variability in y that cannot be explained by the linear relationship between x and y.

The population of all Armand's restaurants can also be viewed as a collection of subpopulations, one for each distinct value of x. For example, one subpopulation consists of all Armand's restaurants located near college campuses with 8000 students; another subpopulation consists of all Armand's restaurants located near college campuses with 9000 students; and so on. Each subpopulation has a corresponding distribution of y values. Thus, a distribution of y values is associated with restaurants located near campuses with 8000 students; a distribution of y values is associated with restaurants located near campuses with 9000 students; and so on. Each distribution of y values has its own mean or expected value. The equation that describes how the expected value of y, denoted $E(y)$, is related to x is called the **regression equation**. The regression equation for simple linear regression follows.

SIMPLE LINEAR REGRESSION EQUATION

$$E(y) = \beta_0 + \beta_1 x \tag{14.2}$$

The graph of the simple linear regression equation is a straight line; β_0 is the y-intercept of the regression line, β_1 is the slope, and $E(y)$ is the mean or expected value of y for a given value of x.

Examples of possible regression lines are shown in Figure 14.1. The regression line in Panel A shows that the mean value of y is related positively to x, with larger values of $E(y)$ associated with larger values of x. The regression line in Panel B shows the mean value of y is related negatively to x, with smaller values of $E(y)$ associated with larger values of x. The regression line in Panel C shows the case in which the mean value of y is not related to x; that is, the mean value of y is the same for every value of x.

Estimated Regression Equation

If the values of the population parameters β_0 and β_1 were known, we could use equation (14.2) to compute the mean value of y for a given value of x. In practice, the parameter values are not known and must be estimated using sample data. Sample statistics (denoted b_0 and b_1) are computed as estimates of the population parameters β_0 and β_1. Substituting the values of the sample statistics b_0 and b_1 for β_0 and β_1 in the regression equation, we obtain the **estimated regression equation**. The estimated regression equation for simple linear regression follows.

ESTIMATED SIMPLE LINEAR REGRESSION EQUATION

$$\hat{y} = b_0 + b_1 x \tag{14.3}$$

FIGURE 14.1   Possible Regression Lines in Simple Linear Regression

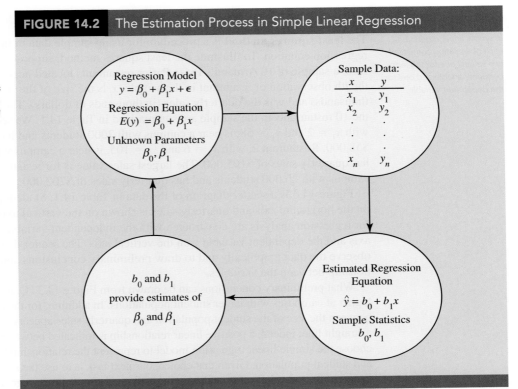

FIGURE 14.2 The Estimation Process in Simple Linear Regression

The estimation of β_0 and β_1 is a statistical process much like the estimation of μ discussed in Chapter 7. β_0 and β_1 are the unknown parameters of interest, and b_0 and b_1 are the sample statistics used to estimate the parameters.

Figure 14.2 provides a summary of the estimation process for simple linear regression.

The graph of the estimated simple linear regression equation is called the *estimated regression line*; b_0 is the y-intercept and b_1 is the slope. In the next section, we show how the least squares method can be used to compute the values of b_0 and b_1 in the estimated regression equation.

In general, $\hat{y}$ is the point estimator of $E(y)$, the mean value of y for a given value of x. Thus, to estimate the mean or expected value of quarterly sales for all restaurants located near campuses with 10,000 students, Armand's would substitute the value of 10,000 for x in equation (14.3). In some cases, however, Armand's may be more interested in predicting sales for one particular restaurant. For example, suppose Armand's would like to predict quarterly sales for the restaurant they are considering building near Talbot College, a school with 10,000 students. As it turns out, the best predictor of y for a given value of x is also provided by $\hat{y}$. Thus, to predict quarterly sales for the restaurant located near Talbot College, Armand's would also substitute the value of 10,000 for x in equation (14.3).

The value of $\hat{y}$ provides both a point estimate of $E(y)$ for a given value of x and a prediction of an individual value of y for a given value of x.

NOTES + COMMENTS

1. Regression analysis cannot be interpreted as a procedure for establishing a cause-and-effect relationship between variables. It can only indicate how or to what extent variables are associated with each other. Any conclusions about cause and effect must be based upon the judgment of those individuals most knowledgeable about the application.

2. The regression equation in simple linear regression is $E(y) = \beta_0 + \beta_1 x$. More advanced texts in regression analysis often write the regression equation as $E(y|x) = \beta_0 + \beta_1 x$ to emphasize that the regression equation provides the mean value of y for a given value of x.

14.2 Least Squares Method

In simple linear regression, each observation consists of two values: one for the independent variable and one for the dependent variable.

The **least squares method** is a procedure for using sample data to find the estimated regression equation. To illustrate the least squares method, suppose data were collected from a sample of 10 Armand's Pizza Parlor restaurants located near college campuses. For the ith observation or restaurant in the sample, x_i is the size of the student population (in thousands) and y_i is the quarterly sales (in thousands of dollars). The values of x_i and y_i for the 10 restaurants in the sample are summarized in Table 14.1. We see that restaurant 1, with $x_1 = 2$ and $y_1 = 58$, is near a campus with 2000 students and has quarterly sales of $58,000. Restaurant 2, with $x_2 = 6$ and $y_2 = 105$, is near a campus with 6000 students and has quarterly sales of $105,000. The largest sales value is for restaurant 10, which is near a campus with 26,000 students and has quarterly sales of $202,000.

Figure 14.3 is a scatter diagram of the data in Table 14.1. Student population is shown on the horizontal axis and quarterly sales is shown on the vertical axis. **Scatter diagrams** for regression analysis are constructed with the independent variable x on the horizontal axis and the dependent variable y on the vertical axis. The scatter diagram enables us to observe the data graphically and to draw preliminary conclusions about the possible relationship between the variables.

What preliminary conclusions can be drawn from Figure 14.3? Quarterly sales appear to be higher at campuses with larger student populations. In addition, for these data the relationship between the size of the student population and quarterly sales appears to be approximated by a straight line; indeed, a positive linear relationship is indicated between x and y. We therefore choose the simple linear regression model to represent the relationship between quarterly sales and student population. Given that choice, our next task is to use the sample data in Table 14.1 to determine the values of b_0 and b_1 in the estimated simple linear regression equation. For the ith restaurant, the estimated regression equation provides

$$\hat{y}_i = b_0 + b_1 x_i \tag{14.4}$$

where

$\hat{y}_i$ = predicted value of quarterly sales ($1000s) for the ith restaurant
b_0 = the y-intercept of the estimated regression line
b_1 = the slope of the estimated regression line
x_i = size of the student population (1000s) for the ith restaurant

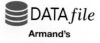

DATA *file*

Armand's

TABLE 14.1	Student Population and Quarterly Sales Data for 10 Armand's Pizza Parlors	
Restaurant i	Student Population (1000s) x_i	Quarterly Sales ($1000s) y_i
1	2	58
2	6	105
3	8	88
4	8	118
5	12	117
6	16	137
7	20	157
8	20	169
9	22	149
10	26	202

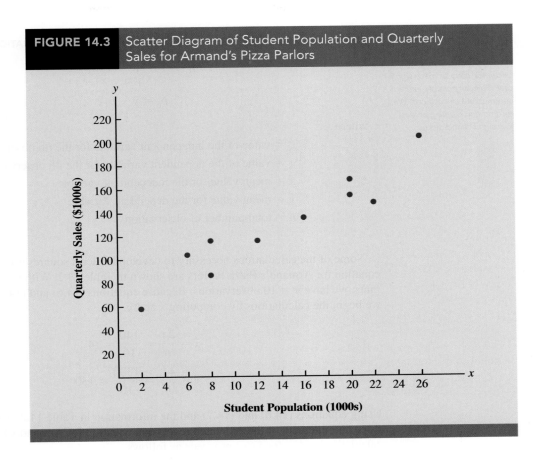

FIGURE 14.3 Scatter Diagram of Student Population and Quarterly Sales for Armand's Pizza Parlors

With y_i denoting the observed (actual) sales for restaurant i and $\hat{y}_i$ in equation (14.4) representing the predicted value of sales for restaurant i, every restaurant in the sample will have an observed value of sales y_i and a predicted value of sales $\hat{y}_i$. For the estimated regression line to provide a good fit to the data, we want the differences between the observed sales values and the predicted sales values to be small.

The least squares method uses the sample data to provide the values of b_0 and b_1 that minimize the *sum of the squares of the deviations* between the observed values of the dependent variable y_i and the predicted values of the dependent variable $\hat{y}_i$. The criterion for the least squares method is given by expression (14.5).

LEAST SQUARES CRITERION

$$\min \Sigma(y_i - \hat{y}_i)^2 \tag{14.5}$$

where

y_i = observed value of the dependent variable for the ith observation
$\hat{y}_i$ = predicted value of the dependent variable for the ith observation

Carl Friedrich Gauss (1777–1855) proposed the least squares method.

Differential calculus can be used to show (see Appendix 14.1) that the values of b_0 and b_1 that minimize expression (14.5) can be found by using equations (14.6) and (14.7).

In computing b_1 with a calculator, carry as many significant digits as possible in the intermediate calculations. We recommend carrying at least four significant digits.

SLOPE AND y-INTERCEPT FOR THE ESTIMATED REGRESSION EQUATION[1]

$$b_1 = \frac{\Sigma(x_i - \bar{x})(y_i - \bar{y})}{\Sigma(x_i - \bar{x})^2} \tag{14.6}$$

$$b_0 = \bar{y} - b_1\bar{x} \tag{14.7}$$

where

x_i = value of the independent variable for the ith observation

y_i = value of the dependent variable for the ith observation

$\bar{x}$ = mean value for the independent variable

$\bar{y}$ = mean value for the dependent variable

n = total number of observations

Some of the calculations necessary to develop the least squares estimated regression equation for Armand's Pizza Parlors are shown in Table 14.2. With the sample of 10 restaurants, we have $n = 10$ observations. Because equations (14.6) and (14.7) require $\bar{x}$ and $\bar{y}$ we begin the calculations by computing $\bar{x}$ and $\bar{y}$.

$$\bar{x} = \frac{\Sigma x_i}{n} = \frac{140}{10} = 14$$

$$\bar{y} = \frac{\Sigma y_i}{n} = \frac{1300}{10} = 130$$

Using equations (14.6) and (14.7) and the information in Table 14.2, we can compute the slope and intercept of the estimated regression equation for Armand's Pizza Parlors. The calculation of the slope (b_1) proceeds as follows.

TABLE 14.2 Calculations for the Least Squares Estimated Regression Equation for Armand's Pizza Parlors

Restaurant i	x_i	y_i	$x_i - \bar{x}$	$y_i - \bar{y}$	$(x_i - \bar{x})(y_i - \bar{y})$	$(x_i - \bar{x})^2$
1	2	58	−12	−72	864	144
2	6	105	−8	−25	200	64
3	8	88	−6	−42	252	36
4	8	118	−6	−12	72	36
5	12	117	−2	−13	26	4
6	16	137	2	7	14	4
7	20	157	6	27	162	36
8	20	169	6	39	234	36
9	22	149	8	19	152	64
10	26	202	12	72	864	144
Totals	140	1300			2840	568
	Σx_i	Σy_i			$\Sigma(x_i - \bar{x})(y_i - \bar{y})$	$\Sigma(x_i - \bar{x})^2$

---

[1]An alternate formula for b_1 is

$$b_1 = \frac{\Sigma x_i y_i - (\Sigma x_i \Sigma y_i)/n}{\Sigma x_i^2 - (\Sigma x_i)^2/n}$$

This form of equation (14.6) is often recommended when using a calculator to compute b_1.

$$b_1 = \frac{\Sigma(x_i - \bar{x})(y_i - \bar{y})}{\Sigma(x_i - \bar{x})^2}$$

$$= \frac{2840}{568}$$

$$= 5$$

The calculation of the y intercept (b_0) follows.

$$b_0 = \bar{y} - b_1\bar{x}$$
$$= 130 - 5(14)$$
$$= 60$$

Thus, the estimated regression equation is

$$\hat{y} = 60 + 5x$$

One should be cautious about making predictions based on regression for values of the independent variable outside the range of values in the data used to estimate the regression equation. We cannot be sure that the relationship is valid outside the experimental region of the data.

Figure 14.4 shows the graph of this equation on the scatter diagram.

The slope of the estimated regression equation ($b_1 = 5$) is positive, implying that as student population increases, sales increase. In fact, we can conclude (based on sales measured in $1000s and student population in 1000s) that an increase in the student population of 1000 is associated with an increase of $5000 in expected sales; that is, quarterly sales are expected to increase by $5 per student.

If we believe the least squares estimated regression equation adequately describes the relationship between x and y, it would seem reasonable to use the estimated regression equation to predict the value of y for a given value of x. For example, if we wanted to

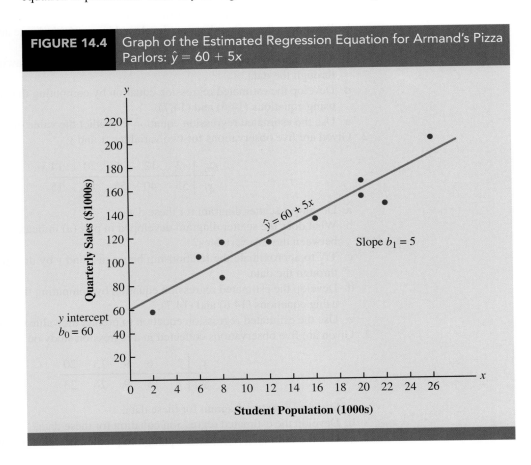

FIGURE 14.4   Graph of the Estimated Regression Equation for Armand's Pizza Parlors: $\hat{y} = 60 + 5x$

predict quarterly sales for a restaurant to be located near a campus with 16,000 students, we would compute

$$\hat{y} = 60 + 5(16) = 140$$

Hence, we would predict quarterly sales of $140,000 for this restaurant. In the following sections we will discuss methods for assessing the appropriateness of using the estimated regression equation for estimation and prediction.

NOTES + COMMENTS

The least squares method provides an estimated regression equation that minimizes the sum of squared deviations between the observed values of the dependent variable y_i and the predicted values of the dependent variable $\hat{y}_i$. This least squares criterion is used to choose the equation that provides the best fit. If some other criterion were used, such as minimizing the sum of the absolute deviations between y_i and $\hat{y}_i$, a different equation would be obtained. In practice, the least squares method is the most widely used.

EXERCISES

Methods

1. Given are five observations for two variables, x and y.

x_i	1	2	3	4	5
y_i	3	7	5	11	14

   a. Develop a scatter diagram for these data.
   b. What does the scatter diagram developed in part (a) indicate about the relationship between the two variables?
   c. Try to approximate the relationship between x and y by drawing a straight line through the data.
   d. Develop the estimated regression equation by computing the values of b_0 and b_1 using equations (14.6) and (14.7).
   e. Use the estimated regression equation to predict the value of y when $x = 4$.

2. Given are five observations for two variables, x and y.

x_i	3	12	6	20	14
y_i	55	40	55	10	15

   a. Develop a scatter diagram for these data.
   b. What does the scatter diagram developed in part (a) indicate about the relationship between the two variables?
   c. Try to approximate the relationship between x and y by drawing a straight line through the data.
   d. Develop the estimated regression equation by computing the values of b_0 and b_1 using equations (14.6) and (14.7).
   e. Use the estimated regression equation to predict the value of y when $x = 10$.

3. Given are five observations collected in a regression study on two variables.

x_i	2	6	9	13	20
y_i	7	18	9	26	23

   a. Develop a scatter diagram for these data.
   b. Develop the estimated regression equation for these data.
   c. Use the estimated regression equation to predict the value of y when $x = 6$.

Applications

4. **Retail and Trade: Female Managers.** The following data give the percentage of women working in five companies in the retail and trade industry. The percentage of management jobs held by women in each company is also shown.

% Working	67	45	73	54	61
% Management	49	21	65	47	33

   a. Develop a scatter diagram for these data with the percentage of women working in the company as the independent variable.
   b. What does the scatter diagram developed in part (a) indicate about the relationship between the two variables?
   c. Try to approximate the relationship between the percentage of women working in the company and the percentage of management jobs held by women in that company.
   d. Develop the estimated regression equation by computing the values of b_0 and b_1.
   e. Predict the percentage of management jobs held by women in a company that has 60% women employees.

5. **Production Line Speed and Quality Control.** Brawdy Plastics, Inc., produces plastic seat belt retainers for General Motors at the Brawdy Plastics plant in Buffalo, New York. After final assembly and painting, the parts are placed on a conveyor belt that moves the parts past a final inspection station. How fast the parts move past the final inspection station depends upon the line speed of the conveyor belt (feet per minute). Although faster line speeds are desirable, management is concerned that increasing the line speed too much may not provide enough time for inspectors to identify which parts are actually defective. To test this theory, Brawdy Plastics conducted an experiment in which the same batch of parts, with a known number of defective parts, was inspected using a variety of line speeds. The following data were collected.

Line Speed	Number of Defective Parts Found
20	23
20	21
30	19
30	16
40	15
40	17
50	14
50	11

   a. Develop a scatter diagram with the line speed as the independent variable.
   b. What does the scatter diagram developed in part (a) indicate about the relationship between the two variables?
   c. Use the least squares method to develop the estimated regression equation.
   d. Predict the number of defective parts found for a line speed of 25 feet per minute.

6. **Passing and Winning in the NFL.** The National Football League (NFL) records a variety of performance data for individuals and teams. To investigate the importance of passing on the percentage of games won by a team, the following data show the average number of passing yards per attempt (Yds/Att) and the percentage of games won (WinPct) in a season for a random sample of 10 NFL teams.

DATA *file*

NFLPassing

Team	Yds/Att	WinPct
Arizona Cardinals	6.5	50
Atlanta Falcons	7.1	63
Carolina Panthers	7.4	38
Chicago Bears	6.4	50
Dallas Cowboys	7.4	50
New England Patriots	8.3	81
Philadelphia Eagles	7.4	50
Seattle Seahawks	6.1	44
St. Louis Rams	5.2	13
Tampa Bay Buccaneers	6.2	25

a. Develop a scatter diagram with the number of passing yards per attempt on the horizontal axis and the percentage of games won on the vertical axis.

b. What does the scatter diagram developed in part (a) indicate about the relationship between the two variables?

c. Develop the estimated regression equation that could be used to predict the percentage of games won given the average number of passing yards per attempt.

d. Provide an interpretation for the slope of the estimated regression equation.

e. For the 2011 season, the average number of passing yards per attempt for the Kansas City Chiefs was 6.2. Use the estimated regression equation developed in part (c) to predict the percentage of games won by the Kansas City Chiefs. (*Note:* For the 2011 season the Kansas City Chiefs record was 7 wins and 9 losses.) Compare your prediction to the actual percentage of games won by the Kansas City Chiefs.

7. **Sales Experience and Performance.** A sales manager collected the following data on annual sales for new customer accounts and the number of years of experience for a sample of 10 salespersons.

DATA *file*

Sales

Salesperson	Years of Experience	Annual Sales ($1000s)
1	1	80
2	3	97
3	4	92
4	4	102
5	6	103
6	8	111
7	10	119
8	10	123
9	11	117
10	13	136

a. Develop a scatter diagram for these data with years of experience as the independent variable.

b. Develop an estimated regression equation that can be used to predict annual sales given the years of experience.

c. Use the estimated regression equation to predict annual sales for a salesperson with 9 years of experience.

8. **Broker Satisfaction.** The American Association of Individual Investors (AAII) On-Line Discount Broker Survey polls members on their experiences with discount brokers. As part of the survey, members were asked to rate the quality of the speed of execution with their broker as well as provide an overall satisfaction rating for electronic trades. Possible responses (scores) were no opinion (0), unsatisfied (1), somewhat satisfied (2), satisfied (3), and very satisfied (4). For each broker summary scores were computed by calculating

a weighted average of the scores provided by each respondent. A portion of the survey results follow (*AAII* website).

BrokerRatings

Brokerage	Speed	Satisfaction
Scottrade, Inc.	3.4	3.5
Charles Schwab	3.3	3.4
Fidelity Brokerage Services	3.4	3.9
TD Ameritrade	3.6	3.7
E*Trade Financial	3.2	2.9
Vanguard Brokerage Services	3.8	2.8
USAA Brokerage Services	3.8	3.6
Thinkorswim	2.6	2.6
Wells Fargo Investments	2.7	2.3
Interactive Brokers	4.0	4.0
Zecco.com	2.5	2.5

Source: AAII website, (https://www.aaii.com/sentimentsurvey)

a. Develop a scatter diagram for these data with the speed of execution as the independent variable.
b. What does the scatter diagram developed in part (a) indicate about the relationship between the two variables?
c. Develop the least squares estimated regression equation.
d. Provide an interpretation for the slope of the estimated regression equation.
e. Suppose Zecco.com developed new software to increase their speed of execution rating. If the new software is able to increase their speed of execution rating from the current value of 2.5 to the average speed of execution rating for the other 10 brokerage firms that were surveyed, what value would you predict for the overall satisfaction rating?

9. **Estimating Landscaping Expenditures.** David's Landscaping has collected data on home values (in thousands of $) and expenditures (in thousands of $) on landscaping with the hope of developing a predictive model to help marketing to potential new clients. Data for 14 households may be found in the file *Landscape*.

a. Develop a scatter diagram with home value as the independent variable.
b. What does the scatter plot developed in part (a) indicate about the relationship between the two variables?
c. Use the least squares method to develop the estimated regression equation.
d. For every additional $1000 in home value, estimate how much additional will be spent on landscaping.
e. Use the equation estimated in part (c) to predict the landscaping expenditures for a home valued at $575,000.

10. **Age and the Price of Wine.** For a particular red wine, the following data show the auction price for a 750-milliliter bottle and the age of the wine in June of 2016 (*WineX* website).

WinePrices

Age (years)	Price ($)
36	256
20	142
29	212
33	255
41	331
27	173
30	209
45	297
34	237
22	182

Source: WineX website, June 2016 (https://www.winex.com/default.php)

a. Develop a scatter diagram for these data with age as the independent variable.
b. What does the scatter diagram developed in part (a) indicate about the relationship between age and price?
c. Develop the least squares estimated regression equation.
d. Provide an interpretation for the slope of the estimated equation.

11. **Laptop Ratings.** To help consumers in purchasing a laptop computer, *Consumer Reports* calculates an overall test score for each computer tested based upon rating factors such as ergonomics, portability, performance, display, and battery life. Higher overall scores indicate better test results. The following data show the average retail price and the overall score for ten 13-inch models (*Consumer Reports* website).

DATA*file*
Computer

Brand & Model	Price ($)	Overall Score
Samsung Ultrabook NP900X3C-A01US	1250	83
Apple MacBook Air MC965LL/A	1300	83
Apple MacBook Air MD231LL/A	1200	82
HP ENVY 13-2050nr Spectre XT	950	79
Sony VAIO SVS13112FXB	800	77
Acer Aspire S5-391-9880 Ultrabook	1200	74
Apple MacBook Pro MD101LL/A	1200	74
Apple MacBook Pro MD313LL/A	1000	73
Dell Inspiron I13Z-6591SLV	700	67
Samsung NP535U3C-A01US	600	63

Source: Consumer Reports website, (https://web.consumerreports.org/laptops/b/v2/index.html?EXTKEY=SG72E00&sitelink=550&gclid=EAIaIQobChMI0-Kjs6D43QIVBySGCh1-YwsnEAAYASABEgKx0_D_BwE&gclsrc=aw.ds&dclid=CLz57rSg-N0CFYQIDAod2AkEag)

a. Develop a scatter diagram with price as the independent variable.
b. What does the scatter diagram developed in part (a) indicate about the relationship between the two variables?
c. Use the least squares method to develop the estimated regression equation.
d. Provide an interpretation of the slope of the estimated regression equation.
e. Another laptop that *Consumer Reports* tested is the Acer Aspire S3-951-6646 Ultrabook; the price for this laptop was $700. Predict the overall score for this laptop using the estimated regression equation developed in part (c).

12. **Stock Beta.** In June of 2016, *Yahoo Finance* reported the beta value for Coca-Cola was .82 (*Yahoo Finance* website). Betas for individual stocks are determined by simple linear regression. The dependent variable is the total return for the stock, and the independent variable is the total return for the stock market, such as the return of the S&P 500. The slope of this regression equation is referred to as the stock's *beta*. Many financial analysts prefer to measure the risk of a stock by computing the stock's beta value.

For more discussion and prac-tice estimating stock betas, see Case 1 at the end of this chapter.

The data contained in the DATAfile named *CocaCola* show the monthly percentage returns for the S&P 500 and the Coca-Cola Company for August 2015 to May 2016.

DATA*file*
CocaCola

Month	S&P 500 % Return	Coca-Cola % Return
August	−3	3
September	8	6
October	0	1
November	−2	1
December	−5	0
January	0	0
February	7	8
March	0	−3
April	2	0
May	−5	−1

Source: Yahoo Finance website, June 30, 2016. (https://finance.yahoo.com/)

a. Develop a scatter diagram with the S&P % Return as the independent variable.
b. What does the scatter diagram developed in part (a) indicate about the relationship between the returns of the S&P 500 and those of the Coca-Cola Company?
c. Develop the least squares estimated regression equation.
d. Provide an interpretation for the slope of the estimated equation (that is, the beta).
e. Is your beta estimate close to .82? If not, why might your estimate be different?

13. **Auditing Itemized Tax Deductions.** To the Internal Revenue Service, the reasonableness of total itemized deductions depends on the taxpayer's adjusted gross income. Large deductions, which include charity and medical deductions, are more reasonable for taxpayers with large adjusted gross incomes. If a taxpayer claims larger than average itemized deductions for a given level of income, the chances of an IRS audit are increased. Data (in thousands of dollars) on adjusted gross income and the average or reasonable amount of itemized deductions follow.

Adjusted Gross Income ($1000s)	Reasonable Amount of Itemized Deductions ($1000s)
22	9.6
27	9.6
32	10.1
48	11.1
65	13.5
85	17.7
120	25.5

a. Develop a scatter diagram for these data with adjusted gross income as the independent variable.
b. Use the least squares method to develop the estimated regression equation.
c. Predict the reasonable level of total itemized deductions for a taxpayer with an adjusted gross income of $52,500. If this taxpayer claimed itemized deductions of $20,400, would the IRS agent's request for an audit appear justified? Explain.

14. **Distance and Absenteeism.** A large city hospital conducted a study to investigate the relationship between the number of unauthorized days that employees are absent per year and the distance (miles) between home and work for the employees. A sample of 10 employees was selected and the following data were collected.

Distance to Work (miles)	Number of Days Absent
1	8
3	5
4	8
6	7
8	6
10	3
12	5
14	2
14	4
18	2

a. Develop a scatter diagram for these data. Does a linear relationship appear reasonable? Explain.
b. Develop the least squares estimated regression equation that relates the distance to work to the number of days absent.
c. Predict the number of days absent for an employee who lives 5 miles from the hospital.

14.3 Coefficient of Determination

For the Armand's Pizza Parlors example, we developed the estimated regression equation $\hat{y} = 60 + 5x$ to approximate the linear relationship between the size of the student population x and quarterly sales y. A question now is: How well does the estimated regression equation fit the data? In this section, we show that the **coefficient of determination** provides a measure of the goodness of fit for the estimated regression equation.

For the ith observation, the difference between the observed value of the dependent variable, y_i, and the predicted value of the dependent variable, $\hat{y}_i$, is called the ith **residual**. The ith residual represents the error in using $\hat{y}_i$ to estimate y_i. Thus, for the ith observation, the residual is $y_i - \hat{y}_i$. The sum of squares of these residuals or errors is the quantity that is minimized by the least squares method. This quantity, also known as the *sum of squares due to error*, is denoted by SSE.

SUM OF SQUARES DUE TO ERROR

$$\text{SSE} = \Sigma(y_i - \hat{y}_i)^2 \tag{14.8}$$

The value of SSE is a measure of the error in using the estimated regression equation to predict the values of the dependent variable in the sample.

In Table 14.3 we show the calculations required to compute the sum of squares due to error for the Armand's Pizza Parlors example. For instance, for restaurant 1 the values of the independent and dependent variables are $x_1 = 2$ and $y_1 = 58$. Using the estimated regression equation, we find that the predicted value of quarterly sales for restaurant 1 is $\hat{y}_1 = 60 + 5(2) = 70$. Thus, the error in using $\hat{y}_1$ to predict y_1 for restaurant 1 is $y_1 - \hat{y}_1 = 58 - 70 = -12$. The squared error, $(-12)^2 = 144$, is shown in the last column of Table 14.3. After computing and squaring the residuals for each restaurant in the sample, we sum them to obtain SSE = 1530. Thus, SSE = 1530 measures the error in using the estimated regression equation $\hat{y} = 60 + 5x$ to predict sales.

Now suppose we are asked to develop an estimate of quarterly sales without knowledge of the size of the student population. Without knowledge of any related variables, we would use the sample mean as an estimate of quarterly sales at any given restaurant.

TABLE 14.3 Calculation of SSE for Armand's Pizza Parlors

Restaurant i	x_i = Student Population (1000s)	y_i = Quarterly Sales ($1000s)	Predicted Sales $\hat{y}_i = 60 + 5x_i$	Error $y_i - \hat{y}_i$	Squared Error $(y_i - \hat{y}_i)^2$
1	2	58	70	−12	144
2	6	105	90	15	225
3	8	88	100	−12	144
4	8	118	100	18	324
5	12	117	120	−3	9
6	16	137	140	−3	9
7	20	157	160	−3	9
8	20	169	160	9	81
9	22	149	170	−21	441
10	26	202	190	12	144
				SSE =	1530

TABLE 14.4	Computation of the Total Sum of Squares for Armand's Pizza Parlors

Restaurant i	x_i = Student Population (1000s)	y_i = Quarterly Sales ($1000s)	Deviation $y_i - \bar{y}$	Squared Deviation $(y_i - \bar{y})^2$
1	2	58	−72	5184
2	6	105	−25	625
3	8	88	−42	1764
4	8	118	−12	144
5	12	117	−13	169
6	16	137	7	49
7	20	157	27	729
8	20	169	39	1521
9	22	149	19	361
10	26	202	72	5184
				SST = 15,730

Table 14.2 showed that for the sales data, $\Sigma y_i = 1300$. Hence, the mean value of quarterly sales for the sample of 10 Armand's restaurants is $\bar{y} = \Sigma y_i / n = 1300/10 = 130$. In Table 14.4 we show the sum of squared deviations obtained by using the sample mean $\bar{y} = 130$ to predict the value of quarterly sales for each restaurant in the sample. For the ith restaurant in the sample, the difference $y_i - \bar{y}$ provides a measure of the error involved in using $\bar{y}$ to predict sales. The corresponding sum of squares, called the *total sum of squares*, is denoted SST.

TOTAL SUM OF SQUARES

$$\text{SST} = \Sigma(y_i - \bar{y})^2 \tag{14.9}$$

The sum at the bottom of the last column in Table 14.4 is the total sum of squares for Armand's Pizza Parlors; it is SST = 15,730.

In Figure 14.5 we show the estimated regression line $\hat{y} = 60 + 5x$ and the line corresponding to $\bar{y} = 130$. Note that the points cluster more closely around the estimated regression line than they do about the line $\bar{y} = 130$. For example, for the 10th restaurant in the sample we see that the error is much larger when $\bar{y} = 130$ is used to predict y_{10} than when $\hat{y}_{10} = 60 + 5(26) = 190$ is used. We can think of SST as a measure of how well the observations cluster about the $\bar{y}$ line and SSE as a measure of how well the observations cluster about the $\hat{y}$ line.

With SST = 15,730 and SSE = 1530, the estimated regression line provides a much better fit to the data than the line y = ȳ.

To measure how much the $\hat{y}$ values on the estimated regression line deviate from $\bar{y}$, another sum of squares is computed. This sum of squares, called the *sum of squares due to regression*, is denoted SSR.

SUM OF SQUARES DUE TO REGRESSION

$$\text{SSR} = \Sigma(\hat{y}_i - \bar{y})^2 \tag{14.10}$$

From the preceding discussion, we should expect that SST, SSR, and SSE are related. Indeed, the relationship among these three sums of squares provides one of the most important results in statistics.

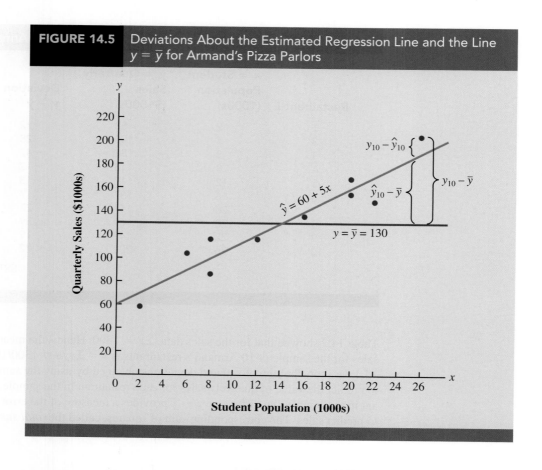

FIGURE 14.5 Deviations About the Estimated Regression Line and the Line $y = \bar{y}$ for Armand's Pizza Parlors

SSR can be thought of as the explained portion of SST, and SSE can be thought of as the unexplained portion of SST.

RELATIONSHIP AMONG SST, SSR, AND SSE

$$SST = SSR + SSE \qquad \qquad (14.11)$$

where

$$SST = \text{total sum of squares}$$
$$SSR = \text{sum of squares due to regression}$$
$$SSE = \text{sum of squares due to error}$$

Equation (14.11) shows that the total sum of squares can be partitioned into two components, the sum of squares due to regression and the sum of squares due to error. Hence, if the values of any two of these sum of squares are known, the third sum of squares can be computed easily. For instance, in the Armand's Pizza Parlors example, we already know that $SSE = 1530$ and $SST = 15{,}730$; therefore, solving for SSR in equation (14.11), we find that the sum of squares due to regression is

$$SSR = SST - SSE = 15{,}730 - 1530 = 14{,}200$$

Now let us see how the three sums of squares, SST, SSR, and SSE, can be used to provide a measure of the goodness of fit for the estimated regression equation. The estimated regression equation would provide a perfect fit if every value of the dependent variable y_i happened to lie on the estimated regression line. In this case, $y_i - \hat{y}_i$ would be zero for each observation, resulting in $SSE = 0$. Because $SST = SSR + SSE$, we see that for a perfect fit SSR must equal SST, and the ratio (SSR/SST) must equal one. Poorer fits will result in larger values for SSE. Solving for SSE in equation (14.11), we see that SSE = SST − SSR. Hence, the largest value for SSE (and hence the poorest fit) occurs when SSR = 0 and SSE = SST.

The ratio SSR/SST, which will take values between zero and one, is used to evaluate the goodness of fit for the estimated regression equation. This ratio is called the *coefficient of determination* and is denoted by r^2.

COEFFICIENT OF DETERMINATION

$$r^2 = \frac{SSR}{SST}$$

(14.12)

For the Armand's Pizza Parlors example, the value of the coefficient of determination is

$$r^2 = \frac{SSR}{SST} = \frac{14,200}{15,730} = .9027$$

When we express the coefficient of determination as a percentage, r^2 can be interpreted as the percentage of the total sum of squares that can be explained by using the estimated regression equation. For Armand's Pizza Parlors, we can conclude that 90.27% of the total sum of squares can be explained by using the estimated regression equation $\hat{y} = 60 + 5x$ to predict quarterly sales. In other words, 90.27% of the variability in sales can be explained by the linear relationship between the size of the student population and sales. We should be pleased to find such a good fit for the estimated regression equation.

Correlation Coefficient

In Chapter 3 we introduced the **correlation coefficient** as a descriptive measure of the strength of linear association between two variables, x and y. Values of the correlation coefficient are always between −1 and +1. A value of +1 indicates that the two variables x and y are perfectly related in a positive linear sense. That is, all data points are on a straight line that has a positive slope. A value of −1 indicates that x and y are perfectly related in a negative linear sense, with all data points on a straight line that has a negative slope. Values of the correlation coefficient close to zero indicate that x and y are not linearly related.

In Section 3.5 we presented the equation for computing the sample correlation coefficient. If a regression analysis has already been performed and the coefficient of determination r^2 computed, the sample correlation coefficient can be computed as follows:

SAMPLE CORRELATION COEFFICIENT

$$r_{xy} = (\text{sign of } b_1)\sqrt{\text{Coefficient of determination}}$$
$$= (\text{sign of } b_1)\sqrt{r^2}$$

(14.13)

where

$$b_1 = \text{the slope of the estimated regression equation } \hat{y} = b_0 + b_1 x$$

The sign for the sample correlation coefficient is positive if the estimated regression equation has a positive slope ($b_1 > 0$) and negative if the estimated regression equation has a negative slope ($b_1 < 0$).

For the Armand's Pizza Parlor example, the value of the coefficient of determination corresponding to the estimated regression equation $\hat{y} = 60 + 5x$ is .9027. Because the slope of the estimated regression equation is positive, equation (14.13) shows that the sample correlation coefficient is $+\sqrt{.9027} = +.9501$. With a sample correlation coefficient of $r_{xy} = +.9501$, we would conclude that a strong positive linear association exists between x and y.

In the case of a linear relationship between two variables, both the coefficient of determination and the sample correlation coefficient provide measures of the strength of the relationship. The coefficient of determination provides a measure between zero and one, whereas the sample correlation coefficient provides a measure between -1 and $+1$. Although the sample correlation coefficient is restricted to a linear relationship between two variables, the coefficient of determination can be used for nonlinear relationships and for relationships that have two or more independent variables. Thus, the coefficient of determination provides a wider range of applicability.

NOTES + COMMENTS

1. In developing the least squares estimated regression equation and computing the coefficient of determination, we made no probabilistic assumptions about the error term ϵ, and no statistical tests for significance of the relationship between x and y were conducted. Larger values of r^2 imply that the least squares line provides a better fit to the data; that is, the observations are more closely grouped about the least squares line. But, using only r^2, we can draw no conclusion about whether the relationship between x and y is statistically significant. Such a conclusion must be based on considerations that involve the sample size and the properties of the appropriate sampling distributions of the least squares estimators.

2. As a practical matter, for typical data found in the social sciences, values of r^2 as low as .25 are often considered useful. For data in the physical and life sciences, r^2 values of .60 or greater are often found; in fact, in some cases, r^2 values greater than .90 can be found. In business applications, r^2 values vary greatly, depending on the unique characteristics of each application.

EXERCISES

Methods

15. The data from exercise 1 follow.

x_i	1	2	3	4	5
y_i	3	7	5	11	14

The estimated regression equation for these data is $\hat{y} = .20 + 2.60x$.
a. Compute SSE, SST, and SSR using equations (14.8), (14.9), and (14.10).
b. Compute the coefficient of determination r^2. Comment on the goodness of fit.
c. Compute the sample correlation coefficient.

16. The data from exercise 2 follow.

x_i	3	12	6	20	14
y_i	55	40	55	10	15

The estimated regression equation for these data is $\hat{y} = 68 - 3x$.
a. Compute SSE, SST, and SSR.
b. Compute the coefficient of determination r^2. Comment on the goodness of fit.
c. Compute the sample correlation coefficient.

17. The data from exercise 3 follow.

x_i	2	6	9	13	20
y_i	7	18	9	26	23

The estimated regression equation for these data is $\hat{y} = 7.6 + .9x$. What percentage of the total sum of squares can be accounted for by the estimated regression equation? What is the value of the sample correlation coefficient?

Applications

18. **Price and Quality of Headphones.** The following data show the brand, price ($), and the overall score for six stereo headphones that were tested by *Consumer Reports* (*Consumer Reports* website). The overall score is based on sound quality and effectiveness of ambient noise reduction. Scores range from 0 (lowest) to 100 (highest). The estimated regression equation for these data is $\hat{y} = 23.194 + .318x$, where x = price ($) and y = overall score.

Brand	Price ($)	Score
Bose	180	76
Skullcandy	150	71
Koss	95	61
Phillips/O'Neill	70	56
Denon	70	40
JVC	35	26

Source: Consumer Reports website, (https://www.consumerreports.org/cro/headphones.htm?EXTKEY =SG72E00&sitelink=527&gclid=EAIaIQobChMIjriWjaH43QIVQkSGCh2BYAxVEAAYASACEgJSXfD_BwE &gclsrc=aw.ds&dclid=CJGT8JCh-N0CFVNTDAodERYNGw)

  a. Compute SST, SSR, and SSE.
  b. Compute the coefficient of determination r^2. Comment on the goodness of fit.
  c. What is the value of the sample correlation coefficient?

19. **Sales Experience and Sales Performance.** In exercise 7 a sales manager collected the following data on x = annual sales and y = years of experience. The estimated regression equation for these data is $\hat{y} = 80 + 4x$.

DATA *file*

Sales

Salesperson	Years of Experience	Annual Sales ($1000s)
1	1	80
2	3	97
3	4	92
4	4	102
5	6	103
6	8	111
7	10	119
8	10	123
9	11	117
10	13	136

  a. Compute SST, SSR, and SSE.
  b. Compute the coefficient of determination r^2. Comment on the goodness of fit.
  c. What is the value of the sample correlation coefficient?

20. **Price and Weight of Bicycles.** *Bicycling,* the world's leading cycling magazine, reviews hundreds of bicycles throughout the year. Their "Road-Race" category contains reviews of bikes used by riders primarily interested in racing. One of the most important factors in selecting a bike for racing is the weight of the bike. The following data show the weight (pounds) and price ($) for 10 racing bikes reviewed by the magazine (*Bicycling* website).

DATA *file*

RacingBicycles

Brand	Weight	Price ($)
FELT F5	17.8	2100
PINARELLO Paris	16.1	6250
ORBEA Orca GDR	14.9	8370
EDDY MERCKX EMX-7	15.9	6200
BH RC1 Ultegra	17.2	4000
BH Ultralight 386	13.1	8600
CERVELO S5 Team	16.2	6000
GIANT TCR Advanced 2	17.1	2580
WILIER TRIESTINA Gran Turismo	17.6	3400
SPECIALIZED S-Works Amira SL4	14.1	8000

Source: Bicycling website, (https://www.bicycling.com/)

a. Use the data to develop an estimated regression equation that could be used to estimate the price for a bike given the weight.
b. Compute r^2. Did the estimated regression equation provide a good fit?
c. Predict the price for a bike that weighs 15 pounds.

21. **Cost Estimation.** An important application of regression analysis in accounting is in the estimation of cost. By collecting data on volume and cost and using the least squares method to develop an estimated regression equation relating volume and cost, an accountant can estimate the cost associated with a particular manufacturing volume. Consider the following sample of production volumes and total cost data for a manufacturing operation.

Production Volume (units)	Total Cost ($)
400	4000
450	5000
550	5400
600	5900
700	6400
750	7000

a. Use these data to develop an estimated regression equation that could be used to predict the total cost for a given production volume.
b. What is the variable cost per unit produced?
c. Compute the coefficient of determination. What percentage of the variation in total cost can be explained by production volume?
d. The company's production schedule shows 500 units must be produced next month. Predict the total cost for this operation.

22. **Rental Car Revenue and Fleet Size.** The following data were used to investigate the relationship between the number of cars in service (1000s) and the annual revenue ($millions) for six smaller car rental companies (*Auto Rental News* website).

Company	Cars (1000s)	Revenue ($ millions)
U-Save Auto Rental System, Inc.	11.5	118
Payless Car Rental System, Inc.	10.0	135
ACE Rent A Car	9.0	100
Rent-A-Wreck of America	5.5	37
Triangle Rent-A-Car	4.2	40
Affordable/Sensible	3.3	32

With x = cars in service (1000s) and y = annual revenue ($ millions), the estimated regression equation is $\hat{y} = -17.005 + 12.966x$. For these data SSE = 1043.03.

a. Compute the coefficient of determination r^2.
b. Did the estimated regression equation provide a good fit? Explain.
c. What is the value of the sample correlation coefficient? Does it reflect a strong or weak relationship between the number of cars in service and the annual revenue?

14.4 Model Assumptions

In conducting a regression analysis, we begin by making an assumption about the appropriate model for the relationship between the dependent and independent variable(s). For the case of simple linear regression, the assumed regression model is

$$y = \beta_0 + \beta_1 x + \epsilon$$

Then the least squares method is used to develop values for b_0 and b_1, the estimates of the model parameters β_0 and β_1, respectively. The resulting estimated regression equation is

$$\hat{y} = b_0 + b_1 x$$

We saw that the value of the coefficient of determination (r^2) is a measure of the goodness of fit of the estimated regression equation. However, even with a large value of r^2, the estimated regression equation should not be used until further analysis of the appropriateness of the assumed model has been conducted. An important step in determining whether the assumed model is appropriate involves testing for the significance of the relationship. The tests of significance in regression analysis are based on the following assumptions about the error term ϵ.

ASSUMPTIONS ABOUT THE ERROR TERM ϵ IN THE REGRESSION MODEL

$$y = \beta_0 + \beta_1 x + \epsilon$$

1. The error term ϵ is a random variable with a mean or expected value of zero; that is, $E(\epsilon) = 0$.
   Implication: β_0 and β_1 are constants, therefore $E(\beta_0) = \beta_0$ and $E(\beta_1) = \beta_1$; thus, for a given value of x, the expected value of y is

   $$E(y) = \beta_0 + \beta_1 x \qquad \textbf{(14.14)}$$

   As we indicated previously, equation (14.14) is referred to as the regression equation.
2. The variance of ϵ, denoted by σ^2, is the same for all values of x.
   Implication: The variance of y about the regression line equals σ^2 and is the same for all values of x.
3. The values of ϵ are independent.
   Implication: The value of ϵ for a particular value of x is not related to the value of ϵ for any other value of x; thus, the value of y for a particular value of x is not related to the value of y for any other value of x.
4. The error term ϵ is a normally distributed random variable for all values of x.
   Implication: Because y is a linear function of ϵ, y is also a normally distributed random variable for all values of x.

Figure 14.6 illustrates the model assumptions and their implications; note that in this graphical interpretation, the value of $E(y)$ changes according to the specific value of x considered. However, regardless of the x value, the probability distribution of ϵ and hence the probability distributions of y are normally distributed, each with the same variance. The

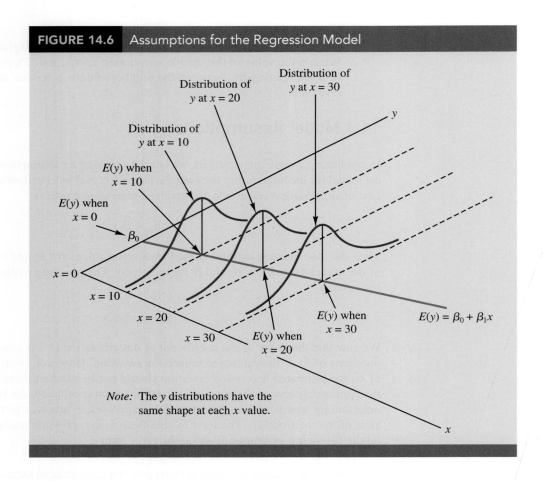

FIGURE 14.6   Assumptions for the Regression Model

Distribution of
y at x = 20

Distribution of
y at x = 30

Distribution of
y at x = 10

$E(y)$ when
$x = 10$

$E(y)$ when
$x = 0$

β_0

y

$x = 0$

$x = 10$

$x = 20$

$x = 30$

$E(y)$ when
$x = 20$

$E(y)$ when
$x = 30$

$E(y) = \beta_0 + \beta_1 x$

x

Note: The y distributions have the
same shape at each x value.

specific value of the error ϵ at any particular point depends on whether the actual value of y is greater than or less than $E(y)$.

At this point, we must keep in mind that we are also making an assumption or hypothesis about the form of the relationship between x and y. That is, we assume that a straight line represented by $\beta_0 + \beta_1 x$ is the basis for the relationship between the variables. We must not lose sight of the fact that some other model, for instance $y = \beta_0 + \beta_1 x^2 + \epsilon$, may turn out to be a better model for the underlying relationship.

14.5 Testing for Significance

In a simple linear regression equation, the mean or expected value of y is a linear function of x: $E(y) = \beta_0 + \beta_1 x$. If the value of β_1 is zero, $E(y) = \beta_0 + (0)x = \beta_0$. In this case, the mean value of y does not depend on the value of x and hence we would conclude that x and y are not linearly related. Alternatively, if the value of β_1 is not equal to zero, we would conclude that the two variables are related. Thus, to test for a significant regression relationship, we must conduct a hypothesis test to determine whether the value of β_1 is zero. Two tests are commonly used. Both require an estimate of σ^2, the variance of ϵ in the regression model.

Estimate of σ^2

From the regression model and its assumptions we can conclude that σ^2, the variance of ϵ, also represents the variance of the y values about the regression line. Recall that the deviations of the y values about the estimated regression line are called residuals. Thus,

SSE, the sum of squared residuals, is a measure of the variability of the actual observations about the estimated regression line. The **mean square error** (MSE) provides the estimate of σ^2; it is SSE divided by its degrees of freedom.

With $\hat{y}_i = b_0 + b_1 x_i$, SSE can be written as

$$\text{SSE} = \Sigma(y_i - \hat{y}_i)^2 = \Sigma(y_i - b_0 - b_1 x_i)^2$$

Every sum of squares has associated with it a number called its degrees of freedom. Statisticians have shown that SSE has $n - 2$ degrees of freedom because two parameters (β_0 and β_1) must be estimated to compute SSE. Thus, the mean square error is computed by dividing SSE by $n - 2$. MSE provides an unbiased estimator of σ^2. Because the value of MSE provides an estimate of σ^2, the notation s^2 is also used.

MEAN SQUARE ERROR (ESTIMATE OF σ^2)

$$s^2 = \text{MSE} = \frac{\text{SSE}}{n - 2} \tag{14.15}$$

In Section 14.3 we showed that for the Armand's Pizza Parlors example, SSE = 1530; hence,

$$s^2 = \text{MSE} = \frac{1530}{8} = 191.25$$

provides an unbiased estimate of σ^2.

To estimate σ we take the square root of s^2. The resulting value, s, is referred to as the **standard error of the estimate**.

STANDARD ERROR OF THE ESTIMATE

$$s = \sqrt{\text{MSE}} = \sqrt{\frac{\text{SSE}}{n - 2}} \tag{14.16}$$

For the Armand's Pizza Parlors example, $s = \sqrt{\text{MSE}} = \sqrt{191.25} = 13.829$. In the following discussion, we use the standard error of the estimate in the tests for a significant relationship between x and y.

t Test

The simple linear regression model is $y = \beta_0 + \beta_1 x + \epsilon$. If x and y are linearly related, we must have $\beta_1 \neq 0$. The purpose of the t test is to see whether we can conclude that $\beta_1 \neq 0$. We will use the sample data to test the following hypotheses about the parameter β_1.

$$H_0: \beta_1 = 0$$
$$H_a: \beta_1 \neq 0$$

If H_0 is rejected, we will conclude that $\beta_1 \neq 0$ and that a statistically significant relationship exists between the two variables. However, if H_0 cannot be rejected, we will have insufficient evidence to conclude that a significant relationship exists. The properties of the sampling distribution of b_1, the least squares estimator of β_1, provide the basis for the hypothesis test.

First, let us consider what would happen if we used a different random sample for the same regression study. For example, suppose that Armand's Pizza Parlors used the sales records of a different sample of 10 restaurants. A regression analysis of this new sample might result in an estimated regression equation similar to our previous estimated regression equation $\hat{y} = 60 + 5x$. However, it is doubtful that we would obtain exactly the same equation (with an intercept of exactly 60 and a slope of exactly 5). Indeed, b_0 and b_1, the least squares estimators, are sample statistics with their own sampling distributions. The properties of the sampling distribution of b_1 follow.

SAMPLING DISTRIBUTION OF b_1

Expected Value

$$E(b_1) = \beta_1$$

Standard Deviation

$$\sigma_{b_1} = \frac{\sigma}{\sqrt{\Sigma(x_i - \bar{x})^2}} \qquad (14.17)$$

Distribution Form

Normal

Note that the expected value of b_1 is equal to β_1, so b_1 is an unbiased estimator of β_1.

Because we do not know the value of σ, we develop an estimate of σ_{b_1}, denoted s_{b_1}, by estimating σ with s in equation (14.17). Thus, we obtain the following estimate of σ_{b_1}.

The standard deviation of b_1 is also referred to as the standard error of b_1. Thus, s_{b_1} provides an estimate of the standard error of b_1.

ESTIMATED STANDARD DEVIATION OF b_1

$$s_{b_1} = \frac{s}{\sqrt{\Sigma(x_i - \bar{x})^2}} \qquad (14.18)$$

For Armand's Pizza Parlors, $s = 13.829$. Hence, using $\Sigma(x_i - \bar{x})^2 = 568$ as shown in Table 14.2, we have

$$s_{b_1} = \frac{13.829}{\sqrt{568}} = .5803$$

as the estimated standard deviation of b_1.

The t test for a significant relationship is based on the fact that the test statistic

$$\frac{b_1 - \beta_1}{s_{b_1}}$$

follows a t distribution with $n - 2$ degrees of freedom. If the null hypothesis is true, then $\beta_1 = 0$ and $t = b_1/s_{b_1}$.

Let us conduct this test of significance for Armand's Pizza Parlors at the $\alpha = .01$ level of significance. The test statistic is

$$t = \frac{b_1}{s_{b_1}} = \frac{5}{.5803} = 8.62$$

Appendixes 14.3 and 14.4 show how JMP and Excel can be used to compute the p-value.

The t distribution table (Table 2 of Appendix D) shows that with $n - 2 = 10 - 2 = 8$ degrees of freedom, $t = 3.355$ provides an area of .005 in the upper tail. Thus, the area in the upper tail of the t distribution corresponding to the test statistic $t = 8.62$ must be less than .005. Because this test is a two-tailed test, we double this value to conclude that the p-value associated with $t = 8.62$ must be less than $2(.005) = .01$. Statistical software shows the p-value $= .000$. Because the p-value is less than $\alpha = .01$, we reject H_0 and conclude that β_1 is not equal to zero. This evidence is sufficient to conclude that a significant relationship exists between student population and quarterly sales. A summary of the t test for significance in simple linear regression follows.

> ### t TEST FOR SIGNIFICANCE IN SIMPLE LINEAR REGRESSION
>
> $$H_0: \beta_1 = 0$$
> $$H_a: \beta_1 \neq 0$$
>
> **TEST STATISTIC**
>
> $$t = \frac{b_1}{s_{b_1}}$$ (14.19)
>
> **REJECTION RULE**
>
> p-value approach: Reject H_0 if p-value $\leq \alpha$
>
> Critical value approach: Reject H_0 if $t \leq -t_{\alpha/2}$ or if $t \geq t_{\alpha/2}$
>
> where $t_{\alpha/2}$ is based on a t distribution with $n - 2$ degrees of freedom.

Confidence Interval for β_1

The form of a confidence interval for β_1 is as follows:

$$b_1 \pm t_{\alpha/2} s_{b_1}$$

The point estimator is b_1 and the margin of error is $t_{\alpha/2} s_{b_1}$. The confidence coefficient associated with this interval is $1 - \alpha$, and $t_{\alpha/2}$ is the t value providing an area of $\alpha/2$ in the upper tail of a t distribution with $n - 2$ degrees of freedom. For example, suppose that we wanted to develop a 99% confidence interval estimate of β_1 for Armand's Pizza Parlors. From Table 2 of Appendix B we find that the t value corresponding to $\alpha = .01$ and $n - 2 = 10 - 2 = 8$ degrees of freedom is $t_{.005} = 3.355$. Thus, the 99% confidence interval estimate of β_1 is

$$b_1 \pm t_{\alpha/2} s_{b_1} = 5 \pm 3.355(.5803) = 5 \pm 1.95$$

or 3.05 to 6.95.

In using the t test for significance, the hypotheses tested were

$$H_0: \beta_1 = 0$$
$$H_a: \beta_1 \neq 0$$

At the $\alpha = .01$ level of significance, we can use the 99% confidence interval as an alternative for drawing the hypothesis testing conclusion for the Armand's data. Because 0, the hypothesized value of β_1, is not included in the confidence interval (3.05 to 6.95), we can reject H_0 and conclude that a significant statistical relationship exists between the size of the student population and quarterly sales. In general, a confidence interval can be used to test any two-sided hypothesis about β_1. If the hypothesized value of β_1 is contained in the confidence interval, do not reject H_0. Otherwise, reject H_0.

F Test

An F test, based on the F probability distribution, can also be used to test for significance in regression. With only one independent variable, the F test will provide the same conclusion as the t test; that is, if the t test indicates $\beta_1 \neq 0$ and hence a significant relationship, the F test will also indicate a significant relationship. But with more than one independent variable, only the F test can be used to test for an overall significant relationship.

The logic behind the use of the F test for determining whether the regression relationship is statistically significant is based on the development of two independent estimates of σ^2. We explained how MSE provides an estimate of σ^2. If the null hypothesis $H_0: \beta_1 = 0$ is true, the sum of squares due to regression, SSR, divided by its degrees of freedom provides another independent estimate of σ^2. This estimate is called the *mean square due to regression,* or simply the *mean square regression,* and is denoted MSR. In general,

$$MSR = \frac{SSR}{Regression\ degrees\ of\ freedom}$$

For the models we consider in this text, the regression degrees of freedom is always equal to the number of independent variables in the model:

$$MSR = \frac{SSR}{Number\ of\ independent\ variables} \tag{14.20}$$

Because we consider only regression models with one independent variable in this chapter, we have MSR = SSR/1 = SSR. Hence, for Armand's Pizza Parlors, MSR = SSR = 14,200.

If the null hypothesis (H_0: $\beta_1 = 0$) is true, MSR and MSE are two independent estimates of σ^2 and the sampling distribution of MSR/MSE follows an F distribution with numerator degrees of freedom equal to one and denominator degrees of freedom equal to $n - 2$. Therefore, when $\beta_1 = 0$, the value of MSR/MSE should be close to one. However, if the null hypothesis is false ($\beta_1 \neq 0$), MSR will overestimate σ^2 and the value of MSR/MSE will be inflated; thus, large values of MSR/MSE lead to the rejection of H_0 and the conclusion that the relationship between x and y is statistically significant.

Let us conduct the F test for the Armand's Pizza Parlors example. The test statistic is

$$F = \frac{MSR}{MSE} = \frac{14,200}{191.25} = 74.25$$

The F test and the t test provide identical results for simple linear regression.

The F distribution table (Table 4 of Appendix B) shows that with one degree of freedom in the numerator and $n - 2 = 10 - 2 = 8$ degrees of freedom in the denominator, $F = 11.26$ provides an area of .01 in the upper tail. Thus, the area in the upper tail of the F distribution corresponding to the test statistic $F = 74.25$ must be less than .01. Thus, we conclude that the p-value must be less than .01. Statistical software shows the p-value = .000. Because the p-value is less than $\alpha = .01$, we reject H_0 and conclude that a significant relationship exists between the size of the student population and quarterly sales. A summary of the F test for significance in simple linear regression follows.

If H_0 is false, MSE still provides an unbiased estimate of σ^2 and MSR overestimates σ^2. If H_0 is true, both MSE and MSR provide unbiased estimates of σ^2; in this case the value of MSR/MSE should be close to 1.

F TEST FOR SIGNIFICANCE IN SIMPLE LINEAR REGRESSION

$$H_0\!: \beta_1 = 0$$
$$H_a\!: \beta_1 \neq 0$$

TEST STATISTIC

$$F = \frac{MSR}{MSE} \tag{14.21}$$

REJECTION RULE

p-value approach: Reject H_0 if p-value $\leq \alpha$

Critical value approach: Reject H_0 if $F \geq F_\alpha$

where F_α is based on an F distribution with 1 degree of freedom in the numerator and $n - 2$ degrees of freedom in the denominator.

In Chapter 13 we covered analysis of variance (ANOVA) and showed how an **ANOVA table** could be used to provide a convenient summary of the computational aspects of analysis of variance. A similar ANOVA table can be used to summarize the results of the F test for significance in regression. Table 14.5 is the general form of the ANOVA table

In every analysis of variance table the total sum of squares is the sum of the regression sum of squares and the error sum of squares; in addition, the total degrees of freedom is the sum of the regression degrees of freedom and the error degrees of freedom.

| | TABLE 14.5 | General Form of the Anova Table for Simple Linear Regression |

Source of Variation	Sum of Squares	Degrees of Freedom	Mean Square	F	p-value
Regression	SSR	1	$MSR = \dfrac{SSR}{1}$	$F = \dfrac{MSR}{MSE}$	
Error	SSE	$n - 2$	$MSE = \dfrac{SSE}{n - 2}$		
Total	SST	$n - 1$			

| | TABLE 14.6 | Anova Table for the Armand's Pizza Parlors Problem |

Source of Variation	Sum of Squares	Degrees of Freedom	Mean Square	F	p-value
Regression	14,200	1	$\dfrac{14{,}200}{1} = 14{,}200$	$\dfrac{14{,}200}{191.25} = 74.25$	.000
Error	1530	8	$\dfrac{1530}{8} = 191.25$		
Total	15,730	9			

for simple linear regression. Table 14.6 is the ANOVA table with the F test computations performed for Armand's Pizza Parlors. Regression, Error, and Total are the labels for the three sources of variation, with SSR, SSE, and SST appearing as the corresponding sum of squares in column 2. The degrees of freedom, 1 for SSR, $n - 2$ for SSE, and $n - 1$ for SST, are shown in column 3. Column 4 contains the values of MSR and MSE, column 5 contains the value of $F = $ MSR/MSE, and column 6 contains the p-value corresponding to the F value in column 5. Almost all computer printouts of regression analysis include an ANOVA table summary of the F test for significance.

Some Cautions About the Interpretation of Significance Tests

Rejecting the null hypothesis $H_0: \beta_1 = 0$ and concluding that the relationship between x and y is significant does not enable us to conclude that a cause-and-effect relationship is present between x and y. Concluding a cause-and-effect relationship is warranted only if the analyst can provide some type of theoretical justification that the relationship is in fact causal. In the Armand's Pizza Parlors example, we can conclude that there is a significant relationship between the size of the student population x and quarterly sales y; moreover, the estimated regression equation $\hat{y} = 60 + 5x$ provides the least squares estimate of the relationship. We cannot, however, conclude that changes in student population x *cause* changes in quarterly sales y just because we identified a statistically significant relationship. The appropriateness of such a cause-and-effect conclusion is left to supporting theoretical justification and to good judgment on the part of the analyst. Armand's managers felt that increases in the student population were a likely cause of increased quarterly sales. Thus, the result of the significance test enabled them to conclude that a cause-and-effect relationship was present.

Regression analysis, which can be used to identify how variables are associated with one another, cannot be used as evidence of a cause-and-effect relationship.

In addition, just because we are able to reject $H_0: \beta_1 = 0$ and demonstrate statistical significance does not enable us to conclude that the relationship between x and y is linear.

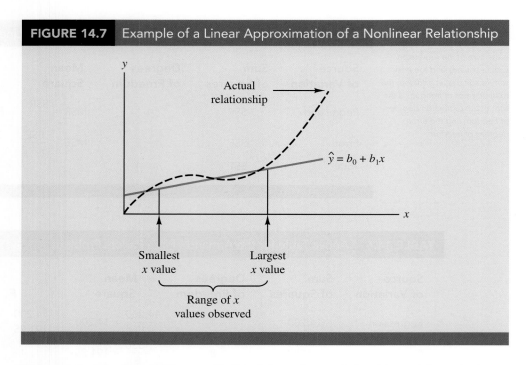

FIGURE 14.7   Example of a Linear Approximation of a Nonlinear Relationship

We can state only that x and y are related and that a linear relationship explains a significant portion of the variability in y over the range of values for x observed in the sample. Figure 14.7 illustrates this situation. The test for significance calls for the rejection of the null hypothesis $H_0: \beta_1 = 0$ and leads to the conclusion that x and y are significantly related, but the figure shows that the actual relationship between x and y is not linear. Although the linear approximation provided by $\hat{y} = b_0 + b_1 x$ is good over the range of x values observed in the sample, it becomes poor for x values outside that range.

Given a significant relationship, we should feel confident in using the estimated regression equation for predictions corresponding to x values within the range of the x values observed in the sample. For Armand's Pizza Parlors, this range corresponds to values of x between 2 and 26. Unless other reasons indicate that the model is valid beyond this range, predictions outside the range of the independent variable should be made with caution. For Armand's Pizza Parlors, because the regression relationship has been found significant at the .01 level, we should feel confident using it to predict sales for restaurants where the associated student population is between 2000 and 26,000.

NOTES + COMMENTS

1. The assumptions made about the error term (Section 14.4) are what allow the tests of statistical significance in this section. The properties of the sampling distribution of b_1 and the subsequent t and F tests follow directly from these assumptions.

2. Do not confuse statistical significance with practical significance. With very large sample sizes, statistically significant results can be obtained for small values of b_1; in such cases, one must exercise care in concluding that the relationship has practical significance.

3. A test of significance for a linear relationship between x and y can also be performed by using the sample correlation coefficient r_{xy}. With ρ_{xy} denoting the population correlation coefficient, the hypotheses are as follows.

$$H_0: \rho_{xy} = 0$$
$$H_a: \rho_{xy} \neq 0$$

A significant relationship can be concluded if H_0 is rejected. The details of this test are provided in Appendix 14.2. However, the t and F tests presented previously in this section give the same result as the test for significance using the correlation coefficient. Conducting a test for significance using the correlation coefficient therefore is not necessary if a t or F test has already been conducted.

EXERCISES

Methods

23. The data from exercise 1 follow.

x_i	1	2	3	4	5
y_i	3	7	5	11	14

    a. Compute the mean square error using equation (14.15).
    b. Compute the standard error of the estimate using equation (14.16).
    c. Compute the estimated standard deviation of b_1 using equation (14.18).
    d. Use the t test to test the following hypotheses ($\alpha = .05$):

$$H_0: \beta_1 = 0$$
$$H_a: \beta_1 \neq 0$$

    e. Use the F test to test the hypotheses in part (d) at a .05 level of significance. Present the results in the analysis of variance table format.

24. The data from exercise 2 follow.

x_i	3	12	6	20	14
y_i	55	40	55	10	15

    a. Compute the mean square error using equation (14.15).
    b. Compute the standard error of the estimate using equation (14.16).
    c. Compute the estimated standard deviation of b_1 using equation (14.18).
    d. Use the t test to test the following hypotheses ($\alpha = .05$):

$$H_0: \beta_1 = 0$$
$$H_a: \beta_1 \neq 0$$

    e. Use the F test to test the hypotheses in part (d) at a .05 level of significance. Present the results in the analysis of variance table format.

25. The data from exercise 3 follow.

x_i	2	6	9	13	20
y_i	7	18	9	26	23

    a. What is the value of the standard error of the estimate?
    b. Test for a significant relationship by using the t test. Use $\alpha = .05$.
    c. Use the F test to test for a significant relationship. Use $\alpha = .05$. What is your conclusion?

Applications

26. **Headphones Conclusion.** In exercise 18, the data on price ($) and the overall score for six stereo headphones tested by *Consumer Reports* were as follows (*Consumer Reports* website).

Brand	Price ($)	Score
Bose	180	76
Skullcandy	150	71
Koss	95	61
Phillips/O'Neill	70	56
Denon	70	40
JVC	35	26

Source: Consumer Reports website, (https://www.consumerreports.org/cro/headphones.htm?EXTKEY =SG72E00&sitelink=527&gclid=EAIaIQobChMIjriWjaH43QIVQkSGCh2BYAxVEAAYASACEgJSXfD_BwE &gclsrc=aw.ds&dclid=CJGT8JCh-N0CFVNTDAodERYNGw)

a. Does the t test indicate a significant relationship between price and the overall score? What is your conclusion? Use $\alpha = .05$.

b. Test for a significant relationship using the F test. What is your conclusion? Use $\alpha = .05$.

c. Show the ANOVA table for these data.

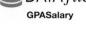
GPASalary

27. **College GPA and Salary.** Do students with higher college grade point averages (GPAs) earn more than those graduates with lower GPAs (*CivicScience*)? Consider the college GPA and salary data (10 years after graduation) provided in the file *GPASalary*.

a. Develop a scatter diagram for these data with college GPA as the independent variable. What does the scatter diagram indicate about the relationship between the two variables?

b. Use these data to develop an estimated regression equation that can be used to predict annual salary 10 years after graduation given college GPA.

c. At the .05 level of significance, does there appear to be a significant statistical relationship between the two variables?

BrokerRatings

28. **Broker Satisfaction Conclusion.** In exercise 8, ratings data on x = the quality of the speed of execution and y = overall satisfaction with electronic trades provided the estimated regression equation $\hat{y} = .2046 + .9077x$. At the .05 level of significance, test whether speed of execution and overall satisfaction are related. Show the ANOVA table. What is your conclusion?

29. **Cost Estimation Conclusion.** Refer to exercise 21, where data on production volume and cost were used to develop an estimated regression equation relating production volume and cost for a particular manufacturing operation. Use $\alpha = .05$ to test whether the production volume is significantly related to the total cost. Show the ANOVA table. What is your conclusion?

30. **Significance of Fleet Size on Rental Car Revenue.** Companies in the U.S. car rental market vary greatly in terms of the size of the fleet, the number of locations, and annual revenue. The following data were used to investigate the relationship between the number of cars in service (1000s) and the annual revenue ($ millions) for six smaller car rental companies (*Auto Rental News* website).

Company	Cars (1000s)	Revenue ($ millions)
U-Save Auto Rental System, Inc.	11.5	118
Payless Car Rental System, Inc.	10.0	135
ACE Rent A Car	9.0	100
Rent-A-Wreck of America	5.5	37
Triangle Rent-A-Car	4.2	40
Affordable/Sensible	3.3	32

Source: Auto Rental News website, (https://www.autorentalnews.com/custom-content/253201/research-statistics)

With x = cars in service (1000s) and y = annual revenue ($ millions), the estimated regression equation is $\hat{y} = -17.005 + 12.966x$. For these data SSE = 1043.03 and SST = 10,568. Do these results indicate a significant relationship between the number of cars in service and the annual revenue?

RacingBicycles

31. **Significance of Racing Bike Weight on Price.** In exercise 20, data on x = weight (pounds) and y = price ($) for 10 road-racing bikes provided the estimated regression equation $\hat{y} = 28,574 - 1439x$. (*Bicycling* website). For these data SSE = 7,102,922.54 and SST = 52,120,800. Use the F test to determine whether the weight for a bike and the price are related at the .05 level of significance.

14.6 Using the Estimated Regression Equation for Estimation and Prediction

When using the simple linear regression model, we are making an assumption about the relationship between x and y. We then use the least squares method to obtain the estimated simple linear regression equation. If a significant relationship exists between x and y and the coefficient of determination shows that the fit is good, the estimated regression equation should be useful for estimation and prediction.

For the Armand's Pizza Parlors example, the estimated regression equation is $\hat{y} = 60 + 5x$. At the end of Section 14.1, we stated that $\hat{y}$ can be used as a *point estimator* of $E(y)$, the mean or expected value of y for a given value of x, and as a predictor of an individual value of y. For example, suppose Armand's managers want to estimate the mean quarterly sales for *all* restaurants located near college campuses with 10,000 students. Using the estimated regression equation $\hat{y} = 60 + 5x$, we see that for $x = 10$ (10,000 students), $\hat{y} = 60 + 5(10) = 110$. Thus, a *point estimate* of the mean quarterly sales for all restaurant locations near campuses with 10,000 students is $110,000. In this case we are using $\hat{y}$ as the point estimator of the mean value of y when $x = 10$.

We can also use the estimated regression equation to *predict* an individual value of y for a given value of x. For example, to predict quarterly sales for a new restaurant Armand's is considering building near Talbot College, a campus with 10,000 students, we would compute $\hat{y} = 60 + 5(10) = 110$. Hence, we would predict quarterly sales of $110,000 for such a new restaurant. In this case, we are using $\hat{y}$ as the *predictor* of y for a new observation when $x = 10$.

When we are using the estimated regression equation to estimate the mean value of y or to predict an individual value of y, it is clear that the estimate or prediction depends on the given value of x. For this reason, as we discuss in more depth the issues concerning estimation and prediction, the following notation will help clarify matters.

$x^* = $ the given value of the independent variable x

$y^* = $ the random variable denoting the possible values of the dependent variable y when $x = x^*$

$E(y^*) = $ the mean or expected value of the dependent variable y when $x = x^*$

$\hat{y}^* = b_0 + b_1 x^* = $ the point estimator of $E(y^*)$ and the predictor of an individual value of y^* when $x = x^*$

To illustrate the use of this notation, suppose we want to estimate the mean value of quarterly sales for *all* Armand's restaurants located near a campus with 10,000 students. For this case, $x^* = 10$ and $E(y^*)$ denotes the unknown mean value of quarterly sales for all restaurants where $x^* = 10$. Thus, the point estimate of $E(y^*)$ is provided by $\hat{y}^* = 60 + 5(10) = 110$, or $110,000. But, using this notation, $\hat{y}^* = 110$ is also the predictor of quarterly sales for the new restaurant located near Talbot College, a school with 10,000 students.

Interval Estimation

Point estimators and predictors do not provide any information about the precision associated with the estimate and/or prediction. For that we must develop confidence intervals and prediction intervals. A **confidence interval** is an interval estimate of the *mean value of y* for a given value of x. A **prediction interval** is used whenever we want to *predict an individual value of y* for a new observation corresponding to a given value of x. Although the predictor of y for a given value of x is the same as the point estimator of the mean value of y for a given value of x, the interval estimates we obtain for the two cases are different. As we will show, the margin of error is larger for a prediction interval. We begin by showing how to develop an interval estimate of the mean value of y.

Confidence Interval for the Mean Value of y

In general, we cannot expect $\hat{y}^*$ to equal $E(y^*)$ exactly. If we want to make an inference about how close $\hat{y}^*$ is to the true mean value $E(y^*)$, we will have to estimate the variance of $\hat{y}^*$. The formula for estimating the variance of $\hat{y}^*$, denoted by $s_{\hat{y}^*}^2$, is

$$ s_{\hat{y}^*}^2 = s^2 \left[\frac{1}{n} + \frac{(x^* - \bar{x})^2}{\Sigma(x_i - \bar{x})^2} \right] \tag{14.22}$$

The estimate of the standard deviation of $\hat{y}^*$ is given by the square root of equation (14.22).

$$s_{\hat{y}*} = s\sqrt{\frac{1}{n} + \frac{(x^* - \bar{x})^2}{\Sigma(x_i - \bar{x})^2}} \tag{14.23}$$

The computational results for Armand's Pizza Parlors in Section 14.5 provided $s = 13.829$. With $x^* = 10$, $\bar{x} = 14$, and $\Sigma(x_i - \bar{x})^2 = 568$, we can use equation (14.23) to obtain

$$s_{\hat{y}*} = 13.829\sqrt{\frac{1}{10} + \frac{(10 - 14)^2}{568}}$$

$$= 13.829\sqrt{.1282} = 4.95$$

The general expression for a confidence interval follows.

CONFIDENCE INTERVAL FOR E(y*)

The margin of error associated with this confidence interval is $t_{\alpha/2}s_{\hat{y}*}$.

$$\hat{y}* \pm t_{\alpha/2}s_{\hat{y}*} \tag{14.24}$$

where the confidence coefficient is $1 - \alpha$ and $t_{\alpha/2}$ is based on the t distribution with $n - 2$ degrees of freedom.

Using expression (14.24) to develop a 95% confidence interval of the mean quarterly sales for all Armand's restaurants located near campuses with 10,000 students, we need the value of t for $\alpha/2 = .025$ and $n - 2 = 10 - 2 = 8$ degrees of freedom. Using Table 2 of Appendix B, we have $t_{.025} = 2.306$. Thus, with $\hat{y}* = 110$ and a margin of error of $t_{\alpha/2}s_{\hat{y}*} = 2.306(4.95) = 11.415$, the 95% confidence interval estimate is

$$110 \pm 11.415$$

In dollars, the 95% confidence interval for the mean quarterly sales of all restaurants near campuses with 10,000 students is $\$110,000 \pm \$11,415$. Therefore, the 95% confidence interval for the mean quarterly sales when the student population is 10,000 is $\$98,585$ to $\$121,415$.

Confidence intervals and prediction intervals show the precision of the regression results. Narrower intervals provide a higher degree of precision.

Note that the estimated standard deviation of $\hat{y}*$ given by equation (14.23) is smallest when $x^* - \bar{x} = 0$. In this case the estimated standard deviation of $\hat{y}*$ becomes

$$s_{\hat{y}*} = s\sqrt{\frac{1}{n} + \frac{(\bar{x} - \bar{x})^2}{\Sigma(x_i - \bar{x})^2}} = s\sqrt{\frac{1}{n}}$$

This result implies that we can make the best or most precise estimate of the mean value of y whenever $x^* = \bar{x}$. In fact, the further x^* is from $\bar{x}$, the larger $x^* - \bar{x}$ becomes. As a result, the confidence interval for the mean value of y will become wider as x^* deviates more from $\bar{x}$. This pattern is shown graphically in Figure 14.8.

Prediction Interval for an Individual Value of y

Instead of estimating the mean value of quarterly sales for all Armand's restaurants located near campuses with 10,000 students, suppose we want to predict quarterly sales for a new restaurant Armand's is considering building near Talbot College, a campus with 10,000 students. As noted previously, the predictor of y^*, the value of y corresponding to the given x^*, is $\hat{y}* = b_0 + b_1x^*$. For the new restaurant located near Talbot College, $x^* = 10$ and the prediction of quarterly sales is $\hat{y}* = 60 + 5(10) = 110$, or $\$110,000$. Note that the prediction of quarterly sales for the new Armand's restaurant near Talbot College is the same as the point estimate of the mean sales for all Armand's restaurants located near campuses with 10,000 students.

To develop a prediction interval, let us first determine the variance associated with using $\hat{y}*$ as a predictor of y when $x = x^*$. This variance is made up of the sum of the following two components.

1. The variance of the y^* values about the mean $E(y^*)$, an estimate of which is given by s^2
2. The variance associated with using $\hat{y}*$ to estimate $E(y^*)$, an estimate of which is given by $s_{\hat{y}*}^2$

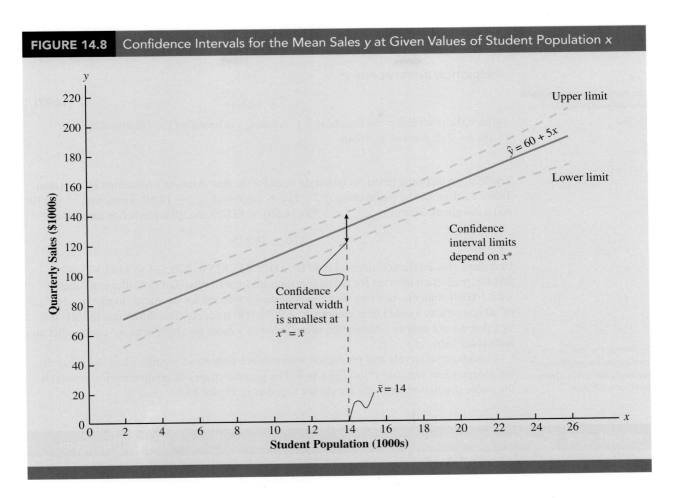

FIGURE 14.8 Confidence Intervals for the Mean Sales y at Given Values of Student Population x

The formula for estimating the variance corresponding to the prediction of the value of y when $x = x^*$, denoted s_{pred}^2, is

$$s_{pred}^2 = s^2 + s_{\hat{y}*}^2$$

$$= s^2 + s^2 \left[\frac{1}{n} + \frac{(x^* - \bar{x})^2}{\Sigma(x_i - \bar{x})^2} \right]$$

$$= s^2 \left[1 + \frac{1}{n} + \frac{(x^* - \bar{x})^2}{\Sigma(x_i - \bar{x})^2} \right] \qquad \textbf{(14.25)}$$

Hence, an estimate of the standard deviation corresponding to the prediction of the value of y^* is

$$s_{pred} = s \sqrt{1 + \frac{1}{n} + \frac{(x^* - \bar{x})^2}{\Sigma(x_i - \bar{x})^2}} \qquad \textbf{(14.26)}$$

For Armand's Pizza Parlors, the estimated standard deviation corresponding to the prediction of quarterly sales for a new restaurant located near Talbot College, a campus with 10,000 students, is computed as follows.

$$s_{pred} = 13.829 \sqrt{1 + \frac{1}{10} + \frac{(10 - 14)^2}{568}}$$

$$= 13.829 \sqrt{1.282}$$

$$= 14.69$$

The general expression for a prediction interval follows.

PREDICTION INTERVAL FOR y*

The margin of error associated with this prediction interval is $t_{a/2} s_{pred}$.

$$\hat{y}^* \pm t_{\alpha/2} s_{pred} \qquad (14.27)$$

where the confidence coefficient is $1 - \alpha$ and $t_{\alpha/2}$ is based on the t distribution with $n - 2$ degrees of freedom.

The 95% prediction interval for quarterly sales for the new Armand's restaurant located near Talbot College can be found using $t_{\alpha/2} = t_{.025} = 2.306$ and $s_{pred} = 14.69$. Thus, with $\hat{y}^* = 110$ and a margin of error of $t_{.025} s_{pred} = 2.306(14.69) = 33.875$, the 95% prediction interval is

$$110 \pm 33.875$$

In dollars, this prediction interval is \$110,000 $\pm$ \$33,875 or \$76,125 to \$143,875. Note that the prediction interval for the new restaurant located near Talbot College, a campus with 10,000 students, is wider than the confidence interval for the mean quarterly sales of all restaurants located near campuses with 10,000 students. The difference reflects the fact that we are able to estimate the mean value of y more precisely than we can predict an individual value of y.

In general, the lines for the confidence interval limits and the prediction interval limits both have curvature.

Confidence intervals and prediction intervals are both more precise when the value of the independent variable x^* is closer to $\bar{x}$. The general shapes of confidence intervals and the wider prediction intervals are shown together in Figure 14.9.

FIGURE 14.9 Confidence and Prediction Intervals for Sales y at Given Values of Student Population x

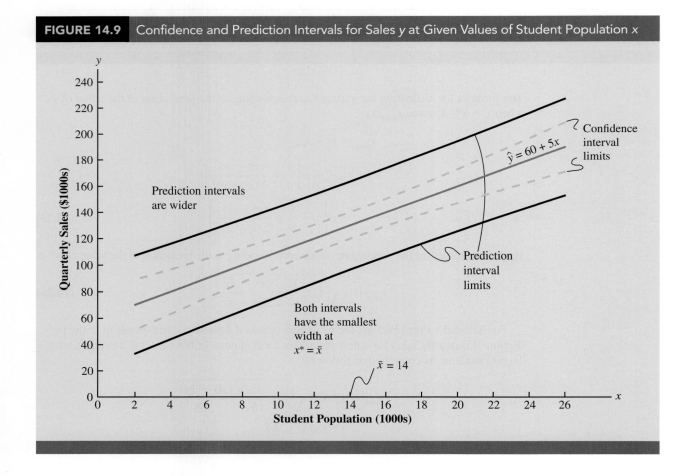

NOTES + COMMENTS

A prediction interval is used to predict the value of the dependent variable y for a *new observation*. As an illustration, we showed how to develop a prediction interval of quarterly sales for a new restaurant that Armand's is considering building near Talbot College, a campus with 10,000 students. The fact that the value of $x = 10$ is not one of the values of student population for the Armand's sample data in Table 14.1 is not meant to imply that prediction intervals cannot be developed for values of x in

the sample data. But, for the ten restaurants that make up the data in Table 14.1, developing a prediction interval for quarterly sales for *one of these restaurants* does not make any sense because we already know the value of quarterly sales for each of these restaurants. In other words, a prediction interval only has meaning for something new, in this case a new observation corresponding to a particular value of x that may or may not equal one of the values of x in the sample.

EXERCISES

Methods

32. The data from exercise 1 follow.

x_i	1	2	3	4	5
y_i	3	7	5	11	14

  a. Use equation (14.23) to estimate the standard deviation of $\hat{y}^*$ when $x = 4$.
  b. Use expression (14.24) to develop a 95% confidence interval for the expected value of y when $x = 4$.
  c. Use equation (14.26) to estimate the standard deviation of an individual value of y when $x = 4$.
  d. Use expression (14.27) to develop a 95% prediction interval for y when $x = 4$.

33. The data from exercise 2 follow.

x_i	3	12	6	20	14
y_i	55	40	55	10	15

  a. Estimate the standard deviation of $\hat{y}^*$ when $x = 8$.
  b. Develop a 95% confidence interval for the expected value of y when $x = 8$.
  c. Estimate the standard deviation of an individual value of y when $x = 8$.
  d. Develop a 95% prediction interval for y when $x = 8$.

34. The data from exercise 3 follow.

x_i	2	6	9	13	20
y_i	7	18	9	26	23

  Develop the 95% confidence and prediction intervals when $x = 12$. Explain why these two intervals are different.

Applications

35. **Restaurant Lines.** Many small restaurants in Portland, Oregon, and other cities across the United States do not take reservations. Owners say that with smaller capacity, no-shows are costly, and they would rather have their staff focused on customer service rather than maintaining a reservation system (*pressherald.com*). However, it is important to be able to give reasonable estimates of waiting time when customers arrive and put their name on the waiting list. The file *RestaurantLine* contains 40 observations of number of people in line ahead of a customer (independent variable x) and actual waiting time (dependent variable y). The estimated regression equation is: $\hat{y} = 4.35 + 8.81x$ and MSE = 94.42.

DATA*file*

RestaurantLine

  a. Develop a point estimate for a customer who arrive with three people on the wait-list.
  b. Develop a 95% confidence interval for the mean waiting time for a customer who arrives with three customers already in line.

c. Develop a 95% prediction interval for Roger and Sherry Davy's waiting time if there are three customers in line when they arrive.

d. Discuss the difference between parts (b) and (c).

DATA *file*

Sales

36. **Sales Performance.** In exercise 7, the data on y = annual sales ($1000s) for new customer accounts and x = number of years of experience for a sample of 10 salespersons provided the estimated regression equation $\hat{y} = 80 + 4x$. For these data $\bar{x} = 7$, $\Sigma(x_i - \bar{x})^2 = 142$, and $s = 4.6098$.

a. Develop a 95% confidence interval for the mean annual sales for all salespersons with nine years of experience.

b. The company is considering hiring Tom Smart, a salesperson with nine years of experience. Develop a 95% prediction interval of annual sales for Tom Smart.

c. Discuss the differences in your answers to parts (a) and (b).

37. **Auditing Itemized Deductions.** In exercise 13, data were given on the adjusted gross income x and the amount of itemized deductions taken by taxpayers. Data were reported in thousands of dollars. With the estimated regression equation $\hat{y} = 4.68 + .16x$, the point estimate of a reasonable level of total itemized deductions for a taxpayer with an adjusted gross income of $52,500 is $13,080.

a. Develop a 95% confidence interval for the mean amount of total itemized deductions for all taxpayers with an adjusted gross income of $52,500.

b. Develop a 95% prediction interval estimate for the amount of total itemized deductions for a particular taxpayer with an adjusted gross income of $52,500.

c. If the particular taxpayer referred to in part (b) claimed total itemized deductions of $20,400, would the IRS agent's request for an audit appear to be justified?

d. Use your answer to part (b) to give the IRS agent a guideline as to the amount of total itemized deductions a taxpayer with an adjusted gross income of $52,500 should claim before an audit is recommended.

38. **Prediction Intervals for Cost Estimation.** Refer to exercise 21, where data on the production volume x and total cost y for a particular manufacturing operation were used to develop the estimated regression equation $\hat{y} = 1246.67 + 7.6x$.

a. The company's production schedule shows that 500 units must be produced next month. What is the point estimate of the total cost for next month?

b. Develop a 99% prediction interval for the total cost for next month.

c. If an accounting cost report at the end of next month shows that the actual production cost during the month was $6000, should managers be concerned about incurring such a high total cost for the month? Discuss.

39. **Entertainment Spend.** *The Wall Street Journal* asked Concur Technologies, Inc., an expense-management company, to examine data from 8.3 million expense reports to provide insights regarding business travel expenses. Their analysis of the data showed that New York was the most expensive city. The following table shows the average daily hotel room rate (x) and the average amount spent on entertainment (y) for a random sample of 9 of the 25 most visited U.S. cities. These data lead to the estimated regression equation $\hat{y} = 17.49 + 1.0334x$. For these data, SSE = 1541.4.

DATA *file*

BusinessTravel

City	Room Rate ($)	Entertainment ($)
Boston	148	161
Denver	96	105
Nashville	91	101
New Orleans	110	142
Phoenix	90	100
San Diego	102	120
San Francisco	136	167
San Jose	90	140
Tampa	82	98

Predict the amount spent on entertainment for a particular city that has a daily room rate of $89.

14.7 Computer Solution

Performing the regression analysis computations without the help of a computer can be quite time consuming. In this section we discuss how the computational burden can be minimized by using a computer software package such as JMP or Excel.

Although the layout of the information may differ by computer software, the information shown in Figure 14.10 is fairly typical. We will use the structure illustrated in Figure 14.10, but be aware that the particular package you use may differ in style and in number of digits shown in the numerical output.

We have highlighted the portions of the output that are topics we have previously discussed in this chapter (the portions of the output not highlighted are beyond the scope of this text, but can be found in more advanced statistics texts).

The interpretation of the highlighted portion of the printout follows.

1. The ANOVA table is printed below the heading Analysis of Variance. The label Error is used for the error source of variation. Note that DF is an abbreviation for degrees of freedom and that MSR is given in the Regression row under the column Adj MS as 14,200 and MSE is given in the Error row under Adj MS as 191.2. The ratio of these two values provides the F value of 74.25 and the corresponding p-value of .000. Because the p-value is zero (to three decimal

---

FIGURE 14.10 Output for the Armand's Pizza Parlors Problem

Analysis of Variance

Source	DF	Adj SS	Adj MS	F-Value	P-Value	
Regression	1	14200.0	14200.0	74.25	.000	} ← **ANOVA table**
Error	8	1530.0	191.2			
Total	9	15730.0				

Model Summary

S	R-sq	R-sq(adj)
13.8293	90.27%	89.06%

For simple linear regression, Adj SS and Adj MS are the same as the SS and MS values as described in this chapter. The interpretation differs for multiple regression, which is discussed in Chapter 15.

Coefficients

Term	Coef	SE Coef	T-Value	P-Value
Constant	60.00	9.23	6.50	.000
Population	5.000	.580	8.62	.000

Regression Equation

Sales = 60.00 + 5.000 Population ← **Estimated Regression Equation**

Prediction for Sales

Variable	Setting
Population	10

Fit	SE Fit	95% CI	95% PI	
110	4.95099	(98.5830, 121.417)	(76.1275, 143.873)	← **Interval Estimates**

places), the relationship between Sales and Population is judged statistically significant.

2. Under the heading Model Summary, the standard error of the estimate, $s = 13.8293$, is given as well as information about the goodness of fit. Note that "R-sq = 90.27%" is the coefficient of determination expressed as a percentage. The value "R-Sq(adj) = 89.06%" is discussed in Chapter 15.

3. A table is printed that shows the values of the coefficients b_0 and b_1, the standard deviation of each coefficient, the t value obtained by dividing each coefficient value by its standard deviation, and the p-value associated with the t test. This appears under the heading Coefficients. Because the p-value is zero (to three decimal places), the sample results indicate that the null hypothesis (H_0: $\beta_1 = 0$) should be rejected. Alternatively, we could compare 8.62 (located in the T-Value column) to the appropriate critical value. This procedure for the t test was described in Section 14.5.

4. Under the heading Regression Equation, the estimated regression equation is given: Sales $= 60.00 + 5.000$ Population.

5. The 95% confidence interval estimate of the expected sales and the 95% prediction interval estimate of sales for an individual restaurant located near a campus with 10,000 students are printed below the ANOVA table. The confidence interval is (98.5830, 121.4417) and the prediction interval is (76.1275, 143.873) as we showed in Section 14.6.

EXERCISES

Applications

40. **Apartment Selling Price.** The commercial division of a real estate firm is conducting a regression analysis of the relationship between x, annual gross rents (in thousands of dollars), and y, selling price (in thousands of dollars) for apartment buildings. Data were collected on several properties recently sold and the following computer output was obtained.

Analysis of Variance

SOURCE	DF	Adj SS
Regression	1	41587.3
Error	7	
Total	8	51984.1

Predictor	Coef	SE Coef	T-Value
Constant	20.000	3.2213	6.21
X	7.210	1.3626	5.29

Regression Equation

$Y = 20.0 + 7.21\ X$

a. How many apartment buildings were in the sample?
b. Write the estimated regression equation.
c. What is the value of s_{b_1}?
d. Use the F statistic to test the significance of the relationship at a .05 level of significance.
e. Predict the selling price of an apartment building with gross annual rents of $50,000.

41. **Computer Maintenance.** Following is a portion of the computer output for a regression analysis relating y = maintenance expense (dollars per month) to x = usage (hours per week) of a particular brand of computer.

Analysis of Variance

SOURCE	DF	Adj SS	Adj MS
Regression	1	1575.76	1575.76
Error	8	349.14	43.64
Total	9	1924.90	

Predictor	Coef	SE Coef
Constant	6.1092	.9361
X	.8951	.1490

Regression Equation

$$Y = 6.1092 + .8951\ X$$

a. Write the estimated regression equation.
b. Use a t test to determine whether monthly maintenance expense is related to usage at the .05 level of significance.
c. Use the estimated regression equation to predict monthly maintenance expense for any computer that is used 25 hours per week.

42. **Annual Sales and Salesforce.** A regression model relating x, number of salespersons at a branch office, to y, annual sales at the office (in thousands of dollars) provided the following computer output from a regression analysis of the data.

Analysis of Variance

SOURCE	DF	Adj SS	Adj MS
Regression	1	6828.6	6828.6
Error	28	2298.8	82.1
Total	29	9127.4	

Predictor	Coef	SE Coef	T
Constant	80.0	11.333	7.06
X	50.0	5.482	9.12

Regression Equation

$$Y = 80.0 + 50.00\ X$$

a. Write the estimated regression equation.
b. How many branch offices were involved in the study?
c. Compute the F statistic and test the significance of the relationship at a .05 level of significance.
d. Predict the annual sales at the Memphis branch office. This branch employs 12 salespersons.

43. **Estimating Setup Time.** Sherry is a production manager for a small manufacturing shop and is interested in developing a predictive model to estimate the time to produce an order of a given size—that is, the total time to produce a certain quantity of the product. She has collected data on the total time to produce 30 different orders of various quantities in the file *Setup*.

DATA *file*

Setup

a. Develop a scatter diagram with quantity as the independent variable.
b. What does the scatter diagram developed in part (a) indicate about the relationship between the two variables?
c. Develop the estimated regression equation. Interpret the intercept and slope.
d. Test for a significant relationship. Use .05.
e. Did the estimated regression equation provide a good fit?

44. **Auto Racing Helmet.** Automobile racing, high-performance driving schools, and driver education programs run by automobile clubs continue to grow in popularity. All these activities require the participant to wear a helmet that is certified by the Snell Memorial Foundation, a not-for-profit organization dedicated to research, education, testing, and development of helmet safety standards. Snell "SA" (Sports Application)-rated professional helmets are designed for auto racing and provide extreme impact resistance and high fire protection. One of the key factors in selecting a helmet is weight, since lower weight helmets tend to place less stress on the neck. Consider the following data showing the weight and price for 18 SA helmets.

DATA *file*

RaceHelmets

Weight (oz)	Price ($)
64	248
64	278
64	200
64	200
58	300
47	700
49	900
59	340
66	199
58	299
58	299
52	479
52	479
63	369
62	369
54	559
63	250
63	280

a. Develop a scatter diagram with weight as the independent variable.
b. Does there appear to be any relationship between these two variables?
c. Develop the estimated regression equation that could be used to predict the price given the weight.
d. Test for the significance of the relationship at the .05 level of significance.
e. Did the estimated regression equation provide a good fit? Explain.

14.8 Residual Analysis: Validating Model Assumptions

Residual analysis is the primary tool for determining whether the assumed regression model is appropriate.

As we noted previously, the *residual* for observation i is the difference between the observed value of the dependent variable (y_i) and the predicted value of the dependent variable ($\hat{y}_i$).

RESIDUAL FOR OBSERVATION i

$$y_i - \hat{y}_i \tag{14.28}$$

where

y_i is the observed value of the dependent variable
$\hat{y}_i$ is the predicted value of the dependent variable

TABLE 14.7	Residuals for Armand's Pizza Parlors		
Student Population x_i	Sales y_i	Predicted Sales $\hat{y}_i = 60 + 5x_i$	Residuals $y_i - \hat{y}_i$
2	58	70	−12
6	105	90	15
8	88	100	−12
8	118	100	18
12	117	120	−3
16	137	140	−3
20	157	160	−3
20	169	160	9
22	149	170	−21
26	202	190	12

In other words, the ith residual is the error resulting from using the estimated regression equation to predict the value of the dependent variable. The residuals for the Armand's Pizza Parlors example are computed in Table 14.7. The observed values of the dependent variable are in the second column and the predicted values of the dependent variable, obtained using the estimated regression equation $\hat{y} = 60 + 5x$, are in the third column. An analysis of the corresponding residuals in the fourth column will help determine whether the assumptions made about the regression model are appropriate.

Let us now review the regression assumptions for the Armand's Pizza Parlors example. A simple linear regression model was assumed.

$$y = \beta_0 + \beta_1 x + \epsilon \tag{14.29}$$

This model indicates that we assumed quarterly sales (y) to be a linear function of the size of the student population (x) plus an error term ϵ. In Section 14.4 we made the following assumptions about the error term ϵ.

1. $E(\epsilon) = 0$.
2. The variance of ϵ, denoted by σ^2, is the same for all values of x.
3. The values of ϵ are independent.
4. The error term ϵ has a normal distribution.

These assumptions provide the theoretical basis for the t test and the F test used to determine whether the relationship between x and y is significant, and for the confidence and prediction interval estimates presented in Section 14.6. If the assumptions about the error term ϵ appear questionable, the hypothesis tests about the significance of the regression relationship and the interval estimation results may not be valid.

The residuals provide the best information about ϵ; hence an analysis of the residuals is an important step in determining whether the assumptions for ϵ are appropriate. Much of residual analysis is based on an examination of graphical plots. In this section, we discuss the following residual plots.

1. A plot of the residuals against values of the independent variable x
2. A plot of residuals against the predicted values of the dependent variable y
3. A standardized residual plot
4. A normal probability plot

Residual Plot Against x

A **residual plot** against the independent variable x is a graph in which the values of the independent variable are represented by the horizontal axis and the corresponding residual values

FIGURE 14.11   Plot of the Residuals Against the Independent Variable x for Armand's Pizza Parlors

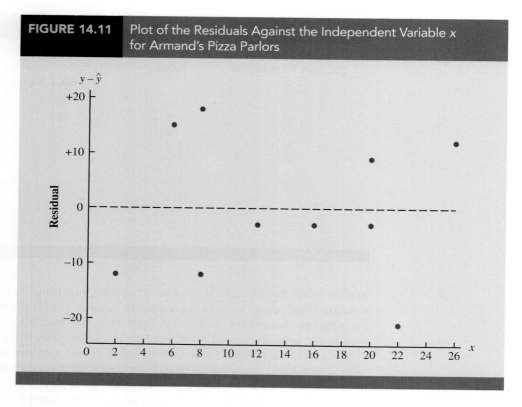

are represented by the vertical axis. A point is plotted for each residual. The first coordinate for each point is given by the value of x_i and the second coordinate is given by the corresponding value of the residual $y_i - \hat{y}_i$. For a residual plot against x with the Armand's Pizza Parlors data from Table 14.7, the coordinates of the first point are $(2, -12)$, corresponding to $x_1 = 2$ and $y_1 - \hat{y}_1 = -12$; the coordinates of the second point are $(6, 15)$, corresponding to $x_2 = 6$ and $y_2 - \hat{y}_2 = 15$; and so on. Figure 14.11 shows the resulting residual plot.

Before interpreting the results for this residual plot, let us consider some general patterns that might be observed in any residual plot. Three examples appear in Figure 14.12. If the assumption that the variance of ϵ is the same for all values of x and the assumed regression model is an adequate representation of the relationship between the variables, the residual plot should give an overall impression of a horizontal band of points such as the one in Panel A of Figure 14.12. However, if the variance of ϵ is not the same for all values of x—for example, if variability about the regression line is greater for larger values of x—a pattern such as the one in Panel B of Figure 14.12 could be observed. In this case, the assumption of a constant variance of ϵ is violated. Another possible residual plot is shown in Panel C. In this case, we would conclude that the assumed regression model is not an adequate representation of the relationship between the variables. A curvilinear regression model or multiple regression model should be considered.

Now let us return to the residual plot for Armand's Pizza Parlors shown in Figure 14.11. The residuals appear to approximate the horizontal pattern in Panel A of Figure 14.12. Hence, we conclude that the residual plot does not provide evidence that the assumptions made for Armand's regression model should be challenged. At this point, we are confident in the conclusion that Armand's simple linear regression model is valid.

Experience and good judgment are always factors in the effective interpretation of residual plots. Seldom does a residual plot conform precisely to one of the patterns in Figure 14.12. Yet analysts who frequently conduct regression studies and frequently review residual plots become adept at understanding the differences between patterns that are reasonable and patterns that indicate the assumptions of the model should be questioned. A residual plot provides one technique to assess the validity of the assumptions for a regression model.

FIGURE 14.12 Residual Plots from Three Regression Studies

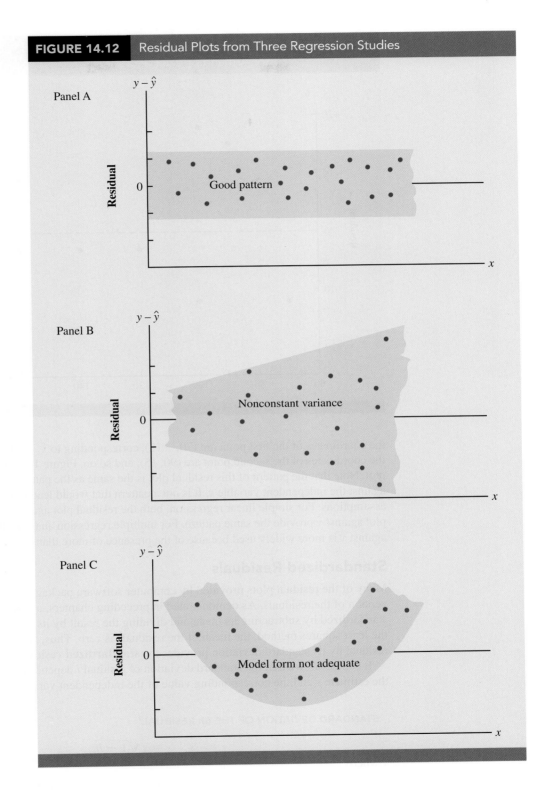

Residual Plot Against $\hat{y}$

Another residual plot represents the predicted value of the dependent variable $\hat{y}$ on the horizontal axis and the residual values on the vertical axis. A point is plotted for each residual. The first coordinate for each point is given by $\hat{y}_i$ and the second coordinate is given by the corresponding value of the ith residual $y_i - \hat{y}_i$. With the Armand's data from Table 14.7,

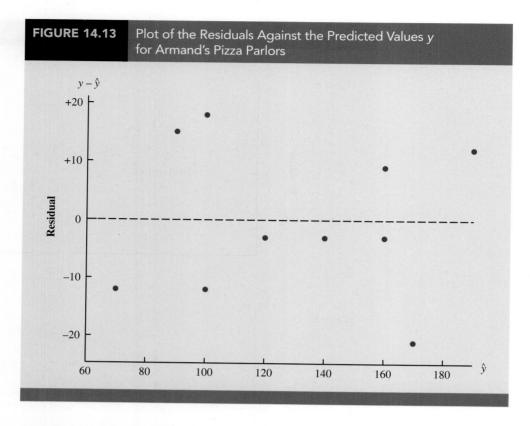

FIGURE 14.13 Plot of the Residuals Against the Predicted Values y for Armand's Pizza Parlors

the coordinates of the first point are $(70, -12)$, corresponding to $\hat{y}_1 = 70$ and $y_1 - \hat{y}_1 = -12$; the coordinates of the second point are $(90, 15)$; and so on. Figure 14.13 provides the residual plot. Note that the pattern of this residual plot is the same as the pattern of the residual plot against the independent variable x. It is not a pattern that would lead us to question the model assumptions. For simple linear regression, both the residual plot against x and the residual plot against $\hat{y}$ provide the same pattern. For multiple regression analysis, the residual plot against $\hat{y}$ is more widely used because of the presence of more than one independent variable.

Standardized Residuals

Many of the residual plots provided by computer software packages use a standardized version of the residuals. As demonstrated in preceding chapters, a random variable is standardized by subtracting its mean and dividing the result by its standard deviation. With the least squares method, the mean of the residuals is zero. Thus, simply dividing each residual by its standard deviation provides the **standardized residual**.

It can be shown that the standard deviation of residual i depends on the standard error of the estimate s and the corresponding value of the independent variable x_i.

STANDARD DEVIATION OF THE ith RESIDUAL[2]

$$s_{y_i - \hat{y}_i} = s\sqrt{1 - h_i} \tag{14.30}$$

where

$$s_{y_i - \hat{y}_i} = \text{the standard deviation of residual } i$$
$$s = \text{the standard error of the estimate}$$
$$h_i = \frac{1}{n} + \frac{(x_i - \bar{x})^2}{\Sigma(x_i - \bar{x})^2} \tag{14.31}$$

[2]This equation actually provides an estimate of the standard deviation of the ith residual, because s is used instead of σ.

Note that equation (14.30) shows that the standard deviation of the ith residual depends on x_i because of the presence of h_i in the formula.[3] Once the standard deviation of each residual is calculated, we can compute the standardized residual by dividing each residual by its corresponding standard deviation.

STANDARDIZED RESIDUAL FOR OBSERVATION i

$$\frac{y_i - \hat{y}_i}{s_{y_i - \hat{y}_i}}$$

(14.32)

Table 14.8 shows the calculation of the standardized residuals for Armand's Pizza Parlors. Recall that previous calculations showed $s = 13.829$. Figure 14.14 is the plot of the standardized residuals against the independent variable x.

The standardized residual plot can provide insight about the assumption that the error term ϵ has a normal distribution. If this assumption is satisfied, the distribution of the standardized residuals should appear to come from a standard normal probability distribution.[4] Thus, when looking at a standardized residual plot, we should expect to see approximately 95% of the standardized residuals between -2 and $+2$. We see in Figure 14.14 that for the Armand's example all standardized residuals are between -2 and $+2$. Therefore, on the basis of the standardized residuals, this plot gives us no reason to question the assumption that ϵ has a normal distribution.

Small departures from normality do not have a great effect on the statistical tests used in regression analysis.

Because of the effort required to compute the estimated values of $\hat{y}$, the residuals, and the standardized residuals, most statistical packages provide these values as optional regression output. Hence, residual plots can be easily obtained. For large problems computer packages are the only practical means for developing the residual plots discussed in this section.

Normal Probability Plot

Another approach for determining the validity of the assumption that the error term has a normal distribution is the **normal probability plot**. To show how a normal probability plot is developed, we introduce the concept of *normal scores*.

TABLE 14.8   Computation of Standardized Residuals for Armand's Pizza Parlors

Restaurant i	x_i	$x_i - \bar{x}$	$(x_i - \bar{x})^2$	$\dfrac{(x_i - \bar{x})^2}{\Sigma(x_i - \bar{x})^2}$	h_i	$s_{y_i - \hat{y}_i}$	$y_i - \hat{y}_i$	Standardized Residual
1	2	−12	144	.2535	.3535	11.1193	−12	−1.0792
2	6	−8	64	.1127	.2127	12.2709	15	1.2224
3	8	−6	36	.0634	.1634	12.6493	−12	−.9487
4	8	−6	36	.0634	.1634	12.6493	18	1.4230
5	12	−2	4	.0070	.1070	13.0682	−3	−.2296
6	16	2	4	.0070	.1070	13.0682	−3	−.2296
7	20	6	36	.0634	.1634	12.6493	−3	−.2372
8	20	6	36	.0634	.1634	12.6493	9	.7115
9	22	8	64	.1127	.2127	12.2709	−21	−1.7114
10	26	12	144	.2535	.3535	11.1193	12	1.0792
		Total	568					

Note: The values of the residuals were computed in Table 14.7.

---

[3]h_i is referred to as the leverage of observation i. Leverage will be discussed further when we consider influential observations in Section 14.9.

[4]Because s is used instead of σ in equation (14.30), the probability distribution of the standardized residuals is not technically normal. However, in most regression studies, the sample size is large enough that a normal approximation is very good.

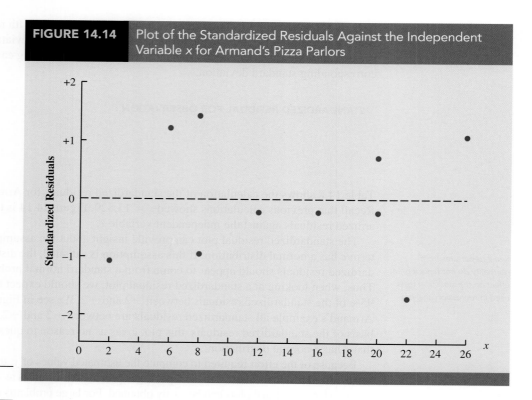

FIGURE 14.14 Plot of the Standardized Residuals Against the Independent Variable x for Armand's Pizza Parlors

TABLE 14.9

Normal Scores
For $n = 10$

Order Statistic	Normal Score
1	−1.55
2	−1.00
3	−.65
4	−.37
5	−.12
6	.12
7	.37
8	.65
9	1.00
10	1.55

TABLE 14.10

Normal Scores and
Ordered Standardized
Residuals for Armand's
Pizza Parlors

Normal Scores	Ordered Standardized Residuals
−1.55	−1.7114
−1.00	−1.0792
−.65	−.9487
−.37	−.2372
−.12	−.2296
.12	−.2296
.37	.7115
.65	1.0792
1.00	1.2224
1.55	1.4230

Suppose 10 values are selected randomly from a normal probability distribution with a mean of zero and a standard deviation of one, and that the sampling process is repeated over and over with the values in each sample of 10 ordered from smallest to largest. For now, let us consider only the smallest value in each sample. The random variable representing the smallest value obtained in repeated sampling is called the first-order statistic.

Statisticians show that for samples of size 10 from a standard normal probability distribution, the expected value of the first-order statistic is −1.55. This expected value is called a normal score. For the case with a sample of size $n = 10$, there are 10 order statistics and 10 normal scores (see Table 14.9). In general, a data set consisting of n observations will have n order statistics and hence n normal scores.

Let us now show how the 10 normal scores can be used to determine whether the standardized residuals for Armand's Pizza Parlors appear to come from a standard normal probability distribution. We begin by ordering the 10 standardized residuals from Table 14.8. The 10 normal scores and the ordered standardized residuals are shown together in Table 14.10. If the normality assumption is satisfied, the smallest standardized residual should be close to the smallest normal score, the next smallest standardized residual should be close to the next smallest normal score, and so on. If we were to develop a plot with the normal scores on the horizontal axis and the corresponding standardized residuals on the vertical axis, the plotted points should cluster closely around a 45-degree line passing through the origin if the standardized residuals are approximately normally distributed. Such a plot is referred to as a *normal probability plot*.

Figure 14.15 is the normal probability plot for the Armand's Pizza Parlors example. Judgment is used to determine whether the pattern observed deviates from the line enough to conclude that the standardized residuals are not from a standard normal probability distribution. In Figure 14.15, we see that the points are grouped closely about the line. We therefore conclude that the assumption of the error term having a normal probability

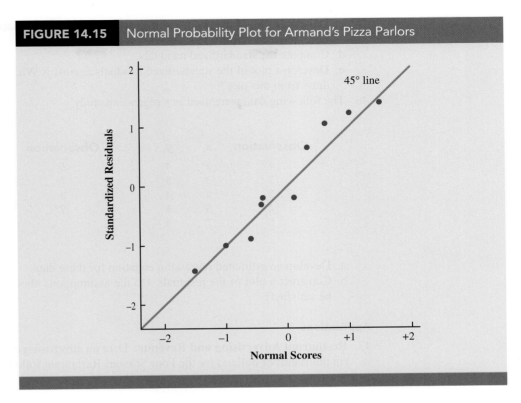

FIGURE 14.15   Normal Probability Plot for Armand's Pizza Parlors

distribution is reasonable. In general, the more closely the points are clustered about the 45-degree line, the stronger the evidence supporting the normality assumption. Any substantial curvature in the normal probability plot is evidence that the residuals have not come from a normal distribution. Normal scores and the associated normal probability plot can be obtained easily from statistical packages.

NOTES + COMMENTS

1. We use residual and normal probability plots to validate the assumptions of a regression model. If our review indicates that one or more assumptions are questionable, a different regression model or a transformation of the data should be considered. The appropriate corrective action when the assumptions are violated must be based on good judgment; recommendations from an experienced statistician can be valuable.

2. Analysis of residuals is the primary method statisticians use to verify that the assumptions associated with a regression model are valid. Even if no violations are found, it does not necessarily follow that the model will yield good predictions. However, if additional statistical tests support the conclusion of significance and the coefficient of determination is large, we should be able to develop good estimates and predictions using the estimated regression equation.

EXERCISES

Methods

45. Given are data for two variables, x and y.

x_i	6	11	15	18	20
y_i	6	8	12	20	30

    a. Develop an estimated regression equation for these data.
    b. Compute the residuals.

     c. Develop a plot of the residuals against the independent variable x. Do the assumptions about the error terms seem to be satisfied?

     d. Compute the standardized residuals.

     e. Develop a plot of the standardized residuals against $\hat{y}$. What conclusions can you draw from this plot?

46. The following data were used in a regression study.

Observation	x_i	y_i	Observation	x_i	y_i
1	2	4	6	7	6
2	3	5	7	7	9
3	4	4	8	8	5
4	5	6	9	9	11
5	7	4			

     a. Develop an estimated regression equation for these data.

     b. Construct a plot of the residuals. Do the assumptions about the error term seem to be satisfied?

Applications

47. **Restaurant Advertising and Revenue.** Data on advertising expenditures and revenue (in thousands of dollars) for the Four Seasons Restaurant follow.

Advertising Expenditures	Revenue
1	19
2	32
4	44
6	40
10	52
14	53
20	54

     a. Let x equal advertising expenditures and y equal revenue. Use the method of least squares to develop a straight line approximation of the relationship between the two variables.

     b. Test whether revenue and advertising expenditures are related at a .05 level of significance.

     c. Prepare a residual plot of $y - \hat{y}$ versus $\hat{y}$. Use the result from part (a) to obtain the values of $\hat{y}$.

     d. What conclusions can you draw from residual analysis? Should this model be used, or should we look for a better one?

48. **Experience and Sales.** Refer to exercise 7, where an estimated regression equation relating years of experience and annual sales was developed.

     a. Compute the residuals and construct a residual plot for this problem.

     b. Do the assumptions about the error terms seem reasonable in light of the residual plot?

49. **Buy Versus Rent.** Occasionally, it has been the case that home prices and mortgage rates dropped so low that in a number of cities the monthly cost of owning a home was less expensive than renting. The following data show the average asking rent for 10 markets and the monthly mortgage on the median priced home (including taxes and insurance) for 10 cities where the average monthly mortgage payment was less than the average asking rent (*The Wall Street Journal*).

City	Rent ($)	Mortgage ($)
Atlanta	840	539
Chicago	1062	1002
Detroit	823	626
Jacksonville, Fla.	779	711
Las Vegas	796	655
Miami	1071	977
Minneapolis	953	776
Orlando, Fla.	851	695
Phoenix	762	651
St. Louis	723	654

Source: The Wall Street Journal, (wsj.com)

a. Develop the estimated regression equation that can be used to predict the monthly mortgage given the average asking rent.
b. Construct a residual plot against the independent variable.
c. Do the assumptions about the error term and model form seem reasonable in light of the residual plot?

14.9 Residual Analysis: Outliers and Influential Observations

In Section 14.8 we showed how residual analysis could be used to determine when violations of assumptions about the regression model occur. In this section, we discuss how residual analysis can be used to identify observations that can be classified as outliers or as being especially influential in determining the estimated regression equation. Some steps that should be taken when such observations occur are discussed.

Detecting Outliers

Figure 14.16 is a scatter diagram for a data set that contains an **outlier**, a data point (observation) that does not fit the trend shown by the remaining data. Outliers represent observations that are suspect and warrant careful examination. They may represent erroneous data; if so, the data should be corrected. They may signal a violation of model assumptions; if so, another model should be considered. Finally, they may simply be unusual values that occurred by chance. In this case, they should be retained.

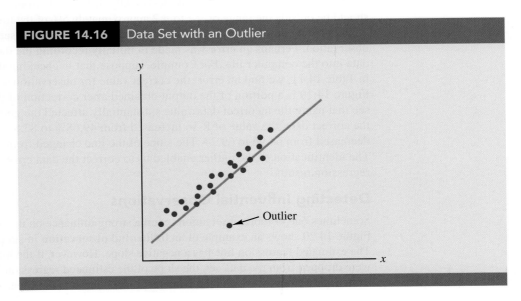

FIGURE 14.16   Data Set with an Outlier

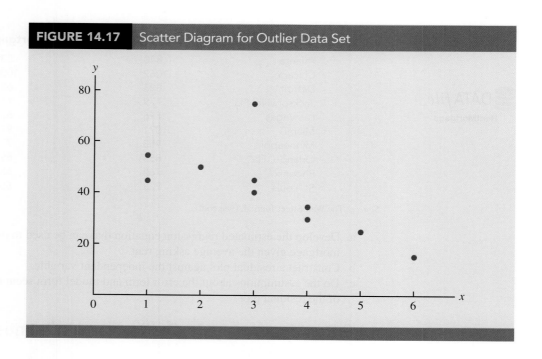

FIGURE 14.17 Scatter Diagram for Outlier Data Set

TABLE 14.11

Data Set Illustrating the Effect of an Outlier

x_i	y_i
1	45
1	55
2	50
3	75
3	40
3	45
4	30
4	35
5	25
6	15

To illustrate the process of detecting outliers, consider the data set in Table 14.11; Figure 14.17 is a scatter diagram. Except for observation 4 ($x_4 = 3$, $y_4 = 75$), a pattern suggesting a negative linear relationship is apparent. Indeed, given the pattern of the rest of the data, we would expect y_4 to be much smaller and hence would identify the corresponding observation as an outlier. For the case of simple linear regression, one can often detect outliers by simply examining the scatter diagram.

The standardized residuals can also be used to identify outliers. If an observation deviates greatly from the pattern of the rest of the data (e.g., the outlier in Figure 14.16), the corresponding standardized residual will be large in absolute value. Many computer packages automatically identify observations with standardized residuals that are large in absolute value. For the data in Table 14.11, Figure 14.18 shows the output from a regression analysis, including the regression equation, the predicted values of y, the residuals, and the standardized residuals. The highlighted portion of the output shows that the standardized residual for observation 4 is 2.67. With normally distributed errors, standardized residuals should be outside the range of -2 to $+2$ approximately 5% of the time.

In deciding how to handle an outlier, we should first check to see whether it is a valid observation. Perhaps an error was made in initially recording the data or in entering the data into the computer file. For example, suppose that in checking the data for the outlier in Table 14.11, we find an error; the correct value for observation 4 is $x_4 = 3$, $y_4 = 30$. Figure 14.19 is a portion of the output obtained after correction of the value of y_4. We see that using the incorrect data value substantially affected the goodness of fit. With the correct data, the value of R-sq increased from 49.68% to 83.8% and the value of b_0 decreased from 64.96 to 59.24. The slope of the line changed from -7.33 to -6.95. The identification of the outlier enabled us to correct the data error and improve the regression results.

Detecting Influential Observations

Sometimes one or more observations exert a strong influence on the results obtained. Figure 14.20 shows an example of an **influential observation** in simple linear regression. The estimated regression line has a negative slope. However, if the influential observation were dropped from the data set, the slope of the estimated regression line would change from negative to positive and the y-intercept would be smaller. Clearly, this one observation

FIGURE 14.18	Output for Regression Analysis of the Outlier Data Set

Analysis of Variance

Source	DF	Adj SS	Adj MS	F-Value	P-Value
Regression	1	1268.2	1268.2	7.90	.023
Error	8	1284.3	160.5		
Total	9	2552.5			

Model Summary

S	R-sq	R-sq(adj)
12.6704	49.68%	43.39%

Coefficients

Term	Coef	SE Coef	T-Value	P-Value
Constant	64.96	9.26	7.02	.000
x	−7.33	2.6	−2.81	.023

Regression Equation

$y = 64.96 - 7.33\,x$

Observation	Predicted y	Residuals	Standard Residuals
1	57.6271	−12.6271	−1.0570
2	57.6271	−2.6271	−.2199
3	50.2966	−.2966	−.0248
4	42.9661	32.0339	2.6816
5	42.9661	−2.9661	−.2483
6	42.9661	2.0339	.1703
7	35.6356	−5.6356	−.4718
8	35.6356	−.6356	−.0532
9	28.3051	−3.3051	−.2767
10	20.9746	−5.9746	−.5001

is much more influential in determining the estimated regression line than any of the others; dropping one of the other observations from the data set would have little effect on the estimated regression equation.

Influential observations can be identified from a scatter diagram when only one independent variable is present. An influential observation may be an outlier (an observation with a y value that deviates substantially from the trend), it may correspond to an x value far away from its mean (e.g., see Figure 14.20), or it may be caused by a combination of the two (a somewhat off-trend y value and a somewhat extreme x value).

Because influential observations may have such a dramatic effect on the estimated regression equation, they must be examined carefully. We should first check to make sure that no error was made in collecting or recording the data. If an error occurred, it can be corrected and a new estimated regression equation can be developed. If the observation is valid, we might consider ourselves fortunate to have it. Such a point, if valid, can contribute to a better understanding of the appropriate model and can lead to a better estimated regression equation. The presence of the influential observation in Figure 14.20, if valid, would suggest trying to obtain data on intermediate values of x to understand better the relationship between x and y.

FIGURE 14.19   Output for the Revised Outlier Data Set

Analysis of Variance

Source	DF	Adj SS	Adj MS	F-Value	P-Value
Regression	1	1139.66	1139.66	41.38	.000
Error	8	220.34	27.54		
Total	9	1360.00			

Model Summary

S	R-sq	R-sq(adj)
5.24808	83.80%	81.77%

Coefficients

Term	Coef	SE Coef	T-Value	P-Value
Constant	59.24	3.83	15.45	.000
x	−6.95	1.08	−6.43	.000

Regression Equation

$y = 59.24 - 6.95\ x$

FIGURE 14.20   Data Set with an Influential Observation

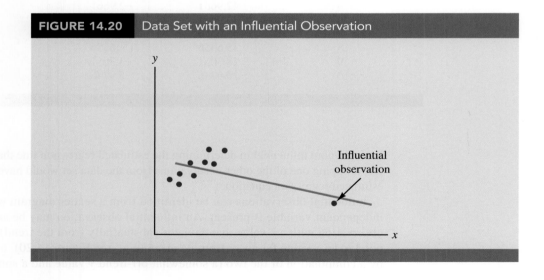

Observations with extreme values for the independent variables are called **high leverage points**. The influential observation in Figure 14.20 is a point with high leverage. The leverage of an observation is determined by how far the values of the independent variables are from their mean values. For the single-independent-variable case, the leverage of the ith observation, denoted h_i, can be computed by using equation (14.33).

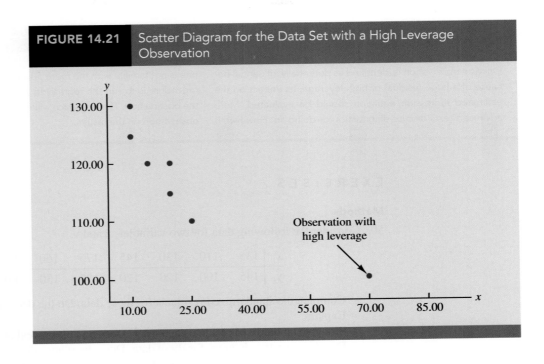

FIGURE 14.21   Scatter Diagram for the Data Set with a High Leverage Observation

LEVERAGE OF OBSERVATION i

$$h_i = \frac{1}{n} + \frac{(x_i - \bar{x})^2}{\Sigma(x_i - \bar{x})^2} \tag{14.33}$$

TABLE 14.12

Data Set with a High Leverage Observation

x_i	y_i
10	125
10	130
15	120
20	115
20	120
25	110
70	100

From the formula, it is clear that the farther x_i is from its mean $\bar{x}$, the higher the leverage of observation i.

Many statistical packages automatically identify observations with high leverage as part of the standard regression output. As an illustration of points with high leverage, let us consider the data set in Table 14.12.

From Figure 14.21, a scatter diagram for the data set in Table 14.12, it is clear that observation 7 ($x = 70$, $y = 100$) is an observation with an extreme value of x. Hence, we would expect it to be identified as a point with high leverage. For this observation, the leverage is computed by using equation (14.33) as follows.

$$h_7 = \frac{1}{n} + \frac{(x_7 - \bar{x})^2}{\Sigma(x_i - \bar{x})^2} = \frac{1}{7} + \frac{(70 - 24.286)^2}{2621.43} = .94$$

For the case of simple linear regression, observations have high leverage if $h_i > 6/n$ or .99, whichever is smaller. For the data set in Table 14.12, $6/n = 6/7 = .86$. Because $h_7 = .94 > .86$, we will identify observation 7 as an observation whose x value gives it large influence.

Influential observations that are caused by an interaction of large residuals and high leverage can be difficult to detect. Diagnostic procedures are available that take both into account in determining when an observation is influential. One such measure, called Cook's D statistic, will be discussed in Chapter 15.

NOTES + COMMENTS

Once an observation is identified as potentially influential because of a large residual or high leverage, its impact on the estimated regression equation should be evaluated. More advanced texts discuss diagnostics for doing so. However, if one is not familiar with the more advanced material, a simple procedure is to run the regression analysis with and without the observation. This approach will reveal the influence of the observation on the results.

EXERCISES

Methods

50. Consider the following data for two variables, x and y.

x_i	135	110	130	145	175	160	120
y_i	145	100	120	120	130	130	110

a. Compute the standardized residuals for these data. Do the data include any outliers? Explain.
b. Plot the standardized residuals against $\hat{y}$. Does this plot reveal any outliers?
c. Develop a scatter diagram for these data. Does the scatter diagram indicate any outliers in the data? In general, what implications does this finding have for simple linear regression?

51. Consider the following data for two variables, x and y.

x_i	4	5	7	8	10	12	12	22
y_i	12	14	16	15	18	20	24	19

a. Compute the standardized residuals for these data. Do the data include any outliers? Explain.
b. Compute the leverage values for these data. Do there appear to be any influential observations in these data? Explain.
c. Develop a scatter diagram for these data. Does the scatter diagram indicate any influential observations? Explain.

Applications

52. **Predicting Charity Expenses.** Charity Navigator is America's leading independent charity evaluator. The following data show the total expenses ($), the percentage of the total budget spent on administrative expenses, the percentage spent on fundraising, and the percentage spent on program expenses for 10 supersized charities (*Charity Navigator* website). Administrative expenses include overhead, administrative staff and associated costs, and organizational meetings. Fundraising expenses are what a charity spends to raise money, and program expenses are what the charity spends on the programs and services it exists to deliver. The sum of the three percentages does not add to 100% because of rounding.

DATA*file*
Charities

Charity	Total Expenses ($)	Administrative Expenses (%)	Fundraising Expenses (%)	Program Expenses (%)
American Red Cross	3,354,177,445	3.9	3.8	92.1
World Vision	1,205,887,020	4.0	7.5	88.3
Smithsonian Institution	1,080,995,083	23.5	2.6	73.7
Food For The Poor	1,050,829,851	.7	2.4	96.8
American Cancer Society	1,003,781,897	6.1	22.2	71.6

Charity	Total Expenses ($)	Administrative Expenses (%)	Fundraising Expenses (%)	Program Expenses (%)
Volunteers of America	929,158,968	8.6	1.9	89.4
Dana-Farber Cancer Institute	877,321,613	13.1	1.6	85.2
AmeriCares	854,604,824	.4	.7	98.8
ALSAC—St. Jude Children's Research Hospital	829,662,076	9.6	16.9	73.4
City of Hope	736,176,619	13.7	3.0	83.1

Source: Charity Navigator website, (https://www.charitynavigator.org/)

a. Develop a scatter diagram with fundraising expenses (%) on the horizontal axis and program expenses (%) on the vertical axis. Looking at the data, do there appear to be any outliers and/or influential observations?
b. Develop an estimated regression equation that could be used to predict program expenses (%) given fundraising expenses (%).
c. Does the value for the slope of the estimated regression equation make sense in the context of this problem situation?
d. Use residual analysis to determine whether any outliers and/or influential observations are present. Briefly summarize your findings and conclusions.

53. **Supermarket Checkout Lines.** Retail chain Kroger has more than 2700 locations and is the largest supermarket in the United States based on revenue. Kroger has invested heavily in data, technology, and analytics. Feeding predictive models with data from an infrared sensor system called QueVision to anticipate when shoppers will reach the checkout counters, Kroger is able to alert workers to open more checkout lines as needed. This has allowed Kroger to lower its average checkout time from four minutes to less than 30 seconds (*Retail Touchpoints*).

Checkout

   Consider the data in the file *Checkout*. The file contains 32 observations. Each observation gives the arrival time (measured in minutes before 6 P.M.) and the shopping time (measured in minutes).
a. Develop a scatter diagram for arrival time as the independent variable.
b. What does the scatter diagram developed in part (a) indicate about the relationship between the two variables? Do there appear to be any outliers or influential observations? Explain.
c. Using the entire data set, develop the estimated regression equation that can be used to predict the shopping time given the arrival time.
d. Use residual analysis to determine whether any outliers or influential observations are present.
e. After looking at the scatter diagram in part (a), suppose you were able to visually identify what appears to be an influential observation. Drop this observation from the data set and fit an estimated regression equation to the remaining data. Compare the estimated slope for the new estimated regression equation to the estimated slope obtained in part (c). Does this approach confirm the conclusion you reached in part (d)? Explain.

54. **Valuation of a Major League Baseball Team.** The following data show the annual revenue ($ millions) and the estimated team value ($ millions) for 30 Major League Baseball teams (*Forbes* website).

MLBValues

Team	Revenue ($ millions)	Value ($ millions)
Arizona Diamondbacks	195	584
Atlanta Braves	225	629
Baltimore Orioles	206	618
Boston Red Sox	336	1312
Chicago Cubs	274	1000

Team	Revenue ($ millions)	Value ($ millions)
Chicago White Sox	216	692
Cincinnati Reds	202	546
Cleveland Indians	186	559
Colorado Rockies	199	537
Detroit Tigers	238	643
Houston Astros	196	626
Kansas City Royals	169	457
Los Angeles Angels of Anaheim	239	718
Los Angeles Dodgers	245	1615
Miami Marlins	195	520
Milwaukee Brewers	201	562
Minnesota Twins	214	578
New York Mets	232	811
New York Yankees	471	2300
Oakland Athletics	173	468
Philadelphia Phillies	279	893
Pittsburgh Pirates	178	479
San Diego Padres	189	600
San Francisco Giants	262	786
Seattle Mariners	215	644
St. Louis Cardinals	239	716
Tampa Bay Rays	167	451
Texas Rangers	239	764
Toronto Blue Jays	203	568
Washington Nationals	225	631

Source: Forbes website, (HYPERLINK "https://www.forbes.com/sites/mikeozanian/2018/04/11/baseball-team-values-2018/"https://www.forbes.com/sites/mikeozanian/2018/04/11/baseball-team-values-2018/#2226481b3fc0)

a. Develop a scatter diagram with Revenue on the horizontal axis and Value on the vertical axis. Looking at the scatter diagram, does it appear that there are any outliers and/or influential observations in the data?

b. Develop the estimated regression equation that can be used to predict team value given the annual revenue.

c. Use residual analysis to determine whether any outliers and/or influential observations are present. Briefly summarize your findings and conclusions.

14.10 Practical Advice: Big Data and Hypothesis Testing in Simple Linear Regression

In Chapter 7, we observed that the standard errors of the sampling distributions of the sample mean $\bar{x}$ (shown in formula 7.2) and the sample proportion of $\bar{p}$ (shown in formula 7.5) decrease as the sample size increases. In Chapters 8 and 9, we observed that this results in narrower confidence interval estimates for μ and p and smaller p-values for the tests of the hypotheses $H_0: \mu \leq \mu_0$ and $H_0: p \leq p_0$ as the sample size increases. These results extend to simple linear regression. In simple linear regression, as the sample size increases,

- the p-value for the t-test used to determine whether a significant relationship exists between the dependent variable and the independent decreases;
- the confidence interval for the slope parameter associated with the independent variable narrows;
- the confidence interval for the mean value of y narrows;
- the prediction interval for an individual value of y narrows.

Thus, we are more likely to reject the hypothesis that a relationship does not exist between the dependent variable and the independent variable and conclude that a relationship exists as the sample size increases. The interval estimates for the slope parameter associated with the independent variable, the mean value of y, and predicted individual value of y will become more precise as the sample size increases. But this does not necessarily mean that these results become more reliable as the sample size increases.

No matter how large the sample used to estimate the simple linear regression equation, we must be concerned about the potential presence of nonsampling error in the data. It is important to carefully consider whether a random sample of the population of interest has actually been taken. If the data to be used for testing the hypothesis of no relationship between the independent and dependent variable are corrupted by nonsampling error, the likelihood of making a Type I or Type II error may be higher than if the sample data are free of nonsampling error. If the relationship between the independent and dependent variable is statistically significant, it is also important to consider whether the relationship in the simple linear regression equation is of *practical* significance.

Although simple linear regression is an extremely powerful statistical tool, it provides evidence that should be considered only in combination with information collected from other sources to make the most informed decision possible. No business decision should be based exclusively on inference in simple linear regression. Nonsampling error may lead to misleading results, and practical significance should always be considered in conjunction with statistical significance. This is particularly important when a hypothesis test is based on an extremely large sample because p-values in such cases can be extremely small. When executed properly, inference based on simple linear regression can be an important component in the business decision-making process.

SUMMARY

In this chapter we showed how regression analysis can be used to determine how a dependent variable y is related to an independent variable x. In simple linear regression, the regression model is $y = \beta_0 + \beta_1 x + \epsilon$. The simple linear regression equation $E(y) = \beta_0 + \beta_1 x$ describes how the mean or expected value of y is related to x. We used sample data and the least squares method to develop the estimated regression equation $\hat{y} = b_0 + b_1 x$. In effect, b_0 and b_1 are the sample statistics used to estimate the unknown model parameters β_0 and β_1.

The coefficient of determination was presented as a measure of the goodness of fit for the estimated regression equation; it can be interpreted as the proportion of the variation in the dependent variable y that can be explained by the estimated regression equation. We reviewed correlation as a descriptive measure of the strength of a linear relationship between two variables.

The assumptions about the regression model and its associated error term ϵ were discussed, and t and F tests, based on those assumptions, were presented as a means for determining whether the relationship between two variables is statistically significant. We showed how to use the estimated regression equation to develop confidence interval estimates of the mean value of y and prediction interval estimates of individual values of y.

The chapter concluded with a section on the computer solution of regression problems, two sections on the use of residual analysis to validate the model assumptions and to identify outliers and influential observations and a section on practical advice when using big data.

GLOSSARY

ANOVA table The analysis of variance table used to summarize the computations associated with the F test for significance.

Coefficient of determination A measure of the goodness of fit of the estimated regression equation. It can be interpreted as the proportion of the variability in the dependent variable y that is explained by the estimated regression equation.

Confidence interval   The interval estimate of the mean value of y for a given value of x.

Correlation coefficient   A measure of the strength of the linear relationship between two variables (previously discussed in Chapter 3).

Dependent variable   The variable that is being predicted or explained. It is denoted by y.

Estimated regression equation   The estimate of the regression equation developed from sample data by using the least squares method. For simple linear regression, the estimated regression equation is $\hat{y} = b_0 + b_1 x$.

High leverage points   Observations with extreme values for the independent variables.

Independent variable   The variable that is doing the predicting or explaining. It is denoted by x.

Influential observation   An observation that has a strong influence or effect on the regression results.

ith residual   The difference between the observed value of the dependent variable and the value predicted using the estimated regression equation; for the ith observation the ith residual is $y_i - \hat{y}_i$.

Least squares method   A procedure used to develop the estimated regression equation. The objective is to minimize $\Sigma(y_i - \hat{y}_i)^2$.

Mean square error   The unbiased estimate of the variance of the error term σ^2. It is denoted by MSE or s^2.

Normal probability plot   A graph of the standardized residuals plotted against values of the normal scores. This plot helps determine whether the assumption that the error term has a normal probability distribution appears to be valid.

Outlier   A data point or observation that does not fit the trend shown by the remaining data.

Prediction interval   The interval estimate of an individual value of y for a given value of x.

Regression equation   The equation that describes how the mean or expected value of the dependent variable is related to the independent variable; in simple linear regression, $E(y) = \beta_0 + \beta_1 x$.

Regression model   The equation that describes how y is related to x and an error term; in simple linear regression, the regression model is $y = \beta_0 + \beta_1 x + \epsilon$.

Residual analysis   The analysis of the residuals used to determine whether the assumptions made about the regression model appear to be valid. Residual analysis is also used to identify outliers and influential observations.

Residual plot   Graphical representation of the residuals that can be used to determine whether the assumptions made about the regression model appear to be valid.

Scatter diagram   A graph of bivariate data in which the independent variable is on the horizontal axis and the dependent variable is on the vertical axis.

Simple linear regression   Regression analysis involving one independent variable and one dependent variable in which the relationship between the variables is approximated by a straight line.

Standard error of the estimate   The square root of the mean square error, denoted by s. It is the estimate of σ, the standard deviation of the error term ϵ.

Standardized residual   The value obtained by dividing a residual by its standard deviation.

KEY FORMULAS

Simple Linear Regression Model

$$y = \beta_0 + \beta_1 x + \epsilon \tag{14.1}$$

Simple Linear Regression Equation

$$E(y) = \beta_0 + \beta_1 x \tag{14.2}$$

Estimated Simple Linear Regression Equation

$$\hat{y} = b_0 + b_1 x \tag{14.3}$$

Least Squares Criterion

$$\min \Sigma(y_i - \hat{y}_i)^2 \tag{14.5}$$

Slope and *y*-Intercept for the Estimated Regression Equation

$$b_1 = \frac{\Sigma(x_i - \bar{x})(y_i - \bar{y})}{\Sigma(x_i - \bar{x})^2} \tag{14.6}$$

$$b_0 = \bar{y} - b_1\bar{x} \tag{14.7}$$

Sum of Squares Due to Error

$$\text{SSE} = \Sigma(y_i - \bar{y}_i)^2 \tag{14.8}$$

Total Sum of Squares

$$\text{SST} = \Sigma(y_i - \bar{y})^2 \tag{14.9}$$

Sum of Squares Due to Regression

$$\text{SSR} = \Sigma(\hat{y}_i - \bar{y})^2 \tag{14.10}$$

Relationship Among SST, SSR, and SSE

$$\text{SST} = \text{SSR} + \text{SSE} \tag{14.11}$$

Coefficient of Determination

$$r^2 = \frac{\text{SSR}}{\text{SST}} \tag{14.12}$$

Sample Correlation Coefficient

$$
\begin{aligned}
r_{xy} &= (\text{sign of } b_1)\sqrt{\text{Coefficient of determination}} \\
&= (\text{sign of } b_1)\sqrt{r^2}
\end{aligned}
\tag{14.13}
$$

Mean Square Error (Estimate of σ^2)

$$s^2 = \text{MSE} = \frac{\text{SSE}}{n - 2} \tag{14.15}$$

Standard Error of the Estimate

$$s = \sqrt{\text{MSE}} = \sqrt{\frac{\text{SSE}}{n - 2}} \tag{14.16}$$

Standard Deviation of b_1

$$\sigma_{b_1} = \frac{\sigma}{\sqrt{\Sigma(x_i - \bar{x})^2}} \tag{14.17}$$

Estimated Standard Deviation of b_1

$$s_{b_1} = \frac{s}{\sqrt{\Sigma(x_i - \bar{x})^2}} \tag{14.18}$$

***t* Test Statistic**

$$t = \frac{b_1}{s_{b_1}} \tag{14.19}$$

Mean Square Regression

$$\text{MSR} = \frac{\text{SSR}}{\text{Number of independent variables}} \tag{14.20}$$

F Test Statistic

$$F = \frac{\text{MSR}}{\text{MSE}} \qquad\qquad (14.21)$$

Estimated Standard Deviation of $\hat{y}^*$

$$s_{\hat{y}^*} = s\sqrt{\frac{1}{n} + \frac{(x^* - \bar{x})^2}{\Sigma(x_i - \bar{x})^2}} \qquad\qquad (14.23)$$

Confidence Interval for $E(y^*)$

$$\hat{y}^* \pm t_{\alpha/2}s_{\hat{y}^*} \qquad\qquad (14.24)$$

Estimated Standard Deviation of an Individual Value

$$s_{\text{pred}} = s\sqrt{1 + \frac{1}{n} + \frac{(x^* - \bar{x})^2}{\Sigma(x_i - \bar{x})^2}} \qquad\qquad (14.26)$$

Prediction Interval for y^*

$$\hat{y}^* \pm t_{\alpha/2}s_{\text{pred}} \qquad\qquad (14.27)$$

Residual for Observation i

$$y_i - \hat{y}_i \qquad\qquad (14.28)$$

Standard Deviation of the ith Residual

$$s_{y_i - \hat{y}_i} = s\sqrt{1 - h_i} \qquad\qquad (14.30)$$

Standardized Residual for Observation i

$$\frac{y_i - \hat{y}_i}{s_{y_i - \hat{y}_i}} \qquad\qquad (14.32)$$

Leverage of Observation i

$$h_i = \frac{1}{n} + \frac{(x_i - \bar{x})^2}{\Sigma(x_i - \bar{x})^2} \qquad\qquad (14.33)$$

SUPPLEMENTARY EXERCISES

55. Does a high value of r^2 imply that two variables are causally related? Explain.
56. In your own words, explain the difference between an interval estimate of the mean value of y for a given x and an interval estimate for an individual value of y for a given x.
57. What is the purpose of testing whether $\beta_1 = 0$? If we reject $\beta_1 = 0$, does it imply a good fit?
58. **Stock Market Performance.** The Dow Jones Industrial Average (DJIA) and the Standard & Poor's 500 (S&P 500) indexes are used as measures of overall movement in the stock market. The DJIA is based on the price movements of 30 large companies; the S&P 500 is an index composed of 500 stocks. Some say the S&P 500 is a better measure of stock market performance because it is broader based. The closing price for the DJIA and the S&P 500 for 15 weeks, of a previous year follow (*Barron*'s website).

Date	DJIA	S&P
January 6	12,360	1278
January 13	12,422	1289
January 20	12,720	1315
January 27	12,660	1316
February 3	12,862	1345

DATA *file*

DJIAS&P500

Date	DJIA	S&P
February 10	12,801	1343
February 17	12,950	1362
February 24	12,983	1366
March 2	12,978	1370
March 9	12,922	1371
March 16	13,233	1404
March 23	13,081	1397
March 30	13,212	1408
April 5	13,060	1398
April 13	12,850	1370

Source: Barron's website, (http://www.barrons.com/data)

   a. Develop a scatter diagram with DJIA as the independent variable.
   b. Develop the estimated regression equation.
   c. Test for a significant relationship. Use $\alpha = .05$.
   d. Did the estimated regression equation provide a good fit? Explain.
   e. Suppose that the closing price for the DJIA is 13,500. Predict the closing price for the S&P 500.
   f. Should we be concerned that the DJIA value of 13,500 used to predict the S&P 500 value in part (e) is beyond the range of the data used to develop the estimated regression equation?

59. **Home Size and Price.** Is the number of square feet of living space a good predictor of a house's selling price? The following data collected in April, 2015, show the square footage and selling price for fifteen houses in Winston Salem, North Carolina (*Zillow.com*).

Size (1000s sq. ft)	Selling Price ($1000s)
1.26	117.5
3.02	299.9
1.99	139.0
.91	45.6
1.87	129.9
2.63	274.9
2.60	259.9
2.27	177.0
2.30	175.0
2.08	189.9
1.12	95.0
1.38	82.1
1.80	169.0
1.57	96.5
1.45	114.9

DATA *file*

WSHouses

Source: Zillow.com, April 5, 2015. (https://www.zillow.com/)

   a. Develop a scatter diagram with square feet of living space as the independent variable and selling price as the dependent variable. What does the scatter diagram indicate about the relationship between the size of a house and the selling price?
   b. Develop the estimated regression equation that could be used to predict the selling price given the number of square feet of living space.
   c. At the .05 level, is there a significant relationship between the two variables?
   d. Use the estimated regression equation to predict the selling price of a 2000 square foot house in Winston Salem, North Carolina.

e. Do you believe the estimated regression equation developed in part (b) will provide a good prediction of selling price of a particular house in Winston Salem, North Carolina? Explain.

f. Would you be comfortable using the estimated regression equation developed in part (b) to predict the selling price of a particular house in Seattle, Washington? Why or why not?

60. **Online Education.** One of the biggest changes in higher education in recent years has been the growth of online universities. The Online Education Database is an independent organization whose mission is to build a comprehensive list of the top accredited online colleges. The following table shows the retention rate (%) and the graduation rate (%) for 29 online colleges.

DATA *file*

OnlineEdu

Retention Rate (%)	Graduation Rate (%)
7	25
51	25
4	28
29	32
33	33
47	33
63	34
45	36
60	36
62	36
67	36
65	37
78	37
75	38
54	39
45	41
38	44
51	45
69	46
60	47
37	48
63	50
73	51
78	52
48	53
95	55
68	56
100	57
100	61

a. Develop a scatter diagram with retention rate as the independent variable. What does the scatter diagram indicate about the relationship between the two variables?

b. Develop the estimated regression equation.

c. Test for a significant relationship. Use $\alpha = .05$.

d. Did the estimated regression equation provide a good fit?

61. **Machine Maintenance.** Jensen Tire & Auto is in the process of deciding whether to purchase a maintenance contract for its new computer wheel alignment and balancing machine. Managers feel that maintenance expense should be related to usage,

and they collected the following information on weekly usage (hours) and annual maintenance expense (in hundreds of dollars).

Jensen

Weekly Usage (hours)	Annual Maintenance Expense
13	17.0
10	22.0
20	30.0
28	37.0
32	47.0
17	30.5
24	32.5
31	39.0
40	51.5
38	40.0

a. Develop the estimated regression equation that relates annual maintenance expense to weekly usage.
b. Test the significance of the relationship in part (a) at a .05 level of significance.
c. Jensen expects to use the new machine 30 hours per week. Develop a 95% prediction interval for the company's annual maintenance expense.
d. If the maintenance contract costs $3000 per year, would you recommend purchasing it? Why or why not?

62. **Production Rate and Quality Control.** In a manufacturing process the assembly line speed (feet per minute) was thought to affect the number of defective parts found during the inspection process. To test this theory, managers devised a situation in which the same batch of parts was inspected visually at a variety of line speeds. They collected the following data.

Line Speed	Number of Defective Parts Found
20	21
20	19
40	15
30	16
60	14
40	17

a. Develop the estimated regression equation that relates line speed to the number of defective parts found.
b. At a .05 level of significance, determine whether line speed and number of defective parts found are related.
c. Did the estimated regression equation provide a good fit to the data?
d. Develop a 95% confidence interval to predict the mean number of defective parts for a line speed of 50 feet per minute.

63. **Absenteeism and Location.** A sociologist was hired by a large city hospital to investigate the relationship between the number of unauthorized days that employees are absent per year and the distance (miles) between home and work for the employees. A sample of 10 employees was chosen, and the following data were collected.

Absent

Distance to Work (miles)	Number of Days Absent
1	8
3	5
4	8
6	7
8	6
10	3
12	5
14	2
14	4
18	2

a. Develop a scatter diagram for these data. Does a linear relationship appear reasonable? Explain.

b. Develop the least squares estimated regression equation.

c. Is there a significant relationship between the two variables? Use $\alpha = .05$.

d. Did the estimated regression equation provide a good fit? Explain.

e. Use the estimated regression equation developed in part (b) to develop a 95% confidence interval for the expected number of days absent for employees living 5 miles from the company.

64. **Bus Maintenance.** The regional transit authority for a major metropolitan area wants to determine whether there is any relationship between the age of a bus and the annual maintenance cost. A sample of 10 buses resulted in the following data.

AgeCost

Age of Bus (years)	Maintenance Cost ($)
1	350
2	370
2	480
2	520
2	590
3	550
4	750
4	800
5	790
5	950

a. Develop the least squares estimated regression equation.

b. Test to see whether the two variables are significantly related with $\alpha = .05$.

c. Did the least squares line provide a good fit to the observed data? Explain.

d. Develop a 95% prediction interval for the maintenance cost for a specific bus that is 4 years old.

65. **Studying and Grades.** A marketing professor at Givens College is interested in the relationship between hours spent studying and total points earned in a course. Data collected on 10 students who took the course last quarter follow.

HoursPts

Hours Spent Studying	Total Points Earned
45	40
30	35
90	75
60	65

Hours Spent Studying	Total Points Earned
105	90
65	50
90	90
80	80
55	45
75	65

a. Develop an estimated regression equation showing how total points earned is related to hours spent studying.
b. Test the significance of the model with $\alpha = .05$.
c. Predict the total points earned by Mark Sweeney. He spent 95 hours studying.
d. Develop a 95% prediction interval for the total points earned by Mark Sweeney.

66. **Market Beta.** Market betas for individual stocks are determined by simple linear regression. For each stock, the dependent variable is its quarterly percentage return (capital appreciation plus dividends) minus the percentage return that could be obtained from a risk-free investment (the Treasury Bill rate is used as the risk-free rate). The independent variable is the quarterly percentage return (capital appreciation plus dividends) for the stock market (S&P 500) minus the percentage return from a risk-free investment. An estimated regression equation is developed with quarterly data; the market beta for the stock is the slope of the estimated regression equation (b_1). The value of the market beta is often interpreted as a measure of the risk associated with the stock. Market betas greater than 1 indicate that the stock is more volatile than the market average; market betas less than 1 indicate that the stock is less volatile than the market average. Suppose that the following figures are the differences between the percentage return and the risk-free return for 10 quarters for the S&P 500 and Horizon Technology.

DATA *file*

MktBeta

S&P 500	Horizon
1.2	−.7
−2.5	−2.0
−3.0	−5.5
2.0	4.7
5.0	1.8
1.2	4.1
3.0	2.6
−1.0	2.0
.5	−1.3
2.5	5.5

a. Develop an estimated regression equation that can be used to predict the market beta for Horizon Technology. What is Horizon Technology's market beta?
b. Test for a significant relationship at the .05 level of significance.
c. Did the estimated regression equation provide a good fit? Explain.

67. **Income and Percent Audited.** The Transactional Records Access Clearinghouse at Syracuse University reported data showing the odds of an Internal Revenue Service audit. The following table shows the average adjusted gross income reported and the percent of the returns that were audited for 20 selected IRS districts.

DATA *file*

IRSAudit

District	Adjusted Gross Income ($)	Percent Audited
Los Angeles	36,664	1.3
Sacramento	38,845	1.1
Atlanta	34,886	1.1
Boise	32,512	1.1
Dallas	34,531	1.0
Providence	35,995	1.0
San Jose	37,799	.9
Cheyenne	33,876	.9
Fargo	30,513	.9
New Orleans	30,174	.9
Oklahoma City	30,060	.8
Houston	37,153	.8
Portland	34,918	.7
Phoenix	33,291	.7
Augusta	31,504	.7
Albuquerque	29,199	.6
Greensboro	33,072	.6
Columbia	30,859	.5
Nashville	32,566	.5
Buffalo	34,296	.5

a. Develop the estimated regression equation that could be used to predict the percent audited given the average adjusted gross income reported.
b. At the .05 level of significance, determine whether the adjusted gross income and the percent audited are related.
c. Did the estimated regression equation provide a good fit? Explain.
d. Use the estimated regression equation developed in part (a) to calculate a 95% confidence interval for the expected percent audited for districts with an average adjusted gross income of $35,000.

68. **Used Car Mileage and Price.** The Toyota Camry is one of the best-selling cars in North America. The cost of a previously owned Camry depends upon many factors, including the model year, mileage, and condition. To investigate the relationship between the car's mileage and the sales price for a 2007 model year Camry, the following data show the mileage and sale price for 19 sales (*PriceHub* website).

DATA *file*

Camry

Miles (1000s)	Price ($1000s)
22	16.2
29	16.0
36	13.8
47	11.5
63	12.5
77	12.9
73	11.2
87	13.0
92	11.8
101	10.8
110	8.3
28	12.5
59	11.1
68	15.0
68	12.2
91	13.0
42	15.6
65	12.7
110	8.3

Source: PriceHub website, (http://www.pricehub.com/)

a. Develop a scatter diagram with the car mileage on the horizontal axis and the price on the vertical axis.
b. What does the scatter diagram developed in part (a) indicate about the relationship between the two variables?
c. Develop the estimated regression equation that could be used to predict the price ($1000s) given the miles (1000s).
d. Test for a significant relationship at the .05 level of significance.
e. Did the estimated regression equation provide a good fit? Explain.
f. Provide an interpretation for the slope of the estimated regression equation.
g. Suppose that you are considering purchasing a previously owned 2007 Camry that has been driven 60,000 miles. Using the estimated regression equation developed in part (c), predict the price for this car. Is this the price you would offer the seller?

CASE PROBLEM 1: MEASURING STOCK MARKET RISK

One measure of the risk or volatility of an individual stock is the standard deviation of the total return (capital appreciation plus dividends) over several periods of time. Although the standard deviation is easy to compute, it does not take into account the extent to which the price of a given stock varies as a function of a standard market index, such as the S&P 500. As a result, many financial analysts prefer to use another measure of risk referred to as *beta*.

DATA*file*

Beta

Betas for individual stocks are determined by simple linear regression. The dependent variable is the total return for the stock and the independent variable is the total return for the stock market.* For this case problem we will use the S&P 500 index as the measure of the total return for the stock market, and an estimated regression equation will be developed using monthly data. The beta for the stock is the slope of the estimated regression equation (b_1). The data contained in the file named Beta provides the total return (capital appreciation plus dividends) over 36 months for eight widely traded common stocks and the S&P 500.

The value of beta for the stock market will always be 1; thus, stocks that tend to rise and fall with the stock market will also have a beta close to 1. Betas greater than 1 indicate that the stock is more volatile than the market, and betas less than 1 indicate that the stock is less volatile than the market. For instance, if a stock has a beta of 1.4, it is 40% *more* volatile than the market, and if a stock has a beta of .4, it is 60% *less* volatile than the market.

Managerial Report

You have been assigned to analyze the risk characteristics of these stocks. Prepare a report that includes but is not limited to the following items.

a. Compute descriptive statistics for each stock and the S&P 500. Comment on your results. Which stocks are the most volatile?
b. Compute the value of beta for each stock. Which of these stocks would you expect to perform best in an up market? Which would you expect to hold their value best in a down market?
c. Comment on how much of the return for the individual stocks is explained by the market.

CASE PROBLEM 2: U.S. DEPARTMENT OF TRANSPORTATION

As part of a study on transportation safety, the U.S. Department of Transportation collected data on the number of fatal accidents per 1000 licenses and the percentage of licensed

---

*Various sources use different approaches for computing betas. For instance, some sources subtract the return that could be obtained from a risk-free investment (e.g., T-bills) from the dependent variable and the independent variable before computing the estimated regression equation. Some also use different indexes for the total return of the stock market; for instance, Value Line computes betas using the New York Stock Exchange composite index.

drivers under the age of 21 in a sample of 42 cities. Data collected over a one-year period follow. These data are contained in the file named Safety.

DATA *file*

Safety

Percent Under 21	Fatal Accidents per 1000 Licenses	Percent Under 21	Fatal Accidents per 1000 Licenses
13	2.962	17	4.100
12	.708	8	2.190
8	.885	16	3.623
12	1.652	15	2.623
11	2.091	9	.835
17	2.627	8	.820
18	3.830	14	2.890
8	.368	8	1.267
13	1.142	15	3.224
8	.645	10	1.014
9	1.028	10	.493
16	2.801	14	1.443
12	1.405	18	3.614
9	1.433	10	1.926
10	.039	14	1.643
9	.338	16	2.943
11	1.849	12	1.913
12	2.246	15	2.814
14	2.855	13	2.634
14	2.352	9	.926
11	1.294	17	3.256

Source: U.S. Department of Transportation, (https://www.transportation.gov/)

Managerial Report

1. Develop numerical and graphical summaries of the data.
2. Use regression analysis to investigate the relationship between the number of fatal accidents and the percentage of drivers under the age of 21. Discuss your findings.
3. What conclusion and recommendations can you derive from your analysis?

CASE PROBLEM 3: SELECTING A POINT-AND-SHOOT DIGITAL CAMERA

Consumer Reports tested 166 different point-and-shoot digital cameras. Based upon factors such as the number of megapixels, weight (oz.), image quality, and ease of use, they developed an overall score for each camera tested. The overall score ranges from 0 to 100, with higher scores indicating better overall test results. Selecting a camera with many options can be a difficult process, and price is certainly a key issue for most consumers. By spending more, will a consumer really get a superior camera? And, do cameras that have more megapixels, a factor often considered to be a good measure of picture quality, cost more than cameras with fewer megapixels? Table 14.13 shows the brand, average retail price ($), number of megapixels, weight (oz.), and the overall score for 13 Canon and 15 Nikon subcompact cameras tested by *Consumer Reports* (*Consumer Reports* website).

Managerial Report

1. Develop numerical summaries of the data.
2. Using overall score as the dependent variable, develop three scatter diagrams, one using price as the independent variable, one using the number of megapixels as the independent variable, and one using weight as the independent variable. Which of the three independent variables appears to be the best predictor of overall score?

		Price		Weight	
Observation	Brand	($)	Megapixels	(oz.)	Score
1	Canon	330	10	7	66
2	Canon	200	12	5	66
3	Canon	300	12	7	65
4	Canon	200	10	6	62
5	Canon	180	12	5	62
6	Canon	200	12	7	61
7	Canon	200	14	5	60
8	Canon	130	10	7	60
9	Canon	130	12	5	59
10	Canon	110	16	5	55
11	Canon	90	14	5	52
12	Canon	100	10	6	51
13	Canon	90	12	7	46
14	Nikon	270	16	5	65
15	Nikon	300	16	7	63
16	Nikon	200	14	6	61
17	Nikon	400	14	7	59
18	Nikon	120	14	5	57
19	Nikon	170	16	6	56
20	Nikon	150	12	5	56
21	Nikon	230	14	6	55
22	Nikon	180	12	6	53
23	Nikon	130	12	6	53
24	Nikon	80	12	7	52
25	Nikon	80	14	7	50
26	Nikon	100	12	4	46
27	Nikon	110	12	5	45
28	Nikon	130	14	4	42

TABLE 14.13 Data for 28 Point-and-Shoot Digital Cameras

DATA *file*

Cameras

3. Using simple linear regression, develop an estimated regression equation that could be used to predict the overall score given the price of the camera. For this estimated regression equation, perform an analysis of the residuals and discuss your findings and conclusions.

4. Analyze the data using only the observations for the Canon cameras. Discuss the appropriateness of using simple linear regression and make any recommendations regarding the prediction of overall score using just the price of the camera.

CASE PROBLEM 4: FINDING THE BEST CAR VALUE

When trying to decide what car to buy, real value is not necessarily determined by how much you spend on the initial purchase. Instead, cars that are reliable and don't cost much to own often represent the best values. But, no matter how reliable or inexpensive a car may cost to own, it must also perform well.

To measure value, *Consumer Reports* developed a statistic referred to as a value score. The value score is based upon five-year owner costs, overall road-test scores, and predicted reliability ratings. Five-year owner costs are based on the expenses incurred in the first five years of ownership, including depreciation, fuel, maintenance and repairs, and so on. Using a national average of 12,000 miles per year, an average cost per mile driven is used as the measure of five-year owner costs. Road-test scores are the results of more than 50 tests and evaluations and are based upon a 100-point scale, with higher scores indicating better performance, comfort, convenience, and fuel economy. The highest road-test score obtained in the tests conducted by *Consumer Reports* was a 99 for a Lexus LS 460L. Predicted-reliability ratings (1 = Poor, 2 = Fair, 3 = Good, 4 = Very Good, and 5 = Excellent) are based on data from *Consumer Reports'* Annual Auto Survey.

A car with a value score of 1.0 is considered to be "average-value." A car with a value score of 2.0 is considered to be twice as good a value as a car with a value score of 1.0; a car with a value score of .5 is considered half as good as average; and so on. The data for 20 family sedans, including the price ($) of each car tested, follow.

DATA *file*

FamilySedans

Car	Price ($)	Cost/Mile	Road-Test Score	Predicted Reliability	Value Score
Nissan Altima 2.5 S (4-cyl.)	23,970	.59	91	4	1.75
Kia Optima LX (2.4)	21,885	.58	81	4	1.73
Subaru Legacy 2.5i Premium	23,830	.59	83	4	1.73
Ford Fusion Hybrid	32,360	.63	84	5	1.70
Honda Accord LX-P (4-cyl.)	23,730	.56	80	4	1.62
Mazda6 i Sport (4-cyl.)	22,035	.58	73	4	1.60
Hyundai Sonata GLS (2.4)	21,800	.56	89	3	1.58
Ford Fusion SE (4-cyl.)	23,625	.57	76	4	1.55
Chevrolet Malibu LT (4-cyl.)	24,115	.57	74	3	1.48
Kia Optima SX (2.0T)	29,050	.72	84	4	1.43
Ford Fusion SEL (V6)	28,400	.67	80	4	1.42
Nissan Altima 3.5 SR (V6)	30,335	.69	93	4	1.42
Hyundai Sonata Limited (2.0T)	28,090	.66	89	3	1.39
Honda Accord EX-L (V6)	28,695	.67	90	3	1.36
Mazda6 s Grand Touring (V6)	30,790	.74	81	4	1.34
Ford Fusion SEL (V6, AWD)	30,055	.71	75	4	1.32
Subaru Legacy 3.6R Limited	30,094	.71	88	3	1.29
Chevrolet Malibu LTZ (V6)	28,045	.67	83	3	1.20
Chrysler 200 Limited (V6)	27,825	.70	52	5	1.20
Chevrolet Impala LT (3.6)	28,995	.67	63	3	1.05

Managerial Report

1. Develop numerical summaries of the data.
2. Use regression analysis to develop an estimated regression equation that could be used to predict the value score given the price of the car.
3. Use regression analysis to develop an estimated regression equation that could be used to predict the value score given the five-year owner costs (cost/mile).
4. Use regression analysis to develop an estimated regression equation that could be used to predict the value score given the road-test score.
5. Use regression analysis to develop an estimated regression equation that could be used to predict the value score given the predicted-reliability.
6. What conclusions can you derive from your analysis?

CASE PROBLEM 5: BUCKEYE CREEK AMUSEMENT PARK

Buckeye Creek Amusement Park is open from the beginning of May to the end of October. Buckeye Creek relies heavily on the sale of season passes. The sale of season passes brings in significant revenue prior to the park opening each season, and season pass holders

BuckeyeCreek

contribute a substantial portion of the food, beverage, and novelty sales in the park. Greg Ross, director of marketing at Buckeye Creek, has been asked to develop a targeted marketing campaign to increase season pass sales.

Greg has data for last season that show the number of season pass holders for each zip code within 50 miles of Buckeye Creek. He has also obtained the total population of each zip code from the U.S. Census bureau website. Greg thinks it may be possible to use regression analysis to predict the number of season pass holders in a zip code given the total population of a zip code. If this is possible, he could then conduct a direct mail campaign that would target zip codes that have fewer than the expected number of season pass holders.

Managerial Report

1. Compute descriptive statistics and construct a scatter diagram for the data. Discuss your findings.
2. Using simple linear regression, develop an estimated regression equation that could be used to predict the number of season pass holders in a zip code given the total population of the zip code.
3. Test for a significant relationship at the .05 level of significance.
4. Did the estimated regression equation provide a good fit?
5. Use residual analysis to determine whether the assumed regression model is appropriate.
6. Discuss if/how the estimated regression equation should be used to guide the marketing campaign.
7. What other data might be useful to predict the number of season pass holders in a zip code?

Chapter 14 Appendix

Appendix 14.1 Calculus-Based Derivation of Least Squares Formulas

As mentioned in the chapter, the least squares method is a procedure for determining the values of b_0 and b_1 that minimize the sum of squared residuals. The sum of squared residuals is given by

$$\Sigma(y_i - \hat{y}_i)^2$$

Substituting $\hat{y}_i = b_0 + b_1 x_i$, we get

$$\Sigma(y_i - b_0 - b_1 x_i)^2 \tag{14.34}$$

as the expression that must be minimized.

To minimize expression (14.34), we must take the partial derivatives with respect to b_0 and b_1, set them equal to zero, and solve. Doing so, we get

$$\frac{\partial \Sigma(y_i - b_0 - b_1 x_i)^2}{\partial b_0} = -2\Sigma(y_i - b_0 - b_1 x_i) = 0 \tag{14.35}$$

$$\frac{\partial \Sigma(y_i - b_0 - b_1 x_i)^2}{\partial b_1} = -2\Sigma x_i(y_i - b_0 - b_1 x_i) = 0 \tag{14.36}$$

Dividing equation (14.35) by two and summing each term individually yields

$$-\Sigma y_i + \Sigma b_0 + \Sigma b_1 x_i = 0$$

Bringing Σy_i to the other side of the equal sign and noting that $\Sigma b_0 = n b_0$, we obtain

$$n b_0 + (\Sigma x_i) b_1 = \Sigma y_i \tag{14.37}$$

Similar algebraic simplification applied to equation (14.36) yields

$$(\Sigma x_i) b_0 + (\Sigma x_i^2) b_1 = \Sigma x_i y_i \tag{14.38}$$

Equations (14.37) and (14.38) are known as the *normal equations*. Solving equation (14.37) for b_0 yields

$$b_0 = \frac{\Sigma y_i}{n} - b_1 \frac{\Sigma x_i}{n} \tag{14.39}$$

Using equation (14.39) to substitute for b_0 in equation (14.38) provides

$$\frac{\Sigma x_i \Sigma y_i}{n} - \frac{(\Sigma x_i)^2}{n} b_1 + (\Sigma x_i^2) b_1 = \Sigma x_i y_i \tag{14.40}$$

By rearranging the terms in equation (14.40), we obtain

$$b_1 = \frac{\Sigma x_i y_i - (\Sigma x_i \Sigma y_i)/n}{\Sigma x_i^2 - (\Sigma x_i)^2/n} = \frac{\Sigma(x_i - \bar{x})(y_i - \bar{y})}{\Sigma(x_i - \bar{x})^2} \tag{14.41}$$

Because $\bar{y} = \Sigma y_i/n$ and $\bar{x} = \Sigma x_i/n$, we can rewrite equation (14.39) as

$$b_0 = \bar{y} - b_1 \bar{x} \tag{14.42}$$

Equations (14.41) and (14.42) are the formulas (14.6) and (14.7) we used in the chapter to compute the coefficients in the estimated regression equation.

Appendix 14.2 A Test for Significance Using Correlation

Using the sample correlation coefficient r_{xy}, we can determine whether the linear relationship between x and y is significant by testing the following hypotheses about the population correlation coefficient ρ_{xy}.

$$H_0: \rho_{xy} = 0$$
$$H_a: \rho_{xy} \neq 0$$

If H_0 is rejected, we can conclude that the population correlation coefficient is not equal to zero and that the linear relationship between the two variables is significant. This test for significance follows.

A TEST FOR SIGNIFICANCE USING CORRELATION

$$H_0: \rho_{xy} = 0$$
$$H_a: \rho_{xy} \neq 0$$

TEST STATISTIC

$$t = r_{xy} \sqrt{\frac{n-2}{1-r_{xy}^2}} \qquad\qquad (14.43)$$

REJECTION RULE

p-value approach: Reject H_0 if p-value $\leq \alpha$

Critical value approach: Reject H_0 if $t \leq -t_{\alpha/2}$ or if $t \geq t_{\alpha/2}$

where $t_{\alpha/2}$ is based on a t distribution with $n-2$ degrees of freedom.

In Section 14.3, we found that the sample with $n = 10$ provided the sample correlation coefficient for student population and quarterly sales of $r_{xy} = .9501$. The test statistic is

$$t = r_{xy} \sqrt{\frac{n-2}{1-r_{xy}^2}} = .9501 \sqrt{\frac{10-2}{1-(.9501)^2}} = 8.61$$

The t distribution table shows that with $n - 2 = 10 - 2 = 8$ degrees of freedom, $t = 3.355$ provides an area of .005 in the upper tail. Thus, the area in the upper tail of the t distribution corresponding to the test statistic $t = 8.61$ must be less than .005. Because this test is a two-tailed test, we double this value to conclude that the p-value associated with $t = 8.61$ must be less than $2(.005) = .01$. Because the p-value is less than $\alpha = .01$, we reject H_0 and conclude that ρ_{xy} is not equal to zero. This evidence is sufficient to conclude that a significant linear relationship exists between student population and quarterly sales.

Note that except for rounding, the test statistic t and the conclusion of a significant relationship are identical to the results obtained in Section 14.5 for the t test conducted using Armand's estimated regression equation $\hat{y} = 60 + 5x$. Performing regression analysis provides the conclusion of a significant relationship between x and y and in addition provides the equation showing how the variables are related. Most analysts therefore use modern computer packages to perform regression analysis and find that using correlation as a test of significance is unnecessary.

Appendix 14.3 Simple Linear Regression with JMP

In this appendix we describe how to use JMP to perform a simple linear regression.

DATA *file*

Armand's

Step 1. Open the file *Armand's* with JMP using the steps provided in Appendix 1.1

Step 2. From the **Data** window containing the population and sales data, click **Analyze** and select **Fit Y by X**

FIGURE JMP 14.1   Simple Linear Regression JMP Output for Armand's Pizza

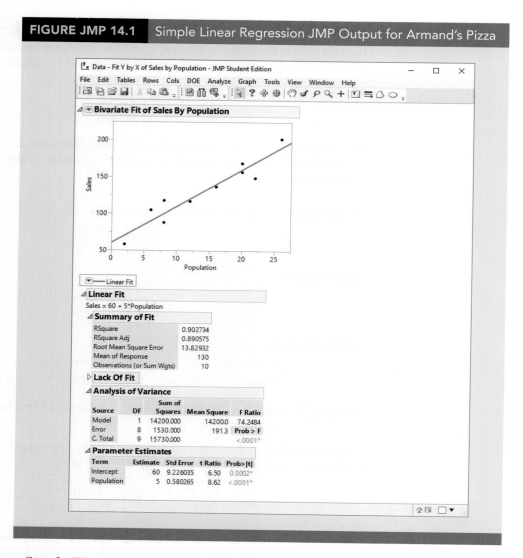

Step 3. When the **Fit Y by X—Contextual** window appears:
   Drag **Sales** in the **Select Columns** area to the **Y, Response** box in the **Cast Selected Columns into Roles** area
   Drag **Population** in the **Select Columns** area to the **X, Factor** box in the **Cast Selected Columns into Roles** area
   Click **OK** in the **Action** area

Step 4. When the **Data—Fit Y by X of Sales by Population** window appears:
   Click on the red triangle ▼ next to **Bivariate Fit of Sales by Population** and select **Fit Line**

The regression output appears as shown in Figure JMP 14.1. We see that the estimated regression equation is Sales = 60 + 5*Population. The R^2 = .902734. The **Analysis of Variance** section indicates that the model is significant at the .01 level (F ratio = 74.2484) and Prob F < .0001 < .01. Similarly, in the **Parameter Estimates** section, we see that Population is significant at the .01 level (Prob > |t| < .001 < .01).

Appendix 14.4 Regression Analysis with Excel

DATA *file*

Armand's

In this appendix we will illustrate how Excel's Regression tool can be used to perform the regression analysis computations for the Armand's Pizza Parlors problem. Refer to Figure Excel 14.1 as we describe the steps involved. The labels Restaurant, Population, and Sales

FIGURE Excel 14.1   Excel Solution to the Armand's Pizza Parlors Problem

	A	B	C	D	E	F	G	H	I	J
1	**Restaurant**	**Population**	**Sales**							
2	1	2	58							
3	2	6	105							
4	3	8	88							
5	4	8	118							
6	5	12	117							
7	6	16	137							
8	7	20	157							
9	8	20	169							
10	9	22	149							
11	10	26	202							
12										
13	SUMMARY OUTPUT									
14										
15	*Regression Statistics*									
16	Multiple R	0.9501								
17	R Square	0.9027								
18	Adjusted R Square	0.8906								
19	Standard Error	13.8293								
20	Observations	10								
21										
22	ANOVA									
23		*df*	*SS*	*MS*	*F*	*Significance F*				
24	Regression	1	14200	14200	74.2484	2.55E-05				
25	Residual	8	1530	191.25						
26	Total	9	15730							
27										
28		*Coefficients*	*Standard Error*	*t Stat*	*P-value*	*Lower 95%*	*Upper 95%*	*Lower 99.0%*	*Upper 99.0%*	
29	Intercept	60	9.2260	6.5033	0.0002	38.7247	81.2753	29.0431	90.9569	
30	Population	5	0.5803	8.6167	2.55E-05	3.6619	6.3381	3.0530	6.9470	
31										

are entered into cells A1:C1 of the worksheet. To identify each of the 10 observations, we entered the numbers 1 through 10 into cells A2:A11. The sample data are entered into cells B2:C11. The following steps describe how to use Excel to produce the regression results.

Step 1. Click the **Data** tab on the Ribbon
Step 2. In the **Analyze** group, click **Data Analysis**
Step 3. Choose **Regression** from the list of Analysis Tools
Step 4. Click **OK**
Step 5. When the Regression dialog box appears:
　　　　　Enter *C1:C11* in the **Input Y Range:** box
　　　　　Enter *B1:B11* in the **Input X Range:** box
　　　　　Select the check box for **Labels**
　　　　　Select the check box for **Confidence Level:** and enter *99* in the box
　　　　　Select **Output Range:** and enter *A13* in the box
　　　　　Click **OK**

The first section of the output, titled *Regression Statistics*, contains summary statistics such as the coefficient of determination (R Square). The second section of the output, titled ANOVA, contains the analysis of variance table. The last section of the output, which is not titled, contains the estimated regression coefficients and related information. We will begin our discussion of the interpretation of the regression output with the information contained in cells A28:I30.

Interpretation of Estimated Regression Equation Output

The y-intercept of the estimated regression line, $b_0 = 60$, is shown in cell B29, and the slope of the estimated regression line, $b_1 = 5$, is shown in cell B30. The label Intercept in cell A29 and the label Population in cell A30 are used to identify these two values.

In Section 14.5 we showed that the estimated standard deviation of b_1 is $s_{b_1} = .5803$. Note that the value in cell C30 is .5803. The label Standard Error in cell C28 is Excel's way of indicating that the value in cell C30 is the standard error, or standard deviation, of b_1. Recall that the t test for a significant relationship required the computation of the t statistic, $t = b_1/s_{b_1}$. For the Armand's data, the value of t that we computed was $t = 5/.5803 = 8.62$. The label in cell D28, t Stat, reminds us that cell D30 contains the value of the t test statistic.

The value in cell E30 is the p-value associated with the t test for significance. Excel has displayed the p-value in cell E30 using scientific notation. To obtain the decimal value, we move the decimal point 5 places to the left, obtaining a value of .0000255. Because the p-value $= .0000255 < \alpha = .01$, we can reject H_0 and conclude that we have a significant relationship between student population and quarterly sales.

The information in cells F28:I30 can be used to develop confidence interval estimates of the y-intercept and slope of the estimated regression equation. Excel always provides the lower and upper limits for a 95% confidence interval. Recall that in step 4 we selected Confidence Level and entered 99 in the Confidence Level box. As a result, Excel's Regression tool also provides the lower and upper limits for a 99% confidence interval. The value in cell H30 is the lower limit for the 99% confidence interval estimate of β_1 and the value in cell I30 is the upper limit. Thus, after rounding, the 99% confidence interval estimate of β_1 is 3.05 to 6.95. The values in cells F30 and G30 provide the lower and upper limits for the 95% confidence interval. Thus, the 95% confidence interval is 3.66 to 6.34.

Interpretation of ANOVA Output

The information in cells A22:F26 is a summary of the analysis of variance computations. The three sources of variation are labeled Regression, Residual, and Total. The label df in cell B23 stands for degrees of freedom, the label SS in cell C23 stands for sum of squares, and the label MS in cell D23 stands for mean square.

In Section 14.5 we stated that the mean square error, obtained by dividing the error or residual sum of squares by its degrees of freedom, provides an estimate of σ^2. The value in cell D25, 191.25, is the mean square error for the Armand's regression output. In Section 14.5 we showed that an F test could also be used to test for significance in regression. The value in cell F24, .0000255, is the p-value associated with the F test for significance. Because the p-value $= .0000255 < \alpha = .01$, we can reject H_0 and conclude that we have a significant relationship between student population and quarterly sales. The label Excel uses to identify the p-value for the F test for significance, shown in cell F23, is $Significance\ F$.

The label Significance F may be more meaningful if you think of the value in cell F24 as the observed level of significance for the F test.

Interpretation of Regression Statistics Output

The coefficient of determination, .9027, appears in cell B17; the corresponding label, R Square, is shown in cell A17. The square root of the coefficient of determination provides the sample correlation coefficient of .9501 shown in cell B16. Note that Excel uses the label Multiple R (cell A16) to identify this value. In cell A19, the label Standard Error is used to identify the value of the standard error of the estimate shown in cell B19. Thus, the standard error of the estimate is 13.8293. We caution the reader to keep in mind that in the Excel output, the label Standard Error appears in two different places. In the Regression Statistics section of the output, the label Standard Error refers to the estimate of σ. In the Estimated Regression Equation section of the output, the label $Standard\ Error$ refers to s_{b_1}, the standard deviation of the sampling distribution of b_1.

Chapter 15

Multiple Regression

CONTENTS

STATISTICS IN PRACTICE

84.51°*

CINCINNATI, OHIO

In 2015, the Kroger Company purchased the remaining 50% stake in a joint venture it had previously with British firm dunnhumby to create a new company called 84.51°. The company name is the longitude of its corporate headquarters. 84.51° specializes in finding clues and patterns as to what customers are buying and why. The company turns its insights into actionable strategies that create dramatic growth and sustainable loyalty, ultimately improving brand value and the customer experience. 84.51° serves a prestigious group of clients, including Bayer, Dannon, Dole, Kellogg's, Kroger, General Electric, Pepsico, Procter and Gamble, Red Bull, and Smuckers.

The company's research begins with data collected about a client's customers. Data come from customer reward or discount card purchase records, electronic point-of-sale transactions, and traditional market research. Analysis of the data often translates billions of data points into detailed insights about the behavior, preferences, and lifestyles of the customers. Such insights allow for more effective merchandising programs to be activated, including strategy recommendations on pricing, promotion, advertising, and product assortment decisions.

Researchers have used a multiple regression technique referred to as logistic regression to help in their analysis of customer-based data. Using logistic regression, an estimated multiple regression equation of the following form is developed.

$$\hat{y} = b_0 + b_1x_1 + b_2x_2 + b_3x_3 + \cdots + b_px_p$$

The dependent variable $\hat{y}$ is a prediction of the probability that a customer belongs to a particular customer group. The independent variables $x_1, x_2, x_3, \ldots, x_p$ are measures of the customer's actual shopping behavior and may include the specific items purchased, number of

dunnhumby uses logistic regression to predict customer shopping behavior.
Source: micro10x/Shutterstock.com

items purchased, amount purchased, day of the week, hour of the day, and so on. The analysis helps identify the independent variables that are most relevant in predicting the customer's group and provides a better understanding of the customer population, enabling further analysis with far greater confidence. The focus of the analysis is on understanding the customer to the point of developing merchandising, marketing, and direct marketing programs that will maximize the relevancy and service to the customer group.

---

*The authors are indebted to Paul Hunter, Senior Vice President of Solutions for dunnhumby for providing the context for this Statistics in Practice.

In this chapter, we will introduce multiple regression and show how the concepts of simple linear regression introduced in Chapter 14 can be extended to the multiple regression case. In addition, we will show how statistical software packages are used for multiple regression. In the final section of the chapter, we introduce logistic regression using an example that illustrates how the technique is used in a marketing research application.

In Chapter 14 we presented simple linear regression and demonstrated its use in developing an estimated regression equation that describes the relationship between two variables. Recall that the variable being predicted or explained is called the dependent variable and the variable being used to predict or explain the dependent variable is called the independent variable. In this chapter, we continue our study of regression analysis by considering situations involving two or more independent variables. This subject area, called **multiple regression analysis**, enables us to consider more factors and thus obtain better predictions than are possible with simple linear regression.

15.1 Multiple Regression Model

Multiple regression analysis is the study of how a dependent variable y is related to two or more independent variables. In the general case, we will use p to denote the number of independent variables.

Regression Model and Regression Equation

The concepts of a regression model and a regression equation introduced in the preceding chapter are applicable in the multiple regression case. The equation that describes how the dependent variable y is related to the independent variables $x_1, x_2, \ldots, x_p$ and an error term is called the **multiple regression model**. We begin with the assumption that the multiple regression model takes the following form.

MULTIPLE REGRESSION MODEL

$$y = \beta_0 + \beta_1 x_1 + \beta_2 x_2 + \cdots + \beta_p x_p + \epsilon \qquad (15.1)$$

In the multiple regression model, $\beta_0, \beta_1, \beta_2, \ldots, \beta_p$ are the parameters and the error term ϵ (the Greek letter epsilon) is a random variable. A close examination of this model reveals that y is a linear function of $x_1, x_2, \ldots, x_p$ (the $\beta_0 + \beta_1 x_1 + \beta_2 x_2 + \cdots + \beta_p x_p$ part) plus the error term ϵ. The error term accounts for the variability in y that cannot be explained by the linear effect of the p independent variables.

In Section 15.4 we will discuss the assumptions for the multiple regression model and ϵ. One of the assumptions is that the mean or expected value of ϵ is zero. A consequence of this assumption is that the mean or expected value of y, denoted $E(y)$, is equal to $\beta_0 + \beta_1 x_1 + \beta_2 x_2 + \cdots + \beta_p x_p$. The equation that describes how the mean value of y is related to $x_1, x_2, \ldots, x_p$ is called the **multiple regression equation**.

MULTIPLE REGRESSION EQUATION

$$E(y) = \beta_0 + \beta_1 x_1 + \beta_2 x_2 + \cdots + \beta_p x_p \qquad (15.2)$$

Estimated Multiple Regression Equation

If the values of $\beta_0, \beta_1, \beta_2, \ldots, \beta_p$ were known, equation (15.2) could be used to compute the mean value of y at given values of $x_1, x_2, \ldots, x_p$. Unfortunately, these parameter values will not, in general, be known and must be estimated from sample data. A simple random

FIGURE 15.1   The Estimation Process for Multiple Regression

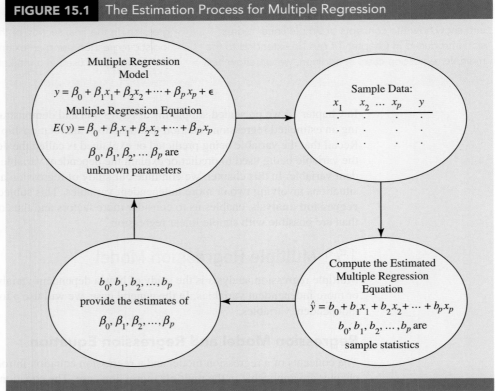

sample is used to compute sample statistics $b_0, b_1, b_2, \ldots, b_p$ that are used as the point estimators of the parameters $\beta_0, \beta_1, \beta_2, \ldots, \beta_p$. These sample statistics provide the following **estimated multiple regression equation**.

ESTIMATED MULTIPLE REGRESSION EQUATION

$$\hat{y} = b_0 + b_1 x_1 + b_2 x_2 + \cdots + b_p x_p \tag{15.3}$$

where

$b_0, b_1, b_2, \ldots, b_p$ are the estimates of $\beta_0, \beta_1, \beta_2, \ldots, \beta_p$
$\hat{y}$ = predicted value of the dependent variable

The estimation process for multiple regression is shown in Figure 15.1.

15.2 Least Squares Method

In Chapter 14, we used the **least squares method** to develop the estimated regression equation that best approximated the straight-line relationship between the dependent and independent variables. This same approach is used to develop the estimated multiple regression equation. The least squares criterion is restated as follows:

LEAST SQUARES CRITERION

$$\min \Sigma(y_i - \hat{y}_i)^2 \tag{15.4}$$

where

y_i = observed value of the dependent variable for the ith observation
$\hat{y}_i$ = predicted value of the dependent variable for the ith observation

The predicted values of the dependent variable are computed by using the estimated multiple regression equation

$$\hat{y} = b_0 + b_1 x_1 + b_2 x_2 + \cdots + b_p x_p$$

As expression (15.4) shows, the least squares method uses sample data to provide the values of $b_0, b_1, b_2, \ldots, b_p$ that make the sum of squared residuals (the deviations between the observed values of the dependent variable (y_i) and the predicted values of the dependent variable ($\hat{y}_i$)) a minimum.

In Chapter 14 we presented formulas for computing the least squares estimators b_0 and b_1 for the estimated simple linear regression equation $\hat{y} = b_0 + b_1 x$. With relatively small data sets, we were able to use those formulas to compute b_0 and b_1 by manual calculations. In multiple regression, however, the presentation of the formulas for the regression coefficients b_0, b_1, $b_2, \ldots, b_p$ involves the use of matrix algebra and is beyond the scope of this text. Therefore, in presenting multiple regression, we focus on how statistical software can be used to obtain the estimated regression equation and other information. The emphasis will be on how to interpret the computer output rather than on how to make the multiple regression computations.

An Example: Butler Trucking Company

As an illustration of multiple regression analysis, we will consider a problem faced by the Butler Trucking Company, an independent trucking company in southern California. A major portion of Butler's business involves deliveries throughout its local area. To develop better work schedules, the managers want to predict the total daily travel time for their drivers.

Initially the managers believed that the total daily travel time would be closely related to the number of miles traveled in making the daily deliveries. A simple random sample of 10 driving assignments provided the data shown in Table 15.1 and the scatter diagram shown in Figure 15.2. After reviewing this scatter diagram, the managers hypothesized that the simple linear regression model $y = \beta_0 + \beta_1 x_1 + \epsilon$ could be used to describe the relationship between the total travel time (y) and the number of miles traveled (x_1). To estimate the parameters β_0 and β_1, the least squares method was used to develop the estimated regression equation.

$$\hat{y} = b_0 + b_1 x_1 \qquad\qquad (15.5)$$

In Figure 15.3, we show statistical software output from applying simple linear regression to the data in Table 15.1. The estimated regression equation is

$$\hat{y} = 1.27 + .0678 x_1$$

At the .05 level of significance, the F value of 15.81 and its corresponding p-value of .004 indicate that the relationship is significant; that is, we can reject $H_0: \beta_1 = 0$ because the

TABLE 15.1	Preliminary Data for Butler Trucking	
Driving Assignment	x_1 = Miles Traveled	y = Travel Time (hours)
1	100	9.3
2	50	4.8
3	100	8.9
4	100	6.5
5	50	4.2
6	80	6.2
7	75	7.4
8	65	6.0
9	90	7.6
10	90	6.1

DATA *file*

Butler

Source: PC Magazine website, April, 2015. (https://www.pcmag.com/reviews/monitors)

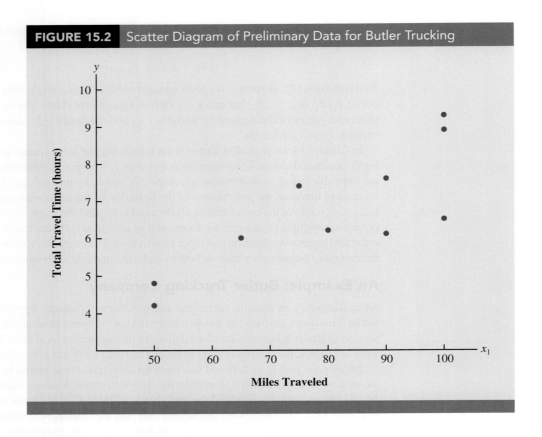

FIGURE 15.2 Scatter Diagram of Preliminary Data for Butler Trucking

FIGURE 15.3 Output for Butler Trucking with One Independent Variable

Analysis of Variance

Source	DF	Adj SS	Adj MS	F-Value	P-Value
Regression	1	15.871	15.8713	15.81	.004
Error	8	8.029	1.0036		
Total	9	23.900			

Model Summary

S	R-sq	R-sq (adj)
1.00179	66.41%	62.21%

Coefficients

Term	Coef	SE Coef	T-Value	P-Value
Constant	1.27	1.40	.91	.390
Miles	.0678	.0171	3.98	.004

Regression Equation

Time = 1.27 + .0678 Miles

TABLE 15.2	Data for Butler Trucking with Miles Traveled (x_1) and Number of Deliveries (x_2) as the Independent Variables		
Driving Assignment	**x_1 = Miles Traveled**	**x_2 = Number of Deliveries**	**y = Travel Time (hours)**
1	100	4	9.3
2	50	3	4.8
3	100	4	8.9
4	100	2	6.5
5	50	2	4.2
6	80	2	6.2
7	75	3	7.4
8	65	4	6.0
9	90	3	7.6
10	90	2	6.1

Butler

p-value is less than $\alpha = .05$. Note that the same conclusion is obtained from the t value of 3.98 and its associated p-value of .004. Thus, we can conclude that the relationship between the total travel time and the number of miles traveled is significant; longer travel times are associated with more miles traveled. With a coefficient of determination (expressed as a percentage) of R-Sq = 66.41%, we see that 66.41% of the variability in travel time can be explained by the linear effect of the number of miles traveled. This finding is fairly good, but the managers might want to consider adding a second independent variable to explain some of the remaining variability in the dependent variable.

In attempting to identify another independent variable, the managers felt that the number of deliveries could also contribute to the total travel time. The Butler Trucking data, with the number of deliveries added, are shown in Table 15.2. Computer output with both miles traveled (x_1) and number of deliveries (x_2) as independent variables is shown in Figure 15.4. The estimated regression equation is

$$\hat{y} = -.869 + .06113x_1 + .923x_2 \tag{15.6}$$

In the next section, we will discuss the use of the coefficient of multiple determination in measuring how good a fit is provided by this estimated regression equation. Before doing so, let us examine more carefully the values of $b_1 = .06113$ and $b_2 = .923$ in equation (15.6).

Note on Interpretation of Coefficients

One observation can be made at this point about the relationship between the estimated regression equation with only the miles traveled as an independent variable and the equation that includes the number of deliveries as a second independent variable. The value of b_1 is not the same in both cases. In simple linear regression, we interpret b_1 as an estimate of the change in y for a one-unit change in the independent variable. In multiple regression analysis, this interpretation must be modified somewhat. That is, in multiple regression analysis, we interpret each regression coefficient as follows: b_i represents an estimate of the change in y corresponding to a one-unit change in x_i when all other independent variables are held constant. In the Butler Trucking example involving two independent variables, $b_1 = .06113$. Thus, .06113 hours is an estimate of the expected increase in travel time corresponding to an increase of one mile in the distance traveled when the number of deliveries is held constant. Similarly, because $b_2 = .923$, an estimate of the expected increase in travel time corresponding to an increase of one delivery when the number of miles traveled is held constant is .923 hours.

FIGURE 15.4   Output for Butler Trucking with Two Independent Variables

Analysis of Variance

Source	DF	Adj SS	Adj MS	F-Value	P-Value
Regression	2	21.6006	10.8003	32.88	.000
Error	7	2.2994	.3285		
Total	9	23.900			

Model Summary

S	R-sq	R-sq (adj)
.573142	90.38%	87.63%

Coefficients

Term	Coef	SE Coef	T-Value	P-Value
Constant	−.869	.952	−.91	.392
Miles	.06113	.00989	6.18	.000
Deliveries	.923	.221	4.18	.004

Regression Equation

Time = −.869 + .06113 Miles + 0.923 Deliveries

EXERCISES

Note to student: The exercises involving data in this and subsequent sections were designed to be solved using a statistical software package.

Methods

1. The estimated regression equation for a model involving two independent variables and 10 observations follows.

$$\hat{y} = 29.1270 + .5906x_1 + .4980x_2$$

   a. Interpret b_1 and b_2 in this estimated regression equation.
   b. Predict y when $x_1 = 180$ and $x_2 = 310$.

2. Consider the following data for a dependent variable y and two independent variables, x_1 and x_2.

x_1	x_2	y
30	12	94
47	10	108
25	17	112
51	16	178
40	5	94
51	19	175
74	7	170
36	12	117
59	13	142
76	16	211

DATA*file*

Exer2

a. Develop an estimated regression equation relating y to x_1. Predict y if $x_1 = 47$.
b. Develop an estimated regression equation relating y to x_2. Predict y if $x_2 = 10$.
c. Develop an estimated regression equation relating y to x_1 and x_2. Predict y if $x_1 = 47$ and $x_2 = 10$.

3. In a regression analysis involving 30 observations, the following estimated regression equation was obtained.

$$\hat{y} = 17.6 + 3.8x_1 - 2.3x_2 + 7.6x_3 + 2.7x_4$$

a. Interpret b_1, b_2, b_3, and b_4 in this estimated regression equation.
b. Predict y when $x_1 = 10$, $x_2 = 5$, $x_3 = 1$, and $x_4 = 2$.

Applications

4. **Shoe Sales.** A shoe store developed the following estimated regression equation relating sales to inventory investment and advertising expenditures.

$$\hat{y} = 25 + 10x_1 + 8x_2$$

where

$$x_1 = \text{inventory investment (\$1000s)}$$
$$x_2 = \text{advertising expenditures (\$1000s)}$$
$$y = \text{sales (\$1000s)}$$

a. Predict the sales resulting from a \$15,000 investment in inventory and an advertising budget of \$10,000.
b. Interpret b_1 and b_2 in this estimated regression equation.

5. **Theater Revenue.** The owner of Showtime Movie Theaters, Inc., would like to predict weekly gross revenue as a function of advertising expenditures. Historical data for a sample of eight weeks follow.

DATA_file_
Showtime

Weekly Gross Revenue ($1000s)	Television Advertising ($1000s)	Newspaper Advertising ($1000s)
96	5.0	1.5
90	2.0	2.0
95	4.0	1.5
92	2.5	2.5
95	3.0	3.3
94	3.5	2.3
94	2.5	4.2
94	3.0	2.5

a. Develop an estimated regression equation with the amount of television advertising as the independent variable.
b. Develop an estimated regression equation with both television advertising and newspaper advertising as the independent variables.
c. Is the estimated regression equation coefficient for television advertising expenditures the same in part (a) and in part (b)? Interpret the coefficient in each case.
d. Predict weekly gross revenue for a week when \$3500 is spent on television advertising and \$2300 is spent on newspaper advertising.

6. **NFL Winning Percentage.** The National Football League (NFL) records a variety of performance data for individuals and teams. To investigate the importance of passing on the percentage of games won by a team, the following data show the conference (Conf), average number of passing yards per attempt (Yds/Att), the number of

interceptions thrown per attempt (Int/Att), and the percentage of games won (Win%) for a random sample of 16 NFL teams for one full season.

Team	Conf	Yds/Att	Int/Att	Win%
Arizona Cardinals	NFC	6.5	.042	50.0
Atlanta Falcons	NFC	7.1	.022	62.5
Carolina Panthers	NFC	7.4	.033	37.5
Cincinnati Bengals	AFC	6.2	.026	56.3
Detroit Lions	NFC	7.2	.024	62.5
Green Bay Packers	NFC	8.9	.014	93.8
Houstan Texans	AFC	7.5	.019	62.5
Indianapolis Colts	AFC	5.6	.026	12.5
Jacksonville Jaguars	AFC	4.6	.032	31.3
Minnesota Vikings	NFC	5.8	.033	18.8
New England Patriots	AFC	8.3	.020	81.3
New Orleans Saints	NFC	8.1	.021	81.3
Oakland Raiders	AFC	7.6	.044	50.0
San Francisco 49ers	NFC	6.5	.011	81.3
Tennessee Titans	AFC	6.7	.024	56.3
Washington Redskins	NFC	6.4	.041	31.3

DATA *file*

PassingNFL

a. Develop the estimated regression equation that could be used to predict the percentage of games won given the average number of passing yards per attempt.
b. Develop the estimated regression equation that could be used to predict the percentage of games won given the number of interceptions thrown per attempt.
c. Develop the estimated regression equation that could be used to predict the percentage of games won given the average number of passing yards per attempt and the number of interceptions thrown per attempt.
d. The average number of passing yards per attempt for the Kansas City Chiefs was 6.2 and the number of interceptions thrown per attempt was .036. Use the estimated regression equation developed in part (c) to predict the percentage of games won by the Kansas City Chiefs. (*Note:* For this season the Kansas City Chiefs' record was 7 wins and 9 losses.) Compare your prediction to the actual percentage of games won by the Kansas City Chiefs.

7. **Rating Computer Monitors.** *PC Magazine* provided ratings for several characteristics of computer monitors, including an overall rating (PC Magazine website). The following data show the rating for contrast ratio, resolution, and the overall rating for ten monitors tested using a 0–100 point scale. The highest rated monitor was the BenQ BL3201PH, with an overall rating of 87.

DATA *file*

MonitorRatings

Model	Contrast Ratio	Resolution	Overall Rating
BenQ BL3201PH	78	89	87
AOC U2868PQU	98	87	86
NEC MultiSync PA322UHD	84	82	85
Acer XB280HK	78	77	82
Asus ROG Swift PG278Q	65	82	82
AOC E1759Fwu	57	78	82
Dell UltraSharp UZ2715H	56	83	81
NEC MultiSync EA244UHD	77	75	79
HP DreamColor Z27x	47	81	77
Dell UltraSharp UZ2315H	55	70	76

Source: PC Magazine website, April, 2015. (https://www.pcmag.com/reviews/monitors)

a. Develop the estimated regression equation that can be used to predict the Overall Rating using the Contrast Ratio Rating.
b. Develop the estimated regression equation that can be used to predict the Overall Rating using both the Contrast Ratio Rating and the Resolution Rating.
c. Predict the Overall Rating for a computer monitor computer that has a Contrast Ratio Rating of 85 and a Resolution Rating of 74.

8. **Scoring Cruise Ships.** The *Condé Nast Traveler* Gold List provides ratings for the top 20 small cruise ships. The data shown below are the scores each ship received based upon the results from *Condé Nast Traveler*'s annual Readers' Choice Survey. Each score represents the percentage of respondents who rated a ship as excellent or very good on several criteria, including Shore Excursions and Food/Dining. An overall score was also reported and used to rank the ships. The highest ranked ship, the *Seabourn Odyssey*, has an overall score of 94.4, the highest component of which is 97.8 for Food/Dining.

DATA *file*

Ships

Ship	Overall	Shore Excursions	Food/Dining
Seabourn Odyssey	94.4	90.9	97.8
Seabourn Pride	93.0	84.2	96.7
National Geographic Endeavor	92.9	100.0	88.5
Seabourn Sojourn	91.3	94.8	97.1
Paul Gauguin	90.5	87.9	91.2
Seabourn Legend	90.3	82.1	98.8
Seabourn Spirit	90.2	86.3	92.0
Silver Explorer	89.9	92.6	88.9
Silver Spirit	89.4	85.9	90.8
Seven Seas Navigator	89.2	83.3	90.5
Silver Whisperer	89.2	82.0	88.6
National Geographic Explorer	89.1	93.1	89.7
Silver Cloud	88.7	78.3	91.3
Celebrity Xpedition	87.2	91.7	73.6
Silver Shadow	87.2	75.0	89.7
Silver Wind	86.6	78.1	91.6
SeaDream II	86.2	77.4	90.9
Wind Star	86.1	76.5	91.5
Wind Surf	86.1	72.3	89.3
Wind Spirit	85.2	77.4	91.9

Source: Condé Nast Traveler, (https://www.cntraveler.com/galleries/2014-10-20/top-cruise-lines-readers-choice-awards-2014)

a. Determine an estimated regression equation that can be used to predict the overall score given the score for Shore Excursions.
b. Consider the addition of the independent variable Food/Dining. Develop the estimated regression equation that can be used to predict the overall score given the scores for Shore Excursions and Food/Dining.
c. Predict the overall score for a cruise ship with a Shore Excursions score of 80 and a Food/Dining Score of 90.

9. **House Prices.** Spring is a peak time for selling houses. The file *SpringHouses* contains the selling price, number of bathrooms, square footage, and number of bedrooms of 26 homes sold in Ft. Thomas, Kentucky, in spring 2018 (*realtor.com* website).
a. Develop scatter plots of selling price versus number of bathrooms, selling price versus square footage, and selling price versus number of bedrooms. Comment on the relationship between selling price and these three variables.

SpringHouses

b. Develop an estimated regression equation that can be used to predict the selling price given the three independent variables (number of baths, square footage, and number of bedrooms).

c. It is argued that we do not need both number of baths and number of bedrooms. Develop an estimated regression equation that can be used to predict selling price given square footage and the number of bedrooms.

d. Suppose your house has four bedrooms and is 2650 square feet. What is the predicted selling price using the model developed in part c.

10. **Baseball Pitcher Performance.** Major League Baseball (MLB) consists of teams that play in the American League and the National League. MLB collects a wide variety of team and player statistics. Some of the statistics often used to evaluate pitching performance are as follows:

ERA: The average number of earned runs given up by the pitcher per nine innings. An earned run is any run that the opponent scores off a particular pitcher except for runs scored as a result of errors.

SO/IP: The average number of strikeouts per inning pitched.

HR/IP: The average number of home runs per inning pitched.

R/IP: The number of runs given up per inning pitched.

The following data show values for these statistics for a random sample of 20 pitchers from the American League for a full season.

PitchingMLB

Player	Team	W	L	ERA	SO/IP	HR/IP	R/IP
Verlander, J	DET	24	5	2.40	1.00	.10	.29
Beckett, J	BOS	13	7	2.89	.91	.11	.34
Wilson, C	TEX	16	7	2.94	.92	.07	.40
Sabathia, C	NYY	19	8	3.00	.97	.07	.37
Haren, D	LAA	16	10	3.17	.81	.08	.38
McCarthy, B	OAK	9	9	3.32	.72	.06	.43
Santana, E	LAA	11	12	3.38	.78	.11	.42
Lester, J	BOS	15	9	3.47	.95	.10	.40
Hernandez, F	SEA	14	14	3.47	.95	.08	.42
Buehrle, M	CWS	13	9	3.59	.53	.10	.45
Pineda, M	SEA	9	10	3.74	1.01	.11	.44
Colon, B	NYY	8	10	4.00	.82	.13	.52
Tomlin, J	CLE	12	7	4.25	.54	.15	.48
Pavano, C	MIN	9	13	4.30	.46	.10	.55
Danks, J	CWS	8	12	4.33	.79	.11	.52
Guthrie, J	BAL	9	17	4.33	.63	.13	.54
Lewis, C	TEX	14	10	4.40	.84	.17	.51
Scherzer, M	DET	15	9	4.43	.89	.15	.52
Davis, W	TB	11	10	4.45	.57	.13	.52
Porcello, R	DET	14	9	4.75	.57	.10	.57

a. Develop an estimated regression equation that can be used to predict the average number of runs given up per inning given the average number of strikeouts per inning pitched.

b. Develop an estimated regression equation that can be used to predict the average number of runs given up per inning given the average number of home runs per inning pitched.

c. Develop an estimated regression equation that can be used to predict the average number of runs given up per inning given the average number of strikeouts per inning pitched and the average number of home runs per inning pitched.

d. A. J. Burnett, a pitcher for the New York Yankees, had an average number of strikeouts per inning pitched of .91 and an average number of home runs per inning of .16. Use the estimated regression equation developed in part (c) to predict the average number of runs given up per inning for A. J. Burnett. (*Note:* The actual value for R/IP was .6.)

e. Suppose a suggestion was made to also use the earned run average as another independent variable in part (c). What do you think of this suggestion?

15.3 Multiple Coefficient of Determination

In simple linear regression, we showed that the total sum of squares can be partitioned into two components: the sum of squares due to regression and the sum of squares due to error. The same procedure applies to the sum of squares in multiple regression.

RELATIONSHIP AMONG SST, SSR, AND SSE

$$SST = SSR + SSE \qquad\qquad (15.7)$$

where

$$SST = \text{total sum of squares} = \Sigma(y_i - \bar{y})^2$$
$$SSR = \text{sum of squares due to regression} = \Sigma(\hat{y}_i - \bar{y})^2$$
$$SSE = \text{sum of squares due to error} = \Sigma(y_i - \hat{y}_i)^2$$

Because of the computational difficulty in computing the three sums of squares, we rely on computer packages to determine those values. The analysis of variance part of the output in Figure 15.4 shows the three values for the Butler Trucking problem with two independent variables: SST = 23.900, SSR = 21.6006, and SSE = 2.2994. With only one independent variable (number of miles traveled), the output in Figure 15.3 shows that SST = 23.900, SSR = 15.871, and SSE = 8.029. The value of SST is the same in both cases because it does not depend on $\hat{y}$, but SSR increases and SSE decreases when a second independent variable (number of deliveries) is added. The implication is that the estimated multiple regression equation provides a better fit for the observed data.

In Chapter 14, we used the coefficient of determination, $r^2 = SSR/SST$, to measure the goodness of fit for the estimated regression equation. The same concept applies to multiple regression. The term **multiple coefficient of determination** indicates that we are measuring the goodness of fit for the estimated multiple regression equation. The multiple coefficient of determination, denoted R^2, is computed as follows:

MULTIPLE COEFFICIENT OF DETERMINATION

$$R^2 = \frac{SSR}{SST} \qquad\qquad (15.8)$$

The multiple coefficient of determination can be interpreted as the proportion of the variability in the dependent variable that can be explained by the estimated multiple regression equation. Hence, when multiplied by 100, it can be interpreted as the percentage of the variability in y that can be explained by the estimated regression equation.

In the two-independent-variable Butler Trucking example, with SSR = 21.6006 and SST = 23.900, we have

$$R^2 = \frac{21.6006}{23.900} = .9038$$

Adding independent variables causes the prediction errors to become smaller, thus reducing the sum of squares due to error, SSE. Because SSR = SST − SSE, when SSE becomes smaller, SSR becomes larger, causing R^2 = SSR/SST to increase.

Therefore, 90.38% of the variability in travel time y is explained by the estimated multiple regression equation with miles traveled and number of deliveries as the independent variables. In Figure 15.4, we see that the multiple coefficient of determination (expressed as a percentage) is also provided; it is denoted by R-sq = 90.38%.

Figure 15.3 shows that the R-sq value for the estimated regression equation with only one independent variable, number of miles traveled (x_1), is 66.41%. Thus, the percentage of the variability in travel times that is explained by the estimated regression equation increases from 66.41% to 90.38% when number of deliveries is added as a second independent variable. In general, R^2 always increases as independent variables are added to the model.

Many analysts prefer adjusting R^2 for the number of independent variables to avoid overestimating the impact of adding an independent variable on the amount of variability explained by the estimated regression equation. With n denoting the number of observations and p denoting the number of independent variables, the **adjusted multiple coefficient of determination** is computed as follows:

If a variable is added to the model, R^2 becomes larger even if the variable added is not statistically significant. The adjusted multiple coefficient of determination compensates for the number of independent variables in the model.

ADJUSTED MULTIPLE COEFFICIENT OF DETERMINATION

$$R_a^2 = 1 - (1 - R^2)\frac{n - 1}{n - p - 1} \qquad (15.9)$$

For the Butler Trucking example with $n = 10$ and $p = 2$, we have

$$R_a^2 = 1 - (1 - .9038)\frac{10 - 1}{10 - 2 - 1} = .8763$$

Thus, after adjusting for the two independent variables, we have an adjusted multiple coefficient of determination of .8763. This value (expressed as a percentage) is provided in the output in Figure 15.4 as R-Sq(adj) = 87.63%.

NOTES + COMMENTS

If the value of R^2 is small and the model contains a large number of independent variables, the adjusted coefficient of determina-

tion can take a negative value; in such cases, statistical software usually sets the adjusted coefficient of determination to zero.

EXERCISES

Methods

11. In exercise 1, the following estimated regression equation based on 10 observations was presented.

$$\hat{y} = 29.1270 + .5906x_1 + .4980x_2$$

The values of SST and SSR are 6724.125 and 6216.375, respectively.
a. Find SSE.
b. Compute R^2.
c. Compute R_a^2.
d. Comment on the goodness of fit.

12. In exercise 2, 10 observations were provided for a dependent variable y and two independent variables x_1 and x_2; for these data SST = 15,182.9, and SSR = 14,052.2.
a. Compute R^2.
b. Compute R_a^2.
c. Does the estimated regression equation explain a large amount of the variability in the data? Explain.

13. In exercise 3, the following estimated regression equation based on 30 observations was presented.

$$\hat{y} = 17.6 + 3.8x_1 - 2.3x_2 + 7.6x_3 + 2.7x_4$$

The values of SST and SSR are 1805 and 1760, respectively.
a. Compute R^2.
b. Compute R_a^2.
c. Comment on the goodness of fit.

Applications

14. **R^2 in Shoe Sales Prediction.** In exercise 4, the following estimated regression equation relating sales to inventory investment and advertising expenditures was given.

$$\hat{y} = 25 + 10x_1 + 8x_2$$

The data used to develop the model came from a survey of 10 stores; for those data, SST = 16,000 and SSR = 12,000.
d. For the estimated regression equation given, compute R^2.
e. Compute R_a^2.
f. Does the model appear to explain a large amount of variability in the data? Explain.

15. **R^2 in Theater Revenue Prediction.** In exercise 5, the owner of Showtime Movie Theaters, Inc., used multiple regression analysis to predict gross revenue (y) as a function of television advertising (x_1) and newspaper advertising (x_2). The estimated regression equation was

$$\hat{y} = 83.2 + 2.29x_1 + 1.30x_2$$

Showtime

The computer solution provided SST = 25.5 and SSR = 23.435.
a. Compute and interpret R^2 and R_a^2.
b. When television advertising was the only independent variable, $R^2 = .653$ and $R_a^2 = .595$. Do you prefer the multiple regression results? Explain.

16. **Quality of Fit in Predicting NFL Wins.** In exercise 6, data were given on the average number of passing yards per attempt (Yds/Att), the number of interceptions thrown per attempt (Int/Att), and the percentage of games won (Win%) for a random sample of 16 National Football League (NFL) teams for one full season.

PassingNFL

a. Did the estimated regression equation that uses only the average number of passing yards per attempt as the independent variable to predict the percentage of games won provide a good fit?
b. Discuss the benefit of using both the average number of passing yards per attempt and the number of interceptions thrown per attempt to predict the percentage of games won.

17. **Quality of Fit in Predicting House Prices.** Revisit exercise 9, where we develop an estimated regression equation that can be used to predict the selling price given the number of bathrooms, square footage, and number of bedrooms in the house.

SpringHouses

a. Does the estimated regression equation provide a good fit to the data? Explain.
b. In part c of exercise 9 you developed an estimated regression equation that predicts selling price given the square footage and number of bedrooms. Compare the fit for this simpler model to that of the model that also includes number of bathrooms as an independent variable.

18. **R^2 in Predicting Baseball Pitcher Performance.** Refer to exercise 10, where Major League Baseball (MLB) pitching statistics were reported for a random sample of 20 pitchers from the American League for one full season.

PitchingMLB

a. In part (c) of exercise 10, an estimated regression equation was developed relating the average number of runs given up per inning pitched given the average number of strikeouts per inning pitched and the average number of home runs per inning pitched. What are the values of R^2 and R_a^2?

b. Does the estimated regression equation provide a good fit to the data? Explain.

c. Suppose the earned run average (ERA) is used as the dependent variable in part (c) instead of the average number of runs given up per inning pitched. Does the estimated regression equation that uses the ERA provide a good fit to the data? Explain.

15.4 Model Assumptions

In Section 15.1 we introduced the following multiple regression model.

MULTIPLE REGRESSION MODEL

$$y = \beta_0 + \beta_1 x_1 + \beta_2 x_2 + \cdots + \beta_p x_p + \epsilon \tag{15.10}$$

The assumptions about the error term ϵ in the multiple regression model parallel those for the simple linear regression model.

ASSUMPTIONS ABOUT THE ERROR TERM ϵ IN THE MULTIPLE REGRESSION MODEL

$y = \beta_0 + \beta_1 x_1 + \cdots + \beta_p x_p + \epsilon$

1. The error term ϵ is a random variable with mean or expected value of zero; that is, $E(\epsilon) = 0$.

    Implication: For given values of $x_1, x_2, \ldots, x_p$, the expected, or average, value of y is given by

    $$E(y) = \beta_0 + \beta_1 x_1 + \beta_2 x_2 + \cdots + \beta_p x_p \tag{15.11}$$

    Equation (15.11) is the multiple regression equation we introduced in Section 15.1. In this equation, $E(y)$ represents the average of all possible values of y that might occur for the given values of $x_1, x_2, \ldots, x_p$.

2. The variance of ϵ is denoted by σ^2 and is the same for all values of the independent variables $x_1, x_2, \ldots, x_p$.

    Implication: The variance of y about the regression line equals σ^2 and is the same for all values of $x_1, x_2, \ldots, x_p$.

3. The values of ϵ are independent.

    Implication: The value of ϵ for a particular set of values for the independent variables is not related to the value of ϵ for any other set of values.

4. The error term ϵ is a normally distributed random variable reflecting the deviation between the y value and the expected value of y given by $\beta_0 + \beta_1 x_1 + \beta_2 x_2 + \cdots + \beta_p x_p$.

    Implication: Because $\beta_0, \beta_1, \ldots, \beta_p$ are constants for the given values of $x_1, x_2, \ldots, x_p$, the dependent variable y is also a normally distributed random variable.

To obtain more insight about the form of the relationship given by equation (15.11), consider the following two-independent-variable multiple regression equation.

$$E(y) = \beta_0 + \beta_1 x_1 + \beta_2 x_2$$

The graph of this equation is a plane in three-dimensional space. Figure 15.5 provides an example of such a graph. Note that the value of ϵ shown is the difference between the actual y value and the expected value of y, $E(y)$, when $x_1 = x_1^*$ and $x_2 = x_2^*$.

In regression analysis, the term *response variable* is often used in place of the term *dependent variable*. Furthermore, since the multiple regression equation generates a plane or surface, its graph is called a *response surface*.

FIGURE 15.5 Graph of the Regression Equation for Multiple Regression Analysis with Two Independent Variables

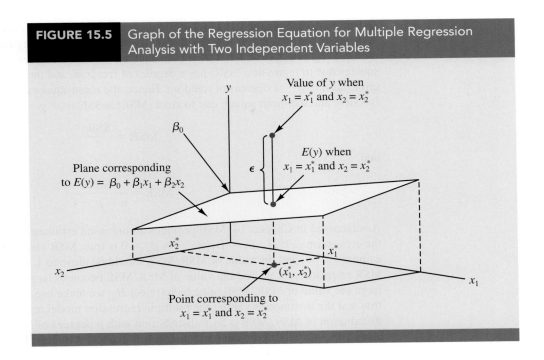

15.5 Testing for Significance

In this section we show how to conduct significance tests for a multiple regression relationship. The significance tests we used in simple linear regression were a t test and an F test. In simple linear regression, both tests provide the same conclusion; that is, if the null hypothesis is rejected, we conclude that $\beta_1 \neq 0$. In multiple regression, the t test and the F test have different purposes.

1. The F test is used to determine whether a significant relationship exists between the dependent variable and the set of all the independent variables; we will refer to the F test as the test for *overall significance*.
2. If the F test shows an overall significance, the t test is used to determine whether each of the individual independent variables is significant. A separate t test is conducted for each of the independent variables in the model; we refer to each of these t tests as a test for *individual significance*.

In the material that follows, we will explain the F test and the t test and apply each to the Butler Trucking Company example.

F Test

The multiple regression model as defined in Section 15.4 is

$$y = \beta_0 + \beta_1 x_1 + \beta_2 x_2 + \cdots + \beta_p x_p + \epsilon$$

The hypotheses for the F test involve the parameters of the multiple regression model.

$$H_0: \beta_1 = \beta_2 = \cdots = \beta_p = 0$$
$$H_a: \text{One or more of the parameters are not equal to zero}$$

If H_0 is rejected, the test gives us sufficient statistical evidence to conclude that one or more of the parameters are not equal to zero and that the overall relationship between y and the set of independent variables $x_1, x_2, \ldots, x_p$ is significant. However, if H_0 cannot be rejected, we do not have sufficient evidence to conclude that a significant relationship is present.

Before describing the steps of the F test, we need to review the concept of *mean square*. A mean square is a sum of squares divided by its corresponding degrees of freedom. In the multiple regression case, the total sum of squares has $n - 1$ degrees of freedom, the sum of squares due to regression (SSR) has p degrees of freedom, and the sum of squares due to error has $n - p - 1$ degrees of freedom. Hence, the mean square due to regression (MSR) is SSR/p and the mean square due to error (MSE) is SSE/$(n - p - 1)$.

$$\text{MSR} = \frac{\text{SSR}}{p} \qquad (15.12)$$

and

$$\text{MSE} = \frac{\text{SSE}}{n - p - 1} \qquad (15.13)$$

As discussed in Chapter 14, MSE provides an unbiased estimate of σ^2, the variance of the error term ϵ. If $H_0: \beta_1 = \beta_2 = \cdots = \beta_p = 0$ is true, MSR also provides an unbiased estimate of σ^2, and the value of MSR/MSE should be close to 1. However, if H_0 is false, MSR overestimates σ^2 and the value of MSR/MSE becomes larger. To determine how large the value of MSR/MSE must be to reject H_0, we make use of the fact that if H_0 is true and the assumptions about the multiple regression model are valid, the sampling distribution of MSR/MSE is an F distribution with p degrees of freedom in the numerator and $n - p - 1$ in the denominator. A summary of the F test for significance in multiple regression follows.

F TEST FOR OVERALL SIGNIFICANCE

$H_0: \beta_1 = \beta_2 = \cdots = \beta_p = 0$

H_a: One or more of the parameters are not equal to zero

TEST STATISTIC

$$F = \frac{\text{MSR}}{\text{MSE}} \qquad (15.14)$$

REJECTION RULE

p-value approach: Reject H_0 if p-value $\leq \alpha$

Critical value approach: Reject H_0 if $F \geq F_\alpha$

where F_α is based on an F distribution with p degrees of freedom in the numerator and $n - p - 1$ degrees of freedom in the denominator.

Let us apply the F test to the Butler Trucking Company multiple regression problem. With two independent variables, the hypotheses are written as follows:

$H_0: \beta_1 = \beta_2 = 0$

$H_a: \beta_1$ and/or β_2 is not equal to zero

Figure 15.6 is the output for the multiple regression model with miles traveled (x_1) and number of deliveries (x_2) as the two independent variables. In the analysis of variance part of the output, we see that MSR = 10.8003 and MSE = .3285. Using equation (15.14), we obtain the test statistic.

$$F = \frac{10.8003}{.3285} = 32.88$$

Using $\alpha = .01$, the p-value = .000 in the last column of the analysis of variance table (Figure 15.6) indicates that we can reject $H_0: \beta_1 = \beta_2 = 0$ because the p-value is less than

$\alpha = .01$. Alternatively, Table 4 of Appendix B shows that with two degrees of freedom in the numerator and seven degrees of freedom in the denominator, $F_{.01} = 9.55$. With $32.88 > 9.55$, we reject $H_0: \beta_1 = \beta_2 = 0$ and conclude that a significant relationship is present between travel time y and the two independent variables, miles traveled and number of deliveries.

As noted previously, the mean square error provides an unbiased estimate of σ^2, the variance of the error term ϵ. Referring to Figure 15.6, we see that the estimate of σ^2 is MSE $= .3285$. The square root of MSE is the estimate of the standard deviation of the error term. As defined in Section 14.5, this standard deviation is called the standard error of the estimate and is denoted s. Hence, we have $s = \sqrt{\text{MSE}} = \sqrt{.3285} = .5731$. Note that the value of the standard error of the estimate appears in the output in Figure 15.6.

Table 15.3 is the general analysis of variance (ANOVA) table that provides the F test results for a multiple regression model. The value of the F test statistic appears in the

---

FIGURE 15.6   Output for Butler Trucking with Two Independent Variables, Miles Traveled (x_1) and Number of Deliveries (x_2)

Analysis of Variance

Source	DF	Adj SS	Adj MS	F-Value	P-Value
Regression	2	21.6006	10.8003	32.88	.000
Error	7	2.2994	.3285		
Total	9	23.900			

Model Summary

S	R-sq	R-sq (adj)
.573142	90.38%	87.63%

Coefficients

Term	Coef	SE Coef	T-Value	P-Value
Constant	−.869	.952	−.91	.392
Miles	.06113	.00989	6.18	.000
Deliveries	.923	.221	4.18	.004

Regression Equation

Time $= -.869 + .06113$ Miles $+ .923$ Deliveries

TABLE 15.3   ANOVA Table for a Multiple Regression Model with p Independent Variables

Source	Sum of Squares	Degrees of Freedom	Mean Square	F
Regression	SSR	p	$\text{MSR} = \dfrac{\text{SSR}}{p}$	$F = \dfrac{\text{MSR}}{\text{MSE}}$
Error	SSE	$n - p - 1$	$\text{MSE} = \dfrac{\text{SSE}}{n - p - 1}$	
Total	SST	$n - 1$		

last column and can be compared to F_α with p degrees of freedom in the numerator and $n - p - 1$ degrees of freedom in the denominator to make the hypothesis test conclusion. By reviewing the output for Butler Trucking Company in Figure 15.6, we see that the analysis of variance table contains this information. Moreover, the p-value corresponding to the F test statistic is also provided.

t Test

If the F test shows that the multiple regression relationship is significant, a t test can be conducted to determine the significance of each of the individual parameters. The t test for individual significance follows.

> **t TEST FOR INDIVIDUAL SIGNIFICANCE**
>
> For any parameter β_i
>
> $$H_0: \beta_i = 0$$
> $$H_a: \beta_i \neq 0$$
>
> **TEST STATISTIC**
>
> $$t = \frac{b_i}{s_{b_i}} \tag{15.15}$$
>
> **REJECTION RULE**
>
> p-value approach: Reject H_0 if p-value $\leq \alpha$
> Critical value approach: Reject H_0 if $t \leq -t_{\alpha/2}$ or if $t \geq t_{\alpha/2}$
>
> where $t_{\alpha/2}$ is based on a t distribution with $n - p - 1$ degrees of freedom.

In the test statistic, s_{b_i} is the estimate of the standard deviation of b_i. The value of s_{b_i} will be provided by the computer software package.

Let us conduct the t test for the Butler Trucking regression problem. Refer to the section of Figure 15.6 that shows the output for the t-ratio calculations. Values of b_1, b_2, s_{b_1}, and s_{b_2} are as follows.

$$b_1 = .06113 \quad s_{b_1} = .00989$$
$$b_2 = .923 \quad s_{b_2} = .221$$

Using equation (15.15), we obtain the test statistic for the hypotheses involving parameters β_1 and β_2.

$$t = .06113/.00989 = 6.18$$
$$t = .923/.221 = 4.18$$

Note that both of these t-ratio values and the corresponding p-values are provided by the output in Figure 15.6. Using $\alpha = .01$, the p-values of .000 and .004 in the output indicate that we can reject $H_0: \beta_1 = 0$ and $H_0: \beta_2 = 0$. Hence, both parameters are statistically significant. Alternatively, Table 2 of Appendix B shows that with $n - p - 1 = 10 - 2 - 1 = 7$ degrees of freedom, $t_{.005} = 3.499$. With $6.18 > 3.499$, we reject $H_0: \beta_1 = 0$. Similarly, with $4.18 > 3.499$, we reject $H_0: \beta_2 = 0$.

Multicollinearity

We use the term *independent variable* in regression analysis to refer to any variable being used to predict or explain the value of the dependent variable. The term does not mean, however, that the independent variables themselves are independent in any statistical sense. On the contrary, most independent variables in a multiple regression problem are correlated to some degree with one another. For example, in the Butler Trucking example involving the two independent variables x_1 (miles traveled) and x_2 (number of deliveries), we could treat the miles traveled as the dependent variable and the number of deliveries as the independent variable to determine whether those two variables are themselves related. We could then compute the sample correlation coefficient $r_{x_1 x_2}$ to determine the extent to which the variables are related. Doing so yields $r_{x_1 x_2} = .16$. Thus, we find some degree of linear association between the two independent variables. In multiple regression analysis, **multicollinearity** refers to the correlation among the independent variables.

To provide a better perspective of the potential problems of multicollinearity, let us consider a modification of the Butler Trucking example. Instead of x_2 being the number of deliveries, let x_2 denote the number of gallons of gasoline consumed. Clearly, x_1 (the miles traveled) and x_2 are related; that is, we know that the number of gallons of gasoline used depends on the number of miles traveled. Hence, we would conclude logically that x_1 and x_2 are highly correlated independent variables.

Assume that we obtain the equation $\hat{y} = b_0 + b_1 x_1 + b_2 x_2$ and find that the F test shows the relationship to be significant. Then suppose we conduct a t test on β_1 to determine whether $\beta_1 \neq 0$, and we cannot reject $H_0: \beta_1 = 0$. Does this result mean that travel time is not related to miles traveled? Not necessarily. What it probably means is that with x_2 already in the model, x_1 does not make a significant contribution to determining the value of y. This interpretation makes sense in our example; if we know the amount of gasoline consumed, we do not gain much additional information useful in predicting y by knowing the miles traveled. Similarly, a t test might lead us to conclude $\beta_2 = 0$ on the grounds that, with x_1 in the model, knowledge of the amount of gasoline consumed does not add much.

To summarize, in t tests for the significance of individual parameters, the difficulty caused by multicollinearity is that it is possible to conclude that none of the individual parameters is significantly different from zero when an F test on the overall multiple regression equation indicates a significant relationship. This problem is avoided when there is little correlation among the independent variables.

A sample correlation coefficient greater than +.7 or less than −.7 for two independent variables is a rule of thumb warning of potential problems with multicollinearity.

When the independent variables are highly correlated, it is not possible to determine the separate effect of any particular independent variable on the dependent variable.

Statisticians have developed several tests for determining whether multicollinearity is high enough to cause problems. According to the rule of thumb test, multicollinearity is a potential problem if the absolute value of the sample correlation coefficient exceeds .7 for any two of the independent variables. The other types of tests are more advanced and beyond the scope of this text.

If possible, every attempt should be made to avoid including independent variables that are highly correlated. In practice, however, strict adherence to this policy is rarely possible. When decision makers have reason to believe substantial multicollinearity is present, they must realize that separating the effects of the individual independent variables on the dependent variable is difficult.

NOTES + COMMENTS

Ordinarily, multicollinearity does not affect the way in which we perform our regression analysis or interpret the output from a study. However, when multicollinearity is severe—that is, when two or more of the independent variables are highly correlated with one another—we can have difficulty interpreting the results of t tests on the individual parameters. In addition to the type of problem illustrated in this section, severe cases of multicollinearity have been shown to result in least squares estimates that have the wrong sign. That is, in simulated studies where researchers created the underlying regression model and then applied the least squares technique to develop estimates of β_0, β_1, β_2, and so on, it has been shown that under conditions of high multicollinearity the least squares estimates can have a sign opposite that of the parameter being estimated. For example, β_2 might actually be $+10$ and b_2, its estimate, might turn out to be -2. Thus, little faith can be placed in the individual coefficients if multicollinearity is present to a high degree.

EXERCISES

Methods

19. In exercise 1, the following estimated regression equation based on 10 observations was presented.

$$\hat{y} = 29.1270 + .5906x_1 + .4980x_2$$

Here SST = 6724.125, SSR = 6216.375, s_{b_1} = .0813, and s_{b_2} = .0567.
a. Compute MSR and MSE.
b. Compute F and perform the appropriate F test. Use $\alpha = .05$.
c. Perform a t test for the significance of β_1. Use $\alpha = .05$.
d. Perform a t test for the significance of β_2. Use $\alpha = .05$.

20. Refer to the data presented in exercise 2. The estimated regression equation for these data is

$$\hat{y} = -18.37 + 2.01x_1 + 4.74x_2$$

Here SST = 15,182.9, SSR = 14,052.2, s_{b_1} = .2471, and s_{b_2} = .9484.
a. Test for a significant relationship among x_1, x_2, and y. Use $\alpha = .05$.
b. Is β_1 significant? Use $\alpha = .05$.
c. Is β_2 significant? Use $\alpha = .05$.

21. The following estimated regression equation was developed for a model involving two independent variables.

$$\hat{y} = 40.7 + 8.63x_1 + 2.71x_2$$

After x_2 was dropped from the model, the least squares method was used to obtain an estimated regression equation involving only x_1 as an independent variable.

$$\hat{y} = 42.0 + 9.01x_1$$

a. Give an interpretation of the coefficient of x_1 in both models.
b. Could multicollinearity explain why the coefficient of x_1 differs in the two models? If so, how?

Applications

22. **Testing Significance in Shoe Sales Prediction.** In exercise 4, the following estimated regression equation relating sales to inventory investment and advertising expenditures was given.

$$\hat{y} = 25 + 10x_1 + 8x_2$$

The data used to develop the model came from a survey of 10 stores; for these data SST = 16,000 and SSR = 12,000.
a. Compute SSE, MSE, and MSR.
b. Use an F test and a .05 level of significance to determine whether there is a relationship among the variables.

23. **Testing Significance in Theater Revenue.** Refer to exercise 5.
a. Use $\alpha = .01$ to test the hypotheses

$$H_0: \beta_1 = \beta_2 = 0$$
$$H_a: \beta_1 \text{ and/or } \beta_2 \text{ is not equal to zero}$$

for the model $y = \beta_0 + \beta_1 x_1 + \beta_2 x_2 + \epsilon$, where

$$x_1 = \text{television advertising (\$1000s)}$$
$$x_2 = \text{newspaper advertising (\$1000s)}$$

b. Use $\alpha = .05$ to test the significance of β_1. Should x_1 be dropped from the model?
c. Use $\alpha = .05$ to test the significance of β_2. Should x_2 be dropped from the model?

NFL 2011

24. **Testing Significance in Predicting NFL Wins.** The National Football League (NFL) records a variety of performance data for individuals and teams. A portion of the data showing the average number of passing yards obtained per game on offense (Off-PassYds/G), the average number of yards given up per game on defense (DefYds/G), and the percentage of games won (Win%), for one full season follows.

Team	OffPassYds/G	DefYds/G	Win%
Arizona	222.9	355.1	50.0
Atlanta	262.0	333.6	62.5
Baltimore	213.9	288.9	75.0
.	.	.	.
.	.	.	.
.	.	.	.
St. Louis	179.4	358.4	12.5
Tampa Bay	228.1	394.4	25.0
Tennessee	245.2	355.1	56.3
Washington	235.8	339.8	31.3

a. Develop an estimated regression equation that can be used to predict the percentage of games won given the average number of passing yards obtained per game on offense and the average number of yards given up per game on defense.
b. Use the F test to determine the overall significance of the relationship. What is your conclusion at the .05 level of significance?
c. Use the t test to determine the significance of each independent variable. What is your conclusion at the .05 level of significance?

AutoResale

25. **Auto Resale Value.** The Honda Accord was named the best midsized car for resale value for 2018 by the Kelley Blue Book (Kelley Blue Book website). The file *AutoResale* contains mileage, age, and selling price for a sample of 33 Honda Accords.
a. Develop an estimated regression equation that predicts the selling price of a used Honda Accord given the mileage and age of the car.
b. Is multicollinearity an issue for this model? Find the correlation between the independent variables to answer this question.
c. Use the F test to determine the overall significance of the relationship. What is your conclusion at the .05 level of significance?
d. Use the t test to determine the significance of each independent variable. What is your conclusion at the .05 level of significance?

PitchingMLB

26. **Testing Significance in Baseball Pitcher Performance.** In exercise 10, data showing the values of several pitching statistics for a random sample of 20 pitchers from the American League of Major League Baseball were provided. In part (c) of this exercise an estimated regression equation was developed to predict the average number of runs given up per inning pitched (R/IP) given the average number of strikeouts per inning pitched (SO/IP) and the average number of home runs per inning pitched (HR/IP).
a. Use the F test to determine the overall significance of the relationship. What is your conclusion at the .05 level of significance?
b. Use the t test to determine the significance of each independent variable. What is your conclusion at the .05 level of significance?

15.6 Using the Estimated Regression Equation for Estimation and Prediction

The procedures for estimating the mean value of y and predicting an individual value of y in multiple regression are similar to those in regression analysis involving one independent variable. First, recall that in Chapter 14 we showed that the point estimate of the expected

TABLE 15.4   The 95% Confidence and Prediction Intervals for Butler Trucking

Value of x_1	Value of x_2	95% Confidence Interval Lower Limit	Upper Limit	95% Prediction Interval Lower Limit	Upper Limit
100	4	8.135	9.742	7.363	10.514
50	3	4.127	5.789	3.369	6.548
100	4	8.135	9.742	7.363	10.514
100	2	6.258	7.925	5.500	8.683
50	2	3.146	4.924	2.414	5.656
80	2	5.232	6.505	4.372	7.366
75	3	6.037	6.936	5.059	7.915
65	4	5.960	7.637	5.205	8.392
90	3	6.917	7.891	5.964	8.844
90	2	5.776	7.184	4.953	8.007
75	4	6.669	8.152	5.865	8.955

value of y for a given value of x was the same as the point estimate of an individual value of y. In both cases, we used $\hat{y} = b_0 + b_1 x$ as the point estimate.

In multiple regression we use the same procedure. That is, we substitute the given values of $x_1, x_2, \ldots, x_p$ into the estimated regression equation and use the corresponding value of $\hat{y}$ as the point estimate. Suppose that for the Butler Trucking example we want to use the estimated regression equation involving x_1 (miles traveled) and x_2 (number of deliveries) to develop two interval estimates:

1. A *confidence interval* of the mean travel time for all trucks that travel 100 miles and make two deliveries
2. A *prediction interval* of the travel time for *one specific* truck that travels 100 miles and makes two deliveries

Using the estimated regression equation $\hat{y} = -.869 + .06113x_1 + .923x_2$ with $x_1 = 100$ and $x_2 = 2$, we obtain the following value of $\hat{y}$.

$$\hat{y} = -.869 + .06113(100) + .923(2) = 7.09$$

Hence, the point estimate of travel time in both cases is approximately seven hours.

To develop interval estimates for the mean value of y and for an individual value of y, we use a procedure similar to that for regression analysis involving one independent variable. The formulas required are beyond the scope of the text, but statistical software for multiple regression analysis will often provide confidence intervals once the values of $x_1, x_2, \ldots, x_p$ are specified by the user. In Table 15.4 we show the 95% confidence and prediction intervals for the Butler Trucking example for selected values of x_1 and x_2; these values were obtained with statistical software. Note that the interval estimate for an individual value of y is wider than the interval estimate for the expected value of y. This difference simply reflects the fact that for given values of x_1 and x_2 we can estimate the mean travel time for all trucks with more precision than we can predict the travel time for one specific truck.

EXERCISES

Methods

27. In exercise 1, the following estimated regression equation based on 10 observations was presented.

$$\hat{y} = 29.1270 + .5906x_1 + .4980x_2$$

a. Develop a point estimate of the mean value of y when $x_1 = 180$ and $x_2 = 310$.

b. Develop a point estimate for an individual value of y when $x_1 = 180$ and $x_2 = 310$.

Exer2

28. Refer to the data in exercise 2. The estimated regression equation for those data is

$$\hat{y} = -18.4 + 2.01x_1 + 4.74x_2$$

a. Develop a 95% confidence interval for the mean value of y when $x_1 = 47$ and $x_2 = 10$.

b. Develop a 95% prediction interval for y when $x_1 = 47$ and $x_2 = 10$.

Applications

Showtime

29. **Confidence and Prediction Intervals for Theater Revenue.** In exercise 5, the owner of Showtime Movie Theaters, Inc., used multiple regression analysis to predict gross revenue (y) as a function of television advertising (x_1) and newspaper advertising (x_2). The estimated regression equation was

$$\hat{y} = 83.23 + 2.29x_1 + 1.30x_2$$

a. What is the gross revenue expected for a week when $3500 is spent on television advertising ($x_1 = 3.5$) and $2300 is spent on newspaper advertising ($x_2 = 2.3$)?

b. Provide a 95% confidence interval for the mean revenue of all weeks with the expenditures listed in part (a).

c. Provide a 95% prediction interval for next week's revenue, assuming that the advertising expenditures will be allocated as in part (a).

NFL2011

30. **Confidence and Prediction Intervals for NFL Wins.** In exercise 24, an estimated regression equation was developed relating the percentage of games won by a team in the National Football League for the 2011 season given the average number of passing yards obtained per game on offense and the average number of yards given up per game on defense (ESPN website, November 3, 2012).

a. Predict the percentage of games won for a particular team that averages 225 passing yards per game on offense and gives up an average of 300 yards per game on defense.

b. Develop a 95% prediction interval for the percentage of games won for a particular team that averages 225 passing yards per game on offense and gives up an average of 300 yards per game on defense.

31. **Confidence and Prediction Intervals for Auto Resale Value.** Refer to Problem 25. Use the estimated regression equation from part (a) to answer the following questions.

AutoResale

a. Estimate the selling price of a four-year-old Honda Accord with mileage of 40,000 miles.

b. Develop a 95% confidence interval for the selling price of a car with the data in part (a).

c. Develop a 95% prediction interval for the selling price of a particular car having the data in part (a).

15.7 Categorical Independent Variables

The independent variables may be categorical or quantitative.

Thus far, the examples we have considered involved quantitative independent variables such as student population, distance traveled, and number of deliveries. In many situations, however, we must work with **categorical independent variables** such as gender (male, female), method of payment (cash, credit card, check), and so on. The purpose of this section is to show how categorical variables are handled in regression analysis. To illustrate the use and interpretation of a categorical independent variable, we will consider a problem facing the managers of Johnson Filtration, Inc.

An Example: Johnson Filtration, Inc.

Johnson Filtration, Inc., provides maintenance service for water-filtration systems throughout southern Florida. Customers contact Johnson with requests for maintenance service on their water-filtration systems. To estimate the service time and the service cost, Johnson's managers want to predict the repair time necessary for each maintenance request. Hence, repair time in hours is the dependent variable. Repair time is believed to be related to two factors, the number of months since the last maintenance service and the type of repair problem (mechanical or electrical). Data for a sample of 10 service calls are reported in Table 15.5.

Let y denote the repair time in hours and x_1 denote the number of months since the last maintenance service. The regression model that uses only x_1 to predict y is

$$y = \beta_0 + \beta_1 x_1 + \epsilon$$

Using statistical software to develop the estimated regression equation, we obtained the output shown in Figure 15.7. The estimated regression equation is

$$\hat{y} = 2.147 + .304x_1 \tag{15.16}$$

At the .05 level of significance, the p-value of .016 for the t (or F) test indicates that the number of months since the last service is significantly related to repair time. R-sq = 53.42% indicates that x_1 alone explains 53.42% of the variability in repair time.

To incorporate the type of repair into the regression model, we define the following variable.

$$x_2 = \begin{cases} 0 \text{ if the type of repair is mechanical} \\ 1 \text{ if the type of repair is electrical} \end{cases}$$

In regression analysis x_2 is called a **dummy** or *indicator* **variable**. Using this dummy variable, we can write the multiple regression model as

$$y = \beta_0 + \beta_1 x_1 + \beta_2 x_2 + \epsilon$$

TABLE 15.5 Data for the Johnson Filtration Example

Service Call	Months Since Last Service	Type of Repair	Repair Time in Hours
1	2	Electrical	2.9
2	6	Mechanical	3.0
3	8	Electrical	4.8
4	3	Mechanical	1.8
5	2	Electrical	2.9
6	7	Electrical	4.9
7	9	Mechanical	4.2
8	8	Mechanical	4.8
9	4	Electrical	4.4
10	6	Electrical	4.5

TABLE 15.6	Data for the Johnson Filtration Example with Type of Repair Indicated by a Dummy Variable ($x_2 = 0$ for Mechanical; $x_2 = 1$ for Electrical)		
Customer	**Months Since Last Service (x_1)**	**Type of Repair (x_2)**	**Repair Time in Hours (y)**
1	2	1	2.9
2	6	0	3.0
3	8	1	4.8
4	3	0	1.8
5	2	1	2.9
6	7	1	4.9
7	9	0	4.2
8	8	0	4.8
9	4	1	4.4
10	6	1	4.5

DATA*file*

Johnson

Table 15.6 is the revised data set that includes the values of the dummy variable. The output in Figure 15.8 shows that the estimated multiple regression equation is

$$\hat{y} = .93 + .3876x_1 + 1.263x_2 \tag{15.17}$$

At the .05 level of significance, the *p*-value of .001 associated with the *F* test ($F = 21.36$) indicates that the regression relationship is significant. The *t* test part of the output in

FIGURE 15.7	Output for Johnson Filtration with Months Since Last Service (x_1) as the Independent Variable

Analysis of Variance

Source	DF	Adj SS	Adj MS	F-Value	P-Value
Regression	1	5.596	5.5960	9.17	.016
Error	8	4.880	.6100		
Total	9	10.476			

Model Summary

S	R-sq	R-sq (adj)
.781022	53.42%	47.59%

Coefficients

Term	Coef	SE Coef	T-Value	P-Value
Constant	2.147	.605	3.55	.008
Months Since Last Service	.304	.100	3.03	.016

Regression Equation

Repair Time (hours) = 2.147 + .304 Months Since Last Service

FIGURE 15.8 Output for Johnson Filtration with Months Since Last Service (x_1) and Type of Repair (x_2) as the Independent Variables

Analysis of Variance

Source	DF	Adj SS	Adj MS	F-Value	P-Value
Regression	2	9.0009	4.50046	21.36	.001
Error	7	1.4751	.21073		
Total	9	10.4760			

Model Summary

S	R-sq	R-sq (adj)
.459048	85.92%	81.90%

Coefficients

Term	Coef	SE Coef	T-Value	P-Value
Constant	.930	.467	1.99	.087
Months Since Last Service	.3876	.0626	6.20	.000
Type of Repair	1.263	.314	4.02	.005

Regression Equation

Repair Time (hours) = .930 + .3876 Months Since Last Service + 1.263 Type of Repair

Figure 15.8 shows that both months since last service (p-value $= .000$) and type of repair (p-value $= .005$) are statistically significant. In addition, R-Sq $= 85.92\%$ and R-Sq (adj) $= 81.9\%$ indicate that the estimated regression equation does a good job of explaining the variability in repair times. Thus, equation (15.17) should prove helpful in predicting the repair time necessary for the various service calls.

Interpreting the Parameters

The multiple regression equation for the Johnson Filtration example is

$$E(y) = \beta_0 + \beta_1 x_1 + \beta_2 x_2 \qquad (15.18)$$

To understand how to interpret the parameters β_0, β_1, and β_2 when a categorical variable is present, consider the case when $x_2 = 0$ (mechanical repair). Using $E(y \mid \text{mechanical})$ to denote the mean or expected value of repair time *given* a mechanical repair, we have

$$E(y \mid \text{mechanical}) = \beta_0 + \beta_1 x_1 + \beta_2(0) = \beta_0 + \beta_1 x_1 \qquad (15.19)$$

Similarly, for an electrical repair ($x_2 = 1$), we have

$$E(y \mid \text{electrical}) = \beta_0 + \beta_1 x_1 + \beta_2(1) = \beta_0 + \beta_1 x_1 + \beta_2 \qquad (15.20)$$
$$= (\beta_0 + \beta_2) + \beta_1 x_1$$

Comparing equations (15.19) and (15.20), we see that the mean repair time is a linear function of x_1 for both mechanical and electrical repairs. The slope of both equations is β_1, but the y-intercept differs. The y-intercept is β_0 in equation (15.19) for mechanical repairs and $(\beta_0 + \beta_2)$ in equation (15.20) for electrical repairs. The interpretation of β_2 is that it indicates the difference between the mean repair time for an electrical repair and the mean repair time for a mechanical repair.

If β_2 is positive, the mean repair time for an electrical repair will be greater than that for a mechanical repair; if β_2 is negative, the mean repair time for an electrical repair will be less than that for a mechanical repair. Finally, if $\beta_2 = 0$, there is no difference in the mean repair time between electrical and mechanical repairs and the type of repair is not related to the repair time.

Using the estimated multiple regression equation $\hat{y} = .93 + .3876x_1 + 1.263x_2$, we see that .93 is the estimate of β_0 and 1.263 is the estimate of β_2. Thus, when $x_2 = 0$ (mechanical repair)

$$\hat{y} = .93 + .3876x_1 \qquad (15.21)$$

and when $x_2 = 1$ (electrical repair)

$$\hat{y} = .93 + .3876x_1 + 1.263(1) \qquad (15.22)$$
$$= 2.193 + .3876x_1$$

In effect, the use of a dummy variable for type of repair provides two estimated regression equations that can be used to predict the repair time, one corresponding to mechanical repairs and one corresponding to electrical repairs. In addition, with $b_2 = 1.263$, we learn that, on average, electrical repairs require 1.263 hours longer than mechanical repairs.

Figure 15.9 is the plot of the Johnson data from Table 15.6. Repair time in hours (y) is represented by the vertical axis and months since last service (x_1) is represented by the horizontal axis. A data point for a mechanical repair is indicated by an M and a data point for an electrical repair is indicated by an E. Equations (15.21) and (15.22) are plotted on the graph to show graphically the two equations that can be used to predict the repair time, one corresponding to mechanical repairs and one corresponding to electrical repairs.

FIGURE 15.9 Scatter Diagram for the Johnson Filtration Repair Data from Table 15.6

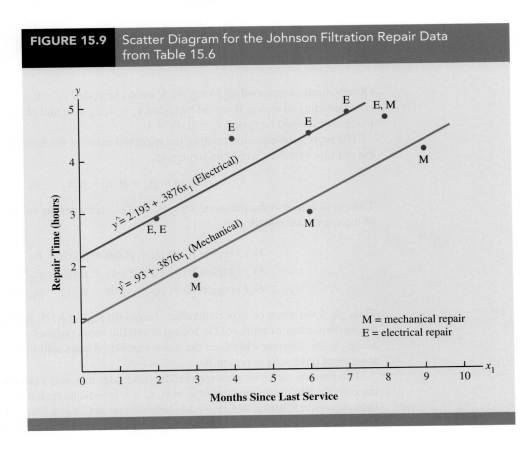

More Complex Categorical Variables

A categorical variable with k levels must be modeled using k − 1 dummy variables. Care must be taken in defining and interpreting the dummy variables.

Because the categorical variable for the Johnson Filtration example had two levels (mechanical and electrical), defining a dummy variable with zero indicating a mechanical repair and one indicating an electrical repair was easy. However, when a categorical variable has more than two levels, care must be taken in both defining and interpreting the dummy variables. As we will show, if a categorical variable has k levels, $k - 1$ dummy variables are required, with each dummy variable being coded as 0 or 1.

For example, suppose a manufacturer of copy machines organized the sales territories for a particular state into three regions: A, B, and C. The managers want to use regression analysis to help predict the number of copiers sold per week. With the number of units sold as the dependent variable, they are considering several independent variables (the number of sales personnel, advertising expenditures, and so on). Suppose the managers believe sales region is also an important factor in predicting the number of copiers sold. Because sales region is a categorical variable with three levels, A, B and C, we will need $3 - 1 = 2$ dummy variables to represent the sales region. Each variable can be coded 0 or 1 as follows.

$$x_1 = \begin{cases} 1 \text{ if sales region B} \\ 0 \text{ otherwise} \end{cases}$$

$$x_2 = \begin{cases} 1 \text{ if sales region C} \\ 0 \text{ otherwise} \end{cases}$$

With this definition, we have the following values of x_1 and x_2.

Region	x_1	x_2
A	0	0
B	1	0
C	0	1

Observations corresponding to region A would be coded $x_1 = 0$, $x_2 = 0$; observations corresponding to region B would be coded $x_1 = 1$, $x_2 = 0$; and observations corresponding to region C would be coded $x_1 = 0$, $x_2 = 1$.

The regression equation relating the expected value of the number of units sold, $E(y)$, to the dummy variables would be written as

$$E(y) = \beta_0 + \beta_1 x_1 + \beta_2 x_2$$

To help us interpret the parameters β_0, β_1, and β_2, consider the following three variations of the regression equation.

$$E(y \mid \text{region A}) = \beta_0 + \beta_1(0) + \beta_2(0) = \beta_0$$
$$E(y \mid \text{region B}) = \beta_0 + \beta_1(1) + \beta_2(0) = \beta_0 + \beta_1$$
$$E(y \mid \text{region C}) = \beta_0 + \beta_1(0) + \beta_2(1) = \beta_0 + \beta_2$$

Thus, β_0 is the mean or expected value of sales for region A; β_1 is the difference between the mean number of units sold in region B and the mean number of units sold in region A; and β_2 is the difference between the mean number of units sold in region C and the mean number of units sold in region A.

Two dummy variables were required because sales region is a categorical variable with three levels. But the assignment of $x_1 = 0$, $x_2 = 0$ to indicate region A, $x_1 = 1$, $x_2 = 0$ to indicate region B, and $x_1 = 0$, $x_2 = 1$ to indicate region C was arbitrary. For example, we could have chosen $x_1 = 1$, $x_2 = 0$ to indicate region A, $x_1 = 0$, $x_2 = 0$ to indicate region B, and

$x_1 = 0, x_2 = 1$ to indicate region C. In that case, β_1 would have been interpreted as the mean difference between regions A and B and β_2 as the mean difference between regions C and B.

The important point to remember is that when a categorical variable has k levels, $k - 1$ dummy variables are required in the multiple regression analysis. Thus, if the sales region example had a fourth region, labeled D, three dummy variables would be necessary. For example, the three dummy variables can be coded as follows.

$$x_1 = \begin{cases} 1 \text{ if sales region B} \\ 0 \text{ otherwise} \end{cases} \qquad x_2 = \begin{cases} 1 \text{ if sales region C} \\ 0 \text{ otherwise} \end{cases} \qquad x_3 = \begin{cases} 1 \text{ if sales region D} \\ 0 \text{ otherwise} \end{cases}$$

EXERCISES

Methods

32. Consider a regression study involving a dependent variable y, a quantitative independent variable x_1, and a categorical independent variable with two levels (level 1 and level 2).
    a. Write a multiple regression equation relating x_1 and the categorical variable to y.
    b. What is the expected value of y corresponding to level 1 of the categorical variable?
    c. What is the expected value of y corresponding to level 2 of the categorical variable?
    d. Interpret the parameters in your regression equation.

33. Consider a regression study involving a dependent variable y, a quantitative independent variable x_1, and a categorical independent variable with three possible levels (level 1, level 2, and level 3).
    a. How many dummy variables are required to represent the categorical variable?
    b. Write a multiple regression equation relating x_1 and the categorical variable to y.
    c. Interpret the parameters in your regression equation.

Applications

34. **Fast Food Sales.** Management proposed the following regression model to predict sales at a fast-food outlet.

$$y = \beta_0 + \beta_1 x_1 + \beta_2 x_2 + \beta_3 x_3 + \epsilon$$

where

$$x_1 = \text{number of competitors within one mile}$$
$$x_2 = \text{population within one mile (1000s)}$$
$$x_3 = \begin{cases} 1 \text{ if drive-up window present} \\ 0 \text{ otherwise} \end{cases}$$
$$y = \text{sales (\$1000s)}$$

The following estimated regression equation was developed after 20 outlets were surveyed.

$$\hat{y} = 10.1 - 4.2x_1 + 6.8x_2 + 15.3x_3$$

    a. What is the expected amount of sales attributable to the drive-up window?
    b. Predict sales for a store with two competitors, a population of 8000 within one mile, and no drive-up window.
    c. Predict sales for a store with one competitor, a population of 3000 within one mile, and a drive-up window.

35. **Repair Time.** Refer to the Johnson Filtration problem introduced in this section. Suppose that in addition to information on the number of months since the machine was serviced and whether a mechanical or an electrical repair was necessary, the managers obtained a list showing which repairperson performed the service. The revised data follow.

DATA *file*

Repair

Repair Time in Hours	Months Since Last Service	Type of Repair	Repairperson
2.9	2	Electrical	Dave Newton
3.0	6	Mechanical	Dave Newton
4.8	8	Electrical	Bob Jones
1.8	3	Mechanical	Dave Newton
2.9	2	Electrical	Dave Newton
4.9	7	Electrical	Bob Jones
4.2	9	Mechanical	Bob Jones
4.8	8	Mechanical	Bob Jones
4.4	4	Electrical	Bob Jones
4.5	6	Electrical	Dave Newton

a. Ignore for now the months since the last maintenance service (x_1) and the repairperson who performed the service. Develop the estimated simple linear regression equation to predict the repair time (y) given the type of repair (x_2). Recall that $x_2 = 0$ if the type of repair is mechanical and 1 if the type of repair is electrical.

b. Does the equation that you developed in part (a) provide a good fit for the observed data? Explain.

c. Ignore for now the months since the last maintenance service and the type of repair associated with the machine. Develop the estimated simple linear regression equation to predict the repair time given the repairperson who performed the service. Let $x_3 = 0$ if Bob Jones performed the service and $x_3 = 1$ if Dave Newton performed the service.

d. Does the equation that you developed in part (c) provide a good fit for the observed data? Explain.

36. **Extending Model for Repair Time.** This problem is an extension of the situation described in exercise 35.

a. Develop the estimated regression equation to predict the repair time given the number of months since the last maintenance service, the type of repair, and the repairperson who performed the service.

b. At the .05 level of significance, test whether the estimated regression equation developed in part (a) represents a significant relationship between the independent variables and the dependent variable.

c. Is the addition of the independent variable x_3, the repairperson who performed the service, statistically significant? Use $\alpha = .05$. What explanation can you give for the results observed?

37. **Pricing Refrigerators.** Best Buy, a nationwide retailer of electronics, computers, and appliances, sells several brands of refrigerators. A random sample of models of full size refrigerators prices sold by Best Buy and the corresponding cubic feet (cu. ft.) and list price follow (Best Buy website).

DATA *file*

Refrigerators

Model	Cu. Ft.	List Price
Frigidaire Gallery Custom-Flex Top-Freezer Refrigerator	18.3	$899.99
GE French Door Refrigerator	24.8	$1,599.99
GE Frost-Free Side-by-Side Refrigerator with Thru-the-Door Ice and Water	25.4	$1,599.99
Whirlpool Top-Freezer Refrigerator	19.3	$749.99
GE Frost-Free Top-Freezer Refrigerator	17.5	$599.99
Whirlpool French Door Refrigerator with Thru-the-Ice and Door Water	19.6	$1,619.99
Samsung French Door Refrigerator	25.0	$999.99

Model	Cu. Ft.	List Price
Samsung Side-by-Side Refrigerator	24.5	$1,299.99
Whirlpool Side-by-Side Refrigerator with Thru-the-Door Ice and Water	25.4	$1,299.99
Frigidaire Gallery Frost-Free Side-by-Side Refrigerator with Thru-the-Door Ice and Water	26.0	$1,299.99
Frigidaire Side-by-Side Refrigerator with Thru-the-Door Ice and Water	25.6	$1,099.99
Frigidaire Top-Freezer Refrigerator	18.0	$579.99
Whirlpool French Door Refrigerator with Thru-the-Door Ice and Water	25.0	$2,199.99
Whirlpool Top-Freezer Refrigerator	20.5	$849.99
GE Frost-Free Top-Freezer Refrigerator	15.5	$549.99
Samsung 4-Door French Door Refrigerator with Thru-the-Door Ice and Water	28.2	$2,599.99
Samsung Showcase 4-Door French Door Refrigerator	27.8	$2,999.99
Samsung 3-Door French Door Refrigerator with Thru-the-Door Ice and Water	24.6	$2,399.99
Frigidaire Side-by-Side Refrigerator with Thru-the-Door Ice and Water	22.6	$1,099.99
GE Side-by-Side Refrigerator with Thru-the-Door Ice and Water	21.8	$1,499.99
GE Bottom-Freezer Refrigerator	20.9	$1,649.99

Source: Best Buy website, (https://www.bestbuy.com/site/searchpage.jsp?st=refrigerator&_dyncharset=UTF-8&id=pcat17071&type=page&sc=Global&cp=1&nrp=&sp=&qp=&list=n&af=true&iht=y&usc=All+Categories&ks=960&keys=keys)

a. Develop the estimated simple linear regression equation to show how list price is related to the independent variable cubic feet.

b. At the .05 level of significance, test whether the estimated regression equation developed in part (a) indicates a significant relationship between list price and cubic feet.

c. Develop a dummy variable that will account for whether the refrigerator has the thru-the-door ice and water feature. Code the dummy variable with a value of 1 if the refrigerator has the thru-the-door ice and water feature and with 0 otherwise. Use this dummy variable to develop the estimated multiple regression equation to show how list price is related to cubic feet and the thru-the-door ice and water feature.

d. At $\alpha = .05$, is the thru-the-door ice and water feature a significant factor in the list price of a refrigerator?

38. **Risk of a Stroke.** A 10-year study conducted by the American Heart Association provided data on how age, blood pressure, and smoking relate to the risk of strokes. Assume that the following data are from a portion of this study. Risk is interpreted as the probability (times 100) that the patient will have a stroke over the next 10-year period. For the smoking variable, define a dummy variable with 1 indicating a smoker and 0 indicating a nonsmoker.

DATA *file*

Stroke

Risk	Age	Pressure	Smoker
12	57	152	No
24	67	163	No
13	58	155	No
56	86	177	Yes
28	59	196	No
51	76	189	Yes
18	56	155	Yes
31	78	120	No
37	80	135	Yes
15	78	98	No

(continued)

Risk	Age	Pressure	Smoker
22	71	152	No
36	70	173	Yes
15	67	135	Yes
48	77	209	Yes
15	60	199	No
36	82	119	Yes
8	66	166	No
34	80	125	Yes
3	62	117	No
37	59	207	Yes

a. Develop an estimated regression equation that relates risk of a stroke to the person's age, blood pressure, and whether the person is a smoker.
b. Is smoking a significant factor in the risk of a stroke? Explain. Use $\alpha = .05$.
c. What is the probability of a stroke over the next 10 years for Art Speen, a 68-year-old smoker who has blood pressure of 175? What action might the physician recommend for this patient?

15.8 Residual Analysis

In Chapter 14 we pointed out that standardized residuals are frequently used in residual plots and in the identification of outliers. The general formula for the standardized residual for observation i follows.

STANDARDIZED RESIDUAL FOR OBSERVATION i

$$\frac{y_i - \hat{y}_i}{s_{y_i - \hat{y}_i}} \tag{15.23}$$

where

$$s_{y_i - \hat{y}_i} = \text{the standard deviation of residual } i$$

The general formula for the standard deviation of residual i is defined as follows.

STANDARD DEVIATION OF RESIDUAL i

$$s_{y_i - \hat{y}_i} = s\sqrt{1 - h_i} \tag{15.24}$$

where

$$s = \text{standard error of the estimate}$$
$$h_i = \text{leverage of observation } i$$

As we stated in Chapter 14, the **leverage** of an observation is determined by how far the values of the independent variables are from their means. The computation of h_i, $s_{y_i - \hat{y}_i}$, and hence the standardized residual for observation i in multiple regression analysis is too complex to be done by hand. However, the standardized residuals can be easily obtained as part of the output from statistical software. Table 15.7 lists the predicted values, the residuals, and the standardized residuals for the Butler Trucking example presented previously in this chapter; we obtained these values by using statistical software. The predicted values in the table are based on the estimated regression equation $\hat{y} = -.869 + .06113x_1 + .923x_2$.

| TABLE 15.7 | Residuals and Standardized Residuals for the Butler Trucking Regression Analysis |

Miles Traveled (x_1)	Deliveries (x_2)	Travel Time (y)	Predicted Value $(\hat{y})$	Residual $(y - \hat{y})$	Standardized Residual
100	4	9.3	8.93846	.361541	.78344
50	3	4.8	4.95830	−.158304	−.34962
100	4	8.9	8.93846	−.038460	−.08334
100	2	6.5	7.09161	−.591609	−1.30929
50	2	4.2	4.03488	.165121	.38167
80	2	6.2	5.86892	.331083	.65431
75	3	7.4	6.48667	.913331	1.68917
65	4	6.0	6.79875	−.798749	−1.77372
90	3	7.6	7.40369	.196311	.36703
90	2	6.1	6.48026	−.380263	−.77639

The standardized residuals and the predicted values of y from Table 15.7 are used in Figure 15.10, the standardized residual plot for the Butler Trucking multiple regression example. This standardized residual plot does not indicate any unusual abnormalities. Also, all the standardized residuals are between −2 and +2; hence, we have no reason to question the assumption that the error term ϵ is normally distributed. We conclude that the model assumptions are reasonable.

A normal probability plot also can be used to determine whether the distribution of ϵ appears to be normal. The procedure and interpretation for a normal probability plot were discussed in Section 14.8. The same procedure is appropriate for multiple regression. Again, we would use a statistical software package to perform the computations and provide the normal probability plot.

| FIGURE 15.10 | Standardized Residual Plot for Butler Trucking |

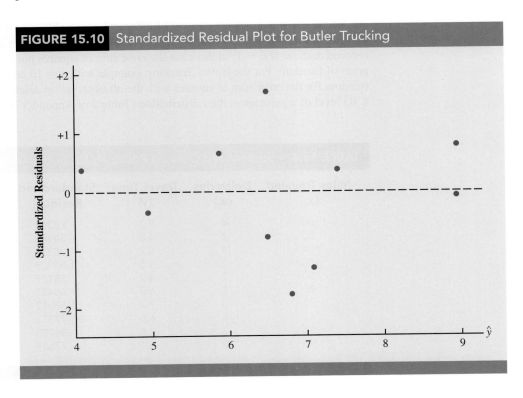

Detecting Outliers

An **outlier** is an observation that is unusual in comparison with the other data; in other words, an outlier does not fit the pattern of the other data. In Chapter 14 we showed an example of an outlier and discussed how standardized residuals can be used to detect outliers. An observation is classified as an outlier if the value of its standardized residual is less than -2 or greater than $+2$. Applying this rule to the standardized residuals for the Butler Trucking example (see Table 15.7), we do not detect any outliers in the data set.

In general, the presence of one or more outliers in a data set tends to increase s, the standard error of the estimate, and hence increase $s_{y-\hat{y}_i}$, the standard deviation of residual i. Because $s_{y_i-\hat{y}_i}$ appears in the denominator of the formula for the standardized residual (15.23), the size of the standardized residual will decrease as s increases. As a result, even though a residual may be unusually large, the large denominator in expression (15.23) may cause the standardized residual rule to fail to identify the observation as being an outlier. We can circumvent this difficulty by using a form of the standardized residuals called **studentized deleted residuals**.

Studentized Deleted Residuals and Outliers

Suppose the ith observation is deleted from the data set and a new estimated regression equation is developed with the remaining $n-1$ observations. Let $s_{(i)}$ denote the standard error of the estimate based on the data set with the ith observation deleted. If we compute the standard deviation of residual i using $s_{(i)}$ instead of s, and then compute the standardized residual for observation i using the revised $s_{y_i-\hat{y}_i}$ value, the resulting standardized residual is called a studentized deleted residual. If the ith observation is an outlier, $s_{(i)}$ will be less than s. The absolute value of the ith studentized deleted residual therefore will be larger than the absolute value of the standardized residual. In this sense, studentized deleted residuals may detect outliers that standardized residuals do not detect.

Many statistical software packages provide an option for obtaining studentized deleted residuals. Using statistical software, we obtained the studentized deleted residuals for the Butler Trucking example; the results are reported in Table 15.8. The t distribution can be used to determine whether the studentized deleted residuals indicate the presence of outliers. Recall that p denotes the number of independent variables and n denotes the number of observations. Hence, if we delete the ith observation, the number of observations in the reduced data set is $n-1$; in this case the error sum of squares has $(n-1)-p-1$ degrees of freedom. For the Butler Trucking example with $n=10$ and $p=2$, the degrees of freedom for the error sum of squares with the ith observation deleted is $9-2-1=6$. At a .05 level of significance, the t distribution (Table 2 of Appendix B) shows that with

TABLE 15.8	Studentized Deleted Residuals for Butler Trucking			
Miles Traveled (x_1)	Deliveries (x_2)	Travel Time (y)	Standardized Residual	Studentized Deleted Residual
100	4	9.3	.78344	.75939
50	3	4.8	−.34962	−.32654
100	4	8.9	−.08334	−.07720
100	2	6.5	−1.30929	−1.39494
50	2	4.2	.38167	.35709
80	2	6.2	.65431	.62519
75	3	7.4	1.68917	2.03187
65	4	6.0	−1.77372	−2.21314
90	3	7.6	.36703	.34312
90	2	6.1	−.77639	−.75190

TABLE 15.9	Leverage and Cook's Distance Measures for Butler Trucking			
Miles Traveled (x_1)	Deliveries (x_2)	Travel Time (y)	Leverage (h_i)	Cook's D (D_i)
100	4	9.3	.351704	.110994
50	3	4.8	.375863	.024536
100	4	8.9	.351704	.001256
100	2	6.5	.378451	.347923
50	2	4.2	.430220	.036663
80	2	6.2	.220557	.040381
75	3	7.4	.110009	.117562
65	4	6.0	.382657	.650029
90	3	7.6	.129098	.006656
90	2	6.1	.269737	.074217

six degrees of freedom, $t_{.025} = 2.447$. If the value of the ith studentized deleted residual is less than -2.447 or greater than $+2.447$, we can conclude that the ith observation is an outlier. The studentized deleted residuals in Table 15.8 do not exceed those limits; therefore, we conclude that outliers are not present in the data set.

Influential Observations

In Section 14.9 we discussed how the leverage of an observation can be used to identify observations for which the value of the independent variable may have a strong influence on the regression results. As we indicated in the discussion of standardized residuals, the leverage of an observation, denoted h_i, measures how far the values of the independent variables are from their mean values. We use the rule of thumb $h_i > 3(p + 1)/n$ to identify **influential observations**. For the Butler Trucking example with $p = 2$ independent variables and $n = 10$ observations, the critical value for leverage is $3(2 + 1)/10 = .9$. The leverage values for the Butler Trucking example obtained by using statistical software are reported in Table 15.9. Because h_i does not exceed .9, we do not detect influential observations in the data set.

Using Cook's Distance Measure to Identify Influential Observations

TABLE 15.10

Data Set Illustrating Potential Problem Using the Leverage Criterion

x_i	y_i	Leverage h_i
1	18	.204170
1	21	.204170
2	22	.164205
3	21	.138141
4	23	.125977
4	24	.125977
5	26	.127715
15	39	.909644

A problem that can arise in using leverage to identify influential observations is that an observation can be identified as having high leverage and not necessarily be influential in terms of the resulting estimated regression equation. For example, Table 15.10 is a data set consisting of eight observations and their corresponding leverage values (obtained by using statistical software). Because the leverage for the eighth observation is .91 > .75 (the critical leverage value), this observation is identified as influential. Before reaching any final conclusions, however, let us consider the situation from a different perspective.

Figure 15.11 shows the scatter diagram corresponding to the data set in Table 15.10. We used statistical software to develop the following estimated regression equation for these data.

$$\hat{y} = 18.2 + 1.39x$$

The straight line in Figure 15.11 is the graph of this equation. Now, let us delete the observation $x = 15$, $y = 39$ from the data set and fit a new estimated regression equation to the remaining seven observations; the new estimated regression equation is

$$\hat{y} = 18.1 + 1.42x$$

FIGURE 15.11 Scatter Diagram for the Data Set in Table 15.10

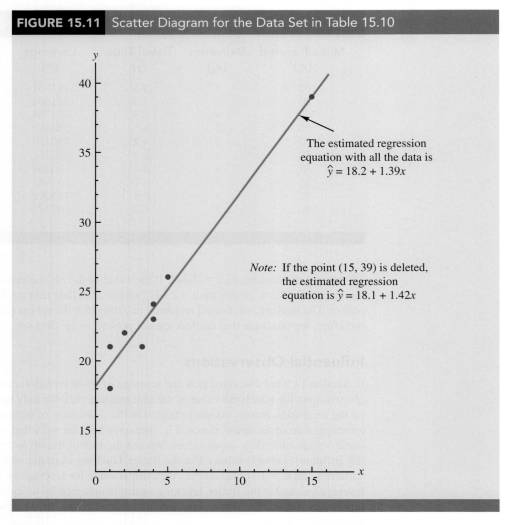

Note: If the point (15, 39) is deleted, the estimated regression equation is $\hat{y} = 18.1 + 1.42x$

The estimated regression equation with all the data is $\hat{y} = 18.2 + 1.39x$

We note that the *y*-intercept and slope of the new estimated regression equation are very close to the values obtained using all the data. Although the leverage criterion identified the eighth observation as influential, this observation clearly had little influence on the results obtained. Thus, in some situations using only leverage to identify influential observations can lead to wrong conclusions.

Cook's distance measure uses both the leverage of observation *i*, h_i, and the residual for observation *i*, $(y_i - \hat{y}_i)$, to determine whether the observation is influential.

COOK'S DISTANCE MEASURE

$$D_i = \frac{(y_i - \hat{y}_i)^2}{(p + 1)s^2}\left[\frac{h_i}{(1 - h_i)^2}\right] \tag{15.25}$$

where

$$D_i = \text{Cook's distance measure for observation } i$$
$$y_i - \hat{y}_i = \text{the residual for observation } i$$
$$h_i = \text{the leverage for observation } i$$
$$p = \text{the number of independent variables}$$
$$s = \text{the standard error of the estimate}$$

The value of Cook's distance measure will be large and indicate an influential observation if the residual or the leverage is large. As a rule of thumb, values of $D_i > 1$ indicate that the ith observation is influential and should be studied further. The last column of Table 15.9 provides Cook's distance measure for the Butler Trucking problem. Observation 8 with $D_i = .650029$ has the most influence. However, applying the rule $D_i > 1$, we should not be concerned about the presence of influential observations in the Butler Trucking data set.

NOTES + COMMENTS

1. The procedures for identifying outliers and influential observations provide warnings about the potential effects some observations may have on the regression results. Each outlier and influential observation warrants careful examination. If data errors are found, the errors can be corrected and the regression analysis repeated. In general, outliers and influential observations should not be removed from the data set unless clear evidence shows that they are not based on elements of the population being studied and should not have been included in the original data set.

2. To determine whether the value of Cook's distance measure D_i is large enough to conclude that the ith observation is influential, we can also compare the value of D_i to the 50th percentile of an F distribution (denoted F_{50}) with $p + 1$ numerator degrees of freedom and $n - p - 1$ denominator degrees of freedom. F tables corresponding to a .50 level of significance must be available to carry out the test. The rule of thumb we provided ($D_i > 1$) is based on the fact that the table value is close to one for a wide variety of cases.

EXERCISES

Methods

39. Data for two variables, x and y, follow.

x_i	1	2	3	4	5
y_i	3	7	5	11	14

a. Develop the estimated regression equation for these data.
b. Plot the standardized residuals versus $\hat{y}$. Do there appear to be any outliers in these data? Explain.
c. Compute the studentized deleted residuals for these data. At the .05 level of significance, can any of these observations be classified as an outlier? Explain.

40. Data for two variables, x and y, follow.

x_i	22	24	26	28	40
y_i	12	21	31	35	70

a. Develop the estimated regression equation for these data.
b. Compute the studentized deleted residuals for these data. At the .05 level of significance, can any of these observations be classified as an outlier? Explain.
c. Compute the leverage values for these data. Do there appear to be any influential observations in these data? Explain.
d. Compute Cook's distance measure for these data. Are any observations influential? Explain.

Applications

41. **Detecting Outliers in Theater Revenue.** Exercise 5 gave the following data on weekly gross revenue, television advertising, and newspaper advertising for Showtime Movie Theaters.

DATAfile

Showtime

Weekly Gross Revenue ($1000s)	Television Advertising ($1000s)	Newspaper Advertising ($1000s)
96	5.0	1.5
90	2.0	2.0
95	4.0	1.5
92	2.5	2.5
95	3.0	3.3
94	3.5	2.3
94	2.5	4.2
94	3.0	2.5

   a. Find an estimated regression equation relating weekly gross revenue to television and newspaper advertising.

   b. Plot the standardized residuals against $\hat{y}$. Does the residual plot support the assumptions about ϵ? Explain.

   c. Check for any outliers in these data. What are your conclusions?

   d. Are there any influential observations? Explain.

42. **Sports Car Prices.** The following data show the curb weight, horsepower, and ¼-mile speed for 16 popular sports and GT cars. Suppose that the price of each sports and GT car is also available. The complete data set is as follows:

DATAfile

Auto2

Sports & GT Car	Price ($1000s)	Curb Weight (lb.)	Horsepower	Speed at ¼ Mile (mph)
Acura Integra Type R	25.035	2577	195	90.7
Acura NSX-T	93.758	3066	290	108.0
BMW Z3 2.8	40.900	2844	189	93.2
Chevrolet Camaro Z28	24.865	3439	305	103.2
Chevrolet Corvette Convertible	50.144	3246	345	102.1
Dodge Viper RT/10	69.742	3319	450	116.2
Ford Mustang GT	23.200	3227	225	91.7
Honda Prelude Type SH	26.382	3042	195	89.7
Mercedes-Benz CLK320	44.988	3240	215	93.0
Mercedes-Benz SLK230	42.762	3025	185	92.3
Mitsubishi 3000GT VR-4	47.518	3737	320	99.0
Nissan 240SX SE	25.066	2862	155	84.6
Pontiac Firebird Trans Am	27.770	3455	305	103.2
Porsche Boxster	45.560	2822	201	93.2
Toyota Supra Turbo	40.989	3505	320	105.0
Volvo C70	41.120	3285	236	97.0

   a. Find the estimated regression equation that uses price and horsepower to predict ¼-mile speed.

   b. Plot the standardized residuals against $\hat{y}$. Does the residual plot support the assumption about ϵ? Explain.

   c. Check for any outliers. What are your conclusions?

   d. Are there any influential observations? Explain.

43. **Golf Scores.** The Ladies Professional Golfers Association (LPGA) maintains statistics on performance and earnings for members of the LPGA Tour. Year-end performance

DATA*file*

LPGA2014

statistics for 134 golfers for 2014 appear in the file named *LPGA2014* (LPGA website, April 2015). Earnings ($1000s) is the total earnings in thousands of dollars; Scoring Avg. is the scoring average for all events; Greens in Reg. is the percentage of time a player is able to hit the greens in regulation; and Putting Avg. is the average number of putts taken on greens hit in regulation. A green is considered hit in regulation if any part of the ball is touching the putting surface and the difference between par for the hole and the number of strokes taken to hit the green is at least 2.

a. Develop an estimated regression equation that can be used to predict the scoring average given the percentage of time a player is able to hit the greens in regulation and the average number of putts taken on green hit in regulation.

b. Plot the standardized residuals against $\hat{y}$. Does the residual plot support the assumption about ϵ? Explain.

c. Check for any outliers. What are your conclusions?

d. Are there any influential observations? Explain.

15.9 Logistic Regression

In many regression applications, the dependent variable may only assume two discrete values. For instance, a bank might want to develop an estimated regression equation for predicting whether a person will be approved for a credit card. The dependent variable can be coded as $y = 1$ if the bank approves the request for a credit card and $y = 0$ if the bank rejects the request for a credit card. Using logistic regression we can estimate the probability that the bank will approve the request for a credit card given a particular set of values for the chosen independent variables.

Let us consider an application of logistic regression involving a direct mail promotion being used by Simmons Stores. Simmons owns and operates a national chain of women's apparel stores. Five thousand copies of an expensive four-color sales catalog have been printed, and each catalog includes a coupon that provides a $50 discount on purchases of $200 or more. The catalogs are expensive and Simmons would like to send them to only those customers who have a high probability of using the coupon.

Management believes that annual spending at Simmons Stores and whether a customer has a Simmons credit card are two variables that might be helpful in predicting whether a customer who receives the catalog will use the coupon. Simmons conducted a pilot study using a random sample of 50 Simmons credit card customers and 50 other customers who do not have a Simmons credit card. Simmons sent the catalog to each of the 100 customers selected. At the end of a test period, Simmons noted whether each customer had used her or his coupon. The sample data for the first 10 catalog recipients are shown in Table 15.11.

TABLE 15.11 Partial Sample Data for the Simmons Stores Example

Customer	Annual Spending ($1000)	Simmons Card	Coupon
1	2.291	1	0
2	3.215	1	0
3	2.135	1	0
4	3.924	0	0
5	2.528	1	0
6	2.473	0	1
7	2.384	0	0
8	7.076	0	1
9	1.182	1	1
10	3.345	0	0

DATA*file*

Simmons

The amount each customer spent last year at Simmons is shown in thousands of dollars and the credit card information has been coded as 1 if the customer has a Simmons credit card and 0 if not. In the Coupon column, a 1 is recorded if the sampled customer used the coupon and 0 if not.

We might think of building a multiple regression model using the data in Table 15.11 to help Simmons estimate whether a catalog recipient will use the coupon. We would use Annual Spending ($1000) and Simmons Card as independent variables and Coupon as the dependent variable. Because the dependent variable may only assume the values of 0 or 1, however, the ordinary multiple regression model is not applicable. This example shows the type of situation for which logistic regression was developed. Let us see how logistic regression can be used to help Simmons estimate which type of customer is most likely to take advantage of their promotion.

Logistic Regression Equation

In many ways logistic regression is like ordinary regression. It requires a dependent variable, y, and one or more independent variables. In multiple regression analysis, the mean or expected value of y is referred to as the multiple regression equation.

$$E(y) = \beta_0 + \beta_1 x_1 + \beta_2 x_2 + \cdots + \beta_p x_p \qquad (15.26)$$

In logistic regression, statistical theory as well as practice has shown that the relationship between $E(y)$ and $x_1, x_2, \ldots, x_p$ is better described by the following nonlinear equation.

LOGISTIC REGRESSION EQUATION

$$E(y) = \frac{e^{\beta_0 + \beta_1 x_1 + \beta_2 x_2 + \cdots + \beta_p x_p}}{1 + e^{\beta_0 + \beta_1 x_1 + \beta_2 x_2 + \cdots + \beta_p x_p}} \qquad (15.27)$$

If the two values of the dependent variable y are coded as 0 or 1, the value of $E(y)$ in equation (15.27) provides the *probability* that $y = 1$ given a particular set of values for the independent variables $x_1, x_2, \ldots, x_p$. Because of the interpretation of $E(y)$ as a probability, the **logistic regression equation** is often written as follows:

INTERPRETATION OF $E(y)$ AS A PROBABILITY IN LOGISTIC REGRESSION

$$E(y) = P(y = 1 | x_1, x_2, \ldots, x_p) \qquad (15.28)$$

To provide a better understanding of the characteristics of the logistic regression equation, suppose the model involves only one independent variable x and the values of the model parameters are $\beta_0 = -7$ and $\beta_1 = 3$. The logistic regression equation corresponding to these parameter values is

$$E(y) = P(y = 1 | x) = \frac{e^{\beta_0 + \beta_1 x}}{1 + e^{\beta_0 + \beta_1 x}} = \frac{e^{-7 + 3x}}{1 + e^{-7 + 3x}} \qquad (15.29)$$

Figure 15.12 shows a graph of equation (15.29). Note that the graph is S-shaped. The value of $E(y)$ ranges from 0 to 1. For example, when $x = 2$, $E(y)$ is approximately .27. Also note that the value of $E(y)$ gradually approaches 1 as the value of x becomes larger and the value of $E(y)$ approaches 0 as the value of x becomes smaller. For example, when $x = 2$, $E(y) = .269$. Note also that the values of $E(y)$, representing probability, increase fairly rapidly as x increases from 2 to 3. The fact that the values of $E(y)$ range from 0 to 1 and that the curve is S-shaped makes equation (15.29) ideally suited to model the probability the dependent variable is equal to 1.

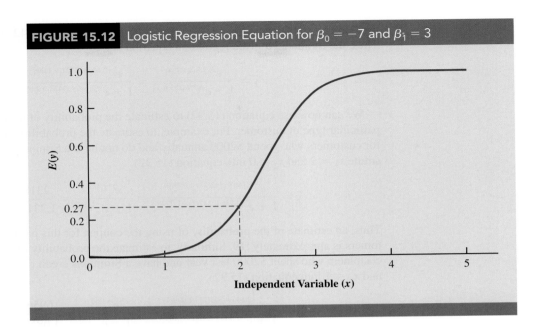

FIGURE 15.12 Logistic Regression Equation for $\beta_0 = -7$ and $\beta_1 = 3$

Estimating the Logistic Regression Equation

In simple linear and multiple regression the least squares method is used to compute b_0, $b_1, \ldots, b_p$ as estimates of the model parameters ($\beta_0, \beta_1, \ldots, \beta_p$). The nonlinear form of the logistic regression equation makes the method of computing estimates more complex and beyond the scope of this text. We use statistical software to provide the estimates. The **estimated logistic regression equation** is

ESTIMATED LOGISTIC REGRESSION EQUATION

$$\hat{y} = \text{estimate of } P(y = 1|x_1, x_2, \ldots, x_p) = \frac{e^{b_0+b_1x_1+b_2x_2+\cdots+b_px_p}}{1 + e^{b_0+b_1x_1+b_2x_2+\cdots+b_px_p}} \qquad (15.30)$$

Here, $\hat{y}$ provides an estimate of the probability that $y = 1$ given a particular set of values for the independent variables.

Let us now return to the Simmons Stores example. The variables in the study are defined as follows:

$$y = \begin{cases} 0 \text{ if the customer did not use the coupon} \\ 1 \text{ if the customer used the coupon} \end{cases}$$

$$x_1 = \text{annual spending at Simmons Stores (\$1000s)}$$

$$x_2 = \begin{cases} 0 \text{ if the customer does not have a Simmons credit card} \\ 1 \text{ if the customer has a Simmons credit card} \end{cases}$$

Thus, we choose a logistic regression equation with two independent variables.

$$E(y) = \frac{e^{\beta_0+\beta_1x_1+\beta_2x_2}}{1 + e^{\beta_0+\beta_1x_1+\beta_2x_2}} \qquad (15.31)$$

In Appendix 15.2 we show how JMP is used to generate the output in Figure 15.13.

Using the sample data (see Table 15.11), we used statistical software to compute estimates of the model parameters β_0, β_1, and β_2. Figure 15.13 displays output commonly provided by statistical software. We see that $b_0 = -2.146$, $b_1 = .342$, and $b_2 = 1.099$. Thus, the estimated logistic regression equation is

$$\hat{y} = \frac{e^{b_0 + b_1 x_1 + b_2 x_2}}{1 + e^{b_0 + b_1 x_1 + b_2 x_2}} = \frac{e^{-2.146 + .342 x_1 + 1.099 x_2}}{1 + e^{-2.146 + .342 x_1 + 1.099 x_2}} \tag{15.32}$$

We can now use equation (15.32) to estimate the probability of using the coupon for a particular type of customer. For example, to estimate the probability of using the coupon for customers who spend \$2000 annually and do not have a Simmons credit card, we substitute $x_1 = 2$ and $x_2 = 0$ into equation (15.32).

$$\hat{y} = \frac{e^{-2.146 + .342(2) + 1.099(0)}}{1 + e^{-2.146 + .342(2) + 1.099(0)}} = \frac{e^{-1.462}}{1 + e^{-1.462}} = \frac{.2318}{1.2318} = .1882$$

Thus, an estimate of the probability of using the coupon for this particular group of customers is approximately .19. Similarly, to estimate the probability of using the coupon for customers who spent \$2000 last year and have a Simmons credit card, we substitute $x_1 = 2$ and $x_2 = 1$ into equation (15.32).

$$\hat{y} = \frac{e^{-2.146 + .342(2) + 1.099(1)}}{1 + e^{-2.146 + .342(2) + 1.099(1)}} = \frac{e^{-.363}}{1 + e^{-.363}} = \frac{.6956}{1.6956} = .4102$$

Thus, for this group of customers, the probability of using the coupon is approximately .41. It appears that the probability of using the coupon is much higher for customers with a Simmons credit card. Before reaching any conclusions, however, we need to assess the statistical significance of our model.

Testing for Significance

Testing for significance in logistic regression is similar to testing for significance in multiple regression. First we conduct a test for overall significance. For the Simmons Stores example, the hypotheses for the test of overall significance follow:

$$H_0: \beta_1 = \beta_2 = 0$$
$$H_a: \text{One or both of the parameters is not equal to zero}$$

The test for overall significance is based upon the value of a χ^2 test statistic. If the null hypothesis is true, the sampling distribution of χ^2 follows a chi-square distribution with degrees of freedom equal to the number of independent variables in the model. While the calculations behind the computation of χ^2 is beyond the scope of the book, Figure 15.13 lists the value of χ^2 and its corresponding p-value in the Whole Model row of the Significance Tests table; we see that the value of χ^2 is 13.63, its degrees of freedom are 2, and its p-value is .0011. Thus, at any level of significance $\alpha \geq .0011$, we would reject the null hypothesis and conclude that the overall model is significant.

If the χ^2 test shows an overall significance, another χ^2 test can be used to determine whether each of the individual independent variables is making a significant contribution to the overall model. For the independent variables x_i, the hypotheses are

$$H_0: \beta_i = 0$$
$$H_a: \beta_i \neq 0$$

The test of significance for an independent variable is also based upon the value of a χ^2 test statistic. If the null hypothesis is true, the sampling distribution of χ^2 follows a chi-square distribution with one degree of freedom. The Spending and Card rows of the Significance Tests table of Figure 15.13 contain the values of χ^2 and their corresponding p-values test for the estimated coefficients. Suppose we use $\alpha = .05$ to test for the significance of the

FIGURE 15.13 Logistic Regression Output for the Simmons Stores Example

Significance Tests

Term	Degrees of Freedom	χ^2	p-Value
Whole Model	2	13.63	.0011
Spending	1	7.56	.0060
Card	1	6.41	.0013

Parameter Estimates

Term	Estimate	Standard Error
Intercept	−2.146	.577
Spending	.342	.129
Card	1.099	.44

Odds Ratios

Term	Odds Ratio	Lower 95%	Upper 95%
Spending	1.4073	1.0936	1.8109
Card	3.0000	1.2550	7.1730

independent variables in the Simmons model. For the independent variable Spending (x_1) the χ^2 value is 7.56 and the corresponding p-value is .0060. Thus, at the .05 level of significance we can reject $H_0: \beta_1 = 0$. In a similar fashion we can also reject $H_0: \beta_2 = 0$ because the p-value corresponding to Card's $\chi^2 = 6.41$ is .0013. Hence, at the .05 level of significance, both independent variables are statistically significant.

Managerial Use

We described how to develop the estimated logistic regression equation and how to test it for significance. Let us now use it to make a decision recommendation concerning the Simmons Stores catalog promotion. For Simmons Stores, we already computed $P(y = 1|x_1 = 2, x_2 = 1) = .4102$ and $P(y = 1|x_1 = 2, x_2 = 0) = .1881$. These probabilities indicate that for customers with annual spending of $2000 the presence of a Simmons credit card increases the probability of using the coupon. In Table 15.12 we show estimated probabilities for values of annual spending ranging from $1000 to $7000 for both customers who have a Simmons credit card and customers who do not have a Simmons credit card. How can Simmons use this information to better target customers for the new promotion? Suppose Simmons wants to send the promotional catalog only to customers who have a .40 or higher probability of using the coupon. Using the estimated probabilities in Table 15.12, Simmons promotion strategy would be:

Customers who have a Simmons credit card: Send the catalog to every customer who spent $2000 or more last year.

Customers who do not have a Simmons credit card: Send the catalog to every customer who spent $6000 or more last year.

Looking at the estimated probabilities further, we see that the probability of using the coupon for customers who do not have a Simmons credit card but spend $5000 annually is .3922. Thus, Simmons may want to consider revising this strategy by including

TABLE 15.12 Estimated Probabilities for Simmons Stores

		Annual Spending						
		$1000	$2000	$3000	$4000	$5000	$6000	$7000
Credit	Yes	.3307	.4102	.4948	.5796	.6599	.7320	.7936
Card	No	.1414	.1881	.2460	.3148	.3927	.4765	.5617

those customers who do not have a credit card, as long as they spent $5000 or more last year.

Interpreting the Logistic Regression Equation

Interpreting a regression equation involves relating the independent variables to the business question that the equation was developed to answer. With logistic regression, it is difficult to interpret the relation between the independent variables and the probability that $y = 1$ directly because the logistic regression equation is nonlinear. However, statisticians have shown that the relationship can be interpreted indirectly using a concept called the odds ratio.

The **odds in favor of an event occurring** is defined as the probability the event will occur divided by the probability the event will not occur. In logistic regression the event of interest is always $y = 1$. Given a particular set of values for the independent variables, the odds in favor of $y = 1$ can be calculated as follows:

$$\text{odds} = \frac{P(y = 1|x_1, x_2, \ldots, x_p)}{P(y = 0|x_1, x_2, \ldots, x_p)} = \frac{P(y = 1|x_1, x_2, \ldots, x_p)}{1 - P(y = 1|x_1, x_2, \ldots, x_p)} \quad \textbf{(15.33)}$$

The **odds ratio** measures the impact on the odds of a one-unit increase in only one of the independent variables. The odds ratio is the odds that $y = 1$ given that one of the independent variables has been increased by one unit (odds_1) divided by the odds that $y = 1$ given no change in the values for the independent variables (odds_0).

ODDS RATIO

$$\text{Odds Ratio} = \frac{\text{odds}_1}{\text{odds}_0} \quad \textbf{(15.34)}$$

For example, suppose we want to compare the odds of using the coupon for customers who spend $2000 annually and have a Simmons credit card ($x_1 = 2$ and $x_2 = 1$) to the odds of using the coupon for customers who spend $2000 annually and do not have a Simmons credit card ($x_1 = 2$ and $x_2 = 0$). We are interested in interpreting the effect of a one-unit increase in the independent variable x_2. In this case

$$\text{odds}_1 = \frac{P(y = 1|x_1 = 2, x_2 = 1)}{1 - P(y = 1|x_1 = 2, x_2 = 1)}$$

and

$$\text{odds}_0 = \frac{P(y = 1|x_1 = 2, x_2 = 0)}{1 - P(y = 1|x_1 = 2, x_2 = 0)}$$

Previously we showed that an estimate of the probability that $y = 1$ given $x_1 = 2$ and $x_2 = 1$ is .4102, and an estimate of the probability that $y = 1$ given $x_1 = 2$ and $x_2 = 0$ is .1881. Thus,

$$\text{estimate of odds}_1 = \frac{.4102}{1 - .4102} = .6956$$

and

$$\text{estimate of odds}_0 = \frac{.1881}{1 - .1881} = .2318$$

The estimated odds ratio is

$$\text{estimated odds ratio} = \frac{.6956}{.2318} = 3.00$$

Thus, we can conclude that the estimated odds in favor of using the coupon for customers who spent \$2000 last year and have a Simmons credit card are 3 times greater than the estimated odds in favor of using the coupon for customers who spent \$2000 last year and do not have a Simmons credit card.

The odds ratio for each independent variable is computed while holding all the other independent variables constant. But it does not matter what constant values are used for the other independent variables. For instance, if we computed the odds ratio for the Simmons credit card variable (x_2) using \$3000, instead of \$2000, as the value for the annual spending variable (x_1), we would still obtain the same value for the estimated odds ratio (3.00). Thus, we can conclude that the estimated odds of using the coupon for customers who have a Simmons credit card are 3 times greater than the estimated odds of using the coupon for customers who do not have a Simmons credit card.

The odds ratio is standard output for most statistical software packages. The Odds Ratios table in Figure 15.13 contains the estimated odds ratios for each of the independent variables. The estimated odds ratio for Spending (x_1) is 1.4073 and the estimated odds ratio for Card (x_2) is 3.0000. We already showed how to interpret the estimated odds ratio for the binary independent variable x_2. Let us now consider the interpretation of the estimated odds ratio for the continuous independent variable x_1.

The value of 1.4073 in the Odds Ratio column of the output tells us that the estimated odds in favor of using the coupon for customers who spent \$3000 last year is 1.4073 times greater than the estimated odds in favor of using the coupon for customers who spent \$2000 last year. Moreover, this interpretation is true for any one-unit change in x_1. For instance, the estimated odds in favor of using the coupon for someone who spent \$5000 last year is 1.4073 times greater than the odds in favor of using the coupon for a customer who spent \$4000 last year. But suppose we are interested in the change in the odds for an increase of more than one unit for an independent variable. Note that x_1 can range from 1 to 7. The odds ratio given by the output does not answer this question. To answer this question we must explore the relationship between the odds ratio and the regression coefficients.

A unique relationship exists between the odds ratio for a variable and its corresponding regression coefficient. For each independent variable in a logistic regression equation it can be shown that

$$\text{Odds ratio} = e^{\beta_i}$$

To illustrate this relationship, consider the independent variable x_1 in the Simmons example. The estimated odds ratio for x_1 is

$$\text{Estimated odds ratio} = e^{b_1} = e^{.342} = 1.407$$

Similarly, the estimated odds ratio for x_2 is

$$\text{Estimated odds ratio} = e^{b_2} = e^{1.099} = 3.000$$

This relationship between the odds ratio and the coefficients of the independent variables makes it easy to compute estimated odds ratios once we develop estimates of the model parameters. Moreover, it also provides us with the ability to investigate changes in the odds ratio of more than or less than one unit for a continuous independent variable.

The odds ratio for an independent variable represents the change in the odds for a one-unit change in the independent variable holding all the other independent variables constant. Suppose that we want to consider the effect of a change of more than one unit, say c units. For instance, suppose in the Simmons example that we want to compare the odds of using the coupon for customers who spend \$5000 annually ($x_1 = 5$) to the odds of using the coupon for customers who spend \$2000 annually ($x_1 = 2$). In this case $c = 5 - 2 = 3$ and the corresponding estimated odds ratio is

$$e^{cb_1} = e^{3(.342)} = e^{1.026} = 2.79$$

This result indicates that the estimated odds of using the coupon for customers who spend \$5000 annually is 2.79 times greater than the estimated odds of using the coupon for customers who spend \$2000 annually. In other words, the estimated odds ratio for an increase of \$3000 in annual spending is 2.79.

In general, the odds ratio enables us to compare the odds for two different events. If the value of the odds ratio is 1, the odds for both events are the same. Thus, if the independent variable we are considering (such as Simmons credit card status) has a positive impact on the probability of the event occurring, the corresponding odds ratio will be greater than 1. Most statistical software packages provide a confidence interval for the odds ratio. The Odds Ratio table in Figure 15.13 provides a 95% confidence interval for each of the odds ratios. For example, the point estimate of the odds ratio for x_1 is 1.4073 and the 95% confidence interval is 1.0936 to 1.8109. Because the confidence interval does not contain the value of 1, we can conclude that x_1 has a significant relationship with the estimated odds ratio. Similarly, the 95% confidence interval for the odds ratio for x_2 is 1.2550 to 7.1730. Because this interval does not contain the value of 1, we can also conclude that x_2 has a significant relationship with the odds ratio.

Logit Transformation

An interesting relationship can be observed between the odds in favor of $y = 1$ and the exponent for e in the logistic regression equation. It can be shown that

$$\ln(\text{odds}) = \beta_0 + \beta_1 x_1 + \beta_2 x_2 + \cdots + \beta_p x_p$$

This equation shows that the natural logarithm of the odds in favor of $y = 1$ is a linear function of the independent variables. This linear function is called the **logit**. We will use the notation $g(x_1, x_2, \ldots, x_p)$ to denote the logit.

LOGIT

$$g(x_1, x_2, \ldots, x_p) = \beta_0 + \beta_1 x_1 + \beta_2 x_2 + \cdots + \beta_p x_p \qquad \textbf{(15.35)}$$

Substituting $g(x_1, x_2, \ldots, x_p)$ for $\beta_1 + \beta_1 x_1 + \beta_2 x_2 + \cdots + \beta_p x_p$ in equation (15.27), we can write the logistic regression equation as

$$E(y) = \frac{e^{g(x_1, x_2, \ldots, x_p)}}{1 + e^{g(x_1, x_2, \ldots, x_p)}} \qquad \textbf{(15.36)}$$

Once we estimate the parameters in the logistic regression equation, we can compute an estimate of the logit. Using $\hat{g}(x_1, x_2, \ldots, x_p)$ to denote the **estimated logit**, we obtain

ESTIMATED LOGIT

$$\hat{g}(x_1, x_2, \ldots, x_p) = b_0 + b_1 x_1 + b_2 x_2 + \cdots + b_p x_p \qquad \textbf{(15.37)}$$

Thus, in terms of the estimated logit, the estimated regression equation is

$$\hat{y} = \frac{e^{b_0 + b_1 x_1 + b_2 x_2 + \cdots + b_p x_p}}{1 + e^{b_0 + b_1 x_1 + b_2 x_2 + \cdots + b_p x_p}} = \frac{e^{\hat{g}(x_1, x_2, \ldots, x_p)}}{1 + e^{\hat{g}(x_1, x_2, \ldots, x_p)}} \qquad (15.38)$$

For the Simmons Stores example, the estimated logit is

$$\hat{g}(x_1, x_2) = -2.146 + .342x_1 + 1.099x_2$$

and the estimated regression equation is

$$\hat{y} = \frac{e^{\hat{g}(x_1, x_2)}}{1 + e^{\hat{g}(x_1, x_2)}} = \frac{e^{-2.146 + .342x_1 + 1.099x_2}}{1 + e^{-2.146 + .342x_1 + 1.099x_2}}$$

Thus, because of the unique relationship between the estimated logit and the estimated logistic regression equation, we can compute the estimated probabilities for Simmons Stores by dividing $e^{\hat{g}(x_1, x_2)}$ by $1 + e^{\hat{g}(x_1, x_2)}$.

NOTES + COMMENTS

1. Because of the unique relationship between the estimated coefficients in the model and the corresponding odds ratios, the overall test for significance based upon the χ^2 statistic is also a test of overall significance for the odds ratios. In addition, the χ^2 test for the individual significance of a model parameter also provides a statistical test of significance for the corresponding odds ratio.

2. In simple and multiple regression, the coefficient of determination is used to measure the goodness of fit. In logistic regression, no single measure provides a similar interpretation. A discussion of goodness of fit is beyond the scope of our introductory treatment of logistic regression.

EXERCISES

Applications

Simmons

44. **Coupon Redemption.** Refer to the Simmons Stores example introduced in this section. The dependent variable is coded as $y = 1$ if the customer used the coupon and 0 if not. Suppose that the only information available to help predict whether the customer will use the coupon is the customer's credit card status, coded as $x = 1$ if the customer has a Simmons credit card and $x = 0$ if not.
    a. Write the logistic regression equation relating x to y.
    b. What is the interpretation of $E(y)$ when $x = 0$?
    c. For the Simmons data in Table 15.11, use statistical software to compute the estimated logit.
    d. Use the estimated logit computed in part (c) to estimate the probability of using the coupon for customers who do not have a Simmons credit card and to estimate the probability of using the coupon for customers who have a Simmons credit card.
    e. What is the estimated odds ratio? What is its interpretation?

45. **Odds Ratio for Coupon Redemption.** In Table 15.12 we provided estimates of the probability of using the coupon in the Simmons Stores catalog promotion. A different value is obtained for each combination of values for the independent variables.
    a. Compute the odds in favor of using the coupon for a customer with annual spending of $4000 who does not have a Simmons credit card ($x_1 = 4$, $x_2 = 0$).
    b. Use the information in Table 15.12 and part (a) to compute the odds ratio for the Simmons credit card variable $x_2 = 0$, holding annual spending constant at $x_1 = 4$.

c. In the text, the odds ratio for the credit card variable was computed using the information in the $2000 column of Table 15.12. Did you get the same value for the odds ratio in part (b)?

46. **Direct Deposit.** Community Bank would like to increase the number of customers who use payroll direct deposit. Management is considering a new sales campaign that will require each branch manager to call each customer who does not currently use payroll direct deposit. As an incentive to sign up for payroll direct deposit, each customer contacted will be offered free checking for two years. Because of the time and cost associated with the new campaign, management would like to focus their efforts on customers who have the highest probability of signing up for payroll direct deposit. Management believes that the average monthly balance in a customer's checking account may be a useful predictor of whether the customer will sign up for direct payroll deposit. To investigate the relationship between these two variables, Community Bank tried the new campaign using a sample of 50 checking account customers who do not currently use payroll direct deposit. The sample data show the average monthly checking account balance (in hundreds of dollars) and whether the customer contacted signed up for payroll direct deposit (coded 1 if the customer signed up for payroll direct deposit and 0 if not). The data are contained in the data set named Bank; a portion of the data follows.

Bank

Customer	x = Monthly Balance	y = Direct Deposit
1	1.22	0
2	1.56	0
3	2.10	0
4	2.25	0
5	2.89	0
6	3.55	0
7	3.56	0
8	3.65	1
.	.	.
.	.	.
.	.	.
48	18.45	1
49	24.98	0
50	26.05	1

a. Write the logistic regression equation relating x to y.
b. For the Community Bank data, use statistical software to compute the estimated logistic regression equation.
c. Conduct a test of significance using the χ^2 test statistic. Use $\alpha = .05$.
d. Estimate the probability that customers with an average monthly balance of $1000 will sign up for direct payroll deposit.
e. Suppose Community Bank only wants to contact customers who have a .50 or higher probability of signing up for direct payroll deposit. What is the average monthly balance required to achieve this level of probability?
f. What is the estimated odds ratio? What is its interpretation?

47. **College Retention.** Over the past few years the percentage of students who leave Lakeland College at the end of the first year has increased. Last year Lakeland started a voluntary one-week orientation program to help first-year students adjust to campus life. If Lakeland is able to show that the orientation program has a positive effect on retention, they will consider making the program a requirement for all first-year students. Lakeland's administration also suspects that students with lower GPAs have a higher probability of leaving Lakeland at the end of the first year. In order to investigate the relation of

these variables to retention, Lakeland selected a random sample of 100 students from last year's entering class. The data are contained in the data set named Lakeland; a portion of the data follows.

DATA *file*

Lakeland

Student	GPA	Program	Return
1	3.78	1	1
2	2.38	0	1
3	1.30	0	0
4	2.19	1	0
5	3.22	1	1
6	2.68	1	1
.	.	.	.
.	.	.	.
.	.	.	.
98	2.57	1	1
99	1.70	1	1
100	3.85	1	1

The dependent variable was coded as $y = 1$ if the student returned to Lakeland for the sophomore year and $y = 0$ if not. The two independent variables are:

$x_1 = $ GPA at the end of the first semester

$x_2 = \begin{cases} 0 \text{ if the student did not attend the orientation program} \\ 1 \text{ if the student attended the orientation program} \end{cases}$

a. Write the logistic regression equation relating x_1 and x_2 to y.
b. What is the interpretation of $E(y)$ when $x_2 = 0$?
c. Use both independent variables and statistical software to compute the estimated logit.
d. Conduct a test for overall significance using $\alpha = .05$.
e. Use $\alpha = .05$ to determine whether each of the independent variables is significant.
f. Use the estimated logit computed in part (c) to estimate the probability that students with a 2.5 grade point average who did not attend the orientation program will return to Lakeland for their sophomore year. What is the estimated probability for students with a 2.5 grade point average who attended the orientation program?
g. What is the estimated odds ratio for the orientation program? Interpret it.
h. Would you recommend making the orientation program a required activity? Why or why not?

48. **Repeat Sales.** The Tire Rack maintains an independent consumer survey to help drivers help each other by sharing their long-term tire experiences. The data contained in the file named TireRatings show survey results for 68 all-season tires. Performance traits are rated using the following 10-point scale.

DATA *file*

TireRatings

Superior		Excellent		Good		Fair		Unacceptable	
10	9	8	7	6	5	4	3	2	1

The values for the variable labeled Wet are the average of the ratings for each tire's wet traction performance and the values for the variable labeled Noise are the average of the ratings for the noise level generated by each tire. Respondents were also asked whether they would buy the tire again using the following 10-point scale:

Definitely		Probably		Possibly		Probably Not	Definitely Not	
10	9	8	7	6	5	4	3	2	1

The values for the variable labeled Buy Again are the average of the buy-again responses. For the purposes of this exercise, we created the following binary dependent variable:

$$\text{Purchase} = \begin{cases} 1 \text{ if the value of the Buy-Again variable is 7 or greater} \\ 0 \text{ if the value of the Buy-Again variable is less than 7} \end{cases}$$

Thus, if Purchase $= 1$, the respondent would probably or definitely buy the tire again.

a. Write the logistic regression equation relating $x_1 =$ Wet performance rating and $x_2 =$ Noise performance rating to $y =$ Purchase.

b. Use statistical software to compute the estimated logit.

c. Use the estimated logit to compute an estimate of the probability that a customer will probably or definitely purchase a particular tire again with a Wet performance rating of 8 and a Noise performance rating of 8.

d. Suppose that the Wet and Noise performance ratings were 7. How does that affect the probability that a customer will probably or definitely purchase a particular tire again with these performance ratings?

e. If you were the CEO of a tire company, what do the results for parts (c) and (d) tell you?

15.10 Practical Advice: Big Data and Hypothesis Testing in Multiple Regression

In Chapter 14, we observed that in simple linear regression, the p-value for the test of the hypothesis $H_0: \beta_1 = 0$ decreases as the sample size increases. Likewise, for a given level of confidence, the confidence interval for β_1, the confidence interval for the mean value of y, and the prediction interval for an individual value of y each narrows as the sample size increases. These results extend to multiple regression. As the sample size increases:

- the p-value for the F test used to determine whether a significant relationship exists between the dependent variable and the set of all independent variables in the regression model decreases;
- the p-value for each of t-test used to determine whether a significant relationship exists between the dependent variable and an individual independent variable in the regression model decreases;
- the confidence interval for the slope parameter associated with each individaul independent variable narrow;
- the confidence interval for the mean value of y narrows;
- the prediction interval for an individual value of y narrows.

Thus the interval estimates for the slope parameter associated with each individual independent variable, the mean value of y, and predicted individual value of y will become more precise as the sample size increases. And we are more likely to reject the hypothesis that a relationship does not exist between the dependent variable and the set of all individual independent variable in the model as the sample size increases. And for each individual independent variable, we are more likely to reject the hypothesis that a relationship does not exist between the dependent variable and the individual independent variable as the sample size increases. Even when servere multicollinearity is present, if the sample is sufficiently large, independent variable that are highly correlated may each have a significant relationship with the dependent variable. But this does not necessariloy mean that these results become more reliable as the sample size increases.

No matter how large the sample used to estimate the multiple regression model, we must be concerned about the potential presence of nonsampling error in the data. It is important to carefully consider whether a random sample of the population of interest has actually been taken. If nonsampling error is introduced in the data cololection process, the likelihood of marking a Type I or Type II error on hypothesis test in multiple regression may be higher than if the sample data are free of nonsampling error. Furthermore, multicollinearity may cause the estimated slope coefficients to be misleading; this problem persists as the size of the sample used to estimate the multiple regression model increases. Finally, it is important to consider whether the statistically significant relationship(s) in the multiple regression model are of practical significance.

Although multiple regression is an extremely powerful statistical tool, no business decision should be based exclusively on hypothsis testing in multiple regression. Nonsampling error may lead to misleading results. If severe multicollinearity is present, we must be cautious in interpreting the estimated slope coefficients. And practical significance should always be considered in conjunction with statistical significance; this is particularly important when a hypothesis test is based on an extremely large sample, because p-values in such cases can be extremely small. When executed properly, hypothesis tests in mutiple regression provide evidence that should be considered in combination with information collected from other sources to make the most informed decision possible.

SUMMARY

In this chapter, we introduced multiple regression analysis as an extension of simple linear regression analysis presented in Chapter 14. Multiple regression analysis enables us to understand how a dependent variable is related to two or more independent variables. The multiple regression equation $E(y) = \beta_0 + \beta_1 x_1 + \beta_2 x_2 + \cdots + \beta_p x_p$ shows that the mean or expected value of the dependent variable y, denoted $E(y)$, is related to the values of the independent variables $x_1, x_2, \ldots, x_p$. Sample data and the least squares method are used to develop the estimated multiple regression equation $\hat{y} = b_0 + b_1 x_1 + b_2 x_2 + \cdots + b_p x_p$. In effect $b_0, b_1, b_2, \ldots, b_p$ are sample statistics used to estimate the unknown model parameters $\beta_0, \beta_1, \beta_2, \ldots, \beta_p$.

The multiple coefficient of determination was presented as a measure of the goodness of fit of the estimated regression equation. It determines the proportion of the variation of y that can be explained by the estimated regression equation. The adjusted multiple coefficient of determination is a similar measure of goodness of fit that adjusts for the number of independent variables and thus avoids overestimating the impact of adding more independent variables.

An F test and a t test were presented as ways to determine statistically whether the relationship among the variables is significant. The F test is used to determine whether there is a significant overall relationship between the dependent variable and the set of all independent variables. The t test is used to determine whether there is a significant relationship between the dependent variable and an individual independent variable given the other independent variables in the regression model. Correlation among the independent variables, known as multicollinearity, was discussed.

The section on categorical independent variables showed how dummy variables can be used to incorporate categorical data into multiple regression analysis. The section on residual analysis showed how residual analysis can be used to validate the model assumptions, detect outliers, and identify influential observations. Standardized residuals, leverage, studentized deleted residuals, and Cook's distance measure were discussed. The section on logistic regression illustrated how to model situations in which the dependent variable may only assume two values. Finally, we discussed the implications of large data sets on the application and interpretation of multiple regression analysis.

GLOSSARY

Adjusted multiple coefficient of determination A measure of the goodness of fit of the estimated multiple regression equation that adjusts for the number of independent variables in the model and thus avoids overestimating the impact of adding more independent variables.

Categorical independent variable An independent variable with categorical data.

Cook's distance measure A measure of the influence of an observation based on both the leverage of observation i and the residual for observation i.

Dummy variable A variable used to model the effect of categorical independent variables. A dummy variable may take only the value zero or one.

Estimated logistic regression equation The estimate of the logistic regression equation based on sample data; that is, $\hat{y} = $ estimate of $P(y = 1 | x_1, x_2, \ldots, x_p) = \dfrac{e^{b_0 + b_1 x_1 + b_2 x_2 + \cdots + b_p x_p}}{1 + e^{b_0 + b_1 x_1 + b_2 x_2 + \cdots + b_p x_p}}$.

Estimated logit An estimate of the logit based on sample data; that is, $\hat{g}(x_1, x_2, \ldots, x_p) = b_0 + b_1 x_1 + b_2 x_2 + \cdots + b_p x_p$.

Estimated multiple regression equation The estimate of the multiple regression equation based on sample data and the least squares method; it is $\hat{y} = b_0 + b_1 x_1 + b_2 x_2 + \cdots + b_p x_p$.

Influential observation An observation that has a strong influence on the regression results.

Least squares method The method used to develop the estimated regression equation. It minimizes the sum of squared residuals (the deviations between the observed values of the dependent variable, y_i, and the predicted values of the dependent variable, $\hat{y}_i$).

Leverage A measure of how far the values of the independent variables are from their mean values.

Logistic regression equation The mathematical equation relating $E(y)$, the probability that $y = 1$, to the values of the independent variables; that is, $E(y) = P(y = 1 | x_1, x_2, \ldots, x_p) = \dfrac{e^{\beta_0 + \beta_1 x_1 + \beta_2 x_2 + \cdots + \beta_p x_p}}{1 + e^{\beta_0 + \beta_1 x_1 + \beta_2 x_2 + \cdots + \beta_p x_p}}$.

Logit The natural logarithm of the odds in favor of $y = 1$; that is, $g(x_1, x_2, \ldots, x_p) = \beta_0 + \beta_1 x_1 + \beta_2 x_2 + \cdots + \beta_p x_p$.

Multicollinearity The term used to describe the correlation among the independent variables.

Multiple coefficient of determination A measure of the goodness of fit of the estimated multiple regression equation. It can be interpreted as the proportion of the variability in the dependent variable that is explained by the estimated regression equation.

Multiple regression analysis Regression analysis involving two or more independent variables.

Multiple regression equation The mathematical equation relating the expected value or mean value of the dependent variable to the values of the independent variables; that is, $E(y) = \beta_0 + \beta_1 x_1 + \beta_2 x_2 + \cdots + \beta_p x_p$.

Multiple regression model The mathematical equation that describes how the dependent variable y is related to the independent variables $x_1, x_2, \ldots, x_p$ and an error term ϵ.

Odds in favor of an event occurring The probability the event will occur divided by the probability the event will not occur.

Odds ratio The odds that $y = 1$ given that one of the independent variables increased by one unit ($odds_1$) divided by the odds that $y = 1$ given no change in the values for the independent variables ($odds_0$); that is, Odds ratio $= odds_1 / odds_0$.

Outlier An observation that does not fit the pattern of the other data.

Studentized deleted residuals Standardized residuals that are based on a revised standard error of the estimate obtained by deleting observation i from the data set and then performing the regression analysis and computations.

KEY FORMULAS

Multiple Regression Model

$$y = \beta_0 + \beta_1 x_1 + \beta_2 x_2 + \cdots + \beta_p x_p + \epsilon \tag{15.1}$$

Multiple Regression Equation

$$E(y) = \beta_0 + \beta_1 x_1 + \beta_2 x_2 + \cdots + \beta_p x_p \tag{15.2}$$

Estimated Multiple Regression Equation

$$\hat{y} = b_0 + b_1x_1 + b_2x_2 + \cdots + b_px_p \tag{15.3}$$

Least Squares Criterion

$$\min \Sigma(y_i - \hat{y}_i)^2 \tag{15.4}$$

Relationship Among SST, SSR, and SSE

$$SST = SSR + SSE \tag{15.7}$$

Multiple Coefficient of Determination

$$R^2 = \frac{SSR}{SST} \tag{15.8}$$

Adjusted Multiple Coefficient of Determination

$$R_a^2 = 1 - (1 - R^2)\frac{n-1}{n-p-1} \tag{15.9}$$

Mean Square Due to Regression

$$MSR = \frac{SSR}{p} \tag{15.12}$$

Mean Square Due to Error

$$MSE = \frac{SSE}{n-p-1} \tag{15.13}$$

_F_ Test Statistic

$$F = \frac{MSR}{MSE} \tag{15.14}$$

_t_ Test Statistic

$$t = \frac{b_i}{s_{b_i}} \tag{15.15}$$

Standardized Residual for Observation _i_

$$\frac{y_i - \hat{y}_i}{s_{y_i - \hat{y}_i}} \tag{15.23}$$

Standard Deviation of Residual _i_

$$s_{y_i - \hat{y}_i} = s\sqrt{1 - h_i} \tag{15.24}$$

Cook's Distance Measure

$$D_i = \frac{(y_i - \hat{y}_i)^2}{(p+1)s^2}\left[\frac{h_i}{(1-h_i)^2}\right] \tag{15.25}$$

Logistic Regression Equation

$$E(y) = \frac{e^{\beta_0+\beta_1x_1+\beta_2x_2+\cdots+\beta_px_p}}{1 + e^{\beta_0+\beta_1x_1+\beta_2x_2+\cdots+\beta_px_p}} \tag{15.27}$$

Estimated Logistic Regression Equation

$$\hat{y} = \text{estimate of } P(y = 1|x_1, x_2, \ldots, x_p) = \frac{e^{b_0+b_1x_1+b_2x_2+\cdots+b_px_p}}{1 + e^{b_0+b_1x_1+b_2x_2+\cdots+b_px_p}} \tag{15.30}$$

Odds Ratio

$$\text{Odds ratio} = \frac{\text{odds}_1}{\text{odds}_0} \qquad\qquad \textbf{15.34)}$$

Logit

$$g(x_1, x_2, \ldots, x_p) = \beta_0 + \beta_1 x_1 + \beta_2 x_2 + \cdots + \beta_p x_p \qquad\qquad \textbf{(15.35)}$$

Estimated Logit

$$\hat{g}(x_1, x_2, \ldots, x_p) = b_0 + b_1 x_1 + b_2 x_2 + \cdots + b_p x_p \qquad\qquad \textbf{(15.37)}$$

SUPPLEMENTARY EXERCISES

49. **College Grade Point Average.** The admissions officer for Clearwater College developed the following estimated regression equation relating the final college GPA to the student's SAT mathematics score and high-school GPA.

$$\hat{y} = -1.41 + .0235x_1 + .00486x_2$$

where

$$x_1 = \text{high-school grade point average}$$
$$x_2 = \text{SAT mathematics score}$$
$$y = \text{final college grade point average}$$

a. Interpret the coefficients in this estimated regression equation.
b. Predict the final college GPA for a student who has a high-school average of 84 and a score of 540 on the SAT mathematics test.

50. **Job Satisfaction.** The personnel director for Electronics Associates developed the following estimated regression equation relating an employee's score on a job satisfaction test to his or her length of service and wage rate.

$$\hat{y} = 14.4 - 8.69x_1 + 13.5x_2$$

where

$$x_1 = \text{length of service (years)}$$
$$x_2 = \text{wage rate (dollars)}$$
$$y = \text{job satisfaction test score (higher scores}$$
$$\text{indicate greater job satisfaction)}$$

a. Interpret the coefficients in this estimated regression equation.
b. Predict the job satisfaction test score for an employee who has four years of service and makes $13.00 per hour.

51. A partial computer output from a regression analysis follows.

```
The regression equation is
Y = 8.13 + 7.602 XI + 3.111 X2

Predictor          Coef        SE Coef            T
Constant        _____        2.667         _____
X1              _____        2.105         _____
X2              _____        0.613         _____

S = 3.335     R-Sq = 92.3%     R-Sq(adj) = _____%


Analysis of Variance

SOURCE            DF            SS          MS         F
Regression      _____        1612       _____    _____
Residual Error    12          _____     _____
Total           _____        _____
```

a. Compute the missing entries in this output.
b. Use the F test and $\alpha = .05$ to see whether a significant relationship is present.
c. Use the t test and $\alpha = .05$ to test $H_0: \beta_1 = 0$ and $H_0: \beta_2 = 0$.

52. **Analyzing College Grade Point Average.** Recall that in exercise 49, the admissions officer for Clearwater College developed the following estimated regression equation relating final college GPA to the student's SAT mathematics score and high-school GPA.

$$\hat{y} = -1.41 + .0235x_1 + .00486x_2$$

where

$$x_1 = \text{high-school grade point average}$$
$$x_2 = \text{SAT mathematics score}$$
$$y = \text{final college grade point average}$$

A portion of the associated computer output follows.

```
The regression equation is
Y = -1.41 + .0235 XI + .00486 X2

Predictor        Coef        SE Coef         T
Constant       -1.4053        .4848        _____
X1              .023467       .008666       _____
X2              _____       .001077       _____

S = .1298    R-Sq = _____        R-Sq (adj) = _____

Analysis of Variance

SOURCE           DF          SS           MS          F
Regression      _____      1.76209       _____       _____
Residual Error  _____      _____       _____
Total             9        1.88000
```

a. Complete the missing entries in this output.
b. Use the F test and a .05 level of significance to see whether a significant relationship is present.
c. Use the t test and $\alpha = .05$ to test $H_0: \beta_1 = 0$ and $H_0: \beta_2 = 0$.
d. Did the estimated regression equation provide a good fit to the data? Explain.

53. **Analyzing Job Satisfaction.** Recall that in exercise 50 the personnel director for Electronics Associates developed the following estimated regression equation relating an employee's score on a job satisfaction test to length of service and wage rate.

$$\hat{y} = 14.41 - 8.69x_1 + 13.52x_2$$

where

$$x_1 = \text{length of service (years)}$$
$$x_2 = \text{wage rate (dollars)}$$
$$y = \text{job satisfaction test score (higher scores}$$
$$\text{indicate greater job satisfaction)}$$

A portion of the associated computer output follows.

```
The regression equation is
Y = 14.4 - 8.69 XI + 13.52 X2

Predictor        Coef         SE Coef            T
Constant       14.448           8.191         1.76
X1                              1.555        _____
X2             13.517           2.085        _____

S = 3.773    R-Sq = _____ %    R-Sq(adj) = _____ %


Analysis of Variance

SOURCE          DF         SS            MS          F
Regression       2       _____         _____       _____
Residual Error  _____    71.17         _____
Total            7      720.0
```

a. Complete the missing entries in this output.
b. Compute F and test using $\alpha = .05$ to see whether a significant relationship is present.
c. Did the estimated regression equation provide a good fit to the data? Explain.
d. Use the t test and $\alpha = .05$ to test $H_0: \beta_1 = 0$ and $H_0: \beta_2 = 0$.

54. **Analyzing Repeat Purchases.** The Tire Rack, America's leading online distributor of tires and wheels, conducts extensive testing to provide customers with
products that are right for their vehicle, driving style, and driving conditions. In
addition, the Tire Rack maintains an independent consumer survey to help drivers
help each other by sharing their long-term tire experiences. The following data
show survey ratings (1 to 10 scale with 10 the highest rating) for 18 maximum
performance summer tires. The variable Steering rates the tire's steering responsiveness, Tread Wear rates quickness of wear based on the driver's expectations,
and Buy Again rates the driver's overall tire satisfaction and desire to purchase the
same tire again.

TireRack

Tire	Steering	Tread Wear	Buy Again
Goodyear Assurance TripleTred	8.9	8.5	8.1
Michelin HydroEdge	8.9	9.0	8.3
Michelin Harmony	8.3	8.8	8.2
Dunlop SP 60	8.2	8.5	7.9
Goodyear Assurance ComforTred	7.9	7.7	7.1
Yokohama Y372	8.4	8.2	8.9
Yokohama Aegis LS4	7.9	7.0	7.1
Kumho Power Star 758	7.9	7.9	8.3
Goodyear Assurance	7.6	5.8	4.5
Hankook H406	7.8	6.8	6.2
Michelin Energy LX4	7.4	5.7	4.8
Michelin MX4	7.0	6.5	5.3
Michelin Symmetry	6.9	5.7	4.2
Kumho 722	7.2	6.6	5.0
Dunlop SP 40 A/S	6.2	4.2	3.4
Bridgestone Insignia SE200	5.7	5.5	3.6
Goodyear Integrity	5.7	5.4	2.9
Dunlop SP20 FE	5.7	5.0	3.3

a. Develop an estimated regression equation that can be used to predict the Buy Again rating given based on the Steering rating. At the .05 level of significance, test for a significant relationship.

b. Did the estimated regression equation developed in part (a) provide a good fit to the data? Explain.

c. Develop an estimated regression equation that can be used to predict the Buy Again rating given the Steering rating and the Tread Wear rating.

d. Is the addition of the Tread Wear independent variable significant? Use $\alpha = .05$.

ZooSpend

55. **Zoo Attendance.** The Cincinnati Zoo and Botanical Gardens had a record attendance of 1.87 million visitors in 2017 (*Cincinnati Business Courier* website). Nonprofit organizations such as zoos and museums are becoming more sophisticated in their use of data to improve the customer experience. Being able to better estimate expected revenue is one use of analytics that allows nonprofits to better manage their operations.

The file *ZooSpend* contains sample data on zoo attendance. The file contains the following data on 125 visits by families to the zoo: amount spent, size of the family, the distance the family lives from the zoo (the gate attendee asks for the zip code of each family entering the zoo), and whether or not the family has a zoo membership (1 = yes, 0 = no).

a. Develop an estimated regression equation that predicts the amount of money spent by a family given family size, whether or not it has a zoo membership, and the distance the family lives from the zoo.

b. Test the significance of the zoo membership independent variable at the .05 level.

c. Give an explanation for the sign of the estimate you tested in part (b).

d. Test the overall significance of the model at the .05 level.

e. Estimate the amount of money spent in a visit by a family of five that lives 125 miles from the zoo and does not have a zoo membership.

56. **Mutual Fund Returns.** A portion of a data set containing information for 45 mutual funds that are part of the *Morningstar Funds 500* follows. The complete data set is available in the file named MutualFunds. The data set includes the following five variables:

Fund Type: The type of fund, labeled DE (Domestic Equity), IE (International Equity), and FI (Fixed Income)

Net Asset Value ($): The closing price per share on December 31, 2007

5-Year Average Return (%): The average annual return for the fund over the past five years

Expense Ratio (%): The percentage of assets deducted each fiscal year for fund expenses

Morningstar Rank: The risk adjusted star rating for each fund; Morningstar ranks go from a low of 1-Star to a high of 5-Stars

DATA*file*

MutualFunds

Fund Name	Fund Type	Net Asset Value ($)	5-Year Average Return (%)	Expense Ratio (%)	Morningstar Rank
Amer Cent Inc & Growth Inv	DE	28.88	12.39	.67	2-Star
American Century Intl. Disc	IE	14.37	30.53	1.41	3-Star
American Century Tax-Free Bond	FI	10.73	3.34	.49	4-Star
American Century Ultra	DE	24.94	10.88	.99	3-Star
Ariel	DE	46.39	11.32	1.03	2-Star
Artisan Intl Val	IE	25.52	24.95	1.23	3-Star
Artisan Small Cap	DE	16.92	15.67	1.18	3-Star
Baron Asset	DE	50.67	16.77	1.31	5-Star
Brandywine	DE	36.58	18.14	1.08	4-Star
.	. .	.	.	.	.
.	. .	.	.	.	.
.	. .	.	.	.	.

a. Develop an estimated regression equation that can be used to predict the 5-year average return given the type of fund. At the .05 level of significance, test for a significant relationship.

b. Did the estimated regression equation developed in part (a) provide a good fit to the data? Explain.

c. Develop the estimated regression equation that can be used to predict the 5-year average return given the type of fund, the net asset value, and the expense ratio. At the .05 level of significance, test for a significant relationship. Do you think any variables should be deleted from the estimated regression equation? Explain.

d. Morningstar Rank is a categorical variable. Because the data set contains only funds with four ranks (2-Star through 5-Star), use the following dummy variables: 3StarRank = 1 for a 3-Star fund, 0 otherwise; 4StarRank = 1 for a 4-Star fund, 0 otherwise; and 5StarRank = 1 for a 5-Star fund, 0 otherwise. Develop an estimated regression equation that can be used to predict the 5-year average return given the type of fund, the expense ratio, and the Morningstar Rank. Using $\alpha = .05$, remove any independent variables that are not significant.

e. Use the estimated regression equation developed in part (d) to predict the 5-year average return for a domestic equity fund with an expense ratio of 1.05% and a 3-Star Morningstar Rank.

GiftCards

57. **Gift Card Sales.** For the holiday season of 2017, nearly 59 percent of consumers planned to buy gift cards. According to the National Retail Federation, millennials like to purchase gift cards (*Dayton Daily News* website). Consider the sample data in the file *GiftCards*. The following data are given for a sample of 600 millennials: the amount they reported spending on gift cards over the last year, annual income, marital status (1 = yes, 0 = no), and whether they are male (1 = yes, 0 = no).

a. Develop an estimated regression equitation that predicts annual spend on gift cards given annual income, marital status, and gender.

b. Test the overall significance at the .05 level.

c. Test the significance of each individual variable using a .05 level of significance.

CASE PROBLEM 1: CONSUMER RESEARCH, INC.

Consumer Research, Inc., is an independent agency that conducts research on consumer attitudes and behaviors for a variety of firms. In one study, a client asked for an investigation of consumer characteristics that can be used to predict the amount charged by credit card users. Data were collected on annual income, household size, and annual credit card charges for a sample of 50 consumers. The following data are contained in the file *Consumer*.

Consumer

Income ($1000s)	Household Size	Amount Charged ($)	Income ($1000s)	Household Size	Amount Charged ($)
54	3	4016	54	6	5573
30	2	3159	30	1	2583
32	4	5100	48	2	3866
50	5	4742	34	5	3586
31	2	1864	67	4	5037
55	2	4070	50	2	3605
37	1	2731	67	5	5345
40	2	3348	55	6	5370
66	4	4764	52	2	3890
51	3	4110	62	3	4705
25	3	4208	64	2	4157
48	4	4219	22	3	3579
27	1	2477	29	4	3890
33	2	2514	39	2	2972

Income ($1000s)	Household Size	Amount Charged ($)	Income ($1000s)	Household Size	Amount Charged ($)
65	3	4214	35	1	3121
63	4	4965	39	4	4183
42	6	4412	54	3	3730
21	2	2448	23	6	4127
44	1	2995	27	2	2921
37	5	4171	26	7	4603
62	6	5678	61	2	4273
21	3	3623	30	2	3067
55	7	5301	22	4	3074
42	2	3020	46	5	4820
41	7	4828	66	4	5149

Source: Consumer Research, Inc. (https://www.bbb.org/us/ny/rochester/profile/secret-shopper/consumer-research-inc-0041-45625697)

Managerial Report

1. Use methods of descriptive statistics to summarize the data. Comment on the findings.
2. Develop estimated regression equations, first using annual income as the independent variable and then using household size as the independent variable. Which variable is the better predictor of annual credit card charges? Discuss your findings.
3. Develop an estimated regression equation with annual income and household size as the independent variables. Discuss your findings.
4. What is the predicted annual credit card charge for a three-person household with an annual income of $40,000?
5. Discuss the need for other independent variables that could be added to the model. What additional variables might be helpful?

CASE PROBLEM 2: PREDICTING WINNINGS FOR NASCAR DRIVERS

Matt Kenseth won the 2012 Daytona 500, the most important race of the NASCAR season. His win was no surprise because for the 2011 season he finished fourth in the point standings with 2330 points, behind Tony Stewart (2403 points), Carl Edwards (2403 points), and Kevin Harvick (2345 points). In 2011 he earned $6,183,580 by winning three Poles (fastest driver in qualifying), winning three races, finishing in the top five 12 times, and finishing in the top ten 20 times. NASCAR's point system in 2011 allocated 43 points to the driver who finished first, 42 points to the driver who finished second, and so on down to 1 point for the driver who finished in the 43rd position. In addition any driver who led a lap received 1 bonus point, the driver who led the most laps received an additional bonus point, and the race winner was awarded 3 bonus points. But, the maximum number of points a driver could earn in any race was 48. Table 15.13 shows data for the 2011 season for the top 35 drivers (NASCAR website).

Managerial Report

1. Suppose you wanted to predict Winnings ($) using only the number of poles won (Poles), the number of wins (Wins), the number of top five finishes (Top 5), or the number of top ten finishes (Top 10). Which of these four variables provides the best single predictor of winnings?
2. Develop an estimated regression equation that can be used to predict Winnings ($) given the number of poles won (Poles), the number of wins (Wins), the number of top five finishes (Top 5), and the number of top ten (Top 10) finishes. Test for individual significance and discuss your findings and conclusions.
3. Create two new independent variables: Top 2–5 and Top 6–10. Top 2–5 represents the number of times the driver finished between second and fifth place and Top 6–10

NASCAR

TABLE 15.13 Nascar Results for the 2011 Season

Driver	Points	Poles	Wins	Top 5	Top 10	Winnings ($)
Tony Stewart	2403	1	5	9	19	6,529,870
Carl Edwards	2403	3	1	19	26	8,485,990
Kevin Harvick	2345	0	4	9	19	6,197,140
Matt Kenseth	2330	3	3	12	20	6,183,580
Brad Keselowski	2319	1	3	10	14	5,087,740
Jimmie Johnson	2304	0	2	14	21	6,296,360
Dale Earnhardt Jr.	2290	1	0	4	12	4,163,690
Jeff Gordon	2287	1	3	13	18	5,912,830
Denny Hamlin	2284	0	1	5	14	5,401,190
Ryan Newman	2284	3	1	9	17	5,303,020
Kurt Busch	2262	3	2	8	16	5,936,470
Kyle Busch	2246	1	4	14	18	6,161,020
Clint Bowyer	1047	0	1	4	16	5,633,950
Kasey Kahne	1041	2	1	8	15	4,775,160
A. J. Allmendinger	1013	0	0	1	10	4,825,560
Greg Biffle	997	3	0	3	10	4,318,050
Paul Menard	947	0	1	4	8	3,853,690
Martin Truex Jr.	937	1	0	3	12	3,955,560
Marcos Ambrose	936	0	1	5	12	4,750,390
Jeff Burton	935	0	0	2	5	3,807,780
Juan Montoya	932	2	0	2	8	5,020,780
Mark Martin	930	2	0	2	10	3,830,910
David Ragan	906	2	1	4	8	4,203,660
Joey Logano	902	2	0	4	6	3,856,010
Brian Vickers	846	0	0	3	7	4,301,880
Regan Smith	820	0	1	2	5	4,579,860
Jamie McMurray	795	1	0	2	4	4,794,770
David Reutimann	757	1	0	1	3	4,374,770
Bobby Labonte	670	0	0	1	2	4,505,650
David Gilliland	572	0	0	1	2	3,878,390
Casey Mears	541	0	0	0	0	2,838,320
Dave Blaney	508	0	0	1	1	3,229,210
Andy Lally	398	0	0	0	0	2,868,220
Robby Gordon	268	0	0	0	0	2,271,890
J. J. Yeley	192	0	0	0	0	2,559,500

Source: NASCAR website, February 28, 2011. (https://www.nascar.com/)

represents the number of times the driver finished between sixth and tenth place. Develop an estimated regression equation that can be used to predict Winnings ($) using Poles, Wins, Top 2–5, and Top 6–10. Test for individual significance and discuss your findings and conclusions.

4. Based upon the results of your analysis, what estimated regression equation would you recommend using to predict Winnings ($)? Provide an interpretation of the estimated regression coefficients for this equation.

CASE PROBLEM 3: FINDING THE BEST CAR VALUE

When trying to decide what car to buy, real value is not necessarily determined by how much you spend on the initial purchase. Instead, cars that are reliable and don't cost much to own often represent the best values. But no matter how reliable or inexpensive a car may cost to own, it must also perform well.

To measure value, *Consumer Reports* developed a statistic referred to as a value score. The value score is based upon five-year owner costs, overall road-test scores, and predicted-reliability ratings. Five-year owner costs are based upon the expenses incurred in the first five years of ownership, including depreciation, fuel, maintenance and repairs, and so on. Using a national average of 12,000 miles per year, an average cost per mile driven is used as the measure of five-year owner costs. Road-test scores are the results of more than 50 tests and evaluations and are based on a 100-point scale, with higher scores indicating better performance, comfort, convenience, and fuel economy. The highest road-test score obtained in the tests conducted by *Consumer Reports* was a 99 for a Lexus LS 460L. Predicted-reliability ratings (1 = Poor, 2 = Fair, 3 = Good, 4 = Very Good, and 5 = Excellent) are based upon data from *Consumer Reports*' Annual Auto Survey.

CarValues

A car with a value score of 1.0 is considered to be an "average-value" car. A car with a value score of 2.0 is considered to be twice as good a value as a car with a value score of 1.0; a car with a value score of .5 is considered half as good as average; and so on. The data for three sizes of cars (13 small sedans, 20 family sedans, and 21 upscale sedans), including the price ($) of each car tested, are contained in the file *CarValues* (*Consumer Reports* website). To incorporate the effect of size of car, a categorical variable with three values (small sedan, family sedan, and upscale sedan), use the following dummy variables:

$$\text{Family-Sedan} = \begin{cases} 1 \text{ if the car is a Family Sedan} \\ 0 \text{ otherwise} \end{cases}$$

$$\text{Upscale-Sedan} = \begin{cases} 1 \text{ if the car is an Upscale Sedan} \\ 0 \text{ otherwise} \end{cases}$$

Managerial Report

1. Treating Cost/Mile as the dependent variable, develop an estimated regression with Family-Sedan and Upscale-Sedan as the independent variables. Discuss your findings.
2. Treating Value Score as the dependent variable, develop an estimated regression equation using Cost/Mile, Road-Test Score, Predicted Reliability, Family-Sedan, and Upscale-Sedan as the independent variables.
3. Delete any independent variables that are not significant from the estimated regression equation developed in part 2 using a .05 level of significance. After deleting any independent variables that are not significant, develop a new estimated regression equation.
4. Suppose someone claims that "smaller cars provide better values than larger cars." For the data in this case, the Small Sedans represent the smallest type of car and the Upscale Sedans represent the largest type of car. Does your analysis support this claim?
5. Use regression analysis to develop an estimated regression equation that could be used to predict the value score given the value of the Road-Test Score.
6. Use regression analysis to develop an estimated regression equation that could be used to predict the value score given the Predicted Reliability.
7. What conclusions can you derive from your analysis?

Chapter 15 Appendix

Appendix 15.1 Multiple Linear Regression with JMP

In this appendix, we describe how to use JMP to estimate the multiple linear regression equation and execute the associated significance tests discussed in Section 15.5. In addition, we demonstrate how to use JMP to apply the estimated regression equation to generate predictions for observations making up a data set as well as a new observation with no value of the dependent variable. Specifically, we will apply JMP to the Butler Trucking example to estimate the relationship between the travel time (y) of a route and its mileage (x_1) and its number of deliveries (x_2). Then we will predict the travel time of a new observation with Miles = 75 and Deliveries = 4.

Butler

Step 1. Open the file *Butler* with JMP using the steps provided in Appendix 1.1

Step 2. In Row 11, enter *75* in the **Miles** column and enter *4* in the **Deliveries** column. Leave the Row 11 entry in the **Assignment** column blank and the **Time** column blank

Step 3. In the **Data** window, click **Analyze** and select **Fit Model**

Step 4. When the **Fit Model – JMP Student Edition** window appears:

Drag **Time** in the **Select Columns** area to the **Y** box in the **Pick Role Variables** area

Click **Miles** in the **Select Columns** area and then click **Add** in the **Construct Model Effects** area

Click **Deliveries** in the **Select Columns** area and then click **Add** in the **Construct Model Effects** area

Click **Run**

Step 5. When the **Data – Fit Least Squares** window appears:

Click the red triangle ▾ next to **Response Time**, select **Save Columns** and click **Predicted Values**

Click the red triangle ▾ next to **Response Time**, select **Save Columns** and click **Mean Confidence Interval**

Click the red triangle ▾ next to **Response Time**, select **Save Columns** and click **Indiv Confidence Interval**

Steps 1 through 4 above create the output shown in Figure JMP 15.1. We observe that the **Analysis of Variance** and **Parameter Estimates** sections of Figure JMP 15.1 match those found in Figure 15.6. The model is significant at the .01 level with an F ratio of 32.88 and a p-value of .0003. Both independent variables, Miles and Deliveries, are both statistically significant with p-values of .0005 and .0042, respectively. The estimated regression equation is:

$$\text{Time} = -.8687 + .06113 \text{ Miles} + .9234 \text{ Deliveries}$$

Step 5. above creates new columns for Predicted Values, Mean Confidence Intervals and Individual Confidence Intervals in the Data window as shown in Figure JMP 15.2. Specifically,

- **Predicted Values**—generates the Predicted Time column, which contains the point estimates of travel time for each observation in the data set.

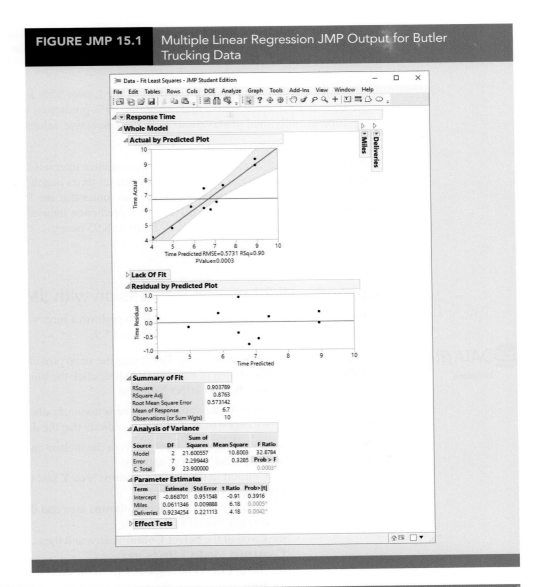

FIGURE JMP 15.1   Multiple Linear Regression JMP Output for Butler Trucking Data

FIGURE JMP 15.2   Generating Multiple Regression Predicted Values and Confidence Intervals in JMP for Butler Trucking Data

- **Mean Confidence Interval**—generates the Lower 95% Mean Time and Upper 95% Mean Time columns making up the 95% confidence interval on the mean travel time of observations with the respective values of the independent variables.
- **Indiv Confidence Interval**—generates the Lower 95% Indiv Time and Upper 95% Indiv Time columns making up the 95% prediction interval on the travel time of individual observations with the respective values of the independent variables.

From Figure JMP 15.2, we see that the 95% confidence intervals on the mean travel times and 95% prediction intervals on the individual travel times match Table 15.4. The 95% confidence interval on the mean travel time of all routes that are 75 miles long with four deliveries is 6.67 hours to 8.15 hours. The 95% prediction interval of a specific route that is 75 miles long with four deliveries is 5.87 hours to 8.95 hours.

Appendix 15.2 Logistic Regression with JMP

In this appendix we describe how to use JMP to perform a binary logistic regression by using the Simmons Stores example from Section 15.9.

DATA *file*

Simmons

Step 1. Open the file *Simmons* with JMP using the steps provided in Appendix 1.1

Step 2. In the **Columns** area of the **Data** window, click the blue triangle next to **Coupon** (Coupon) and select **Nominal**

Step 2 denotes that the data for the variable Coupon is nominal rather than continuous and changes the display for Coupon to ▮▮ Coupon to indicate that the data is on a nominal scale.

Step 3. In the **Data** window, click **Analyze** from the toolbar and select **Fit Model**

Step 4. When the **Fit Model** window appears:

> Drag **Coupon** in the **Select Columns** area **Y** box in the **Pick Role Variables** area
>
> Click **Spending** in the **Select Column**s area and then click **Add** in the **Construct Model Effects** area
>
> Click **Card** in the **Select Columns** area and then click **Add** in the **Construct Model Effects** area
>
> In the **Target Level** box, select **1** form the drop-down menu
>
> Click **Run**

Step 5. When the **Data—Fit Nominal Logistic** window appears:

> Click the red triangle ▾ next to **Nominal Logistic Fit for Coupon** and select **Odds Ratios**

The output shown in Figure JMP 15.3 matches the information in Figure 15.13.

| **FIGURE JMP 15.3** | Logistic Regression JMP Output for Simmons Stores Data |

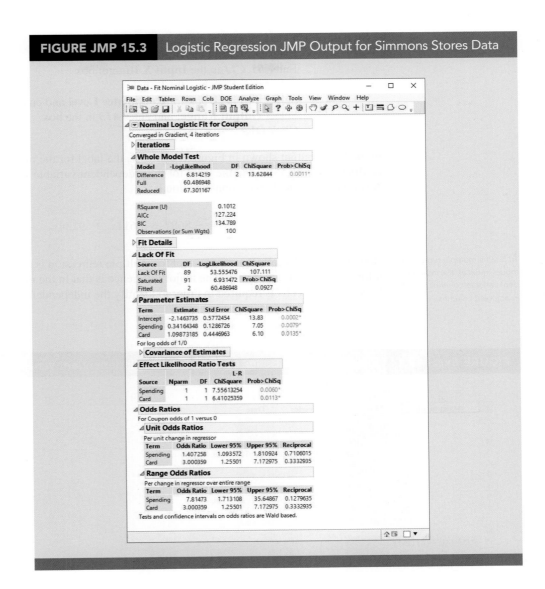

Appendix 15.3 Multiple Regression with Excel

In this appendix we describe how to use Excel's Regression tool to develop the estimated multiple regression equation for the Butler Trucking problem. Refer to Figure Excel 15.1 as we describe the tasks involved. First, the labels Assignment, Miles, Deliveries, and Time are entered into cells A1:D1 of the worksheet, and the sample data are entered into cells B2:D11. The numbers 1–10 in cells A2:A11 identify each observation.

The following steps describe how to use the Regression tool for the multiple regression analysis.

Butler

Step 1. Click the **Data** tab on the Ribbon
Step 2. In the **Analyze** group, click **Data Analysis**
Step 3. Choose **Regression** from the list of Analysis Tools
Click **OK**

Step 4. When the Regression dialog box appears:
  Enter *D1:D11* in the **Input Y Range:** box
  Enter *B1:C11* in the **Input X Range:** box
  Select the check box for **Labels**
  Select the check box for **Confidence Level** and enter *99* in the box
  Select **Output Range:** and enter *A13* in the box
  Click **OK**

In the Excel output shown in Figure Excel 15.1, the label for the independent variable x_1 is Miles (see cell A30), and the label for the independent variable x_2 is Deliveries (see cell A31). The estimated regression equation is

$$\hat{y} = -.8687 + .0611x_1 + .9234x_2$$

To build a multiple regression model in Excel, the independent variable columns must be in adjacent columns.

Note that using Excel's Regression tool for multiple regression is almost the same as using it for simple linear regression. The major difference is that in the multiple regression case a larger range of cells is required in order to identify the independent variables.

FIGURE Excel 15.1   Excel Output for Butler Trucking with Two Independent Variables

	A	B	C	D	E	F	G	H	I	J
1	Assignment	Miles	Deliveries	Time						
2	1	100	4	9.3						
3	2	50	3	4.8						
4	3	100	4	8.9						
5	4	100	2	6.5						
6	5	50	2	4.2						
7	6	80	2	6.2						
8	7	75	3	7.4						
9	8	65	4	6						
10	9	90	3	7.6						
11	10	90	2	6.1						
12										
13	SUMMARY OUTPUT									
14										
15	*Regression Statistics*									
16	Multiple R	0.9507								
17	R Square	0.9038								
18	Adjusted R Square	0.8763								
19	Standard Error	0.5731								
20	Observations	10								
21										
22	ANOVA									
23		*df*	*SS*	*MS*	*F*	*Significance F*				
24	Regression	2	21.6006	10.8003	32.8784	0.0003				
25	Residual	7	2.2994	0.3285						
26	Total	9	23.9							
27										
28		*Coefficients*	*Standard Error*	*t Stat*	*P-value*	*Lower 95%*	*Upper 95%*	*Lower 99.0%*	*Upper 99.0%*	
29	Intercept	-0.8687	0.9515	-0.9129	0.3916	-3.1188	1.3813	-4.1986	2.4612	
30	Miles	0.0611	0.0099	6.1824	0.0005	0.0378	0.0845	0.0265	0.0957	
31	Deliveries	0.9234	0.2211	4.1763	0.0042	0.4006	1.4463	0.1496	1.6972	
32										

Appendixes

CONTENTS

Appendix A—References and Bibliography

General

Freedman, D., R. Pisani, and R. Purves. *Statistics*, 4th ed. W. W. Norton, 2007.

Hogg R. V., E. A. Tanis, and D. L. Zimmerman. *Probability and Statistical Inference*, 9th ed. Prentice Hall, 2015.

McKean, J. W., R. V. Hogg, and A. T. Craig. *Introduction to Mathematical Statistics*, 7th ed. Prentice Hall, 2012.

Miller, I., and M. Miller. *John E. Freund's Mathematical Statistics*, 8th ed. Pearson Prentice Hall, 2012.

Moore, D. S., G. P. McCabe, and B. Craig. *Introduction to the Practice of Statistics*, 9th ed. Freeman, 2016.

Wackerly, D. D., W. Mendenhall, and R. L. Scheaffer. *Mathematical Statistics with Applications*, 7th ed. Cengage Learning, 2008.

Experimental Design

Cochran, W. G., and G. M. Cox. *Experimental Designs*, 2nd ed. Wiley, 1992.

Hicks, C. R., and K. V. Turner. *Fundamental Concepts in the Design of Experiments*, 5th ed. Oxford University Press, 1999.

Montgomery, D. C. *Design and Analysis of Experiments*, 8th ed. Wiley, 2012.

Winer, B. J., K. M. Michels, and D. R. Brown. *Statistical Principles in Experimental Design*, 3rd ed. McGraw-Hill, 1991.

Wu, C. F. Jeff, and M. Hamada. *Experiments: Planning, Analysis, and Optimization*, 2nd ed. Wiley, 2011.

Time Series and Forecasting

Bowerman, B. L., R. T. O'Connell, and A. Koehler. *Forecasting and Time Series: An Applied Approach*, 4th ed. Thomson Learning, 2004.

Box, G. E. P., G. M. Jenkins, and G. C. Reinsel. *Time Series Analysis: Forecasting and Control*, 5th ed. Wiley, 2015.

Makridakis, S. G., S. C. Wheelwright, and R. J. Hyndman. *Forecasting Methods and Applications*, 3rd ed. Wiley, 1997.

Wilson, J. H., B. Keating, and John Galt Solutions, Inc. *Business Forecasting with Accompanying Excel-Based Forecast X*™, 6th ed. McGraw-Hill/Irwin, 2008.

Index Numbers

U.S. Department of Commerce. *Survey of Current Business.*

U.S. Department of Labor, Bureau of Labor Statistics. *CPI Detailed Report.*

U.S. Department of Labor. *Producer Price Indexes.*

Nonparametric Methods

Conover, W. J. *Practical Nonparametric Statistics*, 3rd ed. Wiley, 1999.

Corder, G. W., and D. I. Foreman. *Nonparametric Statistics: A Step-by-Step Approach*, 2nd ed. Wiley, 2014.

Gibbons, J. D., and S. Chakraborti. *Nonparametric Statistical Inference*, 5th ed. CRC Press, 2010.

Higgins, J. J. *Introduction to Modern Nonparametric Statistics.* Thomson-Brooks/Cole, 2003.

Hollander, M., D. A. Wolfe, and E. Chicken. *Non-Parametric Statistical Methods*, 3rd ed. Wiley, 2013.

Jureckova, J., P. K. Sen, and J. Picek. *Methodology in Robust and Nonparametric Statistics*, 7th ed. CRC Press, 2012.

Probability

Hogg R. V., E. A. Tanis, and D. L. Zimmerman. *Probability and Statistical Inference*, 9th ed. Pearson, 2014.

Ross, S. M. *Introduction to Probability Models*, 11th ed. Academic Press, 2014.

Wackerly, D. D., W. Mendenhall, and R. L. Scheaffer. *Mathematical Statistics with Applications*, 7th ed. Cengage Learning, 2008.

Quality Control

DeFeo, J. A., and J. M. Juran, *Juran's Quality Handbook*, 7th ed. McGraw-Hill, 2016.

Evans, J. R., and W. M. Lindsay. *Managing for Quality and Performance Excllence,* 10th ed., Cengage, 2017.

Montgomery, D. C. *Introduction to Statistical Quality Control*, 7th ed. Wiley, 2012.

Regression Analysis

Chatterjee, S., and A. S. Hadi. *Regression Analysis by Example*, 5th ed. Wiley, 2012.

Draper, N. R., and H. Smith. *Applied Regression Analysis*, 3rd ed. Wiley, 1998.

Graybill, F. A., and H. K. Iyer. *Regression Analysis: Concepts and Applications.* Wadsworth, 1994.

Hosmer, D. W., and S. Lemeshow. *Applied Logistic Regression*, 3rd ed. Wiley, 2013.

Kleinbaum, D. G., L. L. Kupper, and K. E. Muller. *Applied Regression Analysis and Other Multivariate Methods*, 4th ed. Cengage Learning, 2007.

Neter, J., W. Wasserman, M. H. Kutner, and C. Nashtsheim. *Applied Linear Statistical Models*, 5th ed. McGraw-Hill, 2004.

Mendenhall, M., T. Sincich., and T. R. Dye. *A Second Course in Statistics: Regression Analysis*, 7th ed. Prentice Hall, 2011.

Decision Analysis

Clemen, R. T., and T. Reilly. *Making Hard Decisions with Decision Tools*, 3rd ed. Cengage Learning, 2014.

Goodwin, P., and G. Wright. *Decision Analysis for Management Judgment*, 5th ed. Wiley, 2014.

Pratt, J. W., H. Raiffa, and R. Schlaifer. *Introduction to Statistical Decision Theory*. MIT Press, 2008.

Sampling

Cochran, W. G. *Sampling Techniques*, 3rd ed. Wiley, 1977.

Hansen, M. H., W. N. Hurwitz, W. G. Madow, and M. N. Hanson. *Sample Survey Methods and Theory*. Wiley, 1993.

Kish, L. *Survey Sampling*. Wiley, 2008.

Levy, P. S., and S. Lemeshow. *Sampling of Populations: Methods and Applications*, 4th ed. Wiley, 2009.

Scheaffer, R. L., W. Mendenhall, and L. Ott. *Elementary Survey Sampling*, 7th ed. Duxbury Press, 2011.

Data Visualization

Cleveland, W. S. *Visualizing Data*. Hobart Press, 1993.

Cleveland, W. S. *The Elements of Graphing Data*, 2nd ed. Hobart Press, 1994.

Few, S. *Show Me the Numbers: Designing Tables and Graphs to Enlighten*, 2nd ed. Analytics Press, 2012.

Few, S. *Information Dashboard Design: The Effective Visual Communication of Data*, 2nd ed. O'Reilly Media, 2012.

Few, S. *Now You See It: Simple Visualization Techniques for Quantitative Analysis*. Analytics Press, 2009.

Fry, B. *Visualizing Data: Exploring and Explaining Data with the Processing Environment*. O'Reilly Media, 2008.

Knaflic, C., N. *Storytelling with Data: A Data Visualization Guide for Business Professionals*, Wiley, 2015.

Robbins, N. B. *Creating More Effective Graphs*. Chart House, 2013.

Telea, A. C. *Data Visualization Principles and Practice*, 2nd ed. A.K. Peters Ltd., 2014.

Tufte, E. R. *Envisioning Information*. Graphics Press, 1990.

Tufte, E. R. *The Visual Display of Quantitative Information*, 2nd ed. Graphics Press, 1990.

Tufte, E. R. *Visual Explanations: Images and Quantities, Evidence and Narrative*. Graphics Press, 1997.

Tufte, E. R. *Visual and Statistical Thinking: Displays of Evidence for Making Decisions*. Graphics Press, 2009.

Tufte, E. R. *Beautiful Evidence*. Graphics Press, 2006.

Wong, D. M. *The Wall Street Journal Guide to Information Graphics*. W. W. Norton & Company, 2013.

Young, F. W., P. M. Valero-Mora, and M. Friendly. *Visual Statistics: Seeing Data with Dynamic Interactive Graphics*. Wiley, 2006.

Business Analytics

Camm, J. D., J. J. Cochran, M. J. Fry, J. W. Ohlmann, D. R. Anderson, D. J. Sweeney, and T. A. Williams *Business Analytics*, 3rd ed. Cengage Learning, 2018.

Appendix B—Tables

TABLE 1 Cumulative Probabilities for the standard Normal Distribution

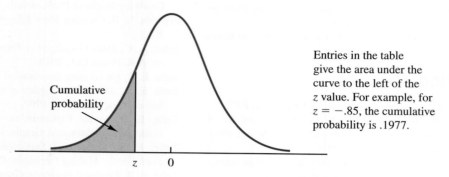

Cumulative probability

Entries in the table give the area under the curve to the left of the z value. For example, for $z = -.85$, the cumulative probability is .1977.

z	.00	.01	.02	.03	.04	.05	.06	.07	.08	.09
−3.0	.0013	.0013	.0013	.0012	.0012	.0011	.0011	.0011	.0010	.0010
−2.9	.0019	.0018	.0018	.0017	.0016	.0016	.0015	.0015	.0014	.0014
−2.8	.0026	.0025	.0024	.0023	.0023	.0022	.0021	.0021	.0020	.0019
−2.7	.0035	.0034	.0033	.0032	.0031	.0030	.0029	.0028	.0027	.0026
−2.6	.0047	.0045	.0044	.0043	.0041	.0040	.0039	.0038	.0037	.0036
−2.5	.0062	.0060	.0059	.0057	.0055	.0054	.0052	.0051	.0049	.0048
−2.4	.0082	.0080	.0078	.0075	.0073	.0071	.0069	.0068	.0066	.0064
−2.3	.0107	.0104	.0102	.0099	.0096	.0094	.0091	.0089	.0087	.0084
−2.2	.0139	.0136	.0132	.0129	.0125	.0122	.0119	.0116	.0113	.0110
−2.1	.0179	.0174	.0170	.0166	.0162	.0158	.0154	.0150	.0146	.0143
−2.0	.0228	.0222	.0217	.0212	.0207	.0202	.0197	.0192	.0188	.0183
−1.9	.0287	.0281	.0274	.0268	.0262	.0256	.0250	.0244	.0239	.0233
−1.8	.0359	.0351	.0344	.0336	.0329	.0322	.0314	.0307	.0301	.0294
−1.7	.0446	.0436	.0427	.0418	.0409	.0401	.0392	.0384	.0375	.0367
−1.6	.0548	.0537	.0526	.0516	.0505	.0495	.0485	.0475	.0465	.0455
−1.5	.0668	.0655	.0643	.0630	.0618	.0606	.0594	.0582	.0571	.0559
−1.4	.0808	.0793	.0778	.0764	.0749	.0735	.0721	.0708	.0694	.0681
−1.3	.0968	.0951	.0934	.0918	.0901	.0885	.0869	.0853	.0838	.0823
−1.2	.1151	.1131	.1112	.1093	.1075	.1056	.1038	.1020	.1003	.0985
−1.1	.1357	.1335	.1314	.1292	.1271	.1251	.1230	.1210	.1190	.1170
−1.0	.1587	.1562	.1539	.1515	.1492	.1469	.1446	.1423	.1401	.1379
−.9	.1841	.1814	.1788	.1762	.1736	.1711	.1685	.1660	.1635	.1611
−.8	.2119	.2090	.2061	.2033	.2005	.1977	.1949	.1922	.1894	.1867
−.7	.2420	.2389	.2358	.2327	.2296	.2266	.2236	.2206	.2177	.2148
−.6	.2743	.2709	.2676	.2643	.2611	.2578	.2546	.2514	.2483	.2451
−.5	.3085	.3050	.3015	.2981	.2946	.2912	.2877	.2843	.2810	.2776
−.4	.3446	.3409	.3372	.3336	.3300	.3264	.3228	.3192	.3156	.3121
−.3	.3821	.3783	.3745	.3707	.3669	.3632	.3594	.3557	.3520	.3483
−.2	.4207	.4168	.4129	.4090	.4052	.4013	.3974	.3936	.3897	.3859
−.1	.4602	.4562	.4522	.4483	.4443	.4404	.4364	.4325	.4286	.4247
−.0	.5000	.4960	.4920	.4880	.4840	.4801	.4761	.4721	.4681	.4641

TABLE 1 Cumulative Probabilities for the standard Normal Distribution
(*Continued*)

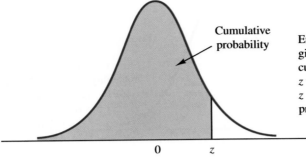

Cumulative probability

Entries in the table give the area under the curve to the left of the *z* value. For example, for *z* = 1.25, the cumulative probability is .8944.

z	.00	.01	.02	.03	.04	.05	.06	.07	.08	.09
.0	.5000	.5040	.5080	.5120	.5160	.5199	.5239	.5279	.5319	.5359
.1	.5398	.5438	.5478	.5517	.5557	.5596	.5636	.5675	.5714	.5753
.2	.5793	.5832	.5871	.5910	.5948	.5987	.6026	.6064	.6103	.6141
.3	.6179	.6217	.6255	.6293	.6331	.6368	.6406	.6443	.6480	.6517
.4	.6554	.6591	.6628	.6664	.6700	.6736	.6772	.6808	.6844	.6879
.5	.6915	.6950	.6985	.7019	.7054	.7088	.7123	.7157	.7190	.7224
.6	.7257	.7291	.7324	.7357	.7389	.7422	.7454	.7486	.7517	.7549
.7	.7580	.7611	.7642	.7673	.7704	.7734	.7764	.7794	.7823	.7852
.8	.7881	.7910	.7939	.7967	.7995	.8023	.8051	.8078	.8106	.8133
.9	.8159	.8186	.8212	.8238	.8264	.8289	.8315	.8340	.8365	.8389
1.0	.8413	.8438	.8461	.8485	.8508	.8531	.8554	.8577	.8599	.8621
1.1	.8643	.8665	.8686	.8708	.8729	.8749	.8770	.8790	.8810	.8830
1.2	.8849	.8869	.8888	.8907	.8925	.8944	.8962	.8980	.8997	.9015
1.3	.9032	.9049	.9066	.9082	.9099	.9115	.9131	.9147	.9162	.9177
1.4	.9192	.9207	.9222	.9236	.9251	.9265	.9279	.9292	.9306	.9319
1.5	.9332	.9345	.9357	.9370	.9382	.9394	.9406	.9418	.9429	.9441
1.6	.9452	.9463	.9474	.9484	.9495	.9505	.9515	.9525	.9535	.9545
1.7	.9554	.9564	.9573	.9582	.9591	.9599	.9608	.9616	.9625	.9633
1.8	.9641	.9649	.9656	.9664	.9671	.9678	.9686	.9693	.9699	.9706
1.9	.9713	.9719	.9726	.9732	.9738	.9744	.9750	.9756	.9761	.9767
2.0	.9772	.9778	.9783	.9788	.9793	.9798	.9803	.9808	.9812	.9817
2.1	.9821	.9826	.9830	.9834	.9838	.9842	.9846	.9850	.9854	.9857
2.2	.9861	.9864	.9868	.9871	.9875	.9878	.9881	.9884	.9887	.9890
2.3	.9893	.9896	.9898	.9901	.9904	.9906	.9909	.9911	.9913	.9916
2.4	.9918	.9920	.9922	.9925	.9927	.9929	.9931	.9932	.9934	.9936
2.5	.9938	.9940	.9941	.9943	.9945	.9946	.9948	.9949	.9951	.9952
2.6	.9953	.9955	.9956	.9957	.9959	.9960	.9961	.9962	.9963	.9964
2.7	.9965	.9966	.9967	.9968	.9969	.9970	.9971	.9972	.9973	.9974
2.8	.9974	.9975	.9976	.9977	.9977	.9978	.9979	.9979	.9980	.9981
2.9	.9981	.9982	.9982	.9983	.9984	.9984	.9985	.9985	.9986	.9986
3.0	.9987	.9987	.9987	.9988	.9988	.9989	.9989	.9989	.9990	.9990

TABLE 2 *t* Distribution

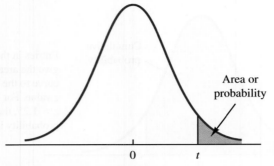

Area or probability

Entries in the table give *t* values for an area or probability in the upper tail of the *t* distribution. For example, with 10 degrees of freedom and a .05 area in the upper tail, $t_{.05} = 1.812$.

Degrees of Freedom	Area in Upper Tail					
	.20	.10	.05	.025	.01	.005
1	1.376	3.078	6.314	12.706	31.821	63.656
2	1.061	1.886	2.920	4.303	6.965	9.925
3	.978	1.638	2.353	3.182	4.541	5.841
4	.941	1.533	2.132	2.776	3.747	4.604
5	.920	1.476	2.015	2.571	3.365	4.032
6	.906	1.440	1.943	2.447	3.143	3.707
7	.896	1.415	1.895	2.365	2.998	3.499
8	.889	1.397	1.860	2.306	2.896	3.355
9	.883	1.383	1.833	2.262	2.821	3.250
10	.879	1.372	1.812	2.228	2.764	3.169
11	.876	1.363	1.796	2.201	2.718	3.106
12	.873	1.356	1.782	2.179	2.681	3.055
13	.870	1.350	1.771	2.160	2.650	3.012
14	.868	1.345	1.761	2.145	2.624	2.977
15	.866	1.341	1.753	2.131	2.602	2.947
16	.865	1.337	1.746	2.120	2.583	2.921
17	.863	1.333	1.740	2.110	2.567	2.898
18	.862	1.330	1.734	2.101	2.552	2.878
19	.861	1.328	1.729	2.093	2.539	2.861
20	.860	1.325	1.725	2.086	2.528	2.845
21	.859	1.323	1.721	2.080	2.518	2.831
22	.858	1.321	1.717	2.074	2.508	2.819
23	.858	1.319	1.714	2.069	2.500	2.807
24	.857	1.318	1.711	2.064	2.492	2.797
25	.856	1.316	1.708	2.060	2.485	2.787
26	.856	1.315	1.706	2.056	2.479	2.779
27	.855	1.314	1.703	2.052	2.473	2.771
28	.855	1.313	1.701	2.048	2.467	2.763
29	.854	1.311	1.699	2.045	2.462	2.756
30	.854	1.310	1.697	2.042	2.457	2.750
31	.853	1.309	1.696	2.040	2.453	2.744
32	.853	1.309	1.694	2.037	2.449	2.738
33	.853	1.308	1.692	2.035	2.445	2.733
34	.852	1.307	1.691	2.032	2.441	2.728

TABLE 2 *t* Distribution (*Continued*)

Degrees of Freedom	Area in Upper Tail					
	.20	.10	.05	.025	.01	.005
35	.852	1.306	1.690	2.030	2.438	2.724
36	.852	1.306	1.688	2.028	2.434	2.719
37	.851	1.305	1.687	2.026	2.431	2.715
38	.851	1.304	1.686	2.024	2.429	2.712
39	.851	1.304	1.685	2.023	2.426	2.708
40	.851	1.303	1.684	2.021	2.423	2.704
41	.850	1.303	1.683	2.020	2.421	2.701
42	.850	1.302	1.682	2.018	2.418	2.698
43	.850	1.302	1.681	2.017	2.416	2.695
44	.850	1.301	1.680	2.015	2.414	2.692
45	.850	1.301	1.679	2.014	2.412	2.690
46	.850	1.300	1.679	2.013	2.410	2.687
47	.849	1.300	1.678	2.012	2.408	2.685
48	.849	1.299	1.677	2.011	2.407	2.682
49	.849	1.299	1.677	2.010	2.405	2.680
50	.849	1.299	1.676	2.009	2.403	2.678
51	.849	1.298	1.675	2.008	2.402	2.676
52	.849	1.298	1.675	2.007	2.400	2.674
53	.848	1.298	1.674	2.006	2.399	2.672
54	.848	1.297	1.674	2.005	2.397	2.670
55	.848	1.297	1.673	2.004	2.396	2.668
56	.848	1.297	1.673	2.003	2.395	2.667
57	.848	1.297	1.672	2.002	2.394	2.665
58	.848	1.296	1.672	2.002	2.392	2.663
59	.848	1.296	1.671	2.001	2.391	2.662
60	.848	1.296	1.671	2.000	2.390	2.660
61	.848	1.296	1.670	2.000	2.389	2.659
62	.847	1.295	1.670	1.999	2.388	2.657
63	.847	1.295	1.669	1.998	2.387	2.656
64	.847	1.295	1.669	1.998	2.386	2.655
65	.847	1.295	1.669	1.997	2.385	2.654
66	.847	1.295	1.668	1.997	2.384	2.652
67	.847	1.294	1.668	1.996	2.383	2.651
68	.847	1.294	1.668	1.995	2.382	2.650
69	.847	1.294	1.667	1.995	2.382	2.649
70	.847	1.294	1.667	1.994	2.381	2.648
71	.847	1.294	1.667	1.994	2.380	2.647
72	.847	1.293	1.666	1.993	2.379	2.646
73	.847	1.293	1.666	1.993	2.379	2.645
74	.847	1.293	1.666	1.993	2.378	2.644
75	.846	1.293	1.665	1.992	2.377	2.643
76	.846	1.293	1.665	1.992	2.376	2.642
77	.846	1.293	1.665	1.991	2.376	2.641
78	.846	1.292	1.665	1.991	2.375	2.640
79	.846	1.292	1.664	1.990	2.374	2.639

TABLE 2 *t* Distribution (*Continued*)

Degrees of Freedom	Area in Upper Tail					
	.20	.10	.05	.025	.01	.005
80	.846	1.292	1.664	1.990	2.374	2.639
81	.846	1.292	1.664	1.990	2.373	2.638
82	.846	1.292	1.664	1.989	2.373	2.637
83	.846	1.292	1.663	1.989	2.372	2.636
84	.846	1.292	1.663	1.989	2.372	2.636
85	.846	1.292	1.663	1.988	2.371	2.635
86	.846	1.291	1.663	1.988	2.370	2.634
87	.846	1.291	1.663	1.988	2.370	2.634
88	.846	1.291	1.662	1.987	2.369	2.633
89	.846	1.291	1.662	1.987	2.369	2.632
90	.846	1.291	1.662	1.987	2.368	2.632
91	.846	1.291	1.662	1.986	2.368	2.631
92	.846	1.291	1.662	1.986	2.368	2.630
93	.846	1.291	1.661	1.986	2.367	2.630
94	.845	1.291	1.661	1.986	2.367	2.629
95	.845	1.291	1.661	1.985	2.366	2.629
96	.845	1.290	1.661	1.985	2.366	2.628
97	.845	1.290	1.661	1.985	2.365	2.627
98	.845	1.290	1.661	1.984	2.365	2.627
99	.845	1.290	1.660	1.984	2.364	2.626
100	.845	1.290	1.660	1.984	2.364	2.626
∞	.842	1.282	1.645	1.960	2.326	2.576

TABLE 3 Chi-Square Distribution

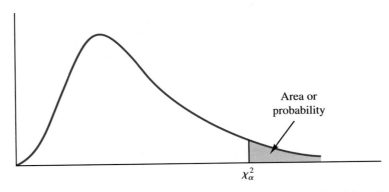

Area or
probability

χ_α^2

Entries in the table give χ_α^2 values, where α is the area or probability in the upper tail of the chi-square distribution.
For example, with 10 degrees of freedom and a .01 area in the upper tail, $\chi_{.01}^2 = 23.209$.

Degrees of Freedom	Area in Upper Tail									
	.995	.99	.975	.95	.90	.10	.05	.025	.01	.005
1	.000	.000	.001	.004	.016	2.706	3.841	5.024	6.635	7.879
2	.010	.020	.051	.103	.211	4.605	5.991	7.378	9.210	10.597
3	.072	.115	.216	.352	.584	6.251	7.815	9.348	11.345	12.838
4	.207	.297	.484	.711	1.064	7.779	9.488	11.143	13.277	14.860
5	.412	.554	.831	1.145	1.610	9.236	11.070	12.832	15.086	16.750
6	.676	.872	1.237	1.635	2.204	10.645	12.592	14.449	16.812	18.548
7	.989	1.239	1.690	2.167	2.833	12.017	14.067	16.013	18.475	20.278
8	1.344	1.647	2.180	2.733	3.490	13.362	15.507	17.535	20.090	21.955
9	1.735	2.088	2.700	3.325	4.168	14.684	16.919	19.023	21.666	23.589
10	2.156	2.558	3.247	3.940	4.865	15.987	18.307	20.483	23.209	25.188
11	2.603	3.053	3.816	4.575	5.578	17.275	19.675	21.920	24.725	26.757
12	3.074	3.571	4.404	5.226	6.304	18.549	21.026	23.337	26.217	28.300
13	3.565	4.107	5.009	5.892	7.041	19.812	22.362	24.736	27.688	29.819
14	4.075	4.660	5.629	6.571	7.790	21.064	23.685	26.119	29.141	31.319
15	4.601	5.229	6.262	7.261	8.547	22.307	24.996	27.488	30.578	32.801
16	5.142	5.812	6.908	7.962	9.312	23.542	26.296	28.845	32.000	34.267
17	5.697	6.408	7.564	8.672	10.085	24.769	27.587	30.191	33.409	35.718
18	6.265	7.015	8.231	9.390	10.865	25.989	28.869	31.526	34.805	37.156
19	6.844	7.633	8.907	10.117	11.651	27.204	30.144	32.852	36.191	38.582
20	7.434	8.260	9.591	10.851	12.443	28.412	31.410	34.170	37.566	39.997
21	8.034	8.897	10.283	11.591	13.240	29.615	32.671	35.479	38.932	41.401
22	8.643	9.542	10.982	12.338	14.041	30.813	33.924	36.781	40.289	42.796
23	9.260	10.196	11.689	13.091	14.848	32.007	35.172	38.076	41.638	44.181
24	9.886	10.856	12.401	13.848	15.659	33.196	36.415	39.364	42.980	45.558
25	10.520	11.524	13.120	14.611	16.473	34.382	37.652	40.646	44.314	46.928
26	11.160	12.198	13.844	15.379	17.292	35.563	38.885	41.923	45.642	48.290
27	11.808	12.878	14.573	16.151	18.114	36.741	40.113	43.195	46.963	49.645
28	12.461	13.565	15.308	16.928	18.939	37.916	41.337	44.461	48.278	50.994
29	13.121	14.256	16.047	17.708	19.768	39.087	42.557	45.722	49.588	52.335

TABLE 3 Chi-Square Distribution (*Continued*)

Degrees of Freedom	Area in Upper Tail									
	.995	.99	.975	.95	.90	.10	.05	.025	.01	.005
30	13.787	14.953	16.791	18.493	20.599	40.256	43.773	46.979	50.892	53.672
35	17.192	18.509	20.569	22.465	24.797	46.059	49.802	53.203	57.342	60.275
40	20.707	22.164	24.433	26.509	29.051	51.805	55.758	59.342	63.691	66.766
45	24.311	25.901	28.366	30.612	33.350	57.505	61.656	65.410	69.957	73.166
50	27.991	29.707	32.357	34.764	37.689	63.167	67.505	71.420	76.154	79.490
55	31.735	33.571	36.398	38.958	42.060	68.796	73.311	77.380	82.292	85.749
60	35.534	37.485	40.482	43.188	46.459	74.397	79.082	83.298	88.379	91.952
65	39.383	41.444	44.603	47.450	50.883	79.973	84.821	89.177	94.422	98.105
70	43.275	45.442	48.758	51.739	55.329	85.527	90.531	95.023	100.425	104.215
75	47.206	49.475	52.942	56.054	59.795	91.061	96.217	100.839	106.393	110.285
80	51.172	53.540	57.153	60.391	64.278	96.578	101.879	106.629	112.329	116.321
85	55.170	57.634	61.389	64.749	68.777	102.079	107.522	112.393	118.236	122.324
90	59.196	61.754	65.647	69.126	73.291	107.565	113.145	118.136	124.116	128.299
95	63.250	65.898	69.925	73.520	77.818	113.038	118.752	123.858	129.973	134.247
100	67.328	70.065	74.222	77.929	82.358	118.498	124.342	129.561	135.807	140.170

TABLE 4 *F* Distribution

Entries in the table give F_α values, where α is the area or probability in the upper tail of the *F* distribution. For example, with 4 numerator degrees of freedom, 8 denominator degrees of freedom, and a .05 area in the upper tail, $F_{.05} = 3.84$.

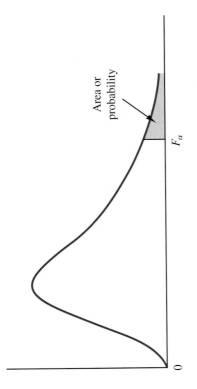

Denominator Degrees of Freedom	Area in Upper Tail	Numerator Degrees of Freedom																	
		1	2	3	4	5	6	7	8	9	10	15	20	25	30	40	60	100	1000
1	.10	39.86	49.50	53.59	55.83	57.24	58.20	58.91	59.44	59.86	60.19	61.22	61.74	62.05	62.26	62.53	62.79	63.01	63.30
	.05	161.45	199.50	215.71	224.58	230.16	233.99	236.77	238.88	240.54	241.88	245.95	248.02	249.26	250.10	251.14	252.20	253.04	254.19
	.025	647.79	799.48	864.15	899.60	921.83	937.11	948.20	956.64	963.28	968.63	984.87	993.08	998.09	1001.40	1005.60	1009.79	1013.16	1017.76
	.01	4052.18	4999.34	5403.53	5624.26	5763.96	5858.95	5928.33	5980.95	6022.40	6055.93	6156.97	6208.66	6239.86	6260.35	6286.43	6312.97	6333.92	6362.80
2	.10	8.53	9.00	9.16	9.24	9.29	9.33	9.35	9.37	9.38	9.39	9.42	9.44	9.45	9.46	9.47	9.47	9.48	9.49
	.05	18.51	19.00	19.16	19.25	19.30	19.33	19.35	19.37	19.38	19.40	19.43	19.45	19.46	19.46	19.47	19.48	19.49	19.49
	.025	38.51	39.00	39.17	39.25	39.30	39.33	39.36	39.37	39.39	39.40	39.43	39.45	39.46	39.46	39.47	39.48	39.49	39.50
	.01	98.50	99.00	99.16	99.25	99.30	99.33	99.36	99.38	99.39	99.40	99.43	99.45	99.46	99.47	99.48	99.48	99.49	99.50
3	.10	5.54	5.46	5.39	5.34	5.31	5.28	5.27	5.25	5.24	5.23	5.20	5.18	5.17	5.17	5.16	5.15	5.14	5.13
	.05	10.13	9.55	9.28	9.12	9.01	8.94	8.89	8.85	8.81	8.79	8.70	8.66	8.63	8.62	8.59	8.57	8.55	8.53
	.025	17.44	16.04	15.44	15.10	14.88	14.73	14.62	14.54	14.47	14.42	14.25	14.17	14.12	14.08	14.04	13.99	13.96	13.91
	.01	34.12	30.82	29.46	28.71	28.24	27.91	27.67	27.49	27.34	27.23	26.87	26.69	26.58	26.50	26.41	26.32	26.24	26.14
4	.10	4.54	4.32	4.19	4.11	4.05	4.01	3.98	3.95	3.94	3.92	3.87	3.84	3.83	3.82	3.80	3.79	3.78	3.76
	.05	7.71	6.94	6.59	6.39	6.26	6.16	6.09	6.04	6.00	5.96	5.86	5.80	5.77	5.75	5.72	5.69	5.66	5.63
	.025	12.22	10.65	9.98	9.60	9.36	9.20	9.07	8.98	8.90	8.84	8.66	8.56	8.50	8.46	8.41	8.36	8.32	8.26
	.01	21.20	18.00	16.69	15.98	15.52	15.21	14.98	14.80	14.66	14.55	14.20	14.02	13.91	13.84	13.75	13.65	13.58	13.47
5	.10	4.06	3.78	3.62	3.52	3.45	3.40	3.37	3.34	3.32	3.30	3.24	3.21	3.19	3.17	3.16	3.14	3.13	3.11
	.05	6.61	5.79	5.41	5.19	5.05	4.95	4.88	4.82	4.77	4.74	4.62	4.56	4.52	4.50	4.46	4.43	4.41	4.37
	.025	10.01	8.43	7.76	7.39	7.15	6.98	6.85	6.76	6.68	6.62	6.43	6.33	6.27	6.23	6.18	6.12	6.08	6.02
	.01	16.26	13.27	12.06	11.39	10.97	10.67	10.46	10.29	10.16	10.05	9.72	9.55	9.45	9.38	9.29	9.20	9.13	9.03

TABLE 4 *F* Distribution (Continued)

Denominator Degrees of Freedom	Area in Upper Tail	Numerator Degrees of Freedom																	
		1	2	3	4	5	6	7	8	9	10	15	20	25	30	40	60	100	1000
6	.10	3.78	3.46	3.29	3.18	3.11	3.05	3.01	2.98	2.96	2.94	2.87	2.84	2.81	2.80	2.78	2.76	2.75	2.72
	.05	5.99	5.14	4.76	4.53	4.39	4.28	4.21	4.15	4.10	4.06	3.94	3.87	3.83	3.81	3.77	3.74	3.71	3.67
	.025	8.81	7.26	6.60	6.23	5.99	5.82	5.70	5.60	5.52	5.46	5.27	5.17	5.11	5.07	5.01	4.96	4.92	4.86
	.01	13.75	10.92	9.78	9.15	8.75	8.47	8.26	8.10	7.98	7.87	7.56	7.40	7.30	7.23	7.14	7.06	6.99	6.89
7	.10	3.59	3.26	3.07	2.96	2.88	2.83	2.78	2.75	2.72	2.70	2.63	2.59	2.57	2.56	2.54	2.51	2.50	2.47
	.05	5.59	4.74	4.35	4.12	3.97	3.87	3.79	3.73	3.68	3.64	3.51	3.44	3.40	3.38	3.34	3.30	3.27	3.23
	.025	8.07	6.54	5.89	5.52	5.29	5.12	4.99	4.90	4.82	4.76	4.57	4.47	4.40	4.36	4.31	4.25	4.21	4.15
	.01	12.25	9.55	8.45	7.85	7.46	7.19	6.99	6.84	6.72	6.62	6.31	6.16	6.06	5.99	5.91	5.82	5.75	5.66
8	.10	3.46	3.11	2.92	2.81	2.73	2.67	2.62	2.59	2.56	2.54	2.46	2.42	2.40	2.38	2.36	2.34	2.32	2.30
	.05	5.32	4.46	4.07	3.84	3.69	3.58	3.50	3.44	3.39	3.35	3.22	3.15	3.11	3.08	3.04	3.01	2.97	2.93
	.025	7.57	6.06	5.42	5.05	4.82	4.65	4.53	4.43	4.36	4.30	4.10	4.00	3.94	3.89	3.84	3.78	3.74	3.68
	.01	11.26	8.65	7.59	7.01	6.63	6.37	6.18	6.03	5.91	5.81	5.52	5.36	5.26	5.20	5.12	5.03	4.96	4.87
9	.10	3.36	3.01	2.81	2.69	2.61	2.55	2.51	2.47	2.44	2.42	2.34	2.30	2.27	2.25	2.23	2.21	2.19	2.16
	.05	5.12	4.26	3.86	3.63	3.48	3.37	3.29	3.23	3.18	3.14	3.01	2.94	2.89	2.86	2.83	2.79	2.76	2.71
	.025	7.21	5.71	5.08	4.72	4.48	4.32	4.20	4.10	4.03	3.96	3.77	3.67	3.60	3.56	3.51	3.45	3.40	3.34
	.01	10.56	8.02	6.99	6.42	6.06	5.80	5.61	5.47	5.35	5.26	4.96	4.81	4.71	4.65	4.57	4.48	4.41	4.32
10	.10	3.29	2.92	2.73	2.61	2.52	2.46	2.41	2.38	2.35	2.32	2.24	2.20	2.17	2.16	2.13	2.11	2.09	2.06
	.05	4.96	4.10	3.71	3.48	3.33	3.22	3.14	3.07	3.02	2.98	2.85	2.77	2.73	2.70	2.66	2.62	2.59	2.54
	.025	6.94	5.46	4.83	4.47	4.24	4.07	3.95	3.85	3.78	3.72	3.52	3.42	3.35	3.31	3.26	3.20	3.15	3.09
	.01	10.04	7.56	6.55	5.99	5.64	5.39	5.20	5.06	4.94	4.85	4.56	4.41	4.31	4.25	4.17	4.08	4.01	3.92
11	.10	3.23	2.86	2.66	2.54	2.45	2.39	2.34	2.30	2.27	2.25	2.17	2.12	2.10	2.08	2.05	2.03	2.01	1.98
	.05	4.84	3.98	3.59	3.36	3.20	3.09	3.01	2.95	2.90	2.85	2.72	2.65	2.60	2.57	2.53	2.49	2.46	2.41
	.025	6.72	5.26	4.63	4.28	4.04	3.88	3.76	3.66	3.59	3.53	3.33	3.23	3.16	3.12	3.06	3.00	2.96	2.89
	.01	9.65	7.21	6.22	5.67	5.32	5.07	4.89	4.74	4.63	4.54	4.25	4.10	4.01	3.94	3.86	3.78	3.71	3.61
12	.10	3.18	2.81	2.61	2.48	2.39	2.33	2.28	2.24	2.21	2.19	2.10	2.06	2.03	2.01	1.99	1.96	1.94	1.91
	.05	4.75	3.89	3.49	3.26	3.11	3.00	2.91	2.85	2.80	2.75	2.62	2.54	2.50	2.47	2.43	2.38	2.35	2.30
	.025	6.55	5.10	4.47	4.12	3.89	3.73	3.61	3.51	3.44	3.37	3.18	3.07	3.01	2.96	2.91	2.85	2.80	2.73
	.01	9.33	6.93	5.95	5.41	5.06	4.82	4.64	4.50	4.39	4.30	4.01	3.86	3.76	3.70	3.62	3.54	3.47	3.37
13	.10	3.14	2.76	2.56	2.43	2.35	2.28	2.23	2.20	2.16	2.14	2.05	2.01	1.98	1.96	1.93	1.90	1.88	1.85
	.05	4.67	3.81	3.41	3.18	3.03	2.92	2.83	2.77	2.71	2.67	2.53	2.46	2.41	2.38	2.34	2.30	2.26	2.21
	.025	6.41	4.97	4.35	4.00	3.77	3.60	3.48	3.39	3.31	3.25	3.05	2.95	2.88	2.84	2.78	2.72	2.67	2.60
	.01	9.07	6.70	5.74	5.21	4.86	4.62	4.44	4.30	4.19	4.10	3.82	3.66	3.57	3.51	3.43	3.34	3.27	3.18
14	.10	3.10	2.73	2.52	2.39	2.31	2.24	2.19	2.15	2.12	2.10	2.01	1.96	1.93	1.91	1.89	1.86	1.83	1.80
	.05	4.60	3.74	3.34	3.11	2.96	2.85	2.76	2.70	2.65	2.60	2.46	2.39	2.34	2.31	2.27	2.22	2.19	2.14
	.025	6.30	4.86	4.24	3.89	3.66	3.50	3.38	3.29	3.21	3.15	2.95	2.84	2.78	2.73	2.67	2.61	2.56	2.50
	.01	8.86	6.51	5.56	5.04	4.69	4.46	4.28	4.14	4.03	3.94	3.66	3.51	3.41	3.35	3.27	3.18	3.11	3.02
15	.10	3.07	2.70	2.49	2.36	2.27	2.21	2.16	2.12	2.09	2.06	1.97	1.92	1.89	1.87	1.85	1.82	1.79	1.76
	.05	4.54	3.68	3.29	3.06	2.90	2.79	2.71	2.64	2.59	2.54	2.40	2.33	2.28	2.25	2.20	2.16	2.12	2.07
	.025	6.20	4.77	4.15	3.80	3.58	3.41	3.29	3.20	3.12	3.06	2.86	2.76	2.69	2.64	2.59	2.52	2.47	2.40
	.01	8.68	6.36	5.42	4.89	4.56	4.32	4.14	4.00	3.89	3.80	3.52	3.37	3.28	3.21	3.13	3.05	2.98	2.88

Denominator Degrees of Freedom	Area in Upper Tail	1	2	3	4	5	6	7	8	9	10	15	20	25	30	40	60	100	1000
16	.10	3.05	2.67	2.46	2.33	2.24	2.18	2.13	2.09	2.06	2.03	1.94	1.89	1.86	1.84	1.81	1.78	1.76	1.72
	.05	4.49	3.63	3.24	3.01	2.85	2.74	2.66	2.59	2.54	2.49	2.35	2.28	2.23	2.19	2.15	2.11	2.07	2.02
	.025	6.12	4.69	4.08	3.73	3.50	3.34	3.22	3.12	3.05	2.99	2.79	2.68	2.61	2.57	2.51	2.45	2.40	2.32
	.01	8.53	6.23	5.29	4.77	4.44	4.20	4.03	3.89	3.78	3.69	3.41	3.26	3.16	3.10	3.02	2.93	2.86	2.76
17	.10	3.03	2.64	2.44	2.31	2.22	2.15	2.10	2.06	2.03	2.00	1.91	1.86	1.83	1.81	1.78	1.75	1.73	1.69
	.05	4.45	3.59	3.20	2.96	2.81	2.70	2.61	2.55	2.49	2.45	2.31	2.23	2.18	2.15	2.10	2.06	2.02	1.97
	.025	6.04	4.62	4.01	3.66	3.44	3.28	3.16	3.06	2.98	2.92	2.72	2.62	2.55	2.50	2.44	2.38	2.33	2.26
	.01	8.40	6.11	5.19	4.67	4.34	4.10	3.93	3.79	3.68	3.59	3.31	3.16	3.07	3.00	2.92	2.83	2.76	2.66
18	.10	3.01	2.62	2.42	2.29	2.20	2.13	2.08	2.04	2.00	1.98	1.89	1.84	1.80	1.78	1.75	1.72	1.70	1.66
	.05	4.41	3.55	3.16	2.93	2.77	2.66	2.58	2.51	2.46	2.41	2.27	2.19	2.14	2.11	2.06	2.02	1.98	1.92
	.025	5.98	4.56	3.95	3.61	3.38	3.22	3.10	3.01	2.93	2.87	2.67	2.56	2.49	2.44	2.38	2.32	2.27	2.20
	.01	8.29	6.01	5.09	4.58	4.25	4.01	3.84	3.71	3.60	3.51	3.23	3.08	2.98	2.92	2.84	2.75	2.68	2.58
19	.10	2.99	2.61	2.40	2.27	2.18	2.11	2.06	2.02	1.98	1.96	1.86	1.81	1.78	1.76	1.73	1.70	1.67	1.64
	.05	4.38	3.52	3.13	2.90	2.74	2.63	2.54	2.48	2.42	2.38	2.23	2.16	2.11	2.07	2.03	1.98	1.94	1.88
	.025	5.92	4.51	3.90	3.56	3.33	3.17	3.05	2.96	2.88	2.82	2.62	2.51	2.44	2.39	2.33	2.27	2.22	2.14
	.01	8.18	5.93	5.01	4.50	4.17	3.94	3.77	3.63	3.52	3.43	3.15	3.00	2.91	2.84	2.76	2.67	2.60	2.50
20	.10	2.97	2.59	2.38	2.25	2.16	2.09	2.04	2.00	1.96	1.94	1.84	1.79	1.76	1.74	1.71	1.68	1.65	1.61
	.05	4.35	3.49	3.10	2.87	2.71	2.60	2.51	2.45	2.39	2.35	2.20	2.12	2.07	2.04	1.99	1.95	1.91	1.85
	.025	5.87	4.46	3.86	3.51	3.29	3.13	3.01	2.91	2.84	2.77	2.57	2.46	2.40	2.35	2.29	2.22	2.17	2.09
	.01	8.10	5.85	4.94	4.43	4.10	3.87	3.70	3.56	3.46	3.37	3.09	2.94	2.84	2.78	2.69	2.61	2.54	2.43
21	.10	2.96	2.57	2.36	2.23	2.14	2.08	2.02	1.98	1.95	1.92	1.83	1.78	1.74	1.72	1.69	1.66	1.63	1.59
	.05	4.32	3.47	3.07	2.84	2.68	2.57	2.49	2.42	2.37	2.32	2.18	2.10	2.05	2.01	1.96	1.92	1.88	1.82
	.025	5.83	4.42	3.82	3.48	3.25	3.09	2.97	2.87	2.80	2.73	2.53	2.42	2.36	2.31	2.25	2.18	2.13	2.05
	.01	8.02	5.78	4.87	4.37	4.04	3.81	3.64	3.51	3.40	3.31	3.03	2.88	2.79	2.72	2.64	2.55	2.48	2.37
22	.10	2.95	2.56	2.35	2.22	2.13	2.06	2.01	1.97	1.93	1.90	1.81	1.76	1.73	1.70	1.67	1.64	1.61	1.57
	.05	4.30	3.44	3.05	2.82	2.66	2.55	2.46	2.40	2.34	2.30	2.15	2.07	2.02	1.98	1.94	1.89	1.85	1.79
	.025	5.79	4.38	3.78	3.44	3.22	3.05	2.93	2.84	2.76	2.70	2.50	2.39	2.32	2.27	2.21	2.14	2.09	2.01
	.01	7.95	5.72	4.82	4.31	3.99	3.76	3.59	3.45	3.35	3.26	2.98	2.83	2.73	2.67	2.58	2.50	2.42	2.32
23	.10	2.94	2.55	2.34	2.21	2.11	2.05	1.99	1.95	1.92	1.89	1.80	1.74	1.71	1.69	1.66	1.62	1.59	1.55
	.05	4.28	3.42	3.03	2.80	2.64	2.53	2.44	2.37	2.32	2.27	2.13	2.05	2.00	1.96	1.91	1.86	1.82	1.76
	.025	5.75	4.35	3.75	3.41	3.18	3.02	2.90	2.81	2.73	2.67	2.47	2.36	2.29	2.24	2.18	2.11	2.06	1.98
	.01	7.88	5.66	4.76	4.26	3.94	3.71	3.54	3.41	3.30	3.21	2.93	2.78	2.69	2.62	2.54	2.45	2.37	2.27
24	.10	2.93	2.54	2.33	2.19	2.10	2.04	1.98	1.94	1.91	1.88	1.78	1.73	1.70	1.67	1.64	1.61	1.58	1.54
	.05	4.26	3.40	3.01	2.78	2.62	2.51	2.42	2.36	2.30	2.25	2.11	2.03	1.97	1.94	1.89	1.84	1.80	1.74
	.025	5.72	4.32	3.72	3.38	3.15	2.99	2.87	2.78	2.70	2.64	2.44	2.33	2.26	2.21	2.15	2.08	2.02	1.94
	.01	7.82	5.61	4.72	4.22	3.90	3.67	3.50	3.36	3.26	3.17	2.89	2.74	2.64	2.58	2.49	2.40	2.33	2.22
25	.10	2.92	2.53	2.32	2.18	2.09	2.02	1.97	1.93	1.89	1.87	1.77	1.72	1.68	1.66	1.63	1.59	1.56	1.52
	.05	4.24	3.39	2.99	2.76	2.60	2.49	2.40	2.34	2.28	2.24	2.09	2.01	1.96	1.92	1.87	1.82	1.78	1.72
	.025	5.69	4.29	3.69	3.35	3.13	2.97	2.85	2.75	2.68	2.61	2.41	2.30	2.23	2.18	2.12	2.05	2.00	1.91
	.01	7.77	5.57	4.68	4.18	3.85	3.63	3.46	3.32	3.22	3.13	2.85	2.70	2.60	2.54	2.45	2.36	2.29	2.18

Numerator Degrees of Freedom

TABLE 4 *F* Distribution (Continued)

Denominator Degrees of Freedom	Area in Upper Tail	Numerator Degrees of Freedom																	
		1	2	3	4	5	6	7	8	9	10	15	20	25	30	40	60	100	1000
26	.10	2.91	2.52	2.31	2.17	2.08	2.01	1.96	1.92	1.88	1.86	1.76	1.71	1.67	1.65	1.61	1.58	1.55	1.51
	.05	4.23	3.37	2.98	2.74	2.59	2.47	2.39	2.32	2.27	2.22	2.07	1.99	1.94	1.90	1.85	1.80	1.76	1.70
	.025	5.66	4.27	3.67	3.33	3.10	2.94	2.82	2.73	2.65	2.59	2.39	2.28	2.21	2.16	2.09	2.03	1.97	1.89
	.01	7.72	5.53	4.64	4.14	3.82	3.59	3.42	3.29	3.18	3.09	2.81	2.66	2.57	2.50	2.42	2.33	2.25	2.14
27	.10	2.90	2.51	2.30	2.17	2.07	2.00	1.95	1.91	1.87	1.85	1.75	1.70	1.66	1.64	1.60	1.57	1.54	1.50
	.05	4.21	3.35	2.96	2.73	2.57	2.46	2.37	2.31	2.25	2.20	2.06	1.97	1.92	1.88	1.84	1.79	1.74	1.68
	.025	5.63	4.24	3.65	3.31	3.08	2.92	2.80	2.71	2.63	2.57	2.36	2.25	2.18	2.13	2.07	2.00	1.94	1.86
	.01	7.68	5.49	4.60	4.11	3.78	3.56	3.39	3.26	3.15	3.06	2.78	2.63	2.54	2.47	2.38	2.29	2.22	2.11
28	.10	2.89	2.50	2.29	2.16	2.06	2.00	1.94	1.90	1.87	1.84	1.74	1.69	1.65	1.63	1.59	1.56	1.53	1.48
	.05	4.20	3.34	2.95	2.71	2.56	2.45	2.36	2.29	2.24	2.19	2.04	1.96	1.91	1.87	1.82	1.77	1.73	1.66
	.025	5.61	4.22	3.63	3.29	3.06	2.90	2.78	2.69	2.61	2.55	2.34	2.23	2.16	2.11	2.05	1.98	1.92	1.84
	.01	7.64	5.45	4.57	4.07	3.75	3.53	3.36	3.23	3.12	3.03	2.75	2.60	2.51	2.44	2.35	2.26	2.19	2.08
29	.10	2.89	2.50	2.28	2.15	2.06	1.99	1.93	1.89	1.86	1.83	1.73	1.68	1.64	1.62	1.58	1.55	1.52	1.47
	.05	4.18	3.33	2.93	2.70	2.55	2.43	2.35	2.28	2.22	2.18	2.03	1.94	1.89	1.85	1.81	1.75	1.71	1.65
	.025	5.59	4.20	3.61	3.27	3.04	2.88	2.76	2.67	2.59	2.53	2.32	2.21	2.14	2.09	2.03	1.96	1.90	1.82
	.01	7.60	5.42	4.54	4.04	3.73	3.50	3.33	3.20	3.09	3.00	2.73	2.57	2.48	2.41	2.33	2.23	2.16	2.05
30	.10	2.88	2.49	2.28	2.14	2.05	1.98	1.93	1.88	1.85	1.82	1.72	1.67	1.63	1.61	1.57	1.54	1.51	1.46
	.05	4.17	3.32	2.92	2.69	2.53	2.42	2.33	2.27	2.21	2.16	2.01	1.93	1.88	1.84	1.79	1.74	1.70	1.63
	.025	5.57	4.18	3.59	3.25	3.03	2.87	2.75	2.65	2.57	2.51	2.31	2.20	2.12	2.07	2.01	1.94	1.88	1.80
	.01	7.56	5.39	4.51	4.02	3.70	3.47	3.30	3.17	3.07	2.98	2.70	2.55	2.45	2.39	2.30	2.21	2.13	2.02
40	.10	2.84	2.44	2.23	2.09	2.00	1.93	1.87	1.83	1.79	1.76	1.66	1.61	1.57	1.54	1.51	1.47	1.43	1.38
	.05	4.08	3.23	2.84	2.61	2.45	2.34	2.25	2.18	2.12	2.08	1.92	1.84	1.78	1.74	1.69	1.64	1.59	1.52
	.025	5.42	4.05	3.46	3.13	2.90	2.74	2.62	2.53	2.45	2.39	2.18	2.07	1.99	1.94	1.88	1.80	1.74	1.65
	.01	7.31	5.18	4.31	3.83	3.51	3.29	3.12	2.99	2.89	2.80	2.52	2.37	2.27	2.20	2.11	2.02	1.94	1.82
60	.10	2.79	2.39	2.18	2.04	1.95	1.87	1.82	1.77	1.74	1.71	1.60	1.54	1.50	1.48	1.44	1.40	1.36	1.30
	.05	4.00	3.15	2.76	2.53	2.37	2.25	2.17	2.10	2.04	1.99	1.84	1.75	1.69	1.65	1.59	1.53	1.48	1.40
	.025	5.29	3.93	3.34	3.01	2.79	2.63	2.51	2.41	2.33	2.27	2.06	1.94	1.87	1.82	1.74	1.67	1.60	1.49
	.01	7.08	4.98	4.13	3.65	3.34	3.12	2.95	2.82	2.72	2.63	2.35	2.20	2.10	2.03	1.94	1.84	1.75	1.62
100	.10	2.76	2.36	2.14	2.00	1.91	1.83	1.78	1.73	1.69	1.66	1.56	1.49	1.45	1.42	1.38	1.34	1.29	1.22
	.05	3.94	3.09	2.70	2.46	2.31	2.19	2.10	2.03	1.97	1.93	1.77	1.68	1.62	1.57	1.52	1.45	1.39	1.30
	.025	5.18	3.83	3.25	2.92	2.70	2.54	2.42	2.32	2.24	2.18	1.97	1.85	1.77	1.71	1.64	1.56	1.48	1.36
	.01	6.90	4.82	3.98	3.51	3.21	2.99	2.82	2.69	2.59	2.50	2.22	2.07	1.97	1.89	1.80	1.69	1.60	1.45
1000	.10	2.71	2.31	2.09	1.95	1.85	1.78	1.72	1.68	1.64	1.61	1.49	1.43	1.38	1.35	1.30	1.25	1.20	1.08
	.05	3.85	3.00	2.61	2.38	2.22	2.11	2.02	1.95	1.89	1.84	1.68	1.58	1.52	1.47	1.41	1.33	1.26	1.11
	.025	5.04	3.70	3.13	2.80	2.58	2.42	2.30	2.20	2.13	2.06	1.85	1.72	1.64	1.58	1.50	1.41	1.32	1.13
	.01	6.66	4.63	3.80	3.34	3.04	2.82	2.66	2.53	2.43	2.34	2.06	1.90	1.79	1.72	1.61	1.50	1.38	1.16

TABLE 5 Binomial Probabilities

Entries in the table give the probability of x successes in n trials of a binomial experiment, where p is the probability of a success on one trial. For example, with six trials and $p = .05$, the probability of two successes is .0305.

						p				
n	x	.01	.02	.03	.04	.05	.06	.07	.08	.09
2	0	.9801	.9604	.9409	.9216	.9025	.8836	.8649	.8464	.8281
	1	.0198	.0392	.0582	.0768	.0950	.1128	.1302	.1472	.1638
	2	.0001	.0004	.0009	.0016	.0025	.0036	.0049	.0064	.0081
3	0	.9703	.9412	.9127	.8847	.8574	.8306	.8044	.7787	.7536
	1	.0294	.0576	.0847	.1106	.1354	.1590	.1816	.2031	.2236
	2	.0003	.0012	.0026	.0046	.0071	.0102	.0137	.0177	.0221
	3	.0000	.0000	.0000	.0001	.0001	.0002	.0003	.0005	.0007
4	0	.9606	.9224	.8853	.8493	.8145	.7807	.7481	.7164	.6857
	1	.0388	.0753	.1095	.1416	.1715	.1993	.2252	.2492	.2713
	2	.0006	.0023	.0051	.0088	.0135	.0191	.0254	.0325	.0402
	3	.0000	.0000	.0001	.0002	.0005	.0008	.0013	.0019	.0027
	4	.0000	.0000	.0000	.0000	.0000	.0000	.0000	.0000	.0001
5	0	.9510	.9039	.8587	.8154	.7738	.7339	.6957	.6591	.6240
	1	.0480	.0922	.1328	.1699	.2036	.2342	.2618	.2866	.3086
	2	.0010	.0038	.0082	.0142	.0214	.0299	.0394	.0498	.0610
	3	.0000	.0001	.0003	.0006	.0011	.0019	.0030	.0043	.0060
	4	.0000	.0000	.0000	.0000	.0000	.0001	.0001	.0002	.0003
	5	.0000	.0000	.0000	.0000	.0000	.0000	.0000	.0000	.0000
6	0	.9415	.8858	.8330	.7828	.7351	.6899	.6470	.6064	.5679
	1	.0571	.1085	.1546	.1957	.2321	.2642	.2922	.3164	.3370
	2	.0014	.0055	.0120	.0204	.0305	.0422	.0550	.0688	.0833
	3	.0000	.0002	.0005	.0011	.0021	.0036	.0055	.0080	.0110
	4	.0000	.0000	.0000	.0000	.0001	.0002	.0003	.0005	.0008
	5	.0000	.0000	.0000	.0000	.0000	.0000	.0000	.0000	.0000
	6	.0000	.0000	.0000	.0000	.0000	.0000	.0000	.0000	.0000
7	0	.9321	.8681	.8080	.7514	.6983	.6485	.6017	.5578	.5168
	1	.0659	.1240	.1749	.2192	.2573	.2897	.3170	.3396	.3578
	2	.0020	.0076	.0162	.0274	.0406	.0555	.0716	.0886	.1061
	3	.0000	.0003	.0008	.0019	.0036	.0059	.0090	.0128	.0175
	4	.0000	.0000	.0000	.0001	.0002	.0004	.0007	.0011	.0017
	5	.0000	.0000	.0000	.0000	.0000	.0000	.0000	.0001	.0001
	6	.0000	.0000	.0000	.0000	.0000	.0000	.0000	.0000	.0000
	7	.0000	.0000	.0000	.0000	.0000	.0000	.0000	.0000	.0000
8	0	.9227	.8508	.7837	.7214	.6634	.6096	.5596	.5132	.4703
	1	.0746	.1389	.1939	.2405	.2793	.3113	.3370	.3570	.3721
	2	.0026	.0099	.0210	.0351	.0515	.0695	.0888	.1087	.1288
	3	.0001	.0004	.0013	.0029	.0054	.0089	.0134	.0189	.0255
	4	.0000	.0000	.0001	.0002	.0004	.0007	.0013	.0021	.0031
	5	.0000	.0000	.0000	.0000	.0000	.0000	.0001	.0001	.0002
	6	.0000	.0000	.0000	.0000	.0000	.0000	.0000	.0000	.0000
	7	.0000	.0000	.0000	.0000	.0000	.0000	.0000	.0000	.0000
	8	.0000	.0000	.0000	.0000	.0000	.0000	.0000	.0000	.0000

TABLE 5 Binomial Probabilities (*Continued*)

n	x	.01	.02	.03	.04	.05	.06	.07	.08	.09
9	0	.9135	.8337	.7602	.6925	.6302	.5730	.5204	.4722	.4279
	1	.0830	.1531	.2116	.2597	.2985	.3292	.3525	.3695	.3809
	2	.0034	.0125	.0262	.0433	.0629	.0840	.1061	.1285	.1507
	3	.0001	.0006	.0019	.0042	.0077	.0125	.0186	.0261	.0348
	4	.0000	.0000	.0001	.0003	.0006	.0012	.0021	.0034	.0052
	5	.0000	.0000	.0000	.0000	.0000	.0001	.0002	.0003	.0005
	6	.0000	.0000	.0000	.0000	.0000	.0000	.0000	.0000	.0000
	7	.0000	.0000	.0000	.0000	.0000	.0000	.0000	.0000	.0000
	8	.0000	.0000	.0000	.0000	.0000	.0000	.0000	.0000	.0000
	9	.0000	.0000	.0000	.0000	.0000	.0000	.0000	.0000	.0000
10	0	.9044	.8171	.7374	.6648	.5987	.5386	.4840	.4344	.3894
	1	.0914	.1667	.2281	.2770	.3151	.3438	.3643	.3777	.3851
	2	.0042	.0153	.0317	.0519	.0746	.0988	.1234	.1478	.1714
	3	.0001	.0008	.0026	.0058	.0105	.0168	.0248	.0343	.0452
	4	.0000	.0000	.0001	.0004	.0010	.0019	.0033	.0052	.0078
	5	.0000	.0000	.0000	.0000	.0001	.0001	.0003	.0005	.0009
	6	.0000	.0000	.0000	.0000	.0000	.0000	.0000	.0000	.0001
	7	.0000	.0000	.0000	.0000	.0000	.0000	.0000	.0000	.0000
	8	.0000	.0000	.0000	.0000	.0000	.0000	.0000	.0000	.0000
	9	.0000	.0000	.0000	.0000	.0000	.0000	.0000	.0000	.0000
	10	.0000	.0000	.0000	.0000	.0000	.0000	.0000	.0000	.0000
12	0	.8864	.7847	.6938	.6127	.5404	.4759	.4186	.3677	.3225
	1	.1074	.1922	.2575	.3064	.3413	.3645	.3781	.3837	.3827
	2	.0060	.0216	.0438	.0702	.0988	.1280	.1565	.1835	.2082
	3	.0002	.0015	.0045	.0098	.0173	.0272	.0393	.0532	.0686
	4	.0000	.0001	.0003	.0009	.0021	.0039	.0067	.0104	.0153
	5	.0000	.0000	.0000	.0001	.0002	.0004	.0008	.0014	.0024
	6	.0000	.0000	.0000	.0000	.0000	.0000	.0001	.0001	.0003
	7	.0000	.0000	.0000	.0000	.0000	.0000	.0000	.0000	.0000
	8	.0000	.0000	.0000	.0000	.0000	.0000	.0000	.0000	.0000
	9	.0000	.0000	.0000	.0000	.0000	.0000	.0000	.0000	.0000
	10	.0000	.0000	.0000	.0000	.0000	.0000	.0000	.0000	.0000
	11	.0000	.0000	.0000	.0000	.0000	.0000	.0000	.0000	.0000
	12	.0000	.0000	.0000	.0000	.0000	.0000	.0000	.0000	.0000
15	0	.8601	.7386	.6333	.5421	.4633	.3953	.3367	.2863	.2430
	1	.1303	.2261	.2938	.3388	.3658	.3785	.3801	.3734	.3605
	2	.0092	.0323	.0636	.0988	.1348	.1691	.2003	.2273	.2496
	3	.0004	.0029	.0085	.0178	.0307	.0468	.0653	.0857	.1070
	4	.0000	.0002	.0008	.0022	.0049	.0090	.0148	.0223	.0317
	5	.0000	.0000	.0001	.0002	.0006	.0013	.0024	.0043	.0069
	6	.0000	.0000	.0000	.0000	.0000	.0001	.0003	.0006	.0011
	7	.0000	.0000	.0000	.0000	.0000	.0000	.0000	.0001	.0001
	8	.0000	.0000	.0000	.0000	.0000	.0000	.0000	.0000	.0000
	9	.0000	.0000	.0000	.0000	.0000	.0000	.0000	.0000	.0000
	10	.0000	.0000	.0000	.0000	.0000	.0000	.0000	.0000	.0000
	11	.0000	.0000	.0000	.0000	.0000	.0000	.0000	.0000	.0000
	12	.0000	.0000	.0000	.0000	.0000	.0000	.0000	.0000	.0000
	13	.0000	.0000	.0000	.0000	.0000	.0000	.0000	.0000	.0000
	14	.0000	.0000	.0000	.0000	.0000	.0000	.0000	.0000	.0000
	15	.0000	.0000	.0000	.0000	.0000	.0000	.0000	.0000	.0000

TABLE 5 Binomial Probabilities (*Continued*)

n	x	.01	.02	.03	.04	.05	.06	.07	.08	.09
18	0	.8345	.6951	.5780	.4796	.3972	.3283	.2708	.2229	.1831
	1	.1517	.2554	.3217	.3597	.3763	.3772	.3669	.3489	.3260
	2	.0130	.0443	.0846	.1274	.1683	.2047	.2348	.2579	.2741
	3	.0007	.0048	.0140	.0283	.0473	.0697	.0942	.1196	.1446
	4	.0000	.0004	.0016	.0044	.0093	.0167	.0266	.0390	.0536
	5	.0000	.0000	.0001	.0005	.0014	.0030	.0056	.0095	.0148
	6	.0000	.0000	.0000	.0000	.0002	.0004	.0009	.0018	.0032
	7	.0000	.0000	.0000	.0000	.0000	.0000	.0001	.0003	.0005
	8	.0000	.0000	.0000	.0000	.0000	.0000	.0000	.0000	.0001
	9	.0000	.0000	.0000	.0000	.0000	.0000	.0000	.0000	.0000
	10	.0000	.0000	.0000	.0000	.0000	.0000	.0000	.0000	.0000
	11	.0000	.0000	.0000	.0000	.0000	.0000	.0000	.0000	.0000
	12	.0000	.0000	.0000	.0000	.0000	.0000	.0000	.0000	.0000
	13	.0000	.0000	.0000	.0000	.0000	.0000	.0000	.0000	.0000
	14	.0000	.0000	.0000	.0000	.0000	.0000	.0000	.0000	.0000
	15	.0000	.0000	.0000	.0000	.0000	.0000	.0000	.0000	.0000
	16	.0000	.0000	.0000	.0000	.0000	.0000	.0000	.0000	.0000
	17	.0000	.0000	.0000	.0000	.0000	.0000	.0000	.0000	.0000
	18	.0000	.0000	.0000	.0000	.0000	.0000	.0000	.0000	.0000
20	0	.8179	.6676	.5438	.4420	.3585	.2901	.2342	.1887	.1516
	1	.1652	.2725	.3364	.3683	.3774	.3703	.3526	.3282	.3000
	2	.0159	.0528	.0988	.1458	.1887	.2246	.2521	.2711	.2818
	3	.0010	.0065	.0183	.0364	.0596	.0860	.1139	.1414	.1672
	4	.0000	.0006	.0024	.0065	.0133	.0233	.0364	.0523	.0703
	5	.0000	.0000	.0002	.0009	.0022	.0048	.0088	.0145	.0222
	6	.0000	.0000	.0000	.0001	.0003	.0008	.0017	.0032	.0055
	7	.0000	.0000	.0000	.0000	.0000	.0001	.0002	.0005	.0011
	8	.0000	.0000	.0000	.0000	.0000	.0000	.0000	.0001	.0002
	9	.0000	.0000	.0000	.0000	.0000	.0000	.0000	.0000	.0000
	10	.0000	.0000	.0000	.0000	.0000	.0000	.0000	.0000	.0000
	11	.0000	.0000	.0000	.0000	.0000	.0000	.0000	.0000	.0000
	12	.0000	.0000	.0000	.0000	.0000	.0000	.0000	.0000	.0000
	13	.0000	.0000	.0000	.0000	.0000	.0000	.0000	.0000	.0000
	14	.0000	.0000	.0000	.0000	.0000	.0000	.0000	.0000	.0000
	15	.0000	.0000	.0000	.0000	.0000	.0000	.0000	.0000	.0000
	16	.0000	.0000	.0000	.0000	.0000	.0000	.0000	.0000	.0000
	17	.0000	.0000	.0000	.0000	.0000	.0000	.0000	.0000	.0000
	18	.0000	.0000	.0000	.0000	.0000	.0000	.0000	.0000	.0000
	19	.0000	.0000	.0000	.0000	.0000	.0000	.0000	.0000	.0000
	20	.0000	.0000	.0000	.0000	.0000	.0000	.0000	.0000	.0000

TABLE 5 Binomial Probabilities (*Continued*)

						p				
n	*x*	.10	.15	.20	.25	.30	.35	.40	.45	.50
2	0	.8100	.7225	.6400	.5625	.4900	.4225	.3600	.3025	.2500
	1	.1800	.2550	.3200	.3750	.4200	.4550	.4800	.4950	.5000
	2	.0100	.0225	.0400	.0625	.0900	.1225	.1600	.2025	.2500
3	0	.7290	.6141	.5120	.4219	.3430	.2746	.2160	.1664	.1250
	1	.2430	.3251	.3840	.4219	.4410	.4436	.4320	.4084	.3750
	2	.0270	.0574	.0960	.1406	.1890	.2389	.2880	.3341	.3750
	3	.0010	.0034	.0080	.0156	.0270	.0429	.0640	.0911	.1250
4	0	.6561	.5220	.4096	.3164	.2401	.1785	.1296	.0915	.0625
	1	.2916	.3685	.4096	.4219	.4116	.3845	.3456	.2995	.2500
	2	.0486	.0975	.1536	.2109	.2646	.3105	.3456	.3675	.3750
	3	.0036	.0115	.0256	.0469	.0756	.1115	.1536	.2005	.2500
	4	.0001	.0005	.0016	.0039	.0081	.0150	.0256	.0410	.0625
5	0	.5905	.4437	.3277	.2373	.1681	.1160	.0778	.0503	.0312
	1	.3280	.3915	.4096	.3955	.3602	.3124	.2592	.2059	.1562
	2	.0729	.1382	.2048	.2637	.3087	.3364	.3456	.3369	.3125
	3	.0081	.0244	.0512	.0879	.1323	.1811	.2304	.2757	.3125
	4	.0004	.0022	.0064	.0146	.0284	.0488	.0768	.1128	.1562
	5	.0000	.0001	.0003	.0010	.0024	.0053	.0102	.0185	.0312
6	0	.5314	.3771	.2621	.1780	.1176	.0754	.0467	.0277	.0156
	1	.3543	.3993	.3932	.3560	.3025	.2437	.1866	.1359	.0938
	2	.0984	.1762	.2458	.2966	.3241	.3280	.3110	.2780	.2344
	3	.0146	.0415	.0819	.1318	.1852	.2355	.2765	.3032	.3125
	4	.0012	.0055	.0154	.0330	.0595	.0951	.1382	.1861	.2344
	5	.0001	.0004	.0015	.0044	.0102	.0205	.0369	.0609	.0938
	6	.0000	.0000	.0001	.0002	.0007	.0018	.0041	.0083	.0156
7	0	.4783	.3206	.2097	.1335	.0824	.0490	.0280	.0152	.0078
	1	.3720	.3960	.3670	.3115	.2471	.1848	.1306	.0872	.0547
	2	.1240	.2097	.2753	.3115	.3177	.2985	.2613	.2140	.1641
	3	.0230	.0617	.1147	.1730	.2269	.2679	.2903	.2918	.2734
	4	.0026	.0109	.0287	.0577	.0972	.1442	.1935	.2388	.2734
	5	.0002	.0012	.0043	.0115	.0250	.0466	.0774	.1172	.1641
	6	.0000	.0001	.0004	.0013	.0036	.0084	.0172	.0320	.0547
	7	.0000	.0000	.0000	.0001	.0002	.0006	.0016	.0037	.0078
8	0	.4305	.2725	.1678	.1001	.0576	.0319	.0168	.0084	.0039
	1	.3826	.3847	.3355	.2670	.1977	.1373	.0896	.0548	.0312
	2	.1488	.2376	.2936	.3115	.2965	.2587	.2090	.1569	.1094
	3	.0331	.0839	.1468	.2076	.2541	.2786	.2787	.2568	.2188
	4	.0046	.0185	.0459	.0865	.1361	.1875	.2322	.2627	.2734
	5	.0004	.0026	.0092	.0231	.0467	.0808	.1239	.1719	.2188
	6	.0000	.0002	.0011	.0038	.0100	.0217	.0413	.0703	.1094
	7	.0000	.0000	.0001	.0004	.0012	.0033	.0079	.0164	.0313
	8	.0000	.0000	.0000	.0000	.0001	.0002	.0007	.0017	.0039

TABLE 5 Binomial Probabilities (*Continued*)

n	x	.10	.15	.20	.25	.30	.35	.40	.45	.50
9	0	.3874	.2316	.1342	.0751	.0404	.0207	.0101	.0046	.0020
	1	.3874	.3679	.3020	.2253	.1556	.1004	.0605	.0339	.0176
	2	.1722	.2597	.3020	.3003	.2668	.2162	.1612	.1110	.0703
	3	.0446	.1069	.1762	.2336	.2668	.2716	.2508	.2119	.1641
	4	.0074	.0283	.0661	.1168	.1715	.2194	.2508	.2600	.2461
	5	.0008	.0050	.0165	.0389	.0735	.1181	.1672	.2128	.2461
	6	.0001	.0006	.0028	.0087	.0210	.0424	.0743	.1160	.1641
	7	.0000	.0000	.0003	.0012	.0039	.0098	.0212	.0407	.0703
	8	.0000	.0000	.0000	.0001	.0004	.0013	.0035	.0083	.0176
	9	.0000	.0000	.0000	.0000	.0000	.0001	.0003	.0008	.0020
10	0	.3487	.1969	.1074	.0563	.0282	.0135	.0060	.0025	.0010
	1	.3874	.3474	.2684	.1877	.1211	.0725	.0403	.0207	.0098
	2	.1937	.2759	.3020	.2816	.2335	.1757	.1209	.0763	.0439
	3	.0574	.1298	.2013	.2503	.2668	.2522	.2150	.1665	.1172
	4	.0112	.0401	.0881	.1460	.2001	.2377	.2508	.2384	.2051
	5	.0015	.0085	.0264	.0584	.1029	.1536	.2007	.2340	.2461
	6	.0001	.0012	.0055	.0162	.0368	.0689	.1115	.1596	.2051
	7	.0000	.0001	.0008	.0031	.0090	.0212	.0425	.0746	.1172
	8	.0000	.0000	.0001	.0004	.0014	.0043	.0106	.0229	.0439
	9	.0000	.0000	.0000	.0000	.0001	.0005	.0016	.0042	.0098
	10	.0000	.0000	.0000	.0000	.0000	.0000	.0001	.0003	.0010
12	0	.2824	.1422	.0687	.0317	.0138	.0057	.0022	.0008	.0002
	1	.3766	.3012	.2062	.1267	.0712	.0368	.0174	.0075	.0029
	2	.2301	.2924	.2835	.2323	.1678	.1088	.0639	.0339	.0161
	3	.0853	.1720	.2362	.2581	.2397	.1954	.1419	.0923	.0537
	4	.0213	.0683	.1329	.1936	.2311	.2367	.2128	.1700	.1208
	5	.0038	.0193	.0532	.1032	.1585	.2039	.2270	.2225	.1934
	6	.0005	.0040	.0155	.0401	.0792	.1281	.1766	.2124	.2256
	7	.0000	.0006	.0033	.0115	.0291	.0591	.1009	.1489	.1934
	8	.0000	.0001	.0005	.0024	.0078	.0199	.0420	.0762	.1208
	9	.0000	.0000	.0001	.0004	.0015	.0048	.0125	.0277	.0537
	10	.0000	.0000	.0000	.0000	.0002	.0008	.0025	.0068	.0161
	11	.0000	.0000	.0000	.0000	.0000	.0001	.0003	.0010	.0029
	12	.0000	.0000	.0000	.0000	.0000	.0000	.0000	.0001	.0002
15	0	.2059	.0874	.0352	.0134	.0047	.0016	.0005	.0001	.0000
	1	.3432	.2312	.1319	.0668	.0305	.0126	.0047	.0016	.0005
	2	.2669	.2856	.2309	.1559	.0916	.0476	.0219	.0090	.0032
	3	.1285	.2184	.2501	.2252	.1700	.1110	.0634	.0318	.0139
	4	.0428	.1156	.1876	.2252	.2186	.1792	.1268	.0780	.0417
	5	.0105	.0449	.1032	.1651	.2061	.2123	.1859	.1404	.0916
	6	.0019	.0132	.0430	.0917	.1472	.1906	.2066	.1914	.1527
	7	.0003	.0030	.0138	.0393	.0811	.1319	.1771	.2013	.1964
	8	.0000	.0005	.0035	.0131	.0348	.0710	.1181	.1647	.1964
	9	.0000	.0001	.0007	.0034	.0016	.0298	.0612	.1048	.1527
	10	.0000	.0000	.0001	.0007	.0030	.0096	.0245	.0515	.0916
	11	.0000	.0000	.0000	.0001	.0006	.0024	.0074	.0191	.0417
	12	.0000	.0000	.0000	.0000	.0001	.0004	.0016	.0052	.0139
	13	.0000	.0000	.0000	.0000	.0000	.0001	.0003	.0010	.0032
	14	.0000	.0000	.0000	.0000	.0000	.0000	.0000	.0001	.0005
	15	.0000	.0000	.0000	.0000	.0000	.0000	.0000	.0000	.0000

TABLE 5 Binomial Probabilities (*Continued*)

						p				
n	*x*	.10	.15	.20	.25	.30	.35	.40	.45	.50
18	0	.1501	.0536	.0180	.0056	.0016	.0004	.0001	.0000	.0000
	1	.3002	.1704	.0811	.0338	.0126	.0042	.0012	.0003	.0001
	2	.2835	.2556	.1723	.0958	.0458	.0190	.0069	.0022	.0006
	3	.1680	.2406	.2297	.1704	.1046	.0547	.0246	.0095	.0031
	4	.0700	.1592	.2153	.2130	.1681	.1104	.0614	.0291	.0117
	5	.0218	.0787	.1507	.1988	.2017	.1664	.1146	.0666	.0327
	6	.0052	.0301	.0816	.1436	.1873	.1941	.1655	.1181	.0708
	7	.0010	.0091	.0350	.0820	.1376	.1792	.1892	.1657	.1214
	8	.0002	.0022	.0120	.0376	.0811	.1327	.1734	.1864	.1669
	9	.0000	.0004	.0033	.0139	.0386	.0794	.1284	.1694	.1855
	10	.0000	.0001	.0008	.0042	.0149	.0385	.0771	.1248	.1669
	11	.0000	.0000	.0001	.0010	.0046	.0151	.0374	.0742	.1214
	12	.0000	.0000	.0000	.0002	.0012	.0047	.0145	.0354	.0708
	13	.0000	.0000	.0000	.0000	.0002	.0012	.0045	.0134	.0327
	14	.0000	.0000	.0000	.0000	.0000	.0002	.0011	.0039	.0117
	15	.0000	.0000	.0000	.0000	.0000	.0000	.0002	.0009	.0031
	16	.0000	.0000	.0000	.0000	.0000	.0000	.0000	.0001	.0006
	17	.0000	.0000	.0000	.0000	.0000	.0000	.0000	.0000	.0001
	18	.0000	.0000	.0000	.0000	.0000	.0000	.0000	.0000	.0000
20	0	.1216	.0388	.0115	.0032	.0008	.0002	.0000	.0000	.0000
	1	.2702	.1368	.0576	.0211	.0068	.0020	.0005	.0001	.0000
	2	.2852	.2293	.1369	.0669	.0278	.0100	.0031	.0008	.0002
	3	.1901	.2428	.2054	.1339	.0716	.0323	.0123	.0040	.0011
	4	.0898	.1821	.2182	.1897	.1304	.0738	.0350	.0139	.0046
	5	.0319	.1028	.1746	.2023	.1789	.1272	.0746	.0365	.0148
	6	.0089	.0454	.1091	.1686	.1916	.1712	.1244	.0746	.0370
	7	.0020	.0160	.0545	.1124	.1643	.1844	.1659	.1221	.0739
	8	.0004	.0046	.0222	.0609	.1144	.1614	.1797	.1623	.1201
	9	.0001	.0011	.0074	.0271	.0654	.1158	.1597	.1771	.1602
	10	.0000	.0002	.0020	.0099	.0308	.0686	.1171	.1593	.1762
	11	.0000	.0000	.0005	.0030	.0120	.0336	.0710	.1185	.1602
	12	.0000	.0000	.0001	.0008	.0039	.0136	.0355	.0727	.1201
	13	.0000	.0000	.0000	.0002	.0010	.0045	.0146	.0366	.0739
	14	.0000	.0000	.0000	.0000	.0002	.0012	.0049	.0150	.0370
	15	.0000	.0000	.0000	.0000	.0000	.0003	.0013	.0049	.0148
	16	.0000	.0000	.0000	.0000	.0000	.0000	.0003	.0013	.0046
	17	.0000	.0000	.0000	.0000	.0000	.0000	.0000	.0002	.0011
	18	.0000	.0000	.0000	.0000	.0000	.0000	.0000	.0000	.0002
	19	.0000	.0000	.0000	.0000	.0000	.0000	.0000	.0000	.0000
	20	.0000	.0000	.0000	.0000	.0000	.0000	.0000	.0000	.0000

TABLE 5 Binomial Probabilities (*Continued*)

n	x	.55	.60	.65	.70	.75	.80	.85	.90	.95
2	0	.2025	.1600	.1225	.0900	.0625	.0400	.0225	.0100	.0025
	1	.4950	.4800	.4550	.4200	.3750	.3200	.2550	.1800	.0950
	2	.3025	.3600	.4225	.4900	.5625	.6400	.7225	.8100	.9025
3	0	.0911	.0640	.0429	.0270	.0156	.0080	.0034	.0010	.0001
	1	.3341	.2880	.2389	.1890	.1406	.0960	.0574	.0270	.0071
	2	.4084	.4320	.4436	.4410	.4219	.3840	.3251	.2430	.1354
	3	.1664	.2160	.2746	.3430	.4219	.5120	.6141	.7290	.8574
4	0	.0410	.0256	.0150	.0081	.0039	.0016	.0005	.0001	.0000
	1	.2005	.1536	.1115	.0756	.0469	.0256	.0115	.0036	.0005
	2	.3675	.3456	.3105	.2646	.2109	.1536	.0975	.0486	.0135
	3	.2995	.3456	.3845	.4116	.4219	.4096	.3685	.2916	.1715
	4	.0915	.1296	.1785	.2401	.3164	.4096	.5220	.6561	.8145
5	0	.0185	.0102	.0053	.0024	.0010	.0003	.0001	.0000	.0000
	1	.1128	.0768	.0488	.0284	.0146	.0064	.0022	.0005	.0000
	2	.2757	.2304	.1811	.1323	.0879	.0512	.0244	.0081	.0011
	3	.3369	.3456	.3364	.3087	.2637	.2048	.1382	.0729	.0214
	4	.2059	.2592	.3124	.3601	.3955	.4096	.3915	.3281	.2036
	5	.0503	.0778	.1160	.1681	.2373	.3277	.4437	.5905	.7738
6	0	.0083	.0041	.0018	.0007	.0002	.0001	.0000	.0000	.0000
	1	.0609	.0369	.0205	.0102	.0044	.0015	.0004	.0001	.0000
	2	.1861	.1382	.0951	.0595	.0330	.0154	.0055	.0012	.0001
	3	.3032	.2765	.2355	.1852	.1318	.0819	.0415	.0146	.0021
	4	.2780	.3110	.3280	.3241	.2966	.2458	.1762	.0984	.0305
	5	.1359	.1866	.2437	.3025	.3560	.3932	.3993	.3543	.2321
	6	.0277	.0467	.0754	.1176	.1780	.2621	.3771	.5314	.7351
7	0	.0037	.0016	.0006	.0002	.0001	.0000	.0000	.0000	.0000
	1	.0320	.0172	.0084	.0036	.0013	.0004	.0001	.0000	.0000
	2	.1172	.0774	.0466	.0250	.0115	.0043	.0012	.0002	.0000
	3	.2388	.1935	.1442	.0972	.0577	.0287	.0109	.0026	.0002
	4	.2918	.2903	.2679	.2269	.1730	.1147	.0617	.0230	.0036
	5	.2140	.2613	.2985	.3177	.3115	.2753	.2097	.1240	.0406
	6	.0872	.1306	.1848	.2471	.3115	.3670	.3960	.3720	.2573
	7	.0152	.0280	.0490	.0824	.1335	.2097	.3206	.4783	.6983
8	0	.0017	.0007	.0002	.0001	.0000	.0000	.0000	.0000	.0000
	1	.0164	.0079	.0033	.0012	.0004	.0001	.0000	.0000	.0000
	2	.0703	.0413	.0217	.0100	.0038	.0011	.0002	.0000	.0000
	3	.1719	.1239	.0808	.0467	.0231	.0092	.0026	.0004	.0000
	4	.2627	.2322	.1875	.1361	.0865	.0459	.0185	.0331	.0004
	5	.2568	.2787	.2786	.2541	.2076	.1468	.0839	.0331	.0054
	6	.1569	.2090	.2587	.2965	.3115	.2936	.2376	.1488	.0515
	7	.0548	.0896	.1373	.1977	.2670	.3355	.3847	.3826	.2793
	8	.0084	.0168	.0319	.0576	.1001	.1678	.2725	.4305	.6634

TABLE 5 Binomial Probabilities (*Continued*)

						p				
n	*x*	.55	.60	.65	.70	.75	.80	.85	.90	.95
9	0	.0008	.0003	.0001	.0000	.0000	.0000	.0000	.0000	.0000
	1	.0083	.0035	.0013	.0004	.0001	.0000	.0000	.0000	.0000
	2	.0407	.0212	.0098	.0039	.0012	.0003	.0000	.0000	.0000
	3	.1160	.0743	.0424	.0210	.0087	.0028	.0006	.0001	.0000
	4	.2128	.1672	.1181	.0735	.0389	.0165	.0050	.0008	.0000
	5	.2600	.2508	.2194	.1715	.1168	.0661	.0283	.0074	.0006
	6	.2119	.2508	.2716	.2668	.2336	.1762	.1069	.0446	.0077
	7	.1110	.1612	.2162	.2668	.3003	.3020	.2597	.1722	.0629
	8	.0339	.0605	.1004	.1556	.2253	.3020	.3679	.3874	.2985
	9	.0046	.0101	.0207	.0404	.0751	.1342	.2316	.3874	.6302
10	0	.0003	.0001	.0000	.0000	.0000	.0000	.0000	.0000	.0000
	1	.0042	.0016	.0005	.0001	.0000	.0000	.0000	.0000	.0000
	2	.0229	.0106	.0043	.0014	.0004	.0001	.0000	.0000	.0000
	3	.0746	.0425	.0212	.0090	.0031	.0008	.0001	.0000	.0000
	4	.1596	.1115	.0689	.0368	.0162	.0055	.0012	.0001	.0000
	5	.2340	.2007	.1536	.1029	.0584	.0264	.0085	.0015	.0001
	6	.2384	.2508	.2377	.2001	.1460	.0881	.0401	.0112	.0010
	7	.1665	.2150	.2522	.2668	.2503	.2013	.1298	.0574	.0105
	8	.0763	.1209	.1757	.2335	.2816	.3020	.2759	.1937	.0746
	9	.0207	.0403	.0725	.1211	.1877	.2684	.3474	.3874	.3151
	10	.0025	.0060	.0135	.0282	.0563	.1074	.1969	.3487	.5987
12	0	.0001	.0000	.0000	.0000	.0000	.0000	.0000	.0000	.0000
	1	.0010	.0003	.0001	.0000	.0000	.0000	.0000	.0000	.0000
	2	.0068	.0025	.0008	.0002	.0000	.0000	.0000	.0000	.0000
	3	.0277	.0125	.0048	.0015	.0004	.0001	.0000	.0000	.0000
	4	.0762	.0420	.0199	.0078	.0024	.0005	.0001	.0000	.0000
	5	.1489	.1009	.0591	.0291	.0115	.0033	.0006	.0000	.0000
	6	.2124	.1766	.1281	.0792	.0401	.0155	.0040	.0005	.0000
	7	.2225	.2270	.2039	.1585	.1032	.0532	.0193	.0038	.0002
	8	.1700	.2128	.2367	.2311	.1936	.1329	.0683	.0213	.0021
	9	.0923	.1419	.1954	.2397	.2581	.2362	.1720	.0852	.0173
	10	.0339	.0639	.1088	.1678	.2323	.2835	.2924	.2301	.0988
	11	.0075	.0174	.0368	.0712	.1267	.2062	.3012	.3766	.3413
	12	.0008	.0022	.0057	.0138	.0317	.0687	.1422	.2824	.5404
15	0	.0000	.0000	.0000	.0000	.0000	.0000	.0000	.0000	.0000
	1	.0001	.0000	.0000	.0000	.0000	.0000	.0000	.0000	.0000
	2	.0010	.0003	.0001	.0000	.0000	.0000	.0000	.0000	.0000
	3	.0052	.0016	.0004	.0001	.0000	.0000	.0000	.0000	.0000
	4	.0191	.0074	.0024	.0006	.0001	.0000	.0000	.0000	.0000
	5	.0515	.0245	.0096	.0030	.0007	.0001	.0000	.0000	.0000
	6	.1048	.0612	.0298	.0116	.0034	.0007	.0001	.0000	.0000
	7	.1647	.1181	.0710	.0348	.0131	.0035	.0005	.0000	.0000
	8	.2013	.1771	.1319	.0811	.0393	.0138	.0030	.0003	.0000
	9	.1914	.2066	.1906	.1472	.0917	.0430	.0132	.0019	.0000
	10	.1404	.1859	.2123	.2061	.1651	.1032	.0449	.0105	.0006
	11	.0780	.1268	.1792	.2186	.2252	.1876	.1156	.0428	.0049
	12	.0318	.0634	.1110	.1700	.2252	.2501	.2184	.1285	.0307
	13	.0090	.0219	.0476	.0916	.1559	.2309	.2856	.2669	.1348
	14	.0016	.0047	.0126	.0305	.0668	.1319	.2312	.3432	.3658
	15	.0001	.0005	.0016	.0047	.0134	.0352	.0874	.2059	.4633

TABLE 5 Binomial Probabilities (*Continued*)

n	x	.55	.60	.65	.70	.75	.80	.85	.90	.95
18	0	.0000	.0000	.0000	.0000	.0000	.0000	.0000	.0000	.0000
	1	.0000	.0000	.0000	.0000	.0000	.0000	.0000	.0000	.0000
	2	.0001	.0000	.0000	.0000	.0000	.0000	.0000	.0000	.0000
	3	.0009	.0002	.0000	.0000	.0000	.0000	.0000	.0000	.0000
	4	.0039	.0011	.0002	.0000	.0000	.0000	.0000	.0000	.0000
	5	.0134	.0045	.0012	.0002	.0000	.0000	.0000	.0000	.0000
	6	.0354	.0145	.0047	.0012	.0002	.0000	.0000	.0000	.0000
	7	.0742	.0374	.0151	.0046	.0010	.0001	.0000	.0000	.0000
	8	.1248	.0771	.0385	.0149	.0042	.0008	.0001	.0000	.0000
	9	.1694	.1284	.0794	.0386	.0139	.0033	.0004	.0000	.0000
	10	.1864	.1734	.1327	.0811	.0376	.0120	.0022	.0002	.0000
	11	.1657	.1892	.1792	.1376	.0820	.0350	.0091	.0010	.0000
	12	.1181	.1655	.1941	.1873	.1436	.0816	.0301	.0052	.0002
	13	.0666	.1146	.1664	.2017	.1988	.1507	.0787	.0218	.0014
	14	.0291	.0614	.1104	.1681	.2130	.2153	.1592	.0700	.0093
	15	.0095	.0246	.0547	.1046	.1704	.2297	.2406	.1680	.0473
	16	.0022	.0069	.0190	.0458	.0958	.1723	.2556	.2835	.1683
	17	.0003	.0012	.0042	.0126	.0338	.0811	.1704	.3002	.3763
	18	.0000	.0001	.0004	.0016	.0056	.0180	.0536	.1501	.3972
20	0	.0000	.0000	.0000	.0000	.0000	.0000	.0000	.0000	.0000
	1	.0000	.0000	.0000	.0000	.0000	.0000	.0000	.0000	.0000
	2	.0000	.0000	.0000	.0000	.0000	.0000	.0000	.0000	.0000
	3	.0002	.0000	.0000	.0000	.0000	.0000	.0000	.0000	.0000
	4	.0013	.0003	.0000	.0000	.0000	.0000	.0000	.0000	.0000
	5	.0049	.0013	.0003	.0000	.0000	.0000	.0000	.0000	.0000
	6	.0150	.0049	.0012	.0002	.0000	.0000	.0000	.0000	.0000
	7	.0366	.0146	.0045	.0010	.0002	.0000	.0000	.0000	.0000
	8	.0727	.0355	.0136	.0039	.0008	.0001	.0000	.0000	.0000
	9	.1185	.0710	.0336	.0120	.0030	.0005	.0000	.0000	.0000
	10	.1593	.1171	.0686	.0308	.0099	.0020	.0002	.0000	.0000
	11	.1771	.1597	.1158	.0654	.0271	.0074	.0011	.0001	.0000
	12	.1623	.1797	.1614	.1144	.0609	.0222	.0046	.0004	.0000
	13	.1221	.1659	.1844	.1643	.1124	.0545	.0160	.0020	.0000
	14	.0746	.1244	.1712	.1916	.1686	.1091	.0454	.0089	.0003
	15	.0365	.0746	.1272	.1789	.2023	.1746	.1028	.0319	.0022
	16	.0139	.0350	.0738	.1304	.1897	.2182	.1821	.0898	.0133
	17	.0040	.0123	.0323	.0716	.1339	.2054	.2428	.1901	.0596
	18	.0008	.0031	.0100	.0278	.0669	.1369	.2293	.2852	.1887
	19	.0001	.0005	.0020	.0068	.0211	.0576	.1368	.2702	.3774
	20	.0000	.0000	.0002	.0008	.0032	.0115	.0388	.1216	.3585

TABLE 6 Values of $e^{-\mu}$

μ	$e^{-\mu}$	μ	$e^{-\mu}$	μ	$e^{-\mu}$
.00	1.0000	2.00	.1353	4.00	.0183
.05	.9512	2.05	.1287	4.05	.0174
.10	.9048	2.10	.1225	4.10	.0166
.15	.8607	2.15	.1165	4.15	.0158
.20	.8187	2.20	.1108	4.20	.0150
.25	.7788	2.25	.1054	4.25	.0143
.30	.7408	2.30	.1003	4.30	.0136
.35	.7047	2.35	.0954	4.35	.0129
.40	.6703	2.40	.0907	4.40	.0123
.45	.6376	2.45	.0863	4.45	.0117
.50	.6065	2.50	.0821	4.50	.0111
.55	.5769	2.55	.0781	4.55	.0106
.60	.5488	2.60	.0743	4.60	.0101
.65	.5220	2.65	.0707	4.65	.0096
.70	.4966	2.70	.0672	4.70	.0091
.75	.4724	2.75	.0639	4.75	.0087
.80	.4493	2.80	.0608	4.80	.0082
.85	.4274	2.85	.0578	4.85	.0078
.90	.4066	2.90	.0550	4.90	.0074
.95	.3867	2.95	.0523	4.95	.0071
1.00	.3679	3.00	.0498	5.00	.0067
1.05	.3499	3.05	.0474	6.00	.0025
1.10	.3329	3.10	.0450	7.00	.0009
1.15	.3166	3.15	.0429	8.00	.000335
1.20	.3012	3.20	.0408	9.00	.000123
				10.00	.000045
1.25	.2865	3.25	.0388		
1.30	.2725	3.30	.0369		
1.35	.2592	3.35	.0351		
1.40	.2466	3.40	.0334		
1.45	.2346	3.45	.0317		
1.50	.2231	3.50	.0302		
1.55	.2122	3.55	.0287		
1.60	.2019	3.60	.0273		
1.65	.1920	3.65	.0260		
1.70	.1827	3.70	.0247		
1.75	.1738	3.75	.0235		
1.80	.1653	3.80	.0224		
1.85	.1572	3.85	.0213		
1.90	.1496	3.90	.0202		
1.95	.1423	3.95	.0193		

TABLE 7 Poisson Probabilities

Entries in the table give the probability of x occurrences for a Poisson process with a mean μ. For example, when $\mu = 2.5$, the probability of four occurrences is .1336.

					μ					
x	0.1	0.2	0.3	0.4	0.5	0.6	0.7	0.8	0.9	1.0
0	.9048	.8187	.7408	.6703	.6065	.5488	.4966	.4493	.4066	.3679
1	.0905	.1637	.2222	.2681	.3033	.3293	.3476	.3595	.3659	.3679
2	.0045	.0164	.0333	.0536	.0758	.0988	.1217	.1438	.1647	.1839
3	.0002	.0011	.0033	.0072	.0126	.0198	.0284	.0383	.0494	.0613
4	.0000	.0001	.0002	.0007	.0016	.0030	.0050	.0077	.0111	.0153
5	.0000	.0000	.0000	.0001	.0002	.0004	.0007	.0012	.0020	.0031
6	.0000	.0000	.0000	.0000	.0000	.0000	.0001	.0002	.0003	.0005
7	.0000	.0000	.0000	.0000	.0000	.0000	.0000	.0000	.0000	.0001

					μ					
x	1.1	1.2	1.3	1.4	1.5	1.6	1.7	1.8	1.9	2.0
0	.3329	.3012	.2725	.2466	.2231	.2019	.1827	.1653	.1496	.1353
1	.3662	.3614	.3543	.3452	.3347	.3230	.3106	.2975	.2842	.2707
2	.2014	.2169	.2303	.2417	.2510	.2584	.2640	.2678	.2700	.2707
3	.0738	.0867	.0998	.1128	.1255	.1378	.1496	.1607	.1710	.1804
4	.0203	.0260	.0324	.0395	.0471	.0551	.0636	.0723	.0812	.0902
5	.0045	.0062	.0084	.0111	.0141	.0176	.0216	.0260	.0309	.0361
6	.0008	.0012	.0018	.0026	.0035	.0047	.0061	.0078	.0098	.0120
7	.0001	.0002	.0003	.0005	.0008	.0011	.0015	.0020	.0027	.0034
8	.0000	.0000	.0001	.0001	.0001	.0002	.0003	.0005	.0006	.0009
9	.0000	.0000	.0000	.0000	.0000	.0000	.0001	.0001	.0001	.0002

					μ					
x	2.1	2.2	2.3	2.4	2.5	2.6	2.7	2.8	2.9	3.0
0	.1225	.1108	.1003	.0907	.0821	.0743	.0672	.0608	.0550	.0498
1	.2572	.2438	.2306	.2177	.2052	.1931	.1815	.1703	.1596	.1494
2	.2700	.2681	.2652	.2613	.2565	.2510	.2450	.2384	.2314	.2240
3	.1890	.1966	.2033	.2090	.2138	.2176	.2205	.2225	.2237	.2240
4	.0992	.1082	.1169	.1254	.1336	.1414	.1488	.1557	.1622	.1680
5	.0417	.0476	.0538	.0602	.0668	.0735	.0804	.0872	.0940	.1008
6	.0146	.0174	.0206	.0241	.0278	.0319	.0362	.0407	.0455	.0504
7	.0044	.0055	.0068	.0083	.0099	.0118	.0139	.0163	.0188	.0216
8	.0011	.0015	.0019	.0025	.0031	.0038	.0047	.0057	.0068	.0081
9	.0003	.0004	.0005	.0007	.0009	.0011	.0014	.0018	.0022	.0027
10	.0001	.0001	.0001	.0002	.0002	.0003	.0004	.0005	.0006	.0008
11	.0000	.0000	.0000	.0000	.0000	.0001	.0001	.0001	.0002	.0002
12	.0000	.0000	.0000	.0000	.0000	.0000	.0000	.0000	.0000	.0001

TABLE 7 Poisson Probabilities (*Continued*)

					μ					
x	3.1	3.2	3.3	3.4	3.5	3.6	3.7	3.8	3.9	4.0
0	.0450	.0408	.0369	.0344	.0302	.0273	.0247	.0224	.0202	.0183
1	.1397	.1304	.1217	.1135	.1057	.0984	.0915	.0850	.0789	.0733
2	.2165	.2087	.2008	.1929	.1850	.1771	.1692	.1615	.1539	.1465
3	.2237	.2226	.2209	.2186	.2158	.2125	.2087	.2046	.2001	.1954
4	.1734	.1781	.1823	.1858	.1888	.1912	.1931	.1944	.1951	.1954
5	.1075	.1140	.1203	.1264	.1322	.1377	.1429	.1477	.1522	.1563
6	.0555	.0608	.0662	.0716	.0771	.0826	.0881	.0936	.0989	.1042
7	.0246	.0278	.0312	.0348	.0385	.0425	.0466	.0508	.0551	.0595
8	.0095	.0111	.0129	.0148	.0169	.0191	.0215	.0241	.0269	.0298
9	.0033	.0040	.0047	.0056	.0066	.0076	.0089	.0102	.0116	.0132
10	.0010	.0013	.0016	.0019	.0023	.0028	.0033	.0039	.0045	.0053
11	.0003	.0004	.0005	.0006	.0007	.0009	.0011	.0013	.0016	.0019
12	.0001	.0001	.0001	.0002	.0002	.0003	.0003	.0004	.0005	.0006
13	.0000	.0000	.0000	.0000	.0001	.0001	.0001	.0001	.0002	.0002
14	.0000	.0000	.0000	.0000	.0000	.0000	.0000	.0000	.0000	.0001

					μ					
x	4.1	4.2	4.3	4.4	4.5	4.6	4.7	4.8	4.9	5.0
0	.0166	.0150	.0136	.0123	.0111	.0101	.0091	.0082	.0074	.0067
1	.0679	.0630	.0583	.0540	.0500	.0462	.0427	.0395	.0365	.0337
2	.1393	.1323	.1254	.1188	.1125	.1063	.1005	.0948	.0894	.0842
3	.1904	.1852	.1798	.1743	.1687	.1631	.1574	.1517	.1460	.1404
4	.1951	.1944	.1933	.1917	.1898	.1875	.1849	.1820	.1789	.1755
5	.1600	.1633	.1662	.1687	.1708	.1725	.1738	.1747	.1753	.1755
6	.1093	.1143	.1191	.1237	.1281	.1323	.1362	.1398	.1432	.1462
7	.0640	.0686	.0732	.0778	.0824	.0869	.0914	.0959	.1002	.1044
8	.0328	.0360	.0393	.0428	.0463	.0500	.0537	.0575	.0614	.0653
9	.0150	.0168	.0188	.0209	.0232	.0255	.0280	.0307	.0334	.0363
10	.0061	.0071	.0081	.0092	.0104	.0118	.0132	.0147	.0164	.0181
11	.0023	.0027	.0032	.0037	.0043	.0049	.0056	.0064	.0073	.0082
12	.0008	.0009	.0011	.0014	.0016	.0019	.0022	.0026	.0030	.0034
13	.0002	.0003	.0004	.0005	.0006	.0007	.0008	.0009	.0011	.0013
14	.0001	.0001	.0001	.0001	.0002	.0002	.0003	.0003	.0004	.0005
15	.0000	.0000	.0000	.0000	.0001	.0001	.0001	.0001	.0001	.0002

					μ					
x	5.1	5.2	5.3	5.4	5.5	5.6	5.7	5.8	5.9	6.0
0	.0061	.0055	.0050	.0045	.0041	.0037	.0033	.0030	.0027	.0025
1	.0311	.0287	.0265	.0244	.0225	.0207	.0191	.0176	.0162	.0149
2	.0793	.0746	.0701	.0659	.0618	.0580	.0544	.0509	.0477	.0446
3	.1348	.1293	.1239	.1185	.1133	.1082	.1033	.0985	.0938	.0892
4	.1719	.1681	.1641	.1600	.1558	.1515	.1472	.1428	.1383	.1339

TABLE 7 Poisson Probabilities (*Continued*)

					μ					
x	5.1	5.2	5.3	5.4	5.5	5.6	5.7	5.8	5.9	6.0
5	.1753	.1748	.1740	.1728	.1714	.1697	.1678	.1656	.1632	.1606
6	.1490	.1515	.1537	.1555	.1571	.1587	.1594	.1601	.1605	.1606
7	.1086	.1125	.1163	.1200	.1234	.1267	.1298	.1326	.1353	.1377
8	.0692	.0731	.0771	.0810	.0849	.0887	.0925	.0962	.0998	.1033
9	.0392	.0423	.0454	.0486	.0519	.0552	.0586	.0620	.0654	.0688
10	.0200	.0220	.0241	.0262	.0285	.0309	.0334	.0359	.0386	.0413
11	.0093	.0104	.0116	.0129	.0143	.0157	.0173	.0190	.0207	.0225
12	.0039	.0045	.0051	.0058	.0065	.0073	.0082	.0092	.0102	.0113
13	.0015	.0018	.0021	.0024	.0028	.0032	.0036	.0041	.0046	.0052
14	.0006	.0007	.0008	.0009	.0011	.0013	.0015	.0017	.0019	.0022
15	.0002	.0002	.0003	.0003	.0004	.0005	.0006	.0007	.0008	.0009
16	.0001	.0001	.0001	.0001	.0001	.0002	.0002	.0002	.0003	.0003
17	.0000	.0000	.0000	.0000	.0000	.0001	.0001	.0001	.0001	.0001

					μ					
x	6.1	6.2	6.3	6.4	6.5	6.6	6.7	6.8	6.9	7.0
0	.0022	.0020	.0018	.0017	.0015	.0014	.0012	.0011	.0010	.0009
1	.0137	.0126	.0116	.0106	.0098	.0090	.0082	.0076	.0070	.0064
2	.0417	.0390	.0364	.0340	.0318	.0296	.0276	.0258	.0240	.0223
3	.0848	.0806	.0765	.0726	.0688	.0652	.0617	.0584	.0552	.0521
4	.1294	.1249	.1205	.1162	.1118	.1076	.1034	.0992	.0952	.0912
5	.1579	.1549	.1519	.1487	.1454	.1420	.1385	.1349	.1314	.1277
6	.1605	.1601	.1595	.1586	.1575	.1562	.1546	.1529	.1511	.1490
7	.1399	.1418	.1435	.1450	.1462	.1472	.1480	.1486	.1489	.1490
8	.1066	.1099	.1130	.1160	.1188	.1215	.1240	.1263	.1284	.1304
9	.0723	.0757	.0791	.0825	.0858	.0891	.0923	.0954	.0985	.1014
10	.0441	.0469	.0498	.0528	.0558	.0588	.0618	.0649	.0679	.0710
11	.0245	.0265	.0285	.0307	.0330	.0353	.0377	.0401	.0426	.0452
12	.0124	.0137	.0150	.0164	.0179	.0194	.0210	.0227	.0245	.0264
13	.0058	.0065	.0073	.0081	.0089	.0098	.0108	.0119	.0130	.0142
14	.0025	.0029	.0033	.0037	.0041	.0046	.0052	.0058	.0064	.0071
15	.0010	.0012	.0014	.0016	.0018	.0020	.0023	.0026	.0029	.0033
16	.0004	.0005	.0005	.0006	.0007	.0008	.0010	.0011	.0013	.0014
17	.0001	.0002	.0002	.0002	.0003	.0003	.0004	.0004	.0005	.0006
18	.0000	.0001	.0001	.0001	.0001	.0001	.0001	.0002	.0002	.0002
19	.0000	.0000	.0000	.0000	.0000	.0000	.0000	.0001	.0001	.0001

					μ					
x	7.1	7.2	7.3	7.4	7.5	7.6	7.7	7.8	7.9	8.0
0	.0008	.0007	.0007	.0006	.0006	.0005	.0005	.0004	.0004	.0003
1	.0059	.0054	.0049	.0045	.0041	.0038	.0035	.0032	.0029	.0027
2	.0208	.0194	.0180	.0167	.0156	.0145	.0134	.0125	.0116	.0107
3	.0492	.0464	.0438	.0413	.0389	.0366	.0345	.0324	.0305	.0286
4	.0874	.0836	.0799	.0764	.0729	.0696	.0663	.0632	.0602	.0573

TABLE 7 Poisson Probabilities (*Continued*)

					μ					
x	7.1	7.2	7.3	7.4	7.5	7.6	7.7	7.8	7.9	8.0
5	.1241	.1204	.1167	.1130	.1094	.1057	.1021	.0986	.0951	.0916
6	.1468	.1445	.1420	.1394	.1367	.1339	.1311	.1282	.1252	.1221
7	.1489	.1486	.1481	.1474	.1465	.1454	.1442	.1428	.1413	.1396
8	.1321	.1337	.1351	.1363	.1373	.1382	.1388	.1392	.1395	.1396
9	.1042	.1070	.1096	.1121	.1144	.1167	.1187	.1207	.1224	.1241
10	.0740	.0770	.0800	.0829	.0858	.0887	.0914	.0941	.0967	.0993
11	.0478	.0504	.0531	.0558	.0585	.0613	.0640	.0667	.0695	.0722
12	.0283	.0303	.0323	.0344	.0366	.0388	.0411	.0434	.0457	.0481
13	.0154	.0168	.0181	.0196	.0211	.0227	.0243	.0260	.0278	.0296
14	.0078	.0086	.0095	.0104	.0113	.0123	.0134	.0145	.0157	.0169
15	.0037	.0041	.0046	.0051	.0057	.0062	.0069	.0075	.0083	.0090
16	.0016	.0019	.0021	.0024	.0026	.0030	.0033	.0037	.0041	.0045
17	.0007	.0008	.0009	.0010	.0012	.0013	.0015	.0017	.0019	.0021
18	.0003	.0003	.0004	.0004	.0005	.0006	.0006	.0007	.0008	.0009
19	.0001	.0001	.0001	.0002	.0002	.0002	.0003	.0003	.0003	.0004
20	.0000	.0000	.0001	.0001	.0001	.0001	.0001	.0001	.0001	.0002
21	.0000	.0000	.0000	.0000	.0000	.0000	.0000	.0000	.0001	.0001

					μ					
x	8.1	8.2	8.3	8.4	8.5	8.6	8.7	8.8	8.9	9.0
0	.0003	.0003	.0002	.0002	.0002	.0002	.0002	.0002	.0001	.0001
1	.0025	.0023	.0021	.0019	.0017	.0016	.0014	.0013	.0012	.0011
2	.0100	.0092	.0086	.0079	.0074	.0068	.0063	.0058	.0054	.0050
3	.0269	.0252	.0237	.0222	.0208	.0195	.0183	.0171	.0160	.0150
4	.0544	.0517	.0491	.0466	.0443	.0420	.0398	.0377	.0357	.0337
5	.0882	.0849	.0816	.0784	.0752	.0722	.0692	.0663	.0635	.0607
6	.1191	.1160	.1128	.1097	.1066	.1034	.1003	.0972	.0941	.0911
7	.1378	.1358	.1338	.1317	.1294	.1271	.1247	.1222	.1197	.1171
8	.1395	.1392	.1388	.1382	.1375	.1366	.1356	.1344	.1332	.1318
9	.1256	.1269	.1280	.1290	.1299	.1306	.1311	.1315	.1317	.1318
10	.1017	.1040	.1063	.1084	.1104	.1123	.1140	.1157	.1172	.1186
11	.0749	.0776	.0802	.0828	.0853	.0878	.0902	.0925	.0948	.0970
12	.0505	.0530	.0555	.0579	.0604	.0629	.0654	.0679	.0703	.0728
13	.0315	.0334	.0354	.0374	.0395	.0416	.0438	.0459	.0481	.0504
14	.0182	.0196	.0210	.0225	.0240	.0256	.0272	.0289	.0306	.0324
15	.0098	.0107	.0116	.0126	.0136	.0147	.0158	.0169	.0182	.1094
16	.0050	.0055	.0060	.0066	.0072	.0079	.0086	.0093	.0101	.0109
17	.0024	.0026	.0029	.0033	.0036	.0040	.0044	.0048	.0053	.0058
18	.0011	.0012	.0014	.0015	.0017	.0019	.0021	.0024	.0026	.0029
19	.0005	.0005	.0006	.0007	.0008	.0009	.0010	.0011	.0012	.0014
20	.0002	.0002	.0002	.0003	.0003	.0004	.0004	.0005	.0005	.0006
21	.0001	.0001	.0001	.0001	.0001	.0002	.0002	.0002	.0002	.0003
22	.0000	.0000	.0000	.0000	.0001	.0001	.0001	.0001	.0001	.0001

TABLE 7 Poisson Probabilities (*Continued*)

					μ					
x	9.1	9.2	9.3	9.4	9.5	9.6	9.7	9.8	9.9	10
0	.0001	.0001	.0001	.0001	.0001	.0001	.0001	.0001	.0001	.0000
1	.0010	.0009	.0009	.0008	.0007	.0007	.0006	.0005	.0005	.0005
2	.0046	.0043	.0040	.0037	.0034	.0031	.0029	.0027	.0025	.0023
3	.0140	.0131	.0123	.0115	.0107	.0100	.0093	.0087	.0081	.0076
4	.0319	.0302	.0285	.0269	.0254	.0240	.0226	.0213	.0201	.0189
5	.0581	.0555	.0530	.0506	.0483	.0460	.0439	.0418	.0398	.0378
6	.0881	.0851	.0822	.0793	.0764	.0736	.0709	.0682	.0656	.0631
7	.1145	.1118	.1091	.1064	.1037	.1010	.0982	.0955	.0928	.0901
8	.1302	.1286	.1269	.1251	.1232	.1212	.1191	.1170	.1148	.1126
9	.1317	.1315	.1311	.1306	.1300	.1293	.1284	.1274	.1263	.1251
10	.1198	.1210	.1219	.1228	.1235	.1241	.1245	.1249	.1250	.1251
11	.0991	.1012	.1031	.1049	.1067	.1083	.1098	.1112	.1125	.1137
12	.0752	.0776	.0799	.0822	.0844	.0866	.0888	.0908	.0928	.0948
13	.0526	.0549	.0572	.0594	.0617	.0640	.0662	.0685	.0707	.0729
14	.0342	.0361	.0380	.0399	.0419	.0439	.0459	.0479	.0500	.0521
15	.0208	.0221	.0235	.0250	.0265	.0281	.0297	.0313	.0330	.0347
16	.0118	.0127	.0137	.0147	.0157	.0168	.0180	.0192	.0204	.0217
17	.0063	.0069	.0075	.0081	.0088	.0095	.0103	.0111	.0119	.0128
18	.0032	.0035	.0039	.0042	.0046	.0051	.0055	.0060	.0065	.0071
19	.0015	.0017	.0019	.0021	.0023	.0026	.0028	.0031	.0034	.0037
20	.0007	.0008	.0009	.0010	.0011	.0012	.0014	.0015	.0017	.0019
21	.0003	.0003	.0004	.0004	.0005	.0006	.0006	.0007	.0008	.0009
22	.0001	.0001	.0002	.0002	.0002	.0002	.0003	.0003	.0004	.0004
23	.0000	.0001	.0001	.0001	.0001	.0001	.0001	.0001	.0002	.0002
24	.0000	.0000	.0000	.0000	.0000	.0000	.0000	.0001	.0001	.0001

					μ					
x	11	12	13	14	15	16	17	18	19	20
0	.0000	.0000	.0000	.0000	.0000	.0000	.0000	.0000	.0000	.0000
1	.0002	.0001	.0000	.0000	.0000	.0000	.0000	.0000	.0000	.0000
2	.0010	.0004	.0002	.0001	.0000	.0000	.0000	.0000	.0000	.0000
3	.0037	.0018	.0008	.0004	.0002	.0001	.0000	.0000	.0000	.0000
4	.0102	.0053	.0027	.0013	.0006	.0003	.0001	.0001	.0000	.0000
5	.0224	.0127	.0070	.0037	.0019	.0010	.0005	.0002	.0001	.0001
6	.0411	.0255	.0152	.0087	.0048	.0026	.0014	.0007	.0004	.0002
7	.0646	.0437	.0281	.0174	.0104	.0060	.0034	.0018	.0010	.0005
8	.0888	.0655	.0457	.0304	.0194	.0120	.0072	.0042	.0024	.0013
9	.1085	.0874	.0661	.0473	.0324	.0213	.0135	.0083	.0050	.0029
10	.1194	.1048	.0859	.0663	.0486	.0341	.0230	.0150	.0095	.0058
11	.1194	.1144	.1015	.0844	.0663	.0496	.0355	.0245	.0164	.0106
12	.1094	.1144	.1099	.0984	.0829	.0661	.0504	.0368	.0259	.0176
13	.0926	.1056	.1099	.1060	.0956	.0814	.0658	.0509	.0378	.0271
14	.0728	.0905	.1021	.1060	.1024	.0930	.0800	.0655	.0514	.0387

TABLE 7 Poisson Probabilities (*Continued*)

					μ					
x	11	12	13	14	15	16	17	18	19	20
15	.0534	.0724	.0885	.0989	.1024	.0992	.0906	.0786	.0650	.0516
16	.0367	.0543	.0719	.0866	.0960	.0992	.0963	.0884	.0772	.0646
17	.0237	.0383	.0550	.0713	.0847	.0934	.0963	.0936	.0863	.0760
18	.0145	.0256	.0397	.0554	.0706	.0830	.0909	.0936	.0911	.0844
19	.0084	.0161	.0272	.0409	.0557	.0699	.0814	.0887	.0911	.0888
20	.0046	.0097	.0177	.0286	.0418	.0559	.0692	.0798	.0866	.0888
21	.0024	.0055	.0109	.0191	.0299	.0426	.0560	.0684	.0783	.0846
22	.0012	.0030	.0065	.0121	.0204	.0310	.0433	.0560	.0676	.0769
23	.0006	.0016	.0037	.0074	.0133	.0216	.0320	.0438	.0559	.0669
24	.0003	.0008	.0020	.0043	.0083	.0144	.0226	.0328	.0442	.0557
25	.0001	.0004	.0010	.0024	.0050	.0092	.0154	.0237	.0336	.0446
26	.0000	.0002	.0005	.0013	.0029	.0057	.0101	.0164	.0246	.0343
27	.0000	.0001	.0002	.0007	.0016	.0034	.0063	.0109	.0173	.0254
28	.0000	.0000	.0001	.0003	.0009	.0019	.0038	.0070	.0117	.0181
29	.0000	.0000	.0001	.0002	.0004	.0011	.0023	.0044	.0077	.0125
30	.0000	.0000	.0000	.0001	.0002	.0006	.0013	.0026	.0049	.0083
31	.0000	.0000	.0000	.0000	.0001	.0003	.0007	.0015	.0030	.0054
32	.0000	.0000	.0000	.0000	.0001	.0001	.0004	.0009	.0018	.0034
33	.0000	.0000	.0000	.0000	.0000	.0001	.0002	.0005	.0010	.0020
34	.0000	.0000	.0000	.0000	.0000	.0000	.0001	.0002	.0006	.0012
35	.0000	.0000	.0000	.0000	.0000	.0000	.0000	.0001	.0003	.0007
36	.0000	.0000	.0000	.0000	.0000	.0000	.0000	.0001	.0002	.0004
37	.0000	.0000	.0000	.0000	.0000	.0000	.0000	.0000	.0001	.0002
38	.0000	.0000	.0000	.0000	.0000	.0000	.0000	.0000	.0000	.0001
39	.0000	.0000	.0000	.0000	.0000	.0000	.0000	.0000	.0000	.0001

Appendix C–Summation Notation

Summations

Definition

$$\sum_{i=1}^{n} x_i = x_1 + x_2 + \cdots + x_n \qquad \text{(C.1)}$$

Example for $x_1 = 5, x_2 = 8, x_3 = 14$:

$$\sum_{i=1}^{3} x_i = x_1 + x_2 + x_3$$
$$= 5 + 8 + 14$$
$$= 27$$

Result 1

For a constant c:

$$\sum_{i=1}^{n} c = \underbrace{(c + c + \cdots + c)}_{n \text{ times}} = nc \qquad \text{(C.2)}$$

Example for $c = 5, n = 10$:

$$\sum_{i=1}^{10} 5 = 10(5) = 50$$

Example for $c = \bar{x}$:

$$\sum_{i=1}^{n} \bar{x} = n\bar{x}$$

Result 2

$$\sum_{i=1}^{n} cx_i = cx_1 + cx_2 + \cdots + cx_n$$
$$= c(x_1 + x_2 + \cdots + x_n) = c \sum_{i=1}^{n} x_i \qquad \text{(C.3)}$$

Example for $x_1 = 5, x_2 = 8, x_3 = 14, c = 2$:

$$\sum_{i=1}^{3} 2x_i = 2 \sum_{i=1}^{3} x_i = 2(27) = 54$$

Result 3

$$\sum_{i=1}^{n} (ax_i + by_i) = a \sum_{i=1}^{n} x_i + b \sum_{i=1}^{n} y_i \qquad \text{(C.4)}$$

Example for $x_1 = 5$, $x_2 = 8$, $x_3 = 14$, $a = 2$, $y_1 = 7$, $y_2 = 3$, $y_3 = 8$, $b = 4$:

$$\sum_{i=1}^{3} (2x_i + 4y_i) = 2 \sum_{i=1}^{3} x_i + 4 \sum_{i=1}^{3} y_i$$
$$= 2(27) + 4(18)$$
$$= 54 + 72$$
$$= 126$$

Double Summations

Consider the following data involving the variable x_{ij}, where i is the subscript denoting the row position and j is the subscript denoting the column position:

		Column		
		1	**2**	**3**
	1	$x_{11} = 10$	$x_{12} = 8$	$x_{13} = 6$
Row				
	2	$x_{21} = 7$	$x_{22} = 4$	$x_{23} = 12$

Definition

$$\sum_{i=1}^{n} \sum_{j=1}^{m} x_{ij} = (x_{11} + x_{12} + \cdots + x_{1m}) + (x_{21} + x_{22} + \cdots + x_{2m})$$
$$+ (x_{31} + x_{32} + \cdots + x_{3m}) + \cdots + (x_{n1} + x_{n2} + \cdots + x_{nm}) \qquad \text{(C.5)}$$

Example:

$$\sum_{i=1}^{2} \sum_{j=1}^{3} x_{ij} = x_{11} + x_{12} + x_{13} + x_{21} + x_{22} + x_{23}$$
$$= 10 + 8 + 6 + 7 + 4 + 12$$
$$= 47$$

Definition

$$\sum_{i=1}^{n} x_{ij} = x_{1j} + x_{2j} + \cdots + x_{nj} \qquad \text{(C.6)}$$

Example:

$$\sum_{i=1}^{2} x_{i2} = x_{12} + x_{22}$$
$$= 8 + 4$$
$$= 12$$

Shorthand Notation

Sometimes when a summation is for all values of the subscript, we use the following shorthand notations:

$$\sum_{i=1}^{n} x_i = \sum x_i \qquad \text{(C.7)}$$

$$\sum_{i=1}^{n} \sum_{j=1}^{m} x_{ij} = \sum \sum x_{ij} \qquad \text{(C.8)}$$

$$\sum_{i=1}^{n} x_{ij} = \sum_{i} x_{ij} \qquad \text{(C.9)}$$

Appendix E—Microsoft Excel 2016 and Tools for Statistical Analysis

Microsoft Excel 2016, part of the Microsoft Office 2016 system, is a spreadsheet program that can be used to organize and analyze data, perform complex calculations, and create a wide variety of graphical displays. We assume that readers are familiar with basic Excel operations such as selecting cells, entering formulas, copying, and so on. But we do not assume readers are familiar with Excel 2016 or the use of Excel for statistical analysis.

The purpose of this appendix is twofold. First, we provide an overview of Excel 2016 and discuss the basic operations needed to work with Excel 2016 workbooks and worksheets. Second, we provide an overview of the tools that are available for conducting statistical analysis with Excel. These include Excel functions and formulas which allow users to conduct their own analyses and add-ins that provide more comprehensive analysis tools.

Excel's Data Analysis add-in, included with the basic Excel system, is a valuable tool for conducting statistical analysis. In the last section of this appendix we provide instruction for installing the Data Analysis add-in. Other add-ins have been developed by outside suppliers to supplement the basic statistical capabilities provided by Excel.

Overview of Microsoft Excel 2016

A workbook is a file containing one or more worksheets.

When using Excel for statistical analysis, data is displayed in workbooks, each of which contains a series of worksheets that typically include the original data as well as any resulting analysis, including charts. Figure E.1 shows the layout of a blank workbook created each time Excel is opened. The workbook is named Book1, and contains one worksheet named Sheet1. Excel highlights the worksheet currently displayed (Sheet1) by setting the name on the worksheet tab in bold. Note that cell A1 is initially selected.

The wide bar located across the top of the workbook is referred to as the Ribbon. Tabs, located at the top of the Ribbon, provide quick access to groups of related commands. There are eight tabs shown on the workbook in Figure E.1: File; Home; Insert; Page Layout; Formulas; Data; Review; and View. Each tab contains a series of groups of related commands. Note that the Home tab is selected when Excel is opened. Figure E.2 displays the groups available when the Home tab is selected. Under the Home tab there are seven groups: Clipboard; Font; Alignment; Number; Styles; Cells; and Editing. Commands are arranged within each group. For example, to change selected text to boldface, click the Home tab and click the Bold ■ button in the Font group.

Figure E.3 illustrates the location of the Quick Access Toolbar and the Formula Bar. The Quick Access Toolbar allows you to quickly access workbook options. To add or remove features on the Quick Access Toolbar, click the Customize Quick Access Toolbar button ⌄ at the end of the Quick Access Toolbar.

The Formula Bar (see Figure E.3) contains a Name box, the Insert Function button f_x, and a Formula box. In Figure E.3, "A1" appears in the name box because cell A1 is selected. You can select any other cell in the worksheet by using the mouse to move the cursor to another cell and clicking or by typing the new cell location in the Name box. The Formula box is used to display the formula in the currently selected cell. For instance, if you enter $=A1+A2$ into cell A3, whenever you select cell A3 the formula $=A1+A2$ will be shown in the Formula box. This feature makes it very easy to see and edit a formula in a particular

FIGURE E.1   Blank Workbook Created When Excel is Opened

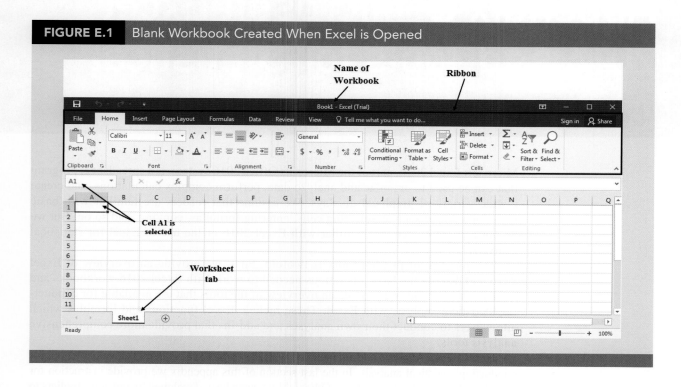

cell. The Insert Function button allows you to quickly access all the functions available in Excel. Later we show how to find and use a particular function.

Basic Workbook Operations

Figure E.4 illustrates the worksheet options that can be performed after right-clicking on a worksheet tab. For instance, to change the name of the current worksheet from "Sheet1" to "Data," right-click the worksheet tab named "Sheet1" and select the Rename option. The

FIGURE E.2   Portion of the Home Tab

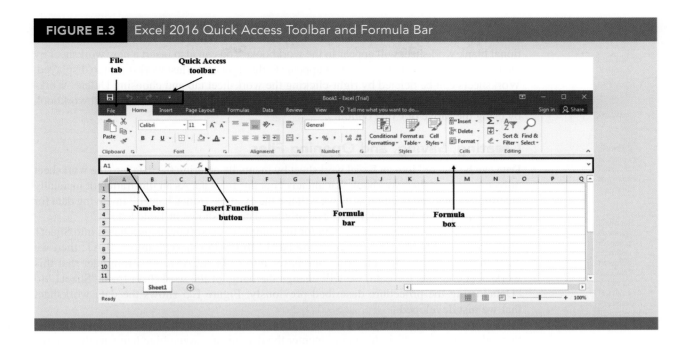

current worksheet name (Sheet1) will be highlighted. Then, simply type the new name (Data) and press the Enter key to rename the worksheet.

Suppose that you wanted to create a copy of "Sheet1." After right-clicking the tab named "Sheet1," select the Move or Copy option. When the Move or Copy dialog box appears, select Create a Copy and click OK. The name of the copied worksheet will appear as "Sheet1 (2)." You can then rename it, if desired.

FIGURE E.4   Worksheet Options Obtained after Right-Clicking on a Worksheet Tab

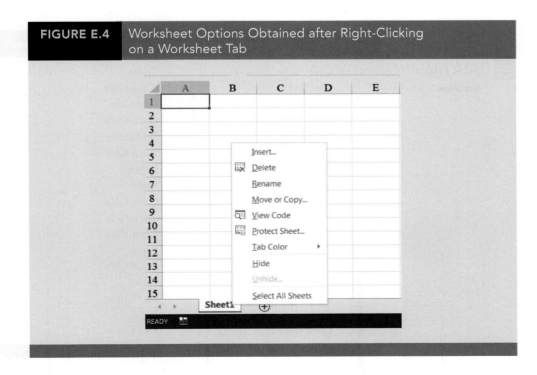

To add a new worksheet to the workbook, right-click any worksheet tab and select the Insert option; when the Insert dialog box appears, select Worksheet and click OK. An additional blank worksheet will appear in the workbook. You can also insert a new worksheet by clicking the New sheet button ⊞ that appears to the right of the last worksheet tab displayed. Worksheets can be deleted by right-clicking the worksheet tab and choosing Delete. Worksheets can also be moved to other workbooks or a different position in the current workbook by using the Move or Copy option.

Creating, Saving, and Opening Files

Data can be entered into an Excel worksheet by manually entering the data into the worksheet or by opening another workbook that already contains the data. As an illustration of manually entering, saving, and opening a file we will use the example from Chapter 2 involving data for a sample of 50 soft drink purchases. The original data are shown in Table E.1.

Suppose we want to enter the data for the sample of 50 soft drink purchases into Sheet1 of the new workbook. First we enter the label "Brand Purchased" into cell A1; then we enter the data for the 50 soft drink purchases into cells A2:A51. As a reminder that this worksheet contains the data, we will change the name of the worksheet from "Sheet1" to "Data" using the procedure described previously. Figure E.5 shows the data worksheet that we just developed.

Before doing any analysis with these data, we recommend that you first save the file; this will prevent you from having to reenter the data in case something happens that causes Excel to close. To save the file as an Excel 2016 workbook using the filename SoftDrink we perform the following steps:

Step 1: Click the **File** tab
Step 2: Click **Save** in the list of options
Step 3: When the **Save As** window appears:
　　　　　Select **This PC**
　　　　　Select Browse
　　　　　Select the location where you want to save the file
　　　　　Type the filename **SoftDrink** in the **File name** box
　　　　　Click **Save**

DATA *file*

SoftDrink

TABLE E.1	Data from a Sample of 50 Soft Drink Purchases	
Coca-Cola	Sprite	Pepsi
Diet Coke	Coca-Cola	Coca-Cola
Pepsi	Diet Coke	Coca-Cola
Diet Coke	Coca-Cola	Coca-Cola
Coca-Cola	Diet Coke	Pepsi
Coca-Cola	Coca-Cola	Dr. Pepper
Dr. Pepper	Sprite	Coca-Cola
Diet Coke	Pepsi	Diet Coke
Pepsi	Coca-Cola	Pepsi
Pepsi	Coca-Cola	Pepsi
Coca-Cola	Coca-Cola	Pepsi
Dr. Pepper	Pepsi	Pepsi
Sprite	Coca-Cola	Coca-Cola
Coca-Cola	Sprite	Dr. Pepper
Diet Coke	Dr. Pepper	Pepsi
Coca-Cola	Pepsi	Sprite
Coca-Cola	Diet Coke	

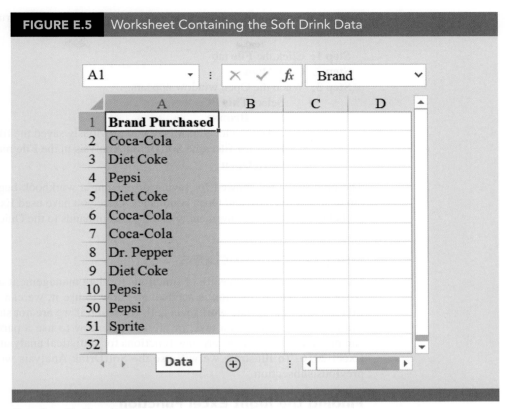

FIGURE E.5 Worksheet Containing the Soft Drink Data

Note: Rows 11–49 are hidden.

Excel's Save command is designed to save the file as an Excel 2016 workbook. As you work with the file to do statistical analysis you should follow the practice of periodically saving the file so you will not lose any statistical analysis you may have performed. Simply click the File tab and select Save in the list of options.

Keyboard shortcut: To save the file, press CTRL+S.

Sometimes you may want to create a copy of an existing file. For instance, suppose you would like to save the soft drink data and any resulting statistical analysis in a new file named "SoftDrink Analysis." The following steps show how to create a copy of the SoftDrink workbook and analysis with the new filename, "SoftDrink Analysis."

Step 1: Click the **File** tab
Step 2: Click **Save As**
Step 3: When the Save As window appears:
Select **This PC**
Select **Browse**
Select the location where you want to save the file
Type the filename **SoftDrink Analysis** in the **File name** box
Click **Save**

Once the workbook has been saved, you can continue to work with the data to perform whatever type of statistical analysis is appropriate. When you are finished working with the file simply click the File tab and then click close in the list of options. To access the SoftDrink

Analysis file at another point in time you can open the file by performing the following steps after launching Excel:

Step 1: Click the **File** tab
Step 2: Click **Open**
Step 3: When the Open window appears:
> Select **This PC**
> Select **Browse**
> Select the location where you previously saved the file
> Enter the filename **SoftDrink Analysis** in the **File name** box
> Click **Open**

The procedures we showed for saving or opening a workbook begin by clicking the File tab to access the Save and Open commands. Once you have used Excel for a while you will probably find it more convenient to add these commands to the Quick Access Toolbar.

Using Excel Functions

Excel 2016 provides a wealth of functions for data management and statistical analysis. If we know which function is needed, and how to use it, we can simply enter the function into the appropriate worksheet cell. However, if we are not sure which functions are available to accomplish a task, or are not sure how to use a particular function, Excel can provide assistance. Many new functions for statistical analysis have been added with Excel 2016. To illustrate we will use the SoftDrink Analysis workbook created in the previous subsection.

Finding the Right Excel Function

To identify the functions available in Excel, select the cell where you want to insert the function; we have selected cell D2. Click the **Formulas** tab on the Ribbon and then click the **Insert Function** button in the **Function Library** group. Alternatively, click the f_x button on the formula bar. Either approach provides the **Insert Function** dialog box shown in Figure E.6.

The **Search for a function** box at the top of the Insert Function dialog box enables us to type a brief description of what we want to do. After doing so and clicking **Go**, Excel will search for and display, in the **Select a function** box, the functions that may accomplish our task. In many situations, however, we may want to browse through an entire category of functions to see what is available. For this task, the **Or select a category** box is helpful. It contains a drop-down list of several categories of functions provided by Excel. Figure E.6 shows that we selected the **Statistical** category. As a result, Excel's statistical functions appear in alphabetic order in the Select a function box. We see the AVEDEV function listed first, followed by the AVERAGE function, and so on.

The AVEDEV function is highlighted in Figure E.6, indicating it is the function currently selected. The proper syntax for the function and a brief description of the function appear below the Select a function box. We can scroll through the list in the Select a function box to display the syntax and a brief description for each of the statistical functions that are available. For instance, scrolling down farther, we select the COUNTIF function as shown in Figure E.7. Note that COUNTIF is now highlighted, and that immediately below the Select a function box we see **COUNTIF(range,criteria)**, which indicates that the COUNTIF function contains two inputs, range and criteria. In addition, we see that the description of the COUNTIF function is "Counts the number of cells within a range that meet the given condition."

If the function selected (highlighted) is the one we want to use, we click **OK**; the **Function Arguments** dialog box then appears. The Function Arguments dialog box for

FIGURE E.6   Insert Function Dialog Box

FIGURE E.7   Description of the Countif Function in the Insert Function Dialog Box

FIGURE E.8   Function Arguments Dialog Box for the Countif Function

the COUNTIF function is shown in Figure E.8. This dialog box assists in creating the appropriate arguments (inputs) for the function selected. When finished entering the arguments, we click **OK**; Excel then inserts the function into a worksheet cell.

Using Excel Add-Ins

Excel's Data Analysis Add-In

Excel's Data Analysis add-in, included with the basic Excel package, is a valuable tool for conducting statistical analysis. Before you can use the Data Analysis add-in it must be installed. To see if the Data Analysis add-in has already been installed, click the Data tab on the Ribbon. In the Analyze group you should see the Data Analysis command. If you do not have an Analyze group and/or the Data Analysis command does not appear in the Analysis group, you will need to install the Data Analysis add-in. The steps needed to install the Data Analysis add-in are as follows:

Step 1. Click the **File** tab
Step 2. Click **Options**
Step 3. When the Excel Options dialog box appears:
  Select **Add-Ins** from the list of options (on the pane on the left)
  In the **Manage** box, select **Excel Add-Ins**
  Click **Go**
Step 4. When the Add-Ins dialog box appears:
  Select **Analysis ToolPak**
  Click **OK**

Appendix F–Computing *p*-Values with JMP and Excel

Here we describe how JMP and Excel can be used to compute *p*-values for the *z*, *t*, χ^2, and *F* statistics that are used in hypothesis tests. As discussed in the text, only approximate *p*-values for the *t*, χ^2, and *F* statistics can be obtained by using tables. This appendix is helpful to a person who has computed the test statistic by hand, or by other means, and wishes to use computer software to compute the exact *p*-value.

Computing *p*-values with JMP

JMP can be used to provide the cumulative probability associated with the *z*, *t*, χ^2, and *F* test statistics.

The *z* test statistic We use the Hilltop Coffee lower tail hypothesis test in Section 9.3 as an illustration; the value of the test statistic is $z = -2.67$. The JMP steps used to compute the cumulative probability corresponding to $z = -2.67$ follow.

DATA *file*
Coffee

Step 1. Select **Help** from the **JMP** ribbon
Step 2. Choose **Teaching Demos**
Step 3. Choose **Distribution Calculator**
Step 4. When the **Distribution Calculator** dialog box appears:
> Select **Normal** from the drop down menu in the **Distribution Characteristics** area
> Select **Input values and calculate probability** in the **Type of Calculation** area
> In the **Calculations** area, select **X < = q** and enter *−2.67* in the **Value** box
> Press **Enter** on your keyboard

Using these steps for the Hilltop Coffee lower tail test, JMP reports a *p*-value of .0038 in the **Calculations area.**

For an upper tail test, select **X > q** and enter the value of *z* in the **Value** box. For a two tail test, select **X < = q1 OR X > q2**, enter *−|z|* in the **Value 1** box, and enter *|z|* in the **Value 2** box

The *t* test statistic We use the Heathrow Airport example from Section 9.4 as an illustration; the value of the test statistic is $t = 1.84$ with 59 degrees of freedom. The JMP steps used to compute the *p*-value follow.

DATA *file*
AirRating

Step 1. Select **Help** from the **JMP** ribbon
Step 2. Choose **Teaching Demos**
Step 3. Choose **Distribution Calculator**
Step 4. When the **Distribution Calculator** dialog box appears:
> Select **t** from the drop down menu in the **Distribution Characteristics** area
> Enter *59* in the in the **DF** box in the **Parameters** section of the **Distribution Characteristics** area
> Select **Input values and calculate probability** in the **Type of Calculation** area
> In the **Calculations** area, select **X > q** and enter *1.84* in the **Value** box
> Press **Enter** on your keyboard

Using these steps for the Heathrow Airport upper tail test, JMP reports a *p*-value of .0354 in the **Calculations** area.

For a lower upper tail test, select **X < = q** and enter the value of *t* in the **Value** box. For a two tail test, select **X < = q1 OR X > q2**, enter $-|t|$ in the **Value 1** box, and enter $|t|$ in the **Value 2** box

The χ^2 test statistic   We use the St. Louis Metro Bus example from Section 11.1 as an illustration; the value of the test statistic is $\chi^2 = 28.18$ with 23 degrees of freedom. The JMP steps used to compute the *p*-value follow.

DATA*file*

BusTimes

Step 1. Select **Help** from the **JMP** ribbon
Step 2. Choose **Teaching Demos**
Step 3. Choose **Distribution Calculator**
Step 4. When the **Distribution Calculator** dialog box appears:
     Select **Chi Square** from the drop down menu in the **Distribution Characteristics** area
     Enter *23* in the in the **DF** box in the **Parameters** section of the **Distribution Characteristics** area
     Select **Input values and calculate probability** in the **Type of Calculation** area
     In the **Calculations** area, select **X > q** and enter *28.18* in the **Value** box
     Press **Enter** on your keyboard

Using these steps for the St. Louis Metro Bus example, JMP reports a *p*-value of .2091 in the **Calculations** area.

The *F* test statistic   We use the Dullus County Schools example from Section 11.2 as an illustration; the test statistic is $F = 2.40$ with 25 numerator degrees of freedom and 15 denominator degrees of freedom. The JMP steps to compute the *p*-value follow.

DATA*file*

SchoolBus

Step 1. Select **Help** from the **JMP** ribbon
Step 2. Choose **Teaching Demos**
Step 3. Choose **Distribution Calculator**
Step 4. When the **Distribution Calculator** dialog box appears:
     Select **F** from the drop down menu in the **Distribution Characteristics** area
     Enter *25* in the in the **Numerator DF** box and *15* in the **Denominator DF** box in the **Parameters** section of the **Distribution Characteristics** area
     Select **Input values and calculate probability** in the **Type of Calculation** area
     In the **Calculations** area, select **X > q** and enter *2.40* in the **Value** box
     Press **Enter** on your keyboard

Using these steps for the Dullus County Schools Bus example, JMP reports a *p*-value of .0406 in the **Calculations** area. Because this is a two-tailed test, we double the *p*-value reported by JMP to obtain the *p*-value of .0812 for this hypothesis test.

Computing *p*-values with Excel

DATA*file*

p-Value

Excel functions and formulas can be used to compute *p*-values associated with the *z*, *t*, χ^2, and *F* test statistics. We provide a template in the data file entitled *p-Value* for use in computing these *p*-values. Using the template, it is only necessary to enter the value of the test statistic and, if necessary, the appropriate degrees of freedom. Refer to Figure F.1 as we describe how the template is used. For users interested in the Excel functions and formulas being used, just click on the appropriate cell in the template.

The z test statistic   We use the Hilltop Coffee lower tail hypothesis test in Section 9.3 as an illustration; the value of the test statistic is $z = -2.67$. To use the p-value template for this hypothesis test, simply enter -2.67 into cell B6 (see Figure F.1). After doing so, p-values for all three types of hypothesis tests will appear. For Hilltop Coffee, we would use the lower tail p-value = .0038 in cell B9. For an upper tail test, we would use the p-value in cell B10, and for a two-tailed test we would use the p-value in cell B11.

The t Test Statistic   We use the Heathrow Airport example from Section 9.4 as an illustration; the value of the test statistic is $t = 1.84$ with 59 degrees of freedom. To use the p-value template for this hypothesis test, enter 1.84 into cell E6 and enter 59 into cell E7 (see Figure F.1). After doing so, p-values for all three types of hypothesis tests will appear. The Heathrow Airport example involves an upper tail test, so we would use the upper tail p-value = .0354 provided in cell E10 for the hypothesis test.

The χ^2 test statistic   We use the St. Louis Metro Bus example from Section 11.1 as an illustration; the value of the test statistic is $\chi^2 = 28.18$ with 23 degrees of freedom. To use the p-value template for this hypothesis test, enter 28.18 into cell B18 and enter 23 into cell B19 (see Figure F.1). After doing so, p-values for all three types of hypothesis tests will appear. The St. Louis Metro Bus example involves an upper tail test, so we would use the upper tail p-value = .2091 provided in cell B23 for the hypothesis test.

FIGURE F.1   Excel Worksheet for Computing p-Values

The *F* test statistic We use the Dullus County Schools example from Section 11.2 as an illustration; the test statistic is $F = 2.40$ with 25 numerator degrees of freedom and 15 denominator degrees of freedom. To use the *p*-value template for this hypothesis test, enter 2.40 into cell E18, enter 25 into cell E19, and enter 15 into cell E20 (see Figure F.1). After doing so, *p*-values for all three types of hypothesis tests will appear. The Dullus County Schools example involves a two-tailed test, so we would use the two-tailed *p*-value = .0812 provided in cell E24 for the hypothesis test.

Index

Note: Chapter 22 can be found with the Online Content for this book. Index entries found in these chapters are denoted by the chapter number (bolded), hyphen, and page number. Page numbers followed by f indicate figures; n indicate footnotes; and t indicate tables.